Periodic Table of The Elements

Legend:
- Metals
- Nonmetals
- Metalloids

1A (1)	2A (2)		3B (3)	4B (4)	5B (5)	6B (6)	7B (7)	8B (8)	8B (9)	8B (10)	1B (11)	2B (12)	3A (13)	4A (14)	5A (15)	6A (16)	7A (17)	8A (18)
1 **H** 1.008																	1 **H** 1.008	2 **He** 4.0026
3 **Li** 6.941	4 **Be** 9.0122												5 **B** 10.81	6 **C** 12.011	7 **N** 14.007	8 **O** 15.9994	9 **F** 18.9984	10 **Ne** 20.1797
11 **Na** 22.9898	12 **Mg** 24.3050												13 **Al** 26.9815	14 **Si** 28.085	15 **P** 30.9738	16 **S** 32.06	17 **Cl** 35.45	18 **Ar** 39.948
19 **K** 39.0983	20 **Ca** 40.078		21 **Sc** 44.9559	22 **Ti** 47.867	23 **V** 50.9415	24 **Cr** 51.9961	25 **Mn** 54.9380	26 **Fe** 55.845	27 **Co** 58.9332	28 **Ni** 58.6934	29 **Cu** 63.546	30 **Zn** 65.38	31 **Ga** 69.723	32 **Ge** 72.63	33 **As** 74.9216	34 **Se** 78.96	35 **Br** 79.904	36 **Kr** 83.798
37 **Rb** 85.4678	38 **Sr** 87.62		39 **Y** 88.9059	40 **Zr** 91.224	41 **Nb** 92.9064	42 **Mo** 95.94	43 **Tc** (98)	44 **Ru** 101.07	45 **Rh** 102.9055	46 **Pd** 106.42	47 **Ag** 107.8682	48 **Cd** 112.411	49 **In** 114.818	50 **Sn** 118.710	51 **Sb** 121.760	52 **Te** 127.60	53 **I** 126.9045	54 **Xe** 131.293
55 **Cs** 132.9055	56 **Ba** 137.327	57 **La** 138.9055 *	72 **Hf** 178.49	73 **Ta** 180.9479	74 **W** 183.84	75 **Re** 186.207	76 **Os** 190.23	77 **Ir** 192.217	78 **Pt** 195.084	79 **Au** 196.9666	80 **Hg** 200.59	81 **Tl** 204.38	82 **Pb** 207.2	83 **Bi** 208.9804	84 **Po** (209)	85 **At** (210)	86 **Rn** (222)
87 **Fr** (223)	88 **Ra** (226)	89 **Ac** (227) **	104 **Rf** (265)	105 **Db** (268)	106 **Sg** (271)	107 **Bh** (270)	108 **Hs** (277)	109 **Mt** (268)	110 **Ds** (281)	111 **Rg** (280)	112 **Cn** (285)	113 **Uut** (284)	114 **Fl** (289)	115 **Uup** (288)	116 **Lv** (293)	117 **Uus** (294)	118 **Uuo** (294)

*Lanthanide Series

58 **Ce** 140.116	59 **Pr** 140.9076	60 **Nd** 144.242	61 **Pm** (145)	62 **Sm** 150.36	63 **Eu** 151.964	64 **Gd** 157.25	65 **Tb** 158.9253	66 **Dy** 162.500	67 **Ho** 164.9303	68 **Er** 167.259	69 **Tm** 168.9342	70 **Yb** 173.054	71 **Lu** 174.9668

** Actinide Series

90 **Th** 232.0381	91 **Pa** 231.0359	92 **U** 238.0289	93 **Np** (237)	94 **Pu** (244)	95 **Am** (243)	96 **Cm** (247)	97 **Bk** (247)	98 **Cf** (251)	99 **Es** (252)	100 **Fm** (257)	101 **Md** (258)	102 **No** (259)	103 **Lr** (262)

Note: Atomic masses are IUPAC values (2009, up to four decimal places). More accurate values for some elements are given in the International Table of Atomic Weights on the facing page.

Chemistry

For CHM 1045

Revised Selections from the 10th ed. of Whitten, Chemistry

Kenneth W. Whitten | Raymond E. Davis | M. Larry Peck | George G. Stanley

CENGAGE
Learning·

Australia • Brazil • Japan • Korea • Mexico • Singapore • Spain • United Kingdom • United States

Chemistry: For CHM 1045, Revised Selections from the 10th ed. of Whitten, Chemistry

Chemistry, Tenth Edition
Kenneth W. Whitten | Raymond E. Davis | M. Larry Peck | George G. Stanley

© 2014, 2010 Cengage Learning. All rights reserved.

General Chemistry, Seventh Edition
Kenneth W. Whitten | Raymond E. Davis | M. Larry Peck | George G. Stanley

© 2004 Cengage Learning. All rights reserved.

Student Solutions Manual: Chemistry, 10th Edition
Kenneth W. Whitten | Raymond E. Davis | M. Larry Peck | George G. Stanley

© 2014 Cengage Learning. All rights reserved.

Senior Project Development Manager:
 Linda deStefano

Market Development Manager:
 Heather Kramer

Senior Production/Manufacturing Manager:
 Donna M. Brown

Production Editorial Manager:
 Kim Fry

Sr. Rights Acquisition Account Manager:
 Todd Osborne

For product information and technology assistance, contact us at
Cengage Learning Customer & Sales Support, 1-800-354-9706
For permission to use material from this text or product,
submit all requests online at **cengage.com/permissions**
Further permissions questions can be emailed to
permissionrequest@cengage.com

This book contains select works from existing Cengage Learning resources and was produced by Cengage Learning Custom Solutions for collegiate use. As such, those adopting and/or contributing to this work are responsible for editorial content accuracy, continuity and completeness.

Compilation © 2013 Cengage Learning
ISBN-13: 978-1-285-88469-1

ISBN-10: 1-285-88469-8

Cengage Learning
5191 Natorp Boulevard
Mason, Ohio 45040
USA
Cengage Learning is a leading provider of customized learning solutions with office locations around the globe, including Singapore, the United Kingdom, Australia, Mexico, Brazil, and Japan. Locate your local office at:
international.cengage.com/region.

Cengage Learning products are represented in Canada by Nelson Education, Ltd. For your lifelong learning solutions, visit **www.cengage.com/custom.**
Visit our corporate website at **www.cengage.com.**

Printed in the United States of America

Brief Contents

Excerpted from:
Student Solutions Manual: Chemistry, Tenth Edition by Whitten, Davis, Peck, and Stanley

The Foundations of Chemistry

1

Chemistry is everywhere! From the combustion of wood to the synthetic fibers that make up much of our clothing. The steel cooking grate is an alloy of iron and carbon (and if it is stainless steel it has other metals such as chromium and nickel mixed in). The plants in the background use a remarkable photochemical reaction to convert CO_2 and water into complex carbohydrates. Our bodies are filled with both inorganic and bioorganic compounds such as bone and proteins, and run on a myriad of chemical reactions needed to keep us alive. Construction materials are made from both natural and recycled sources. Aluminum has many uses, based on its low density and its resistance to corrosion. Heat from a fire can cook food as well as cause skin damage. Clouds consist of tiny droplets of water formed by condensation of water vapor.

oliveromg/Shutterstock.com

OBJECTIVES

After you have studied this chapter, you should be able to

► Use the basic vocabulary of matter and energy

► Recognize models of selected atoms and molecules

► Distinguish between chemical and physical properties and between chemical and physical changes

► Recognize various forms of matter: homogeneous and heterogeneous mixtures, substances, compounds, and elements and their molecular representations

► Apply the concept of significant figures

► Apply appropriate units to describe the results of measurement

► Use the unit factor method to carry out conversions among units

► Describe temperature measurements on various common scales, and convert between these scales

► Carry out calculations relating temperature change to heat gained or lost

Thousands of practical questions are studied by chemists. A few of them are

How can we modify a useful drug so as to improve its effectiveness while minimizing any harmful or unpleasant side effects?

How can we develop better materials to be used as synthetic organs for replacement surgery?

Which substances could help to prevent rejection of foreign tissue in organ transplants?

What improvements in fertilizers or pesticides can increase agricultural yields? How can this be done with minimal environmental danger?

How can we get the maximum work from a fuel while producing the least harmful emissions possible?

Which really poses the greater environmental threat—the burning of fossil fuels and the resulting contribution to the greenhouse effect and climatic change, or the use of nuclear power and the related radiation and disposal problems?

How can we develop suitable materials for the semiconductor and microelectronics industry? Can we develop a battery that is cheaper, lighter, and more powerful?

What changes in structural materials could help to make aircraft lighter and more economical, yet at the same time stronger and safer?

What relationship is there between the substances we eat, drink, or breathe and the possibility of developing cancer? How can we develop substances that are effective in killing cancer cells preferentially over normal cells?

Can we economically produce fresh water from seawater for irrigation or consumption?

How can we slow down unfavorable reactions, such as the corrosion of metals, while speeding up favorable ones, such as the growth of foodstuffs?

Chemistry touches almost every aspect of our lives, our culture, and our environment. Its scope encompasses the air we breathe, the food we eat, the fluids we drink, the clothing we wear, the dwellings we live in, and the transportation and fuel supplies we use, as well as our fellow creatures.

Chemistry is the science that describes matter—its properties, the changes it undergoes, and the energy changes that accompany those processes.

Enormous numbers of chemical reactions are necessary to produce a human being.

Matter includes everything that is tangible, from our bodies and the stuff of our everyday lives to the grandest objects in the universe. Some call chemistry the central science. It rests on the foundation of mathematics and physics and in turn underlies the life sciences—biology and medicine. To understand living systems fully, we must first understand the chemical reactions and the factors that control and affect them. The chemicals in our bodies profoundly affect even the personal world of our thoughts and emotions.

▶ Lithium ions, for example, are effective in the treatment of some manic-depressive disorders.

No one can be expert in all aspects of such a broad science as chemistry. Sometimes we arbitrarily divide the study of chemistry into various branches. Of all the elements, carbon is the most versatile in its bonding. It is a key element in many substances that are essential to life. All forms of living matter contain compounds with carbon combined with hydrogen and sometimes with a few other elements such as oxygen, nitrogen, and sulfur. **Organic chemistry** is the study of all such compounds. **Inorganic chemistry** is the study of all other compounds, but also includes some of the simpler carbon-containing compounds such as carbon monoxide, carbon dioxide, carbonates, and bicarbonates. In the early days of chemistry, living matter and inanimate matter were believed to be entirely different. We now know that many of the compounds found in living matter can be made from nonliving, or "inorganic," sources. Thus, the terms "organic" and "inorganic" have different meanings than they did originally. The branch of chemistry that is concerned with the detection or identification of substances present in a sample (*qualitative analysis*) or with the amount of each substance that is present (*quantitative analysis*) is called **analytical chemistry**. **Physical chemistry** applies the mathematical theories and methods of physics to the properties of matter and to the study of chemical processes and their accompanying energy changes. As its name suggests, **biochemistry** is the study of the chemistry of processes in living organisms. Such divisions are arbitrary, and most chemical studies involve more than one of these traditional areas of chemistry. The principles you will learn in a general chemistry course are the foundation of all branches of chemistry.

We understand simple chemical systems well. They lie near chemistry's fuzzy boundary with physics, so they can often be described quite well by mathematical equations. We fare less well with more complicated systems. Even where our understanding is fairly thorough, we must make approximations, and often our knowledge is far from complete. Each year researchers provide new insights into the nature of matter and its interactions. Our scientific knowledge has been described as an expanding sphere that, as it grows, encounters an ever-enlarging frontier.

In our search for understanding, we must ask fundamental questions, such as:

How do substances combine to form other substances? How much energy is involved in changes that we observe?

How is matter constructed in its intimate detail? How are atoms and the ways that they combine related to properties that we can measure, such as color, hardness, chemical reactivity, and electrical conductivity?

What fundamental factors influence the stability of a substance? How can we force a desired (but energetically unfavorable) change to take place? What factors control the rate at which a chemical change takes place?

In your study of chemistry, you will learn about these and many other basic ideas that chemists have developed to help them describe and understand the behavior of matter. Along the way, we hope that you come to appreciate the development of this science, one of the grandest intellectual achievements of human endeavor. You will also learn how to apply these fundamental principles to solve real problems. One of your major goals in the study of chemistry should be to develop the ability to think critically and to solve problems (not just do numerical calculations!). In other words, you need to learn to manipulate not only numbers, but also ideas, words, and concepts.

In this chapter, our main goals are (1) to begin to get an idea of what chemistry is about and the ways in which chemists view and describe the material world and (2) to acquire some skills that are useful and necessary in the understanding of chemistry, its contribution to science and engineering, and its role in our daily lives.

1-1 Matter and Energy

Matter is anything that has mass and occupies space. **Mass** is a measure of the quantity of matter in a sample of any material. The more massive an object is, the more force is needed to put it in motion. All bodies consist of matter. Our senses of sight and touch usually tell us that an object occupies space. In the case of colorless, odorless, tasteless gases (such as air), our senses may fail us.

Energy is defined as the capacity to do work or to transfer heat. We are familiar with many forms of energy, including mechanical energy, light energy, electrical energy, and heat energy. Light energy from the sun is used by plants as they grow, electrical energy allows us to light a room by flicking a switch, and heat energy cooks our food and warms our homes. Energy can be classified into two principal types: kinetic energy and potential energy.

A body in motion, such as a rolling boulder, possesses energy because of its motion. Such energy is called **kinetic energy**. Kinetic energy represents the capacity for doing work directly. It is easily transferred between objects. **Potential energy** is the energy an object possesses because of its position, condition, or composition. Coal, for example, possesses chemical energy, a form of potential energy, because of its composition. Many electrical generating plants burn coal, producing heat, which is converted to electrical energy. A boulder located atop a mountain possesses potential energy because of its height and the presence of gravity. It can roll down the mountainside and convert its potential energy into kinetic energy.

We discuss energy because all chemical processes are accompanied by energy changes. As some processes occur, energy is released to the surroundings, usually as heat energy. We call such processes **exothermic**. Any combustion (burning) reaction is exothermic. Some chemical reactions and physical changes, however, are **endothermic**; that is, they absorb energy from their surroundings. An example of a physical change that is endothermic is the melting of ice.

The Law of Conservation of Matter

When we burn a sample of metallic magnesium in oxygen, the magnesium combines with the oxygen (Figure 1-1) to form magnesium oxide, a white powder. This chemical reaction is accompanied by the release of large amounts of energy in the form of heat and light. When we weigh the product of the reaction, magnesium oxide, we find that it is heavier than the original piece of magnesium. The increase in the mass of the solid is due to the combination of oxygen with magnesium to form magnesium oxide. Many experiments have shown that the mass of the magnesium oxide is exactly the sum of the masses of magnesium and oxygen that combined to form it. Similar statements can be made for all chemical reactions. These observations are summarized in the **Law of Conservation of Matter**:

> There is no observable change in the quantity of matter during a chemical reaction or during a physical change.

This statement is an example of a **scientific (natural) law**, a general statement based on the observed behavior of matter to which no exceptions are known. A nuclear reaction, in which mass is converted into energy, or sometimes energy into mass, is *not* a chemical reaction.

The Law of Conservation of Energy

In exothermic chemical reactions, *chemical energy* is usually converted into *heat energy*. Some exothermic processes involve other kinds of energy changes. For example, some liberate light energy without heat, and others produce electrical energy without heat or light. In *endothermic* reactions, heat energy, light energy, or electrical energy is converted into chemical energy. Although chemical changes always involve energy changes, some energy transformations do not involve chemical changes at all. For example, heat energy may be converted into electrical energy or into mechanical energy without any simultane-

▶ We might say that we can "touch" air when it blows in our faces, but we depend on other evidence to show that a still body of air fits our definition of matter.

▶ The term "kinetic" comes from the Greek word *kinein*, meaning "to move." The word "cinema" is derived from the same Greek word.

▶ Nuclear energy is an important kind of potential energy.

Figure 1-1 Magnesium burns in oxygen to form magnesium oxide, a white solid. The mass of magnesium oxide formed is equal to the sum of the masses of oxygen and magnesium that formed it.

ous chemical changes. Many experiments have demonstrated that all the energy involved in any chemical or physical change appears in some form after the change. These observations are summarized in the **Law of Conservation of Energy**:

Energy cannot be created or destroyed in a chemical reaction or in a physical change. It can only be converted from one form to another.

▶ Electricity is produced in hydroelectric plants by the conversion of mechanical energy (from flowing water) into electrical energy.

The Law of Conservation of Matter and Energy

With the dawn of the nuclear age in the 1940s, scientists, and then the world, became aware that matter can be converted into energy. In nuclear reactions (Chapter 22), matter is transformed into energy. The relationship between matter and energy is given by Albert Einstein's now famous equation

$$E = mc^2$$

This equation says that the amount of energy released when matter is transformed into energy is the mass of matter transformed times the speed of light squared. Even a hydrogen bomb converts only a small amount of matter into energy. At the present time, we have not (knowingly) observed the transformation of energy into matter on a large scale. Matter-to-energy conversions do happen frequently on an extremely small scale in "atom smashers" (particle accelerators) used to induce nuclear reactions. Now that the equivalence of matter and energy is recognized, the **Law of Conservation of Matter and Energy** can be stated in a single sentence:

▶ Einstein formulated this equation in 1905 as a part of his theory of relativity. Its validity was demonstrated in 1939 with the first controlled nuclear reaction.

The combined amount of matter and energy available in the universe is fixed.

1-2 Chemistry—A Molecular View of Matter

The tremendous variety of matter present in our world consists of combinations of only about 100 basic substances called *elements*. Our everyday experiences with matter take place at the **macroscale**, that is, dealing with samples of matter of a size that we can see, handle, and manipulate. But the basic building blocks of matter are atoms and molecules, which make up elements and compounds. In our interactions with matter, we do not handle or typically observe these exceedingly tiny individual particles. Atoms and molecules exist at the **nanoscale**. (The general meaning of the prefix "nano" is *exceedingly small*; as we shall see later in this chapter, it has a definite numerical meaning of *one-billionth of*.) The chemical view of nature is that everything in the world around us is made up of atoms combined in very definite ways. Most substances are made up of small units called *molecules*. All of the properties and behavior of matter result from the properties of their atoms and molecules and the ways that they interact with one another. Throughout our study of chemistry, we always try to relate our macroscopic observations of matter to the nanoscale properties and behavior of its constituent atoms and molecules. Understanding these relationships is the very essence of chemistry; it provides us with a powerful way to describe the world around us and with the hope of exercising some responsible control over it as we seek answers to questions such as those that opened this chapter.

STOP & THINK
One nanometer, nm, is equivalent to 10 angstroms, Å, a unit commonly used for atomic distances. All atoms and many small molecules are less than 1 nm in size and are, therefore, subnano.

Throughout this book, we will study atoms and molecules in much more detail. For now, let's look at some of the basic ways that chemists represent and think about these important particles.

The Greek philosopher Democritus (470–400 BC) suggested that all matter is composed of tiny, discrete, indivisible particles that he called *atoms*. His ideas, based entirely on philosophical speculation rather than experimental evidence, were rejected for 2000 years. By the late 1700s, scientists began to realize that the concept of atoms provided an explanation for many experimental observations about the nature of matter.

By the early 1800s, the Law of Conservation of Matter (see Section 1-1) and the Law of Definite Proportions (see Section 1-6) were both accepted as general descriptions of how

▶ The term "atom" comes from the Greek language and means "not divided" or "indivisible." We now know that atoms are "divisible" and are composed of smaller subatomic particles.

matter behaves. John Dalton (1766–1844), an English schoolteacher, tried to explain why matter behaves in such systematic ways as those expressed here. In 1808, he published the first "modern" ideas about the existence and nature of atoms. Dalton's explanation summarized and expanded the nebulous concepts of early philosophers and scientists; more importantly, his ideas were based on *reproducible experimental results* of measurements by many scientists. These ideas form the core of **Dalton's Atomic Theory**, one of the highlights in the history of scientific thought. In condensed form, Dalton's ideas may be stated as follows:

▶ The radius of a calcium atom is only 0.000 000 019 7 cm, and its mass is 0.000 000 000 000 000 000 000 066 6 g. Later in this chapter, we will learn a better way to represent these numbers.

1. An element is composed of extremely small, indivisible particles called *atoms*.
2. All atoms of a given element have identical properties that differ from those of other elements.
3. Atoms cannot be created, destroyed, or transformed into atoms of another element via chemical or physical changes.
4. Compounds are formed when atoms of different elements combine with one another in small whole-number ratios.
5. The relative numbers and kinds of atoms are constant in a given compound.

Dalton believed that atoms were solid, indivisible spheres, an idea we now reject. But he showed remarkable insight into the nature of matter and its interactions. Some of his ideas could not be verified (or refuted) experimentally at the time. They were based on the limited experimental observations of his day. Even with their shortcomings, Dalton's ideas provided a framework that could be modified and expanded by later scientists. Thus John Dalton is often considered to be the father of modern atomic theory.

The smallest particle of an element that maintains its chemical identity through all chemical and physical changes is called an **atom** (Figure 1-2). In Chapter 4, we will study the structure of the atom in detail; let us simply summarize here the main features of atomic composition. Atoms, and therefore *all* matter, consist principally of three **fundamental particles**: *electrons*, *protons*, and *neutrons*. These are the basic building blocks of atoms. The masses and charges of the three fundamental particles are shown in Table 1-1. The masses of protons and neutrons are nearly equal, but the mass of an electron is much smaller. Neutrons carry no charge. The charge on a proton is equal in magnitude, but opposite in sign, to the charge on an electron. Because any atom is electrically neutral it contains an equal number of electrons and protons.

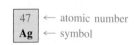

atomic number — 47

symbol — **Ag**

The **atomic number** (symbol is Z) of an element is defined as the number of protons in the nucleus. In the periodic table, elements are arranged in order of increasing atomic numbers. These are the red numbers above the symbols for the elements in the periodic table on the inside front cover. For example, the atomic number of silver is 47.

▶ For the elements in column 8A, the noble gases, a molecule contains only one atom, so an atom and a molecule are the same (see Figure 1-2).

A **molecule** is the smallest particle of an element or compound that can have a stable independent existence. In nearly all molecules, two or more atoms are bonded together in very small, discrete units (particles) that are electrically neutral.

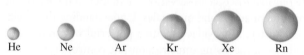

He   Ne   Ar   Kr   Xe   Rn

Figure 1-2 Relative sizes for atoms of the noble gases.

Table 1-1 Fundamental Particles of Matter

Particle (symbol)	Approximate Mass (amu)*	Charge (relative scale)
electron (e^-)	0.0	$1-$
proton (p or p^+)	1.0	$1+$
neutron (n or n^0)	1.0	none

* 1 amu $= 1.6605 \times 10^{-24}$ g.

Individual oxygen atoms, for example, are not stable at room temperature and atmospheric pressure. At these conditions, atoms of oxygen quickly combine to form pairs connected by chemical bonds. The oxygen with which we are all familiar is made up of two atoms of oxygen; it is a *diatomic* molecule with the formula O_2. Hydrogen, nitrogen, fluorine, chlorine, bromine, and iodine are other examples of diatomic molecules (Figure 1-3).

Some other elements exist as more complex molecules. One form of phosphorus molecules consists of four atoms, and sulfur exists as eight-atom ring-shaped molecules at ordinary temperatures and pressures. Molecules that contain two or more atoms are called *polyatomic* molecules (Figure 1-4).

In modern terminology, O_2 is named dioxygen, H_2 is dihydrogen, P_4 is tetraphosphorus, and so on. Even though such terminology is officially preferred, it has not yet gained wide acceptance. Most chemists still refer to O_2 as oxygen, H_2 as hydrogen, P_4 as phosphorus, and so on.

Molecules of compounds are composed of more than one kind of atom in a definite ratio. A water molecule consists of two atoms of hydrogen and one atom of oxygen. A molecule of methane consists of one carbon atom and four hydrogen atoms. The shapes of a few molecules are shown in Figure 1-5 as ball-and-stick models.

▶ You should remember the common elements that exist as diatomic molecules: H_2, N_2, O_2, F_2, Cl_2, Br_2, I_2.

Some common prefixes:
di = two
tri = three
tetra = four
penta = five
hexa = six
poly = more than one

▶ Methane, CH_4, is the principal component of natural gas.

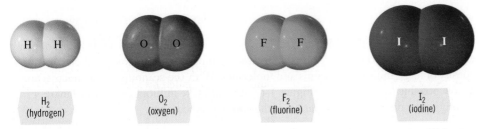

H₂
(hydrogen)

O₂
(oxygen)

F₂
(fluorine)

I₂
(iodine)

Figure 1-3 Models of diatomic molecules of some elements, approximately to scale. These are called *space-filling models* because they show the atoms with their approximate relative sizes.

Ⓐ A model of the P₄ molecule of white phosphorus

Ⓑ A model of the S₈ ring found in rhombic sulfur

Ⓒ Top view of the S₈ ring in rhombic sulfur

Figure 1-4 Space-filling models of some polyatomic elements.

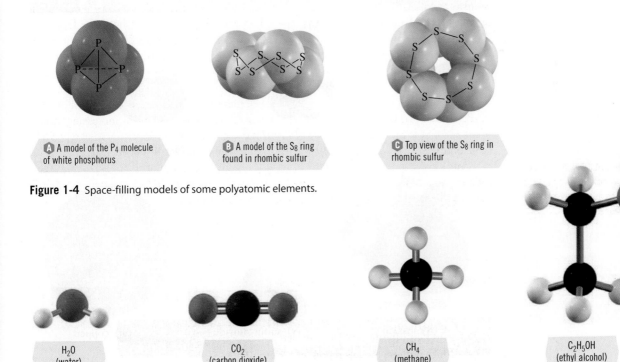

H₂O
(water)

CO₂
(carbon dioxide)

CH₄
(methane)

C₂H₅OH
(ethyl alcohol)

Figure 1-5 Formulas and ball-and-stick models for molecules of some compounds. Ball-and-stick models represent the atoms as smaller spheres than in space-filling models, in order to show the chemical bonds between the atoms as "sticks." Single "sticks" between atoms represent single bonds, two sticks represent double bonds, three sticks represent triple bonds, etc.

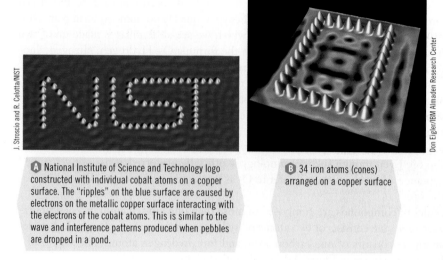

A National Institute of Science and Technology logo constructed with individual cobalt atoms on a copper surface. The "ripples" on the blue surface are caused by electrons on the metallic copper surface interacting with the electrons of the cobalt atoms. This is similar to the wave and interference patterns produced when pebbles are dropped in a pond.

B 34 iron atoms (cones) arranged on a copper surface

Figure 1-6

Atoms are the building blocks of molecules, and molecules are the stable forms of many elements and compounds. We are able to study samples of compounds and elements that consist of large numbers of atoms and molecules. With the scanning probe microscope it is now possible to "see" atoms (Figure 1-6). It would take millions of atoms to make a row as long as the diameter of the period at the end of this sentence.

EXAMPLE 1-1 Models

MOLECULAR REASONING

Look at each of the following models:

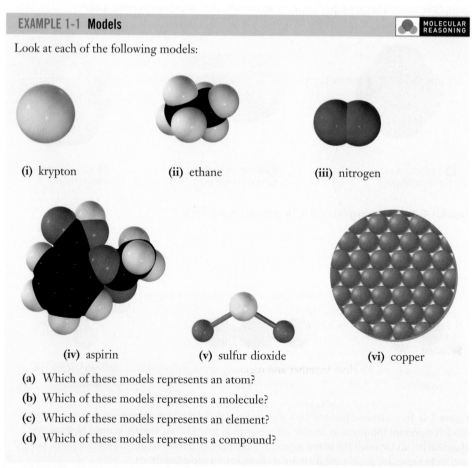

(i) krypton   **(ii)** ethane   **(iii)** nitrogen

(iv) aspirin   **(v)** sulfur dioxide   **(vi)** copper

(a) Which of these models represents an atom?

(b) Which of these models represents a molecule?

(c) Which of these models represents an element?

(d) Which of these models represents a compound?

Plan

We use the descriptions of atoms, molecules, elements, and compounds given earlier in this section.

Solution

(a) An atom is the smallest particle of an element. Only model i represents a single atom.

(b) A molecule can be a single stable atom of an element or it can consist of a definite number of atoms (the same or different). Models i, ii, iii, iv, and v represent molecules.

(c) An element contains a single kind of atom. Models i, iii, and vi represent elements.

(d) A compound contains atoms of two or more different elements. Models ii, iv, and v represent compounds.

You should now work Exercise 18.

▶ With many examples we suggest selected exercises from the end of the chapter. These exercises use the skills or concepts from that example.

1-3 States of Matter

Matter can be classified into three states (Figure 1-7), although we might think of examples that do not fit neatly into any of the three categories. In the **solid** state, substances are rigid and have definite shapes. Volumes of solids do not vary much with changes in temperature and pressure. In crystalline solids, the individual particles that make up the solid occupy definite positions in the crystal structure. The strengths of interaction between the individual particles determine how hard and how strong the crystals are. In the **liquid** state, the individual particles are confined to a given volume. A liquid flows and assumes the shape of its container up to the volume of the liquid because the molecules are randomly oriented and have weaker forces of attraction between them relative to solids.

▶ We often represent the physical state of a substance with notations in parenthesis: (g) for gases, (ℓ) for liquids, (s) for solids.

EXAMPLE 1-2 Models

Identify the state of matter represented by each of the following models.

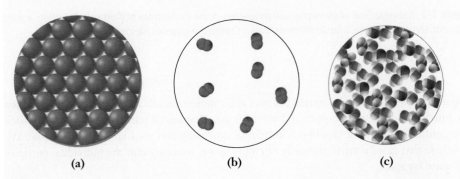

| (a) | (b) | (c) |

Plan

In a solid, the molecules are held close together in a regular arrangement. In a liquid, the molecules are close together but are randomly arranged because they flow past one another. In a gas, molecules are far apart.

Solution

(a) The atoms are close together and regularly arranged, so this model represents the surface of a solid.

(b) The molecules are far apart, so this model represents a gas.

(c) The molecules are close together but randomly arranged, so this model represents a liquid.

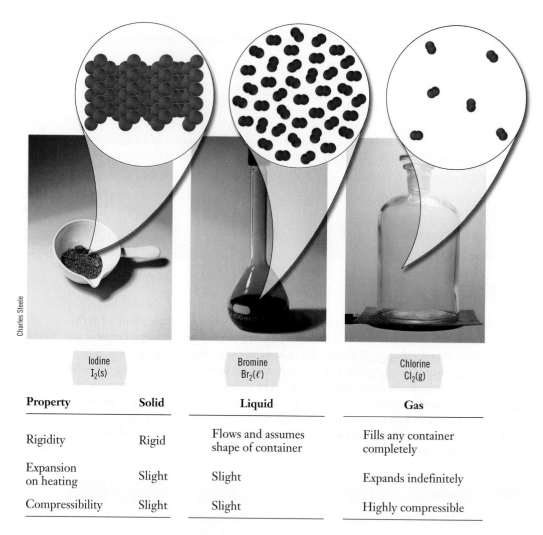

Charles Steele

Property	Solid	Liquid	Gas
Rigidity	Rigid	Flows and assumes shape of container	Fills any container completely
Expansion on heating	Slight	Slight	Expands indefinitely
Compressibility	Slight	Slight	Highly compressible

Figure 1-7 A comparison of some physical properties of the three states of matter. (*left*) Iodine, a solid element. (*center*) Bromine, a liquid element. (*right*) Chlorine, a gaseous element.

Liquids are very hard to compress because their molecules are very close together. **Gases** are much less dense than liquids and solids. A gas occupies all parts of any vessel in which it is confined. Gases are capable of indefinite expansion and are highly compressible. We conclude that gases consist primarily of empty space, meaning that the individual particles are quite far apart.

1-4 Chemical and Physical Properties

To distinguish among samples of different kinds of matter, we determine and compare their **properties**. We recognize different kinds of matter by their properties. We can broadly classify these into chemical properties and physical properties.

▶ The properties of a person include height, weight, sex, skin and hair color, and the many subtle features that constitute that person's general appearance.

Chemical properties are exhibited by matter as it undergoes changes in composition. These properties of substances are related to the kinds of chemical changes that the substances undergo. For instance, we have already described the combination of metallic magnesium with gaseous oxygen to form magnesium oxide, a white powder. A chemical property of magnesium is that it can combine with oxygen, releasing energy in the process. A chemical property of oxygen is that it can combine with magnesium.

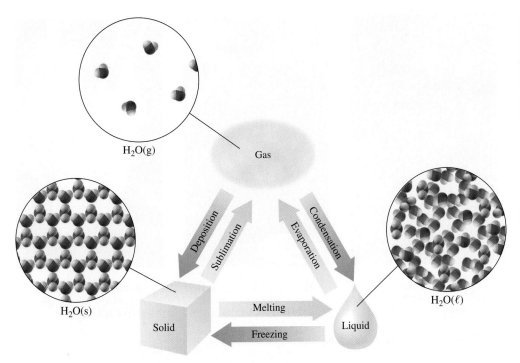

Figure 1-8 Physical changes that occur among the three states of matter. *Sublimation* is the conversion of a solid directly to a gas without passing through the liquid state; the reverse of that process is called *deposition*. The changes shown in blue are endothermic (absorb heat); those shown in red are exothermic (release heat). Water is a substance that is familiar to us in all three physical states. Molecules are close together in a solid and a liquid but far apart in a gas. The molecules in the solid are relatively fixed in position, but those in the liquid and gas can flow around each other.

All substances also exhibit **physical properties** that can be observed in the *absence of any change in composition*. Color, density, hardness, melting point, boiling point, and electrical and thermal conductivities are physical properties. Some physical properties of a substance depend on the conditions, such as temperature and pressure, under which they are measured. For instance, water is a solid (ice) at low temperatures but is a liquid at higher temperatures. At still higher temperatures, it is a gas (steam). As water is converted from one state to another, its composition is constant. Its chemical properties change very little. On the other hand, the physical properties of ice, liquid water, and steam are very different (Figure 1-8).

Properties of matter can be further classified according to whether they depend on the *amount* of substance present. The volume and the mass of a sample depend on (and are directly proportional to) the amount of matter in that sample. Such properties, which depend on the amount of material examined, are called **extensive properties**. By contrast, the color and the melting point of a substance are the same for a small sample as for a large one. Properties such as these are independent of the amount of material examined; they are called **intensive properties**. All chemical properties are intensive properties.

Because no two different substances have identical sets of chemical and physical properties under the same conditions, we can identify and distinguish among different substances. For instance, water is the only clear, colorless liquid that freezes at 0°C, boils at 100°C at one atmosphere of pressure, dissolves a wide variety of substances (e.g., copper(II) sulfate), and reacts violently with sodium (Figure 1-9). Table 1-2 compares several physical properties of a few substances. A sample of any of these substances can be distinguished from the others by observing their properties.

▶ Many compilations of chemical and physical properties of matter can be found on the internet. One site is maintained by the U.S. National Institute of Standards and Technology (NIST) at **webbook.nist.gov**. Perhaps you can find other sites.

▶ *One atmosphere* of pressure is the average atmospheric pressure at sea level.

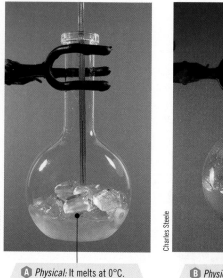

A *Physical:* It melts at 0°C.

B *Physical:* It boils at 100°C (at normal atmospheric pressure).

C *Physical:* It dissolves a wide range of substances, including copper(II) sulfate, a blue solid.

D *Chemical:* It reacts violently with sodium to form hydrogen gas and sodium hydroxide.

Figure 1-9 Some physical and chemical properties of water.

acetic acid

benzene

bromine

methane

oxygen

water

Table 1-2 Physical Properties of a Few Common Substances (at 1 atm pressure)

| Substance | Melting Point (°C) | Boiling Point (°C) | Solubility at 25° C (g/100 g) | | Density (g/cm³) |
			In water	*In ethyl alcohol*	
acetic acid	16.6	118.1	infinite	infinite	1.05
benzene	5.5	80.1	0.07	infinite	0.879
bromine	−7.1	58.8	3.51	infinite	3.12
iron	1530	3000	insoluble	insoluble	7.86
methane	−182.5	−161.5	0.0022	0.033	0.000667
oxygen	−218.8	−183.0	0.0040	0.037	0.00133
sodium chloride	801	1473	36.5	0.065	2.16
water	0	100	—	infinite	1.00

1-5 Chemical and Physical Changes

We described the reaction of magnesium as it burns in oxygen (see Figure 1-1). This is a *chemical change* or *chemical reaction*. In any **chemical change**, (1) one or more substances are used up (at least partially), (2) one or more new substances are formed, and (3) energy is absorbed or released. As substances undergo chemical changes, they demonstrate their chemical properties. A **physical change**, on the other hand, occurs with *no change in chemical composition*. Physical properties are usually altered significantly as matter undergoes physical changes (see Figure 1-8). In addition, a physical change *may* suggest that a chemical change has also taken place. For instance, a color change, a warming, or the formation of a solid when two solutions are mixed could indicate a chemical change.

Energy is always released or absorbed when chemical or physical changes occur. Energy is absorbed when ice melts, and energy is absorbed when water boils. Conversely, the condensation of steam to form liquid water always releases energy, as does the freezing of liquid water to form ice. The changes in energy that accompany these physical changes for

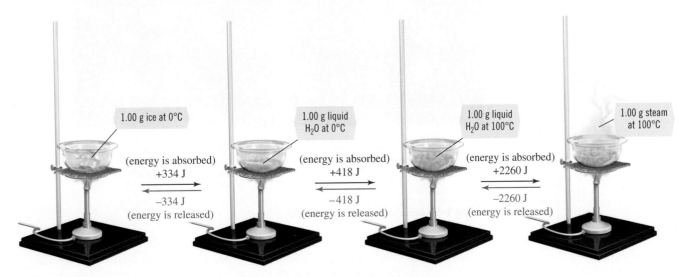

Figure 1-10 Changes in energy that accompany some physical changes for water. The energy unit joules (J) is defined in Section 1-13. Absorption of energy is denoted with a positive sign. Release of energy is denoted with a negative sign.

water are shown in Figure 1-10. At a pressure of one atmosphere, ice always melts at the same temperature (0°C), and pure water always boils at the same temperature (100°C).

1-6 Mixtures, Substances, Compounds, and Elements

A **mixture** is a combination of two or more pure substances in which each substance retains its own composition and properties. Almost every sample of matter that we ordinarily encounter is a mixture. The most easily recognized type of mixture is one that is not uniform throughout. Such a mixture, in which different portions of the sample have recognizably different properties, is called **heterogeneous**. Examples include mixtures of salt and charcoal (in which two components with different colors can be distinguished readily from each other by sight), foggy air (which includes a suspended mist of water droplets), and vegetable soup. Another kind of mixture has uniform properties throughout; such a mixture is described as a **homogeneous mixture** and is also called a **solution**. Examples include salt water; some *alloys*, which are homogeneous mixtures of metals in the solid state; and air (free of particulate matter or mists). Air is a mixture of nitrogen, oxygen, argon, carbon dioxide, and water vapor. There are only trace amounts of other substances in the atmosphere.

▶ By "composition of a mixture," we mean both the identities of the substances present and their relative amounts in the mixture.

▶ The blue copper(II) sulfate solution in Figure 1-9c is a homogeneous mixture.

An important characteristic of all mixtures is that they can have variable composition. (For instance, we can make an infinite number of different mixtures of salt and sugar by varying the relative amounts of the two components used.) Consequently, repeating the same experiment on mixtures from different sources may give different results, whereas the same treatment of a pure sample will always give the same results. When the distinction between homogeneous mixtures and pure substances was realized and methods were developed (in the late 1700s) for separating mixtures and studying pure substances, consistent results were obtained. This resulted in reproducible chemical properties, which formed the basis of real progress in the development of chemistry.

A mixture can be separated by physical means because each component retains its properties (Figures 1-11 and 1-12). For example, a mixture of salt and water can be separated by evaporating the water and leaving the solid salt behind. To separate a mixture of sand and salt, we could treat it with water to dissolve the salt, collect the sand by filtration, and then evaporate the water to reclaim the solid salt. Very fine iron powder can be mixed with powdered sulfur to give what appears to the naked eye to be a homogeneous mixture of the two. Separation of the components of this mixture is easy, however. The iron may be removed by a magnet (see Figure 1-11), or the sulfur may be dissolved in carbon disulfide, which does not dissolve iron.

A T-bone steak is a heterogeneous mixture of white fat, bone, and red meat. Each of these macroscopic items is in turn heterogeneous. For example, the meat is composed of blood vessels, protein structures, fine tendons, etc.

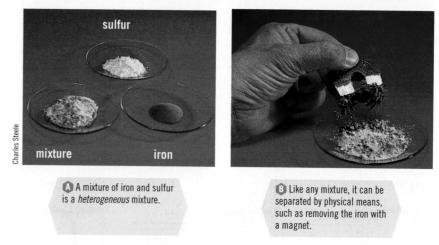

A mixture of iron and sulfur is a *heterogeneous* mixture.

B Like any mixture, it can be separated by physical means, such as removing the iron with a magnet.

Figure 1-11 Separation by physical means.

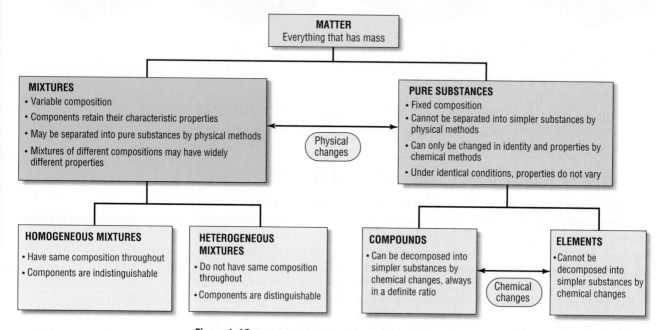

Figure 1-12 One scheme for classification of matter. Arrows indicate the general means by which matter can be separated.

In *any* mixture, (1) the composition can be varied and (2) each component of the mixture retains its own properties.

▶ The first ice that forms is quite pure. The dissolved solids tend to stay behind in the remaining liquid.

Suppose we have a sample of muddy river water (a heterogeneous mixture). We might first separate the suspended dirt from the liquid by filtration. Then we could remove dissolved air by warming the water. Dissolved solids might be removed by cooling the sample until some of it freezes, pouring off the liquid, and then melting the ice. Other dissolved components might be separated by distillation or other methods. Eventually we would obtain a sample of pure water that could not be further separated by any physical separation methods. No matter what the original source of the impure water—the ocean, the Mississippi River, a can of tomato juice—water samples obtained by purification all have identical composition, and, under identical conditions, they all have identical properties. Any such sample is called a *substance*, or sometimes a *pure substance*.

▶ If we use the definition given here of a *substance*, the phrase *pure substance* may appear to be redundant.

A **substance** cannot be further broken down or purified by physical means. A substance is matter of a particular kind. Each substance has its own characteristic properties that are different from the set of properties of any other substance.

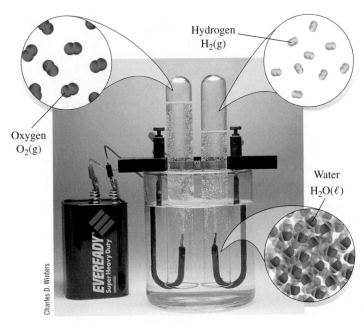

Figure 1-13 Electrolysis apparatus for small-scale chemical decomposition of liquid water by electrical energy. The volume of hydrogen gas produced (*right*) is twice that of oxygen gas (*left*). Some dilute sulfuric acid is added to increase the conductivity.

Now suppose we decompose some water by passing electricity through it (Figure 1-13). (This *electrolysis* process is a chemical reaction.) We find that the water is converted into two simpler substances, hydrogen and oxygen; furthermore, hydrogen and oxygen are *always* present in the same ratio by mass, 11.1% to 88.9%. These observations allow us to identify water as a compound.

A **compound** is a substance that can be decomposed by chemical means into simpler substances, always in the same ratio by mass.

As we continue such a process starting with any substance, we eventually reach a stage at which the new substances formed cannot be further broken down by chemical means. The substances at the end of this chain are called *elements*.

An **element** is a substance that cannot be decomposed into simpler substances by chemical changes.

For instance, neither of the two gases obtained by the electrolysis of water—hydrogen and oxygen—can be further decomposed, so we know that they are elements.

As another illustration (Figure 1-14), pure calcium carbonate (a white solid present in limestone and seashells) can be broken down by heating to give another white solid (call it A) and a gas (call it B) in the mass ratio 56.0:44.0. This observation tells us that calcium carbonate is a compound. The white solid A obtained from calcium carbonate can be further broken down into a solid and a gas in a definite ratio by mass, 71.5:28.5. But neither of these can be further decomposed, so they must be elements. The gas is identical to the oxygen obtained from the electrolysis of water; the solid is a metallic element called calcium. Similarly, the gas B, originally obtained from calcium carbonate, can be decomposed into two elements, carbon and oxygen, in a fixed mass ratio, 27.3:72.7. This sequence illustrates that a compound can be broken apart into simpler substances with a fixed mass ratio; these may be either elements or simpler compounds.

Furthermore, we may say that *a compound is a pure substance consisting of two or more different elements in a fixed ratio*. Water is 11.1% hydrogen and 88.9% oxygen by mass.

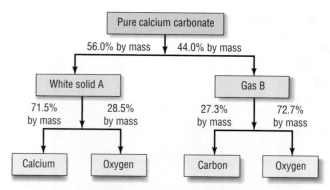

Figure 1-14 Diagram of the decomposition of calcium carbonate to give a white solid A (56.0% by mass) and a gas B (44.0% by mass). This decomposition into simpler substances at a fixed ratio proves that calcium carbonate is a compound. The white solid A further decomposes to give the elements calcium (71.5% by mass) and oxygen (28.5% by mass). This proves that the white solid A is a compound; it is known as calcium oxide. The gas B also can be broken down to give the elements carbon (27.3% by mass) and oxygen (72.7% by mass). This establishes that gas B is a compound; it is known as carbon dioxide.

Similarly, carbon dioxide is 27.3% carbon and 72.7% oxygen by mass, and calcium oxide (the white solid A in the previous discussion) is 71.5% calcium and 28.5% oxygen by mass. We could also combine the numbers in the previous paragraph to show that calcium carbonate is 40.1% calcium, 12.0% carbon, and 47.9% oxygen by mass. Observations such as these on many pure compounds led to the statement of the **Law of Definite Proportions** (also known as the **Law of Constant Composition**):

> Different samples of any pure compound contain the same elements in the same proportions by mass.

The physical and chemical properties of a compound are different from the properties of its constituent elements. Sodium chloride is a white solid that we ordinarily use as table salt (Figure 1-15). This compound is formed by the combination of the element sodium (a soft, silvery white metal that reacts violently with water; see Figure 1-9d) and the element chlorine (a pale green, corrosive, poisonous gas; see the right panel of Figure 1-7).

Recall that elements are substances that cannot be decomposed into simpler substances by chemical changes. Nitrogen, silver, aluminum, copper, gold, and sulfur are other examples of elements.

We use a set of **symbols** to represent the elements. These symbols can be written more quickly than names, and they occupy less space. The symbols for the first 109 elements consist of either a capital letter *or* a capital letter and a lowercase letter, such as C (carbon) or Ca (calcium). A list of the known elements and their symbols is given inside the front cover.

In the past, the discoverers of elements claimed the right to name them, although the question of who had actually discovered the elements first was sometimes disputed. In modern times, each new element is given a temporary name and a three-letter symbol based on a numerical system. This designation is used until the question of the right to name the newly discovered element is resolved. Decisions resolving the names of elements 104 through 112 have been announced by the International Union of Pure and Applied Chemistry (IUPAC), an international organization that represents chemical societies from 40 countries. IUPAC makes recommendations regarding many matters of convention and terminology in chemistry. These recommendations carry no legal force, but they are normally viewed as authoritative throughout the world.

A short list of symbols of common elements is given in Table 1-3. Many symbols consist of the first one or two letters of the element's English name. Some are derived from the element's Latin name (indicated in parentheses in Table 1-3) and one, W for tungsten, is from the German *Wolfram*. You should learn the list in Table 1-3. Names and symbols for additional elements should be learned as they are needed.

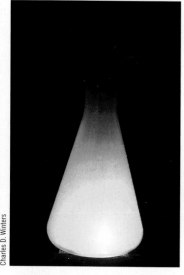

Figure 1-15 The reaction of sodium, a solid element, and chlorine, a gaseous element, to produce sodium chloride (table salt). This reaction gives off considerable energy in the form of heat and light.

▶ See the essay "Names of the Elements" on page 18.

Most of the earth's crust is made up of a relatively small number of elements. Only 10 of the 88 naturally occurring elements make up more than 99% by mass of the earth's crust, oceans, and atmosphere (Table 1-4). Oxygen accounts for roughly half, mainly in the form of water or oxide minerals. Relatively few elements, approximately one-fourth of the naturally occurring ones, occur in nature as free elements. The rest are always found chemically combined with other elements.

A very small amount of the matter in the earth's crust, oceans, and atmosphere is involved in living matter. The main element in living matter is carbon, but only a tiny fraction of the carbon in the environment occurs in living organisms. More than one-quarter of the total mass of the earth's crust, oceans, and atmosphere is made up of silicon, yet it has almost no biological role.

▶ The other known elements have been made artificially in laboratories, as described in Chapter 22.

Table 1-3 Some Common Elements and Their Symbols

Symbol	Element	Symbol	Element	Symbol	Element
Ag	silver (*argentum*)	F	fluorine	Ni	nickel
Al	aluminum	Fe	iron (*ferrum*)	O	oxygen
Au	gold (*aurum*)	H	hydrogen	P	phosphorus
B	boron	He	helium	Pb	lead (*plumbum*)
Ba	barium	Hg	mercury (*hydrargyrum*)	Pt	platinum
Bi	bismuth	I	iodine	S	sulfur
Br	bromine	K	potassium (*kalium*)	Sb	antimony (*stibium*)
C	carbon	Kr	krypton	Si	silicon
Ca	calcium	Li	lithium	Sn	tin (*stannum*)
Cd	cadmium	Mg	magnesium	Sr	strontium
Cl	chlorine	Mn	manganese	Ti	titanium
Co	cobalt	N	nitrogen	U	uranium
Cr	chromium	Na	sodium (*natrium*)	W	tungsten (*Wolfram*)
Cu	copper (*cuprum*)	Ne	neon	Zn	zinc

Mercury is the only metal that is a liquid at room temperature.

Table 1-4 Abundance of Elements in the Earth's Crust, Oceans, and Atmosphere

Element	Symbol	% by Mass		Element	Symbol	% by Mass	
oxygen	O	49.5%		chlorine	Cl	0.19%	
silicon	Si	25.7		phosphorus	P	0.12	
aluminum	Al	7.5		manganese	Mn	0.09	
iron	Fe	4.7		carbon	C	0.08	
calcium	Ca	3.4	99.2%	sulfur	S	0.06	0.7%
sodium	Na	2.6		barium	Ba	0.04	
potassium	K	2.4		chromium	Cr	0.033	
magnesium	Mg	1.9		nitrogen	N	0.030	
hydrogen	H	0.87		fluorine	F	0.027	
titanium	Ti	0.58		zirconium	Zr	0.023	
				all others combined		≈0.1%	

The stable form of sulfur at room temperature is a solid.

Names of the Elements

If you were to discover a new element, how would you name it? Throughout history, scientists have answered this question in different ways. Most have chosen to honor a person or place or to describe the new substance.

Until the Middle Ages only nine elements were known: gold, silver, tin, mercury, copper, lead, iron, sulfur, and carbon. The metals' chemical symbols are taken from descriptive Latin names: *aurum* ("yellow"), *argentum* ("shining"), *stannum* ("dripping" or "easily melted"), *hydrargyrum* ("silvery water"), *cuprum* ("Cyprus," where many copper mines were located), *plumbum* (exact meaning unknown—possibly "heavy"), and *ferrum* (also unknown). Mercury is named after the planet, one reminder that the ancients associated metals with gods and celestial bodies. In turn, both the planet, which moves rapidly across the sky, and the element, which is the only metal that is liquid at room temperature and thus flows rapidly, are named for the fleet god of messengers in Roman mythology. In English, mercury is nicknamed "quicksilver."

Prior to the reforms of Antoine Lavoisier (1743–1794), chemistry was a largely nonquantitative, unsystematic science in which experimenters had little contact with each other. In 1787, Lavoisier published his *Methode de Nomenclature Chimique,* which proposed, among other changes, that all new elements be named descriptively. For the next 125 years, most elements were given names that corresponded to their properties. Greek roots were one popular source, as evidenced by hydrogen (*hydros-gen,* "water-producing"), oxygen (*oksys-gen,* "acid-producing"), nitrogen (*nitron-gen,* "soda-producing"), bromine (*bromos,* "stink"), and argon (*a-er-gon,* "no reaction"). The discoverers of argon, Sir William Ramsay (1852–1916) and Baron Rayleigh (1842–1919), originally proposed the name *aeron* (from *aer* or "air"), but critics thought it was too close to the biblical name Aaron! Latin roots, such as *radius* ("ray"), were also used (radium and radon are both naturally radioactive elements that emit "rays"). Color was often the determining property, especially after the invention of the spectroscope in 1859, because different elements (or the light that they emit) have prominent characteristic colors. Cesium, indium, iodine, rubidium, and thallium were all named in this manner. Their respective Greek and Latin roots denote blue-gray, indigo, violet, red, and green (*thallus* means "tree sprout"). Because of the great variety of colors of its compounds, iridium takes its name from the Latin *iris,* meaning "rainbow." Alternatively, an element name might suggest a mineral or the ore that contained it. One example is Wolfram or tungsten (W), which was isolated from wolframite. Two other "inconsistent" elemental symbols, K and Na, arose from occurrence as well. *Kalium* was first obtained from the saltwort plant, *Salsola kali,* and *natrium* from niter. Their English names, potassium and sodium, are derived from the ores potash and soda.

Other elements, contrary to Lavoisier's suggestion, were named after planets, mythological figures, places, or superstitions. "Celestial elements" include helium ("sun"), tellurium ("earth"), selenium ("moon"—the element was discovered in close proximity to tellurium), cerium (the asteroid Ceres, which was discovered only two years before the element), and uranium (the planet Uranus, discovered a few years earlier). The first two transuranium elements (those *beyond* uranium) to be produced were named neptunium and plutonium for the next two planets, Neptune and Pluto. The names promethium (Prometheus, who stole fire from heaven), vanadium (Scandinavian goddess Vanadis), titanium (Titans, the first sons of the earth), tantalum (Tantalos, father of the Greek goddess Niobe), and thorium (Thor, Scandinavian god of war) all arise from Greek or Norse mythology.

"Geographical elements," shown on the map, sometimes honored the discoverer's native country or workplace. The Latin names for Russia (*ruthenium*), France (*gallium*), Paris (*lutetium*), and Germany (*germanium*) were among those used. Marie Sklodowska Curie named one of the elements that she discovered, polonium, after her native Poland. Often the locale of discovery lends its name to the element; the record holder is certainly the Swedish village Ytterby, the site of ores from which the four elements terbium, erbium, ytterbium, and yttrium were isolated. Elements honoring important scientists include curium, einsteinium, nobelium, fermium, and lawrencium.

Most of the elements now known were given titles peacefully, but a few were not. Niobium, isolated in 1803 by Ekeberg from an ore that also contained tantalum, and named after Niobe (daughter of Tantalos), was later found to be identical to an 1802 discovery of C. Hatchett, columbium. (Interestingly, Hatchett first found the element in an ore sample that had been sent to England more than a century earlier by John Winthrop, the first governor of Connecticut.) Although "niobium" became the accepted designation in Europe, the Americans, not surprisingly, chose "columbium." It was not until 1949—when the International Union of Pure and Applied Chemistry (IUPAC) ended more than a century of controversy by ruling in favor of mythology—that element 41 received a unique name.

In 1978, the IUPAC recommended that elements beyond 103 be known temporarily by systematic names based on numerical roots; element 104 is unnilquadium (*un* for 1, *nil* for 0, *quad* for 4, plus the *-ium* ending), followed by unnilpentium, unnilhexium, and so on. Arguments over the names of elements 104 and 105 prompted the IUPAC to begin hearing claims of priority to numbers 104 to 109. The IUPAC's final recommendations for these element names were announced in 1997. The names and symbols recommended by that report are: element 104, rutherfordium, Rf; element 105, dubnium, Db; element 106, seaborgium, Sg; element 107, bohrium, Bh; element 108, hassium, Hs; and element 109, meitnerium, Mt. Some of these (Rf and Bh) are derived from the names of scientists prominent in the development of atomic theory; others (Sg, Hs, and Mt) are named for scientists who were involved in the discovery of heavy elements. Dubnium is named in honor of the Dubna laboratory in the former Soviet Union, where important contributions to the creation of heavy elements have originated.

LISA SAUNDERS BAUGH

Many chemical elements were named after places. From Vivi Ringnes, "Origin and Names of Chemical Elements," *Journal of Chemical Education,* **66, 1989, 731–737. Reprinted by permission.**

1-7 Measurements in Chemistry

In the next section, we will introduce the standards for basic units of measurement. These standards were selected because they are reproducible and unchanging and because they allow us to make precise measurements. The values of fundamental units are arbitrary.[1] In the United States, all units of measure are set by the National Institute of Standards and Technology, NIST (formerly the National Bureau of Standards, NBS). Measurements in the scientific world are usually expressed in the units of the metric system or its modernized successor, the International System of Units (SI). The SI, adopted by the National Bureau of Standards in 1964, is based on the seven fundamental units listed in Table 1-5. All other units of measurement are derived from them.

▶ The abbreviation SI comes from the French *le Système International.*

In this text we shall use both metric units and SI units. Conversions between non-SI and SI units are usually straightforward. Appendix C lists some important units of measurement and their relationships to one another. Appendix D lists several useful physical constants. The most frequently used of these appear on the inside back cover.

The metric and SI systems are *decimal systems, in which prefixes are used to indicate fractions and multiples of ten.* The same prefixes are used with all units of measurement. The distances and masses in Table 1-6 illustrate the use of some common prefixes and the relationships among them.

Table 1-5 The Seven Fundamental Units of Measurement (SI)

Physical Property	Name of Unit	Symbol
length	meter	m
mass	kilogram	kg
time	second	s
electric current	ampere	A
temperature	kelvin	K
luminous intensity	candela	cd
amount of substance	mole	mol

Table 1-6 Common Prefixes Used in the SI and Metric Systems

Prefix	Abbreviation	Meaning	Example
mega-	M	10^6	1 megameter (Mm) = 1×10^6 m
kilo-*	k	10^3	1 kilometer (km) = 1×10^3 m
deci-	d	10^{-1}	1 decimeter (dm) = 1×10^{-1} m
centi-*	c	10^{-2}	1 centimeter (cm) = 1×10^{-2} m
milli-*	m	10^{-3}	1 milligram (mg) = 1×10^{-3} g
micro-*	μ[†]	10^{-6}	1 microgram (μg) = 1×10^{-6} g
nano-*	n	10^{-9}	1 nanogram (ng) = 1×10^{-9} g
pico-*	p	10^{-12}	1 picogram (pg) = 1×10^{-12} g

▶ The prefixes used in the SI and metric systems may be thought of as *multipliers.* For example, the prefix *kilo-* indicates multiplication by 1000 or 10^3, and *milli-* indicates multiplication by 0.001 or 10^{-3}.

*These prefixes are commonly used in chemistry.
[†]This is the Greek letter μ (pronounced "mew").

[1]Prior to the establishment of the National Bureau of Standards in 1901, at least 50 different distances had been used as "1 foot" in measuring land within New York City. Thus the size of a 100-ft by 200-ft lot in New York City depended on the generosity of the seller and did not necessarily represent the expected dimensions.

1-8 Units of Measurement

Mass and Weight

We distinguish between mass and weight. **Mass** is the measure of the quantity of matter a body contains (see Section 1-1). The mass of a body does not vary as its position changes. On the other hand, the **weight** of a body is a measure of the gravitational attraction of the earth for the body, and this varies with distance from the center of the earth. An object weighs very slightly less high up on a mountain than at the bottom of a deep valley. Because the mass of a body does not vary with its position, the mass of a body is a more fundamental property than its weight. We have become accustomed, however, to using the term "weight" when we mean mass, because weighing is one way of measuring mass (Figure 1-16). Because we usually discuss chemical reactions at constant gravity, weight relationships are just as valid as mass relationships. Nevertheless, we should keep in mind that the two are not identical.

The basic unit of mass in the SI system is the **kilogram** (Table 1-7). The kilogram is defined as the mass of a platinum–iridium cylinder stored in a vault in Sèvres, near Paris, France. A 1-lb object has a mass of 0.4536 kg. The basic mass unit in the earlier *metric system* was the gram. A U.S. five-cent coin (a "nickel") has a mass of about 5 g.

Length

The **meter** is the standard unit of length (distance) in both SI and metric systems. The meter is defined as the distance light travels in a vacuum in 1/299,792,468 second. It is approximately 39.37 inches. In situations in which the English system would use inches, the

Table 1-7 Some SI Units of Mass

*kilo*gram, kg	base unit
gram, g	1,000 g = 1 kg
*milli*gram, mg	1,000 mg = 1 g
*micro*gram, μg	1,000,000 μg = 1 g

Ⓐ A triple-beam balance used for determining mass to about ±0.01 g

Ⓑ A modern electronic top-loading balance that gives a direct readout of mass to ±0.001 g

Ⓒ A modern analytical balance that can be used to determine mass to ±0.0001 g. Analytical balances are used when masses must be determined as precisely as possible.

Figure 1-16 Three types of laboratory balances.

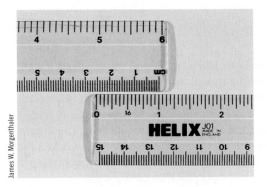

James W. Morgenthaler

Figure 1-17 The relationship between inches and centimeters: 1 in. = 2.54 cm (exactly).

metric centimeter (1/100 meter) is convenient. The relationship between inches and centimeters is shown in Figure 1-17.

Volume

Volumes are often measured in liters or milliliters in the metric system. One liter (1 L) is one cubic decimeter (1 dm³), or 1000 cubic centimeters (1000 cm³). One milliliter (1 mL) is 1 cm³. In medical laboratories, the cubic centimeter (cm³) is often abbreviated cc. In the SI, the cubic meter is the basic volume unit and the cubic decimeter replaces the metric unit, liter. Different kinds of glassware are used to measure the volume of liquids. The one we choose depends on the accuracy we desire. For example, the volume of a liquid dispensed can be measured more accurately with a buret than with a small graduated cylinder (Figure 1-18). Some equivalences between common English units and metric units are summarized in Table 1-8.

Sometimes we must combine two or more units to describe a quantity. For instance, we might express the speed of a car as 60 mi/h (also mph). Recall that the algebraic notation x^{-1} means $1/x$; applying this notation to units, we see that h^{-1} means $1/h$, or "per hour." So the unit of speed could also be expressed as $mi \cdot h^{-1}$.

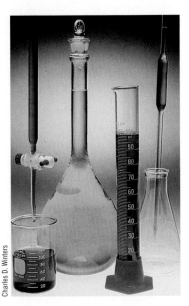

Charles D. Winters

Figure 1-18 Some laboratory apparatus used to measure volumes of liquids: 150-mL beaker (*bottom left*, green liquid); 25-mL buret (*top left*, red); 1000-mL volumetric flask (*center*, yellow); 100-mL graduated cylinder (*right front*, blue); and 10-mL volumetric pipet (*right rear*, green).

▶ The meter was originally defined (1791) as one ten-millionth of the distance between the North Pole and the equator.

Table 1-8 Some Conversion Factors Relating Length, Volume, and Mass (Weight) Units

	Metric		English		Metric-English Equivalents	
Length	1 km	= 10^3 m	1 ft	= 12 in.	2.54 cm	= 1 in.
	1 cm	= 10^{-2} m	1 yd	= 3 ft	39.37 in.*	= 1 m
	1 mm	= 10^{-3} m	1 mi	= 5280 ft	1.609 km*	= 1 mi
	1 nm	= 10^{-9} m				
	1 Å	= 10^{-10} m				
Volume	1 mL	= 1 cm³ = 10^{-3} L	1 gal	= 4 qt = 8 pt	1 L	= 1.057qt*
	1 m³	= 10^6 cm³ = 10^3 L	1 qt	= 57.75 in.³*	28.32 L	= 1 ft³*
Mass	1 kg	= 10^3 g	1 lb	= 16 oz	453.6 g*	= 1 lb
	1 mg	= 10^{-3} g			1 g	= 0.03527 oz*
	1 metric tonne	= 10^3 kg	1 short ton	= 2000 lb	1 metric tonne	= 1.102 short ton*

*These conversion factors, unlike the others listed, are inexact. They are quoted to four significant figures, which is ordinarily sufficient.

1-9 The Unit Factor Method (Dimensional Analysis)

Many chemical and physical processes can be described by numerical relationships. In fact, many of the most useful ideas in science must be treated mathematically. In chemistry, we measure and calculate many things, so we must understand how to use numbers. Two aspects of numbers are: (1) the notation of very large and very small numbers (scientific notation) and (2) an indication of how well we actually know the numbers we are using (significant figures). You will carry out many calculations with calculators. Please refer to Appendix A for a review of scientific notation and significant figures, and for some instructions about the use of electronic calculators. In this section, we review some problem-solving skills.

▶ It would be meaningless to say that the length of a piece of cloth is 4.7. We must specify units with the number—4.7 inches, 4.7 feet, or 4.7 meters, for instance.

Units must *always* accompany the numeric value of a measurement, whether we are writing about the quantity, talking about it, or using it in calculations.

Multiplication by unity (by one) does not change the value of an expression. If we represent "one" in a useful way, we can do many conversions by just "multiplying by one." This method of performing calculations is known as **dimensional analysis**, the **factor-label method**, or the **unit factor method**. Regardless of the name chosen, it is a powerful mathematical tool that is almost foolproof.

Unit factors may be constructed from any two terms that describe the same or equivalent "amounts" of whatever we may consider. For example, 1 foot is equal to exactly 12 inches, by definition. We may write an equation to describe this equality:

$$1 \text{ ft} = 12 \text{ in.}$$

Dividing both sides of the equation by 1 ft gives

$$\frac{1 \text{ ft}}{1 \text{ ft}} = \frac{12 \text{ in.}}{1 \text{ ft}} \quad \text{or} \quad 1 = \frac{12 \text{ in.}}{1 \text{ ft}}$$

The factor (fraction) 12 in./1 ft is a unit factor because the numerator and denominator describe the same distance. Dividing both sides of the original equation by 12 in. gives $1 = 1 \text{ ft}/12 \text{ in.}$, a second unit factor that is the reciprocal of the first. *The reciprocal of any unit factor is also a unit factor.* Stated differently, division of an amount by the same amount always yields one!

In the English system, we can write many unit factors, such as

$$\frac{1 \text{ yd}}{3 \text{ ft}}, \frac{1 \text{ yd}}{36 \text{ in.}}, \frac{1 \text{ mi}}{5280 \text{ ft}}, \frac{4 \text{ qt}}{1 \text{ gal}}, \frac{2000 \text{ lb}}{1 \text{ ton}}$$

▶ Unless otherwise indicated, a "ton" refers to a "short ton," 2000 lb. There are also the "long ton," which is 2240 lb, and the metric tonne, which is 1000 kg.

The reciprocal of each of these is also a unit factor. Items in retail stores are frequently priced with unit factors, such as 39¢/lb and $3.98/gal. When all the quantities in a unit factor come from definitions, the unit is known to an unlimited (infinite) number of significant figures. For instance, if you bought eight 1-gallon jugs of something priced at $3.98/gal, the total cost would be 8 × $3.98, or $31.84; the merchant would not round this to $31.80, let alone to $30.

In science, nearly all numbers have units. What does 12 mean? Usually we must supply appropriate units, such as 12 eggs or 12 people. In the unit factor method, the units guide us through calculations in a step-by-step process, because all units except those in the desired result cancel.

EXAMPLE 1-3 Unit Factors

Express 1.47 miles in inches.

Plan

First we write down the units of what we wish to know, preceded by a question mark. Then we set it equal to whatever we are given:

$$? \text{ inches} = 1.47 \text{ miles}$$

Then we choose unit factors to convert the given units (miles) to the desired units (inches):

$$\text{miles} \longrightarrow \text{feet} \longrightarrow \text{inches}$$

▶ We relate (a) miles to feet and then (b) feet to inches.

Solution

$$? \text{ in.} = 1.47 \text{ mi} \times \frac{5280 \text{ ft}}{1 \text{ mi}} \times \frac{12 \text{ in.}}{1 \text{ ft}} = 9.31 \times 10^4 \text{ in. (calculator gives 93139.2)}$$

Note that both miles and feet cancel, leaving only inches, the desired unit. Thus, there is no ambiguity as to how the unit factors should be written. The answer contains three significant figures because there are three significant figures in 1.47 miles.

Problem-Solving Tip Significant Figures

"How do defined quantities affect significant figures?" Any quantity that comes from a *definition* is exact, that is, it is known to an unlimited number of significant figures. In Example 1-3, the quantities 5280 ft, 1 mile, 12 in., and 1 ft all come from definitions, so they do not limit the significant figures in the answer.

Problem-Solving Tip Think About Your Answer!

It is often helpful to ask yourself, "Does the answer make sense?" In Example 1-3, the distance involved is more than a mile. We expect this distance to be many inches, so a large answer is not surprising. Suppose we had mistakenly multiplied by the unit factor $\frac{1 \text{ mile}}{5280 \text{ feet}}$ (and not noticed that the units did not cancel properly); we would have gotten the answer 3.34×10^{-3} in. (0.00334 in.), which we should have immediately recognized as nonsense!

Within the SI and metric systems, many measurements are related to one another by powers of ten.

EXAMPLE 1-4 Unit Conversions

The Ångstrom (Å) is a unit of length, 1×10^{-10} m, that provides a convenient scale on which to express the radii of atoms. Radii of atoms are often expressed in picometers. The radius of a phosphorus atom is 1.10 Å. What is the distance expressed in centimeters and picometers?

▶ Å → m → cm
Å → m → pm

Plan

We use the equalities $1 \text{ Å} = 1 \times 10^{-10}$ m, $1 \text{ cm} = 1 \times 10^{-2}$ m, and $1 \text{ pm} = 1 \times 10^{-12}$ m to construct the unit factors that convert 1.10 Å to the desired units.

Solution

$$? \text{ cm} = 1.10 \text{ Å} \times \frac{1 \times 10^{-10} \text{ m}}{1 \text{ Å}} \times \frac{1 \text{ cm}}{1 \times 10^{-2} \text{ m}} = 1.10 \times 10^{-8} \text{ cm}$$

$$? \text{ pm} = 1.10 \text{ Å} \times \frac{1.0 \times 10^{-10} \text{ m}}{1 \text{ Å}} \times \frac{1 \text{ pm}}{1 \times 10^{-12} \text{ m}} = 1.10 \times 10^2 \text{ pm}$$

You should now work Exercise 36.

> **S TOP & THINK**
> The conversion factors give correct units (inches). An inch is much shorter than a mile, so it makes sense that the number of inches is much larger than the number of miles. Cancellation of units will be omitted in the remainder of this book, but you may find it useful to continue cancelling units.

> **S TOP & THINK**
> All the unit factors in Example 1-4 are exact numbers. One cm is longer than one Å, so the number of cm is less than the number of Å. One pm is shorter than one Å, so the number of pm is greater than the number of Å.

EXAMPLE 1-5 Volume Calculation

Assuming a phosphorus atom is spherical, calculate its volume in $Å^3$, cm^3, and nm^3. The formula for the volume of a sphere is $V = (\frac{4}{3})\pi r^3$. Refer to Example 1-4.

Plan

We use the results of Example 1-4 to calculate the volume in each of the desired units.

Solution

$$\underline{?}\ Å^3 = \left(\frac{4}{3}\right)\pi(1.10\ Å)^3 = 5.38\ Å^3$$

$$\underline{?}\ cm^3 = \left(\frac{4}{3}\right)\pi(1.10 \times 10^{-8}\ cm)^3 = 5.58 \times 10^{-24}\ cm^3$$

$$\underline{?}\ nm^3 = \left(\frac{4}{3}\right)\pi(1.10 \times 10^{-1}\ nm)^3 = 5.58 \times 10^{-3}\ nm^3$$

You should now work Exercise 38.

STOP & THINK

$1Å = 10^{-10}\ m = 10^{-8}\ cm$

Be sure to cube each unit of distance as well as its magnitude.

EXAMPLE 1-6 Mass Conversion

A sample of gold has a mass of 0.234 mg. What is its mass in g? in kg?

Plan

We use the relationships $1\ g = 1000\ mg$ and $1\ kg = 1000\ g$ to write the required unit factors.

Solution

$$\underline{?}\ g = 0.234\ mg \times \frac{1\ g}{1000\ mg} = 2.34 \times 10^{-4}\ g$$

$$\underline{?}\ kg = 2.34 \times 10^{-4}\ g \times \frac{1\ kg}{1000\ g} = 2.34 \times 10^{-7}\ kg$$

This example includes unit factors that contain only exact numbers.

STOP & THINK

All the unit factors in this example are exact numbers. The units of the answers are correct. One gram is a larger mass than one milligram, so the mass expressed in g should be less than that in mg. One kilogram is even larger, so the mass expressed in kg should be even smaller.

Problem-Solving Tip Conversions Within the Metric or SI System

The SI and metric systems of units are based on powers of ten. This means that many unit conversions *within* these systems can be carried out just by shifting the decimal point. For instance, the conversion from milligrams to grams in Example 1-6 just involves shifting the decimal point to the *left* by three places. How do we know to move it to the left? We know that the gram is a larger unit of mass than the milligram, so the number of grams in a given mass must be a *smaller* number than the number of milligrams. After you carry out many such conversions using unit factors, you will probably begin to take such shortcuts. Always think about the answer, to see whether it should be larger or smaller than the quantity was before conversion.

Unity raised to *any* power is 1. *Any* unit factor raised to a power is still a unit factor, as the next example shows.

EXAMPLE 1-7 Volume Conversion

One liter is exactly 1000 cm³. How many cubic inches are there in 1000 cm³?

Plan

We would multiply by the unit factor $\dfrac{1 \text{ in.}}{2.54 \text{ cm}}$ to convert cm to in. Here we require the *cube* of this unit factor.

Solution

$$\underline{?} \text{ in.}^3 = 1000 \text{ cm}^3 \times \left(\frac{1 \text{ in.}}{2.54 \text{ cm}}\right)^3 = 1000 \text{ cm}^3 \times \frac{1 \text{ in.}^3}{16.4 \text{ cm}^3} = \boxed{61.0 \text{ in}^3}$$

► Suppose we start with the equality

$$1 \text{ in.} = 2.54 \text{ cm}$$

We can perform the same operation on both sides of the equation. Let's cube both sides:

$$(1 \text{ in.})^3 = (2.54 \text{ cm})^3 = 16.4 \text{ cm}^3$$

so the quantity

$$\left(\frac{1 \text{ in.}}{2.54 \text{ cm}}\right)^3$$

is a unit factor.

Example 1-7 shows that a unit factor *cubed* is still a unit factor.

EXAMPLE 1-8 Energy Conversion

A common unit of energy is the erg. Convert 3.74×10^{-2} erg to the SI units of energy, joules and kilojoules. One erg is exactly 1×10^{-7} joule (J).

Plan

The definition that relates ergs and joules is used to generate the needed unit factor. The second conversion uses a unit factor that is based on the definition of the prefix *kilo-*.

Solution

$$\underline{?} \text{ J} = 3.74 \times 10^{-2} \text{ erg} \times \frac{1 \times 10^{-7} \text{ J}}{1 \text{ erg}} = 3.74 \times 10^{-9} \text{ J}$$

$$\underline{?} \text{ kJ} = 3.74 \times 10^{-9} \text{ J} \times \frac{1 \text{ kJ}}{1000 \text{ J}} = \boxed{3.74 \times 10^{-12} \text{ kJ}}$$

S TOP & THINK

The erg is a smaller energy unit than the joule (or than a kilojoule, which is even larger than a joule), so the energy expressed in J or in kJ must be smaller than when it is expressed in ergs.

Conversions between the English and SI (metric) systems are conveniently made by the unit factor method. Several conversion factors are listed in Table 1-8. It may be helpful to remember one each for

length	1 in. = 2.54 cm (exact)
mass and weight	1 lb = 454 g (near sea level)
volume	1 qt = 0.946 L or 1 L = 1.06 qt

► We relate
(a) gallons to quarts, then
(b) quarts to liters, and then
(c) liters to milliliters.

EXAMPLE 1-9 English-Metric Conversion

Express 1.0 gallon in milliliters.

Plan

We ask $\underline{?}$ mL = 1.0 gal and multiply by the appropriate factors.

$$\text{gallons} \rightarrow \text{quarts} \rightarrow \text{liters} \rightarrow \text{milliliters}$$

Solution

$$\underline{?} \text{ mL} = 1.0 \text{ gal} \times \frac{4 \text{ qt}}{1 \text{ gal}} \times \frac{1 \text{ L}}{1.06 \text{ qt}} \times \frac{1000 \text{ mL}}{1 \text{ L}} = \boxed{3.8 \times 10^3 \text{ mL}}$$

You should now work Exercise 40.

S TOP & THINK

One milliliter is a smaller volume than one liter, which is about the same as one quart; one quart is a smaller volume than one gallon. Thus it makes sense that the volume expressed in milliliters is greater than that expressed in gallons.

The fact that all other units cancel to give the desired unit, milliliters, shows that we used the correct unit factors. The factors 4 qt/gal and 1000 mL/L contain only exact numbers. The factor 1 L/1.06 qt contains three significant figures. Because 1.0 gal contains only two, the answer contains only two significant figures.

Examples 1-3 through 1-9 show that multiplication by one or more unit factors changes the units and the number of units, but not the amount of whatever we are calculating.

1-10 Percentage

We often use percentages to describe quantitatively how a total is made up of its parts. In Table 1-4, we described the amounts of elements present in terms of the percentage of each element.

Percentages can be treated as unit factors. For any mixture containing substance A,

$$\frac{\% \text{ A}}{(\text{by mass})} = \frac{\text{parts A (by mass)}}{100 \text{ parts mixture (by mass)}}$$

mass A ⟷ mass mixture

If we say that a sample is 24.4% carbon by mass, we mean that out of every 100 parts (exactly) by mass of sample, 24.4 parts by mass are carbon. This relationship can be represented by whichever of the two unit factors we find useful:

$$\frac{24.4 \text{ parts carbon}}{100 \text{ parts sample}} \quad \text{or} \quad \frac{100 \text{ parts sample}}{24.4 \text{ parts carbon}}$$

This ratio can be expressed in terms of grams of carbon for every 100 grams of sample, pounds of carbon for every 100 pounds of sample, or any other mass or weight unit. The next example illustrates the use of dimensional analysis involving percentage.

EXAMPLE 1-10 Percentage

U.S. pennies made since 1982 consist of 97.6% zinc and 2.4% copper. The mass of a particular penny is measured to be 1.494 grams. How many grams of zinc does this penny contain?

Plan

From the percentage information given, we may write the required unit factor

$$\frac{97.6 \text{ g zinc}}{100 \text{ g sample}}$$

Solution

$$\underline{?} \text{ g zinc} = 1.494 \text{ g sample} \times \frac{97.6 \text{ g zinc}}{100 \text{ g sample}} = 1.46 \text{ g zinc}$$

The number of significant figures in the result is limited by the three significant figures in 97.6%. Because the definition of percentage involves *exactly* 100 parts, the number 100 is known to an infinite number of significant figures. The value "97.6% zinc" tells us that the penny is almost all zinc; thus the mass of zinc present is only slightly smaller than the total mass of the penny.

You should now work Exercises 67 and 68.

1-11 Density and Specific Gravity

In science, we use many terms that involve combinations of different units. Such quantities may be thought of as unit factors that can be used to convert among these units. The **density** of a sample of matter is defined as the mass per unit volume:

$$\text{density} = \frac{\text{mass}}{\text{volume}} \quad \text{or} \quad D = \frac{m}{V}$$

Charles Steele

Six materials with different densities. The liquid layers are gasoline (*top*), water (*middle*), and mercury (*bottom*). A cork floats on gasoline. A piece of oak wood sinks in gasoline but floats on water. Brass sinks in water but floats on mercury.

Table 1-9 Densities of Common Substances*

Substance	Density (g/cm³)	Substance	Density (g/cm³)
hydrogen (gas)	0.000089	sand*	2.32
carbon dioxide (gas)	0.0019	aluminum	2.70
cork*	0.21	iron	7.86
oak wood*	0.71	copper	8.92
ethyl alcohol	0.789	silver	10.50
water	1.00	lead	11.34
magnesium	1.74	mercury	13.59
table salt	2.16	gold	19.30

*Cork, oak wood, and sand are common materials that have been included to provide familiar reference points. They are *not* pure elements or compounds as are the other substances listed.

Densities may be used to distinguish between two substances or to assist in identifying a particular substance. They are usually expressed as g/cm³ or g/mL for liquids and solids and as g/L for gases. These units can also be expressed as $g \cdot cm^{-3}$, $g \cdot mL^{-1}$, and $g \cdot L^{-1}$, respectively. Densities of several substances are listed in Table 1-9.

EXAMPLE 1-11 Density, Mass, Volume

A 47.3-mL sample of ethyl alcohol (ethanol) has a mass of 37.32 g. What is its density?

Plan

We use the definition of density.

Solution

$$D = \frac{m}{V} = \frac{37.32 \text{ g}}{47.3 \text{ mL}} = \boxed{0.789 \text{ g/mL}}$$

You should now work Exercise 44.

EXAMPLE 1-12 Density, Mass, Volume

If 116 g of ethanol is needed for a chemical reaction, what volume of liquid would you use?

Plan

We determined the density of ethanol in Example 1-11. Here we are given the mass, m, of a sample of ethanol. So we know values for D and m in the relationship

$$D = \frac{m}{V}$$

We rearrange this relationship to solve for V, put in the known values, and carry out the calculation. Alternatively, we can use the unit factor method to solve the problem.

Solution

The density of ethanol is 0.789 g/mL (see Table 1-9).

$$D = \frac{m}{V}, \quad \text{so} \quad V = \frac{m}{D} = \frac{116 \text{ g}}{0.789 \text{ g/mL}} = 147 \text{ mL}$$

Alternatively,

$$\underline{?} \text{ mL} = 116 \text{ g} \times \frac{1 \text{ mL}}{0.789 \text{ g}} = \boxed{147 \text{ mL}}$$

You should now work Exercise 46.

▶ These densities are given at room temperature and *one atmosphere* of pressure, the average atmospheric pressure at sea level. Densities of solids and liquids change only slightly, but densities of gases change greatly, with changes in temperature and pressure.

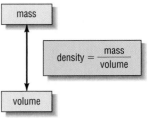

$$\text{density} = \frac{\text{mass}}{\text{volume}}$$

The intensive property *density* relates the two extensive properties: *mass* and *volume*.

S TOP & THINK

The mass in grams is a smaller number than the volume in milliliters. Thus the density in g/mL must be less than one.

▶ Observe that density gives two unit factors. In this case, they are

$$\frac{0.789 \text{ g}}{1 \text{ mL}} \quad \text{and} \quad \frac{1 \text{ mL}}{0.789 \text{ g}}.$$

S TOP & THINK

Cancellation of units leads to the correct final units (mL). A density less than one (0.789 g/mL) tells us that one mL has a mass less than one gram. Thus the number of mL needed must be numerically greater than the number of grams required.

Charles D. Winters

Ice is slightly less dense than liquid water, so ice floats in water.

Charles D. Winters

Solid ethyl alcohol is more dense than liquid ethyl alcohol. This is true of nearly every known substance.

EXAMPLE 1-13 Unit Conversion

Express the density of mercury in lb/ft³.

Plan

The density of mercury is 13.59 g/cm³ (see Table 1-9). To convert this value to the desired units, we can use unit factors constructed from the conversion factors in Table 1-8.

Solution

$$\underline{?}\ \frac{lb}{ft^3} = 13.59\ \frac{g}{cm^3} \times \frac{1\ lb}{453.6\ g} \times \left(\frac{2.54\ cm}{1\ in.}\right)^3 \times \left(\frac{12\ in.}{1\ ft}\right)^3 = 848.4\ lb/ft^3$$

It would take a very strong person to lift a cubic foot of mercury!

▶ Density and specific gravity are both intensive properties; that is, they do not depend on the size of the sample. Specific gravities are dimensionless numbers.

The **specific gravity** (Sp. Gr.) of a substance is the ratio of its density to the density of water, both at the same temperature.

$$\text{Sp. Gr.} = \frac{D_{substance}}{D_{water}}$$

The density of water is 1.000 g/mL at 3.98°C, the temperature at which the density of water is greatest. Variations in the density of water with changes in temperature, however, are small enough that we can use 1.00 g/mL up to 25°C without introducing significant errors into our calculations.

EXAMPLE 1-14 Density, Specific Gravity

The density of table salt is 2.16 g/mL at 20°C. What is its specific gravity?

Plan

We use the preceding definition of specific gravity. The numerator and denominator have the same units, so the result is dimensionless.

Solution

$$\text{Sp. Gr.} = \frac{D_{salt}}{D_{water}} = \frac{2.16\ g/mL}{1.00\ g/mL} = 2.16$$

Labels on commercial solutions of acids give specific gravities and the percentage by mass of the acid present in the solution. From this information, the amount of acid present in a given volume of solution can be calculated.

Specific Gravity, Volume, Percentage by Mass

Battery acid is 40.0% sulfuric acid, H_2SO_4, and 60.0% water by mass. Its specific gravity is 1.31. Calculate the mass of pure H_2SO_4 in 100.0 mL of battery acid.

Plan

The percentages are given on a mass basis, so we must first convert the 100.0 mL of acid solution (soln) to mass. To do this, we need a value for the density. We have demonstrated that density and specific gravity are numerically equal at 20°C because the density of water is 1.00 g/mL. We can use the density as a unit factor to convert the given volume of the solution to mass of the solution. Then we use the percentage by mass to convert the mass of the solution to the mass of the acid.

Solution

From the given value for specific gravity, we may write

$$\text{Density} = 1.31 \text{ g/mL}$$

The solution is 40.0% H_2SO_4 and 60.0% H_2O by mass. From this information we can construct the desired unit factor:

$$\frac{40.0 \text{ g } H_2SO_4}{100 \text{ g soln}} \longrightarrow \boxed{\text{because 100 g of solution contains 40.0 g of } H_2SO_4}$$

We can now solve the problem:

$$\underline{?} \; H_2SO_4 = 100.0 \text{ mL soln} \times \frac{1.31 \text{ g soln}}{1 \text{ mL soln}} \times \frac{40.0 \text{ g } H_2SO_4}{100 \text{ g soln}} = 52.4 \text{ g } H_2SO_4$$

You should now work Exercise 52.

> **S TOP & THINK**
> Careful use of unit factors helps you set up the solution to Example 1-15.

1-12 Heat and Temperature

In Section 1-1 you learned that heat is one form of energy. You also learned that the many forms of energy can be interconverted and that in chemical reactions, chemical energy is converted to heat energy or vice versa. The amount of heat a process uses (*endothermic*) or gives off (*exothermic*) can tell us a great deal about that process. For this reason, it is important for us to be able to measure the intensity of heat.

Temperature measures the intensity of heat, the "hotness" or "coldness" of a body. A piece of metal at 100°C feels hot to the touch, whereas an ice cube at 0°C feels cold. Why? Because the temperature of the metal is higher, and that of the ice cube lower, than body temperature. **Heat** is a form of energy that *always flows spontaneously from a hotter body to a colder body*—it never flows in the reverse direction.

Temperatures can be measured with liquid-in-glass thermometers. This kind of thermometer consists of a reservoir of liquid at the base of a glass tube, open to a very thin (capillary) column extending upward. Any liquid expands as its temperature rises. As it expands, its movement up into the evacuated column can be seen.

Anders Celsius (1701–1744), a Swedish astronomer, developed the Celsius temperature scale, formerly called the centigrade temperature scale. When we place a Celsius thermometer in a beaker of crushed ice and water, the liquid level stands at exactly 0°C, the lower reference point. In a beaker of water boiling at one atmosphere pressure, the liquid level stands at exactly 100°C, the higher reference point. There are 100 equal steps between these two liquid levels. They correspond to an interval of 100 degrees between the melting point of ice and the boiling point of water at one atmosphere. Figure 1-19 shows how temperature marks between the reference points are established.

In the United States, temperatures are frequently measured on the temperature scale devised by Gabriel Fahrenheit (1686–1736), a German instrument maker. On this scale,

Figure 1-19 At 45°C, as read on a liquid-in-glass thermometer, d equals 0.45 d_0, where d_0 is the distance from the liquid level at 0°C to the level at 100°C.

the freezing and boiling points of water are now defined as 32°F and 212°F, respectively. In scientific work, temperatures are often expressed on the **Kelvin** (absolute) temperature scale. As we shall see in Section 12-5, the zero point of the Kelvin temperature scale is derived from the observed behavior of all matter.

Relationships among the three temperature scales are illustrated in Figure 1-20. Between the freezing point of water and the boiling point of water, there are 100 steps (°C or kelvins, respectively) on the Celsius and Kelvin scales. Thus the "degree" is the same size on the Celsius and Kelvin scales. But every Kelvin temperature is 273.15 units above the corresponding Celsius temperature. The relationship between these two scales is as follows:

▶ We will usually round 273.15 to 273.

$$\underline{?}\ K = °C + 273.15° \qquad or \qquad \underline{?}\ °C = K - 273.15°$$

In the SI system, "degrees Kelvin" are abbreviated simply as K rather than °K and are called **kelvins**.

Any temperature *change* has the same numerical value whether expressed on the Celsius scale or on the Kelvin scale. For example, a change from 25°C to 59°C represents a *change* of 34 Celsius degrees. Converting these to the Kelvin scale, the same change is expressed as (273 + 25) = 298 K to (59 + 273) = 332 K, or a *change* of 34 kelvins.

Comparing the Fahrenheit and Celsius scales, we find that the intervals between the same reference points are 180 Fahrenheit degrees and 100 Celsius degrees, respectively. Thus a Fahrenheit degree must be smaller than a Celsius degree. It takes 180 Fahrenheit degrees to cover the same temperature *interval* as 100 Celsius degrees. From this information, we can construct the unit factors for temperature *changes*:

▶ The numbers in these ratios are *exact* numbers, so they do not affect the number of significant figures in the calculated result.

$$\frac{180°F}{100°C} \quad or \quad \frac{1.8°F}{1.0°C} \quad and \quad \frac{100°C}{180°F} \quad or \quad \frac{1.0°C}{1.8°F}$$

But the starting points of the two scales are different, so we *cannot convert* a temperature on one scale to a temperature on the other just by multiplying by the unit factor. In converting from °F to °C, we must also subtract 32 Fahrenheit degrees to reach the zero point on the Celsius scale (see Figure 1-20).

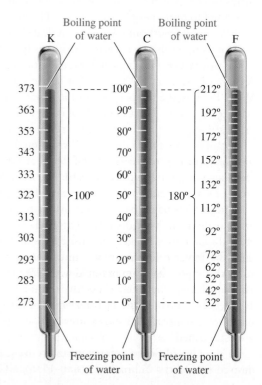

Figure 1-20 The relationships among the Kelvin, Celsius (centigrade), and Fahrenheit temperature scales.

$$\underline{?}\ {}^\circ C = \frac{1.0^\circ C}{1.8^\circ F}\,(x^\circ F - 32^\circ F) \qquad \text{or} \qquad \underline{?}\ {}^\circ F = \left(x^\circ C \times \frac{1.8^\circ F}{1.0^\circ C}\right) + 32^\circ F$$

▶ These are often remembered in abbreviated form:

$$^\circ C = \frac{(^\circ F - 32^\circ)}{1.8}$$
$$^\circ F = 1.8^\circ C + 32^\circ$$

Either of these equations can be rearranged to obtain the other one, so you need to learn only one of them.

EXAMPLE 1-16 Temperature Conversion

When the temperature reaches "100. °F in the shade," it's hot. What is this temperature on the Celsius scale?

Plan

We use the relationship $\underline{?}\ {}^\circ C = \dfrac{1.0^\circ C}{1.8^\circ F}\,(x^\circ F - 32^\circ F)$ to carry out the desired conversion.

Solution

$$\underline{?}\ {}^\circ C = \frac{1.0^\circ C}{1.8^\circ F}\,(100.^\circ F - 32^\circ F) = \frac{1.0^\circ C}{1.8^\circ F}\,(68^\circ F) = \boxed{38^\circ C}$$

▶ A temperature of 100.°F is 38°C.

EXAMPLE 1-17 Temperature Conversion

When the absolute temperature is 400 K, what is the Fahrenheit temperature?

Plan

We first use the relationship $\underline{?}\ {}^\circ C = K - 273^\circ$ to convert from kelvins to degrees Celsius; then we carry out the further conversion from degrees Celsius to degrees Fahrenheit.

Solution

$$\underline{?}\ {}^\circ C = (400\ K - 273\ K)\frac{1.0^\circ C}{1.0\ K} = 127^\circ C$$

$$\underline{?}\ {}^\circ F = \left(127^\circ C \times \frac{1.8^\circ F}{1.0^\circ C}\right) + 32^\circ F = 261^\circ F$$

You should now work Exercise 54.

1-13 Heat Transfer and the Measurement of Heat

Chemical reactions and physical changes occur with either the simultaneous evolution of heat (**exothermic processes**) or the absorption of heat (**endothermic processes**). The amount of heat transferred in a process is usually expressed in joules or in calories.

The SI unit of energy and work is the **joule (J)**, which is defined as $1\ kg \cdot m^2/s^2$. The kinetic energy (KE) of a body of mass m moving at speed v is given by $\frac{1}{2}mv^2$. A 2-kg object moving at one meter per second has $KE = \frac{1}{2}(2\ kg)(1\ m/s)^2 = 1\ kg \cdot m^2/s^2 = 1J$. You may find it more convenient to think in terms of the amount of heat required to raise the temperature of one gram of liquid water from 14.5°C to 15.5°C, which is 4.184 J.

▶ In terms of electrical energy, one joule is equal to one watt · second. Thus, one joule is enough energy to operate a 10-watt light bulb for $\frac{1}{10}$ second.

One **calorie** is defined as exactly 4.184 J. The so-called "large calorie," used to indicate the energy content of foods, is really one kilocalorie, that is, 1000 calories. In this text, we shall do most calculations in joules.

The **specific heat** of a substance is the amount of heat required to raise the temperature of one gram of the substance by one degree Celsius (also one kelvin) with no change in phase. Changes in phase (physical state) absorb or liberate relatively large amounts of energy (see Figure 1-5). The specific heat of each substance, a physical property, is different for the solid, liquid, and gaseous phases of the substance. For example, the specific heat of ice is 2.09 J/g · °C near 0°C; for liquid water it is 4.18 J/g · °C; and for steam it is 2.03 J/g · °C near 100°C. The specific heat for water is quite high. A table of specific heats is provided in Appendix E.

$$\text{specific heat} = \frac{(\text{amount of heat in J})}{(\text{mass of substance in g})(\text{temperature change in °C})}$$

The units of specific heat are $\frac{J}{g \cdot °C}$ or $J \cdot g^{-1} \cdot °C^{-1}$.

The **heat capacity** of a body is the amount of heat required to raise its temperature 1°C. The heat capacity of a body is its mass in grams times its specific heat. The heat capacity refers to the mass of that particular body, so its units do not include mass. The units are J/°C or $J \cdot °C^{-1}$.

► In this example, we calculate the amount of heat needed to prepare a cup of hot tea.

EXAMPLE 1-18 Specific Heat

How much heat, in joules, is required to raise the temperature of 205 g of water from 21.2°C to 91.4°C?

Plan

The specific heat of a substance is the amount of heat required to raise the temperature of 1 g of the substance by 1°C:

$$\text{specific heat} = \frac{(\text{amount of heat in J})}{(\text{mass of substance in g})(\text{temperature change in °C})}$$

We can rearrange the equation so that

(amount of heat) = (mass of substance)(specific heat)(temperature change)

Alternatively, we can use the unit factor approach.

Solution

$$\text{amount of heat} = (205 \text{ g})(4.18 \text{ J/g} \cdot °C)(70.2°C) = 6.02 \times 10^4 \text{ J}$$

By the unit factor approach,

$$\text{amount of heat} = (205 \text{ g})\left(\frac{4.18 \text{ J}}{1 \text{ g} \cdot °C}\right)(70.2°C) = 6.02 \times 10^4 \text{ J} \quad \text{or} \quad 60.2 \text{ kJ}$$

All units except joules cancel. To cool 205 g of water from 91.4°C to 21.2°C, it would be necessary to remove exactly the same amount of heat, 60.2 kJ.

You should now work Exercises 62 and 63.

When two objects at different temperatures are brought into contact, heat flows from the hotter to the colder body (Figure 1-21); this continues until the two are at the same temperature. We say that the two objects are then in *thermal equilibrium*. The temperature change that occurs for each object depends on the initial temperatures and the relative masses and specific heats of the two materials.

A Heat is transferred from the hotter metal bar to the cooler water until the two reach the same temperature.

B We say that they are then at *thermal equilibrium.*

Figure 1-21 A hot object, such as a heated piece of metal, is placed into cooler water.

EXAMPLE 1-19 Specific Heat

A 588-gram chunk of iron is heated to 97.5°C. Then it is immersed in 247 grams of water originally at 20.7°C. When thermal equilibrium has been reached, the water and iron are both at 36.2°C. Calculate the specific heat of iron.

Plan

The amount of heat gained by the water as it is warmed from 20.7°C to 36.2°C is the same as the amount of heat lost by the iron as it cools from 97.5°C to 36.2°C. We can equate these two amounts of heat and solve for the unknown specific heat.

Solution

$$\text{temperature change of water} = 36.2°\text{C} - 20.7°\text{C} = 15.5°\text{C}$$

$$\text{temperature change of iron} = 97.5°\text{C} - 36.2°\text{C} = 61.3°\text{C}$$

$$\text{number of joules gained by water} = (247 \text{ g})\left(4.18 \frac{\text{J}}{\text{g} \cdot °\text{C}}\right)(15.5°\text{C})$$

Let x = specific heat of iron

$$\text{number of joules lost by iron} = (588 \text{ g})\left(x \frac{\text{J}}{\text{g} \cdot °\text{C}}\right)(61.3°\text{C})$$

We set these two quantities equal to one another and solve for x.

$$(247 \text{ g})\left(4.18 \frac{\text{J}}{\text{g} \cdot °\text{C}}\right)(15.5°\text{C}) = (588 \text{ g})\left(x \frac{\text{J}}{\text{g} \cdot °\text{C}}\right)(61.3°\text{C})$$

$$x = \frac{(247 \text{ g})\left(4.18 \dfrac{\text{J}}{\text{g} \cdot °\text{C}}\right)(15.5°\text{C})}{(588 \text{ g})(61.3°\text{C})} = 0.444 \frac{\text{J}}{\text{g} \cdot °\text{C}}$$

You should now work Exercise 66.

▶ In specific heat calculations, we use the *magnitude* of the temperature change (i.e., a positive number), so we subtract the lower temperature from the higher one in both cases.

The specific heat of iron is much smaller than the specific heat of water.

$$\frac{\text{specific heat of iron}}{\text{specific heat of water}} = \frac{0.444 \text{ J/g} \cdot °\text{C}}{4.18 \text{ J/g} \cdot °\text{C}} = 0.106$$

Charles D. Winters

The amount of heat required to raise the temperature of 205 g of iron by 70.2°C (as we calculated for water in Example 1-18) is

$$\text{amount of heat} = (205 \text{ g})\left(\frac{0.444 \text{ J}}{\text{g} \cdot °\text{C}}\right)(70.2°\text{C}) = 6.39 \times 10^3 \text{ J, or } 6.39 \text{ kJ}$$

We see that the amount of heat required to accomplish a given change in temperature for a given quantity of iron is less than that for the same quantity of water, by the same ratio.

$$\frac{\text{number of joules required to warm 205 g of iron by 70.2°C}}{\text{number of joules required to warm 205 g of water by 70.2°C}} = \frac{6.39 \text{ kJ}}{60.2 \text{ kJ}} = 0.106$$

It might not be necessary to carry out explicit calculations when we are looking only for qualitative comparisons.

EXAMPLE 1-20   Comparing Specific Heats

We add the same amount of heat to 10.0 grams of each of the following substances starting at 20.0°C: liquid water, $H_2O\,(\ell)$; liquid mercury, $Hg\,(\ell)$; liquid benzene, $C_6H_6\,(\ell)$; and solid aluminum, Al(s). Rank the samples from lowest to highest final temperature. Refer to Appendix E for required data.

Plan

We can obtain the values of specific heats (Sp. Ht.) for these substances from Appendix E. The higher the specific heat for a substance, the more heat is required to raise a given mass of sample by a given temperature change, so the less its temperature changes by a given amount of heat. The substance with the lowest specific heat undergoes the largest temperature change, and the one with the highest specific heat undergoes the smallest temperature change. *It is not necessary to calculate the amount of heat required to answer this question.*

Solution

The specific heats obtained from Appendix E are as follows:

Substance	Sp. Ht. $\left(\dfrac{\text{J}}{\text{g} \cdot °\text{C}}\right)$
$H_2O\,(\ell)$	4.18
$Hg\,(\ell)$	0.138
$C_6H_6\,(\ell)$	1.74
Al(s)	0.900

Ranked from highest to lowest specific heats: $H_2O\,(\ell) > C_6H_6\,(\ell) > \text{Al(s)} > Hg\,(\ell)$. Adding the same amount of heat to the same size sample of these substances changes the temperature of $H_2O\,(\ell)$ the least and that of $Hg\,(\ell)$ the most. The ranking from lowest to highest final temperature is

$$H_2O\,(\ell) < C_6H_6\,(\ell) < \text{Al(s)} < Hg\,(\ell)$$

You should now work Exercise 75.

KEY TERMS

Accuracy How closely a measured value agrees with the correct value (see Appendix A-4).

Atom The smallest particle of an element that maintains its chemical identity through all chemical and physical changes.

Atomic number The number of protons in the nucleus of an atom.

Calorie Defined as exactly 4.184 joules. Originally defined as the amount of heat required to raise the temperature of one gram of water from 14.5°C to 15.5°C.

Chemical change A change in which one or more new substances are formed; also known as *chemical reaction* or just *reaction.*

Chemical property See *Properties.*

Compound A substance composed of two or more elements in fixed proportions. Compounds can be decomposed into their constituent elements.

Density Mass per unit volume, $D = m/V$.

Element A substance that cannot be decomposed into simpler substances by chemical means.

Endothermic Describes processes that absorb heat energy.

Energy The capacity to do work or transfer heat.

Exothermic Describes processes that release heat energy.

Extensive property A property that depends on the amount of material in a sample.

Heat A form of energy that flows between two samples of matter because of their difference in temperature.

Heat capacity The amount of heat required to raise the temperature of a body one degree Celsius.

Heterogeneous mixture A mixture that does not have uniform composition and properties throughout.

Homogeneous mixture A mixture that has uniform composition and properties throughout.

Intensive property A property that is independent of the amount of material in a sample.

Joule A unit of energy in the SI system. One joule is $1 \text{ kg} \cdot \text{m}^2/\text{s}^2$, which is also 0.2390 cal.

Kinetic energy Energy that matter possesses by virtue of its motion.

Law of Conservation of Energy Energy cannot be created or destroyed in a chemical reaction or in a physical change; it may be changed from one form to another.

Law of Conservation of Matter No detectable change occurs in the total quantity of matter during a chemical reaction or during a physical change.

Law of Conservation of Matter and Energy The combined amount of matter and energy in the universe is fixed.

Law of Constant Composition See *Law of Definite Proportions.*

Law of Definite Proportions Different samples of any pure compound contain the same elements in the same proportions by mass; also known as the *Law of Constant Composition.*

Mass A measure of the amount of matter in an object. Mass is usually measured in grams or kilograms.

Matter Anything that has mass and occupies space.

Mixture A sample of matter composed of variable amounts of two or more substances, each of which retains its identity and properties.

Molecule The smallest particle of an element or compound that can have a stable independent existence.

Physical change A change in which a substance changes from one physical state to another, but no substances with different compositions are formed.

Physical property See *Properties.*

Potential energy Energy that matter possesses by virtue of its position, condition, or composition.

Precision How closely repeated measurements of the same quantity agree with one another (see Appendix A-4).

Properties Characteristics that describe samples of matter. Chemical properties are exhibited as matter undergoes chemical changes. Physical properties are exhibited by matter with no changes in chemical composition.

Scientific (natural) law A general statement based on the observed behavior of matter, to which no exceptions are known.

Significant figures Digits that indicate the precision of measurements—digits of a measured number that have uncertainty only in the last digit (see Appendix A-4).

Specific gravity The ratio of the density of a substance to the density of water at the same temperature.

Specific heat The amount of heat required to raise the temperature of one gram of a substance by one degree Celsius.

Substance Any kind of matter all specimens of which have the same chemical composition and physical properties.

Symbol (of an element) A letter or group of letters that represents (identifies) an element.

Temperature A measure of the intensity of heat, that is, the hotness or coldness of a sample or object.

Unit factor A factor in which the numerator and denominator are expressed in different units but represent the same or equivalent amounts. Multiplying by a unit factor is the same as multiplying by one.

Weight A measure of the gravitational attraction of the earth for a body.

EXERCISES

Matter and Energy

1. Define the following subdivisions of chemistry:
   (a) biochemistry; (b) analytical chemistry;
   (c) geochemistry; (d) nuclear chemistry; (e) inorganic chemistry. (*Hint:* You may need to consult a dictionary for answers to this question.)

2. Define the following subdivisions of chemistry:
   (a) organic chemistry; (b) forensic chemistry;
   (c) physical chemistry; (d) medicinal chemistry. (*Hint:* You may need to consult a dictionary for answers to this question.)

3. Define the following terms, and illustrate each with a specific example: (a) matter; (b) kinetic energy; (c) mass; (d) exothermic process; (e) intensive property.

4. Define the following terms, and illustrate each with a specific example: (a) weight; (b) potential energy; (c) temperature; (d) endothermic process; (e) extensive property.

5. State the Law of Conservation of Matter and Energy, and explain how it differs from the Law of Conservation of Matter and the Law of Conservation of Energy.

6. Describe why you can refer to the following processes as being exothermic even though very little or no heat is being released: (a) discharge of a flashlight battery; (b) the production of light by an activated light stick.

7. Describe why you can refer to the following processes as being exothermic even though very little or no heat is being released: (a) the production of light by a fluorescent light; (b) the production of light by a glow-in-the-dark object.

8. Which of the following processes are exothermic? endothermic? How can you tell? (a) combustion; (b) freezing water; (c) melting ice; (d) boiling water; (e) condensing steam; (f) burning paper.

9. Which of the following processes are exothermic? endothermic? How can you tell? (a) burning gasoline; (b) freezing ice cream; (c) melting chocolate; (d) cooling hot water; (e) condensing water vapor; (f) burning a match.

10. Write Einstein's equation, and describe how it can be used to relate the mass change in a nuclear reaction to energy.

© Bettmann/Corbis

11. State the following laws, and illustrate each: (a) the Law of Conservation of Matter; (b) the Law of Conservation of Energy; (c) the Law of Conservation of Matter and Energy.

12. All electrical motors are less than 100% efficient in converting electrical energy into useable work. How can their efficiency be less than 100% and the Law of Conservation of Energy still be valid?

13. An incandescent light bulb functions because of the flow of electric current. Does the incandescent light bulb convert all of the electrical energy to light? Observe a functioning incandescent light bulb, and explain what occurs with reference to the Law of Conservation of Energy.

States of Matter

14. 🐟 List the three states of matter and some characteristics of each. How are they alike? Different? Draw a molecular representation that illustrates differences in the amount of space between molecules in the gaseous and the liquid or solid states.

15. What is a homogeneous mixture? Which of the following are pure substances? Which of the following are homogeneous mixtures? Explain your answers:
    (a) salt dissolved in water; (b) tea and ice; (c) chicken noodle soup; (d) mud; (e) gasoline; (f) carbon dioxide; (g) mint chocolate-chip ice cream.

© Danilo Calilung/Corbis

16. Define the following terms clearly and concisely. Give two examples of each: (a) substance; (b) mixture; (c) element; (d) compound.

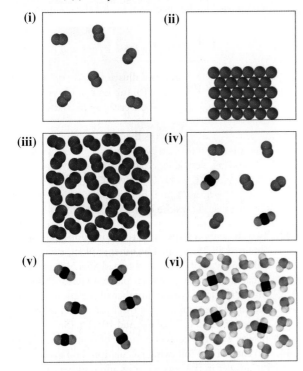

(i)   **(ii)**

(iii)   **(iv)**

(v)   **(vi)**

17. 🪨 The preceding boxes include models of (a) a gaseous element; (b) a gaseous compound; (c) a homogeneous gaseous mixture; (d) a liquid solution; (e) a solid; (f) a pure liquid. Identify each type and provide other examples of each type. Explain your answers.

18. Classify each of the following as an element, a compound, or a mixture. Justify your classification: (a) gasoline; (b) tap water; (c) calcium carbonate; (d) ink from a ballpoint pen; (e) vegetable soup; (f) aluminum foil.

19. What experiment can you use to
    (a) separate salt from water?
    (b) separate iron filings from small pieces of lead?
    (c) separate elemental sulfur from sugar?

20. A $10 gold piece minted in the early 1900s appeared to have a dirty area. The dirty appearance could not be removed by careful cleaning. Close examination of the coin revealed that the "dirty" area was really pure copper. Is the mixture of gold and copper in this coin a heterogeneous or homogeneous mixture?

Chemical and Physical Properties

21. Distinguish between the following pairs of terms, and give two specific examples of each: (a) chemical properties and physical properties; (b) intensive properties and extensive properties; (c) chemical changes and physical changes; (d) mass and weight.

22. Which of the following are chemical properties, and which are physical properties? (a) striking a match

causes it to burst into flames; (b) a particular type of steel is very hard and consists of 95% iron, 4% carbon, and 1% other elements; (c) the density of gold is 19.3 g/mL; (d) baking soda dissolves in water and releases gaseous carbon dioxide; (e) fine steel wool burns in air; (f) refrigeration slows the rate at which fruit ripens.

23. Label each of the following as either a physical process or a chemical process: (a) rusting of an iron nail; (b) melting of ice; (c) burning of a wooden stick; (d) digestion of a baked potato; (e) dissolving of sugar in water.

24. Eight observations are listed below. What observations identify chemical properties?
    (a) Sugar is soluble in water.
    (b) Water boils at 100°C.
    (c) Ultraviolet light converts O_3 (ozone) to O_2 (oxygen).
    (d) Ice is less dense than water.
    (e) Sodium metal reacts violently with water.
    (f) CO_2 does not support combustion.
    (g) Chlorine is a green gas.
    (h) Heat is required to melt ice.

25. Which of the following illustrate the concept of potential energy, and which illustrate kinetic energy? (a) a car moving at 55 miles per hour; (b) a rubber band stretched around a newspaper; (c) a frozen pint of ice cream; (d) a comet moving through space; (e) a basketball dropping through a net; (f) the roof of a house.

26. Which of the following illustrate the concept of potential energy, and which illustrate kinetic energy? (a) a moving car; (b) an inflated balloon; (c) a pitched baseball just as it is being released by the pitcher; (d) a flashlight battery; (e) a frozen lake; (f) a car as it moves along the highway.

27. Tongs are used to hold a sugar cube in a flame. When a portion of the cube begins to turn brown, the cube is removed from the flame. After cooling, the heated portion of the cube is brown and has a burnt aroma. Analysis tells us that the cube lost mass. Is the browning of the sugar a chemical or a physical change? Propose an explanation for these observations.

28. A weighed sample of yellow sulfur is placed in a flask. The flask is gently heated using a Bunsen burner. Observation indicates that nothing appears to happen to the sulfur during the heating, but the mass of sulfur is less than before the heating, and there is a sharp odor that was not present before the heating. Propose an explanation of what caused the change in the mass

🪨 **Molecular Reasoning** exercises   ▲ **More Challenging** exercises   Blue-Numbered exercises solved in Student Solutions Manual

Unless otherwise noted, all content on this page is © Cengage Learning.

of the sulfur. Is your hypothesis of the mass change a chemical or physical change?

Charles D. Winters

Sulfur

Measurements and Calculations

29. Express the following numbers in scientific notation: (a) 650.; (b) 0.0630; (c) 8600 (assume that this number is measured to 10); (d) 8600 (assume that this number is measured to 1); (e) 16,000.; (f) 0.100010.

30. For each of the following quantities, underline the zeros that are significant figures, determine the number of significant figures in the quantity, and rewrite the quantity using scientific notation: (a) 423.006 mL; (b) 0.001073040 g; (c) 1,081.02 pounds.

31. Which of the following are likely to be exact numbers? Why? (a) 128 students; (b) 7 railroad cars; (c) $20,355.47; (d) 25 lb of sugar; (e) 12.5 gal of diesel fuel; (f) 5446 ants.

32. Express the following exponentials as ordinary numbers: (a) 5.06×10^4; (b) 4.060×10^{-4}; (c) 16.10×10^{-2}; (d) 0.206×10^{-3}; (e) 9.000×10^4; (f) 9.000×10^{-4}.

33. The circumference of a circle is given by πd, where d is the diameter of the circle. Calculate the circumference of a circle with a diameter of 7.41 cm. Use the value of 3.141593 for π. (Show your answer with the correct number of significant figures.)

34. A box is 252.56 cm wide, 18.23 cm deep, and 6.5 cm tall. Calculate the volume of the box. (Show your answer with the correct number of significant figures.)

35. Indicate the multiple or fraction of 10 by which a quantity is multiplied when it is preceded by each of the following prefixes. (a) M; (b) m; (c) c; (d) d; (e) k; (f) n.

36. Carry out each of the following conversions: (a) 453.4 m to km; (b) 36.3 km to m; (c) 487 kg to g; (d) 1.32 L to mL; (e) 55.9 dL to L; (f) 6251 L to cm³.

37. Express 5.31 centimeters in meters, millimeters, kilometers, and micrometers.

38. If the price of gasoline is $3.119/gal, what is its price in cents per liter?

39. Suppose your automobile gas tank holds 14 gal and the price of gasoline is $0.861/L. How much would it cost to fill your gas tank?

40. Express (a) 0.750 cubic foot in units of liters; (b) 1.00 liter in units of pints; (c) miles per gallon in kilometers per liter.

41. The screen of a netbook computer measures 8.25 in. wide and 6.25 in. tall. If this computer were being sold in Europe, what would be the metric size, in cm, of the screen used in the specifications for the computer?

Alex Wilson/Getty Images

42. Two students ran the same reaction. One student obtained 58.2% yield. The other student, using a different type of balance, obtained 56.474% yield. What is the average of their percent yields? (Show your answer with the correct number of significant figures.)

43. Calculate the total mass of three samples that have the masses of 10.25 g, 5.5654 g, and 105.4 g. (Show your answer with the correct number of significant figures.)

44. Do each of the following calculations and give the answer in the correct units and number of significant figures: (a) 18 pints × 1 qt/2 pints; ; (b) 55.0 miles per hour × 1.609 km/mile; (c) 15.45 seconds + 2.2 seconds +55 seconds.

45. What is the mass of a rectangular piece of copper 24.4 cm × 11.4 cm × 7.9 cm? The density of copper is 8.92 g/cm³.

46. A small crystal of sucrose (table sugar) had a mass of 6.080 mg. The dimensions of the box-like crystal were 2.20 mm × 1.36 mm × 1.23 mm. What is the density of sucrose expressed in g/cm³?

47. Vinegar has a density of 1.0056 g/cm³. What is the mass of three liters of vinegar?

Charles D. Winters

48. The density of silver is 10.5 g/cm³. (a) What is the volume, in cm³, of an ingot of silver with mass 0.443 kg? (b) If this sample of silver is a cube, how long is each edge in cm? (c) How long is the edge of this cube in inches?

49. ▲ A container has a mass of 78.91 g when empty and 92.44 g when filled with water. The density of water is 1.0000 g/cm³. (a) Calculate the volume of the container. (b) When filled with an unknown liquid, the container had a mass of 88.42 g. Calculate the density of the unknown liquid.

50. ▲ Wire is often sold in pound spools according to the wire gauge number. That number refers to the diameter of the wire. How many meters are in a 10-lb spool of 12-gauge aluminum wire? A 12-gauge wire has a diameter of 0.0808 in. Aluminum has a density of 2.70 g/cm³. ($V = \pi r^2 \ell$)

51. A solution is 40.0% acetic acid (the characteristic component in vinegar) by mass. The density of this solution is 1.049 g/mL at 20°C. Calculate the mass of pure acetic acid in 250.0 mL of this solution at 20°C.

52. A solution that is 11% iron(III) chloride by mass has a density of 1.149 g/mL. What mass of iron(III) chloride, in g, is present in 2.50 L of this solution?

Heat Transfer and Temperature Measurement

53. Express (a) 245°C in K; (b) 25.2 K in °C; (c) −42.0°C in °F; (d) 110.0°F in K.

54. Express (a) 15°F in °C; (b) 32.6°F in K; (c) 328 K in °F; (d) 11.3°C in °F.

55. Which temperature is higher? (a) 20°C or 20°F; (b) 100°C or 180°F; (c) 60°C or 100°F; (d) −12°C or 20°F.

56. ▲ On the Réamur scale, which is no longer used, water freezes at 0°R and boils at 80°R. (a) Derive an equation that relates this to the Celsius scale. (b) Derive an equation that relates this to the Fahrenheit scale. (c) Mercury is a liquid metal at room temperature. It boils at 356.6°C (673.9°F). What is the boiling point of mercury on the Réamur scale?

57. Liquefied gases have boiling points well below room temperature. On the Kelvin scale the boiling points of the following gases are: He, 4.2 K; N_2, 77.4 K. Convert these temperatures to the Celsius and the Fahrenheit scales.

58. Convert the temperatures at which the following metals melt to the Celsius and Fahrenheit scales: Al, 933.6 K; Ag, 1235.1 K.

59. At what point is the temperature in °F exactly twice that in °C?

60. The average temperature of a healthy German shepherd is 102.0°F. Express this temperature (a) in degrees Celsius; (b) in kelvins.

61. Calculate the amount of heat required to raise the temperature of 78.2 g of water from 10.0°C to 32.0°C. The specific heat of water is 4.184 J/g · °C.

62. The specific heat of aluminum is 0.895 J/g· °C. Calculate the amount of heat required to raise the temperature of 45.3 g of aluminum from 27.0°C to 62.5°C.

63. How much heat must be removed from 15.5 g of water at 90.0°C to cool it to 38.2°C?

64. ▲ In some solar-heated homes, heat from the sun is stored in rocks during the day and then released during the cooler night. (a) Calculate the amount of heat required to raise the temperature of 69.7 kg of rocks from 25.0°C to 41.0°C. Assume that the rocks are limestone, which is essentially pure calcium carbonate. The specific heat of calcium carbonate is 0.818 J/g · °C. (b) Suppose that when the rocks in part (a) cool to 30.0°C, all the heat released goes to warm the 10,000 ft³ (2.83×10^5 L) of air in the house, originally at 10.0°C. To what final temperature would the air be heated? The specific heat of air is 1.004 J/g · °C, and its density is 1.20×10^{-3} g/mL.

65. ▲ A small immersion heater is used to heat water for a cup of coffee. We wish to use it to heat 245 mL of water (about a teacupful) from 25°C to 85°C in 2.00 min. What must be the heat rating of the heater, in kJ/min, to accomplish this? Ignore the heat that goes to heat the cup itself. The density of water is 0.997 g/mL.

66. When 50.0 grams of metal at 75.0°C is added to 100. grams of water at 15.0°C, the temperature of the water rises to 18.3°C. Assume that no heat is lost to the surroundings. What is the specific heat of the metal?

Mixed Exercises

67. A sample is marked as containing 25.8% calcium carbonate by mass. (a) How many grams of calcium carbonate are contained in 75.45 g of the sample? (b) How many grams of the sample would contain 18.8 g of calcium carbonate?

68. An iron ore is found to contain 9.24% hematite (a compound that contains iron). (a) How many tons of this ore would contain 5.79 tons of hematite? (b) How many kilograms of this ore would contain 6.40 kg of hematite?

69. ▲ The radius of a hydrogen atom is about 0.37 Å, and the average radius of the earth's orbit around the sun is about 1.5×10^8 km. Find the ratio of the average radius of the earth's orbit to the radius of the hydrogen atom.

70. A notice on a bridge informs drivers that the height of the bridge is 23.5 ft. How tall in meters is an 18-wheel tractor-trailer combination if it just touches the bridge?

71. Some American car manufacturers install speedometers that indicate speed in the English system and in the metric system (mi/h and km/h). What is the metric speed if the car is traveling at 65 mi/h?

72. ▲ The lethal dose of a specific drug taken orally is 1.5 mg/kg of body weight. Calculate the lethal dose of the drug taken orally by a 165-lb person.

73. Suppose you ran a mile in 4.90 min. (a) What would be your average speed in km/h? (b) What would be your average speed in cm/s? (c) What would be your time (in minutes: seconds) for 1500 m?

74. Household ammonia is 5% ammonia by mass and has a density of 1.006 g/mL. What volume of this solution must a person purchase to obtain 25.8 g of ammonia?

⬢ **Molecular Reasoning** exercises   ▲ **More Challenging** exercises   Blue-Numbered exercises solved in Student Solutions Manual

Conceptual Exercises

75. If you were given the job of choosing the materials from which pots and pans were to be made, what kinds of materials would you choose on the basis of specific heat? Why?

76. 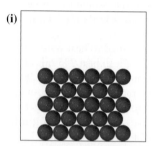 The following shows an element in each of its three physical states.

(i)

(ii)

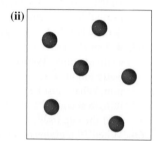

(iii)

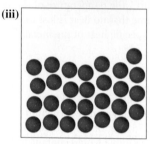

(a) Which drawing represents a solid? (b) Which drawing represents a liquid? (c) Which drawing represents a gas? (d) Rank these physical states from least dense to most dense.

77. Although newly minted pennies look as though they are composed of copper, they actually contain only 2.7% copper. The remainder of the metal is zinc. If the densities of copper and zinc are 8.72 g/cm³ and 7.14 g/cm³ respectively, what is the density of a newly minted penny?

78. When she discovered that a piece of shiny gray zinc was too large to fit through the opening of an Erlenmeyer flask, a student cut the zinc into smaller pieces so they would fit. She then poured enough blue copper chloride solution into the flask to cover the zinc pieces. After 20 min the solution became colorless, the bottom of the flask was slightly warm to the touch, the zinc pieces were visibly reduced in size, and brown granular material appeared in the mixture. List the physical properties, physical changes, and chemical changes the student should have noted and recorded in her laboratory notebook.

79. Which is denser at 0°C, ice or water? How do you know?

80. 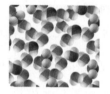 Based upon the answer you gave for Exercise 79, which of the following drawings is a molecular representation for ice and which is for liquid water?

 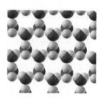

81.  The drawing in the circle (at the bottom left) is a greatly expanded representation of the molecules in the liquid of the thermometer on its left. The thermometer registers 20°C. Which of the figures (a–d) is the best representation of the liquid in this same thermometer at 10°C? (Assume that the same volume of liquid is shown in each expanded representation.)

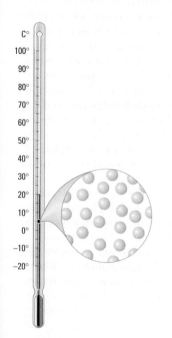 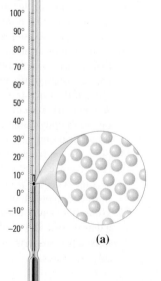

(a)

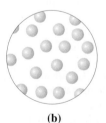

(b)

(c)

(d)

82. During the past several years, you have gained chemical vocabulary and understanding from a variety of academic and entertainment venues. List three events that occurred early in the development of your current chemical knowledge.

83. ▲ At what temperature will a Fahrenheit thermometer give (a) the same reading as a Celsius thermometer; (b) a reading that is twice that on the Celsius thermometer; (c) a reading that is numerically the same but opposite in sign from that on the Celsius thermometer?

84. ▲ Cesium atoms are the largest naturally occurring atoms. The radius of a cesium atom is 2.65 Å. How many cesium atoms would have to be laid side by side to give a row of cesium atoms 1.00 in. long? Assume that the atoms are spherical.

85. Four balloons are each filled with a different gas of varying density:

helium, $d = 0.164$ g/L;
neon, $d = 0.825$ g/L;
argon, $d = 1.633$ g/L;
krypton, $d = 4.425$ g/L.

If the density of dry air is 1.12 g/L, which balloon or balloons float in air?

86. As you write out the answer to an end-of-chapter exercise, what chemical changes occur? Did your answer involve knowledge not covered in Chapter 1?

87. *Combustion* is discussed later in this textbook; however, you probably already know what the term means. (Look it up to be sure.) List two other chemical terms that were in your vocabulary before you read Chapter 1.

88. Which has the higher temperature, a sample of water at 65°C or a sample of iron at 65°F?

89. Answer the following questions using figures (i) to (ix). Each question may have more than one answer. (a) Which represents nanoscale particles in a sample of gas? (b) Which represents nanoscale particles in a sample of liquid? (c) Which represents nanoscale particles in a sample of solid? (d) Which represents nanoscale particles in a sample of an element? (e) Which represents nanoscale particles in a sample of a compound? (f) Which represents nanoscale particles in a sample of a mixture? (g) Which represents nanoscale particles in a sample of a pure substance?

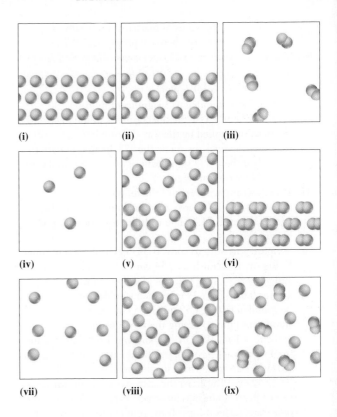

(i)   (ii)   (iii)

(iv)   (v)   (vi)

(vii)   (viii)   (ix)

90. When nitrogen (N_2) reacts with oxygen (O_2), several compounds can be produced: NO, NO_2, N_2O, N_2O_3, N_2O_4, and N_2O_5. If a nitrogen atom is represented by ●, and an oxygen atom is represented by ●, identify by its formula each of the following oxides of nitrogen:

91. Draw models representing an atom of chlorine and a molecule of chlorine. How are they different? Draw models representing an atom of carbon and a molecule of methane. How is methane different from chlorine?

92. Draw models representing samples (several atoms or molecules) of sulfur and oxygen at room temperature. In what ways are the two elements alike? How are they different? Sulfur can combine chemically with oxygen to produce sulfur dioxide. Draw models representing samples of sulfur dioxide and a mixture of sulfur and oxygen. In what ways are the compound and the mixture alike? How are they different? Is the mixture homogeneous or heterogeneous?

93. Charcoal is wood that has been heated in the absence of oxygen to eliminate the volatile organic compounds, leaving carbon and minerals (ash). When charcoal burns, the carbon alone combines with oxygen in the air, producing carbon dioxide. The carbon is a black solid, while the oxygen and the carbon dioxide are both colorless gases. Is the change from solid, black carbon and colorless oxygen gas to colorless carbon dioxide gas a physical change or a chemical change? Why? Are

🔷 **Molecular Reasoning** exercises   ▲ **More Challenging** exercises   Blue-Numbered exercises solved in Student Solutions Manual

the colors and the states of matter of these substances physical properties or chemical properties? Why?

94. When the volume of 53.275 g of copper ($D = 8.92$ g/cm^3) is calculated ($V = \dfrac{m}{D} = \dfrac{53.275 \text{ g}}{8.92 \text{ g/cm}^3} = 5.97253$ cm^3), the answer is rounded to 3 significant figures ($V = 5.97$ cm^3). Use the uncertainties in the mass and the density, implied by the way the numbers are written, to justify the final answer. Is the "7" the first uncertain digit? Is it the "9" (2 significant figures)? Or could it be the "2" (4 significant figures)?

95. What's wrong with each of the following measurements? "There's an animal out in the hallway, and its length is 51." "The width of this room is 7.36 bleams."

96. Suppose you were to convert 3475 centimeters to miles. Using the relationships 2.54 cm = 1 in., 12 in. = 1 ft, and 5280 ft = 1 mi, you would arrive at the answer 0.021 592 649 mi, which would then be rounded to 0.021 59 mi (3475 cm has 4 significant figures). Using the relationships 100 cm = 1 m, 1000 m = 1 km, and 1.609 km = 1 mi (to 4 significant figures), you would arrive at the answer 0.021 597 265 mi, which would then be rounded to 0.021 60 mi. Why aren't the answers exactly the same? Is one of the relationships incorrect? Which calculation uses only exact relationships? Is the result of that calculation exact? Is it more accurate than the result of the other calculation?

97. The temperature of the surface of the sun (the photosphere) ranges from 5500°C to 6000°C. Convert 5500°C to kelvins and °F. Suppose a famous astronomer, in a public lecture for the general public, said that the temperature of the surface of the sun is 10,000°. Would she be referring to the Celsius, Kelvin, or Fahrenheit temperature scale (or is she just confused)?

98. Amount of heat, specific heat, and temperature are such closely related properties of a substance that they are often confused. How are they related to each other? How are they different, by definition? One way to distinguish these three properties is by the unit used. What units might be used by a scientist for each of these properties?

Beyond the Textbook

NOTE: *Whenever the answer to an exercise depends on information obtained from a source other than this textbook, the source must be included as an essential part of the answer.*

99. Use an internet search engine (such as **http://www.google.com**) to locate the total surface area of the state of Idaho. Report your answer in square meters. Repeat the search but this time for Ohio. How does the surface area of the two states compare?

100. Go to **http://www.google.com** or another internet search engine to locate the information needed to answer the following: (a) Which of the world's oceans has the largest area? (b) What is the area of that ocean in square kilometers? (c) What is the area of that ocean in square miles?

101. Go to **http://www.google.com** or another internet search engine to locate the information needed to answer the following: (a) Which of the world's oceans has the largest volume? (b) What is the volume of that ocean in cubic kilometers? (c) What is the volume of that ocean in cubic miles? (d) What is the volume of that ocean in gallons?

102. Go to **chemistry.about.com/od/branchesofchemistry** or another suitable internet site and locate the four central concerns (branches) of chemistry. List the four central concerns for chemistry.

103. Go to **chemistry.about.com/od/branchesofchemistry** or another suitable internet site and locate the description of one of the branches of chemistry. Define the branch of chemistry that you have selected.

104. The definition of the meter has changed several times. Use an internet search engine (such as **http://www.google.com**) to locate the origin and various earlier definitions of the meter. Comment on some advantages of the present definition compared to earlier ones.

105. (a) Since the copyright date (2010) of the 9th edition of this text, the discovery of element 117 has been verified. What is the currently accepted name for element 117? (b) During that time period, names for elements 112, 114, and 116 have been recommended by the IUPAC for approval. Give the current names and symbols for elements 112, 114, and 116; tell for what (or whom) each of these latter three elements is named and describe the origin of the name.

🔷 **Molecular Reasoning** exercises   ▲ **More Challenging** exercises   Blue-Numbered exercises solved in Student Solutions Manual

Unless otherwise noted, all content on this page is © Cengage Learning.

Chemical Formulas and Composition Stoichiometry

2

Rock candy is composed of large crystals of sucrose (sugar, $C_{12}O_{11}H_{22}$). A ball-and-stick model (C = black, O = red, H = white) of sucrose is superimposed on an electrostatic charge potential surface that shows the relative charges on the atoms (red = most negative, green = neutral, blue = most positive).

Courtesy of Dena Diglio Betz

Four Different Representations of the Sucrose Molecule

A Flat structural representation showing all atoms

B Organic line drawing using shorthand notation where carbon and attached hydrogen atoms are not indicated by their elemental symbols

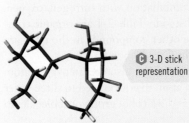

C 3-D stick representation

D A space-filling model

OBJECTIVES

After you have studied this chapter, you should be able to

▶ Use chemical formulas to solve various kinds of chemical problems

▶ Relate names to formulas and charges of simple ions

▶ Combine simple ions to write formulas and names of some ionic compounds

▶ Recognize and use formula weights and mole relationships

▶ Interconvert masses, moles, and formulas

▶ Determine percent compositions in compounds

▶ Determine formulas from composition data

▶ Recognize models from calculated molecular formulas

▶ Perform calculations on the purity of substances

The language we use to describe the forms of matter and the changes in its composition is not limited to use in chemistry courses; it appears throughout the scientific world. Chemical symbols, formulas, and equations are used in such diverse areas as agriculture, home economics, engineering, geology, physics, biology, medicine, and dentistry. In this chapter we will use the simplest atomic theory as we represent the chemical formulas of elements and compounds. Later, after additional facts have been introduced, this theory will be expanded.

The word "stoichiometry" is derived from the Greek *stoicheion*, which means "first principle or element," and *metron*, which means "measure." **Stoichiometry** describes the quantitative relationships among elements in compounds (composition stoichiometry) and among substances as they undergo chemical changes (reaction stoichiometry). In this chapter we are concerned with chemical formulas and **composition stoichiometry**. In Chapter 3 we will discuss chemical equations and **reaction stoichiometry**.

2-1 Chemical Formulas

▶ It is important to learn this fundamental material well as it is the basis of all chemistry.

O_2 molecule

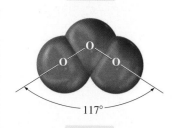

117°

O_3 molecule

The **chemical formula** for a substance shows its chemical composition as elements present and the ratio in which the atoms of the elements occur. The formula for a single atom is the same as the symbol for the element. Thus, Na can represent a single sodium atom. It is quite unusual to find such isolated atoms in nature, with the exception of the noble gases (He, Ne, Ar, Kr, Xe, and Rn). A subscript following the symbol of an element indicates the number of atoms in a molecule. For instance, F_2 indicates a molecule containing two fluorine atoms, and P_4 a molecule containing four phosphorus atoms.

Some elements exist in more than one form. Familiar examples include (1) oxygen, found as O_2 molecules, and ozone, found as O_3 molecules, and (2) two crystalline forms of carbon—diamond and graphite (see Figure 13-32). Different structural forms of the same element are called **allotropic modifications**, or **allotropes**.

Compounds contain two or more elements in chemical combination in fixed proportions. Many compounds exist as molecules (Table 2-1). Hence, each molecule of hydrogen chloride, HCl, contains one atom of hydrogen and one atom of chlorine; each molecule of acetic acid, CH_3COOH, contains two carbon atoms, four hydrogen atoms, and two oxygen atoms. Writing it as CH_3COOH (instead of $C_2H_4O_2$) includes useful bonding and structural information. An aspirin molecule, $C_9H_8O_4$, contains nine carbon atoms, eight hydrogen atoms, and four oxygen atoms.

Many of the molecules found in nature are organic compounds. **Organic compounds** contain C — C or C — H bonds or both, often in combination with nitrogen, oxygen, sulfur, and other elements. Eleven of the compounds listed in Table 2-1 are organic compounds (acetic acid and the last ten entries). All of the other compounds in the table are **inorganic compounds** (compounds that do not contain C — H bonds).

Some groups of atoms behave chemically as single entities. For instance, an oxygen atom that is bonded to a hydrogen atom and also to a carbon atom that is bonded to three other atoms forms the reactive combination of atoms known as the alcohol group or molecule. In

Table 2-1 Names and Formulas of Some Common Molecular Compounds

Name	Formula	Name	Formula	Name	Formula
water	H_2O	sulfur dioxide	SO_2	butane	C_4H_{10}
hydrogen peroxide	H_2O_2	sulfur trioxide	SO_3	pentane	C_5H_{12}
hydrogen chloride*	HCl	carbon monoxide	CO	benzene	C_6H_6
sulfuric acid	H_2SO_4	carbon dioxide	CO_2	methanol (methyl alcohol)	CH_3OH
nitric acid	HNO_3	methane	CH_4	ethanol (ethyl alcohol)	CH_3CH_2OH
acetic acid	CH_3COOH	ethane	C_2H_6	acetone	CH_3COCH_3
ammonia	NH_3	propane	C_3H_8	diethyl ether (ether)	$CH_3CH_2OCH_2CH_3$

*Called hydrochloric acid if dissolved in water.

formulas of compounds containing two or more of the same group, the group formula is enclosed in parentheses. Thus $C_2H_4(OH)_2$ contains two *alcohol groups* (see margin); it is called ethylene glycol. When you count the number of atoms in this molecule from its formula, you must multiply the numbers of hydrogen and oxygen atoms in the OH group by 2. There are *two* carbon atoms, *six* hydrogen atoms and *two* oxygen atoms in a molecule of ethylene glycol. Thus, another way to write this formula is $C_2H_6O_2$, but this is not as informative to chemists (see Section 23-9).

Compounds were first recognized as distinct substances because of their different physical properties and because they could be separated from one another by physical methods. Once the concept of atoms and molecules was established, the reason for these differences in properties could be understood: Two compounds differ from each other because their molecules are different. Conversely, if two molecules contain the same number of the same kinds of atoms, arranged the same way, then both are molecules of the same compound. Thus, the atomic theory explains the **Law of Definite Proportions** (see Section 1-6).

This law, also known as the **Law of Constant Composition**, can now be extended to include its interpretation in terms of atoms. It is so important for performing the calculations in this chapter that we restate it here:

> Different pure samples of a compound always contain the same elements in the same proportion by mass; this corresponds to atoms of these elements combined in fixed numerical ratios.

So we see that for a substance composed of molecules, the **chemical formula** gives the number of atoms of each type in the molecule. But this formula does not express the order in which the atoms in the molecules are bonded together. The **structural formula** shows the order in which atoms are connected. The lines connecting atomic symbols represent chemical bonds between atoms. The bonds are forces that tend to hold atoms at certain distances and angles from one another. For instance, the structural formula of propane, C_3H_8, shows that the three C atoms are linked in a chain, with three H atoms bonded to each of the end C atoms and two H atoms bonded to the center C. Chemists sometimes write out the formula in a way to better convey the connectivity information, e.g., $CH_3CH_2CH_3$, which is a longer representation of the propane chemical formula. Structural formulas are drawn flat and two-dimensional and do not usually indicate any specific three-dimensional information about the molecule. **Ball-and-stick** molecular models and **space-filling** molecular models help us to see the shapes and relative sizes of molecules. These four representations are shown in Figure 2-1. The ball-and-stick and space-filling models show (1) the *bonding sequence*, which is the order in which the atoms are connected to each other, and (2) the *geometrical arrangements* of the atoms in the molecule. As we will see later, both are extremely important because they determine the properties of compounds.

A Ball-and-stick model

B Space-filling model of ethylene glycol, the main constituent of automobile antifreeze

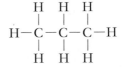

Chemical Formula	Structural Formula	Ball-and-Stick Model	Space-Filling Model
H_2O, water	H—O—H		
H_2O_2, hydrogen peroxide	H—O—O—H		
CCl_4, carbon tetrachloride	$\begin{array}{c} Cl \\ \mid \\ Cl-C-Cl \\ \mid \\ Cl \end{array}$		
C_2H_5OH, ethanol	$\begin{array}{c} H \quad H \\ \mid \quad \mid \\ H-C-C-O-H \\ \mid \quad \mid \\ H \quad H \end{array}$		

Figure 2-1 Formulas and models for some molecules. Structural formulas show the order in which atoms are connected but do not represent true molecular shapes. Ball-and-stick models use balls of different colors to represent atoms and sticks to represent bonds; they show the three-dimensional shapes of molecules. Space-filling models show the (approximate) relative sizes of atoms and the shapes of molecules, but the bonds between the atoms are hidden by the overlapping spheres that represent the atoms.

EXAMPLE 2-1 Chemical Formulas   MOLECULAR REASONING

Look at each of the following molecular models. For each one, write the structural formula and the chemical formula. (Color code: black = carbon; white = hydrogen; red = oxygen; blue = nitrogen; light green = fluorine; dark green = chlorine.)

(a) 1-butanol (occurs in some fruits, dried beans, cheese, and nuts; used as an additive in certain plastics, detergents, and some medicinal formulations)

(b) Freon-12 (formerly used as a refrigerant; implicated in atmospheric ozone depletion)

(c) nitrogen mustard HN1 (a highly toxic substance, used as a chemotherapy drug in the treatment of Hodgkin's disease and of some forms of chronic leukemia)

Plan

We identify each atom present from its color in the model. The structural formula shows which atoms are bonded to one another. We count the number of atoms of each type and represent the chemical formula with element symbols and subscripts, as described in this section.

▶ At this stage, you should not worry if you don't know the order in which the elements should appear in the chemical formula.

Solution

(a) This ball-and-stick model shows that the atoms are bonded together as shown by the structural formula.

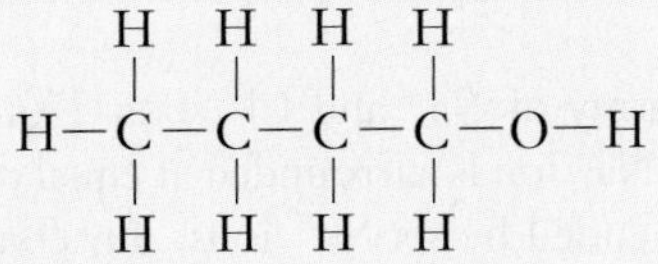

$$
\begin{array}{c}
\quad\; H \quad H \quad H \quad H \\
\quad\; | \quad\; | \quad\; | \quad\; | \\
H-C-C-C-C-O-H \\
\quad\; | \quad\; | \quad\; | \quad\; | \\
\quad\; H \quad H \quad H \quad H
\end{array}
$$

The model shows four carbon atoms (C), ten hydrogen atoms (H), and one oxygen atom (O), so the chemical formula is $C_4H_{10}O$.

(b) This space-filling model shows that the atoms are bonded together as shown by the structural formula.

$$
\begin{array}{c}
\quad\; Cl \\
\quad\; | \\
F-C-Cl \\
\quad\; | \\
\quad\; F
\end{array}
$$

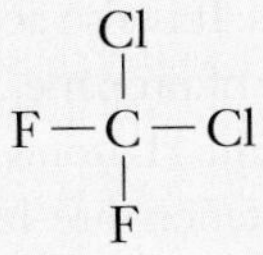

The model shows one carbon atom (C), two fluorine atoms (F), and two chlorine atoms (Cl), so the chemical formula is CF_2Cl_2.

(c) This ball-and-stick model shows that the atoms are bonded together as shown by the structural formula.

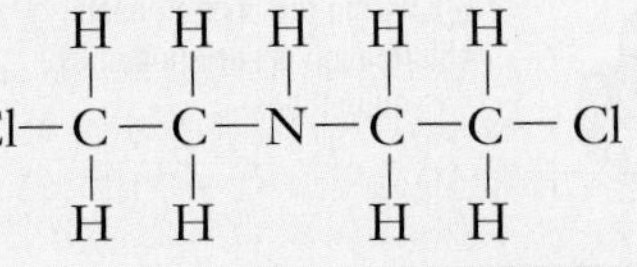

$$
\begin{array}{c}
\quad\; H \quad H \quad\quad H \quad H \quad H \\
\quad\; | \quad\; | \quad\quad | \quad\; | \quad\; | \\
Cl-C-C-N-C-C-Cl \\
\quad\; | \quad\; | \quad\quad\quad | \quad\; | \\
\quad\; H \quad H \quad\quad\quad H \quad H
\end{array}
$$

The model shows four carbon atoms (C), nine hydrogen atoms (H), one nitrogen atom (N), and two chlorine atoms (Cl), so the chemical formula is $C_4N_9NCl_2$.

> **S** **TOP & THINK**
>
> Chemists use a shorthand system for drawing the structures of organic compounds. Carbon and hydrogen atoms bonded to the carbon atoms are sometimes not drawn using their elemental symbols. Carbons are understood to be located at ends and corners of bond lines and have enough hydrogen atoms attached to give each carbon a total of four bonds. This is sometimes called *organic line notation*; examples of the three structures in Example 2-1 are shown below.
>
> ⌁⌁⌁OH
>
> (structure with Cl, F, F, Cl)
>
> (structure: Cl⌁⌁N(H)⌁⌁Cl)

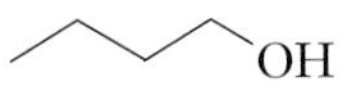

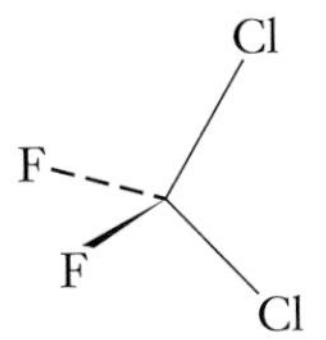

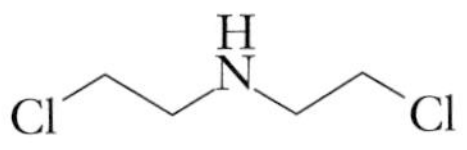

During your study of chemistry you will have many occasions to refer to compounds by name. In these early chapters, we will see how a few compounds should be named. More comprehensive rules for naming compounds are presented at the appropriate places later in the text.

Table 2-1 includes examples of names for a few common molecular compounds. You should learn that short list before proceeding much farther in this textbook. We will name many more molecular compounds as we encounter them in later chapters.

2-2 Ions and Ionic Compounds

So far we have discussed only compounds that exist as discrete molecules. Some compounds, such as sodium chloride, NaCl, consist of collections of large numbers of ions. An **ion** is an atom or group of atoms that carries an electric charge. Ions that possess a *positive* charge, such as the sodium ion, Na^+, are called **cations**. Those carrying a *negative* charge, such as the chloride ion, Cl^-, are called **anions**. The charge on an ion *must* be included as a superscript on the right side of the chemical symbol(s) when we write the formula for the individual ion.

► The words "cation" (kat'-i-on) and "anion" (an'-i-on) and their relationship to cathode and anode will be described in Chapter 21.

As we will discuss in detail in Chapter 4, an atom consists of a very small, very dense, positively charged *nucleus* surrounded by a diffuse distribution of negatively charged particles called *electrons*. The number of positive charges in the nucleus defines the identity of the element to which the atom corresponds. Electrically neutral atoms contain the same number of electrons outside the nucleus as positive charges (protons) within the nucleus. Ions are formed when neutral atoms lose or gain electrons. An Na^+ ion is formed when a sodium atom loses one electron, and a Cl^- ion is formed when a chlorine atom gains one electron.

The compound NaCl consists of an extended array of Na^+ and Cl^- ions (Figure 2-2). Within the crystal (though not on the surface) each Na^+ ion is surrounded at equal distances by six Cl^- ions, and each Cl^- ion is similarly surrounded by six Na^+ ions. *Any* compound, whether ionic or molecular, is electrically neutral; that is, it has no net charge. In NaCl this means that the Na^+ and Cl^- ions are present in a 1:1 ratio, and this is indicated by the formula NaCl.

► The general term "formula unit" applies to molecular or ionic compounds, whereas the more specific term "molecule" applies only to elements and compounds that exist as discrete molecules.

Because there are no "molecules" of ionic substances, we should not refer to "a molecule of sodium chloride, NaCl," for example. Instead, we refer to a **formula unit** of NaCl, which consists of one Na^+ ion and one Cl^- ion. Likewise, one formula unit of $CaCl_2$ consists of one Ca^{2+} ion and two Cl^- ions. We speak of the formula unit of all ionic compounds as the smallest, whole-number ratios of ions that yield neutral representations. It is also acceptable to refer to a formula unit of a molecular compound. One formula unit of propane, C_3H_8, is the same as one molecule of C_3H_8; it contains three C atoms and eight H atoms bonded together into a group. For the present, we will tell you which substances are ionic and which are molecular when it is important to know. Later you will learn to make the distinction yourself.

► In this text, we use the standard convention of representing multiple charges with the number before the sign, e.g., Ca^{2+}, *not* Ca^{+2} and SO_4^{2-}, *not* SO_4^{-2}.

Polyatomic ions are groups of atoms that bear an electric charge. The first atom in the formula is usually the central atom to which the other atoms are bonded to make a stable unit. Examples include the ammonium ion, NH_4^+; the sulfate ion, SO_4^{2-}; and the

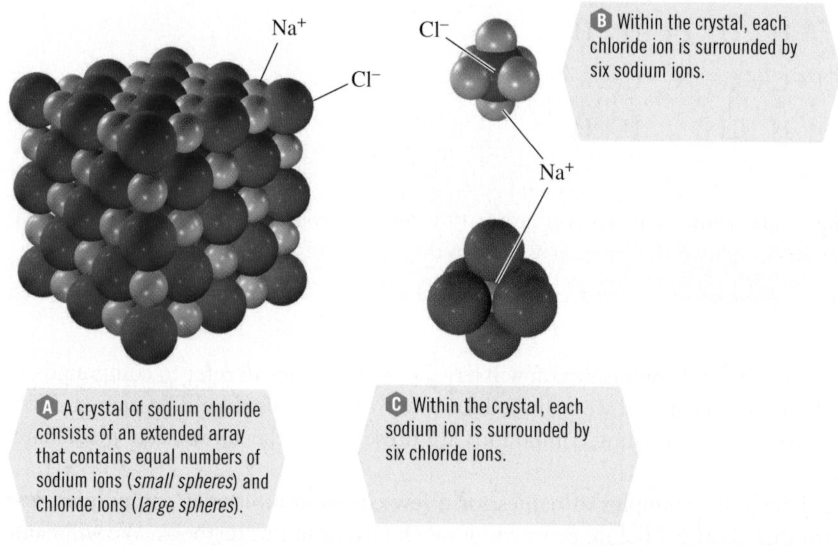

B Within the crystal, each chloride ion is surrounded by six sodium ions.

A A crystal of sodium chloride consists of an extended array that contains equal numbers of sodium ions (*small spheres*) and chloride ions (*large spheres*).

C Within the crystal, each sodium ion is surrounded by six chloride ions.

Figure 2-2 The arrangement of ions in NaCl.

Table 2-2 Formulas, Ionic Charges, and Names of Some Common Ions

Common Cations (positive ions)			Common Anions (negative ions)		
Formula	*Charge*	*Name*	*Formula*	*Charge*	*Name*
Li^+	1+	lithium	F^-	1−	fluoride
Na^+	1+	sodium	Cl^-	1−	chloride
K^+	1+	potassium	Br^-	1−	bromide
NH_4^+	1+	ammonium	I^-	1−	iodide
Ag^+	1+	silver	OH^-	1−	hydroxide
			CH_3COO^-	1−	acetate
Mg^{2+}	2+	magnesium	NO_3^-	1−	nitrate
Ca^{2+}	2+	calcium			
Zn^{2+}	2+	zinc	O^{2-}	2−	oxide
Cu^+	1+	copper(I)	S^{2-}	2−	sulfide
Cu^{2+}	2+	copper(II)	SO_4^{2-}	2−	sulfate
Fe^{2+}	2+	iron(II)	SO_3^{2-}	2−	sulfite
			CO_3^{2-}	2−	carbonate
Fe^{3+}	3+	iron(III)			
Al^{3+}	3+	aluminum	PO_4^{3-}	3−	phosphate

S **TOP & THINK**
It is very important to learn the names, formulas, and charges of the common polyatomic ions listed in Table 2-2 and recognize them in chemical formulas.

▶ As we will see, some metals can form more than one kind of ion with a positive charge. For such metals, we specify which ion we mean with a Roman numeral, for example, iron(II) or iron(III). Because zinc forms no stable ions other than Zn^{2+}, we do not need to use Roman numerals in its name.

nitrate ion, NO_3^-. Table 2-2 shows the formulas, ionic charges, and names of some common ions. When writing the formula of a polyatomic compound, we show groups in parentheses when they appear more than once. For example, $(NH_4)_2SO_4$ represents a compound that has two NH_4^+ ions for each SO_4^{2-} ion.

2-3 Names and Formulas of Some Ionic Compounds

The names of some common ions appear in Table 2-2. You will need to know the names and formulas of these frequently encountered ions. They can be used to write the formulas and names of many ionic compounds. We write the formula of an ionic compound by adjusting the relative numbers of positive and negative ions so their total charges cancel (i.e., add to zero). The name of an ionic compound is formed by giving the names of the ions, with the positive ion named first.

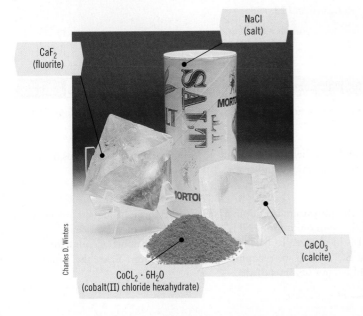

NaCl (salt)

CaF_2 (fluorite)

$CaCO_3$ (calcite)

$CoCL_2 \cdot 6H_2O$ (cobalt(II) chloride hexahydrate)

Charles D. Winters

Ionic compounds *(clockwise, from top)*: salt (sodium chloride, NaCl), calcite (calcium carbonate, $CaCO_3$), cobalt(II) chloride hexahydrate ($CoCl_2 \cdot 6H_2O$), fluorite (calcium fluoride, CaF_2).

> **Problem-Solving Tip** Where to Start in Learning to Name Compounds
>
> You may not be sure of the best point to start learning the naming of compounds. It has been found that before rules for naming can make much sense or before we can expand our knowledge to more complex compounds, we need to know the names and formulas in Tables 2-1 and 2-2. If you are unsure of your ability to recall a name or a formula in Tables 2-1 and 2-2 when given the other, prepare flash cards, lists, and so on that you can use to learn these tables.

EXAMPLE 2-2 Formulas for Ionic Compounds

Write the formulas for the following ionic compounds: (a) sodium fluoride, (b) calcium fluoride, (c) iron(II) sulfate, (d) zinc phosphate.

Plan

In each case, we identify the chemical formulas of the ions from Table 2-2. These ions must be present in the simplest whole-number ratio that gives the compound *no net charge*. Recall that the formulas and names of ionic compounds are written by giving the positively charged ion first.

Solution

(a) The formula for the sodium ion is Na^+, and the formula for the fluoride ion is F^- (see Table 2-2). Because the charges on these two ions are equal in magnitude, the ions must be present in equal numbers, or in a 1:1 ratio. Thus, the formula for sodium fluoride is NaF.

(b) The formula for the calcium ion is Ca^{2+} and the formula for the fluoride ion is F^-. Now each positive ion (Ca^{2+}) provides twice as much charge as each negative ion (F^-). So there must be twice as many F^- ions as Ca^{2+} ions to equalize the charge. This means that the ratio of calcium to fluoride ions is 1:2. So the formula for calcium fluoride is CaF_2.

(c) The iron(II) ion is Fe^{2+}, and the sulfate ion is SO_4^{2-}. As in part (a), the equal magnitudes of positive and negative charges tell us that the ions must be present in equal numbers, or in a 1:1 ratio. The formula for iron(II) sulfate is $FeSO_4$.

(d) The zinc ion is Zn^{2+}, and the phosphate ion is PO_4^{3-}. Now it will take *three* Zn^{2+} ions to account for as much charge (6+ total) as would be present in *two* PO_4^{3-} ions (6− total). So the formula for zinc phosphate is $Zn_3(PO_4)_2$.

You should now work Exercises 16 and 23.

Phosphate ion, PO_4^{3-}

EXAMPLE 2-3 Names for Ionic Compounds

Name the following ionic compounds: (a) $(NH_4)_2S$, (b) $Cu(NO_3)_2$, (c) $ZnCl_2$, (d) $Fe_2(CO_3)_3$.

Plan

In naming ionic compounds, it is helpful to inspect the formula for atoms or groups of atoms that we recognize as representing familiar ions.

Solution

(a) The presence of the polyatomic grouping NH_4 in the formula suggests to us the presence of the ammonium ion, NH_4^+. There are two of these, each accounting for 1+ in charge. To balance this, the single S must account for 2− in charge, or S^{2-}, which we recognize as the sulfide ion. Thus, the name of the compound is ammonium sulfide.

Ammonium ion, NH_4^+

(b) The NO_3 grouping in the formula tells us that the nitrate ion, NO_3^-, is present. Two of these nitrate ions account for $2 \times 1 - \ = 2-$ in negative charge. To balance this, copper must account for $2+$ charge and be the copper(II) ion. The name of the compound is copper(II) nitrate.

(c) The positive ion present is zinc ion, Zn^{2+}, and the negative ion is chloride, Cl^-. The name of the compound is zinc chloride.

(d) Each CO_3 grouping in the formula must represent the carbonate ion, CO_3^{2-}. The presence of *three* such ions accounts for a total of $6-$ in negative charge, so there must be a total of $6+$ present in positive charge to balance this. It takes two iron ions to provide this $6+$, so each ion must have a charge of $3+$ and be Fe^{3+}, the iron(III) ion, or ferric ion. The name of the compound is iron(III) carbonate.

You should now work Exercises 15 and 22.

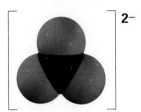

Carbonate ion, CO_3^{2-}

▶ We use the information that the carbonate ion has a 2– charge to find the charge on the iron ions. The total charges must add up to zero.

A more extensive discussion on naming compounds appears in Chapter 6.

2-4 Atomic Weights

As the chemists of the eighteenth and nineteenth centuries painstakingly sought information about the compositions of compounds and tried to systematize their knowledge, it became apparent that each element has a characteristic mass relative to every other element. Although these early scientists did not have the experimental means to measure the mass of each kind of atom, they succeeded in defining a *relative* scale of atomic masses.

An early observation was that carbon and hydrogen have relative atomic masses, also traditionally called **atomic weights (AW)**, of approximately 12 and 1, respectively. Thousands of experiments on the compositions of compounds have resulted in the establishment of a scale of relative atomic weights based on the **atomic mass unit (amu)**, which is defined as *exactly $\frac{1}{12}$ of the mass of an atom of a particular kind of carbon atom, called carbon-12.*

On this scale, the atomic weight of hydrogen (H) is 1.00794 amu, that of sodium (Na) is 22.989768 amu, and that of magnesium (Mg) is 24.3050 amu. This tells us that Na atoms have nearly 23 times the mass of H atoms, and Mg atoms are about 24 times heavier than H atoms.

When you need values of atomic weights, consult the periodic table or the alphabetical listing of elements on the inside covers of this book.

▶ The term "atomic weight" is widely accepted because of its traditional use, although it is properly a mass rather than a weight. "Atomic mass" is often used and is technically more accurate. As you probably know, the weight of an object of a particular mass is the result of a gravitational attraction on the object. In chemistry, we are always comparing amounts of substances under the same gravitation, so any weight ratio is the same as the mass ratio.

2-5 The Mole

Even the smallest bit of matter that can be handled reliably contains an enormous number of atoms. So we must deal with large numbers of atoms in any real situation, and some unit for conveniently describing a large number of atoms is desirable. The idea of using a unit to describe a particular number (amount) of objects has been around for a long time. You are already familiar with the dozen (12 items) and the gross (144 items).

The SI unit for amount is the **mole**, abbreviated mol. It is *defined* as the amount of substance that contains as many entities (atoms, molecules, or other particles) as there are atoms in exactly 0.012 kg of pure carbon-12 atoms. Many experiments have refined the number, and the currently accepted value is

▶ "Mole" is derived from the Latin word *moles*, which means "a mass." "Molecule" is the diminutive form of this word and means "a small mass."

$$1 \text{ mole} = 6.02214179 \times 10^{23} \text{ particles}$$

This number, often rounded to 6.022×10^{23}, is called **Avogadro's number** in honor of Amedeo Avogadro (1776–1856), whose contributions to chemistry are discussed in Section 12-8.

According to its definition, the mole unit refers to a fixed number of items, the identities of which must be specified. Just as we speak of a dozen eggs or a pair of aces, we refer to a mole of atoms or a mole of molecules (or a mole of ions, electrons, or other particles). We could even think about a mole of eggs, although the size of the required carton staggers the imagination! Helium exists as discrete He atoms, so one mole of helium consists of 6.022×10^{23} He *atoms*. Hydrogen commonly exists as diatomic (two-atom) molecules, so one mole of hydrogen is 6.022×10^{23} H_2 *molecules* and $2(6.022 \times 10^{23})$ H atoms.

Every kind of atom, molecule, or ion has a definite characteristic mass. It follows that one mole of a given pure substance also has a definite mass, regardless of the source of the sample. This idea is of central importance in many calculations throughout the study of chemistry and the related sciences.

Because the mole is defined as the number of atoms in 0.012 kg (or 12 g) of carbon-12, and the atomic mass unit is defined as $\frac{1}{12}$ of the mass of a carbon-12 atom, the following convenient relationship is true:

> The mass of one mole of *atoms* of a pure element in grams is numerically equal to the atomic weight of that element in atomic mass units. This is also called the **molar mass** of the element; its units are grams/mole, also written as g/mol or $g \cdot mol^{-1}$.

For instance, if you obtain a pure sample of the metallic element titanium (Ti), whose atomic weight is 47.88 amu, and measure out 47.88 g of it, you will have one mole, or 6.022×10^{23} titanium atoms.

▶ The atomic weight of iron (Fe) is 55.847 amu. Assume that one dozen large eggs weighs 24 oz.

The symbol for an element is used in several ways: (1) to identify the element, (2) to represent one atom of the element, or (3) to represent one mole of atoms of the element. The last interpretation will be extremely useful in calculations in Chapter 3.

A quantity of a substance may be expressed in a variety of ways. For example, consider a dozen eggs and 55.847 grams (or one mole) of iron (Figure 2-3). We can express the amount of eggs or iron present in any of several units. We can then construct unit factors to relate an amount of the substance expressed in one kind of unit to the same amount expressed in another unit.

12 large eggs
or
1 dozen eggs
or
24 ounces of eggs

6.022×10^{23} Fe atoms
or
1 mole of Fe atoms
or
55.847 grams of iron

Figure 2-3 Three ways of representing amounts.

Unit Factors for Eggs	Unit Factors for Iron
$\dfrac{12 \text{ eggs}}{1 \text{ doz eggs}}$	$\dfrac{6.022 \times 10^{23} \text{ Fe atoms}}{1 \text{ mol Fe atoms}}$
$\dfrac{12 \text{ eggs}}{24 \text{ oz eggs}}$	$\dfrac{6.022 \times 10^{23} \text{ Fe atoms}}{55.847 \text{ g Fe}}$
and so on	and so on

As Table 2-3 suggests, the concept of a mole as applied to atoms is especially useful. It provides a convenient basis for comparing the masses of equal numbers of atoms of different elements.

Figure 2-4 shows what one mole of atoms of each of some common elements looks like. Each of the examples in Figure 2-4 represents 6.022×10^{23} *atoms* of the element.

The relationship between the mass of a sample of an element and the number of moles of atoms in the sample is illustrated in Example 2-4.

Table 2-3 Mass of One Mole of Atoms of Some Common Elements

Element	Atomic Weight	A Sample with a Mass of	Contains
carbon	12.0	12.0 g C	6.02×10^{23} C atoms or 1 mol of C atoms
titanium	47.9	47.9 g Ti	6.02×10^{23} Ti atoms or 1 mol of Ti atoms
bromine	79.9	79.9 g Br_2	6.02×10^{23} Br atoms or 1 mol of Br atoms (3.01×10^{23} Br_2 molecules or $\frac{1}{2}$ mole of Br_2 molecules)
hydrogen	1.0	1.0 g H_2	6.02×10^{23} H atoms or 1 mol of H atoms (3.01×10^{23} H_2 molecules or $\frac{1}{2}$ mol of H_2 molecules)
sulfur	32.1	32.1 g S_8	6.02×10^{23} S atoms or 1 mol of S atoms (0.753×10^{23} S_8 molecules or $\frac{1}{8}$ mol of S_8 molecules)

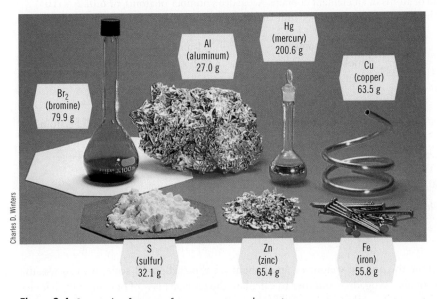

Figure 2-4 One mole of atoms of some common elements.

Charles D. Winters

In this textbook we usually work problems involving atomic weights (masses) or formula weights (masses) rounded to only one decimal place. We round the answer further if initial data do not support the number of significant figures obtained using the rounded atomic weights. Similarly, if the initial data indicate that more significant figures are justified, we will work such problems using atomic weights and formula weights containing values beyond the tenths place.

EXAMPLE 2-4 Moles of Atoms

How many moles of atoms does 136.9 g of iron metal contain?

Plan

▶ To the required four significant figures, 1 mol Fe atoms = 55.85 g Fe.

The atomic weight of iron is 55.85 amu. This tells us that the molar mass of iron is 55.85 g/mol, or that one mole of iron atoms is 55.85 g of iron. We can express this as either of two unit factors:

$$\frac{1 \text{ mol Fe atoms}}{55.85 \text{ g Fe}} \quad \text{or} \quad \frac{55.85 \text{ g Fe}}{1 \text{ mol Fe atoms}}$$

Because one mole of iron has a mass of 55.85 g, we expect that 136.9 g will be a fairly small number of moles (greater than 1, but less than 10).

Solution

$$\underline{?} \text{ mol Fe atoms} = 136.9 \text{ g Fe} \times \frac{1 \text{ mol Fe atoms}}{55.85 \text{ g Fe}} = 2.451 \text{ mol Fe atoms}$$

You should now work Exercises 32 and 40.

> **S** TOP & THINK
> When you are given the mass (or weight) of any substance in grams (or any other mass or weight unit) you almost always need to convert it into moles to do chemical calculations. Formula weight is always greater than 1 (except for H atoms), so the number of moles in a sample is always a smaller number than the mass in grams.

Once the number of moles of atoms of an element is known, the number of atoms in the sample can be calculated, as Example 2-5 illustrates.

EXAMPLE 2-5 Numbers of Atoms

How many atoms are contained in 2.451 mol of iron?

Plan

One mole of atoms of an element contains Avogadro's number of atoms, or 6.022×10^{23} atoms. This lets us generate the two unit factors

$$\frac{6.022 \times 10^{23} \text{ atoms}}{1 \text{ mol atoms}} \quad \text{and} \quad \frac{1 \text{ mol atoms}}{6.022 \times 10^{23} \text{ atoms}}$$

Solution

$$\underline{?} \text{ Fe atoms} = 2.451 \text{ mol Fe atoms} \times \frac{6.022 \times 10^{23} \text{ Fe atoms}}{1 \text{ mol Fe atoms}} = 1.476 \times 10^{24} \text{ Fe atoms}$$

We expected the number of atoms in more than two moles of atoms to be a very large number. Written in nonscientific notation, the answer to this example is: 1,476,000,000,000,000,000,000,000.

You should now work Exercise 42.

> **S** TOP & THINK
> Try to name this number with its many zeroes. One mole of anything contains a huge number of atoms or molecules (Avogadro's number). Thus the number of atoms or molecules is always *much* larger than the number of moles or the mass in grams. Be sure to carry units through every calculation.

If we know the atomic weight of an element on the carbon-12 scale, we can use the mole concept and Avogadro's number to calculate the *average* mass of one atom of that element in grams (or any other mass unit we choose).

CHEMISTRY IN USE

ogadro's Number

ou think that the value of Avogadro's number, 6×10^{23}, is too e to be useful to anyone but chemists, look up into the sky on a r night. You may be able to see about 3000 stars with the na- eye, but the total number of stars swirling around you in the wn universe is approximately equal to Avogadro's number. Just k, the known universe contains approximately one mole of s! You don't have to leave Earth to encounter such large num- s. The water in the Pacific Ocean has a volume of about 10^{23} mL and a mass of about 6×10^{23} g.

vogadro's number is almost incomprehensibly large. For mple, if one mole of dollars had been given away at the rate million dollars per second beginning when the earth first ned some 4.5 billion years ago, would any remain today? Sur- ingly, about three-fourths of the original mole of dollars would eft today; it would take about 14,500,000,000 more years to away the remaining money at $1 million per second.

Computers can be used to provide another illustration of the gnitude of Avogadro's number. If a computer can count up ne billion in one second, it would take that computer about million years to count up to 6×10^{23}. In contrast, recorded nan history goes back only a few thousand years.

The impressively large size of Avogadro's number can give very important insights into the very small sizes of indi- ual molecules. Suppose one drop of water evaporates in

one hour. There are about 20 drops in one milliliter of water, which weighs one gram. So one drop of water is about 0.05 g of water. How many H_2O molecules evaporate per second?

$$\frac{H_2O \text{ molecules}}{1 \text{ s}} = \frac{0.05 \text{ g } H_2O}{1 \text{ h}} \times \frac{1 \text{ mol } H_2O}{18 \text{ g } H_2O} \times$$

$$\frac{6 \times 10^{23} H_2O \text{ molecules}}{1 \text{ mol } H_2O} \times \frac{1 \text{ h}}{60 \text{ min}} \times \frac{1 \text{ min}}{60 \text{ s}}$$

$$= 5 \times 10^{17} H_2O \text{ molecules/s}$$

5×10^{17} H_2O molecules evaporating per second is five hun- dred million billion H_2O molecules evaporating per second—a number that is beyond our comprehension! This calculation helps us to recognize that water molecules are incredibly small. There are approximately 1.7×10^{21} water molecules in a single drop of water.

By gaining some appreciation of the vastness of Avogadro's number, we gain a greater appreciation of the extremely tiny volumes occupied by individual atoms, molecules, and ions.

RONALD DELORENZO

MIDDLE GEORGIA COLLEGE

ORIGINAL CONCEPT BY LARRY NORDELL

EXAMPLE 2-6 Masses of Atoms

Calculate the average mass of one iron atom in grams.

Plan

We expect that the mass of a single atom in grams would be a *very* small number. We know that one mole of Fe atoms has a mass of 55.85 g and contains 6.022×10^{23} Fe atoms. We use this information to generate unit factors to carry out the desired conversion.

Solution

$$\frac{? \text{ g Fe}}{\text{Fe atom}} = \frac{55.85 \text{ g Fe}}{1 \text{ mol Fe atoms}} \times \frac{1 \text{ mol Fe atoms}}{6.022 \times 10^{23} \text{ Fe atoms}} = 9.274 \times 10^{-23} \text{ g Fe/Fe atom}$$

Thus, we see that the average mass of one Fe atom is only 9.274×10^{-23} g, that is, 0.00000000000000000000009274 g.

STOP & THINK
For any substance, the amount that we can manipulate or measure contains a huge number of atoms or molecules, so the mass of any atom or molecule must be a tiny fraction of a gram.

Example 2-6 demonstrates how small atoms are and why it is necessary to use large numbers of atoms in practical work. Example 2-7 will help you to appreciate the huge magnitude of Avogadro's number.

EXAMPLE 2-7 Avogadro's Number

A stack of 500 sheets of typing paper is 1.9 inches thick. Calculate the thickness, in inches and in miles, of a stack of typing paper that contains one mole (Avogadro's number) of sheets.

Plan

We construct unit factors from the data given, from conversion factors in Table 1-8, and from Avogadro's number.

Solution

$$\underline{?}\ \text{in.} = 1\ \text{mol sheets} \times \frac{6.022 \times 10^{23}\ \text{sheets}}{1\ \text{mol sheets}} \times \frac{1.9\ \text{in.}}{500\ \text{sheets}} = 2.3 \times 10^{21}\ \text{in.}$$

$$\underline{?}\ \text{mi} = 2.3 \times 10^{21}\ \text{in.} \times \frac{1\ \text{ft}}{12\ \text{in.}} \times \frac{1\ \text{mi}}{5280\ \text{ft}} = 3.6 \times 10^{16}\ \text{mi.}$$

By comparison, the sun is about 93 million miles from the earth. This stack of paper would make 390 million stacks that reach from the earth to the sun.

▶ Imagine the number of trees required to make this much paper! This would weigh about 5×10^{20} kg, which far exceeds the total mass of all the trees on earth. The mass of the earth is about 6×10^{24} kg.

Problem-Solving Tip When Do We Round?

Even though the number 1.9 has two significant figures, we carry the other numbers in Example 2-7 to more significant figures. Then we round at the end to the appropriate number of significant figures. The numbers in the distance conversions are exact numbers.

2-6 Formula Weights, Molecular Weights, and Moles

▶ Formula weight is more accurately called formula mass.

> The **formula weight (FW)** of a substance is the sum of the atomic weights (AW) of the elements in the formula, each taken the number of times the element occurs. Hence a formula weight gives the mass of one formula unit in atomic mass units.

Formula weights, like the atomic weights on which they are based, are relative masses. The formula weight for sodium hydroxide, NaOH (rounded off to the nearest 0.1 amu), is found as follows.

Number of Atoms of Stated Kind	× Mass of One Atom	= Mass Due to Element
$1 \times \text{Na} = 1$	$\times\ 23.0$ amu	$=\ 23.0$ amu of Na
$1 \times \text{H} = 1$	$\times\ \ 1.0$ amu	$=\ \ \ 1.0$ amu of H
$1 \times \text{O} = 1$	$\times\ 16.0$ amu	$=\ 16.0$ amu of O

Formula weight of NaOH = 40.0 amu

The term "formula weight" is correctly used for either ionic or molecular substances. When we refer specifically to molecular (non-ionic) substances, that is, substances that exist as discrete molecules, we often use the term **molecular weight (MW)**.

EXAMPLE 2-8 Formula Weights

Calculate the formula weight (molecular weight) of acetic acid (the active ingredient in vinegar), CH_3COOH, using rounded values for atomic weights given in the International Table of Atomic Weights inside the front cover of the text.

Plan

We add the atomic weights of the elements in the formula, each multiplied by the number of times the element occurs.

Solution

Number of Atoms of Stated Kind	× Mass of One Atom	= Mass Due to Element
$2 \times C = 2$	$\times$ 12.0 amu	= 24.0 amu of C
$4 \times H = 4$	$\times$ 1.0 amu	= 4.0 amu of H
$2 \times O = 2$	$\times$ 16.0 amu	= 32.0 amu of O

Formula weight (molecular weight) of acetic acid = 60.0 amu

You should now work Exercise 28.

A Ball-and-stick model, CH_3COOH

B Space-filling model of an acetic acid molecule, CH_3COOH

The amount of substance that contains the mass in grams numerically equal to its formula weight in amu contains 6.022×10^{23} formula units, or one *mole* of the substance. This is sometimes called the *molar mass* of the substance. Molar mass is *numerically equal* to the formula weight of the substance (the atomic weight for atoms of elements) and has the units grams/mole (g/mol).

One mole of sodium hydroxide is 40.0 g of NaOH, and one mole of acetic acid is 60.0 g of CH_3COOH. One mole of any molecular substance contains 6.02×10^{23} molecules of that substance, as Table 2-4 illustrates.

Because no simple NaCl molecules exist at ordinary temperatures, it is inappropriate to refer to the "molecular weight" of NaCl or any ionic compound. One mole of an ionic compound contains 6.02×10^{23} *formula units* of the substance. Recall that one formula unit of sodium chloride consists of one sodium ion, Na^+ and one chloride ion, Cl^-. One mole, or 58.4 g, of NaCl contains 6.02×10^{23} Na^+ ions and 6.02×10^{23} ions (Table 2-5).

> **S TOP & THINK**
> The formula weight is the sum of atomic weights. The smallest atomic weight (H) is 1.0, so all other formula weights must be greater than 1 amu.

Table 2-4 One Mole of Some Common Molecular Substances

Substance	Molecular Weight	A Sample with a Mass of	Contains
oxygen	32.0 g/mol	32.0 g O_2	1 mol of O_2 molecules or 6.02×10^{23} molecules O_2 ($2 \times 6.02 \times 10^{23}$ atoms of O)
water	18.0 g/mol	18.0 g H_2O	1 mol of H_2O molecules or 6.02×10^{23} molecules of H_2O ($2 \times 6.02 \times 10^{23}$ atoms of H and 6.02×10^{23} atoms of O)
methane	16.0 g/mol	16.0 g CH_4	1 mol of CH_4 molecules or 6.02×10^{23} molecules of CH_4 ($4 \times 6.02 \times 10^{23}$ atoms of H and 6.02×10^{23} atoms of C)
sucrose (sugar)	342.3 g/mol	342.3 g $C_{12}H_{22}O_{11}$	1 mol of $C_{12}H_{22}O_{11}$ molecules or 6.02×10^{23} molecules of sucrose ($12 \times 6.02 \times 10^{23}$ atoms of C, $22 \times 6.02 \times 10^{23}$ atoms of H, and $11 \times 6.02 \times 10^{23}$ atoms of O)

Table 2-5 One Mole of Some Ionic Compounds

Compound	Formula Weight	A Sample with a Mass of 1 Mol	Contains
sodium chloride	58.4 g/mol	58.4 g NaCl	(6.02×10^{23} Na^+ ions or 1 mol of Na^+ ions) *and* (6.02×10^{23} Cl^- ions or 1 mol of Cl^- ions)
calcium chloride	111.0 g/mol	111.0 g $CaCl_2$	(6.02×10^{23} Ca^{2+} ions or 1 mol of Ca^{2+} ions) *and* ($2 \times 6.02 \times 10^{23}$ Cl^- ions or 2 mol of Cl^- ions)
aluminum sulfate	342.1 g/mol	342.1 g $Al_2(SO_4)_3$	($2 \times 6.02 \times 10^{23}$ Al^{3+} ions or 2 mol of Al^{3+} ions) *and* ($3 \times 6.02 \times 10^{23}$ SO_4^{2-} ions or 3 mol of SO_4^{2-} ions)

The mole concept, together with Avogadro's number, provides important connections among the extensive properties mass of substance, number of moles of substance, and number of molecules or ions. These are summarized as follows:

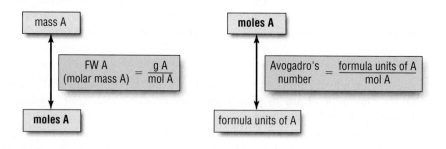

The following examples show the relations between numbers of molecules, atoms, or formula units and their masses.

EXAMPLE 2-9 Masses of Molecules

What is the mass in grams of 10.0 million SO_2 molecules?

Plan

One mole of SO_2 contains 6.02×10^{23} SO_2 molecules and has a mass of 64.1 grams.

Solution

$$\underline{?} \text{ g } SO_2 = 10.0 \times 10^6 \text{ } SO_2 \text{ molecules} \times \frac{64.1 \text{ g } SO_2}{6.02 \times 10^{23} \text{ } SO_2 \text{ molecules}}$$

$$= 1.06 \times 10^{-15} \text{ g } SO_2$$

Ten million SO_2 molecules have a mass of only 0.00000000000000106 g. Commonly used analytical balances are capable of weighing to ± 0.0001 g.

You should now work Exercise 44.

STOP & THINK
When fewer than four significant figures are needed in calculations, Avogadro's number may be rounded to 6.02×10^{23}. The mass of any molecule is a very tiny number of grams.

EXAMPLE 2-10 Moles

How many (a) moles of O_2, (b) O_2 molecules, and (c) O atoms are contained in 40.0 g of oxygen gas (dioxygen) at 25°C?

Plan

We construct the needed unit factors from the following equalities: (a) the mass of one mole of O_2 is 32.0 g (molar mass O_2 = 32.0 g/mol); (b) one mole of O_2 contains 6.02×10^{23} O_2 molecules; (c) one O_2 molecule contains two O atoms.

Solution

One mole of O_2 contains 6.02×10^{23} O_2 molecules, and its mass is 32.0 g.

(a) $\underline{?}$ mol $O_2 = 40.0$ g $O_2 \times \dfrac{1 \text{ mol } O_2}{32.0 \text{ g } O_2} = 1.25$ mol O_2

(b) $\underline{?}$ O_2 molecules $= 40.0$ g $O_2 \times \dfrac{6.02 \times 10^{23} \text{ } O_2 \text{ molecules}}{32.0 \text{ g } O_2}$

$= 7.52 \times 10^{23}$ molecules

Or, we can use the number of moles of O_2 calculated in part (a) to find the number of O_2 molecules.

$\underline{?}$ O_2 molecules $= 1.25$ mol $O_2 \times \dfrac{6.02 \times 10^{23} \text{ } O_2 \text{ molecules}}{1 \text{ mol } O_2} = 7.52 \times 10^{23}$ O_2 molecules

(c) $\underline{?}$ O atoms $= 40.0$ g $O_2 \times \dfrac{6.02 \times 10^{23} \text{ } O_2 \text{ molecules}}{32.0 \text{ g } O_2} \times \dfrac{2 \text{ O atoms}}{1 \text{ } O_2 \text{ molecule}}$

$= 1.50 \times 10^{24}$ O atoms

You should now work Exercise 36.

S TOP & THINK
Use unit factors to help you with all conversions. (a) Number of moles is always less than the mass in grams. (b, c) Number of molecules and number of atoms is always *much* greater than the number of moles present.

EXAMPLE 2-11 Numbers of Atoms

Calculate the number of hydrogen atoms in 39.6 g of ammonium sulfate, $(NH_4)_2SO_4$.

Plan

One mole of $(NH_4)_2SO_4$ is 6.02×10^{23} formula units and has a mass of 132.1 g.

| g of $(NH_4)_2SO_4$ | $\longrightarrow$ | mol of $(NH_4)_2SO_4$ | $\longrightarrow$ | formula units of $(NH_4)_2SO_4$ | $\longrightarrow$ | H atoms |

Solution

$\underline{?}$ H atoms $= 39.6$ g $(NH_4)_2SO_4 \times \dfrac{1 \text{ mol} (NH_4)_2SO_4}{132.1 \text{ g} (NH_4)_2SO_4} \times$

$\dfrac{6.02 \times 10^{23} \text{ formula units } (NH_4)_2SO_4}{1 \text{ mol} (NH_4)_2SO_4} \times \dfrac{8 \text{ H atoms}}{1 \text{ formula units} (NH_4)_2SO_4}$

$= 1.44 \times 10^{24}$ H atoms

You should now work Exercise 34.

▶ In Example 2-11, we relate (a) grams to moles, (b) moles to formula units, and (c) formula units to H atoms.

S TOP & THINK
Remember to include both "types" of subscripts in figuring out the number of atoms! It is pretty easy to remember that the 4-subscript in $(NH_4)_2$ means that there are four H atoms. But don't forget to include the 2-subscript, which means that there are two NH_4 units present for a total of 8 H atoms.

2-7 Percent Composition and Formulas of Compounds

▶ AW = atomic weight (mass)
MW = molecular weight (mass)

As a check, we see that the percentages add to 100%.

If the formula of a compound is known, its chemical composition can be expressed as the mass percent of each element in the compound (percent composition). For example, one carbon dioxide molecule, CO_2, contains one C atom and two O atoms. Percentage is the part divided by the whole times 100% (or simply parts per hundred), so we can represent the percent composition of carbon dioxide as follows:

$$\% C = \frac{\text{mass of C}}{\text{mass of } CO_2} \times 100\% = \frac{\text{AW of C}}{\text{MW of } CO_2} \times 100\% = \frac{12.0 \text{ amu}}{44.0 \text{ amu}} \times 100\% = 27.3\% \text{ C}$$

$$\% O = \frac{\text{mass of O}}{\text{mass of } CO_2} \times 100\% = \frac{2 \times \text{AW of O}}{\text{MW of } CO_2} \times 100\% = \frac{2(16.0 \text{ amu})}{44.0 \text{ amu}} \times 100\% = 72.7\% \text{ O}$$

One *mole* of CO_2 (44.0 g) contains one *mole* of C atoms (12.0 g) and two *moles* of O atoms (32.0 g). We could therefore have used these masses in the preceding calculation. These numbers are the same as the ones used—only the units are different. In Example 2-12 we will base our calculation on one *mole* rather than one *molecule*.

EXAMPLE 2-12 Percent Composition

Calculate the percent composition by mass of HNO_3.

Plan

We first calculate the mass of one mole as in Example 2-8. Then we express the mass of each element as a percent of the total.

Solution

The molar mass of HNO_3 is calculated first.

▶ When chemists use the % notation, they mean percent by mass unless they specify otherwise.

Number of Mol of Atoms	× Mass of One Mol of Atoms	= Mass Due to Element
1 × H = 1	× 1.0 g	= 1.0 g of H
1 × N = 1	× 14.0 g	= 14.0 g of N
3 × O = 3	× 16.0 g	= 48.0 g of O

Mass of 1 mol of HNO_3 = 63.0 g

Now, its percent composition is

$$\% H = \frac{\text{mass of H}}{\text{mass of } HNO_3} \times 100\% = \frac{1.0 \text{ g}}{63.0 \text{ g}} \times 100\% = 1.6\% \text{ H}$$

$$\% N = \frac{\text{mass of N}}{\text{mass of } HNO_3} \times 100\% = \frac{14.0 \text{ g}}{63.0 \text{ g}} \times 100\% = 22.2\% \text{ N}$$

$$\% O = \frac{\text{mass of O}}{\text{mass of } HNO_3} \times 100\% = \frac{48.0 \text{ g}}{63.0 \text{ g}} \times 100\% = 76.2\% \text{ O}$$

Total = 100.0%

You should now work Exercise 62.

Nitric acid is 1.6% H, 22.2% N, and 76.2% O by mass. All samples of pure HNO_3 have this composition, according to the Law of Definite Proportions.

Problem-Solving Tip The Whole Is Equal to the Sum of Its Parts

Percentages must add to 100%. Roundoff errors may not cancel, however, and totals such as 99.9% or 100.1% may be obtained in calculations. As an alternative method of calculation, if we know all of the percentages except one, we can subtract their sum from 100% to obtain the remaining value.

2-8 Derivation of Formulas from Elemental Composition

The **simplest**, or **empirical**, **formula** for a compound is the smallest whole-number ratio of atoms present. For molecular compounds the **molecular formula** indicates the *actual* numbers of atoms present in a molecule of the compound. It may be the same as the simplest formula or else some whole-number multiple of it. For example, the simplest and molecular formulas for water are both H_2O; however, for hydrogen peroxide, the empirical formula is HO, and the molecular formula is H_2O_2.

A ball-and-stick model of (a) a molecule of water, H_2O, and (b) a molecule of hydrogen peroxide, H_2O_2

Each year thousands of new compounds are made in laboratories or discovered in nature. One of the first steps in characterizing a new compound is the determination of its percent composition. A *qualitative* analysis is performed to determine which elements are present in the compound. Then a *quantitative* analysis is performed to determine the *amount* of each element. Once the percent composition of a compound (or its elemental composition by mass) is known, the simplest formula can be determined.

EXAMPLE 2-13 Simplest Formulas

Compounds containing sulfur and oxygen are serious air pollutants; they represent the major cause of acid rain. Analysis of a sample of a pure compound reveals that it contains 50.1% sulfur and 49.9% oxygen by mass. What is the simplest formula of the compound?

Plan

One mole of atoms of any element is 6.02×10^{23} atoms, so the ratio of moles of atoms in any sample of a compound is the same as the ratio of atoms in that compound. This calculation is carried out in two steps.

Step 1: Let's consider 100.0 g of compound, which contains 50.1 g of S and 49.9 g of O. We calculate the number of moles of atoms of each.

▶ Remember that *percent* means "parts per hundred."

Step 2: We then obtain a whole-number ratio between these numbers that gives the ratio of atoms in the sample and hence in the simplest formula for the compound.

Solution

Step 1: $\underline{?}$ mol S atoms $= 50.1 \text{ g S} \times \dfrac{1 \text{ mol S atoms}}{32.1 \text{ g S}} = 1.56 \text{ mol S atoms}$

$\underline{?}$ mol O atoms $= 49.9 \text{ g O} \times \dfrac{1 \text{ mol O atoms}}{16.0 \text{ g O}} = 3.12 \text{ mol O atoms}$

▶ A simple and useful way to obtain whole-number ratios among several numbers follows: (a) Divide each number by the smallest number, and then, (b) if necessary, multiply all the resulting numbers by the smallest whole number that will eliminate fractions

Step 2:   Now we know that 100.0 g of the compound contains 1.56 mol of S atoms and 3.12 mol of O atoms. We obtain a whole-number ratio between these numbers that gives the ratio of atoms in the simplest formula.

$$\frac{1.56}{1.56} = 1.00 \text{ S}$$

$$\frac{3.12}{1.56} = 2.00 \text{ O}$$

SO_2

You should now work Exercise 54.

The solution for Example 2-13 can be set up in tabular form.

▶ The "Relative Mass of Element" column is proportional to the mass of each element in grams. With this interpretation, the next column could be headed "Relative Number of *Moles* of Atoms." Then the last column would represent the smallest whole-number ratios of *moles* of atoms. But because a mole is always the same number of items (atoms), that ratio is the same as the smallest whole-number ratio of atoms.

Element	Relative Mass of Element	Relative Number of Atoms (divide mass by AW)	Divide by Smallest Number	Smallest Whole-Number Ratio of Atoms
S	50.1	$\frac{50.1}{32.1} = 1.56$	$\frac{1.56}{1.56} = 1.00 \text{ S}$	
O	49.9	$\frac{49.9}{16.0} = 3.12$	$\frac{3.12}{1.56} = 2.00 \text{ O}$	SO_2

This tabular format provides a convenient way to solve simplest-formula problems, as the next example illustrates.

EXAMPLE 2-14   Simplest Formula

A 20.882-g sample of an ionic compound is found to contain 6.072 g of Na, 8.474 g of S, and 6.336 g of O. What is its simplest formula?

Plan

We reason as in Example 2-13, calculating the number of moles of each element and the ratio among them. Here we use the tabular format that was introduced earlier.

Solution

Element	Relative Mass of Element	Relative Number of Atoms (divide mass by AW)	Divide by Smallest Number	Convert Fractions to Whole Numbers (multiply by integer)	Smallest Whole-Number Ratio of Atoms
Na	6.072	$\frac{6.072}{23.0} = 0.264$	$\frac{0.264}{0.264} = 1.00$	$1.00 \times 2 = 2\,\text{Na}$	
S	8.474	$\frac{8.474}{32.1} = 0.264$	$\frac{0.264}{0.264} = 1.00$	$1.00 \times 2 = 2\,\text{S}$	$Na_2S_2O_3$
O	6.336	$\frac{6.336}{16.0} = 0.396$	$\frac{0.396}{0.264} = 1.50$	$1.50 \times 2 = 3\,\text{O}$	

The ratio of atoms in the simplest formula *must be a whole-number ratio* (by definition). To convert the ratio 1:1:1.5 to a whole-number ratio, each number in the ratio was multiplied by 2, which gave the simplest formula $Na_2S_2O_3$.

You should now work Exercise 56.

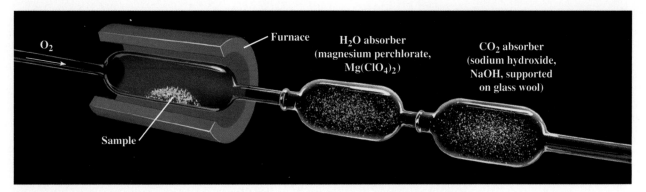

Figure 2-5 A combustion train used for carbon–hydrogen analysis. The increase in weight of the H_2O absorber can be converted into the amount of hydrogen present, while the increase in weight of the CO_2 absorber can be used to calculate the amount of carbon present.

Problem-Solving Tip Know Common Fractions in Decimal Form

As Example 2-14 illustrates, sometimes we must convert a fraction to a whole number by multiplying the fraction by the correct integer. But we must first recognize which fraction is represented by a nonzero part of a number. The decimal equivalents of the following fractions may be useful.

Decimal Equivalent (to two places)	Fraction	To convert to integer, multiply by
0.50	$\frac{1}{2}$	2
0.33	$\frac{1}{3}$	3
0.67	$\frac{2}{3}$	3
0.25	$\frac{1}{4}$	4
0.75	$\frac{3}{4}$	4
0.20	$\frac{1}{5}$	5

The fractions $\frac{2}{5}$, $\frac{3}{5}$, and $\frac{4}{5}$ are equal to 0.40, 0.60, and 0.80, respectively; these should be multiplied by 5.

When we use the procedure given in this section, we often obtain numbers such as 0.99 and 1.52. Because the results obtained by analysis of samples usually contain some error (as well as roundoff errors), we would interpret 0.99 as 1.0 and 1.52 as 1.5.

S TOP & THINK
A simplest (empirical) formula must have only integer subscripts with no common factors.

S TOP & THINK
Don't forget to multiply *all* calculated coefficients by this common factor to obtain the final integer coefficients!

Millions of compounds are composed of carbon, hydrogen, and oxygen. Analyses for C and H can be performed in a C-H combustion system (Figure 2-5). An accurately known mass of a compound is burned in a furnace in a stream of oxygen. This technique is often termed *combustion analysis*. The carbon and hydrogen in the sample are converted to carbon dioxide and water vapor, respectively. The resulting increases in masses of the CO_2 and H_2O absorbers can then be related to the masses and percentages of carbon and hydrogen in the original sample.

▶ Hydrocarbons are obtained from coal and coal tar and from oil and gas wells. The main use of hydrocarbons is as fuels. The simplest hydrocarbons are

methane	CH_4
ethane	C_2H_6
propane	C_3H_8
butane	C_4H_{10}

EXAMPLE 2-15 Percent Composition

Hydrocarbons are organic compounds composed entirely of hydrogen and carbon. A 0.1647-g sample of a pure hydrocarbon was burned in a C-H combustion train to produce 0.4931 g of CO_2 and 0.2691 g of H_2O. Determine the masses of C and H in the sample and the percentages of these elements in this hydrocarbon.

Plan

Step 1: We use the observed mass of CO_2, 0.4931 g, to determine the mass of carbon in the original sample. There is one mole of carbon atoms, 12.01 g, in each mole of CO_2, 44.01 g; we use this information to construct the unit factor

$$\frac{12.01 \text{ g C}}{44.01 \text{ g } CO_2}$$

Step 2: Likewise, we can use the observed mass of H_2O, 0.2691 g, to calculate the amount of hydrogen in the original sample. We use the fact that there are two moles of hydrogen atoms, 2.016 g, in each mole of H_2O, 18.02 g, to construct the unit factor

$$\frac{2.016 \text{ g H}}{18.02 \text{ g } H_2O}$$

▶ We could calculate the mass of H by subtracting the mass of C from the mass of the sample. It is good experimental practice, however, when possible, to base both on experimental measurements, as we have done here. This helps to check for errors in the analysis or calculation.

Step 3: Then we calculate the percentages by mass of each element in turn, using the relationship

$$\% \text{element} = \frac{\text{g element}}{\text{g sample}} \times 100\%$$

Solution

Step 1: $\underline{? \text{ g C}} = 0.4931 \text{ g } CO_2 \times \dfrac{12.01 \text{ g C}}{44.01 \text{ g } CO_2} = \quad 0.1346 \text{ g C}$

Step 2: $\underline{? \text{ g H}} = 0.2691 \text{ g } H_2O \times \dfrac{2.016 \text{ g H}}{18.02 \text{ g } H_2O} = \quad 0.03010 \text{ g H}$

Step 3: $\% \text{ C} = \dfrac{0.1346 \text{ g C}}{0.1647 \text{ g sample}} \times 100\% = \quad 81.72\% \text{ C}$

$\% \text{ H} = \dfrac{0.03010 \text{ g H}}{0.1647 \text{ g sample}} \times 100\% = \quad 18.28\% \text{ H}$

Total = 100.00%

Can you show that the hydrocarbon in Example 2-15 is propane, C_3H_8?

You should now work Exercise 66.

When the compound to be analyzed contains oxygen, the calculation of the amount or percentage of oxygen in the sample is somewhat different. Part of the oxygen that goes to form CO_2 and H_2O comes from the sample, and part comes from the oxygen stream supplied. For that reason, we cannot directly determine the amount of oxygen already in the sample. The approach is to analyze as we did in Example 2-15 for all elements *except* oxygen. Then we subtract the sum of their masses from the mass of the original sample to obtain the mass of oxygen. The next example illustrates such a calculation.

EXAMPLE 2-16 Percent Composition

A 0.1014-g sample of purified glucose was burned in a C-H combustion train to produce 0.1486 g of CO_2 and 0.0609 g of H_2O. An elemental analysis showed that glucose contains only carbon, hydrogen, and oxygen. Determine the masses of C, H, and O in the sample and the percentages of these elements in glucose.

Plan

Steps 1 and 2:   We first calculate the masses of carbon and hydrogen as we did in Example 2-15.

Step 3:   The rest of the sample must be oxygen because glucose has been shown to contain only C, H, and O. So we subtract the masses of C and H from the total mass of sample.

Glucose, a simple sugar, is the main component of intravenous feeding liquids. Its common name is dextrose. It is also one of the products of carbohydrate metabolism.

C. Paxton & J. Farrow/Photo Researchers, Inc.

Step 4:   Then we calculate the percentage by mass for each element.

Solution

Step 1: $? \text{ g C} = 0.1486 \text{ g CO}_2 \times \dfrac{12.01 \text{ g C}}{44.01 \text{ g CO}_2} = 0.04055 \text{ g C}$

Step 2: $? \text{ g H} = 0.0609 \text{ g H}_2\text{O} \times \dfrac{2.016 \text{ g H}}{18.02 \text{ g H}_2\text{O}} = 0.00681 \text{ g H}$

Step 3: $? \text{ g O} = 0.1014 \text{ g sample} - [0.04055 \text{ g C} + 0.00681 \text{ g H}] = 0.0540 \text{ g O}$

▶ We say that the mass of O in the sample is calculated by *difference*.

Step 4:   Now we can calculate the percentages by mass for each element:

$$\% \text{ C} = \dfrac{0.04055 \text{ g C}}{0.1014 \text{ g}} \times 100\% = 39.99\% \text{ C}$$

$$\% \text{ H} = \dfrac{0.00681 \text{ g H}}{0.1014 \text{ g}} \times 100\% = 6.72\% \text{ H}$$

$$\% \text{ O} = \dfrac{0.0540 \text{ g O}}{0.1014 \text{ g}} \times 100\% = 53.2\% \text{ O}$$

Total = 99.9%

You should now work Exercise 68.

2-9 Determination of Molecular Formulas

Percent composition data yield only simplest formulas. To determine the molecular formula for a molecular compound, *both* its *empirical* formula and its molecular weight must be known. Some methods for experimental determination of molecular weights are introduced in Chapters 12 and 14.

For many compounds the molecular formula is a multiple of the simplest formula. Consider butane, C_4H_{10}. The *empirical* formula for butane is C_2H_5, but the molecular formula contains twice as many atoms; that is, $2 \times (C_2H_5) = C_4H_{10}$. Benzene, C_6H_6, is another example. The simplest formula for benzene is CH, but the molecular formula contains six times as many atoms; that is, $6 \times (CH) = C_6H_6$.

The molecular formula for a compound is either the same as, or an *integer* multiple of, the (*empirical*) formula.

$$\text{molecular formula} = n \times \text{simplest formula}$$

So we can write

$$\text{molecular weight} = n \times \text{simplest formula weight}$$

$$n = \dfrac{\text{molecular weight}}{\text{simplest formula weight}}$$

The molecular formula is then obtained by multiplying the *empirical* formula by the integer, n.

EXAMPLE 2–17 Molecular Formula

In Example 2–16, we found the elemental composition of glucose. Other experiments show that its molecular weight is approximately 180 amu. Determine the simplest formula and the molecular formula of glucose.

Plan

Step 1:   We first use the masses of C, H, and O found in Example 2-16 to determine the simplest formula.

▶ As an alternative, we could have used the percentages by mass from Example 2–16. Using the earliest available numbers helps to minimize the effects of rounding errors.

Step 2:   We can use the simplest formula to calculate the simplest formula weight. Because the molecular weight of glucose is known (approximately 180 amu), we can determine the molecular formula by dividing the molecular weight by the simplest formula weight.

$$n = \frac{\text{molecular weight}}{\text{simplest formula weight}}$$

The molecular weight is n times the *empirical* formula weight, so the molecular *formula* of glucose is n times the *empirical formula*.

Solution

Step 1:

Element	Relative Mass of Element	Relative Number of Atoms (divide mass by AW)	Divide by Smallest	Smallest Whole-Number Ratio of Atoms
C	0.04055	$\frac{0.04055}{12.01} = 0.003376$	$\frac{0.003376}{0.003376} = 1.00\ \text{C}$	
H	0.00681	$\frac{0.00681}{1.008} = 0.00676$	$\frac{0.00676}{0.003376} = 2.00\ \text{H}$	CH_2O
O	0.0540	$\frac{0.0540}{16.00} = 0.00338$	$\frac{0.00338}{0.003376} = 1.00\ \text{O}$	

S TOP & THINK

The molecular formula is always the simplest formula multiplied by some positive integer; this integer can be 1.

Step 2:   The simplest formula is CH_2O, which has a formula weight of 30.03 amu. Because the molecular weight of glucose is approximately 180 amu, we can determine the molecular formula by dividing the molecular weight by the *empirical* formula weight.

$$n = \frac{180\ \text{amu}}{30.03\ \text{amu}} = 6.00$$

The molecular weight is six times the simplest formula weight, so the molecular formula of glucose must be six times the empirical formula.

$$\text{molecular formula} = 6 \times (CH_2O) = C_6H_{12}O_6$$

You should now work Exercises 49 and 50.

► Many sugars are rich sources in our diet. The most familiar is ordinary table sugar, which is sucrose, $C_{12}H_{22}O_{11}$. An enzyme in our saliva readily splits sucrose into two simple sugars, glucose and fructose.

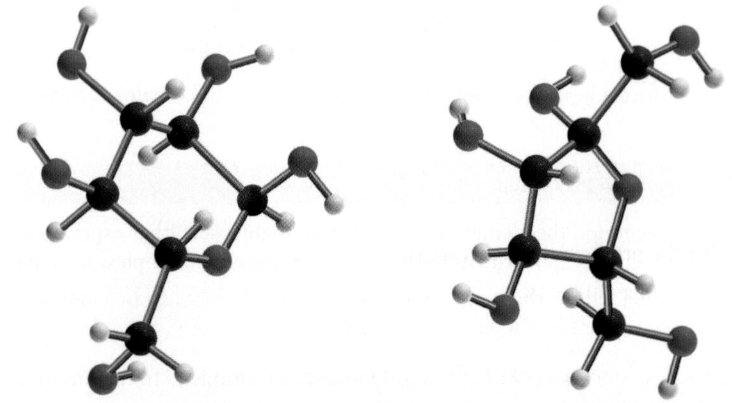

Ball-and-stick models of glucose (*left*) and fructose (*right*). Both have the formula $C_6H_{12}O_6$, but they have different structures and properties, so they are different compounds. Black atoms = carbon, white atoms = hydrogen, and red atoms = oxygen.

As we shall see when we discuss the composition of compounds in some detail, two (and sometimes more) elements may form more than one compound. The **Law of Multiple Proportions** summarizes many experiments on such compounds. It is usually stated:

> When two elements, A and B, form more than one compound, the ratio of the masses of element B that combine with a given mass of element A in each of the compounds can be expressed by small whole numbers.

Water, H_2O, and hydrogen peroxide, H_2O_2, provide an example. The ratio of masses of oxygen that combine with a given mass of hydrogen in H_2O and H_2O_2 is 1:2. In H_2O, one mole of oxygen combines with two moles of hydrogen atoms, while in hydrogen peroxide, H_2O_2, two moles of oxygen combine with two moles of hydrogen atoms. Thus the ratio of oxygen atoms in the two compounds compared to a given number of hydrogen atoms is 1:2. Many similar examples, such as CO and CO_2 (1:2 oxygen ratio) and SO_2 and SO_3 (2:3 oxygen ratio), are known. The Law of Multiple Proportions had been recognized from studies of elemental composition before the time of Dalton. It provided additional support for his atomic theory.

EXAMPLE 2–18 Law of Multiple Proportions

What is the ratio of the numbers of oxygen atoms that are combined with a given number of nitrogen atoms in the compounds N_2O_3 and NO?

Plan

To compare the number of oxygen atoms, we need to have *equal numbers of nitrogen atoms*.

Solution

Because NO has half as many nitrogen atoms in its formula relative to N_2O_3, we must multiply it by a factor of 2 to compare the two elements on the basis of an equal number of nitrogen atoms. Once we show the number of atoms of each element present, we can cancel out the equal amounts of nitrogen atoms, leaving the ratio of oxygen atoms.

$$\text{oxygen ratio} = \frac{N_2O_3}{2(NO)} = \frac{3O/2\cancel{N}}{2O/2\cancel{N}} = \frac{3O}{2O} = \frac{3}{2}$$

You should now work Exercises 71 and 72.

▶ In Example 2-18, we could equalize the number of N atoms by dividing N_2O_3 by a factor of two, to produce fractional subscripts, which most chemists prefer to avoid. That approach would, however, give us the same answer.

2-10 Some Other Interpretations of Chemical Formulas

Once we master the mole concept and the meaning of chemical formulas, we can use them in many ways. The examples in this section illustrate some of the other kinds of information we can get from a chemical formula and the mole concept.

EXAMPLE 2-19 Composition of Compounds

What mass of chromium is contained in 35.8 g of $(NH_4)_2Cr_2O_7$?

Plan

Let us first solve the problem in several steps.

Step 1:   The formula tells us that each mole of $(NH_4)_2Cr_2O_7$ contains two moles of Cr atoms, so we first find the number of moles of $(NH_4)_2Cr_2O_7$, using the unit factor

$$\frac{1 \text{ mol}(NH_4)_2Cr_2O_7}{252.0 \text{ g}(NH_4)_2Cr_2O_7}$$

▶ Chemists often use the term "equivalents" instead of moles when talking about the relative amounts or ratios of atoms or molecules. So Step 1 could also be written as "each equivalent of $(NH_4)_2Cr_2O_7$ contains two equivalents of Cr atoms".

Step 2:   Then we convert the number of moles of $(NH_4)_2Cr_2O_7$ into the number of moles of Cr atoms it contains, using the unit factor

$$\frac{2 \text{ mol Cr atoms}}{1 \text{ mol}(NH_4)_2Cr_2O_7}$$

Step 3:   We then use the atomic weight of Cr to convert the number of moles of chromium atoms to the mass of chromium.

$$\text{mass } (NH_4)_2Cr_2O_7 \longrightarrow \text{mol } (NH_4)_2Cr_2O_7 \longrightarrow \text{mol Cr} \longrightarrow \text{mass Cr}$$

Solution

Step 1: $\underline{?} \text{ mol}(NH_4)_2Cr_2O_7 = 35.8 \text{ g } (NH_4)_2Cr_2O_7 \times \dfrac{1 \text{ mol}(NH_4)_2Cr_2O_7}{252.0 \text{ g}(NH_4)_2Cr_2O_7}$

$= 0.142 \text{ mol}(NH_4)_2Cr_2O_7$

Step 2: $\underline{?} \text{ mol Cr atoms} = 0.142 \text{ mol } (NH_4)_2Cr_2O_7 \times \dfrac{2 \text{ mol Cr atoms}}{1 \text{ mol}(NH_4)_2Cr_2O_7}$

$= 0.284 \text{ mol Cr atoms}$

Step 3: $\underline{?} \text{ g Cr} = 0.284 \text{ mol Cr atoms} \times \dfrac{52.0 \text{ g Cr}}{1 \text{ mol Cr atoms}} = 14.8 \text{ g Cr}$

If you understand the reasoning in these conversions, you should be able to solve this problem in a single setup:

$$\underline{?} \text{ g Cr} = 35.8 \text{ g}(NH_4)_2Cr_2O_7 \times \frac{1 \text{ mol}(NH_4)_2Cr_2O_7}{252.0 \text{ g } (NH_4)_2Cr_2O_7} \times \frac{2 \text{ mol Cr atoms}}{1 \text{ mol}(NH_4)_2Cr_2O_7} \times \frac{52.0 \text{ g Cr}}{1 \text{ mol Cr}} = \boxed{14.8 \text{ g Cr}}$$

You should now work Exercise 76.

EXAMPLE 2-20 Composition of Compounds

What mass of potassium chlorate, $KClO_3$, would contain 40.0 g of oxygen?

Plan

The formula $KClO_3$ tells us that each mole of $KClO_3$ contains three moles of oxygen atoms. Each mole of oxygen atoms weighs 16.0 g. So we can set up the solution to convert:

$$\text{mass O} \longrightarrow \text{mol O} \longrightarrow \text{mol } KClO_3 \longrightarrow \text{mass } KClO_3$$

Solution

$$\underline{?} \text{ g } KClO_3 = 40.0 \text{ g O} \times \frac{1 \text{ mol O atoms}}{16.0 \text{ g O atoms}} \times \frac{1 \text{ mol } KClO_3}{3 \text{ mol O atoms}} \times \frac{122.6 \text{ g } KClO_3}{1 \text{ mol } KClO_3}$$

$$= 102 \text{ g } KClO_3$$

You should now work Exercise 78.

STOP & THINK

The mass of a compound must always be greater than the mass of any element contained in the compound.

Problem-Solving Tip How Do We Know When...?

How do we know when to represent oxygen as O and when as O_2? A *compound* that contains oxygen *does not* contain O_2 molecules. So we solve problems such as Example 2-20 in terms of moles of O atoms. Thus, we must use the formula weight for O, which is 16.0 g O atoms/1 mol O atoms. Similar reasoning applies to compounds containing other elements that are polyatomic molecules in *pure elemental form*, such as H_2, Cl_2, or P_4.

EXAMPLE 2-21 Composition of Compounds

(a) What mass of sulfur dioxide, SO_2, would contain the same mass of oxygen as is contained in 33.7 g of arsenic pentoxide, As_2O_5?

(b) What mass of calcium chloride, $CaCl_2$, would contain the same number of chloride ions as are contained in 48.6 g of sodium chloride, NaCl?

Plan

(a) We need only convert to *moles* of O (because this is the same mass of O regardless of its environment) and then to moles of SO_2 to obtain the mass of SO_2.

$$\text{mass } As_2O_5 \longrightarrow \text{mol } As_2O_5 \longrightarrow \text{mol O atoms} \longrightarrow \text{mol } SO_2 \longrightarrow \text{mass } SO_2$$

Alternatively, we could find explicitly the number of grams of O in 33.7 g of As_2O_5, and then find the mass of SO_2 that contains that same number of grams of O. But this alternate method includes some unnecessary calculation.

(b) Because one mole always consists of the same number (Avogadro's number) of items, we can reason in terms of *moles* of Cl^- ions and solve as in part (a).

$$\text{mass NaCl} \longrightarrow \text{mol NaCl} \longrightarrow \text{mol } Cl^- \text{ ions} \longrightarrow \text{mol } CaCl_2 \longrightarrow \text{mass } CaCl_2$$

Solution

(a) $\underline{?}$ g SO_2 = 33.7 g As_2O_5 $\times \dfrac{1 \text{ mol } As_2O_5}{229.8 \text{ g } As_2O_5} \times \dfrac{5 \text{ mol O atoms}}{1 \text{ mol } As_2O_5}$

$\times \dfrac{1 \text{ mol } SO_2}{2 \text{ mol O atoms}} \times \dfrac{64.1 \text{ g } SO_2}{1 \text{ mol } SO_2} = 23.5$ g SO_2

(b) $\underline{?}$ g $CaCl_2$ = 48.6 g NaCl $\times \dfrac{1 \text{ mol NaCl}}{58.4 \text{ g NaCl}} \times \dfrac{1 \text{ mol } Cl^-}{1 \text{ mol NaCl}}$

$\times \dfrac{1 \text{ mol } CaCl_2}{2 \text{ mol } Cl^-} \times \dfrac{111.0 \text{ g } CaCl_2}{1 \text{ mol } CaCl_2} = 46.2$ g $CaCl_2$

STOP & THINK

In problems such as those in Example 2-21, it is very important to use complete units. Keep track of g of *what*, mol of *what*, etc. by including them in the units.

You should now work Exercise 80.

The physical appearance of one mole of each of some compounds is illustrated in Figure 2-6. Two different forms of oxalic acid are shown. The formula unit (molecule) of oxalic acid is $(COOH)_2$ (FW = 90.0 amu; molar mass = 90.0 g/mol). When oxalic acid is obtained by crystallization from a water solution, however, the resulting crystals contain two molecules of water for each molecule of oxalic acid (even though it appears "dry"). The formula of this **hydrate** is $(COOH)_2 \cdot 2H_2O$ (FW = 126.1 amu; molar mass = 126.1 g/mol). The dot shows that the crystals contain two H_2O molecules per $(COOH)_2$ molecule. The water can be driven out of the crystals by heating to leave **anhydrous** oxalic acid, $(COOH)_2$. "Anhydrous" means "without water." Copper(II) sulfate, an *ionic* compound, shows similar behavior. Anhydrous copper(II) sulfate ($CuSO_4$; FW = 159.6 amu; molar mass = 159.6 g/mol) is almost white. Hydrated copper(II) sulfate ($CuSO_4 \cdot 5H_2O$; FW = 249.7 amu; molar mass = 249.7 g/mol) is deep blue. Example 2-22 illustrates how we might find and use the formula of a hydrate.

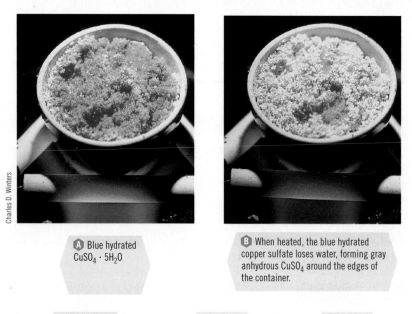

Charles D. Winters

A Blue hydrated $CuSO_4 \cdot 5H_2O$

B When heated, the blue hydrated copper sulfate loses water, forming gray anhydrous $CuSO_4$ around the edges of the container.

Figure 2-6 One mole of some compounds. The colorless liquid is water, H_2O (1 mol = 18.0 g). The solids are *anhydrous* oxalic acid, $(COOH)_2$; *hydrated* oxalic acid, $(COOH)_2 \cdot 2H_2O$; hydrated copper(II) sulfate, $CuSO_4 \cdot 5H_2O$; and mercury(II) oxide.

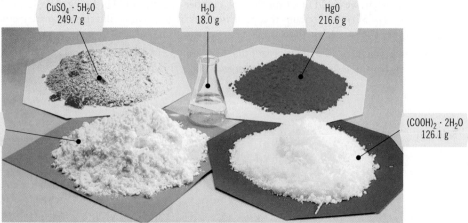

$CuSO_4 \cdot 5H_2O$
249.7 g

H_2O
18.0 g

HgO
216.6 g

$(COOH)_2$
90.0 g

$(COOH)_2 \cdot 2H_2O$
126.1 g

Charles Steele

EXAMPLE 2-22 Composition of Compounds

A reaction requires pure anhydrous calcium sulfate, $CaSO_4$. Only an unidentified hydrate of calcium sulfate, $CaSO_4 \cdot xH_2O$, is available.

(a) We heat 67.5 g of unknown hydrate until all the water has been driven off. The resulting mass of pure $CaSO_4$ is 53.4 g. What is the formula of the hydrate, and what is its formula weight?

(b) Suppose we wish to obtain enough of this hydrate to supply 95.5 g of $CaSO_4$ after heating. How many grams should we weigh out?

Plan

(a) To determine the formula of the hydrate, we must find the value of x in the formula $CaSO_4 \cdot xH_2O$. The mass of water removed from the sample is equal to the difference in the two masses given. The value of x is the number of moles of H_2O per mole of $CaSO_4$ in the hydrate.

(b) The formula weights of $CaSO_4$, 136.2 g/mol, and of $CaSO_4 \cdot xH_2O$, $(136.2 + x18.0)$ g/mol, allow us to write the conversion factor required for the calculation.

Solution

(a) $\underline{?}$ g water driven off $= 67.5$ g $CaSO_4 \cdot xH_2O - 53.4$ g $CaSO_4 = 14.1$ g H_2O

$$x = \frac{\underline{?} \text{ mol } H_2O}{\text{mol } CaSO_4} = \frac{14.1 \text{ g } H_2O}{53.4 \text{ g } CaSO_4} \times \frac{1 \text{ mol } H_2O}{18.0 \text{ g } H_2O} \times \frac{136.2 \text{ g } CaSO_4}{1 \text{ mol } CaSO_4} = \frac{2.00 \text{ mol } H_2O}{\text{mol } CaSO_4}$$

Thus, the formula of the hydrate is $CaSO_4 \cdot 2H_2O$. Its formula weight is

$$FW = 1 \times (\text{formula weight } CaSO_4) + 2 \times (\text{formula weight } H_2O)$$

$$= 136.2 \text{ g/mol} + 2(18.0 \text{ g/mol}) = 172.2 \text{ g/mol}$$

(b) The formula weights of $CaSO_4$ (136.2 g/mol) and of $CaSO_4 \cdot 2H_2O$ (172.2 g/mol) allow us to write the unit factor

$$\frac{172.2 \text{ g } CaSO_4 \cdot 2H_2O}{136.2 \text{ g } CaSO_4}$$

We use this factor to perform the required conversion:

$$\underline{?} \text{ g } CaSO_4 \times 2H_2O = 95.5 \text{ g } CaSO_4 \text{ desired} \times \frac{172.2 \text{ g } CaSO_4 \cdot 2H_2O}{136.2 \text{ g } CaSO_4}$$

$$= 121 \text{ g } CaSO_4 \cdot 2H_2O$$

You should now work Exercise 82.

> **S TOP & THINK**
> A hydrate consists of water *plus* another substance, so the total mass of the hydrate present must always be *greater than* the mass of the other substance present.

2-11 Purity of Samples

The **percent purity** is the mass percentage of a specified substance in an impure sample. Most substances obtained from laboratory reagent shelves are not 100% pure. When impure samples are used for precise work, account must be taken of impurities. The photo in the margin shows the label from reagent-grade sodium hydroxide, NaOH, which is 98.2% pure by mass. From this information we know that total impurities represent 1.8% of the mass of this material. We can write several unit factors:

$$\frac{98.2 \text{ g } NaOH}{100 \text{ g sample}}, \quad \frac{1.8 \text{ g impurities}}{100 \text{ g sample}}, \quad \text{and} \quad \frac{1.8 \text{ g impurities}}{98.2 \text{ g } NaOH}$$

The inverse of each of these gives us a total of six unit factors.

ACTUAL ANALYSIS, LOT G22931

Meets A.C.S. Specifications		
Assay (NaOH) (by acidimetry)	98.2	%
Sodium Carbonate (Na₂CO₃)	0.2	%
Chloride (Cl)	< 0.0005	%
Ammonium Hydroxide Precipitate	< 0.01	%
Heavy Metals (as Ag)	< 0.0005	%
Copper (Cu)	0.0003	%
Potassium (K) (by FES)	0.002	%
Trace Impurities (in ppm):		
Nitrogen Compounds (as N)	< 2	
Phosphate (PO₄)	< 1	
Sulfate (SO₄)	< 5	
Iron (Fe)	< 2	
Mercury (Hg) (by AAS)	< 0.003	
Nickel (Ni)	< 2	

A label from a bottle of sodium hydroxide, NaOH

EXAMPLE 2-23 Percent Purity

Calculate the masses of NaOH and impurities in 45.2 g of 98.2% pure NaOH.

Plan

The percentage of NaOH in the sample gives the unit factor $\dfrac{98.2 \text{ g } NaOH}{100 \text{ g sample}}$. The remainder of the sample is $100\% - 98.2\% = 1.8\%$ impurities; this gives the unit factor $\dfrac{1.8 \text{ g impurities}}{100 \text{ g sample}}$.

Solution

$$\underline{?} \text{ g } NaOH = 45.2 \text{ g sample} \times \frac{98.2 \text{ g } NaOH}{100 \text{ g sample}} = 44.4 \text{ g } NaOH$$

$$\underline{?} \text{ g impurities} = 45.2 \text{ g sample} \times \frac{1.8 \text{ g impurities}}{100 \text{ g sample}} = 0.81 \text{ g impurities}$$

You should now work Exercises 86 and 87.

> ▶ Impurities are not necessarily bad. For example, inclusion of 0.02% KI, potassium iodide, in ordinary table salt has nearly eliminated goiter in the United States. Goiter is a disorder of the thyroid gland caused by a deficiency of iodine. Mineral water tastes better than purer, distilled water.

> **Problem-Solving Tip** Utility of the Unit Factor Method
>
> Observe the beauty of the unit factor approach to problem solving! Such questions as "do we multiply by 0.982 or divide by 0.982?" never arise. The units always point toward the correct answer because we use unit factors constructed so that units *always* cancel out and we arrive at the desired unit.

Many important relationships have been introduced in this chapter. Some of the most important transformations you have seen in Chapters 1 and 2 are summarized in Figure 2-7.

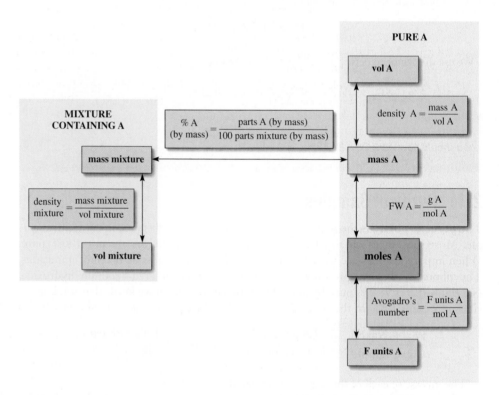

Figure 2-7 Some important relationships from Chapters 1 and 2. The relationships that provide unit factors are enclosed in green boxes. F units = formula units (molecules for molecular systems).

KEY TERMS

Allotropic modifications (allotropes) Different structural forms of the same element.

Anhydrous Without water.

Anion An ion with a negative charge.

Atomic mass unit (amu) One-twelfth of the mass of an atom of the carbon-12 isotope; a unit used for stating atomic and formula weights.

Atomic weight Weighted average of the masses of the constituent isotopes of an element; the relative mass of atoms of different elements.

Avogadro's number 6.022×10^{23} units of a specified item. See *Mole*.

Cation An ion with a positive charge.

Chemical formula Combination of element symbols that indicates the chemical composition of a substance.

Composition stoichiometry Describes the quantitative (mass) relationships among elements in compounds.

Empirical formula See *Simplest formula*.

Formula Combination of element symbols that indicates the chemical composition of a substance.

Formula unit The smallest repeating unit of a substance—for non-ionic substances, the molecule.

Formula weight The mass, in atomic mass units, of one formula unit of a substance. Numerically equal to the mass, in grams, of one mole of the substance (see *Molar mass*). This number is obtained by adding the atomic weights of the atoms specified in the formula.

Hydrate A crystalline sample that contains water, H_2O, and another compound in a fixed mole ratio. Examples include $CuSO_4 \cdot 5H_2O$ and $(COOH)_2 \cdot 2H_2O$.

Ion   An atom or group of atoms that carries an electric charge. A positive ion is a *cation*; a negative ion is an *anion*.

Ionic compound   A compound that is composed of cations and anions. An example is sodium chloride, NaCl.

Law of Constant Composition   See *Law of Definite Proportions*.

Law of Definite Proportions   Different samples of a pure compound always contain the same elements in the same proportions by mass; this corresponds to atoms of these elements in fixed numerical ratios. Also known as the Law of Constant Composition.

Law of Multiple Proportions   When two elements, A and B, form more than one compound, the ratio of the masses of element B that combine with a given mass of element A in each of the compounds can be expressed by small whole numbers.

Molar mass   The mass, in grams, of one mole of a substance; numerically equal to the formula weight of the substance. See *Formula weight*; see *Molecular weight*.

Mole 6.022×10^{23} (Avogadro's number of) formula units (or molecules, for a molecular substance) of a substance. The mass, in grams, of one mole is numerically equal to the formula (molecular) weight of the substance.

Molecular formula   A formula that indicates the actual number of atoms present in a molecule of a molecular substance. Compare with *Simplest (empirical) formula*.

Molecular weight   The mass, in atomic mass units, of one molecule of a non-ionic (molecular) substance. Numerically equal to the mass, in grams, of one mole of such a substance. This number is obtained by adding the atomic weights of the atoms specified in the formula.

Percent composition   The mass percentage of each element in a compound.

Percent purity   The mass percentage of a specified compound or element in an impure sample.

Polyatomic   Consisting of more than one atom. Elements such as Cl_2, P_4, and S_8 exist as polyatomic molecules. Examples of polyatomic ions are the ammonium ion, NH_4^+, and the sulfate ion, SO_4^{2-}.

Simplest formula   The smallest whole-number ratio of atoms present in a compound; also called *empirical formula*. Compare with *Molecular formula*.

Stoichiometry   Description of the quantitative relationships among elements in compounds (composition stoichiometry) and among substances as they undergo chemical changes (reaction stoichiometry).

Structural formula   A representation that shows how atoms are connected in a compound.

EXERCISES

🌐 **Molecular Reasoning** exercises

▲ **More Challenging** exercises

Blue-Numbered exercises are solved in the Student Solutions Manual

Basic Ideas

1. (a) Define "stoichiometry." (b) Distinguish between composition stoichiometry and reaction stoichiometry.
2. Give two examples of molecules that represent allotropes. Which of the compounds you selected are diatomic?
3. List the common ions present in each of the formula units: (a) $MgCl_2$; (b) $(NH_4)_2CO_3$; (c) $Zn(NO_3)_2$.
4. 🌐 Draw the structural formulas and the ball-and-stick models of water and ethanol (CH_3CH_2OH). What arrangement of atoms is alike in these two compounds?
5. 🌐 Draw the space-filling and ball-and-stick models of ethanol (CH_3CH_2OH) and methanol (CH_3OH). What structural features do they have in common?
6. 🌐 What structural feature distinguishes organic compounds from inorganic compounds? Draw a molecular model of an organic compound and an inorganic compound.
7. Give the names and formulas of the compounds in Table 2-1 that are organic compounds.
8. 🌐 Select a compound from Table 2-1 that contains only carbon and hydrogen and is not one of the compounds in Figure 1-5. Draw a ball-and-stick model of the selected compound.
9. 🌐 Select a compound from Table 2-1 that contains carbon, hydrogen and oxygen and is not one of the compounds in Figure 1-5. Draw a ball-and-stick model of the selected compound.
10. Give examples of molecules that contain (a) three atoms of oxygen; (b) only two atoms of hydrogen; (c) four atoms total; (d) eight atoms total; (e) eight atoms of hydrogen.
11. Define the following terms: (a) formula weight (or formula mass); (b) molecular weight (or molecular mass); (c) structural formula; (d) ion.

Names and Formulas

12. Name the following compounds: (a) HNO_3; (b) C_5H_{12}; (c) NH_3; (d) CH_3OH.
13. Write formulas for the following compounds: (a) butane; (b) ethyl alcohol; (c) sulfur trioxide; (d) acetone; (e) carbon tetrachloride.
14. Write the chemical symbol for each of the following ions. Classify each as a monatomic or polyatomic ion. Classify each as a cation or an anion. (a) magnesium ion; (b) sulfite ion; (c) copper(I) ion; (d) ammonium ion; (e) oxide ion.

🌐 **Molecular Reasoning** exercises   ▲ **More Challenging** exercises   Blue-Numbered exercises solved in Student Solutions Manual

Unless otherwise noted, all content on this page is © Cengage Learning.

15. Name each of the following compounds: (a) $MgCl_2$; (b) $Fe(NO_3)_2$; (c) Na_2SO_4; (d) $Ca(OH)_2$; (e) $FeSO_4$.

16. Determine the chemical formulas for barium sulfate, magnesium nitrate, and sodium acetate. Each compound contains a monatomic cation and a polyatomic anion. What are the names and electrical charges of these ions?

17. Write the chemical formula for the ionic compound formed between each of the following pairs of ions. Name each compound. (a) Na^+ and OH^-; (b) Al^{3+} and CO_3^{2-}; (c) Na^+ and PO_4^{3-}; (d) Ca^{2+} and NO_3^-; (e) Fe^{2+} and CO_3^{2-}.

18. Write the chemical formula for the ionic compound formed between each of the following pairs of ions. Name each compound. (a) Cu^{2+} and CO_3^{2-}; (b) Sr^{2+} and Br^-; (c) NH_4^+ and CO_3^{2-}; (d) Zn^{2+} and O^{2-}; (e) Fe^{3+} and SO_4^{2-}.

19. A student was asked to write the chemical formulas for the following compounds. If the formulas are correct, say so. Explain why any that are incorrect are in error, and correct them. (a) potassium iodide, PI; (b) copper(I) nitrate, $CuNO_3$; (c) silver carbonate, $AgCO_4$.

20. Convert each of the following into a correct formula represented with correct notation: (a) $NaCO_3$; (b) Mg_2Cl; (c) $Zn(OH)_3$; (d) $(NH_4)_3S$; (e) $Na_2(I)_2$.

21. Convert each of the following into a correct formula represented with correct notation: (a) AlO_3H_3; (b) Mg_3CO_3; (c) $Zn(CO_3)_2$; (d) $(NH_4)_3SO_4$; (e) $Zn_2(SO_4)_2$.

22. Write the formula of the compound produced by the combination of each of the following pairs of elements. Name each compound. (a) sodium and bromine; (b) magnesium and bromine; (c) sulfur and oxygen; (d) calcium and oxygen; (e) potassium and sulfur; (f) aluminum and bromine.

Aluminum reacting with bromine

23. Write the chemical formula of each of the following: (a) calcium carbonate—major component of coral, seashells, and limestone—found in antacid preparations; (b) magnesium hydroxide—found in milk of magnesia; (c) acetic acid—the acid in vinegar; (d) sodium hydroxide—common name is lye; (e) zinc oxide—used to protect from sunlight's UV rays when blended in an ointment.

Zinc oxide used as a sunscreen

Atomic and Formula Weights

24. What is the mass ratio (four significant figures) of one atom of Rb to one atom of Br?

25. An atom of an element has a mass ever so slightly greater than twice the mass of an Ni atom. Identify the element.

26. (a) What is the atomic weight of an element? (b) Why can atomic weights be referred to as relative numbers?

27. (a) What is the atomic mass unit (amu)? (b) The atomic weight of aluminum is 26.98 amu, and the atomic weight of cobalt is 58.93 amu. What can we say about the relative masses of Al and Co atoms?

28. Determine the formula weight (molecular mass) of each of the following substances: (a) bromine, Br_2; (b) hydrogen peroxide, H_2O_2; (c) saccharin, $C_7H_5NSO_3$; (d) potassium chromate, K_2CrO_4.

29. Determine the formula weight (molecular mass) of each of the following substances: (a) calcium sulfate, $CaSO_4$; (b) propane, C_3H_8; (c) the sulfa drug sulfanilamide, $C_6H_4SO_2(NH_2)_2$; (d) uranyl phosphate, $(UO_2)_3(PO_4)_2$.

30. ⬤ Determine the formula weight (molecular mass) of each of the following common acids:

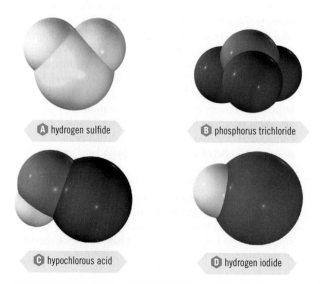

Ⓐ hydrogen sulfide

Ⓑ phosphorus trichloride

Ⓒ hypochlorous acid

Ⓓ hydrogen iodide

⬤ **Molecular Reasoning** exercises   ▲ **More Challenging** exercises   Blue-Numbered exercises solved in Student Solutions Manual

31. A sample of 1.76 g of barium combines exactly with 0.487 g of fluorine, forming barium fluoride, BaF_2. Find the relative masses of the atoms of barium and fluorine. Check your answer using a table of atomic weights. If the formula were not known, could you still do this calculation?

The Mole Concept

32. Calculate the mass in grams and kilograms of 2.371 moles of

$$Cl-\overset{\displaystyle \overset{Cl}{|}}{\underset{\displaystyle \underset{Cl}{|}}{C}}-Cl$$

33. What mass, in grams, should be weighed for an experiment that requires 1.24 mol of $H-O-O-H$?

34. How many hydrogen atoms are contained in 167 grams of propane?

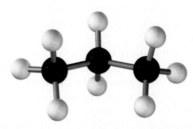

35. (a) How many formula units are contained in 154.3 g of K_2CrO_4? (b) How many potassium ions? (c) How many CrO_4^{2-} ions? (d) How many atoms of all kinds?

36. How many moles of NH_3 are in a 12.50-gram sample?

37. A large neon sign is to be filled with a mixture of gases, including 6.438 g neon. What number of moles is this?

Neon discharge tube

38. How many molecules are in 31.6 g of each of the following substances? (a) CO_2; (b) N_2; (c) P_4; (d) P_2. (e) Do parts (c) and (d) contain the same number of atoms of phosphorus?

39. Sulfur molecules exist under various conditions as S_8, S_6, S_4, S_2, and S. (a) Is the mass of one mole of each of these molecules the same? (b) Is the number of molecules in one mole of each of these molecules the same? (c) Is the mass of sulfur in one mole of each of these molecules the same? (d) Is the number of atoms of sulfur in one mole of each of these molecules the same?

40. Complete the following table. Refer to a table of atomic weights.

Element	Atomic Weight	Mass of One Mole of Atoms
(a) Sn	_____	_____
(b) _____	79.904	_____
(c) Mg	_____	_____
(d) _____	_____	51.9961 g

41. Complete the following table. Refer to a table of atomic weights.

Element	Formula	Mass of One Mole of Molecules
(a) Br	Br_2	_____
(b) _____	O_2	_____
(c) _____	P_4	_____
(d) _____	_____	20.1797 g
(e) S	_____	256.528 g
(f) O	_____	_____

42. Complete the following table.

Moles of Compound	Moles of Cations	Moles of Anions
1 mol $NaClO_4$	_____	_____
2 mol K_2SO_4	_____	_____
0.2 mol calcium sulfate	_____	_____
_____	0.50 mol NH_4^+	0.25 mol SO_4^{2-}

43. What is the average mass of one copper atom?

44. What is the mass of 6.00 million methane, CH_4, molecules?

45. A sample of propane, C_3H_8, has the same mass as 8.00 million molecules of methane, CH_4. How many C_3H_8 molecules does the sample contain?

46. Referring to the compounds in Exercise 30, which will contain the largest number of moles of atoms per 100.0 grams of compound?

Composition Stoichiometry

47. What percent by mass of iron(II) phosphate is iron?

48. Calculate the percent by mass of silver found in a particular mineral that is determined to be silver carbonate.

 Molecular Reasoning exercises   ▲ **More Challenging** exercises   Blue-Numbered exercises solved in Student Solutions Manual

Unless otherwise noted, all content on this page is © Cengage Learning.

49. 🔵 An alcohol is 60.00% C, 13.33% H, and 26.67% O by mass. Another experiment shows that its molecular weight (mass) is approximately 60 amu. What is the molecular formula of the alcohol?

50. Skatole is found in coal tar and in human feces. It contains three elements: C, H, and N. It is 82.40% C and 6.92% H by mass. Its simplest formula is its molecular formula. What are (a) the formula and (b) the molecular weight of skatole?

51. Testosterone, the male sex hormone, contains only C, H, and O. It is 79.12% C and 9.79% H by mass. Each molecule contains two O atoms. What are (a) the molecular weight and (b) the molecular formula for testosterone?

52. ▲ The beta-blocker drug, timolol, is expected to reduce the need for heart bypass surgery. Its composition by mass is 49.4% C, 7.64% H, 17.7% N, 15.2% O, and 10.1% S. The mass of 0.0100 mol of timolol is 3.16 g. (a) What is the simplest formula of timolol? (b) What is the molecular formula of timolol?

53. Determine the simplest formula for each of the following compounds: (a) copper(II) tartrate: 30.03% Cu, 22.70% C, 1.91% H, 45.37% O; (b) nitrosyl fluoroborate: 11.99% N, 13.70% O, 9.25% B, 65.06% F.

54. The hormone norepinephrine is released in the human body during stress and increases the body's metabolic rate. Like many biochemical compounds, norepinephrine is composed of carbon, hydrogen, oxygen, and nitrogen. The percent composition of this hormone is 56.8% C, 6.56% H, 28.4% O, and 8.28% N. What is the simplest formula of norepinephrine?

55. (a) A sample of a compound is found to contain 5.60 g N, 14.2 g Cl, and 0.800 g H. What is the simplest formula of this compound? (b) A sample of another compound containing the same elements is found to be 26.2% N, 66.4% Cl, and 7.5% H. What is the simplest formula of this compound?

56. A common product found in nearly every kitchen contains 27.37% sodium, 1.20% hydrogen, 14.30% carbon, and 57.14% oxygen. The simplest formula is the same as the formula of the compound. Find the formula of this compound.

57. Bupropion is present in a medication that is an antidepressant and is also used to aid in quitting smoking. The composition of bupropion is 65.13% carbon, 7.57% hydrogen, 14.79% chlorine, 5.84% nitrogen, and 6.67% oxygen. The simplest formula is the same as the molecular formula of this compound. Determine the formula.

58. Lysine is an essential amino acid. One experiment showed that each molecule of lysine contains two nitrogen atoms. Another experiment showed that lysine contains 19.2% N, 9.64% H, 49.3% C, and 21.9% O by mass. What is the molecular formula for lysine?

59. Cocaine has the following percent composition by mass: 67.30% C, 6.930% H, 21.15% O, and 4.62% N. What is the simplest formula of cocaine?

60. A compound with the molecular weight of 56.0 g was found as a component of photochemical smog. The compound is composed of carbon and oxygen, 42.9%

and 57.1%, respectively. What is the formula of this compound?

61. Calculate the percent composition of each of the following compounds: (a) aspartame, $C_{14}H_{18}N_2O_5$; (b) carborundum, SiC; (c) aspirin, $C_9H_8O_4$.

62. Calculate the percent composition of each of the following compounds: (a) L-DOPA, $C_9H_{11}NO_4$; (b) vitamin E, $C_{29}H_{50}O_2$; (c) vanillin, $C_8H_8O_3$.

Determination of Simplest and Molecular Formulas

63. 🔵 Write the chemical formula and the simplest formula of each of the following compounds: (a) hydrogen peroxide; (b) water; (c) ethylene glycol.

64. ▲ Copper is obtained from ores containing the following minerals: azurite, $Cu_3(CO_3)_2(OH)_2$; chalcocite, Cu_2S; chalcopyrite, $CuFeS_2$; covelite, CuS; cuprite, Cu_2O; and malachite, $Cu_2CO_3(OH)_2$. Which mineral has the lowest copper content as a percent by mass?

65. A 1.20-g sample of a compound gave 2.92 g of CO_2 and 1.22 g of H_2O on combustion in oxygen. The compound is known to contain only C, H, and O. What is its simplest formula?

66. A 0.1153-gram sample of a pure hydrocarbon was burned in a C — H combustion train to produce 0.3986 gram of CO_2 and 0.0578 gram of H_2O. Determine the masses of C and H in the sample and the percentages of these elements in this hydrocarbon.

67. Dimethylhydrazine, the fuel used in the Apollo lunar descent module, has a molar mass of 60.10 g/mol. It is made up of carbon, hydrogen, and nitrogen atoms. The combustion of 3.302 g of the fuel in excess oxygen yields 4.839 g of carbon dioxide and 3.959 g of water. What are the simplest and molecular formulas for dimethylhydrazine?

68. 🔵 What is the maximum mass of carbon dioxide that can be produced by the combustion of 0.377 g of the following compound?

69. ▲ Complicated chemical reactions occur at hot springs on the ocean floor. One compound obtained from such a hot spring consists of Mg, Si, H, and O. From a 0.301-g sample, the Mg is recovered as 0.104 g of MgO; H is recovered as 23.1 mg of H_2O; and Si is recovered as 0.155 g of SiO_2. What is the simplest formula of this compound?

70. A 1.000-gram sample of an alcohol was burned in oxygen to produce 1.913 g of CO_2 and 1.174 g of H_2O. The alcohol contained only C, H, and O. What is the simplest formula of the alcohol?

The Law of Multiple Proportions

71. Show that the compounds water, H_2O, and hydrogen peroxide, H_2O_2, obey the Law of Multiple Proportions.

🔵 **Molecular Reasoning** exercises   ▲ **More Challenging** exercises   Blue-Numbered exercises solved in Student Solutions Manual

Unless otherwise noted, all content on this page is © Cengage Learning.

72. Nitric oxide, NO, is produced in internal combustion engines. When NO comes in contact with air, it is quickly converted into nitrogen dioxide, NO_2, a very poisonous, corrosive gas. What mass of O is combined with 3.00 g of N in (a) NO and (b) NO_2? Show that NO and NO_2 obey the Law of Multiple Proportions.

73. A certain metal, M, forms two oxides, M_2O and MO. If the percent by mass of M in M_2O is 73.4%, what is its percent by mass in MO?

74. What mass of oxygen is combined with 9.04 g of sulfur in (a) sulfur dioxide, SO_2, and (b) sulfur trioxide, SO_3?

Interpretation of Chemical Formulas

75. One prominent ore of copper contains chalcopyrite, $CuFeS_2$. How many pounds of copper are contained in 6.63 pounds of pure $CuFeS_2$?

76. Mercury occurs as a sulfide ore called *cinnabar*, HgS. How many grams of mercury are contained in 578 g of pure HgS?

A sample of cinnabar

77. (a) How many grams of copper are contained in 253 g of $CuSO_4$? (b) How many grams of copper are contained in 573 g of $CuSO_4 \cdot 5H_2O$?

78. What mass of $KMnO_4$ would contain 72.6 g of manganese?

79. What mass of azurite, $Cu_3(CO_3)_2(OH)_2$, would contain 685 g of copper?

A sample of azurite

80. Two minerals that contain copper are chalcopyrite, $CuFeS_2$, and chalcocite, Cu_2S. What mass of chalcocite would contain the same mass of copper as is contained in 418 pounds of chalcopyrite?

81. Tungsten is a very dense metal (19.3 g/cm^3) with extremely high melting and boiling points (3370°C and 5900°C). When a small amount of it is included in steel, the resulting alloy is far harder and stronger than ordinary steel. Two important ores of tungsten are $FeWO_4$ and $CaWO_4$. How many grams of $CaWO_4$ would contain the same mass of tungsten that is present in 657 g of $FeWO_4$?

82. ▲ When a mole of $CuSO_4 \cdot 5H_2O$ is heated to 110°C, it loses four moles of H_2O to form $CuSO_4 \cdot H_2O$. When it is heated to temperatures above 150°C, the other mole of H_2O is lost. (a) How many grams of $CuSO_4 \cdot H_2O$ could be obtained by heating 495 g of $CuSO_4 \cdot 5H_2O$ to 110°C? (b) How many grams of anhydrous $CuSO_4$ could be obtained by heating 463 g of $CuSO_4 \cdot 5H_2O$ to 180°C?

Percent Purity

83. A particular ore of lead, galena, is 10.0% lead sulfide, PbS, and 90.0% impurities by weight. What mass of lead is contained in 110.5 grams of this ore?

A sample of galena

84. What mass of chromium is present in 234 grams of an ore of chromium that is 55.0% iron(II) dichromate, $FeCr_2O_7$, and 45.0% impurities by mass? If 90.0% of the chromium can be recovered from 400.0 grams of the ore, what mass of pure chromium is obtained?

85. What masses of (a) Sr and (b) N are contained in 267.7 g of 88.2% pure $Sr(NO_3)_2$? Assume that the impurities do not contain the elements mentioned.

86. (a) What weight of magnesium carbonate is contained in 275 pounds of an ore that is 26.7% magnesium carbonate by weight? (b) What weight of impurities is contained in the sample? (c) What weight of magnesium is contained in the sample? (Assume that no magnesium is present in the impurities.)

87. Vinegar is 5.0% acetic acid, $C_2H_4O_2$, by mass. (a) How many grams of acetic acid are contained in 143.7 g of vinegar? (b) How many pounds of acetic acid are contained in 143.7 pounds of vinegar? (c) How many grams of sodium chloride, NaCl, are contained in 34.0 g of saline solution that is 5.0% NaCl by mass?

88. ▲ What is the percent by mass of copper sulfate, $CuSO_4$, in a sample of copper sulfate pentahydrate, $CuSO_4 \cdot 5H_2O$? (b) What is the percent by mass of $CuSO_4$ in a sample that is 74.4% $CuSO_4 \cdot 5H_2O$ by mass?

Mixed Examples

89. Ammonium sulfate, $(NH_4)_2SO_4$, and urea, CH_4N_2O, are both commonly used as sources of nitrogen in commercial fertilizers. If ammonium sulfate costs $7.00 for 20 lb and urea costs $21.00 for 6 lb, which has the more nitrogen for the dollar?

90. (a) How many moles of ozone molecules are contained in 96.0 g of ozone, O_3? (b) How many moles of oxygen atoms

● **Molecular Reasoning** exercises   ▲ **More Challenging** exercises   Blue-Numbered exercises solved in Student Solutions Manual

Unless otherwise noted, all content on this page is © Cengage Learning.

are contained in 96.0 g of ozone? (c) What mass of O_2 would contain the same number of oxygen atoms as 96.0 g of ozone? (d) What mass of oxygen gas, O_2, would contain the same number of molecules as 96.0 g of ozone?

91. The recommended daily dietary allowance of calcium is 1200 mg. Calcium carbonate is an inexpensive source of calcium and useful as a dietary supplement as long as it is taken along with vitamin D, which is essential to calcium absorption. How many grams of calcium carbonate must an individual take per day to provide for his/her recommended daily allowance of calcium?

92. Vitamin E is an antioxidant that plays an especially important role protecting cellular structures in the lungs. Combustion of a 0.497-g sample of vitamin E produced 1.47 g of carbon dioxide and 0.518 g of water. Determine the empirical formula of vitamin E.

93. A metal, M, forms an oxide having the simplest formula M_2O_3. This oxide contains 52.9% of the metal by mass. (a) Calculate the atomic weight of the metal. (b) Identify the metal.

94. Three samples of magnesium oxide were analyzed to determine the mass ratios O/Mg, giving the following results:

$$\frac{1.60 \text{ g O}}{2.43 \text{ g Mg}}; \quad \frac{0.658 \text{ g O}}{1.00 \text{ g Mg}}; \quad \frac{2.29 \text{ g O}}{3.48 \text{ g Mg}}$$

Which law of chemical combination is illustrated by these data?

95. ▲ The molecular weight of hemoglobin is about 65,000 g/mol. Hemoglobin contains 0.35% Fe by mass. How many iron atoms are in a hemoglobin molecule?

96. ▲ More than 1 billion pounds of adipic acid (MW 146.1 g/mol) is manufactured in the United States each year. Most of it is used to make synthetic fabrics. Adipic acid contains only C, H, and O. Combustion of a 1.6380-g sample of adipic acid gives 2.960 g of CO_2 and 1.010 g of H_2O. (a) What is the simplest formula for adipic acid? (b) What is its molecular formula?

97. Crystals of hydroxyapatite, $Ca_{10}(PO_4)_6(OH)_2$, provide the hardness associated with bones. In hydroxyapatite crystals, what is (a) the percent calcium and (b) the percent phosphorus?

Conceptual Exercises

98. 🔬 In 2003 researchers at Columbia University demonstrated that β-hydroxybutyric acid may be a cheap and easy way to treat Parkinson's disease. From the molecular model shown below determine the structural formula and the chemical formula of β-hydroxybutyric acid. (Color code: black = carbon, white = hydrogen, red = oxygen.)

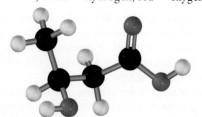

In a structural formula, each line connecting two chemical symbols represents a pair of electrons that is shared between the two atoms. Based upon your examination of this and other structures in this chapter, how many pairs of electrons does a carbon atom generally share with other atoms? Does an oxygen atom or a hydrogen atom share this same number of pairs of electrons with other atoms?

99. For each of the following simple ions, locate the element on the periodic table: Li^+, Na^+, K^+, Mg^{2+}, Ca^{2+}, and Al^{3+}. There is a pattern here. How is the charge of a cation related to the group number (the label at the top of the column)? What charge is a cation formed from a rubidium atom likely to have? Write the formula for the cation formed from a barium atom. Locate the elements that form the following anions on the periodic table: F^-, Cl^-, Br^-, I^-, O^{2-}, and S^{2-}. What is the formula for the anion formed from a nitrogen atom?

100. Determine what is wrong with the formula for each of the following substances. Then write the correct formula.

lithium fluoride, LiF_2
iron(III) sulfide, Fe_3S
aluminum hydroxide, $AlOH_3$
zinc nitrate, $Zn_3(NO)_2$
calcium chloride, $CaCl^+$

101. Currently, Avogadro's number is defined as the number of "atoms in exactly 0.012 kg of pure carbon-12," which has been measured to be approximately 6.0221479×10^{23}, depending upon the stability of the standard kilogram. R. F. Fox and T. P. Hill (American Scientist, March–April 2007, 104) have proposed that it be defined as an integer, namely $84,446,888^3$ or 602,214,141,070,409,084,099,072, exactly. How different is this number from the current value? The mass of the standard kilogram may have changed about 50 μg since it was constructed. That's roughly 150 quadrillion (1.5×10^{17}) atoms of platinum and iridium. How does this uncertainty compare with the difference between the two values for Avogadro's number?

102. Calculate the percentage by mass of rhenium, Re, in each of the following oxides: ReO_2, ReO_3, Re_2O_3, Re_2O_7. Determine the charge that rhenium has in each of these compounds. Arrange the formulas in order of increasing charge on the rhenium ion. How does the percentage of rhenium in these oxides change as the charge of the rhenium ion changes?

103. Some compounds with different molecular formulas have the same empirical formula. Acetic acid, CH_3COOH, is found in vinegar. Erythrulose, $HOCH_2COCH(OH)$ CH_2OH, is used in sunless tanning products. Embalming fluids may contain formaldehyde, H_2CO. An important component of sour milk and sore muscles is lactic acid, $CH_3CH(OH)COOH$. Ribose, $HOCH_2CH(OH)CH(OH)$ $CH(OH)CHO$, is an important part of ribonucleic acid. Determine the molecular and empirical formulas for each of these compounds, listing the elements in this order: carbon, hydrogen, and oxygen. Calculate the molecular weight of each compound. What is the ratio of each of the molecular weights to the formula weight of the empirical formula?

104. If a 3.2-mole sample of each of the following compounds is completely burned, which one would produce the most moles of water? Which would produce the fewest? (a) CH_3CH_2OH; (b) CH_3OH; (c) CH_3OCH_3.

105. When a sample is burned in a combustion train, the percent oxygen in the sample cannot be determined directly from the mass of water and carbon dioxide formed. Why?

106. What mass of NaCl would contain the same *total* number of ions as 284 g of $MgCl_2$?

107. Two deposits of minerals containing silver are found. One of the deposits contains silver oxide, and the other contains silver sulfide. The deposits can be mined at the same price per ton of the original silver-containing compound, but only one deposit can be mined by your company. Which of the deposits would you recommend and why?

108. A decision is to be made as to the least expensive source of zinc. One source of zinc is zinc sulfate, $ZnSO_4$, and another is zinc acetate dihydrate, $Zn(CH_3COO)_2 \cdot 2H_2O$. These two sources of zinc can be purchased at the same price per kilogram of compound. Which is the most economical source of zinc and by how much?

109. Assume that a penny is 1/16 in. thick and that the moon is 222,000 mi at its closest approach to the earth (perigee). Show by calculation whether or not a picomole of pennies stacked on their faces would reach from the earth to the moon.

110. Calculate the mass in grams of 13.5 mol of (a) vinyl chloride, C_2H_3Cl, the starting material for a plastic; (b) capsaicin, $C_{18}H_{27}NO_3$, the substance that makes red chili peppers "hot"; (c) stearic acid, $C_{18}H_{36}O_2$, used in soaps.

Building Your Knowledge

NOTE: *Beginning with this chapter, exercises under the "Building Your Knowledge" heading will often require that you use skills, concepts, or information that you should have mastered in earlier chapters. This provides you an excellent opportunity to "tie things together" as you study.*

111. Vegetarians sometimes suffer from the lack of vitamin B12. Each molecule of vitamin B12 contains a single atom of cobalt and is 4.35% cobalt by mass. What is the molecular weight of vitamin B12?

112. A student wants to determine the empirical and molecular formulas of a compound containing only carbon, hydrogen, and oxygen. To do so, he combusted a 0.625-g sample of the compound and collected

1.114 g of CO_2 and 0.455 g of water. An independent analysis indicated that the molar mass of the compound is 74.1 g/mol. What are the empirical and molecular formulas of this compound?

113. Elemental lead is needed in the construction of storage batteries. The lead is obtained by first roasting galena (PbS) in limited air to produce sulfur dioxide and lead oxide. The lead oxide formed is 92.83% lead. The lead is then obtained from the lead oxide in a process that is nearly 100% efficient. What is the simplest formula of the lead oxide formed?

114. Near room temperature, the density of water is 1.00 g/mL, and the density of ethanol (grain alcohol) is 0.789 g/mL. What volume of ethanol contains the same number of molecules as are present in 380. mL of H_2O?

115. A drop of water has a volume of about 0.050 mL. How many molecules of water are in a drop of water? (Assume water has a density of 1.00 g/cm³.)

116. Use the molecular volume provided with each compound to calculate its density in g/mL: (a) $NaHCO_3$, sodium bicarbonate or sodium hydrogen carbonate (also called baking soda), 0.0389 L/mol; (b) I_2, iodine, 0.05148 L/mol; (c) Hg, liquid mercury, 0.01476 L/mol; (d) NaCl, common table salt, 0.02699 L/mol.

Beyond the Textbook

NOTE: *Whenever the answer to an exercise depends on information obtained from a source other than this textbook, the source must be included as an essential part of the answer.*

117. Use an internet search engine (such as **http://www.google.com**) to locate the history and properties of the element zinc. When was it first isolated? What are three common uses of zinc? Describe the reported effects of a zinc deficiency in one's diet.

118. Use an internet search engine (such as **http://www.google.com**) to locate the history and properties of the element iodine. When was it first isolated? What are three common uses of iodine? Describe three health effects associated with iodine or iodine-containing compounds.

119. Use an internet search engine (such as **http://www.google.com**) to locate a source of chemistry jokes or puns. Quote a joke or pun that involves the name of an element. Quote a joke or pun that involves a low formula weight compound.

120. Use an internet search engine (such as **http://www.google.com**) to locate the history of Louis Joseph Gay-Lussac. Which element did he discover and isolate?

Molecular Reasoning exercises ▲ **More Challenging** exercises Blue-Numbered exercises solved in Student Solutions Manual

Chemical Equations and Reaction Stoichiometry

3

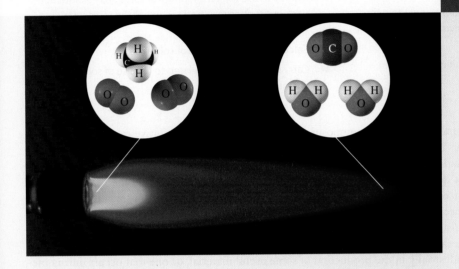

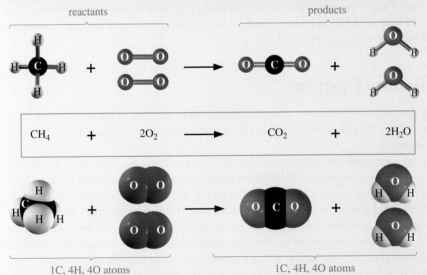

reactants $\longrightarrow$ products

$$CH_4 + 2O_2 \longrightarrow CO_2 + 2H_2O$$

1C, 4H, 4O atoms   1C, 4H, 4O atoms

The combustion (burning) of methane (CH_4) with oxygen (O_2) produces mainly carbon dioxide (CO_2) and water (H_2O). Methane is the main component of natural gas.

Charles D. Winters

OBJECTIVES

After you have studied this chapter, you should be able to

▶ Write balanced chemical equations to describe chemical reactions with chemical formulas and with molecular models

▶ Interpret balanced chemical equations to calculate the moles of reactants and products involved in each of the reactions

▶ Interpret balanced chemical equations to calculate the masses of reactants and products involved in each of the reactions

▶ Determine which reactant is the limiting reactant in reactions

▶ Use the limiting reactant concept in calculations involving chemical equations

▶ Compare the amount of substance formed in a reaction (actual yield) with the predicted amount (theoretical yield), and determine the percent yield

▶ Work with sequential reactions

▶ Learn and use the terminology of solutions—solute, solvent, concentration—and recognize the molecular significance

▶ Calculate concentrations of solutions

▶ Carry out calculations related to the use of solutions in chemical reactions

In Chapter 2 we studied composition stoichiometry, the quantitative relationships among elements in compounds. In this chapter we will study **reaction stoichiometry**—the quantitative relationships among substances as they participate in chemical reactions. Several important questions will be asked and answered. *How* can we describe the reaction of one substance with another? *How much* of one substance reacts with a given amount of another substance? *Which reactant* determines the amounts of products formed in a chemical reaction? *How* can we describe reactions in aqueous solutions?

Whether we are concerned with describing a reaction used in a chemical analysis, one used industrially in the production of some useful material, or one that occurs during metabolism in the body, we must describe it accurately. Chemical equations represent a very precise, yet a very versatile, language that describes chemical changes. We begin our study by examining chemical equations.

3-1 Chemical Equations

Chemical reactions always involve changing one or more substances into one or more different substances. In other words, chemical reactions rearrange atoms or ions to form other substances.

Chemical equations are used to describe chemical reactions, and they show (1) *the substances that react*, called **reactants**; (2) *the substances formed*, called **products**; and (3) *the relative amounts of the substances involved*. We write the reactants to the *left* of an arrow and the products to the *right* of the arrow. The numbers placed in front of compounds in a chemical equation are called *coefficients* and represent the number of molecules (or formula units) of each reactant or product needed to balance the equation. As a typical example, let's consider the combustion (burning) of natural gas, a reaction used to heat buildings and cook food. Natural gas is a mixture of several substances, but the principal component is methane, CH_4. The equation that describes the reaction of methane with excess oxygen is:

▶ Sometimes it is not possible to represent a chemical change with a single chemical equation. For example, when too little O_2 is present, both CO_2 and CO are found as products, and a second chemical equation must be used to describe the process. In the present case with sufficient or excess oxygen, only one equation is required. We refer to this as the "complete" combustion of methane.

Coefficients indicate the amount of each compound or element and can be changed to balance the equation; omitted coefficients are assumed to be 1.

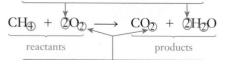

$$CH_4 + 2O_2 \longrightarrow CO_2 + 2H_2O$$

reactants   products

Subscripts indicate the number of atoms of each element in the compound or element and CANNOT be changed when balancing an equation.

How do we interpret this equation? In the simplest terms, it tells us that methane reacts with oxygen to produce carbon dioxide, CO_2, and water. More specifically, it says that for every CH_4 molecule that reacts, two molecules of O_2 also react, and that one CO_2 molecule and two H_2O molecules are formed. That is,

$$CH_4 \ + \ 2O_2 \ \xrightarrow{\text{heat}} \ CO_2 \ + \ 2H_2O$$

1 molecule   2 molecules   1 molecule   2 molecules

▶ The arrow may be read "yields." The capital Greek letter delta (Δ) is often used in place of the word "heat."

This description of the reaction of CH_4 with O_2 is based on *experimental observations*. Many experiments have shown that when one CH_4 molecule reacts with two O_2 molecules, one CO_2 molecule and two H_2O molecules are formed. *Chemical equations are based on experimental observations.* Special conditions required for some reactions are indicated by a notation above or below the arrow. Figure 3-1 is a pictorial representation of the rearrangement of atoms described by this equation.

In Section 1-1, we learned the **Law of Conservation of Matter**: *there is no detectable change in the quantity of matter during an ordinary chemical reaction.* This guiding principle is the basis for "balancing" chemical equations and for performing calculations based on those equations. Because matter is neither created nor destroyed during a chemical reaction,

a balanced chemical equation must always include the same number of each kind of atom on both sides of the equation.

Chemists usually write equations with the smallest possible whole-number coefficients.

Before we attempt to balance an equation, all substances must be represented by formulas that describe them *as they exist*. For instance, we must write H_2 to represent diatomic hydrogen molecules—not H, which represents individual hydrogen atoms, which are unstable and do not exist by themselves under normal conditions. Once the correct formulas are written, the subscripts in the formulas may not be changed. Different subscripts in formulas specify different substances, so changing the formulas would mean that the equation would no longer describe the same reaction.

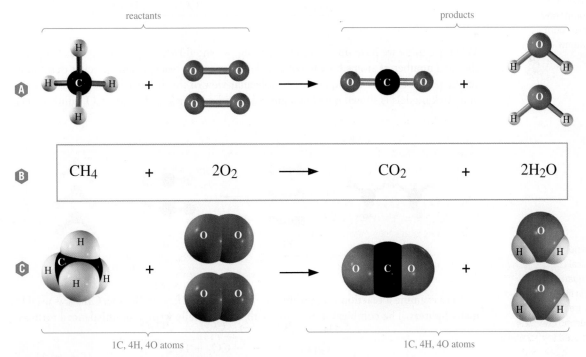

1C, 4H, 4O atoms   1C, 4H, 4O atoms

Figure 3-1 Three representations of the reaction of methane with oxygen to form carbon dioxide and water. Chemical bonds are broken and new ones are formed in each representation. Part (a) illustrates the reaction using ball-and-stick models, (b) uses chemical formulas, and (c) uses space-filling models.

Dimethyl ether, C_2H_6O, burns in an excess of oxygen to give carbon dioxide and water. Let's balance the equation for this reaction. In unbalanced form, the equation is

$$C_2H_6O + O_2 \longrightarrow CO_2 + H_2O$$

Carbon appears in only one compound on each side, and the same is true for hydrogen. We begin by balancing these elements. The subscripts on the carbon and hydrogen atoms in C_2H_6O guide us in assigning the coefficients on the product side:

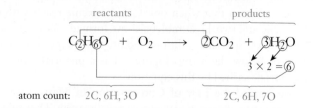

reactants   products

atom count: 2C, 6H, 3O   2C, 6H, 7O

Now we have a different total number of O atoms on each side: 3 on the reactant side and 7 on the product side. We now need to balance the oxygen count by adding 4 more oxygen atoms to the reactant side. This is done by adding 2 more O_2 molecules (total of 4 oxygen atoms) to the one already present giving a total of $3O_2$ molecules on the reactant side:

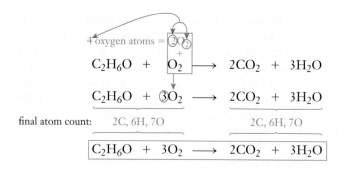

4 oxygen atoms $= 2O_2$

$$C_2H_6O + O_2 \longrightarrow 2CO_2 + 3H_2O$$

$$C_2H_6O + 3O_2 \longrightarrow 2CO_2 + 3H_2O$$

final atom count: 2C, 6H, 7O   2C, 6H, 7O

$$\boxed{C_2H_6O + 3O_2 \longrightarrow 2CO_2 + 3H_2O}$$

When we think we have finished the balancing, we should *always* do a complete check that the total number of atoms for each of the elements on the reactant side matches that found on the product side of the equation. A molecular view of this balanced equation using ball-and-stick models is shown next (element color coding: black = C, red = O, white = H).

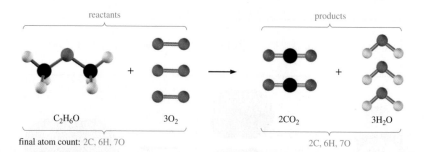

reactants   products

C_2H_6O $3O_2$ $2CO_2$ $3H_2O$

final atom count: 2C, 6H, 7O   2C, 6H, 7O

Let's examine a reaction that produces a fractional coefficient. Butane, C_4H_{10}, is used in many lighters. The combustion reaction with O_2 is initially written in unbalanced form as:

$$C_4H_{10} + O_2 \longrightarrow CO_2 + H_2O$$

Once again, carbon only appears in one compound on each side and the same is true for hydrogen. We begin by balancing these elements. The subscripts on the carbon and hydrogen atoms in C_4H_{10} guide us in assigning the coefficients on the product side:

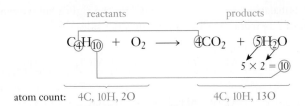

atom count: 4C, 10H, 2O   4C, 10H, 13O

There are different total numbers of O atoms on each side: 2 on the reactant and 13 on the product side. We need to balance the oxygen count by adding 11 oxygen atoms to the reactant side. This is done by adding 1½ = 5.5 O_2 molecules to the one that is currently there, giving a total of 6½ or 6.5 O_2 molecules on the reactant side:

$$C_4H_{10} + 6.5\,O_2 \longrightarrow 4CO_2 + 5H_2O$$

final atom count: 4C, 10H, 13O   4C, 10H, 13O

► If you are going to express a coefficient as a fractional value it is best to list it as a decimal number, e.g., 6.5 instead of 6½ or 13/2.

Although this is considered a properly balanced equation, many chemists do not ordinarily use fractional coefficients in chemical equations. To convert the fractional coefficient into an integer value, one simply multiplies the entire balanced equation by the proper integer value to convert the fractional value into the smallest integer value. In this case, one would multiply the entire equation by a factor of 2 to produce the final balanced equation with all integer coefficients:

$$2\,[\,C_4H_{10} + 6.5\,O_2 \longrightarrow 4CO_2 + 5H_2O\,]$$

$$2C_4H_{10} + 13\,O_2 \longrightarrow 8CO_2 + 10H_2O$$

final atom count: 8C, 20H, 26O   8C, 20H, 26O

Let's generate the balanced equation for the reaction of aluminum metal with hydrogen chloride to produce aluminum chloride and hydrogen. The unbalanced "equation" is

$$Al + HCl \longrightarrow AlCl_3 + H_2$$

As it now stands, the "equation" does not satisfy the Law of Conservation of Matter because there are two H atoms in the H_2 molecule and three Cl atoms in one formula unit of $AlCl_3$ (product side), but only one H atom and one Cl atom in the HCl molecule (reactant side).

Let's first balance chlorine by putting a coefficient of 3 in front of HCl.

reactants   products

$$Al + 3HCl \longrightarrow AlCl_3 + H_2$$

atom count: Al, 3H, 3Cl   Al, 2H, 3Cl

Now there are 3H on the left and 2H on the right. We can add hydrogen only as two atoms at a time (as H_2) on the product side. So we need to find the least common multiple of 3 and 2, which is 6, in order to balance the H atoms. To get a total of 6H atoms on each side, we multiply the 3HCl by 2 and the lone H_2 by 3. This now gives

$$Al + \boxed{3HCl}_{\times 2} \longrightarrow AlCl_3 + \boxed{H_2}_{\times 3}$$

$$Al + 6HCl \longrightarrow AlCl_3 + 3H_2$$

atom count: Al, 6H, 6Cl   Al, 6H, 3Cl

Now Cl is again unbalanced (6Cl on the left, 3Cl on the right), but we can fix this by putting a coefficient of 2 in front of $AlCl_3$ on the product side.

$$Al \ + \ 6HCl \ \longrightarrow \ \boxed{AlCl_3}_{\times 2} \ + \ 3H_2$$

$$\underbrace{Al \ + \ 6HCl}_{} \ \longrightarrow \ \underbrace{\textcircled{2}AlCl_3 \ + \ 3H_2}_{}$$

atom count: Al, 6H, 6Cl   2Al, 6H, 6Cl

Now all elements except Al are balanced (1Al on the left, 2Al on the right); we complete the balancing by putting a coefficient of 2 in front of Al on the reactant side.

$$\boxed{Al}_{\times 2} \ + \ 6HCl \ \longrightarrow \ 2AlCl_3 \ + \ 3H_2$$

$$\underbrace{\textcircled{2}Al \ + \ 6HCl}_{} \ \longrightarrow \ \underbrace{2AlCl_3 \ + \ 3H_2}_{}$$

final atom count: 2Al, 6H, 6Cl   2Al, 6H, 6Cl

$$\boxed{2Al \ + \ 6HCl \ \longrightarrow \ 2AlCl_3 \ + \ 3H_2}$$

▶ Note the iterative nature of this balancing process. It is important to keep track of the total reactant and product atom counts to help decide which material to balance next.

Balancing chemical equations "by inspection" is a *trial-and-error* approach. It requires a great deal of practice, but it is *very important!* Remember that we use the smallest whole-number coefficients. Some chemical equations are difficult to balance by inspection or "trial and error." In Chapter 11 we will learn methods for balancing complex equations.

Problem-Solving Tip Balancing Chemical Equations

There is no one best place to start when balancing a chemical equation, but the following suggestions might be helpful:

1. Look for elements that appear in only one place on each side of the equation (in only one reactant and in only one product), and balance those elements first.

2. A good starting point is usually to pick a pair of compounds with a common element. Then focus on the compound with the largest subscript for the element in question to see if you can use that subscript as the coefficient for the other compound.

3. If free, uncombined elements appear on either side, balance them last.

Notice how these suggestions worked in the procedures illustrated in this section. Above all, remember that we should *never* change subscripts in formulas, because doing so would describe different substances. We adjust only the coefficients to balance the equation.

EXAMPLE 3-1 Balancing Chemical Equations

Balance the following chemical equations:

(a) $P_4 + Cl_2 \longrightarrow PCl_3$

(b) $RbOH + SO_2 \longrightarrow Rb_2SO_3 + H_2O$

(c) $P_4O_{10} + Ca(OH)_2 \longrightarrow Ca_3(PO_4)_2 + H_2O$

Plan

For each equation, we balance one element at a time by inspection, making sure that there are the same numbers of each type of element on the reactant and product sides of the equations.

Solution

(a) Let's first balance P.

$$P_4 + Cl_2 \longrightarrow 4PCl_3$$

atom count: 4P, 2Cl   4P, 12Cl

Cl₂(g)

P₄(s)

Now we need 10 more Cl atoms on the reactant side. But Cl_2 comes in increments of 2Cl atoms, so we need 5 *more* Cl_2 molecules, or a total of $6Cl_2$:

$$P_4 + 6Cl_2 \longrightarrow 4PCl_3$$

final atom count: 4P, 12Cl   4P, 12Cl

A molecular view of this balanced reaction using ball-and-stick models is shown next (element color coding: orange = P, green = Cl).

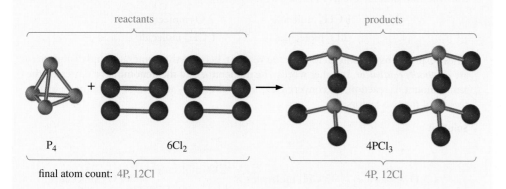

reactants   products

P_4 $6Cl_2$ $4PCl_3$

final atom count: 4P, 12Cl   4P, 12Cl

As a check, we see that there are 4P and 12Cl on each side, so the equation is balanced.

(b) We can first balance Rb.

$$2RbOH + SO_2 \longrightarrow Rb_2SO_3 + H_2O$$

We see that each side now has 2Rb, 1S, 2H, and 4O, so the equation is balanced.

(c) Let's balance P first. There are two P on the right and 4P on the left, so we multiply $Ca_3(PO_4)_2$ by 2.

$$P_4O_{10} + Ca(OH)_2 \longrightarrow 2Ca_3(PO_4)_2 + H_2O$$

Next we can balance Ca by multiplying $Ca(OH)_2$ by 6.

$$P_4O_{10} + 6Ca(OH)_2 \longrightarrow 2Ca_3(PO_4)_2 + H_2O$$

Now we see that there are 12H on the left and only 2H on the right, so we multiply H_2O by 6.

$$P_4O_{10} + 6Ca(OH)_2 \longrightarrow 2Ca_3(PO_4)_2 + 6H_2O$$

Checking the O balance we see that there are $(10 + (2 \times 6)) = 22O$ on the left and $((2 \times 4 \times 2) + (6 \times 1)) = 22O$ on the right. All other elements are also balanced so the equation is balanced.

You should now work Exercises 8 and 10.

3-2 Calculations Based on Chemical Equations

We are now ready to use chemical equations to calculate the relative *amounts* of substances involved in chemical reactions. Let us again consider the combustion of methane in oxygen. The balanced chemical equation for that reaction is

$$CH_4 + 2O_2 \longrightarrow CO_2 + 2H_2O$$

On a quantitative basis, at the molecular level, the equation says

$$CH_4 \quad + \quad 2O_2 \quad \longrightarrow \quad CO_2 \quad + \quad 2H_2O$$

| 1 molecule of methane | 2 molecules of oxygen | 1 molecule of carbon dioxide | 2 molecules of water |

> ▶ A balanced chemical equation may be interpreted on a *molecular* basis.

EXAMPLE 3-2 Number of Molecules

How many O_2 molecules react with 47 CH_4 molecules according to the preceding equation?

Plan

The *balanced* equation tells us that *one* CH_4 molecule reacts with *two* O_2 molecules. We can construct two unit factors from this fact:

$$\frac{1 \; CH_4 \; \text{molecule}}{2 \; O_2 \; \text{molecules}} \quad \text{and} \quad \frac{2 \; O_2 \; \text{molecules}}{1 \; CH_4 \; \text{molecule}}$$

These expressions are unit factors for *this* reaction because the numerator and denominator are *chemically equivalent*. In other words, the numerator and the denominator represent the same amount of reaction. To convert CH_4 molecules to O_2 molecules, we multiply by the second of the two factors.

> **S**TOP & THINK
> The balanced equation shows two O_2 molecules and only one CH_4 molecule, so it is reasonable that the number of O_2 molecules that react is twice the number of CH_4 molecules that react.

Solution

$$\underline{?} \; O_2 \; \text{molecules} = 47 \; CH_4 \; \text{molecules} \times \overbrace{\frac{2 \; O_2 \; \text{molecules}}{1 \; CH_4 \; \text{molecule}}}^{\text{reaction ratio from balanced equation}} = 94 \; O_2 \; \text{molecules}$$

You should now work Exercise 12.

> ▶ We usually cannot work with individual molecules; a mole of a substance is an amount we might use in a laboratory experiment.

A chemical equation also indicates the relative amounts of each reactant and product in a given chemical reaction. We showed earlier that formulas can represent moles of substances. Suppose Avogadro's number of CH_4 molecules, rather than just one CH_4 molecule, undergo this reaction. Then the equation can be written

$$CH_4 \qquad + \qquad 2O_2 \qquad \longrightarrow \qquad CO_2 \qquad + \qquad 2H_2O$$

| 6.02×10^{23} molecules | $2(6.02 \times 10^{23}$ molecules$)$ | 6.02×10^{23} molecules | $2(6.02 \times 10^{23}$ molecules$)$ |
| = 1 mol | = 2 mol | = 1 mol | = 2 mol |

> ▶ A balanced chemical equation may be interpreted in terms of *moles* of reactants and products.

This interpretation tells us that *one* mole of methane reacts with *two* moles of oxygen to produce *one* mole of carbon dioxide and *two* moles of water.

EXAMPLE 3-3 Number of Moles Formed

How many moles of water could be produced by the reaction of 3.5 moles of methane with excess oxygen (i.e., more than a sufficient amount of oxygen is present)?

Plan

> ▶ Please don't try to memorize unit factors for chemical reactions; instead, learn the general *method* for constructing them from balanced chemical equations.

The equation for the combustion of methane

$$CH_4 + 2O_2 \longrightarrow CO_2 + 2H_2O$$

| 1 mol | 2 mol | 1 mol | 2 mol |

shows that 1 mol of methane reacts with 2 mol of oxygen to produce 2 mol of water. From this information we construct two *unit factors*:

$$\frac{1 \text{ mol } CH_4}{2 \text{ mol } H_2O} \quad \text{and} \quad \frac{2 \text{ mol } H_2O}{1 \text{ mol } CH_4}$$

We use the second factor in this calculation.

Solution

$$\underline{?} \text{ mol } H_2O = 3.5 \text{ mol } CH_4 \times \overset{\substack{\text{reaction ratio from} \\ \text{balanced equation}}}{\boxed{\frac{2 \text{ mol } H_2O}{1 \text{ mol } CH_4}}} = 7.0 \text{ mol } H_2O$$

You should now work Exercises 14 and 18.

<aside>TOP & THINK

The balanced equation shows 2 moles of H_2O and only 1 mole of CH_4, so it is reasonable that the number of moles of H_2O produced is twice the number of moles of CH_4 that react.</aside>

We know the mass of 1 mol of each of these substances, so we can also write

$$
\begin{array}{ccccccc}
CH_4 & + & 2O_2 & \longrightarrow & CO_2 & + & 2H_2O \\
1 \text{ mol} & & 2 \text{ mol} & & 1 \text{ mol} & & 2 \text{ mol} \\
16.0 \text{ g} & & 2(32.0 \text{ g}) & & 44.0 \text{ g} & & 2(18.0 \text{ g}) \\
\underline{16.0 \text{ g}} & & \underline{64.0 \text{ g}} & & \underline{44.0 \text{ g}} & & \underline{36.0 \text{ g}} \\
\end{array}
$$

$$\underbrace{\phantom{16.0 \text{ g} \quad 64.0 \text{ g}}}_{80.0 \text{ g reactants}} \qquad \underbrace{\phantom{44.0 \text{ g} \quad 36.0 \text{ g}}}_{80.0 \text{ g products}}$$

The equation now tells us that 16.0 g of CH_4 reacts with 64.0 g of O_2 to form 44.0 g of CO_2 and 36.0 g of H_2O. The Law of Conservation of Matter is satisfied. Chemical equations describe **reaction ratios**, that is, the *mole ratios* of reactants and products as well as the *mass ratios* of reactants and products.

▶ A balanced equation may be interpreted on a *mass* basis.

Problem-Solving Tip Use the Reaction Ratio in Calculations with Balanced Chemical Equations

The most important way of interpreting the balanced chemical equation is in terms of moles. We use the coefficients to find the reaction ratio (in moles) of any two substances we want to relate. Then we apply it as

$$
\begin{pmatrix} \text{moles of} \\ \text{desired} \\ \text{substance} \end{pmatrix} = \begin{pmatrix} \text{moles of} \\ \text{substance} \\ \text{given} \end{pmatrix} \times \begin{pmatrix} \text{reaction ratio} \\ \text{from balanced} \\ \text{chemical equation} \end{pmatrix}
$$

It is important to include the substance formulas as part of the units; this can help us decide how to set up the unit factors. Notice that in Example 3-3 we want to cancel the term mol CH_4, so we know that mol CH_4 must be in the denominator of the mole ratio by which we multiply; we want mol H_2O as the answer, so mol H_2O must appear in the numerator of the mole ratio. In other words, do not just write $\dfrac{\text{mol}}{\text{mol}}$; write

$\dfrac{\text{mol of something}}{\text{mol of something else}}$, giving the formulas of the two substances involved.

EXAMPLE 3-4 Mass of a Reactant Required

What mass of oxygen is required to react completely with 1.20 moles of CH_4?

Plan

The balanced equation

$$
\begin{array}{ccccccc}
CH_4 & + & 2O_2 & \longrightarrow & CO_2 & + & 2H_2O \\
1 \text{ mol} & & 2 \text{ mol} & & 1 \text{ mol} & & 2 \text{ mol} \\
16.0 \text{ g} & & 2(32.0 \text{ g}) & & 44.0 \text{ g} & & 2(18.0 \text{ g}) \\
\end{array}
$$

gives the relationships among moles and grams of reactants and products.

$$\boxed{\text{mol } CH_4} \longrightarrow \boxed{\text{mol } O_2} \longrightarrow g\ O_2$$

Solution

◄ **TOP & THINK**
Remember to use the proper coefficient from the balanced equation to set up this reaction ratio expression.

$$\underline{?}\ g\ O_2 = 1.20\ \text{mol } CH_4 \times \overset{\substack{\text{reaction ratio from} \\ \text{balanced equation}}}{\frac{2\ \text{mol } O_2}{1\ \text{mol } CH_4}} \times \frac{32.0\ g\ O_2}{1\ \text{mol } O_2} = \boxed{76.8\ g\ O_2}$$

EXAMPLE 3-5 Mass of a Reactant Required

What mass of oxygen is required to react completely with 24.0 g of CH_4?

Plan

Recall the balanced equation in Example 3-4.

$$\begin{array}{ccccccc} CH_4 & + & 2O_2 & \longrightarrow & CO_2 & + & 2H_2O \\ 1\ \text{mol} & & 2\ \text{mol} & & 1\ \text{mol} & & 2\ \text{mol} \\ 16.0\ g & & 2(32.0\ g) & & 44.0\ g & & 2(18.0\ g) \end{array}$$

This shows that 1 mol of CH_4 reacts with 2 mol of O_2. These two quantities are chemically equivalent, so we can construct *unit factors*.

Solution

$$\begin{array}{ccccccc} CH_4 & + & 2O_2 & \longrightarrow & CO_2 & + & 2H_2O \\ 1\ \text{mol} & & 2\ \text{mol} & & 1\ \text{mol} & & 2\ \text{mol} \end{array}$$

► Here we solve the problem in three steps; we convert

1. g $CH_4 \longrightarrow$ mol CH_4

2. mol $CH_4 \longrightarrow$ mol O_2

3. mol $O_2 \longrightarrow$ g O_2

$$\underline{?}\ \text{mol } CH_4 = 24.0\ g\ CH_4 \times \frac{1\ \text{mol } CH_4}{16.0\ g\ CH_4} = \underline{1.50\ \text{mol } CH_4}$$

$$\underline{?}\ \text{mol } O_2 = 1.50\ \text{mol } CH_4 \times \frac{2\ \text{mol } O_2}{1\ \text{mol } CH_4} = \underline{3.00\ \text{mol } O_2}$$

$$\underline{?}\ g\ O_2 = 3.00\ \text{mol } O_2 \times \frac{32.0\ g\ O_2}{1\ \text{mol } O_2} = \boxed{96.0\ g\ O_2}$$

All these steps could be combined into one setup in which we convert

◄ **TOP & THINK**
The balanced equation shows more moles of O_2 than of CH_4; furthermore, a mole of O_2 has a greater mass (32.0 g) than a mole of CH_4 (16.0 g). Thus it is reasonable that the mass of O_2 that reacts is considerably greater than the mass of CH_4.

$$\boxed{\text{g of } CH_4} \longrightarrow \boxed{\text{mol of } CH_4} \longrightarrow \boxed{\text{mol of } O_2} \longrightarrow g\ \text{of } O_2$$

$$\underline{?}\ g\ O_2 = 24.0\ g\ CH_4 \times \frac{1\ \text{mol } CH_4}{16.0\ g\ CH_4} \times \frac{2\ \text{mol } O_2}{1\ \text{mol } CH_4} \times \frac{32.0\ g\ O_2}{1\ \text{mol } O_2} = \boxed{96.0\ g\ O_2}$$

The same answer, 96.0 g of O_2, is obtained by both methods.

You should now work Exercise 22.

The question posed in Example 3-5 may be reversed, as in Example 3-6.

EXAMPLE 3-6 Mass of a Reactant Required

What mass of CH_4, in grams, is required to react with 96.0 g of O_2?

Plan

We recall that 1 mole of CH_4 reacts with 2 moles of O_2.

Solution

◄ **TOP & THINK**
When a problem such as this gives the amount of a substance in grams, you almost always have to convert it to moles as the first step. These unit factors are the reciprocals of those used in Example 3-5.

$$\underline{?}\ g\ CH_4 = 96.0\ g\ O_2 \times \frac{1\ \text{mol } O_2}{32.0\ g\ O_2} \times \frac{1\ \text{mol } CH_4}{2\ \text{mol } O_2} \times \frac{16.0\ g\ CH_4}{1\ \text{mol } CH_4} = \boxed{24.0\ g\ CH_4}$$

You should now work Exercise 24.

This is the amount of CH_4 in Example 3-5 that reacted with 96.0 g of O_2.

EXAMPLE 3-7 Mass of a Product Formed

Most combustion reactions occur in excess O_2, that is, more than enough O_2 to burn the substance completely. Calculate the mass of CO_2, in grams, that can be produced by burning 6.00 moles of CH_4 in excess O_2.

▶ It is important to recognize that the reaction must stop when the 6.00 moles of CH_4 has been used up. Some O_2 will remain unreacted.

Plan

The balanced equation tells us that 1 mole of CH_4 produces 1 mole of CO_2.

$$CH_4 \ + \ 2O_2 \ \longrightarrow \ CO_2 \ + \ 2H_2O$$

1 mol	2 mol	1 mol	2 mol
16.0 g	2(32.0 g)	44.0 g	2(18.0 g)

STOP & THINK
Note that even though there is excess O_2 present, we still use the balanced chemical equation to solve the problem.

Solution

$$\underline{?} \text{ g } CO_2 = 6.00 \text{ mol } CH_4 \times \overbrace{\frac{1 \text{ mol } CO_2}{1 \text{ mol } CH_4}}^{\substack{\text{reaction ratio from} \\ \text{balanced equation}}} \times \frac{44.0 \text{ g } CO_2}{1 \text{ mol } CO_2} = \boxed{2.64 \times 10^2 \text{ g } CO_2}$$

You should now work Exercise 26.

Reaction stoichiometry usually involves interpreting a balanced chemical equation to relate a *given* bit of information to the *desired* bit of information.

EXAMPLE 3-8 Mass of a Reactant Required

Phosphorus, P_4, burns with excess oxygen to form tetraphosphorus decoxide, P_4O_{10}. In this reaction, what mass of P_4 reacts with 1.50 moles of O_2?

Plan

The balanced equation tells us that 1 mole of P_4 reacts with 5 moles of O_2.

$$P_4 \ + \ 5O_2 \longrightarrow \ P_4O_{10}$$

1 mol	5 mol	1 mol

$$\boxed{\text{mol } O_2} \ \longrightarrow \ \boxed{\text{mol } P_4} \ \longrightarrow \ \boxed{\text{mass } P_4}$$

STOP & THINK
Never start a calculation involving a chemical reaction without first checking that the equation is balanced.

Solution

$$\underline{?} \text{ g } P_4 = 1.50 \text{ mol } O_2 \times \overbrace{\frac{1 \text{ mol } P_4}{5 \text{ mol } O_2}}^{\substack{\text{reaction ratio from} \\ \text{balanced equation}}} \times \frac{124.0 \text{ g } P_4}{\text{mol } P_4} = \boxed{37.2 \text{ g } P_4}$$

You should now work Exercise 28.

The possibilities for this kind of problem solving are limitless. Exercises 12–29 at the end of the chapter will give you important practice with such calculations.

3-3 The Limiting Reactant (Reagent) Concept

In the problems we have worked thus far, the presence of an excess of one reactant was stated or implied. The calculations were based on the substance that was used up first, called the **limiting reactant** or **reagent**. Before we study the concept of the limiting reactant in stoichiometry, let's develop the basic idea by considering a simple but analogous nonchemical example.

▶ Chemists often refer to the limiting reagent concept.

Suppose you have four slices of ham and six slices of bread and you wish to make as many ham sandwiches as possible using only one slice of ham and two slices of bread per sandwich. Obviously, you can make only three sandwiches, at which point you run out of bread. (In a chemical reaction this would correspond to one of the reactants being used up—so the reaction would stop.) The bread is therefore the *limiting reactant*, and the extra slice of ham is the *excess reactant*. The amount of product, ham sandwiches, is determined by the amount of the limiting reactant, bread in this case. The limiting reactant is not necessarily the reactant present in the smallest amount. We have four slices of ham, the smallest amount, and six slices of bread, but the *reaction ratio* is two slices of bread to one piece of ham, so bread is the limiting reactant.

Consider the following balanced equation:

$$CO + 2H_2 \longrightarrow CH_3OH$$

Suppose we have the following mixture shown here using ball-and-stick models (element color coding: black = C, red = O, white = H).

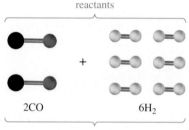

atom count: 2C, 12H, 2O

These can react to make only two molecules of CH_3OH (methanol), leaving two molecules of H_2 left over, as shown here.

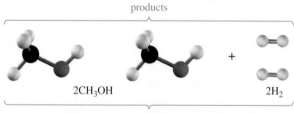

atom count: 2C, 12H, 2O

In this example, H_2 molecules are present in excess (two more than needed to react with the CO molecules present). The other (and equal) way of looking at this reaction is that there are not enough CO molecules to react with all the H_2 molecules. The CO in this example is called the limiting reactant (chemists generally use the term *limiting reagent*).

The following examples show how the limiting reactant concept is applied to chemical calculations.

EXAMPLE 3-9 Limiting Reactant   MOLECULAR REASONING

What mass of CO_2 could be formed by the reaction of 16.0 g of CH_4 with 48.0 g of O_2?

Plan

The balanced equation tells us that 1 mole of CH_4 reacts with 2 moles of O_2.

$$
\begin{array}{ccccccc}
CH_4 & + & 2O_2 & \longrightarrow & CO_2 & + & 2H_2O \\
1\ mol & & 2\ mol & & 1\ mol & & 2\ mol \\
16.0\ g & & 2(32.0\ g) & & 44.0\ g & & 2(18.0\ g)
\end{array}
$$

We are given masses of both CH_4 and O_2, so we calculate the number of moles of each reactant, and then determine the number of moles of each reactant required to react with the other. From these calculations we identify the limiting reactant. Then we base the calculation on it.

Solution

$$? \text{ mol CH}_4 = 16.0 \text{ g CH}_4 \times \frac{1 \text{ mol CH}_4}{16.0 \text{ g CH}_4} = \underline{1.00 \text{ mol CH}_4}$$

$$? \text{ mol O}_2 = 48.0 \text{ g O}_2 \times \frac{1 \text{ mol O}_2}{32.0 \text{ g O}_2} = \underline{1.50 \text{ mol O}_2}$$

Now we return to the balanced equation. First we calculate the number of moles of O_2 that would be required to react with 1.00 mole of CH_4.

$$? \text{ mol O}_2 = 1.00 \text{ mol CH}_4 \times \overbrace{\frac{2 \text{ mol O}_2}{1 \text{ mol CH}_4}}^{\substack{\text{reaction ratio from} \\ \text{balanced equation}}} = 2.00 \text{ mol O}_2$$

We see that 2.00 moles of O_2 are required, but we have only 1.50 moles of O_2, so O_2 is the limiting reactant. Alternatively, we can calculate the number of moles of CH_4 that would react with 1.50 moles of O_2.

$$? \text{ mol CH}_4 = 1.50 \text{ mol O}_2 \times \frac{1 \text{ mol CH}_4}{2 \text{ mol O}_2} = 0.750 \text{ mol CH}_4$$

This tells us that only 0.750 mole of CH_4 would be required to react with 1.50 moles of O_2. But we have 1.00 mole of CH_4, so we see again that O_2 is the limiting reactant. The reaction must stop when the limiting reactant, O_2, is used up, so we base the calculation on O_2.

$$\boxed{\text{g of O}_2} \longrightarrow \boxed{\text{mol O}_2} \longrightarrow \boxed{\text{mol CO}_2} \longrightarrow \boxed{\text{g of CO}_2}$$

$$? \text{ g CO}_2 = 48.0 \text{ g O}_2 \times \frac{1 \text{ mol O}_2}{32.0 \text{ g O}_2} \times \frac{1 \text{ mol CO}_2}{2 \text{ mol O}_2} \times \frac{44.0 \text{ g CO}_2}{1 \text{ mol CO}_2} = \boxed{33.0 \text{ g CO}_2}$$

You should now work Exercise 30.

> **S**TOP & THINK
> The chain of conversions gives the correct units (g CO_2).

Thus, 33.0 g of CO_2 is the most CO_2 that can be produced from 16.0 g of CH_4 and 48.0 g of O_2. If we had based our calculation simply on CH_4 rather than O_2, our answer would be too big (44.0 g) and *wrong* because more O_2 than we have would be required. This is why the limiting reagent concept is so important.

Another approach to problems like Example 3-9 is to calculate the number of moles of each reactant:

$$? \text{ mol CH}_4 = 16.0 \text{ g CH}_4 \times \frac{1 \text{ mol CH}_4}{16.0 \text{ g CH}_4} = \underline{1.00 \text{ mol CH}_4}$$

$$? \text{ mol O}_2 = 48.0 \text{ g O}_2 \times \frac{1 \text{ mol O}_2}{32.0 \text{ g O}_2} = \underline{1.50 \text{ mol O}_2}$$

Then we return to the balanced equation. We first calculate the *required ratio* of reactants as indicated by the balanced chemical equation. We then calculate the *available ratio* of reactants and compare the two:

Required Ratio	**Available Ratio**
$\dfrac{1 \text{ mol CH}_4}{2 \text{ mol O}_2} = \dfrac{0.500 \text{ mol CH}_4}{1.00 \text{ mol O}_2}$	$\dfrac{1.00 \text{ mol CH}_4}{1.50 \text{ mol O}_2} = \dfrac{0.667 \text{ mol CH}_4}{1.00 \text{ mol O}_2}$

We see that each mole of O_2 requires exactly 0.500 mole of CH_4 to be completely used up. We have 0.667 mole of CH_4 for each mole of O_2, so there is more than enough CH_4 to react with the O_2 present. That means that there is *insufficient* O_2 to react with all the available CH_4. The reaction must stop when the O_2 is gone; O_2 is the limiting reactant, and we must base the calculation on it. (Suppose the available ratio of CH_4 to O_2 had been *smaller than* the required ratio. Then we would have concluded that there is not enough CH_4 to react with all the O_2, so CH_4 would have been the limiting reactant.)

Problem-Solving Tip Choosing the Limiting Reactant

Students often wonder how to know which ratio to calculate to help find the limiting reactant.

1. The ratio must involve the two reactants whose amounts are given in the problem.

2. It doesn't matter which way you calculate the ratios, as long as you calculate both required ratio and available ratio in the same order. For example, we could calculate the required and available ratios of $\dfrac{\text{mol } O_2}{\text{mol } CH_4}$ in the approach we just illustrated.

3. If you can't decide how to solve a limiting reactant problem, as a last resort you could do the entire calculation twice—once based on each reactant amount given. The *smaller* answer is the correct one.

EXAMPLE 3-10 Limiting Reactant

> **S TOP & THINK**
> When we are given the amounts of *two (or more)* reactants, we should suspect that we are dealing with a limiting reactant problem. It is very unlikely that *exactly* the stoichiometric amounts of both reactants are present in a reaction mixture.

What is the maximum mass of $Ni(OH)_2$ that could be prepared by mixing two solutions that contain 25.9 g of $NiCl_2$ and 10.0 g of NaOH, respectively?

$$NiCl_2 + 2NaOH \longrightarrow Ni(OH)_2 + 2NaCl$$

Plan

Interpreting the balanced equation as usual, we have

$$NiCl_2 + 2NaOH \longrightarrow Ni(OH)_2 + 2NaCl$$

	1 mol	2 mol	1 mol	2 mol
	129.6 g	2(40.0 g)	92.7 g	2(58.4 g)

We determine the number of moles of $NiCl_2$ and NaOH present. Then we find the number of moles of each reactant required to react with the other reactant. These calculations identify the limiting reactant. We base the calculation on it.

▶ Even though the reaction occurs in aqueous solution, this calculation is similar to earlier examples because we are given the amounts of pure reactants.

Solution

$$\underline{?}\ \text{mol } NiCl_2 = 25.9\ \text{g } NiCl_2 \times \frac{1\ \text{mol } NiCl_2}{129.6\ \text{g } NiCl_2} = 0.200\ \text{mol } NiCl_2$$

$$\underline{?}\ \text{mol NaOH} = 10.0\ \text{g NaOH} \times \frac{1\ \text{mol NaOH}}{40.0\ \text{g NaOH}} = 0.250\ \text{mol NaOH}$$

We return to the balanced equation and calculate the number of moles of NaOH required to react with 0.200 mole of $NiCl_2$.

$$\underline{?}\ \text{mol NaOH} = 0.200\ \text{mol } NiCl_2 \times \frac{2\ \text{mol NaOH}}{1\ \text{mol } NiCl_2} = 0.400\ \text{mol NaOH}$$

But we have only 0.250 mole of NaOH, so NaOH is the limiting reactant.

$$\boxed{\text{g of NaOH}} \longrightarrow \boxed{\text{mol NaOH}} \longrightarrow \boxed{\text{mol } Ni(OH)_2} \longrightarrow \boxed{\text{g of } Ni(OH)_2}$$

reaction ratio from balanced equation

$$\underline{?}\ \text{g } Ni(OH)_2 = 10.0\ \text{g NaOH} \times \frac{1\ \text{mol NaOH}}{40.0\ \text{g NaOH}} \times \frac{1\ \text{mol } Ni(OH)_2}{2\ \text{mol NaOH}} \times \frac{92.7\ \text{g } Ni(OH)_2}{1\ \text{mol } Ni(OH)_2}$$

$$= 11.6\ \text{g } Ni(OH)_2$$

A precipitate of solid $Ni(OH)_2$ forms when colorless NaOH solution is added to green $NiCl_2$ solution. (Example 3-10.)

Charles Steele

You should now work Exercises 34 and 36.

3-4 Percent Yields from Chemical Reactions

The **theoretical yield** from a chemical reaction is the yield calculated by assuming that the reaction goes to completion. In practice we often do not obtain as much product from a reaction mixture as is theoretically possible. There are several reasons for this. (1) Many reactions do not go to completion; that is, the reactants are not completely converted to products. (2) In some cases, a particular set of reactants undergoes two or more reactions simultaneously, forming undesired products as well as desired products. Reactions other than the desired one are called *side reactions*. (3) In some cases, separation of the desired product from the reaction mixture is so difficult that not all of the product formed is successfully isolated. The **actual** or **isolated yield** is the amount of a specified pure product actually obtained from a given reaction.

▶ In the examples we have worked to this point, the amounts of products that we calculated were theoretical yields.

The term **percent yield** is used to indicate how much of a desired product is obtained from a reaction.

$$\text{percent yield} = \frac{\text{actual yield of product}}{\text{theoretical yield of product}} \times 100\%$$

Consider the preparation of nitrobenzene, $C_6H_5NO_2$, by the reaction of a limited amount of benzene, C_6H_6, with excess nitric acid, HNO_3. The balanced equation for the reaction may be written as

$$C_6H_6 + HNO_3 \longrightarrow C_6H_5NO_2 + H_2O$$

1 mol	1 mol	1 mol	1 mol
78.1 g	63.0 g	123.1 g	18.0 g

EXAMPLE 3-11 Percent Yield

A 15.6-g sample of C_6H_6 is mixed with excess HNO_3. We isolate 18.0 g of $C_6H_5NO_2$. What is the percent yield of $C_6H_5NO_2$ in this reaction?

Plan

First we interpret the balanced chemical equation to calculate the theoretical yield of $C_6H_5NO_2$. Then we use the actual (isolated) yield and the previous definition to calculate the percent yield.

Solution

We calculate the theoretical yield of $C_6H_5NO_2$.

$$\underline{?}\ g\ C_6H_5NO_2 = 15.6\ g\ C_6H_6 \times \frac{1\ mol\ C_6H_6}{78.1\ g\ C_6H_6} \times \overbrace{\frac{1\ mol\ C_6H_5NO_2}{1\ mol\ C_6H_6}}^{\substack{\text{reaction ratio from} \\ \text{balanced equation}}} \times \frac{123.1\ g\ C_6H_5NO_2}{1\ mol\ C_6H_5NO_2}$$

$$= 24.6\ g\ C_6H_5NO_2 \quad \longleftarrow \quad \text{theoretical yield}$$

This tells us that if *all* the C_6H_6 were converted to $C_6H_5NO_2$ and isolated, we should obtain 24.6 g of $C_6H_5NO_2$ (100% yield). We isolate only 18.0 g of $C_6H_5NO_2$, however.

$$\text{percent yield} = \frac{\text{actual yield of product}}{\text{theoretical yield of product}} \times 100\% = \frac{18.0\ g}{24.6\ g} \times 100\% = 73.2\%$$

▶ It is not necessary to know the mass of 1 mole of HNO_3 to solve this problem.

You should now work Exercise 44.

S TOP & THINK
Percent yield can never exceed 100%, so this answer is reasonable.

The amount of nitrobenzene obtained *in this experiment* is 73.2% of the amount that would be expected *if* the reaction had gone to completion, *if* there were no side reactions, and *if* we could have recovered all the product as a pure substance.

3-5 Sequential Reactions

Often more than one reaction is required to convert starting materials into the desired products. This is true for many reactions that we carry out in the laboratory and for many industrial processes. These are called **sequential reactions**. The amount of desired product from each reaction is taken as the starting material for the next reaction.

EXAMPLE 3-12 Sequential Reactions

At high temperatures, carbon reacts with water to produce a mixture of carbon monoxide, CO, and hydrogen, H_2.

$$C + H_2O \xrightarrow{\text{heat}} CO + H_2$$

Carbon monoxide is separated from H_2 and then used to separate nickel from cobalt by forming a gaseous compound, nickel tetracarbonyl, $Ni(CO)_4$.

$$Ni + 4CO \longrightarrow Ni(CO)_4$$

What mass of $Ni(CO)_4$ could be obtained from the CO produced by the reaction of 75.0 g of carbon? Assume 100% yield.

Plan

We interpret both chemical equations in the usual way, and solve the problem in two steps. They tell us that one mole of C produces one mole of CO and that four moles of CO is required to produce one mole of $Ni(CO)_4$.

1. We determine the number of moles of CO formed in the first reaction.

2. From the number of moles of CO produced in the first reaction, we calculate the number of grams of $Ni(CO)_4$ formed in the second reaction.

Solution

1.
$$\begin{array}{ccccccc}
\text{C} & + & \text{H}_2\text{O} & \longrightarrow & \text{CO} & + & \text{H}_2 \\
1\text{ mol} & & 1\text{ mol} & & 1\text{ mol} & & 1\text{ mol} \\
12.0\text{ g} & & & & & &
\end{array}$$

$$\underset{\text{?}}{\text{? mol CO}} = 75.0\text{ g C} \times \frac{1\text{ mol C}}{12.0\text{ g C}} \times \overbrace{\frac{1\text{ mol CO}}{1\text{ mol C}}}^{\substack{\text{reaction ratio from} \\ \text{balanced equation}}} = 6.25\text{ mol CO}$$

2.
$$\begin{array}{ccccc}
\text{Ni} & + & 4\text{CO} & \longrightarrow & \text{Ni(CO)}_4 \\
1\text{ mol} & & 4\text{ mol} & & 1\text{ mol} \\
& & & & 171\text{ g}
\end{array}$$

$$\text{? g Ni(CO)}_4 = 6.25\text{ mol CO} \times \overbrace{\frac{1\text{ mol Ni(CO)}_4}{4\text{ mol CO}}}^{\substack{\text{reaction ratio from} \\ \text{balanced equation}}} \times \frac{171\text{ g Ni(CO)}_4}{1\text{ mol Ni(CO)}_4} = 267\text{ g Ni(CO)}_4$$

Alternatively, we can set up a series of unit factors based on the conversions in the reaction sequence and solve the problem in one setup.

$$\boxed{\text{g C}} \longrightarrow \boxed{\text{mol C}} \longrightarrow \boxed{\text{mol CO}} \longrightarrow \boxed{\text{mol Ni(CO)}_4} \longrightarrow \boxed{\text{g Ni(CO)}_4}$$

$$\text{? g Ni(CO)}_4 = 75.0\text{ g C} \times \frac{1\text{ mol C}}{12.0\text{ g C}} \times \overbrace{\frac{1\text{ mol CO}}{1\text{ mol C}}}^{\substack{\text{reaction ratio from} \\ \text{equations 1 \& 2}}} \times \frac{1\text{ mol Ni(CO)}_4}{4\text{ mol CO}} \times \frac{171\text{ g Ni(CO)}_4}{1\text{ mol Ni(CO)}_4}$$

$$= 267\text{ g Ni(CO)}_4$$

You should now work Exercise 50.

EXAMPLE 3-13 Sequential Reactions, Percent Yield

Phosphoric acid, H_3PO_4, is a very important compound used to make fertilizers. It is also present in cola drinks.

H_3PO_4 can be prepared in a two-step process.

$$\text{Reaction 1: } P_4 + 5O_2 \longrightarrow P_4O_{10}$$

$$\text{Reaction 2: } P_4O_{10} + 6H_2O \longrightarrow 4H_3PO_4$$

We allow 272 g of phosphorus to react with excess oxygen, which forms tetraphosphorus decoxide, P_4O_{10}, in 89.5% yield. In the second step reaction, a 96.8% yield of H_3PO_4 is obtained. What mass of H_3PO_4 is obtained?

Plan

1. We interpret the first equation as usual and calculate the amount of P_4O_{10} *obtained.*

$$
\begin{array}{ccc}
P_4 & + \quad 5O_2 & \longrightarrow \quad P_4O_{10} \\
1\ \text{mol} & 5\ \text{mol} & 1\ \text{mol} \\
124\ \text{g} & 5(32.0\ \text{g}) & 284\ \text{g}
\end{array}
$$

$$\boxed{\text{g } P_4} \longrightarrow \boxed{\text{mol } P_4} \longrightarrow \boxed{\text{mol } P_4O_{10}} \longrightarrow \boxed{\text{g } P_4O_{10}}$$

2. Then we interpret the second equation and calculate the amount of H_3PO_4 *obtained* from the P_4O_{10} from the first step.

$$
\begin{array}{ccc}
P_4O_{10} & + \quad 6H_2O & \longrightarrow \quad 4H_3PO_4 \\
1\ \text{mol} & 6\ \text{mol} & 4\ \text{mol} \\
284\ \text{g} & 6(18.0\ \text{g}) & 4(98.0\ \text{g})
\end{array}
$$

$$\boxed{\text{g } P_4O_{10}} \longrightarrow \boxed{\text{mol } P_4O_{10}} \longrightarrow \boxed{H_3PO_4} \longrightarrow \boxed{\text{g } H_3PO_4}$$

Solution

1. $\underline{\text{?}} \ \text{g } P_4O_{10} = 272 \text{ g } P_4 \times \dfrac{1 \text{ mol } P_4}{124 \text{ g } P_4} \times \underbrace{\dfrac{1 \text{ mol } P_4O_{10}}{1 \text{ mol } P_4}}_{\substack{\text{reaction ratio from} \\ \text{balanced equation}}} \times \dfrac{284 \text{ g } P_4O_{10} \text{ theoretical}}{1 \text{ mol } P_4O_{10} \text{ theoretical}}$

$$\times \left(\dfrac{89.5 \text{ g } P_4O_{10} \text{ actual}}{100 \text{ g } P_4O_{10} \text{ theoretical}} \right) = 558 \text{ g } P_4O_{10}$$

2. $\underline{\text{?}} \ \text{g } H_3PO_4 = 558 \text{ g } P_4O_{10} \times \dfrac{1 \text{ mol } P_4O_{10}}{284 \text{ g } P_4O_{10}} \times \dfrac{4 \text{ mol } H_3PO_4}{1 \text{ mol } P_4O_{10}}$

$$\times \dfrac{98.0 \text{ g } H_3PO_4 \text{ theoretical}}{1 \text{ mol } H_3PO_4 \text{ theoretical}} \times \left(\dfrac{96.8 \text{ g } H_3PO_4 \text{ actual}}{100 \text{ g } H_3PO_4 \text{ theoretical}} \right) = 746 \text{ g } H_3PO_4$$

You should now work Exercises 52 and 54.

Charles Steele

Two important uses for H_3PO_4 are in fertilizers and in cola drinks. Approximately 100 lb of H_3PO_4–based fertilizer are used per person per year in America.

S TOP & THINK
The unit factors that represent less than 100% reaction and/or less than 100% recovery are shown in parentheses. If you write "actual" and "theoretical" as part of the units, it will help you to generate the correct unit factors.

3-6 Concentrations of Solutions

Many chemical reactions are more conveniently carried out with the reactants mixed in solution rather than as pure substances. A **solution** is a homogeneous mixture, at the molecular level, of two or more substances. Simple solutions usually consist of one substance, the **solute**, dissolved in another substance, the **solvent**. For example, solutions of hydrochloric acid can be prepared by dissolving hydrogen chloride (HCl, a gas at room temperature and atmospheric pressure) in water. Solutions of sodium hydroxide are prepared by dissolving solid NaOH in water. The solutions used in the laboratory are usually liquids, and the solvent is often water. These are called **aqueous solutions**.

We often use solutions to supply the reactants for chemical reactions. Solutions allow intimate mixing of the reacting substances at the molecular level, much more than would be possible in solid form. (A practical example is drain cleaner, shown in the photo.) We

▶ For some solutions, such as a nearly equal mixture of ethyl alcohol and water, the distinction between *solute* and *solvent* is arbitrary.

The sodium hydroxide and aluminum in some drain cleaners do not react while they are stored in solid form. When water is added, the NaOH dissolves and begins to act on trapped grease. At the same time, NaOH and Al react to produce H_2 gas; the resulting turbulence helps to dislodge the blockage. Do you see why the drain cleaner container should be kept tightly closed?

A 10.0% solution of $Ca(C_6H_{11}O_7)_2$ is sometimes administered intravenously for emergency treatment of black widow spider bites.

sometimes adjust the concentrations of solutions to speed up or slow down the rate of a reaction. In this section we study methods for expressing the quantities of the various components present in a given amount of solution.

Concentrations of solutions are expressed in terms of *either* the amount of solute present in a given mass or volume of *solution, or* the amount of solute dissolved in a given mass or volume of *solvent*.

Percent by Mass

Concentrations of solutions may be expressed in terms of **percent by mass** of solute, which gives the mass of solute per 100 mass units of solution. The gram is the usual mass unit.

$$\text{percent solute} = \frac{\text{mass of solute}}{\text{mass of solution}} \times 100\%$$

$$\text{percent solute} = \frac{\text{mass of solute}}{\text{mass of solute} + \text{mass of solvent}} \times 100\%$$

Thus, a solution that is 10.0% calcium gluconate, $Ca(C_6H_{11}O_7)_2$, by mass contains 10.0 grams of calcium gluconate in 100.0 grams of *solution*. This could be described as 10.0 grams of calcium gluconate in 90.0 grams of water. The density of a 10.0% solution of calcium gluconate is 1.07 g/mL, so 100 mL of a 10.0% solution of calcium gluconate has a mass of 107 grams. Observe that 100 grams of a solution usually does *not* occupy 100 mL. Unless otherwise specified, percent means percent by *mass*, and water is the solvent.

EXAMPLE 3-14 Percent of Solute

Calculate the mass of nickel(II) sulfate, $NiSO_4$, contained in 200. g of a 6.00% solution of $NiSO_4$.

Plan

The percentage information tells us that the solution contains 6.00 g of $NiSO_4$ per 100. g of solution. The desired information is the mass of $NiSO_4$ in 200. g of solution. A unit factor is constructed by placing 6.00 g $NiSO_4$ over 100. g of solution. Multiplication of the mass of the solution, 200. g, by this unit factor gives the mass of $NiSO_4$ in the solution.

Solution

$$\underline{?}\ \text{g}\ NiSO_4 = 200.\ \text{g soln} \times \frac{6.00\ \text{g}\ NiSO_4}{100.\ \text{g soln}} = \boxed{12.0\ \text{g}\ NiSO_4}$$

EXAMPLE 3-15 Mass of Solution

A 6.00% $NiSO_4$ solution contains 40.0 g of $NiSO_4$. Calculate the mass of the solution.

Plan

Placing 100. g of solution over 6.00 g of $NiSO_4$ gives the desired unit factor.

Solution

$$\underline{?}\ \text{g soln} = 40.0\ \text{g}\ NiSO_4 \times \frac{100.\ \text{g soln}}{6.00\ \text{g}\ NiSO_4} = \boxed{667\ \text{g soln}}$$

S **TOP & THINK**
The solution contains only a small percent $NiSO_4$, so it is reasonable that the total mass of solution must be much greater than the mass of $NiSO_4$.

EXAMPLE 3-16 Mass of Solute

Calculate the mass of $NiSO_4$ present in 200. mL of a 6.00% solution of $NiSO_4$. The density of the solution is 1.06 g/mL at 25°C.

Plan

The volume of a solution multiplied by its density gives the mass of the solution (see Section 1-12). The mass of the solution is then multiplied by the mass fraction due to $NiSO_4$ (6.00 g $NiSO_4$/100. g soln) to give the mass of $NiSO_4$ in 200. mL of solution.

Solution

$$\underline{?}\ g\ NiSO_4 = \underbrace{200.\ mL\ soln \times \frac{1.06\ g\ soln}{1.00\ mL\ soln}}_{212\ g\ soln} \times \frac{6.00\ g\ NiSO_4}{100.\ g\ soln} = 12.7\ g\ NiSO_4$$

You should now work Exercise 58.

Solid $NiSO_4$ and a 6% solution of $NiSO_4$ in water (Examples 3-14, 3-15, and 3-16).

EXAMPLE 3-17 Percent Solute and Density

What volume of a solution that is 15.0% iron(III) nitrate contains 30.0 g of $Fe(NO_3)_3$? The density of the solution is 1.16 g/mL at 25°C.

Plan

Two unit factors relate mass of $Fe(NO_3)_3$ and mass of solution, 15.0 g $Fe(NO_3)_3$/100 g and 100 g/15.0 g $Fe(NO_3)_3$. The second factor converts grams of $Fe(NO_3)_3$ to grams of solution.

Solution

$$\underline{?}\ mL\ soln = \underbrace{30.0\ g\ Fe(NO_3)_3 \times \frac{100\ g\ soln}{15.0\ g\ Fe(NO_3)_3}}_{200\ g\ soln} \times \frac{1.00\ mL\ soln}{1.16\ g\ soln} = 172\ mL$$

Note that the answer is not 200. mL but considerably less because 1.00 mL of solution has a mass of 1.16 g; however, 172 mL of the solution has a mass of 200 g.

You should now work Exercise 60.

S TOP & THINK

Write units "g of *what*" and "mL of *what*" to help you generate the correct unit factors. The solution is only a small percent $Fe(NO_3)_3$, so it is reasonable that the required mass of solution is considerably greater than the mass of $Fe(NO_3)_3$ it contains. The density (1.16 g/mL) tells us that each mL of solution has mass greater than 1 g, so the mL of solution required is numerically less than its mass in g.

Molarity

Molarity (*M*), or molar concentration, is a common unit for expressing the concentrations of solutions. **Molarity** is defined as the number of moles of solute per liter of solution:

$$molarity = \frac{number\ of\ moles\ of\ solute}{number\ of\ liters\ of\ solution}$$

To prepare one liter of a one molar solution, one mole of solute is placed in a one-liter volumetric flask, enough solvent is added to dissolve the solute, and solvent is then added until the volume of the solution is exactly one liter. A 0.100 *M* solution contains 0.100 mole of solute per liter of solution, and a 0.0100 *M* solution contains 0.0100 mole of solute per liter of solution (Figure 3-2).

Water is the solvent in *most* of the solutions that we encounter. Unless otherwise indicated, we assume that water is the solvent. When the solvent is other than water, we state this explicitly.

S TOP & THINK

Students sometimes make the mistake of assuming that one molar solution contains one mole of solute in a liter of solvent. This is not the case; one liter of solvent plus one mole of solute usually has a total volume of more than one liter.

Charles Steele

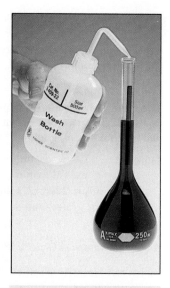

Charles D. Winters

Ⓐ 0.395 g of $KMnO_4$ (0.00250 mol) is weighed out carefully and transferred into a 250.-mL volumetric flask.

Ⓑ The $KMnO_4$ is dissolved in water.

Ⓒ Distilled H_2O is added to the volumetric flask until the volume of solution is 250. mL. The flask is then stoppered, and its contents are mixed thoroughly to give a homogeneous solution.

Figure 3-2 Preparation of 0.0100 *M* solution of $KMnO_4$, potassium permanganate. A 250.-mL sample of 0.0100 *M* $KMnO_4$ solution contains 0.395 g of $KMnO_4$ (1 mol = 158 g).

EXAMPLE 3-18 Molarity

Calculate the molarity (*M*) of a solution that contains 3.65 g of HCl in 2.00 L of solution.

Plan

We are given the number of grams of HCl in 2.00 L of solution. We apply the definition of molarity, remembering to convert grams of HCl to moles of HCl.

Solution

▶ We place 3.65 g HCl over 2.00 L of solution, and then convert g HCl to mol HCl.

$$\frac{?\ \text{mol HCl}}{\text{L soln}} = \frac{3.65\ \text{g HCl}}{2.00\ \text{L soln}} \times \frac{1\ \text{mol HCl}}{36.5\ \text{g HCl}} = 0.0500\ \text{mol HCl/L soln}$$

The concentration of the HCl solution is 0.0500 molar, and the solution is called 0.0500 *M* hydrochloric acid. One liter of the solution contains 0.0500 mole of HCl.

You should now work Exercise 62.

🛑 **TOP & THINK**

Remember to write explicit units. Moles of *what*? Grams of *what*? Although it takes more time, writing out the units and the substance formula (or name) will help you keep track of everything and minimize mistakes.

EXAMPLE 3-19 Mass of Solute

Calculate the mass of $Ba(OH)_2$ required to prepare 2.50 L of a 0.0600 *M* solution of barium hydroxide.

Plan

The volume of the solution, 2.50 L, is multiplied by the concentration, 0.0600 mol $Ba(OH)_2$/L, to give the number of moles of $Ba(OH)_2$. The number of moles of $Ba(OH)_2$ is then multiplied by the mass of $Ba(OH)_2$ in one mole, 171.3 g $Ba(OH)_2$/mol $Ba(OH)_2$, to give the mass of $Ba(OH)_2$ in the solution.

Solution

$$\underline{?} \text{ g Ba(OH)}_2 = 2.50 \text{ L soln} \times \frac{0.0600 \text{ mol Ba(OH)}_2}{1 \text{ L soln}} \times \frac{171.3 \text{ g Ba(OH)}_2}{1 \text{ mol Ba(OH)}_2}$$

$$= 25.7 \text{ g Ba(OH)}_2$$

You should now work Exercise 64.

The solutions of acids and bases that are sold commercially are too concentrated for most laboratory uses. We often dilute these solutions before we use them. We must know the molar concentration of a stock solution before it is diluted. This can be calculated from the specific gravity and the percentage data given on the label of the bottle.

EXAMPLE 3-20 Molarity

A sample of commercial sulfuric acid is 96.4% H_2SO_4 by mass, and its specific gravity is 1.84. Calculate the molarity of this sulfuric acid solution.

Plan

The density of a solution, grams per milliliter, is numerically equal to its specific gravity, so the density of the solution is 1.84 g/mL. The solution is 96.4% H_2SO_4 by mass; therefore, 100. g of solution contains 96.4 g of pure H_2SO_4. From this information, we can find the molarity of the solution. First, we calculate the mass of 1 L of solution.

Solution

$$\frac{\underline{?} \text{ g soln}}{\text{L soln}} = \frac{1.84 \text{ g soln}}{\text{mL soln}} \times \frac{1000 \text{ mL soln}}{\text{L soln}} = 1.84 \times 10^3 \text{ g soln/L soln}$$

The solution is 96.4% H_2SO_4 by mass, so the mass of H_2SO_4 in 1 L is

$$\frac{\underline{?} \text{ g } H_2SO_4}{\text{L soln}} = \frac{1.84 \times 10^3 \text{ g soln}}{\text{L soln}} \times \frac{96.4 \text{ g } H_2SO_4}{100. \text{ g soln}} = 1.77 \times 10^3 \text{ g } H_2SO_4/\text{L soln}$$

The molarity is the number of moles of H_2SO_4 per liter of solution.

$$\frac{\underline{?} \text{ mol } H_2SO_4}{\text{L soln}} = \frac{1.77 \times 10^3 \text{ g } H_2SO_4}{\text{L soln}} \times \frac{1 \text{ mol } H_2SO_4}{98.1 \text{ g } H_2SO_4} = 18.0 \text{ mol } H_2SO_4/\text{L soln}$$

Thus, the solution is an 18.0 M H_2SO_4 solution. This problem can also be solved by using a series of three unit factors.

$$\frac{\underline{?} \text{ mol } H_2SO_4}{\text{L soln}} = \frac{1.84 \text{ g soln}}{\text{mL soln}} \times \frac{1000 \text{ mL soln}}{\text{L soln}} \times \frac{96.4 \text{ g } H_2SO_4}{100. \text{ g soln}} \times \frac{1 \text{ mol } H_2SO_4}{98.1 \text{ g } H_2SO_4}$$

$$= 18.1 \text{ mol } H_2SO_4/\text{L soln} = 18.1 \text{ } M \text{ } H_2SO_4$$

You should now work Exercise 70.

ANALYSIS

Assay (H_2SO_4) W/W...Min. 95.0%--Max. 98.0%

MAXIMUM LIMITS OF IMPURITIES
Appearance........Passes A.C.S. Test
Color (APHA)....................10 Max.
Residue after Ignition............4 ppm
Chloride (Cl)....................0.2 ppm
Nitrate (NO_3)....................0.5 ppm
Ammonium (NH_4)................1 ppm
Substances Reducing $KMnO_4$ (limit about 2ppm as SO_2).........Passes A.C.S. Test
Arsenic (As)...................0.004 ppm
Heavy Metals (as Pb)..........0.8 ppm
Iron (Fe)........................0.2 ppm
Mercury (Hg)......................5 ppb
Specific Gravity...................~1.84
Normality.............................~36

Suitable for Mercury Determinations

A label that shows the analysis of sulfuric acid.

STOP & THINK
Careful application of unit factors will help you solve this problem.

▶ The small difference between these two answers is due to rounding.

Problem-Solving Tip Write Complete Units

A common pitfall is to write units that are not complete enough to be helpful. For instance writing the density in Example 3-20 as just $\dfrac{1.84 \text{ g}}{\text{mL}}$ doesn't help us figure out the required conversions. It is much safer to write $\dfrac{1.84 \text{ g soln}}{\text{mL soln}}$, $\dfrac{1000 \text{ mL soln}}{\text{L soln}}$, $\dfrac{96.4 \text{ g } H_2SO_4}{100 \text{ g soln}}$, and so on. In Example 3-20, we have written complete units to help guide us through the problem.

3-7 Dilution of Solutions

Recall that the definition of molarity is the number of moles of solute divided by the volume of the solution in liters:

$$\text{molarity} = \frac{\text{number of moles of solute}}{\text{number of liters of solution}}$$

Multiplying both sides of the equation by the volume, we obtain

$$\text{volume (in L)} \times \text{molarity} = \text{number of moles of solute}$$

> Multiplication of the volume of a solution, in liters, by its molar concentration gives the amount of solute in the solution.

▶ A can of frozen orange juice contains a certain mass (or moles) of vitamin C. After the frozen contents of the can are diluted by addition of water, the amount of vitamin C in the resulting total amount of solution will be unchanged. The concentration, or amount per a selected volume, will be less in the final solution, however.

When we dilute a solution by mixing it with more solvent, the amount of solute present does not change. But the volume and the concentration of the solution *do* change. Because the same number of moles of solute is divided by a larger number of liters of solution, the molarity decreases. Using a subscript 1 to represent the original concentrated solution and a subscript 2 to represent the dilute solution, we obtain

$$\text{volume}_1 \times \text{molarity}_1 = \text{number of moles of solute} = \text{volume}_2 \times \text{molarity}_2$$

⑤ TOP & THINK
Never use this equation to relate two different substances in a chemical reaction. It applies only to dilution calculations. ▶

or

$$V_1M_1 = V_2M_2 \qquad \text{(for dilution only)}$$

▶ We could use any volume unit as long as we use the same unit on both sides of the equation. This relationship also applies when the concentration is changed by evaporating some solvent.

This expression can be used to calculate any one of four quantities when the other three are known (Figure 3-3). We frequently need a certain volume of dilute solution of a given molarity for use in the laboratory, and we know the concentration of the initial solution available. Then we can calculate the amount of initial solution that must be used to make the dilute solution.

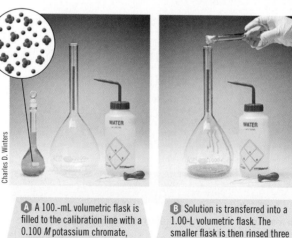

$CrO_4^{2-} =$ ⬤ $K^+ =$ ●
Water molecules not shown for clarity

Charles D. Winters

Ⓐ A 100.-mL volumetric flask is filled to the calibration line with a 0.100 M potassium chromate, K_2CrO_4 solution.

Ⓑ Solution is transferred into a 1.00-L volumetric flask. The smaller flask is then rinsed three times with a small amount of distilled H_2O, which is also transferred into the larger flask.

Ⓒ Distilled water is added to the 1.00-L flask until the liquid level coincides with its calibration line. The flask is stoppered and its contents are mixed thoroughly.

Figure 3-3 Dilution of a solution. The new solution is 0.0100 M K_2CrO_4. (100. mL of 0.100 M K_2CrO_4 solution has been diluted to 1000. mL.) The 100. mL of original solution and the 1000. mL of final solution both contain the amount of K_2CrO_4 dissolved in the original 100. mL of 0.100 M K_2CrO_4.

CAUTION!

Dilution of a concentrated solution, especially of a strong acid or base, frequently liberates a great deal of heat. This can vaporize drops of water as they hit the concentrated solution and can cause dangerous spattering. As a safety precaution, *concentrated solutions of acids or bases are always poured slowly into water*, allowing the heat to be absorbed by the larger quantity of water. Calculations are usually simpler to visualize, however, by assuming that the water is added to the concentrated solution.

Charles D. Winters

Pouring concentrated H₂SO₄ into an equal volume of H₂O liberates a lot of heat— enough to raise the temperature of the resulting solution by as much as 100°C.

EXAMPLE 3-21 Dilution

How many milliliters of 18.0 M H_2SO_4 are required to prepare 1.00 L of a 0.900 M solution of H_2SO_4?

Plan

The volume (1.00 L) and molarity (0.900 M) of the final solution and the molarity (18.0 M) of the original solution are given. We can use the relationship $V_1M_1 = V_2M_2$ with subscript 1 for the initial acid solution and subscript 2 for the dilute solution. We solve

$$V_1M_1 = V_2M_2 \qquad \text{for } V_1$$

Solution

$$V_1 = \frac{V_2M_2}{M_1} = \frac{1.00 \text{ L} \times 0.900 \, M}{18.0 \, M} = 0.0500 \text{ L} = 50.0 \text{ mL}$$

The dilute solution contains 1.00 L × 0.900 M = 0.900 mole of H_2SO_4, so 0.900 mole of H_2SO_4 must also be present in the original concentrated solution. Indeed, 0.0500 L × 18.0 M = 0.900 mole of H_2SO_4.

You should now work Exercises 72 and 74.

3-8 Using Solutions in Chemical Reactions

When we plan to carry out a reaction in a solution, we must calculate the amount of solution that we need. If we know the molarity of a solution, we can calculate the amount of solute contained in a specified volume of that solution. This procedure is illustrated in Example 3-22.

EXAMPLE 3-22 Amount of Solute

Calculate (a) the number of moles of H_2SO_4 and (b) the number of grams of H_2SO_4 in 500. mL of 0.324 M H_2SO_4 solution.

Plan

Because we have two parallel calculations in this example, we state the plan for each step just before the calculation is done.

Solution

(a) The volume of a solution in liters multiplied by its molarity gives the number of moles of solute, H_2SO_4 in this case.

$$\underline{?} \text{ mol } H_2SO_4 = 0.500 \text{ L soln} \times \overset{\text{molarity}}{\frac{0.324 \text{ mol } H_2SO_4}{\text{L soln}}} = 0.162 \text{ mol } H_2SO_4$$

▶ 500. mL is more conveniently expressed as 0.500 L in this problem. By now, you should be able to convert mL to L (and the reverse) without writing out the conversion.

(b) We may use the results of part (a) to calculate the mass of H_2SO_4 in the solution.

$$\underline{?} \text{ g } H_2SO_4 = 0.162 \text{ mol } H_2SO_4 \times \overset{\text{ratio from formula weight}}{\frac{98.1 \text{ g } H_2SO_4}{1 \text{ mol } H_2SO_4}} = 15.9 \text{ g } H_2SO_4$$

▶ A mole of H_2SO_4 is 98.1 g.

▶ Molarity can be used as a unit factor, that is, $\dfrac{\text{mol solute}}{\text{L soln}}$.

The mass of H_2SO_4 in the solution can be calculated without solving explicitly for the number of moles of H_2SO_4.

$$\underline{}\text{ g } H_2SO_4 = 0.500 \text{ L soln} \times \frac{0.324 \text{ mol } H_2SO_4}{\text{L soln}} \times \frac{98.1 \text{ g } H_2SO_4}{1 \text{ mol } H_2SO_4} = \boxed{15.9 \text{ g } H_2SO_4}$$

S **TOP & THINK**
We have less than one liter of solution, and the molarity tells us that there is less than one mole in each liter of solution. Thus it is reasonable that (a) the number of moles of H_2SO_4 present is less than one, so (b) the mass of H_2SO_4 present is less than the formula weight (98.1 g/mol).

One of the most important uses of molarity relates the volume of a solution of known concentration of one reactant to the mass of the other reactant.

EXAMPLE 3-23 Solution Stoichiometry

Calculate the volume in liters and in milliliters of a 0.324 M solution of sulfuric acid required to react completely with 2.792 g of Na_2CO_3 according to the equation

$$H_2SO_4(aq) + Na_2CO_3(aq) \longrightarrow Na_2SO_4(aq) + CO_2(g) + H_2O(\ell)$$

Plan

▶ Aqueous solutions (those in water) are indicated by (aq).

The balanced equation tells us that 1 mol H_2SO_4 reacts with 1 mol Na_2CO_3, and we can write

$$H_2SO_4 + Na_2CO_3 \longrightarrow Na_2SO_4 + CO_2 + H_2O$$

| 1 mol | 1 mol | 1 mol | 1 mol | 1 mol |

106.0 g

We convert (1) grams of Na_2CO_3 to moles of Na_2CO_3, (2) moles of Na_2CO_3 to moles of H_2SO_4, and (3) moles of H_2SO_4 to liters of H_2SO_4 solution.

| g Na_2CO_3 | $\longrightarrow$ | mol Na_2CO_3 | $\longrightarrow$ | mol H_2SO_4 | $\longrightarrow$ | L H_2SO_4 soln |

Solution

reaction ratio from balanced equation   molarity

$$\underline{}\text{ L } H_2SO_4 = 2.792 \text{ g } Na_2CO_3 \times \frac{1 \text{ mol } Na_2CO_3}{106.0 \text{ g } Na_2CO_3} \times \frac{1 \text{ mol } H_2SO_4}{1 \text{ mol } Na_2CO_3} \times \frac{1 \text{ L } H_2SO_4 \text{ soln}}{0.324 \text{ mol } H_2SO_4}$$

$$= \boxed{0.0813 \text{ L } H_2SO_4 \text{ soln}} \quad \text{or} \quad \boxed{81.3 \text{ mL } H_2SO_4 \text{ soln}}$$

You should now work Exercise 78.

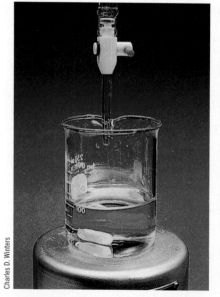

▶ The indicator methyl orange changes from yellow, its color in basic solutions, to orange, its color in acidic solutions, when the reaction in Example 3-23 reaches completion.

Charles D. Winters

Often we must calculate the volume of a solution of known molarity that is required to react with a specified volume of another solution. We always examine the balanced chemical equation for the reaction to determine the *reaction ratio*, that is, the relative numbers of moles of reactants.

EXAMPLE 3-24 Volume of Solution Required

Find the volume in liters and in milliliters of a 0.505 M NaOH solution required to react with 40.0 mL of 0.505 M H_2SO_4 solution according to the reaction

$$H_2SO_4 + 2NaOH \longrightarrow Na_2SO_4 + 2H_2O$$

Plan

We shall work this example in several steps, stating the "plan," or reasoning, just before each step in the calculation. Then we shall use a single setup to solve the problem.

Solution

The balanced equation tells us that the reaction ratio is 1 mol H_2SO_4 to 2 mol NaOH.

$$H_2SO_4 + 2NaOH \longrightarrow Na_2SO_4 + 2H_2O$$
$$\text{1 mol} \quad\quad \text{2 mol} \quad\quad\quad \text{1 mol} \quad\quad \text{2 mol}$$

From the volume and the molarity of the H_2SO_4 solution, we can calculate the number of moles of H_2SO_4.

$$\underline{?}\ \text{mol}\ H_2SO_4 = 0.0400\ \text{L}\ H_2SO_4\ \text{soln} \times \overbrace{\frac{0.505\ \text{mol}\ H_2SO_4}{\text{L soln}}}^{\text{molarity}} = 0.0202\ \text{mol}\ H_2SO_4$$

The number of moles of H_2SO_4 is related to the number of moles of NaOH by the reaction ratio, 1 mol H_2SO_4/2 mol NaOH:

$$\underline{?}\ \text{mol}\ NaOH = 0.0202\ \text{mol}\ H_2SO_4 \times \overbrace{\frac{2\ \text{mol}\ NaOH}{1\ \text{mol}\ H_2SO_4}}^{\substack{\text{reaction ratio from} \\ \text{balanced equation}}} = 0.0404\ \text{mol}\ NaOH$$

Now we can calculate the volume of 0.505 M NaOH solution that contains 0.0404 mole of NaOH:

$$\underline{?}\ \text{L NaOH soln} = 0.0404\ \text{mol}\ NaOH \times \overbrace{\frac{1.00\ \text{L NaOH soln}}{0.505\ \text{mol}\ NaOH}}^{\text{(molarity)}^{-1}} = 0.0800\ \text{L NaOH soln}$$

which we usually call 80.0 mL of NaOH solution .

We have worked through the problem stepwise; let us solve it in a single setup.

$$\boxed{\begin{array}{c}\text{L}\ H_2SO_4\ \text{soln}\\\text{available}\end{array}} \longrightarrow \boxed{\begin{array}{c}\text{mol}\ H_2SO_4\\\text{available}\end{array}} \longrightarrow \boxed{\begin{array}{c}\text{mol NaOH}\\\text{soln needed}\end{array}} \longrightarrow \boxed{\begin{array}{c}\text{L NaOH}\\\text{soln needed}\end{array}}$$

$$\underline{?}\ \text{L NaOH soln} = 0.0400\ \text{L}\ H_2SO_4\ \text{soln} \times \frac{0.505\ \text{mol}\ H_2SO_4}{\text{L}\ H_2SO_4\ \text{soln}} \times \overbrace{\frac{2\ \text{mol}\ NaOH}{1\ \text{mol}\ H_2SO_4}}^{\substack{\text{reaction ratio from}\\ \text{balanced equation}}}$$

$$\times \frac{1.00\ \text{L NaOH soln}}{0.505\ \text{mol}\ NaOH}$$

$$= 0.0800\ \text{L NaOH soln or } 80.0\ \text{mL NaOH soln}$$

You should now work Exercise 80.

S TOP & THINK

A common mistake is to use the dilution equation $V_1M_1 = V_2M_2$ to solve problems involving reactions. Though it can sometimes give the correct answer, this is coincidental; for Example 3-24 it would give the wrong answer.

▶ The volume of H_2SO_4 solution is expressed as 0.0400 L rather than 40.0 mL.

▶ Again we see that molarity can be used as a unit factor. In this case,

$$\frac{1.00\ \text{L NaOH soln}}{0.505\ \text{mol}\ NaOH}$$

KEY TERMS

Actual yield   The amount of a specified pure product actually obtained from a given reaction. Compare with *Theoretical yield*.

Aqueous solution   A solution in which the solvent is water.

Chemical equation   Description of a chemical reaction by placing the formulas of reactants on the left and the formulas of products on the right of an arrow. A chemical equation must be balanced; that is, it must have the same number of each kind of atom on both sides.

Concentration   The amount of solute per unit volume or mass of solvent or of solution.

Dilution   The process of reducing the concentration of a solute in solution, usually simply by adding more solvent.

Isolated yield   see *Actual yield*.

Limiting reactant (or reagent)   A substance that stoichiometrically limits the amount of product(s) that can be formed in a reaction.

Molarity (M)   The number of moles of solute per liter of solution.

Percent by mass   100% multiplied by the mass of a solute divided by the mass of the solution in which it is contained.

Percent yield   100% times actual yield divided by theoretical yield.

Products   Substances produced in a chemical reaction.

Reactants   Substances consumed in a chemical reaction.

Reaction ratio   The relative amounts of reactants and products involved in a reaction; may be the ratio of moles, or masses. Also called *Stoichiometric ratio*.

Reaction stoichiometry   Description of the quantitative relationships among substances as they participate in chemical reactions.

Sequential reaction   A chemical process in which several reaction steps are required to convert starting materials into products.

Solute   The dispersed (dissolved) phase of a solution.

Solution   A homogeneous mixture of two or more substances.

Solvent   The dispersing medium of a solution.

Stoichiometric ratio   see *Reaction ratio*.

Stoichiometry   Description of the quantitative relationships among elements and compounds as they undergo chemical changes.

Theoretical yield   The maximum amount of a specified product that could be obtained from specified amounts of reactants, assuming complete consumption of the limiting reactant according to only one reaction and complete recovery of the product. Compare with *Actual yield*.

EXERCISES

🌐 **Molecular Reasoning** exercises

▲ **More Challenging** exercises

Blue-Numbered exercises are solved in the Student Solutions Manual

Chemical Equations

1. In a chemical equation, what are the products? What information must an unbalanced chemical equation contain?

2. In a balanced chemical equation there must be the same number of atoms of each element on both sides of the equation. What scientific (natural) law requires that there be equal numbers of atoms of each element in both the products and the reactants?

3. 🌐 (a) Write a balanced chemical equation for the following reaction. In sunlight hydrogen gas reacts explosively with chlorine gas to produce hydrogen chloride gas.
   (b) Use ball-and-stick models to illustrate the balanced chemical equation.

4. 🌐 (a) Write a balanced chemical equation for the following reaction. In the presence of a spark, hydrogen gas reacts explosively with oxygen gas to produce gaseous water.
   (b) Use ball-and-stick models to illustrate the balanced chemical equation.

5. 🌐 Use words to state explicitly the relationships among numbers of molecules of reactants and products in the equation for the combustion of butane, C_4H_{10}.

$$2C_4H_{10} + 13O_2 \longrightarrow 8CO_2 + 10H_2O$$

Charles D. Winters

A butane-fueled lighter

6. 🌐 Use words to state explicitly at the molecular level the information given in the following equation.

$$S(s) + O_2(g) \longrightarrow SO_2(g)$$

7. Write the chemical equation for the production of lithium oxide by the reaction of lithium and oxygen.

Balance each "equation" in Exercises 8-11 by inspection.

8. (a) $Na + O_2 \longrightarrow Na_2O$
   (b) $Mg_3N_2 + H_2O \longrightarrow NH_3 + Mg(OH)_2$
   (c) $LiCl + Pb(NO_3)_2 \longrightarrow PbCl_2 + LiNO_3$
   (d) $H_2O + KO_2 \longrightarrow KOH + O_2$
   (e) $H_2SO_4 + NH_3 \longrightarrow (NH_4)_2SO_4$

🌐 **Molecular Reasoning** exercises   ▲ **More Challenging** exercises   Blue-Numbered exercises solved in Student Solutions Manual

Unless otherwise noted, all content on this page is © Cengage Learning.

9. (a) $Na + O_2 \longrightarrow Na_2O_2$
   (b) $P_4 + O_2 \longrightarrow P_4O_{10}$
   (c) $Ca(HCO_3)_2 + Na_2CO_3 \longrightarrow CaCO_3 + NaHCO_3$
   (d) $NH_3 + O_2 \longrightarrow NO + H_2O$
   (e) $Rb + H_2O \longrightarrow RbOH + H_2$
10. (a) $Fe_2O_3 + CO \longrightarrow Fe + CO_2$
    (b) $Rb + H_2O \longrightarrow RbOH + H_2$
    (c) $K + KNO_3 \longrightarrow K_2O + N_2$
    (d) $(NH_4)_2Cr_2O_7 \longrightarrow N_2 + H_2O + Cr_2O_3$
    (e) $Al + Cr_2O_3 \longrightarrow Al_2O_3 + Cr$
11. (a) $Al + H_2SO_4 \longrightarrow Al_2(SO_4)_3 + H_2$
    (b) $C_5H_{10} + O_2 \longrightarrow CO_2 + H_2O$
    (c) $Li + N_2 \longrightarrow Li_3N$
    (d) $Ba(ClO_4)_2 \longrightarrow BaCl_2 + O_2$
    (e) $C_2H_6O + O_2 \longrightarrow CO_2 + H_2O$

Calculations Based on Chemical Equations

In Exercises 12–15, (a) write the balanced chemical equation that represents the reaction described by words, and then perform calculations to answer parts (b) and (c).

12. ♣ (a) Nitrogen, N_2, combines with hydrogen, H_2, to form ammonia, NH_3.
    (b) How many hydrogen molecules are required to react with 150. nitrogen molecules?
    (c) How many ammonia molecules are formed in part (b)?
13. ♣ (a) Sulfur, S_8, combines with oxygen at elevated temperatures to form sulfur dioxide.
    (b) If 160. oxygen molecules are used up in this reaction, how many sulfur molecules react?
    (c) How many sulfur dioxide molecules are formed in part (b)?
14. (a) Limestone, $CaCO_3$, dissolves in hydrochloric acid, HCl, to form calcium chloride, $CaCl_2$, carbon dioxide, and water.
    (b) How many moles of HCl are required to dissolve 2.6 mol of $CaCO_3$?
    (c) How many moles of water are formed in part (b)?

Charles D. Winters

Limestone dissolving in HCl

15. (a) Aluminum building materials have a hard, transparent, protective coating of aluminum oxide, Al_2O_3, formed by reaction with oxygen in the air. The sulfuric acid, H_2SO_4, in acid rain dissolves this protective coating and forms aluminum sulfate, $Al_2(SO_4)_3$, and water.
    (b) How many moles of H_2SO_4 are required to react with 2.6 mol of Al_2O_3?
    (c) How many moles of $Al_2(SO_4)_3$ are formed in part (b)?
16. Calculate the number of grams of baking soda, $NaHCO_3$, that contain 10.5 moles of carbon.

Charles D. Winters

Baking soda

17. Limestone, coral, seashells, and marble are composed primarily of calcium carbonate. The test for the identification of a carbonate is to use a few drops of hydrochloric acid. The unbalanced equation is

$$CaCO_3 + HCl \longrightarrow CaCl_2 + CO_2 + H_2O$$

(a) Balance the equation.
(b) How many atoms are in 0.150 mol of calcium carbonate?
(c) What number of carbon dioxide molecules is released by the reaction of 0.150 mol of calcium carbonate?
18. How many moles of oxygen can be obtained by the decomposition of 6.4 mol of reactant in each of the following reactions?
    (a) $2KClO_3 \longrightarrow 2KCl + 3O_2$
    (b) $2H_2O_2 \longrightarrow 2H_2O + O_2$
    (c) $2HgO \longrightarrow 2Hg + O_2$
    (d) $2NaNO_3 \longrightarrow 2NaNO_2 + O_2$
    (e) $KClO_4 \longrightarrow KCl + 2O_2$
19. For the formation of 6.5 mol of water, which reaction uses the most nitric acid?
    (a) $3Cu + 8HNO_3 \longrightarrow 3Cu(NO_3)_2 + 2NO + 4H_2O$
    (b) $Al_2O_3 + 6HNO_3 \longrightarrow 2Al(NO_3)_3 + 3H_2O$
    (c) $4Zn + 10HNO_3 \longrightarrow 4Zn(NO_3)_2 + NH_4NO_3 + 3H_2O$
20. Consider the reaction

$$NH_3 + O_2 \xrightarrow{\text{not balanced}} NO + H_2O$$

For every 6.40 mol of NH_3, (a) how many moles of O_2 are required, (b) how many moles of NO are produced, and (c) how many moles of H_2O are produced?

♣ **Molecular Reasoning** exercises   ▲ **More Challenging** exercises   Blue-Numbered exercises solved in Student Solutions Manual

Unless otherwise noted, all content on this page is © Cengage Learning.

21. ♣ Consider the reaction

$$2NO + Br_2 \longrightarrow 2NOBr$$

For every 6.25 mol of bromine that reacts, how many moles of (a) NO react and (b) NOBr are produced? (c) Represent the balanced equation with ball-and-stick models.

22. We allow 44.5 g of methane, CH_4, to react as completely as possible with excess oxygen, O_2, to form CO_2 and water. Write the balanced equation for this reaction. What mass of oxygen reacts?

23. Iron(III) oxide, Fe_2O_3, is a result of the reaction of iron with the oxygen in air.
    (a) What is the balanced equation for this reaction?
    (b) What number of moles of iron reacts with 15.25 mol of oxygen from the air?
    (c) What mass of iron is required to react with 15.25 mol of oxygen?

24. A sample of magnetic iron oxide, Fe_3O_4, reacts completely with hydrogen at red heat. The water vapor formed by the reaction

$$Fe_3O_4 + 4H_2 \xrightarrow{\text{heat}} 3Fe + 4H_2O$$

is condensed and found to weigh 27.15 g. Calculate the mass of Fe_3O_4 that reacted.

25. What masses of cobalt(II) chloride, $CoCl_2$, and of hydrogen fluoride are needed to prepare 5.25 mol of cobalt(II) fluoride, CoF_2, by the following reaction?

$$CoCl_2 + 2HF \longrightarrow CoF_2 + 2HCl$$

26. ▲ Sodium iodide, NaI, is a source of iodine used to produce iodized salt. (a) Write the balanced chemical equation for the reaction of sodium and iodine. (b) How many grams of sodium iodide are produced by the reaction of 47.24 grams of iodine?

27. ▲ Calculate the mass of calcium required to react with 1.885 g of carbon during the production of calcium carbide, CaC_2.

28. Calculate the mass of propane, C_3H_8, that will produce 7.25 moles of water when burned in excess oxygen.

$$C_3H_8 + O_2 \xrightarrow{\text{not balanced}} CO_2 + H_2O$$

29. What mass of pentane, C_5H_{12}, produces 9.033×10^{22} CO_2 molecules when burned in excess oxygen?

Limiting Reactant

30. ♣ Carbon monoxide and oxygen react to give carbon dioxide.

$$2CO + O_2 \longrightarrow 2CO_2$$

Imagine that we mix 8 CO molecules and 6 O_2 molecules and allow them to react as completely as possible.
    (a) Draw a molecular representation of the mixture of reactants.
    (b) Draw a molecular representation of the product mixture, including any remaining reactant molecules.
    (c) How many grams of CO_2 can be prepared from 134.67 g of CO and 77.25 g of O_2?

31. ▲ Silver nitrate solution reacts with calcium chloride solution according to the equation

$$2AgNO_3 + CaCl_2 \longrightarrow Ca(NO_3)_2 + 2AgCl$$

All of the substances involved in this reaction are soluble in water except silver chloride, AgCl, which forms a solid (precipitate) at the bottom of the flask. Suppose we mix together a solution containing 9.45 g of $AgNO_3$ and one containing 6.30 g of $CaCl_2$. What mass of AgCl is formed?

32. ▲ "Superphosphate," a water-soluble fertilizer, is sometimes marketed as "triple phosphate." It is a mixture of $Ca(H_2PO_4)_2$ and $CaSO_4$ on a 1:2 *mole* basis. It is formed by the reaction

$$Ca_3(PO_4)_2 + 2H_2SO_4 \longrightarrow Ca(H_2PO_4)_2 + 2CaSO_4$$

We treat 200.0 g of $Ca_3(PO_4)_2$ with 133.5 g of H_2SO_4. How many grams of superphosphate could be formed?

33. Gasoline is produced from crude oil, a nonrenewable resource. Ethanol is mixed with gasoline to produce a fuel called gasohol. Calculate the mass of water produced when 100.0 g of ethanol, C_2H_5OH, is burned in 82.82 g of oxygen.

34. Disulfur dichloride, S_2Cl_2, is used to vulcanize rubber. It can be made by treating molten sulfur with gaseous chlorine:

$$S_8(\ell) + 4Cl_2(g) \longrightarrow 4S_2Cl_2(\ell)$$

Starting with a mixture of 32.0 g of sulfur and 71.0 g of Cl_2,
    (a) Which is the limiting reactant?
    (b) What is the theoretical yield of S_2Cl_2?
    (c) What mass of the excess reactant remains when the reaction is completed?

35. Silicon carbide, an abrasive, is made by the reaction of silicon dioxide with graphite.

$$SiO_2 + C \xrightarrow{\text{heat}} SiC + CO \qquad (\text{balanced?})$$

We mix 300. g of SiO_2 and 203 g of C. If the reaction proceeds as far as possible, which reactant is left over? How much of this reactant remains?

36. What is the maximum amount of $Ca_3(PO_4)_2$ that can be prepared from 12.9 g of $Ca(OH)_2$ and 18.37 g of H_3PO_4?

$$3Ca(OH)_2 + 2H_3PO_4 \longrightarrow Ca_3(PO_4)_2 + 6H_2O$$

37. Aluminum chloride, Al_2Cl_6, is an inexpensive reagent used in many industrial processes. It is made by treating scrap aluminum with chlorine according to the balanced equation

$$2Al(s) + 3Cl_2(g) \longrightarrow Al_2Cl_6(s)$$

    (a) Which reactant is limiting if 2.70 g Al and 4.05 g Cl_2 are mixed?
    (b) What mass of Al_2Cl_6 can be produced?
    (c) What mass of the excess reactant will remain when the reaction is complete?

♣ **Molecular Reasoning** exercises   ▲ **More Challenging** exercises   Blue-Numbered exercises solved in Student Solutions Manual

38. The following equation represents a reaction between aqueous solutions of silver nitrate and barium chloride.

$$2AgNO_3(aq) + BaCl_2(aq) \longrightarrow 2AgCl(s) + Ba(NO_3)_2(aq)$$

According to this equation, if a solution that contains 62.4 g $AgNO_3$ is mixed with a solution that contains 53.1 g $BaCl_2$, (a) which is the limiting reactant? (b) How many grams of which reactant will be left over? (c) How many grams of AgCl will be formed?

39. The following reaction takes place at high temperatures.

$$Cr_2O_3(s) + 2Al(\ell) \longrightarrow 2Cr(\ell) + Al_2O_3(\ell)$$

If 42.7 g Cr_2O_3 and 9.8 g Al are mixed and allowed to react until one of the reactants is used up, (a) which reactant will be left over? (b) How much will be left? (c) How many grams of chromium will be formed?

Percent Yield from Chemical Reactions

40. The percent yield for the reaction

$$PCl_3 + Cl_2 \longrightarrow PCl_5$$

is 76.5%. What mass of PCl_5 is obtained from the reaction of 92.5 g of PCl_3 with excess chlorine?

41. The percent yield for the following reaction carried out in carbon tetrachloride solution is 66.0%.

$$Br_2 + Cl_2 \longrightarrow 2BrCl$$

(a) What amount of BrCl is formed from the reaction of 0.0350 mole of Br_2 with 0.0350 mole of Cl_2?
(b) What amount of Br_2 is left unchanged?

42. When heated, potassium chlorate, $KClO_3$, melts and decomposes to potassium chloride and diatomic oxygen.
(a) What is the theoretical yield of O_2 from 5.79 g $KClO_3$?
(b) If 1.05 g of O_2 is obtained, what is the percent yield?

43. The percent yield of the following reaction is consistently 92%.

$$CH_4(g) + 4S(g) \longrightarrow CS_2(g) + 2H_2S(g)$$

How many grams of sulfur would be needed to obtain 80.0 g of CS_2?

44. Solid silver nitrate undergoes thermal decomposition to form silver metal, nitrogen dioxide, and oxygen. Write the chemical equation for this reaction. A 0.665-g sample of silver metal is isolated from the decomposition of a 1.099-g sample of $AgNO_3$. What is the percent yield of the reaction?

45. Tin(IV) chloride is produced in 81.1% yield by the reaction of tin with chlorine. How much tin is required to produce a kilogram of tin(IV) chloride?

46. What is the percent yield if 108 mg SO_2 is isolated from the combustion of 85.9 mg of carbon disulfide according to the reaction:

$$CS_2 + 3O_2 \longrightarrow CO_2 + 2SO_2?$$

47. From a 45.0-g sample of an iron ore containing Fe_3O_4, 1.56 g of Fe is obtained by the reaction:

$$Fe_3O_4 + 2C \longrightarrow 3Fe + 2CO_2$$

What is the percent of Fe_3O_4 in the ore?

48. The reaction of finely divided aluminum and iron(III) oxide, Fe_2O_3, is called the thermite reaction. It produces a tremendous amount of heat, making the welding of railroad track possible. The reaction of 500.0 grams of aluminum and 500.0 grams of iron(III) oxide produces 166.5 grams of iron. (a) Calculate the mass of iron that should be released by this reaction. (b) What is the percent yield of iron?

$$Fe_2O_3 + 2Al \longrightarrow 2Fe + Al_2O_3 + heat$$

Charles D. Winters

Thermite reaction

49. Lime, $Ca(OH)_2$, can be used to neutralize an acid spill. A 5.57-g sample of $Ca(OH)_2$ reacts with an excess of hydrochloric acid; 7.41 g of calcium chloride is collected. What is the percent yield of this experiment?

$$Ca(OH)_2 + 2HCl \longrightarrow CaCl_2 + 2H_2O$$

Sequential Reactions

50. Consider the two-step process for the formation of tellurous acid described by the following equations:

$$TeO_2 + 2OH^- \longrightarrow TeO_3^{2-} + H_2O$$

$$TeO_3^{2-} + 2H^+ \longrightarrow H_2TeO_3$$

What mass of H_2TeO_3 is formed from 74.2 g of TeO_2, assuming 100% yield?

51. Consider the formation of cyanogen, C_2N_2, and its subsequent decomposition in water given by the equations

$$2Cu^{2+} + 6CN^- \longrightarrow 2[Cu(CN)_2]^- + C_2N_2$$

$$C_2N_2 + H_2O \longrightarrow HCN + HOCN$$

How much hydrocyanic acid, HCN, can be produced from 85.77 g of KCN, assuming 100% yield?

52. What mass of potassium chlorate is required to supply the proper amount of oxygen needed to burn 78.88 g of methane, CH_4?

$$2KClO_3 \longrightarrow 2KCl + 3O_2$$

$$CH_4 + 2O_2 \longrightarrow CO_2 + 2H_2O$$

● **Molecular Reasoning** exercises   ▲ **More Challenging** exercises   Blue-Numbered exercises solved in Student Solutions Manual

Unless otherwise noted, all content on this page is © Cengage Learning.

53. Hydrogen, obtained by the electrical decomposition of water, is combined with chlorine to produce 444.2 g of hydrogen chloride. Calculate the mass of water decomposed.

$$2H_2O \longrightarrow 2H_2 + O_2$$

$$H_2 + Cl_2 \longrightarrow 2HCl$$

54. Ammonium nitrate, known for its use in agriculture, can be produced from ammonia by the following sequence of reactions:

$$NH_3(g) + O_2(g) \longrightarrow NO(g) + H_2O(g)$$

$$NO(g) + O_2(g) \longrightarrow NO_2(g)$$

$$NO_2(g) + H_2O(\ell) \longrightarrow HNO_3(aq) + NO(g)$$

$$HNO_3(aq) + NH_3(g) \longrightarrow NH_4NO_3(aq)$$

(a) Balance each equation.
(b) How many moles of nitrogen atoms are required for every mole of ammonium nitrate (NH_4NO_3)?
(c) How much ammonia is needed to prepare 200.0 grams of ammonium nitrate (NH_4NO_3)?

55. Calcium sulfate is the essential component of plaster and sheet rock. Waste calcium sulfate can be converted into quicklime, CaO, by reaction with carbon at high temperatures. The following two reactions represent a sequence of reactions that might take place:

$$CaSO_4(s) + 4C(s) \longrightarrow CaS(\ell) + 4CO(g)$$

$$CaS(\ell) + 3CaSO_4(s) \longrightarrow 4CaO(s) + 4SO_2(g)$$

What weight of sulfur dioxide (in grams) could be obtained from 1.500 kg of calcium sulfate?

56. ▲ The chief ore of zinc is the sulfide, ZnS. The ore is concentrated by flotation and then heated in air, which converts the ZnS to ZnO.

$$2ZnS + 3O_2 \longrightarrow 2ZnO + 2SO_2$$

The ZnO is then treated with dilute H_2SO_4

$$ZnO + H_2SO_4 \longrightarrow ZnSO_4 + H_2O$$

to produce an aqueous solution containing the zinc as $ZnSO_4$. An electric current is passed through the solution to produce the metal.

$$2ZnSO_4 + 2H_2O \longrightarrow 2Zn + 2H_2SO_4 + O_2$$

What mass of Zn is obtained from an ore containing 454 kg of ZnS? Assume the flotation process to be 89.6% efficient, the electrolysis step to be 92.2% efficient, and the other steps to be 100% efficient.

Concentrations of Solutions—Percent by Mass

57. (a) How many moles of solute are contained in 500. g of a 15.00% aqueous solution of $K_2Cr_2O_7$?
(b) How many grams of solute are contained in the solution of part (a)?
(c) How many grams of water (the solvent) are contained in the solution of part (a)?

58. The density of an 18.0% solution of ammonium sulfate, $(NH_4)_2SO_4$, is 1.10 g/mL. What mass of $(NH_4)_2SO_4$ is required to prepare 750.0 mL of this solution?

59. The density of an 18.0% solution of ammonium chloride, NH_4Cl, solution is 1.05 g/mL. What mass of NH_4Cl does 450. mL of this solution contain?

60. What volume of the solution of $(NH_4)_2SO_4$ described in Exercise 58 contains 125 g of $(NH_4)_2SO_4$?

61. ▲ A reaction requires 65.6 g of NH_4Cl. What volume of the solution described in Exercise 59 do you need if you want to use a 25.0% excess of NH_4Cl?

Concentrations of Solutions—Molarity

62. What is the molarity of a solution prepared by dissolving 355 g of sodium phosphate, Na_3PO_4, in water and diluting to 2.50 L of solution?

63. What is the molarity of a solution prepared by dissolving 4.49 g of sodium chloride in water and diluting to 40.0 mL of solution?

64. What volume of 0.123 M NaOH, in milliliters, contains 25.0 g NaOH?

65. ♣ (a) Ethylene glycol, $C_2H_6O_2$ (antifreeze), is mixed with water in the radiators of cars to protect them against freezing. Draw a molecular representation of a solution of ethylene glycol in water. (Molecular models of ethylene glycol can be found in the margin of Section 2-1.)
(b) How many kilograms of ethylene glycol, $C_2H_6O_2$, are needed to prepare a 9.00 M solution for use in a 12.0-L car radiator?

Antifreeze being poured into water

66. A solution made by dissolving 16.0 g of $CaCl_2$ in 64.0 g of water has a density of 1.180 g/mL at 20°C. (a) What is the percent by mass of $CaCl_2$ in the solution? (b) What is the molarity of $CaCl_2$ in the solution?

67. A solution contains 0.100 mol/L of each of the following acids: HCl, H_2SO_4, H_3PO_4. (a) Is the molarity the same for each acid? (b) Is the number of molecules per liter the same for each acid? (c) Is the mass per liter the same for each acid? Give your reasoning in each case.

68. What is the molarity of a barium chloride solution prepared by dissolving 1.72 g of $BaCl_2 \cdot 2H_2O$ in enough water to make 750. mL of solution?

♣ **Molecular Reasoning** exercises   ▲ **More Challenging** exercises   Blue-Numbered exercises solved in Student Solutions Manual

Unless otherwise noted, all content on this page is © Cengage Learning.

69. How many grams of potassium benzoate trihydrate, $KC_7H_5O_2 \cdot 3H_2O$, are needed to prepare 1.0 L of a 0.150 M solution of potassium benzoate?

70. Stock hydrofluoric acid solution is 49.0% HF and has a specific gravity of 1.17. What is the molarity of the solution?

71. Stock phosphoric acid solution is 85.0% H_3PO_4 and has a specific gravity of 1.70. What is the molarity of the solution?

Dilution of Solutions

72. Commercial concentrated hydrochloric acid is 12.0 M HCl. What volume of concentrated hydrochloric acid is required to prepare 2.00 L of 1.50 M HCl solution?

73. Commercially available concentrated sulfuric acid is 18.0 M H_2SO_4. Calculate the volume of concentrated sulfuric acid required to prepare 2.00 L of 1.50 M H_2SO_4 solution.

74. ▲ You want to clean a 1.00-L bottle that has been used to store a 0.500 M solution. Each time the bottle is emptied, 1.00 mL of solution adheres to the walls, and thus remains in the bottle. One method (method 1) of cleaning the bottle is to empty it, fill to 1.00 L with solvent, and then empty it again. An alternate method (method 2) is to empty the bottle, pour 9.00 mL of solvent into the bottle (to make 10.00 mL total), swirl to mix uniformly, and then empty it. This process is repeated twice, for a total of three rinses. (a) What is the concentration of the solution that remains in the flask after the single rinse in method 1? (b) What is the concentration of the solution that remains in the bottle after the triple rinse in method 2? (c) Compare these two methods of rinsing, in terms of the amount of solvent used. (d) Discuss the implications of this comparison for an industrial process in which many such bottles must be rinsed.

75. You want to clean a 0.500-L flask that has been used to store a 0.8 M solution. Each time the flask is emptied, 1.00 mL of solution adheres to the walls, and thus remains in the bottle. For each rinse cycle, you pour 9.00 mL of solvent into the flask (to make 10.00 mL total), swirl to mix uniformly, and then empty it. What is the minimum number of such rinses necessary to reduce the residual concentration to 0.0001 M (or below)?

76. Calculate the final volume of solution obtained if 100. mL of 12.0 M NaOH are diluted to 5.20 M.

77. In a laboratory preparation room one may find a reagent bottle containing 5.00 L of 12.0 M NaOH. Write a set of instructions for the production of 250. mL of 3.50 M NaOH from such a solution.

Using Solutions in Chemical Reactions

78. Calculate the volume of a 0.157 M solution of potassium hydroxide, KOH, required to react with 0.385 g of acetic acid, CH_3COOH, according to the following reaction.

$$KOH + CH_3COOH \longrightarrow KCH_3COO + H_2O$$

79. Calculate the number of grams of carbon dioxide, CO_2, that can react with 54.55 mL of a 0.957 M solution of potassium hydroxide, KOH, according to the following reaction.

$$2KOH + CO_2 \longrightarrow K_2CO_3 + H_2O$$

80. What volume of 0.558 M HNO_3 solution is required to react completely with 45.55 mL of 0.0515 M $Ba(OH)_2$?

$$Ba(OH)_2 + 2HNO_3 \longrightarrow Ba(NO_3)_2 + 2H_2O$$

81. What volume of 0.558 M HBr is required to react completely with 0.960 mole of $Ca(OH)_2$?

$$2HBr + Ca(OH)_2 \longrightarrow CaBr_2 + 2H_2O$$

82. An excess of $AgNO_3$ reacts with 110.5 mL of an $AlCl_3$ solution to give 0.215 g of AgCl. What is the concentration, in moles per liter, of the $AlCl_3$ solution?

$$AlCl_3 + 3AgNO_3 \longrightarrow 3AgCl + Al(NO_3)_3$$

83. An impure sample of solid Na_2CO_3 is allowed to react with 0.1755 M HCl.

$$Na_2CO_3 + 2HCl \longrightarrow 2NaCl + CO_2 + H_2O$$

A 0.2337-g sample of sodium carbonate requires 15.55 mL of HCl solution. What is the purity of the sodium carbonate?

Mixed Exercises

84. ▲ An iron ore that contains Fe_3O_4 reacts according to the reaction

$$Fe_3O_4 + 2C \longrightarrow 3Fe + 2CO_2$$

We obtain 2.11 g of Fe from the reaction of 75.0 g of the ore. What is the percent Fe_3O_4 in the ore?

85. ▲ If 86.3% of the iron can be recovered from an ore that is 43.2% magnetic iron oxide, Fe_3O_4, what mass of iron could be recovered from 2.50 kg of this ore? The reduction of magnetic iron oxide is a complex process that can be represented in simplified form as

$$Fe_3O_4 + 4CO \longrightarrow 3Fe + 4CO_2$$

86. Gaseous chlorine will displace bromide ion from an aqueous solution of potassium bromide to form aqueous potassium chloride and aqueous bromine. Write the chemical equation for this reaction. What mass of bromine is produced if 0.631 g of chlorine undergoes reaction?

87. Calculate the volume of 2.25 M phosphoric acid solution necessary to react with 45.0 mL of 0.150 M $Mg(OH)_2$.

$$2H_3PO_4 + 3Mg(OH)_2 \longrightarrow Mg_3(PO_4)_2 + 6H_2O$$

Conceptual Exercises

88. 🔵 Using your own words, give a definition of a chemical reaction. Using drawings of ball-and-stick models, illustrate an example of a chemical reaction.

🔵 **Molecular Reasoning** exercises   ▲ **More Challenging** exercises   Blue-Numbered exercises solved in Student Solutions Manual

89. When magnesium metal is burned in air, most of it reacts with oxygen, producing magnesium oxide, MgO. However, at the high temperature of this reaction, some of the magnesium reacts with nitrogen in the air to produce magnesium nitride, Mg_3N_2. This magnesium nitride can be eliminated by adding water, which reacts with the magnesium nitride to produce magnesium hydroxide, $Mg(OH)_2$, and ammonia, NH_3. The balanced equation for that reaction can be represented by the following:

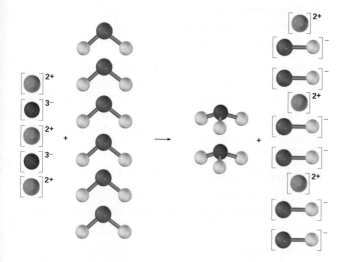

For each element, verify that the same number of atoms appears on both sides of the equation. Write the balanced equation using molecular formulas.

90. A pink solution of cobalt(II) chloride is mixed with a colorless solution of potassium phosphate producing a suspended purple solid. Write the complete, balanced equation for this reaction. (Note: Most potassium salts are soluble and do not form suspensions.)

91. In 1774 Lavoisier repeated Priestley's experiment in which he discovered oxygen by heating red mercury(II) oxide. The unbalanced equation is:

$$HgO(s) \xrightarrow{\Delta} Hg(\ell) + O_2(g)$$

Balance this equation. Using the balanced equation, describe the amounts of each reactant and product in terms of atoms, molecules, and formula units (for any ionic compound). Then describe the amounts of each reactant and product in terms of moles. Finally, describe the amounts of each reactant and product in terms of mass, in grams. How did you determine the numbers of moles? Are the masses in the same proportions as the numbers of moles? Compare the mass of the mercury(II) oxide with the total mass of mercury and oxygen.

92. ♣ Beryllium nitride (Be_3N_2) is a gray solid that melts at 2200°C in the absence of air. (It reacts in air at 600°C.) It can be prepared by heating a mixture of beryllium powder and nitrogen gas at high temperatures. Write the complete, balanced equation for this reaction. How many moles of beryllium are required to react completely with

one mole of nitrogen? How many grams of beryllium are required to react completely with one gram of nitrogen? If the amount of beryllium is less than the amount of nitrogen, will the beryllium be the limiting reagent? In comparing those amounts, would you express them in moles or grams? Does it matter?

93. Write directions for the preparation of 1.000 L of 0.0500 M NaCl solution from a 0.558 M solution of NaCl.

94. Without making any calculations, arrange the following three solutions in order of increasing molarity. (a) 1.0% (by mass) NaCl; (b) 1.0% (by mass) $SnCl_2$; (c) 1.0% (by mass) $AlCl_3$. (Assume that these solutions have nearly equal densities.)

95. To what volume must a student dilute 50. mL of a solution containing 25 mg of $AlCl_3$/mL so that the Al^{3+} concentration in the new solution is 0.022 M?

96. Bismuth dissolves in nitric acid according to the reaction below. What volume of 30.0% HNO_3 by mass (density = 1.182 g/mL) would be required to dissolve 20.0 g of Bi?

$$Bi + 4HNO_3 + 3H_2O \longrightarrow Bi(NO_3)_3 \cdot 5H_2O + NO$$

97. How would you prepare 1.00 L of 1.25×10^{-6} M NaCl (molecular weight 58.44 g/mol) solution by using a balance that can measure mass only to the nearest 0.01 g?

98. ♣ The drawings shown below represent beakers of aqueous solutions. Each sphere represents a dissolved solute particle.
(a) Which solution is most concentrated?
(b) Which solution is least concentrated?
(c) Which two solutions have the same concentration?
(d) When solutions E and F are combined, the resulting solution has the same concentration as solution _____.

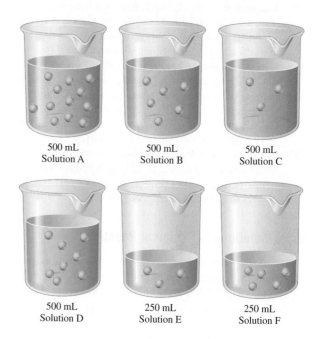

500 mL
Solution A

500 mL
Solution B

500 mL
Solution C

500 mL
Solution D

250 mL
Solution E

250 mL
Solution F

♣ **Molecular Reasoning** exercises   ▲ **More Challenging** exercises   Blue-Numbered exercises solved in Student Solutions Manual

Unless otherwise noted, all content on this page is © Cengage Learning.

99. You prepared a NaCl solution by adding 58.44 g of NaCl to a 1-L volumetric flask and then adding water to dissolve it. When finished, the final volume in your flask looked like the illustration. The solution you prepared is

(a) greater than 1 *M* because you added more solvent than necessary.

(b) less than 1 *M* because you added less solvent than necessary.

(c) greater than 1 *M* because you added less solvent than necessary.

(d) less than 1 *M* because you added more solvent than necessary.

(e) 1 *M* because the amount of solute, not solvent, determines the concentration.

1.00-L flask

100. Zinc is more active chemically than is silver; it can be used to remove ionic silver from solution.

$$Zn(s) + 2AgNO_3(aq) \longrightarrow Zn(NO_3)_2(aq) + 2Ag(s)$$

The concentration of a silver nitrate solution is determined to be 1.330 mol/L. Pieces of zinc totaling 100.0 g are added to 1.000 L of the solution; 90.0 g of silver is collected. (a) Calculate the percent yield of silver. (b) Suggest a reason why the yield is less than 100.0%.

101. 🟣 Ammonia is formed in a direct reaction of nitrogen and hydrogen.

$$N_2(g) + 3H_2(g) \longrightarrow 2NH_3(g)$$

A tiny portion of the starting mixture is represented by the first diagram, where the blue spheres represent N and the white spheres represent H. Which of the numbered diagrams best represents the product mixture?

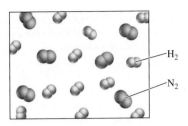

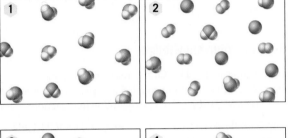

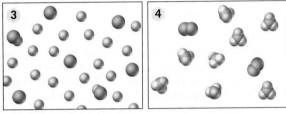

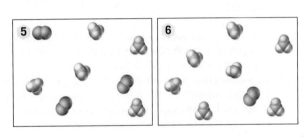

For the reaction of the given sample, which of the following is true?

(a) N_2 is the limiting reactant.

(b) H_2 is the limiting reactant.

(c) NH_3 is the limiting reactant.

(d) No reactant is limiting; they are present in the correct stoichiometric ratio.

102. Given the amount of reactant used and the amount of product actually produced, how would you determine the theoretical amount of product and the percent yield? If the percent yield were calculated by using the number of moles of the product, would the result be the same as the percent yield calculated by using the mass of the product?

103. Carbon disulfide, CS_2, reacts with chlorine, Cl_2, in the presence of a catalyst at 105°C to 130°C, to form carbon tetrachloride, CCl_4.

$$\text{Reaction 1: } CS_2 + 3Cl_2 \longrightarrow CCl_4 + S_2Cl_2$$

🟣 **Molecular Reasoning** exercises   ▲ **More Challenging** exercises   Blue-Numbered exercises solved in Student Solutions Manual

Unless otherwise noted, all content on this page is © Cengage Learning.

The carbon tetrachloride can react with antimony trifluoride, SbF_3, to produce freon-12, CCl_2F_2, a gas that was used in air conditioners.

Reaction 2: $3CCl_4(\ell) + 2SbF_3(s) \longrightarrow 3CCl_2F_2(g) + 2SbCl_3(s)$

If CCl_4 is produced from CS_2 (Reaction 1) with 62.5% yield and CCl_2F_2 is produced from CCl_4 (Reaction 2) with 71.5% yield, what mass of CS_2 must be chlorinated to obtain 125.0 grams of CCl_2F_2 from the CCl_4 produced?

Building Your Knowledge

104. Acetic acid, CH_3COOH, reacts with ethanol, CH_3CH_2OH, to form ethyl acetate, $CH_3COOCH_2CH_3$, (density 0.902 g/mL) by the following reaction:

$CH_3COOH + CH_3CH_2OH \longrightarrow CH_3COOCH_2CH_3 + H_2O$

We combine 20.2 mL of acetic acid with 20.1 mL of ethanol.
(a) Which compound is the limiting reactant?
(b) If 27.5 mL of pure ethyl acetate is produced, what is the percent yield? [Hint: See Tables 1-2 and 1-9.]

105. The following compounds are water-soluble. What ions are produced by each compound in aqueous solution?
(a) KOH   (c) $LiNO_3$
(b) K_2SO_4 (d) $(NH_4)_2SO_4$

106. What is the molarity of a solution prepared by mixing 35.0 mL of 0.375 M NaCl solution with 47.5 mL of a 0.632 M NaCl solution?

107. ▲ Concentrated hydrochloric acid solution is 37.0% HCl and has a density of 1.19 g/mL. A dilute solution of HCl is prepared by diluting 4.50 mL of this concentrated HCl solution to 100.00 mL with water. Then 10.0 mL of this dilute HCl solution reacts with an $AgNO_3$ solution according to the following reaction:

$HCl(aq) + AgNO_3(aq) \longrightarrow HNO_3(aq) + AgCl(s)$

How many milliliters of 0.1105 M $AgNO_3$ solution is required to precipitate all of the chloride as $AgCl(s)$?

108. In a particular experiment, 225 g of phosphorus, P_4, reacted with excess oxygen to form tetraphosphorus decoxide, P_4O_{10}, in 89.5% yield. In a second step reaction with water, a 97.8% yield of H_3PO_4 was obtained.
(a) Write the balanced equations for these two reaction steps.
(b) What mass of H_3PO_4 was obtained?

109. ▲ A mixture of potassium chloride and potassium bromide weighing 3.595 g is heated with chlorine, which converts the KBr completely to potassium chloride. The total mass of potassium chloride after the reaction is 3.129 g. What percentage of the original mixture was potassium bromide?

110. What mass of AgCl could be formed by mixing 10.0 mL of a 1.20% NaCl by mass solution ($D = 1.02$ g/mL) with 50.0 mL of 1.21×10^{-2} M $AgNO_3$? The chemical equation for the reaction of these two solutions is:

$NaCl(aq) + AgNO_3(aq) \longrightarrow AgCl(s) + NaNO_3(aq)$

111. Magnesium displaces copper from a dilute solution of copper(II) sulfate; the pure copper will settle out of the solution.

$Mg(s) + CuSO_4(aq) \longrightarrow MgSO_4(aq) + Cu(s)$

A copper(II) sulfate solution is mixed by dissolving 25.000 g of copper(II) sulfate, and then it is treated with an excess of magnesium metal. The mass of copper collected is 8.786 g after drying. Calculate the percent yield of copper.

112. Suppose you are designing an experiment for the preparation of hydrogen. For the production of equal amounts of hydrogen, which metal, Zn or Al, is less expensive if Zn costs about half as much as Al on a mass basis?

$Zn + 2HCl \longrightarrow ZnCl_2 + H_2$

$2Al + 6HCl \longrightarrow 2AlCl_3 + 3H_2$

113. Gaseous chlorine and gaseous fluorine undergo a combination reaction to form the interhalogen compound ClF.
(a) Write the chemical equation for this reaction.
(b) Calculate the mass of fluorine needed to react with 3.47 g of Cl_2.
(c) How many grams of ClF are formed?

Beyond the Textbook

NOTE: *Whenever the answer to an exercise depends on information obtained from a source other than this textbook, the source must be included as an essential part of the answer.*

114. Use an internet search engine (such as **http://www.google.com**) to locate "drinking water standards" or locate the standards at **www.epa.gov/safewater**. List four inorganic contaminants in drinking water and their maximum contaminant levels (MCLs) allowed.

115. Using the website found in Exercise 114 or another website, list the potential health effects from ingestion of drinking water with excess (a) copper; (b) cadmium.

116. Using the website found in Exercise 114 or another website, list the potential health effects from ingestion of drinking water with excess (a) antimony; (b) beryllium.

117. Consider the websites used in Exercise 114. What is the molarity of the copper atoms or ions in a drinking water sample that has a concentration of copper just equal to the indicated MCLs (maximum contamination levels) allowed for copper in drinking water?

118. There has been considerable controversy over the addition of fluoride (typically in the form of NaF) to drinking water. Fluoridation strengthens tooth enamel, making it more resistant to decay. Search the web to find typical concentrations of fluoride in water that are used for fluoridation. Convert the ppm (or ppb) concentration you find to molarity.

  Molecular Reasoning exercises   ▲ **More Challenging** exercises   Blue-Numbered exercises solved in Student Solutions Manual

The Structure of Atoms

The Lagoon nebula taken by NASA's Spitzer Space Telescope. Atomic excited state emissions produce the following colors in *visible* spectrum photos: red (hydrogen, oxygen), green (oxygen), blue (doubly ionized oxygen, nitrogen), violet (nitrogen). This photo, however, was taken in the infrared region so the colors are "false" (computer assigned) and correspond to different infrared frequencies. Here most of the infrared radiation is coming from carbon atoms that are heated by the stars in the central area.

NASA/JPL-Caltech

OBJECTIVES

After you have studied this chapter, you should be able to

▶ Describe the evidence for the existence and properties of electrons, protons, and neutrons

▶ Predict the arrangements of the particles in atoms

▶ Describe isotopes and their composition

▶ Calculate atomic weights from isotopic abundance

▶ Describe the periodic table and some of the relationships that it summarizes

▶ Describe the wave properties of light and how wavelength, frequency, and speed are related

▶ Use the particle description of light, and explain how it is related to the wave description

▶ Relate atomic emission and absorption spectra to important advances in atomic theory

▶ Describe the main features of the quantum mechanical picture of the atom

▶ Describe the four quantum numbers, and give possible combinations of their values for specific atomic orbitals

▶ Describe the shapes of orbitals and recall the usual order of their relative energies

▶ Write the electron configurations of atoms

▶ Relate the electron configuration of an atom to its position in the periodic table

The Dalton theory of the atom and related ideas were the basis for our study of *composition stoichiometry* (see Chapter 2) and *reaction stoichiometry* (see Chapter 3). That level of atomic theory, however, leaves many questions unanswered. *Why* do atoms combine to form compounds? *Why* do they combine only in simple numerical ratios? *Why* are particular numerical ratios of atoms observed in compounds? *Why* do different elements have different properties? *Why* are they gases, liquids, solids, metals, nonmetals, and so on? *Why* do some groups of elements have similar properties and form compounds with similar formulas? The answers to these and many other important questions in chemistry are supplied by our modern understanding of the nature of atoms. But how can we study something as small as an atom?

Much of the development of modern atomic theory was based on two broad types of research carried out by dozens of scientists just before and after 1900. The first type dealt with the electrical nature of matter. These studies led scientists to recognize that atoms are composed of more fundamental particles and helped them to describe the approximate arrangements of these particles in atoms. The second broad area of research dealt with the interaction of matter with energy in the form of light. Such research included studies of the colors of the light that substances give off or absorb. These studies led to a much more detailed understanding of the arrangements of particles in atoms. It then became clear that the arrangement of the particles determines the chemical and physical properties of each element. As we learn more about the structures of atoms, we are able to organize chemical facts in ways that help us to understand the behavior of matter.

We will first study the particles that make up atoms, and the basic structure of atoms, along with some history and the organization of the periodic table of elements. Then we will take a look at the quantum mechanical theory of atoms and see how this theory describes the arrangement of the electrons in atoms. Current atomic theory is by no means complete. Even so, it is a powerful tool that helps us describe the bonding forces that hold atoms together to form the vast array of matter that makes up the universe.

▶ Accounts of some important developments in atomic theory appear on the World Wide Web; for example, an interesting online history of the discovery of the electron is at **www.aip.org/history/electron**

Subatomic Particles

4-1 Fundamental Particles

▶ Many other subatomic particles, such as quarks, positrons, neutrinos, pions, and muons, have also been discovered. It is not necessary to study their characteristics to understand the fundamentals of atomic structure that are important for chemical properties.

In our study of atomic structure, we look first at the **fundamental particles**. Atoms, and hence *all* matter, consist principally of three fundamental particles: *electrons, protons,* and *neutrons,* which are the basic building blocks for atomic structure. Knowledge of the nature and functions of these particles is essential for understanding chemical interactions.

Table 4-1 Fundamental Particles of Matter

Particle	Mass	Charge (relative scale)
electron (e^-)	0.00054858 amu	1−
proton (p or p^+)	1.0073 amu	1+
neutron (n or n^0)	1.0087 amu	none

The relative masses and charges of the three fundamental particles are shown in Table 4-1. The mass of an electron is very small compared with the mass of either a proton or a neutron. The charge on a proton is equal in magnitude, but opposite in sign, to the charge on an electron. Let's examine these particles in more detail.

4-2 The Discovery of Electrons

Some of the earliest evidence about atomic structure was supplied in the early 1800s by the English chemist Humphry Davy (1778–1829). He found that when he passed electric current through some substances, the substances decomposed. He therefore suggested that the elements of a chemical compound are held together by electrical forces. In 1832–1833, Michael Faraday (1791–1867), who was Davy's student, determined the quantitative relationship between the amount of electricity used in electrolysis and the amount of chemical reaction that occurs. Studies of Faraday's work by George Stoney (1826–1911) led him to suggest in 1874 that units of electric charge are associated with atoms. In 1891, he suggested that these electrical charges be named *electrons*.

▶ The process is called chemical electrolysis. *Lysis* means "splitting apart."

The most convincing evidence for the existence of electrons came from experiments using **cathode-ray tubes** (Figure 4-1). Two electrodes are sealed in a glass tube containing gas at a very low pressure. When a high voltage is applied, current flows and rays are given off by the cathode (negative electrode). These rays travel in straight lines toward the anode (positive electrode) and cause the walls opposite the cathode to glow. An object placed in the path of the cathode rays casts a shadow on a zinc sulfide fluorescent screen placed near the anode. The shadow shows that the rays travel from the negatively charged cathode toward the positively charged anode. This tells us that the rays must be negatively charged. Furthermore, they are deflected by electric and magnetic fields in the directions expected for negatively charged particles.

▶ Study Figures 4-1 and 4-2 as you read this section.

In 1897 J. J. Thomson (1856–1940) studied these negatively charged particles more carefully. He called them **electrons**, as Stoney had suggested. By studying the degree of deflections of cathode rays in different strengths of electric and magnetic fields, Thomson determined the ratio of the charge (e) of the electron to its mass (m). The modern value for this ratio (to six significant figures) is

▶ The coulomb (C) is the standard unit of *quantity* of electric charge. It is defined as the quantity of electricity transported in one second by a current of one ampere. It corresponds to the amount of electricity that will deposit 0.00111798 g of silver in an apparatus set up for plating silver.

$$e/m = 1.75882 \times 10^8 \text{ coulomb (C)/g}$$

This ratio is the same regardless of the type of gas in the tube, the composition of the electrodes, or the nature of the electric power source. Thomson's work suggested that electrons are fundamental particles that are present in all atoms. We now know that this is true and that all atoms contain integral (whole) numbers of electrons.

After the charge-to-mass ratio for the electron had been determined, additional experiments were necessary to determine the value of either its mass or its charge so that the other could be calculated. In 1909, Robert Millikan (1868–1953) solved this dilemma with the famous "oil-drop experiment," in which he determined the charge of the electron. This experiment is described in Figure 4-2. All of the charges measured by Millikan turned out to be integral multiples of the same number. He assumed that this smallest charge was the charge on one electron. This value is 1.60218×10^{-19} coulomb (modern value to six significant figures).

▶ The charge on one mole (Avogadro's number) of electrons is 96,485 coulombs.

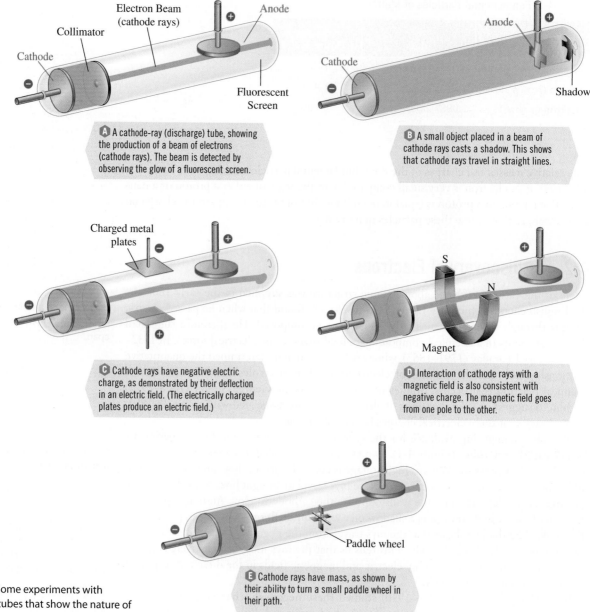

Figure 4-1 Some experiments with cathode-ray tubes that show the nature of cathode rays.

The charge-to-mass ratio, $e/m = 1.75882 \times 10^8$C/g, can be used in inverse form to calculate the mass of the electron:

$$m = \frac{1\,\text{g}}{1.75882 \times 10^8\,\text{C}} \times 1.60218 \times 10^{-19}\,\text{C}$$

$$= 9.10940 \times 10^{-28}\,\text{g}$$

▶ The value of e/m obtained by Thomson and the values of e and m obtained by Millikan differ slightly from the modern values given in this text because early measurements were not as accurate as modern ones.

This is only about 1/1836 the mass of a hydrogen atom, the lightest of all atoms. Millikan's simple oil-drop experiment stands as one of the cleverest, yet most fundamental, of all classic scientific experiments. It was the first experiment to suggest that atoms contain integral numbers of electrons; we now know this to be true.

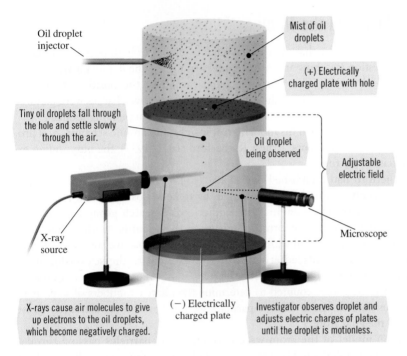

Figure 4-2 The Millikan oil-drop experiment. Tiny spherical oil droplets are produced by an atomizer. The mass of the spherical drop can be calculated from its volume (obtained from a measurement of the radius of the drop with a microscope) and the known density of the oil. A few droplets fall through the hole in the upper plate. Irradiation with X-rays gives some of these oil droplets a negative charge. When the voltage between the plates is increased, a negatively charged drop falls more slowly because it is attracted by the positively charged upper plate and repelled by the negatively charged lower plate. At one particular voltage, the electrical force (up) and the gravitational force (down) on the drop are exactly balanced, and the drop remains stationary. Knowing this voltage and the mass of the drop, we can calculate the charge on the drop.

4-3 Canal Rays and Protons

In 1886 Eugen Goldstein (1850–1930) first observed that a cathode-ray tube also generates a stream of positively charged particles that moves toward the cathode. These were called **canal rays** because they were observed occasionally to pass through a channel, or "canal," drilled in the negative electrode (Figure 4-3). These *positive rays*, or *positive ions*, are created when the gaseous atoms in the tube lose electrons. Positive ions are formed by the process

$$\text{Atom} \longrightarrow \text{cation}^+ + e^- \qquad \text{or} \qquad X \longrightarrow X^+ + e^- \qquad \text{(energy absorbed)}$$

Different elements give positive ions with different e/m ratios. The regularity of the e/m values for different ions led to the idea that there is a subatomic particle with one unit of positive charge, called the **proton**. The proton is a fundamental particle with a charge equal in magnitude but opposite in sign to the charge on the electron. Its mass is almost 1836 times that of the electron.

▶ The proton was observed by Ernest Rutherford and James Chadwick in 1919 as a particle that is emitted by bombardment of certain atoms with α-particles.

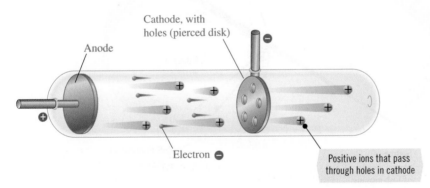

Figure 4-3 A cathode-ray tube with a different design and with a perforated cathode. Such a tube was used to produce canal rays and to demonstrate that they travel toward the cathode. Like cathode rays, these *positive* rays are deflected by electric or magnetic fields, but in the opposite direction from cathode rays (electron beam). Canal ray particles have e/m ratios many times smaller than those of electrons because of their much greater masses. When different elements are in the tube, positive ions with different e/m ratios are observed.

4-4 Rutherford and the Nuclear Atom

By the early 1900s, it was clear that each atom contains regions of both positive and negative charge. The question was, how are these charges arranged? The dominant view of that time was summarized in J. J. Thomson's model of the atom; the positive charge was thought to be distributed evenly throughout the atom. The negative charges were pictured as being imbedded in the atom like plums in a pudding (the "plum pudding model").

Soon after Thomson developed his model, great insight into atomic structure was provided by one of his former students, Ernest Rutherford (1871–1937), the outstanding experimental physicist of his time.

By 1909, Rutherford had established that alpha- (α-) particles are positively charged particles. They are emitted at high kinetic energies by some radioactive atoms, that is, atoms that disintegrate spontaneously. In 1910 Rutherford's research group carried out a series of experiments that had an enormous impact on the scientific world. They bombarded a very thin piece of gold foil with α-particles from a radioactive source. A fluorescent zinc sulfide screen was placed around the foil to indicate the scattering of the α-particles by the gold foil (Figure 4-4). Scintillations (flashes) on the screen, caused by the individual α-particles, were counted to determine the relative numbers of α-particles deflected at various angles. At the time, α-particles were believed to be extremely dense, much denser than the gold atom.

If the Thomson model of the atom were correct, any α-particles passing through the foil would have been deflected by very small angles. Quite unexpectedly, nearly all of the α-particles passed through the foil with little or no deflection. A few, however, were deflected through large angles, and a very small number of α-particles even returned from the gold foil in the direction from which they had come! Rutherford was astounded. In his own words,

> *It was quite the most incredible event that has ever happened to me in my life. It was almost as if you fired a 15-inch shell into a piece of tissue paper and it came back and hit you.*

Rutherford's mathematical analysis of his results showed that the scattering of positively charged α-particles was caused by repulsion from very dense regions of positive charge in the gold foil. He concluded that the mass of one of these regions is nearly equal to that of a gold atom, but that the diameter is no more than 1/10,000 that of an

▶ α-Particles are now known to be He^{2+} ions, that is, helium atoms without their two electrons (see Chapter 22).

▶ Radioactivity is contrary to the Daltonian idea of the indivisibility of atoms.

Ernest Rutherford was one of the giants in the development of our understanding of atomic structure. While working with J. J. Thomson at Cambridge University, he discovered α- and β-radiation. He spent the years 1899–1907 at McGill University in Canada where he proved the nature of these two radiations, for which he received the Nobel Prize in chemistry in 1908. He returned to England in 1908, and it was there, at Manchester University, that he and his coworkers Hans Geiger and Ernst Marsden performed the famous gold foil experiments that led to the nuclear model of the atom. Not only did he perform much important research in physics and chemistry, but he also guided the work of ten future recipients of the Nobel Prize.

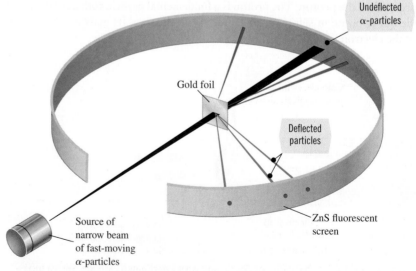

Figure 4-4 The Rutherford scattering experiment. A narrow beam of α-particles from a radioactive source was directed at a very thin sheet of gold foil. Most of the particles passed through the gold foil with no deflection (*shown in black*). Many were deflected through moderate angles (*shown in red*). These deflections were surprising, but the 0.001% of the total that were reflected at acute angles (*shown in blue*) were totally unexpected.

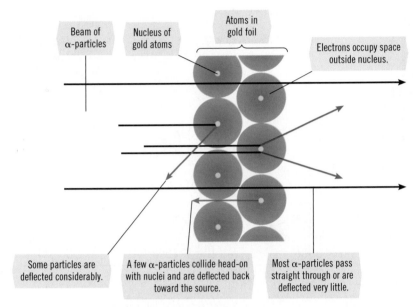

Figure 4-5 An interpretation of the Rutherford scattering experiment. The atom is pictured as consisting mostly of "open" space. The electrons are thinly distributed throughout the "open" space. Most of the positively charged α-particles (*black arrows*) pass through the open space undeflected, not coming near any gold nuclei. The few that pass fairly close to a nucleus (*red arrows*) are repelled by electrostatic forces and thereby deflected. The very few particles that are on a path to collide with gold nuclei are repelled backward at acute angles (*blue arrows*).

atom. Many experiments with foils of different metals yielded similar results. Realizing that these observations were inconsistent with previous theories about atomic structure, Rutherford discarded the old theory and proposed a better one. He suggested that each atom contains a *tiny, but massive, positively charged center* that he called the atomic **nucleus**. Most α-particles pass through metal foils undeflected because atoms are *primarily* empty space populated only by the very light electrons. The few particles that are deflected are the ones that come close to the heavy, highly charged metal nuclei (Figure 4-5).

Rutherford was able to determine the magnitudes of the positive charges on the atomic nuclei. The picture of atomic structure that he developed is called the Rutherford model of the atom.

> Atoms consist of very small, very dense positively charged nuclei surrounded by clouds of electrons at relatively large distances from the nuclei.

4-5 Atomic Number

Only a few years after Rutherford's scattering experiments, H. G. J. Moseley (1887–1915) studied X-rays given off by various elements. Max von Laue (1879–1960) had shown that X-rays could be diffracted by crystals into a spectrum in much the same way that visible light can be separated into its component colors. X-rays can be generated by aiming a beam of high-energy electrons at a solid target made of a single pure element (Figure 4-6a).

The spectra of X-rays produced by targets of different elements were recorded photographically. Each photograph consisted of a series of lines representing X-rays at various wavelengths; each element produced its own distinct set of wavelengths. Comparison of results from different elements revealed that corresponding lines were displaced toward shorter wavelengths as atomic weights of the target materials increased, with a few exceptions. But in 1913 Moseley showed that the X-ray wavelengths could be better correlated

► This representation is *not* to scale. If nuclei were as large as the dots that represent them, each region that represents the size of an atom would have a diameter of more than 100 feet!

► In a modern technique known as "X-ray fluorescence spectroscopy," the wavelengths of X-rays given off by a sample target indicate which elements are present in the sample.

H. G. J. Moseley was one of the many remarkable scientists who worked with Ernest Rutherford. Moseley's scientific career was very short. He enlisted in the British army during World War I and died in battle in the Gallipoli campaign in 1915.

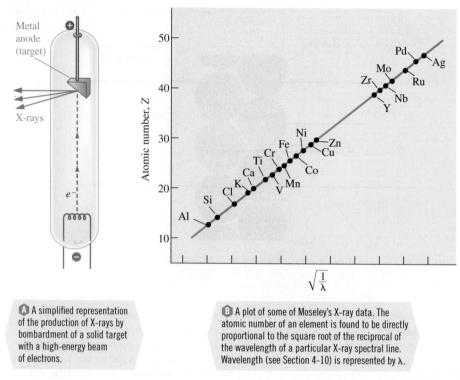

A A simplified representation of the production of X-rays by bombardment of a solid target with a high-energy beam of electrons.

B A plot of some of Moseley's X-ray data. The atomic number of an element is found to be directly proportional to the square root of the reciprocal of the wavelength of a particular X-ray spectral line. Wavelength (see Section 4-10) is represented by λ.

Figure 4-6 Production of X-rays and effect of atomic number on wavelength.

with the atomic number. A plot illustrating this interpretation of Moseley's data appears in Figure 4-6b. On the basis of his mathematical analysis of these X-ray data, he concluded that

each element differs from the preceding element by having one more positive charge in its nucleus.

For the first time it was possible to arrange all known elements in order of increasing nuclear charge. This discovery led to the realization that atomic number, related to the electrical properties of the atom, was more fundamental to determining the properties of the elements than atomic weight was. This discovery put the ideas of the periodic table on a more fundamental footing.

We now know that every nucleus contains an integral number of protons exactly equal to the number of electrons in a neutral atom of the element. Every hydrogen nucleus contains one proton, every helium nucleus contains two protons, every lithium nucleus contains three protons, and so on.

The number of protons in the nucleus of an atom determines its identity; this number is known as the **atomic number** of that element.

▶ This does not mean that elements above number 19 do not have neutrons, only that neutrons are not generally knocked out of atoms of higher atomic number by α-particle bombardment until one reaches the radioactive actinide elements and beyond.

4-6 Neutrons

The third fundamental particle, the neutron, eluded discovery until 1932. James Chadwick (1891–1974) correctly interpreted experiments on the bombardment of beryllium with high-energy α-particles. Later experiments showed that nearly all elements up to potassium, element 19, produce neutrons when they are bombarded with high-energy α-particles. The **neutron** is an uncharged particle with a mass slightly greater than that of the proton.

> Atoms consist of very small, very dense nuclei surrounded by clouds of electrons at relatively great distances from the nuclei. All nuclei contain protons; nuclei of all atoms except the common form of hydrogen also contain neutrons.

Nuclear diameters are about 10^{-5} nanometers (nm); atomic diameters are about 10^{-1} nm. To put this difference in perspective, suppose that you wish to build a model of an atom using a basketball (diameter about 9.5 inches) as the nucleus; on this scale, the atomic model would be nearly 6 miles across!

4-7 Mass Number and Isotopes

Most elements consist of atoms of different masses, called **isotopes**. The isotopes of a given element contain the same number of protons (and also the same number of electrons) because they are atoms of the same element. They differ in mass because they contain different numbers of neutrons in their nuclei.

> Isotopes are atoms of the same element with different masses; they are atoms containing the same number of protons but different numbers of neutrons.

For example, there are three distinct kinds of hydrogen atoms, commonly called hydrogen, deuterium, and tritium. (This is the only element for which we give each isotope a different name.) Each contains one proton in the atomic nucleus. The predominant form of hydrogen contains no neutrons, but each deuterium atom contains one neutron and each tritium atom contains two neutrons in its nucleus (Table 4-2). All three forms of hydrogen display very similar chemical properties.

The **mass number** of an atom is the sum of the number of protons and the number of neutrons in its nucleus; that is

$$\text{Mass number} = \text{number of protons} + \text{number of neutrons}$$
$$= \text{atomic number} + \text{neutron number}$$

The mass number for normal hydrogen atoms is 1; for deuterium, 2; and for tritium, 3. The composition of a nucleus is indicated by its **nuclide symbol**. This consists of the symbol for the element (E), with the atomic number (Z) written as a subscript at the lower left and the mass number (A) as a superscript at the upper left, $_{Z}^{A}E$ (Figure 4-7). By this system, the three isotopes of hydrogen are designated as $_{1}^{1}H$, $_{1}^{2}H$, and $_{1}^{3}H$.

▶ A mass number is a count of the *number* of protons plus neutrons present, so it must be a whole number. Because the masses of the proton and the neutron are both about 1 amu, the mass number is *approximately* equal to the actual mass of the isotope (which is not a whole number).

Table 4-2 The Three Isotopes of Hydrogen

Name	Symbol	Nuclide Symbol	Mass (amu)	Atomic Abundance in Nature	No. of Protons	No. of Neutrons	No. of Electrons (in neutral atoms)
hydrogen	H	$_{1}^{1}H$	1.007825	99.985%	1	0	1
deuterium	D	$_{1}^{2}H$	2.01400	0.015%	1	1	1
tritium*	T	$_{1}^{3}H$	3.01605	0.000%	1	2	1

*No known natural sources; produced by decomposition of artificial isotopes.

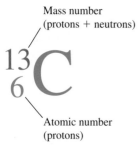

Mass number
(protons + neutrons)

$^{13}_{6}C$

Atomic number
(protons)

Figure 4-7 Interpretation of a nuclide symbol. Chemists often omit the subscripted atomic number because the element symbol implies the atomic number.

EXAMPLE 4-1 Determination of Atomic Makeup

Determine the number of protons, neutrons, and electrons in each of the following species. Are the members within each pair isotopes?

   (a) $^{35}_{17}Cl$ and $^{37}_{17}Cl$ **(b)** $^{63}_{29}Cu$ and $^{65}_{29}Cu$

Plan

We know that the number at the bottom left of the nuclide symbol is the atomic number or number of protons. This lets us verify the identity of the element in addition to knowing the number of protons per nuclide. From the mass number at the top left, we know the number of protons plus neutrons. The number of protons (atomic number) minus the number of electrons must equal the charge, if any, shown at the top right. From these data one can determine if two nuclides have the same number of protons and are therefore the same element. If they are the same element, they will be isotopes only if their mass numbers differ.

Solution

  (a) For $^{35}_{17}Cl$:   Atomic number = 17. There are therefore 17 protons per nucleus.
                  Mass number = 35. There are therefore 35 protons plus neutrons or, because we know that there are 17 protons, there are 18 neutrons. Because no charge is indicated, there must be equal numbers of protons and electrons, or 17 electrons

      For $^{37}_{17}Cl$:   There are 17 protons, 20 neutrons, and 17 electrons per atom.

These are isotopes of the same element. Both have 17 protons, but they differ in their numbers of neutrons: one has 18 neutrons and the other has 20.

  (b) For $^{63}_{29}Cu$:   Atomic number = 29. There are 29 protons per nucleus.
                  Mass number = 63. There are 29 protons plus 34 neutrons. Because no charge is indicated, there must be equal numbers of protons and electrons, or 29 electrons.

      For $^{65}_{29}Cu$:   There are 29 protons, 36 neutrons, and 29 electrons per atom.

These are isotopes. Both have 29 protons, but they differ in their numbers of neutrons: one isotope has 34 neutrons and the other has 36.

You should now work Exercises 18 and 20.

STOP & THINK
Isotopes of an element differ only in the number of neutrons they contain.

4-8 Mass Spectrometry and Isotopic Abundance

Mass spectrometers are instruments that measure the charge-to-mass ratio of charged particles. A gas sample at very low pressure is bombarded with high-energy electrons. This causes electrons to be ejected from some of the gas molecules, creating positive ions. The positive ions are then focused into a very narrow beam and accelerated by an electric field. One type of mass spectrometer uses a magnetic field to deflect the ions from their straight-line path (Figure 4-8). The extent to which the beam of ions is deflected depends on four factors:

  1. *Magnitude of the accelerating voltage (electric field strength).* Higher voltages result in beams of more rapidly moving particles that are deflected less than the beams of the more slowly moving particles produced by lower voltages.

  2. *Magnetic field strength.* Stronger fields deflect a given beam more than weaker fields.

  3. *Masses of the particles.* Because of their inertia, heavier particles are deflected less than lighter particles that carry the same charge.

  4. *Charges on the particles.* Particles with higher charges interact more strongly with magnetic fields and are thus deflected more than particles of equal mass with smaller charges.

▶ Newer mass spectrometers use a simple time-of-flight detector that measures the time the positively charged particles take to travel to the part of the detector that records the impact of the ion. The longer a particle takes to travel the distance, the greater its mass. Another common type of mass spectrometer uses a quadrupolar electrostatic field to sort ions by their masses.

The mass spectrometer can be used to measure masses of isotopes as well as isotopic abundances, that is, the relative amounts of the isotopes. Helium occurs in nature almost exclusively as ^{4}He. Its atomic mass can be determined in an experiment such as that illustrated in Figure 4-8. Modern mass spectrometers are capable of great accuracy in their mass measurements.

▶ We can omit the atomic number subscript 2 for He, because all helium atoms have atomic number 2.

A beam of Ne^+ ions in the mass spectrometer is split into three segments. The mass spectrum of these ions (a graph of the relative numbers of ions of each mass) is shown in Figure 4-9. This indicates that neon occurs in nature as three isotopes: ^{20}Ne, ^{21}Ne, and ^{22}Ne. In Figure 4-9 we see that the isotope ^{20}Ne, mass 19.99244 amu, is the most abundant isotope (has the tallest peak). It accounts for 90.48% of the atoms. ^{22}Ne, mass 21.99138, accounts for 9.25%, and ^{21}Ne, mass 20.99384, for only 0.27% of the atoms.

▶ Isotopes are two or more forms of atoms of the same element with different masses; the atoms contain the same number of protons but different numbers of neutrons.

Figure 4-10 shows a modern mass spectrometer. In nature, some elements, such as fluorine and phosphorus, exist in only one form, but most elements occur as isotopic mixtures. Some examples of natural isotopic abundances are given in Table 4-3. The percentages are based on the numbers of naturally occurring atoms of each isotope, not on their masses.

The distribution of isotopic masses, although nearly constant, does vary somewhat depending on the source of the element. For example, the abundance of ^{13}C in atmospheric CO_2 is slightly different from that in seashells. The chemical history of a sample can often be inferred from small differences in isotope ratios. See the Chemistry in Use essay on Stable Isotope Ratio Analysis.

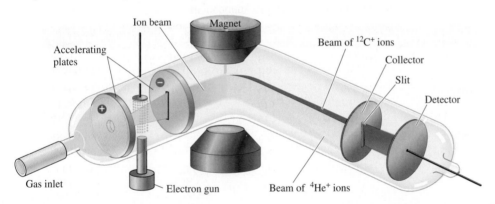

Figure 4-8 A mass spectrometer that uses a magnetic field to separate atoms or molecules with different masses. In this type of mass spectrometer, gas molecules at low pressure are ionized and accelerated by an electric field. The ion beam is then passed through a magnetic field. In that field the beam is resolved into components, each containing particles of equal charge-to-mass ratio. Lighter particles are deflected more strongly than heavy ones with the same charge. In a beam containing $^{12}C^+$ and $^4He^+$ ions, the lighter $^4He^+$ ions would be deflected more than the heavier $^{12}C^+$ ions. The spectrometer shown is adjusted to detect the $^{12}C^+$ ions. By changing the magnitude of the magnetic or electric field, we can move the beam of $^4He^+$ ions striking the collector so that it passes through the slit to reach the detector. The relative masses of the ions are calculated from the changes required to refocus the beam.

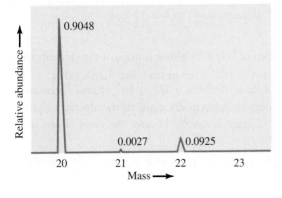

Figure 4-9 Mass spectrum of neon (1+ ions only). Neon consists of three isotopes, of which neon-20 is by far the most abundant (90.48%). The mass of that isotope, to five decimal places, is 19.99244 amu on the carbon-12 (^{12}C) scale. The number by each peak corresponds to the fraction of all ions represented by the isotope with that mass.

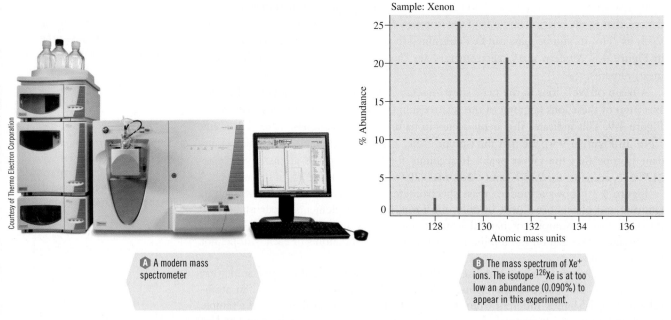

Courtesy of Thermo Electron Corporation

A A modern mass spectrometer

Sample: Xenon

B The mass spectrum of Xe⁺ ions. The isotope ^{126}Xe is at too low an abundance (0.090%) to appear in this experiment.

Figure 4-10 Mass spectrometer and mass spectrum of Xenon.

Table 4.3 Some Naturally Occurring Isotopic Abundances

Element	Atomic Weight (amu)	Isotope	% Natural Abundance	Mass (amu)
boron	10.81	^{10}B	19.91	10.01294
		^{11}B	80.09	11.00931
oxygen	15.999	^{16}O	99.762	15.99492
		^{17}O	0.038	16.99913
		^{18}O	0.200	17.99916
chlorine	35.45	^{35}Cl	75.770	34.96885
		^{37}Cl	24.230	36.96590
uranium	238.0289	^{234}U	0.0055	234.0409
		^{235}U	0.720	235.0439
		^{238}U	99.2745	238.0508

The 20 elements that have only one naturally occurring isotope are ^{9}Be, ^{19}F, ^{23}Na, ^{27}Al, ^{31}P, ^{45}Sc, ^{55}Mn, ^{59}Co, ^{75}As, ^{89}Y, ^{93}Nb, ^{103}Rh, ^{127}I, ^{133}Cs, ^{141}Pr, ^{159}Tb, ^{165}Ho, ^{169}Tm, ^{197}Au, and ^{209}Bi. There are, however, other artificially produced isotopes of these elements.

4-9 The Atomic Weight Scale and Atomic Weights

We learned in Section 2-4 that the *atomic weight scale* is based on the mass of the carbon-12 (^{12}C) isotope. As a result of action taken by the International Union of Pure and Applied Chemistry (IUPAC) in 1962,

▶ Described another way, the mass of one atom of ^{12}C is *exactly* 12 amu.

one **amu** is exactly 1/12 of the mass of a carbon-12 atom.

This is approximately the mass of one atom of ^{1}H, the lightest isotope of the element with lowest mass.

In Section 2-5 we saw that one mole of atoms contains 6.022×10^{23} atoms. The mass of one mole of atoms of any element, in grams, is numerically equal to the atomic weight of the element. Because the mass of one ^{12}C atom is exactly 12 amu, the mass of one mole of carbon-12 atoms is exactly 12 grams.

To show the relationship between atomic mass units and grams, let's calculate the mass, in amu, of 1.000 gram of ^{12}C atoms.

CHEMISTRY IN USE

Stable Isotope Ratio Analysis

Many elements exist as two or more stable isotopes, although one isotope is usually present in far greater abundance. For example, there are two stable isotopes of carbon, ^{13}C and ^{12}C of which ^{12}C is the more abundant, constituting 98.89% of all carbon. Similarly, there are two stable isotopes of nitrogen, ^{14}N and ^{15}N of which ^{14}N makes up 99.63% of all nitrogen.

Differences in chemical and physical properties that arise from differences in atomic mass of an element are known as isotope effects. We know that the extranuclear structure of an element (the number of electrons and their arrangement) essentially determines its chemical behavior, whereas the nucleus has more influence on many of the physical properties of the element. Because all isotopes of a given element contain the same number and arrangement of electrons, it was assumed for a long time that isotopes would behave identically in chemical reactions. In reality, although isotopes behave very similarly in chemical reactions, the correspondence is not perfect. The mass differences between different isotopes of the same element cause them to have slightly different physical and chemical properties. For example, the presence of only one additional neutron in the nucleus of the heavier isotope can cause it to react a little more slowly than its lighter counterpart. Such an effect often results in a ratio of heavy isotope to light isotope in the product of a reaction that is different from the ratio found in the reactant.

Stable isotope ratio analysis (SIRA) is an analytical method that takes advantage of the chemical and physical properties of isotopes as measured by isotope ratio mass spectrometry (IRMS). In this technique, the isotopic composition of a sample is measured using a mass spectrometer. This composition is then expressed as the relative ratios of two or more of the stable isotopes of a specific element. For instance, the ratio of ^{13}C to ^{12}C in a sample can be determined. This ratio is then compared with the isotope ratio of a defined standard. Because mass differences are most pronounced among the lightest elements, those elements experience the greatest isotope effects. Thus, the isotopes of the elements H, C, N, O, and S are used most frequently for SIRA. These elements have further significance because they are among the most abundant elements in biological systems.

The isotopic composition of a sample can be expressed as a "del" value (∂), defined as

$$\partial X_{sample}(‰) = \frac{(R_{sample} - R_{standard})}{R_{standard}} \times 1000$$

where ∂X_{sample} is the isotope ratio relative to a standard, and R_{sample} and $R_{standard}$ are the absolute isotope ratios of the sample and standard, respectively. Multiplying by 1000 allows the values to be expressed in parts per thousand (‰). If the del value is a positive number, the sample has a greater amount of the heavier isotope than does the standard.

An interesting application of SIRA is the determination of the adulteration of food. As already mentioned, the isotope ratios of different plants and animals have been determined. For instance, corn has a $\partial^{13}C$ value of about $-12‰$ and most flowering plants have $\partial^{13}C$ values of about $-26‰$. The difference in these $\partial^{13}C$ values arises because these plants carry out photosynthesis by slightly different chemical reactions. In the first reaction of photosynthesis, corn produces a molecule that contains four carbons, whereas flowering plants produce a molecule that has only three carbons. High-fructose corn syrup (HFCS) is thus derived from a "C$_4$" plant, whereas the nectar that bees gather comes from "C$_3$" plants. The slight differences in the photosynthetic pathways of C$_3$ and C$_4$ plants create the major differences in their $\partial^{13}C$ values. Brokers who buy and sell huge quantities of "sweet" products are able to monitor HFCS adulteration of honey, maple syrup, apple juice, and so on by taking advantage of the SIRA technique. If the $\partial^{13}C$ value of one of these products is not appropriate, then the product obviously has had other substances added to it; that is, it has been adulterated. The U.S. Department of Agriculture conducts routine isotope analyses to ensure the purity of those products submitted for subsidy programs. Similarly, the honey industry monitors itself with the SIRA approach.

Stable isotope ratio analysis is a powerful tool; many of its potential uses are now being recognized by researchers. Recent SIRA studies have included investigations of the geographical origins of olive oils and of cheeses from various localities, as well as the origins and dietary history of various meat sources such as beef, lamb, and fish. The use of stable isotope methods in research is becoming increasingly common, and through these methods scientists are attaining new levels of understanding of chemical, biological, and geological processes.

BETH A. TRUST

$$? \text{ amu} = 1.000 \text{ g } ^{12}\text{C atoms} \times \frac{1 \text{ mol } ^{12}\text{C}}{12 \text{ g } ^{12}\text{C atoms}} \times \frac{6.022 \times 10^{23} \text{ } ^{12}\text{C atoms}}{1 \text{ mol } ^{12}\text{C atoms}} \times \frac{12 \text{ amu}}{^{12}\text{C atom}}$$

$$= 6.022 \times 10^{23} \text{ amu (in 1 g)}$$

Thus,

$$1 \text{ g} = 6.022 \times 10^{23} \text{ amu} \quad or \quad 1 \text{ amu} = 1.660 \times 10^{-24} \text{ g}$$

► We saw in Chapter 2 that Avogadro's number is the number of particles of a substance in one mole of that substance. We now see that Avogadro's number also represents the number of amu in one gram. You may wish to verify that the same result is obtained regardless of the element or isotope chosen.

At this point, we emphasize the following:

1. The *atomic number*, Z, is an integer equal to the number of protons in the nucleus of an atom of the element. It is also equal to the number of electrons in a neutral atom. It is the same for all atoms of an element.

2. The *mass number*, A, is an integer equal to the *sum* of the number of protons and the number of neutrons in the nucleus of an atom of a *particular isotope* of an element. It is different for different isotopes of the same element.

3. Many elements occur in nature as mixtures of isotopes. The *atomic weight* of such an element is the weighted average of the masses of its isotopes. Atomic weights are fractional numbers, not integers.

The atomic weight that we determine experimentally (for an element that consists of more than one isotope) is such a weighted average. The following example shows how an atomic weight can be calculated from measured isotopic abundances.

EXAMPLE 4-2 Calculation of Atomic Weight

Three isotopes of magnesium occur in nature. Their abundances and masses, determined by mass spectrometry, are listed in the following table. Use this information to calculate the atomic weight of magnesium.

Isotope	% Abundance	Mass (amu)
^{24}Mg	78.99	23.98504
^{25}Mg	10.00	24.98584
^{26}Mg	11.01	25.98259

Plan

We multiply the fraction (percent divided by 100) of each isotope by its mass and add these numbers to obtain the atomic weight of magnesium.

Solution

Atomic weight $= 0.7899(23.98504 \text{ amu}) + 0.1000(24.98584 \text{ amu}) + 0.1101(25.98259 \text{ amu})$

$\qquad = 18.946 \text{ amu} \qquad\qquad + 2.4986 \text{ amu} \qquad\qquad + 2.8607 \text{ amu}$

$\qquad = 24.30 \text{ amu} \quad$ (to four significant figures)

You should now work Exercises 28 and 30.

S TOP & THINK
The two heavier isotopes make small contributions to the atomic weight of magnesium because many more magnesium atoms are the lightest isotope, ^{24}Mg. Thus the atomic weight of magnesium is close to 24 amu.

Problem-Solving Tip "Weighted" Averages

Consider the following analogy to the calculation of atomic weights. Suppose you want to calculate the average weight of your classmates. Imagine that one-half of them weigh 100 pounds each, and the other half weigh 200 pounds each. The average weight would be

$$\text{Average weight} = \frac{1}{2}(100 \text{ lb}) + \frac{1}{2}(200 \text{ lb}) = 150 \text{ lb}$$

Imagine, however, that three-quarters of the class members weigh 100 pounds each, and the other quarter weigh 200 pounds each. Now, the average weight would be

$$\text{Average weight} = \frac{3}{4}(100 \text{ lb}) + \frac{1}{4}(200 \text{ lb}) = 125 \text{ lb}$$

We can express the fractions in this calculation in decimal form:

$$\text{Average weight} = 0.750(100 \text{ lb}) + 0.250(200 \text{ lb}) = 125 \text{ lb}$$

In such a calculation, the value (in this case, the weight) of each thing (people, atoms) is multiplied by the fraction of things that have that value. In Example 4-2 we expressed each percentage as a decimal fraction, such as

$$78.99\% = \frac{78.99 \text{ parts}}{100 \text{ parts total}} = 0.7899$$

Example 4-3 shows how the process can be reversed. Isotopic abundances can be calculated from isotopic masses and from the atomic weight of an element that occurs in nature as a mixture of only two isotopes.

EXAMPLE 4-3 Calculation of Isotopic Abundance

The atomic weight of gallium is 69.72 amu. The masses of the naturally occurring isotopes are 68.9257 amu for ^{69}Ga and 70.9249 amu for ^{71}Ga. Calculate the percent abundance of each isotope.

Plan

We represent the fraction of each isotope algebraically. Atomic weight is the weighted average of the masses of the constituent isotopes. So the fraction of each isotope is multiplied by its mass, and the sum of the results is equal to the atomic weight.

▶ When a quantity is represented by fractions, the sum of the fractions must always be one. In this case, $x + (1 - x) = 1$.

Solution

Let x = fraction of ^{69}Ga. Then $(1 - x)$ = fraction of ^{71}Ga.

$$x(68.9257 \text{ amu}) + (1 - x)(70.9249 \text{ amu}) = 69.72 \text{ amu}$$

$$68.9257x + 70.9249 - 70.9249x = 69.72$$

$$-1.9992x = -1.20$$

$$x = 0.600$$

$$x = 0.600 = \text{fraction of } ^{69}\text{Ga} \quad \therefore \quad 60.0\% \ ^{69}\text{Ga}$$

$$(1 - x) = 0.400 = \text{fraction of } ^{71}\text{Ga} \quad \therefore \quad 40.0\% \ ^{71}\text{Ga}$$

You should now work Exercise 32.

S TOP & THINK
The observed atomic weight, 69.72, is closer to the mass of ^{69}Ga (68.9257) than to the other isotope. It is reasonable that there is more ^{69}Ga present (60.0%) than the heavier isotope, ^{71}Ga (40.0%).

4-10 The Periodic Table: Metals, Nonmetals, and Metalloids

In 1869, the Russian chemist Dmitri Mendeleev (1834–1907) and the German chemist Lothar Meyer (1830–1895) independently published arrangements of known elements that are much like the periodic table in use today. Mendeleev's classification was based primarily on chemical properties of the elements, whereas Meyer's classification was based largely on physical properties. The tabulations were surprisingly similar. Both emphasized the *periodicity*, or regular periodic repetition, of properties with increasing atomic weight.

Mendeleev arranged the known elements in order of increasing atomic weight in successive sequences so that elements with similar chemical properties fell into the same column. He

▶ When Mendeleev (pronounced "men-del-lay-ev") and Meyer developed their tabulations, the concept of atomic number was not yet known. Their classifications were based on the atomic weights known at that time.

Not all properties of the elements can be predicted from the trends in the periodic table. For example, gallium's melting point being low enough to melt from the heat of the hand is inconsistent with the properties of the elements above and below it.

noted that both physical and chemical properties of the elements vary in a periodic fashion with atomic weight. His periodic table of 1872 contained the 62 known elements (Figure 4-11). Mendeleev placed H, Li, Na, and K in his table as "Gruppe I." These were known to combine with F, Cl, Br, and I of "Gruppe VII" to produce compounds that have similar formulas such as HF, LiCl, NaCl, and KI. All these compounds dissolve in water to produce solutions that conduct electricity. The "Gruppe II" elements were known to form compounds such as $BeCl_2$, $MgBr_2$, and $CaCl_2$, as well as compounds with O and S from "Gruppe VI" such as MgO, CaO, MgS, and CaS. These and other chemical properties led him to devise a table in which the elements were arranged by increasing atomic weights and grouped into vertical families.

In most areas of human endeavor progress is slow and faltering. Occasionally, however, an individual develops concepts and techniques that clarify confused situations. Mendeleev was such an individual. One of the brilliant successes of his periodic table was that it provided for elements that were unknown at the time. When he encountered "missing"

REIHEN	GRUPPE I – R^2O	GRUPPE II – RO	GRUPPE III – R^2O^3	GRUPPE IV RH^4 RO^2	GRUPPE V RH^3 R^2O^5	GRUPPE VI RH^2 RO^3	GRUPPE VII RH R^2O^7	GRUPPE VIII – RO^4
1	H = 1							
2	Li = 7	Be = 9.4	B = 11	C = 12	N = 14	O = 16	F = 19	
3	Na = 23	Mg = 24	Al = 27.3	Si = 28	P = 31	S = 32	Cl = 35.5	
4	K = 39	Ca = 40	– = 44	Ti = 48	V = 51	Cr = 52	Mn = 55	Fe = 56, Co = 59, Ni = 59, Cu = 63.
5	(Cu = 63)	Zn = 65	– = 68	– = 72	As = 75	Se = 78	Br = 80	
6	Rb = 85	Sr = 87	?Yt = 88	Zr = 90	Nb = 94	Mo = 96	– = 100	Ru = 104, Rh = 104, Pd = 106, Ag = 108.
7	(Ag = 108)	Cd = 112	In = 113	Sn = 118	Sb = 122	Te = 125	J = 127	
8	Cs = 133	Ba = 137	?Di = 138	?Ce = 140	–	–	–	– – – –
9	(–)	–	–	–	–	–	–	
10	–	–	?Er = 178	?La = 180	Ta = 182	W = 184	–	Os = 195, Ir = 197, Pt = 198, Au = 199.
11	(Au = 199)	Hg = 200	Tl = 204	Pb = 207	Bi = 208	–	–	
12	–	–	–	Th = 231	–	U = 240	–	– – – –

Figure 4-11 Mendeleev's early periodic table (1872). "J" is the German symbol for iodine.

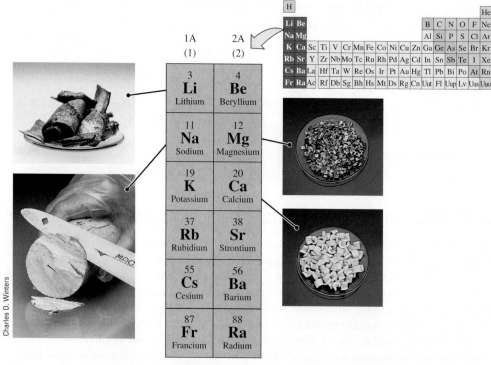

Lithium (*top left*) and sodium (*bottom left*) from Group 1A. Magnesium (*top right*) and calcium (*bottom right*) from Group 2A.

elements, Mendeleev left blank spaces. Some appreciation of his genius in constructing the table as he did can be gained by comparing the predicted (1871) and observed properties of germanium, which was not discovered until 1886. Mendeleev called the undiscovered element eka-silicon (Es) because it fell below silicon in his table. He was familiar with the properties of germanium's neighboring elements. They served as the basis for his predictions of properties of germanium (Table 4-4). Some modern values for the properties of germanium differ significantly from those reported in 1886. But many of the values on which Mendeleev based his predictions were also inaccurate.

Charles Steele

Three of the halogens, elements from Group 7A (*left to right*): chlorine, bromine, iodine.

Table 4-4 Predicted and Observed Properties of Germanium

Property	Eka-Silicon Predicted, 1871	Germanium Reported, 1886	Modern Values
Atomic weight	72	72.32	72.61
Atomic volume	13 cm³/mol	13.22 cm³/mol	13.5 cm³/mol
Specific gravity	5.5	5.47	5.35
Specific heat	0.073 cal/g°C	0.076 cal/g°C	0.074 cal/g°C
Maximum valence*	4	4	4
Color	Dark gray	Grayish white	Grayish white
Reaction with water	Will decompose steam with difficulty	Does not decompose water	Does not decompose water
Reactions with acids and alkalis	Slight with acids; more pronounced with alkalis	Not attacked by HCl or dilute aqueous NaOH; reacts vigorously with molten NaOH	Not dissolved by HCl or H_2SO_4 or dilute NaOH; dissolved by concentrated NaOH
Formula of oxide	EsO_2	GeO_2	GeO_2
Specific gravity of oxide	4.7	4.703	4.228
Specific gravity of tetrachloride	1.9 at 0°C	1.887 at 18°C	1.8443 at 30°C
Boiling point of tetrachloride	100°C	86°C	84°C
Boiling point of tetraethyl derivative	160°C	160°C	186°C

*"Valence" refers to the combining power of a specific element.

Because Mendeleev's arrangement of the elements was based on increasing *atomic weights*, several elements would have been out of place in his table. Mendeleev put the controversial elements (Te and I, Co and Ni) in locations consistent with their properties, however. He thought the apparent reversal of atomic weights was due to inaccurate values for those weights. Careful redetermination showed that the values were correct. Explanation of the locations of these "out-of-place" elements had to await the development of the concept of *atomic number*, approximately 50 years after Mendeleev's work. The **atomic number** (see Section 4-5) of an element is the number of protons in the nucleus of its atoms. (It is also the number of electrons in a neutral atom of an element.) This quantity is fundamental to the identity of each element. Elements are now arranged in the periodic table in order of increasing atomic number. With the development of this concept, the **periodic law** attained its present form:

The properties of the elements are periodic functions of their atomic numbers.

The periodic law tells us that if we arrange the elements in order of increasing atomic number, we periodically encounter elements that have similar chemical and physical properties. The presently used "long form" of the periodic table (Table 4-5 and inside the front cover) is such an arrangement. The vertical columns are referred to as **groups** or **families**, and the horizontal rows are called **periods**. Elements in a *group* have similar chemical and physical properties, and those within a *period* have properties that change progressively across the table. Several groups of elements have common names that are used so frequently they should be learned. The Group 1A elements, except H, are referred to as **alkali metals**, and the Group 2A elements are called the **alkaline earth metals**.

▶ Alkaline means basic. The character of basic compounds is described in Section 10-4.

Table 4-5 The Periodic Table

There are other systems for numbering the groups in the periodic table. We number the groups by the standard American system of A and B groups. An alternative system, recommended by IUPAC, in which the groups are numbered 1 through 18 is shown in parentheses.

The Group 7A elements are called **halogens**, which means "salt formers," and the Group 8A elements are called **noble** (or **rare**) **gases**.

The general properties of metals and nonmetals are distinct. Physical and chemical properties that distinguish metals from nonmetals are summarized in Tables 4-6 and 4-7. Not all metals and nonmetals possess all these properties, but they share most of them to varying degrees. The physical properties of metals can be explained on the basis of metallic bonding in solids (see Section 13-17).

Table 4-5, The Periodic Table, shows how we classify the known elements as **metals** (shown in blue), **nonmetals** (tan), and **metalloids** (green). The elements to the left of those touching the heavy stairstep line are metals (except hydrogen), and those to the right are nonmetals. Such a classification is somewhat arbitrary, and several elements do not fit neatly into either class. Most elements adjacent to the heavy line are often called **metalloids** (or semimetals), because they are metallic (or nonmetallic) only to a limited degree.

> *Metallic character* increases from top to bottom and decreases from left to right with respect to position in the periodic table.

Cesium, atomic number 55, is the most active naturally occurring metal. Francium and radium are radioactive and do not occur in nature in appreciable amounts. Noble gases seldom bond with other elements. They are unreactive, monatomic gases. The most active nonmetal is fluorine, atomic number 9.

> *Nonmetallic character* decreases from top to bottom and increases from left to right in the periodic table.

▶ About 80% of the elements are metals.

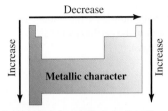

General trends in metallic character of A group elements with position in the periodic table.

Silicon, a metalloid, is widely used in the manufacture of electronic chips.

Table 4-6 Some Physical Properties of Metals and Nonmetals

Metals	Nonmetals
1. High electrical conductivity that decreases with increasing temperature	1. Poor electrical conductivity (except carbon in the form of graphite)
2. High thermal conductivity	2. Good heat insulators (except carbon)
3. Metallic gray or silver luster*	3. No metallic luster
4. Almost all are solids†	4. Solids, liquids, or gases
5. Malleable (can be hammered into sheets)	5. Brittle in solid state
6. Ductile (can be drawn into wires)	6. Nonductile

*Except copper and gold.

†Except mercury; cesium and gallium melt at body temperature (37°C).

Table 4-7 Some Chemical Properties of Metals and Nonmetals

Metals	Nonmetals
1. Outer shells contain few electrons—usually three or fewer	1. Outer shells contain four or more electrons*
2. Form cations (positive ions) by losing electrons	2. Form anions (negative ions) by gaining electrons†
3. Form ionic compounds with nonmetals	3. Form ionic compounds with metals† and molecular (covalent) compounds with nonmetals
4. Solid state characterized by metallic bonding	4. Covalently bonded molecules; noble gases are monatomic

*Except hydrogen and helium.

†Except the noble gases.

▶ Aluminum is the most abundant metal in the earth's crust (7.5% by mass).

Metalloids show some properties that are characteristic of both metals and nonmetals. Many of the metalloids, such as silicon, germanium, and antimony, act as semiconductors, which are important in solid-state electronic circuits. **Semiconductors** are insulators at lower temperatures but become conductors at higher temperatures (see Section 13-17). The conductivities of metals, by contrast, decrease with increasing temperature.

Aluminum is the least metallic of the metals and is sometimes classified as a metalloid. It is metallic in appearance and an excellent conductor of electricity.

In later chapters we will study some chemical reactions of elements and their compounds and relate the reactions to the locations of the elements in the periodic table. First, we will describe the arrangements of electrons in atoms. A knowledge of these arrangements not only provides the physical basis for the periodic table, but also explains chemical bonding and properties.

The Electronic Structures of Atoms

The Rutherford model of the atom is consistent with the evidence presented so far, but it has some serious limitations. It does not answer such important questions as: *Why* do different elements have such different chemical and physical properties? *Why* do chemical and physical properties fall into the regular patterns summarized by the periodic table? *Why* does chemical bonding occur? *Why* does each element form compounds with characteristic formulas? *How* can atoms of different elements give off or absorb light only of characteristic colors (as was known long before 1900)?

To improve our understanding, we must first learn more about the arrangements of electrons in atoms. The theory of these arrangements is based largely on the study of the light given off and absorbed by atoms. Then we will develop a detailed picture of the *electron configurations* of different elements. A knowledge of these arrangements will help us to understand the periodic table and chemical bonding.

White light is dispersed by a prism into a *continuous* spectrum.

4-11 Electromagnetic Radiation

▶ One cycle per second is also called one *hertz* (Hz), after Heinrich Hertz (1857–1894). In about 1887, Hertz discovered electromagnetic radiation outside the visible range and measured its speed and wavelengths.

Our ideas about the arrangements of electrons in atoms have evolved slowly. Much information has been derived from atomic **emission spectra**. These are the bright lines, or bands, produced on photographic film by radiation that has passed through a refracting glass prism after being emitted from electrically or thermally excited atoms. To help us understand the nature of atomic spectra, we first describe electromagnetic radiation.

All types of electromagnetic radiation, or radiant energy, can be described in the terminology of waves. To help characterize any wave, we specify its *wavelength* (or its *frequency*). Let's use a familiar kind of wave, that on the surface of water (Figure 4-12), to illustrate these terms. The significant feature of wave motion is its repetitive nature. The **wavelength**, λ (Greek letter "lambda"), is the distance between any two adjacent identical points of the wave, for instance, two adjacent crests. The **frequency** is the number of wave crests passing a given point per unit time; it is represented by the symbol ν (Greek letter "nu") and is usually expressed in cycles per second or, more commonly, simply as $1/s$ or s^{-1} with "cycles" understood. For a wave that is "traveling" at some speed, the wavelength and the frequency are related to each other by

$$\lambda\nu = \text{speed of propagation} \quad \text{or} \quad \lambda\nu = c \text{ (for light)} \quad \text{or} \quad \lambda\nu = v \text{ (for all other waves)}$$
$$\text{of the wave}$$

The diffraction of white light by the closely spaced grooves of a compact disk spreads the light into its component colors. Diffraction is due to the constructive and destructive interference of light waves.

Thus, wavelength and frequency are inversely proportional to each other; for the same wave speed, shorter wavelengths correspond to higher frequencies.

For water waves, it is the surface of the water that changes repetitively; for a vibrating violin string, it is the displacement of any point on the string. Electromagnetic radiation is a form of energy that consists of electric and magnetic fields that vary repetitively (Figure 4-13).

Alfred Pasieka/Peter Arnold/Getty Images

Spike Mafford/Photodisc/Getty Images

The electromagnetic radiation most obvious to us is visible light. It has wavelengths ranging from about 4.0×10^{-7} m (violet) to about 7.5×10^{-7} m (red). Expressed in frequencies, this range is about 7.5×10^{14} Hz (violet) to about 4.0×10^{14} Hz (red).

Isaac Newton (1642–1727) first recorded the separation of sunlight into its component colors by allowing it to pass through a glass prism. Because sunlight (white light) contains all wavelengths of visible light, it gives the **continuous spectrum** observed in a rainbow (Figure 4-14a). But visible light represents only a tiny segment of the electromagnetic radiation spectrum (Figure 4-14b). In addition to all wavelengths of visible light, sunlight also contains shorter wavelength (ultraviolet) radiation as well as longer wavelength (infrared) radiation. Neither ultraviolet nor infrared radiation can be detected by the human eye. Both may be detected and recorded photographically or by detectors designed for that purpose. Many other familiar kinds of radiation are simply electromagnetic radiation of longer or shorter wavelengths.

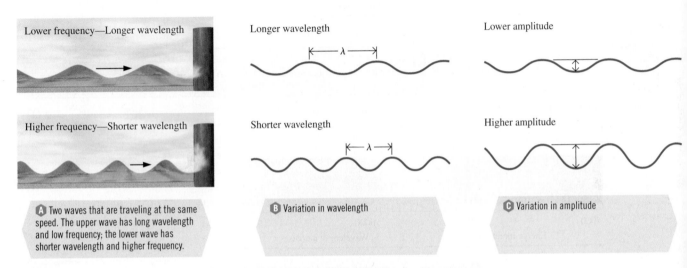

Lower frequency—Longer wavelength

Higher frequency—Shorter wavelength

A Two waves that are traveling at the same speed. The upper wave has long wavelength and low frequency; the lower wave has shorter wavelength and higher frequency.

Longer wavelength

Shorter wavelength

B Variation in wavelength

Lower amplitude

Higher amplitude

C Variation in amplitude

Figure 4-12 Illustrations of the wavelength and frequency of water waves. The distance between any two identical points, such as crests, is the wavelength, λ. We could measure the frequency, ν, of the wave by observing how often the level rises and falls at a fixed point in its path—for instance, at the post—or how often crests hit the post.

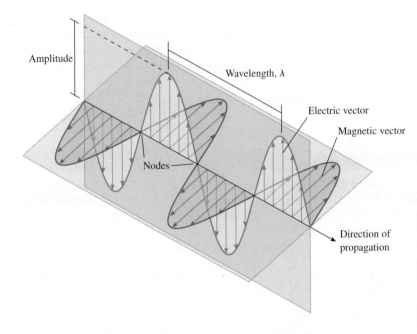

Amplitude

Wavelength, λ

Electric vector

Magnetic vector

Nodes

Direction of propagation

Figure 4-13 All forms of radiation, including visible light, consist of electric and magnetic fields that vary repetitively at right angles to each other. A more intense beam corresponds to a higher amplitude of electric and magnetic fields. This combination of waves moves in the direction of travel of the light beam, similar to the motion of the water waves in Figure 4-12.

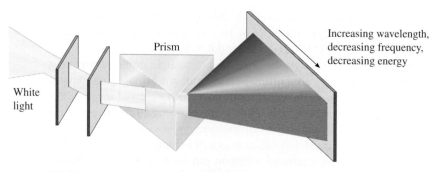

A Dispersion of visible light by a prism. Light from a source of white light is passed through a slit and then through a prism. It is spread into a continuous spectrum of all wavelengths of visible light.

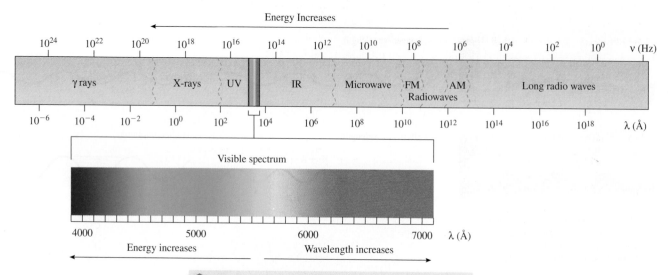

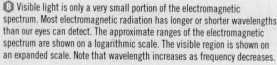

B Visible light is only a very small portion of the electromagnetic spectrum. Most electromagnetic radiation has longer or shorter wavelengths than our eyes can detect. The approximate ranges of the electromagnetic spectrum are shown on a logarithmic scale. The visible region is shown on an expanded scale. Note that wavelength increases as frequency decreases.

Figure 4-14 The electromagnetic spectrum.

In a vacuum, the speed of electromagnetic radiation, c, is the same for all wavelengths, 2.99792458×10^8 m/s. The relationship between the wavelength and frequency of electromagnetic radiation, with c rounded to three significant figures, is

$$\lambda\nu = c = 3.00 \times 10^8 \text{ m/s (or 186,000 miles/s)}$$

EXAMPLE 4-4 Wavelength of Light

Light near the middle of the ultraviolet region of the electromagnetic radiation spectrum has a frequency of 2.73×10^{16} s^{-1}. Yellow light near the middle of the visible region of the spectrum has a frequency of 5.26×10^{14} s^{-1}. Calculate the wavelength that corresponds to each of these two frequencies of light.

Plan

Wavelength and frequency are inversely proportional to each other, $\lambda\nu = c$. We solve this relationship for λ and calculate the wavelengths.

Sir Isaac Newton, one of the giants of science. You probably know of him from his theory of gravitation. In addition, he made enormous contributions to the understanding of many other aspects of physics, including the nature and behavior of light, optics, and the laws of motion. He is credited with the invention of differential calculus and of expansions into infinite series.

© Bettmann/Corbis

Solution

(ultraviolet light) $\lambda = \dfrac{c}{\nu} = \dfrac{3.00 \times 10^8 \text{ m} \cdot \text{s}^{-1}}{2.73 \times 10^{16} \text{ s}^{-1}} = \boxed{1.10 \times 10^{-8} \text{ m} \ (1.10 \times 10^2 \text{ Å})}$

(yellow light) $\lambda = \dfrac{c}{\nu} = \dfrac{3.00 \times 10^8 \text{ m} \cdot \text{s}^{-1}}{5.26 \times 10^{14} \text{ s}^{-1}} = \boxed{5.70 \times 10^{-7} \text{ m} \ (5.70 \times 10^3 \text{ Å})}$

You should now work Exercise 54.

S TOP & THINK
Wavelength and frequency are inversely proportional to one another. Thus the radiation with the higher frequency (ultraviolet) has the shorter wavelength.

We have described light in terms of wave behavior. Under certain conditions, it is also possible to describe light as composed of *particles*, or **photons**. According to the ideas presented by Max Planck (1858–1947) in 1900, each photon of light corresponds to a particular amount (a **quantum**) of energy. The energy of a photon depends on the frequency of the light. The energy of a photon of light is given by Planck's equation

$$E = h\nu \quad \text{or} \quad E = \frac{hc}{\lambda}$$

where h is Planck's constant, $6.62606896 \times 10^{-34}$ J·s, and ν is the frequency of the light. Thus, energy is directly proportional to frequency. Planck's equation is used in Example 4-5 to show that a photon of ultraviolet light has more energy than a photon of yellow light.

EXAMPLE 4-5 Energy of Light

In Example 4-4 we calculated the wavelengths of ultraviolet light of frequency $2.73 \times 10^{16} \text{s}^{-1}$ and of yellow light of frequency $5.26 \times 10^{14} \text{s}^{-1}$. Calculate the energy, in joules, of an individual photon of each. Compare these photons by calculating the ratio of their energies.

Plan

We use each frequency to calculate the photon energy from the relationship $E = h\nu$. Then we calculate the required ratio.

Solution

(ultraviolet light) $E = h\nu = (6.626 \times 10^{-34} \text{ J} \cdot \text{s})(2.73 \times 10^{16} \text{ s}^{-1}) = \boxed{1.81 \times 10^{-17} \text{ J}}$

(yellow light) $E = h\nu = (6.626 \times 10^{-34} \text{ J} \cdot \text{s})(5.26 \times 10^{14} \text{ s}^{-1}) = \boxed{3.49 \times 10^{-19} \text{ J}}$

(You can check these answers by calculating the energies directly from the wavelengths, using the equation $E = hc/\lambda$.)

Now, we compare the energies of these two photons.

$$\frac{E_{\text{uv}}}{E_{\text{yellow}}} = \frac{1.81 \times 10^{-17} \text{ J}}{3.49 \times 10^{-19} \text{ J}} = \boxed{51.9}$$

A photon of light near the middle of the ultraviolet region is more than 51 times as energetic than a photon of light near the middle of the visible region. Photon energy is proportional to frequency, so the light with highest frequency (ultraviolet) has the highest photon energy.

You should now work Exercise 55.

▶ This is one reason why ultraviolet (UV) light damages your skin much more rapidly than visible light. Another reason is that many of the organic compounds in the skin absorb UV light more readily than visible light. For many biologically important molecules, a single photon of ultraviolet light is enough energy to break a chemical bond, often producing very reactive and damaging molecular fragments.

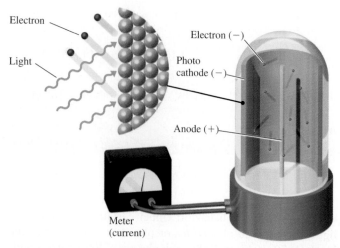

Figure 4-15 The photoelectric effect. When electromagnetic radiation of sufficient minimum energy strikes the surface of a metal (negative electrode or cathode) inside an evacuated tube, electrons are stripped off the metal to create an electric current. The current increases with increasing radiation intensity.

4-12 The Photoelectric Effect

One phenomenon that had not been satisfactorily explained with the wave theory of light was the **photoelectric effect**. The apparatus for the photoelectric effect is shown in Figure 4-15. The negative electrode (cathode) in the evacuated tube is made of a pure metal such as cesium. When light of a sufficiently high energy strikes the metal, electrons are knocked off its surface. They then travel to the positive electrode (anode) to produce a current flowing through the circuit. The important observations follow.

1. Electrons are ejected only if the light is of sufficiently short wavelength (has sufficiently high energy), no matter how long or how brightly the light shines. This wavelength limit is different for different metals.

2. If the photon energy of the light is high enough to start the photoelectric effect, the number of electrons emitted per second (the current) increases as the brightness (intensity) of the light increases. The amount of current does not depend on the wavelength (color) of the light used after the minimum photon energy needed to initiate the photoelectric effect is reached.

▶ The intensity of light is the brightness of the light. In wave terms, it is related to the amplitude of the light waves. In photon terms, it is the number of photons hitting the target.

Classical theory said that even "low-" energy light should cause current to flow if the metal is irradiated long enough. Electrons should accumulate energy and be released when they have enough energy to escape from the metal atoms. According to the old theory, if the light is made more energetic, then the current should increase even though the light intensity remains the same. Such is *not* the case.

The answer to the puzzle was provided by Albert Einstein (1879–1955). In 1905 he extended Planck's idea that light behaves as though it were composed of *photons*, each with a particular amount (a quantum) of energy. According to Einstein, each photon can transfer all of its energy to a single electron during a collision. When we say that the intensity of light is increased, we mean that the number of photons striking a given area per second is increased. The picture is now one of a particle of light striking an electron near the surface of the metal and giving up its energy to the electron. If that energy is equal to or greater than the amount needed to liberate the electron, it can escape to join the photoelectric current. For this explanation, Einstein received the 1921 Nobel Prize in Physics.

The sensor for each "pixel" in a digital camera is a tiny photoelectric device. The photoelectric sensors that open some supermarket and elevator doors also utilize this effect.

4-13 Atomic Spectra and the Bohr Atom

Incandescent ("red hot" or "white hot") solids, liquids, and high-pressure gases give continuous spectra. When an electric current is passed through a gas in a vacuum tube at very low pressures, however, the light that the gas emits can be dispersed by a prism into distinct lines (Figure 4-16a). The resulting **emission spectrum** is described as a *bright line spectrum*. The lines can be recorded photographically, and the wavelength of light that produced each line can be calculated from the position of that line on the photograph.

Similarly, we can shine a beam of white light (containing a continuous distribution of wavelengths) through a gas and analyze the beam that emerges. We find that only certain wavelengths have been absorbed (Figure 4-16b). The wavelengths that are absorbed in this **absorption spectrum** are the same as those given off in the emission experiment. Each spectral line corresponds to a specific wavelength of light and thus to a specific amount of energy that is either absorbed or emitted. Each element displays its own characteristic set of lines in its emission or absorption spectrum (Figure 4-17). These spectra can serve as "fingerprints" that allow us to identify different elements present in a sample, even in trace amounts.

EXAMPLE 4-6   Energy of Light

A green line of wavelength 4.86×10^{-7} m is observed in the emission spectrum of hydrogen. Calculate the energy of one photon of this green light.

Plan

We know the wavelength of the light, and we calculate its frequency so that we can then calculate the energy of each photon.

Solution

$$E = \frac{hc}{\lambda} = \frac{(6.626 \times 10^{-34}\,\text{J} \cdot \text{s})(3.00 \times 10^{8}\,\text{m/s})}{(4.86 \times 10^{-7}\,\text{m})} = 4.09 \times 10^{-19}\,\text{J/photon}$$

> **S TOP & THINK**
> Be careful of unit conversions in calculations such as this.

To gain a better appreciation of the amount of energy involved, let's calculate the total energy, in kilojoules, emitted by one mole of atoms. (Each atom emits one photon.)

$$\frac{?\ \text{kJ}}{\text{mol}} = 4.09 \times 10^{-19}\,\frac{\text{J}}{\text{atom}} \times \frac{1\ \text{kJ}}{1 \times 10^{3}\,\text{J}} \times \frac{6.02 \times 10^{23}\ \text{atoms}}{\text{mol}} = 2.46 \times 10^{2}\ \text{kJ/mol}$$

This calculation shows that when each atom in one mole of hydrogen atoms emits light of wavelength 4.86×10^{-7} m, the mole of atoms loses 246 kJ of energy as green light. (This would be enough energy to operate a 100-watt light bulb for more than 40 minutes.)

You should now work Exercises 56 and 58.

When an electric current is passed through hydrogen gas at very low pressures, several series of lines in the spectrum of hydrogen are produced. These lines were studied intensely by many scientists. In the late 19th century, Johann Balmer (1825–1898) and Johannes Rydberg (1854–1919) showed that the wavelengths of the various lines in the hydrogen spectrum can be related by a mathematical equation:

$$\frac{1}{\lambda} = R\left(\frac{1}{n_1^2} - \frac{1}{n_2^2}\right)$$

Here R is $1.097 \times 10^{7}\,\text{m}^{-1}$ and is known as the Rydberg constant. The n's are positive integers, and n_1 is smaller than n_2. The Balmer–Rydberg equation was derived from numerous observations, not from theory. It is thus an empirical equation.

In 1913 Niels Bohr (1885–1962), a Danish physicist, provided an explanation for Balmer and Rydberg's observations. He wrote equations that described the electron of a hydrogen atom as revolving around its nucleus in one of a discrete set of circular orbits. He added the condition that the electronic energy is *quantized*; that is, only certain values of electronic energy are possible. This led him to suggest that electrons can only be in certain discrete orbits, and that they absorb or emit energy in discrete

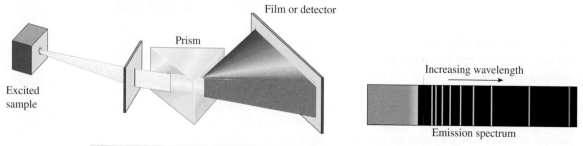

A *Atomic emission.* The light emitted by a sample of excited hydrogen atoms (or any other element) can be passed through a prism and separated into discrete wavelengths. Thus, an emission spectrum, which is a photographic recording of the separated wavelengths, is called a line spectrum. Any sample of reasonable size contains an enormous number of atoms. Although a single atom can be in only one excited state at a time, the collection of atoms contains many possible excited states. The light emitted as these atoms fall to lower energy states is responsible for the spectrum.

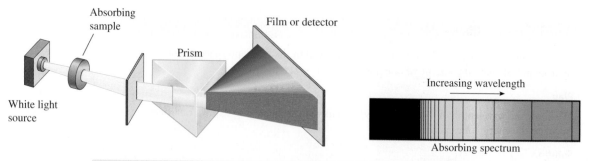

B *Atomic absorption.* When white light is passed through unexcited hydrogen and then through a slit and a prism, the transmitted light is lacking in intensity at the same wavelengths as are emitted in part (a). The recorded absorption spectrum is also a line spectrum and the photographic negative of the emission spectrum.

Figure 4-16

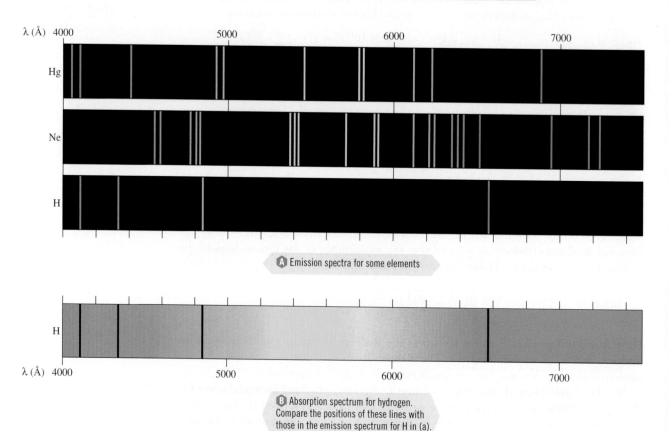

A Emission spectra for some elements

B Absorption spectrum for hydrogen. Compare the positions of these lines with those in the emission spectrum for H in (a).

Figure 4-17 Atomic spectra in the visible region for some elements. Figure 4-16 shows how such spectra are produced.

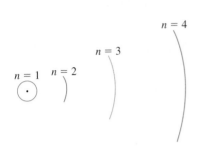

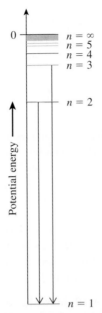

The lightning flashes produced in electrical storms and the light produced by neon gas in neon signs are two familiar examples of visible light produced by electronic transitions.

A The radii of the first four Bohr orbits for a hydrogen atom. The dot at the center represents the nuclear position. The radius of each orbit is proportional to n^2, so the orbits are more widely spaced as the n value increases. These four radii are in the ratio 1:4:9:16.

B Relative values for the energies associated with some Bohr energy levels in a hydrogen atom. By convention, the potential energy of the electron is defined as zero when it is at an infinite distance from the nucleus. Any more stable arrangement would have a lower potential energy. The energy spacing between orbits gets smaller as the n value increases. For very large values of n, the energy levels are so close together that they form a continuum. Some possible electronic transitions corresponding to lines in the hydrogen emission spectrum are indicated by arrows. Transitions in the opposite direction account for lines in the absorption spectrum. The biggest energy *change* occurs when an electron jumps between $n = 1$ and $n = 2$; a considerably smaller energy change occurs when the electron jumps between $n = 3$ and $n = 4$.

S TOP & THINK
Remember that the orbits get farther apart as n increases, but their energies get closer together.

Figure 4-18

amounts as they move from one orbit to another. Each orbit thus corresponds to a definite *energy level* for the electron. When an electron is excited from a lower energy level to a higher one, it absorbs a definite (quantized) amount of energy. When the electron falls back to the original energy level, it emits exactly the same amount of energy that it absorbed in moving from the lower to the higher energy level. Figure 4-18 illustrates these transitions schematically. The values of n_1 and n_2 in the Balmer–Rydberg equation identify the lower and higher levels, respectively, of these electronic transitions.

ENRICHMENT

The Bohr Theory and the Balmer–Rydberg Equation

From mathematical equations describing the orbits for the hydrogen atom, together with the assumption of quantization of energy, Bohr was able to determine two significant aspects of each allowed orbit:

1. *Where* the electron can be with respect to the nucleus—that is, the radius, r, of the circular orbit. This is given by

$$r = n^2 a_0$$

▶ *Note: r* is proportional to n^2. Higher values of *n* correspond to larger *r*, with the electron farther from the nucleus.

▶ *Note: E* is proportional to $-\dfrac{1}{n^2}$. Higher values of *n* correspond to higher (less negative) energies, with the electron less stable.

▶ We define the potential energy of a set of charged particles to be zero when the particles are infinitely far apart.

where *n* is a positive integer $(1, 2, 3, \ldots)$ that tells which orbit is being described and a_0 is the *Bohr radius*. Using a combination of Planck's constant, the charge of the electron, and the mass of the electron, Bohr was able to calculate the value of a_0 as

$$a_0 = 5.292 \times 10^{-11} \text{ m} = 0.5292 \text{ Å}$$

2. *How stable* the electron would be in that orbit—that is, its potential energy, *E*. This is given by

$$E = -\frac{1}{n^2}\left(\frac{h^2}{8\pi^2 ma_0^2}\right) = -\frac{2.180 \times 10^{-18} \text{ J}}{n^2}$$

where *h* = Planck's constant, *m* = the mass of the electron, and the other symbols have the same meaning as before. *E* is always negative when the electron is in the atom; *E* = 0 when the electron is completely removed from the atom (*n* = infinity).

Figure 4-19 shows the results of evaluating these equations for some of the possible values of *n* $(1, 2, 3, \ldots)$. The larger the value of *n*, the farther from the nucleus is the orbit being described, and the radius of this orbit increases as the *square of n* increases. As *n* increases, n^2 increases, $1/n^2$ decreases, and thus the electronic energy increases (becomes less negative). For orbits farther from the nucleus, the electronic potential energy is higher (less negative—the electron is in a *higher* energy level or in a less stable state). Going away from the nucleus, the allowable orbits are farther apart in distance but closer together in energy. Consider the two possible limits of these equations. One limit is when *n* = 1; this describes the electron at the smallest possible distance from the nucleus and at its lowest (most negative) energy; the electron is at its most stable location. The other limit is for very large values of *n*, that is, as *n* approaches infinity. As this limit is approached, the electron is very far from the nucleus, or effectively removed from the atom; the potential energy is as high as possible, approaching zero; the electron is at its least stable location.

Each line in the emission spectrum represents the *difference in energies* between two allowed energy levels for the electron. When the electron goes from energy level n_2 to energy level n_1, the difference in energy is given off as a single photon. The energy of this photon can be calculated from Bohr's equation for the energy, as follows.

$$E \text{ of photon} = E_2 - E_1 = \left(-\frac{2.180 \times 10^{-18} \text{ J}}{n_2^2}\right) - \left(-\frac{2.180 \times 10^{-18} \text{ J}}{n_1^2}\right)$$

Factoring out the constant 2.180×10^{-18} J and rearranging, we get

$$E \text{ of photon} = 2.180 \times 10^{-18} \text{ J}\left(\frac{1}{n_1^2} - \frac{1}{n_2^2}\right)$$

The Planck equation, $E = hc/\lambda$, relates the energy of the photon to the wavelength of the light, so

$$\frac{hc}{\lambda} = 2.180 \times 10^{-18} \text{ J}\left(\frac{1}{n_1^2} - \frac{1}{n_2^2}\right)$$

Rearranging for $1/\lambda$, we obtain

$$\frac{1}{\lambda} = \frac{2.180 \times 10^{-18} \text{ J}}{hc}\left(\frac{1}{n_1^2} - \frac{1}{n_2^2}\right)$$

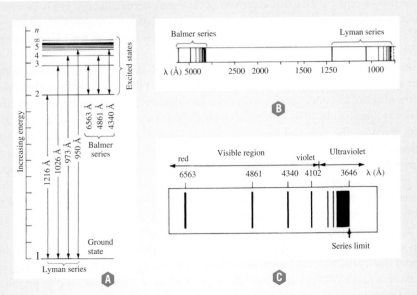

Figure 4-19 (a) The energy levels that the electron can occupy in a hydrogen atom and a few of the transitions that cause the emission spectrum of hydrogen. The numbers on the vertical lines show the wavelengths of light emitted when the electron falls to a lower energy level. (Light of the same wavelength is absorbed when the electron is excited to the higher energy level.) The difference in energy between two given levels is exactly the same for all hydrogen atoms, so it corresponds to a specific wavelength and to a specific line in the emission spectrum of hydrogen. In a given sample, some hydrogen atoms could have their electrons excited to the $n = 2$ level. These electrons could then fall to the $n = 1$ energy level, giving off the *difference* in energy in the form of light (the 1216-Å transition). Other hydrogen atoms might have their electrons excited to the $n = 3$ level; subsequently some could fall to the $n = 1$ level (the 1026-Å transition). Because higher energy levels become closer and closer in energy, *differences* in energy between successive transitions become smaller and smaller. The corresponding lines in the emission spectrum become closer together and eventually result in a continuum, a series of lines so close together that they are indistinguishable. (b) The emission spectrum of hydrogen. The series of lines produced by the electron falling to the $n = 1$ level is known as the *Lyman series*; it is in the ultraviolet region. A transition in which the electron falls to the $n = 2$ level gives rise to a similar set of lines in the visible region of the spectrum, known as the *Balmer series*. Other series involving transitions to energy levels with higher values of n are not shown. (c) The Balmer series shown on an expanded scale. The line at 6563 Å (the $n = 3 \rightarrow n = 2$ transition) is much more intense than the line at 4861 Å (the $n = 4 \rightarrow n = 2$ transition) because the first transition occurs much more frequently than the second. Successive lines in the spectrum become less intense as the series limit is approached because the transitions that correspond to these lines are less probable.

The Danish physicist Niels Bohr was one of the most influential scientists of the 20th century. Like many other now-famous physicists of his time, he worked for a time in England with J. J. Thomson and later with Ernest Rutherford. During this period, he began to develop the ideas that led to the publication of his explanation of atomic spectra and his theory of atomic structure, for which he received the Nobel Prize in Physics in 1922. After escaping from Nazi-occupied Denmark to Sweden in 1943, he helped to arrange the escape of hundreds of Danish Jews from the Hitler regime. He later went to the United States, where, until 1945, he worked with other scientists at Los Alamos, New Mexico, on the development of the atomic bomb. From then until his death in 1962, he worked for the development and use of atomic energy for peaceful purposes.

Comparing this to the Balmer–Rydberg equation, Bohr showed that the Rydberg constant is equivalent to 2.180×10^{-18} J/hc. We can use the values for h and c to obtain the same value, 1.097×10^{7} m^{-1}, that was obtained by Rydberg on a solely empirical basis. Furthermore, Bohr showed the physical meaning of the two whole numbers n_1 and n_2; they represent the two energy states between which the transition takes place. Using this approach, Bohr was able to use fundamental constants to calculate the wavelengths of the observed lines in the hydrogen emission spectrum. Thus, Bohr's application of the idea of quantization of energy to the electron in an atom provided the answer to a half-century-old puzzle concerning the discrete colors observed in emission and absorption spectra.

Various metals emit distinctive colors of visible light when heated to a high enough temperature (flame test). This is the basis for all fireworks, which use the salts of different metals such as strontium (red), barium (green), and copper (blue) to produce the beautiful colors.

We now accept the fact that electrons occupy only certain energy levels in atoms. In most atoms, some of the energy differences between levels correspond to the energy of visible light. Thus, colors associated with electronic transitions in such elements can be observed by the human eye.

Although the Bohr theory satisfactorily explained the spectra of hydrogen and of other species containing one electron (He^+, Li^{2+}, etc.) the wavelengths in the observed spectra of more complex species could not be calculated. Bohr's assumption of circular orbits was modified in 1916 by Arnold Sommerfeld (1868–1951), who assumed elliptical orbits. Even so, the Bohr approach was doomed to failure, because it modified classical mechanics to solve a problem that could not be solved by classical mechanics. It was a contrived solution. This failure of classical mechanics set the stage for the development of a new physics, quantum mechanics, to deal with small particles. The Bohr theory, however, did introduce the ideas that only certain energy levels are possible, that these energy levels are described by quantum numbers that can have only certain allowed values, and that the quantum numbers indicate something about where and how stable the electrons are in these energy levels. The ideas of modern atomic theory have replaced Bohr's original theory. But his achievement in showing a link between electronic arrangements and Balmer and Rydberg's empirical description of light absorption, and in establishing the quantization of electronic energy, was a very important step toward an understanding of atomic structure.

Two big questions remained about electrons in atoms: (1) How are electrons arranged in atoms? (2) How do these electrons behave? We now have the background to describe how modern atomic theory answers these questions.

4-14 The Wave Nature of the Electron

▶ Be careful to distinguish between the letter v, which represents velocity, and the Greek letter nu, ν, which represents frequency (see Section 4-10).

Einstein's idea that light can exhibit both wave properties and particle properties suggested to Louis de Broglie (1892–1987) that very small particles, such as electrons, might also display wave properties under the proper circumstances. In his doctoral thesis in 1925, de Broglie predicted that a particle with a mass m and velocity v should have a wavelength associated with it. The numerical value of this de Broglie wavelength is given by

$$\lambda = h/mv \text{ (where } h = \text{Plank's constant)}$$

Two years after de Broglie's prediction, C. Davisson (1882–1958) and L. H. Germer (1896–1971) at the Bell Telephone Laboratories demonstrated diffraction of electrons by a crystal of nickel. This behavior is an important characteristic of waves. It shows conclusively that electrons do have wave properties. Davisson and Germer found that the wavelength associated with electrons of known energy is exactly that predicted by de Broglie. Similar diffraction experiments have been successfully performed with other particles, such as neutrons.

Materials scientists study electron diffraction patterns to learn about the surfaces of solids.

EXAMPLE 4-7 de Broglie Equation

(a) Calculate the wavelength in meters of an electron traveling at 1.24×10^7 m/s. The mass of an electron is 9.11×10^{-28} g.
(b) Calculate the wavelength of a baseball of mass 5.25 oz traveling at 92.5 mph. Recall that $1\,J = 1\,kg \cdot m^2/s^2$.

Plan

For each calculation, we use the de Broglie equation

$$\lambda = \frac{h}{mv}$$

where

$$h \text{ (Planck's constant)} = 6.626 \times 10^{-34} \, J \cdot s \times \frac{1 \frac{kg \cdot m^2}{s^2}}{1 \, J}$$

$$= 6.626 \times 10^{-34} \frac{kg \cdot m^2}{s}$$

For consistency of units, mass must be expressed in kilograms. In part (b), we must also convert the speed to meters per second.

Solution

(a)
$$m = 9.11 \times 10^{-28} \, g \times \frac{1 \, kg}{1000 \, g} = 9.11 \times 10^{-31} \, kg$$

Substituting into the de Broglie equation,

$$\lambda = \frac{h}{mv} = \frac{6.626 \times 10^{-34} \frac{kg \cdot m^2}{s}}{(9.11 \times 10^{-31} \, kg)\left(1.24 \times 10^7 \frac{m}{s}\right)} = \boxed{5.87 \times 10^{-11} \, m}$$

Though this seems like a very short wavelength, it is similar to the spacing between atoms in many crystals. A stream of such electrons hitting a crystal gives measurable diffraction patterns.

(b)
$$m = 5.25 \, oz \times \frac{1 \, lb}{16 \, oz} \times \frac{1 \, kg}{2.205 \, lb} = 0.149 \, kg$$

$$v = \frac{92.5 \, miles}{h} \times \frac{1 \, h}{3600 \, s} \times \frac{1.609 \, km}{1 \, mile} \times \frac{1000 \, m}{1 \, km} = 41.3 \frac{m}{s}$$

Now, we substitute into the de Broglie equation.

$$\lambda = \frac{h}{mv} = \frac{6.626 \times 10^{-34} \frac{kg \cdot m^2}{s}}{(0.149 \, kg)\left(41.3 \frac{m}{s}\right)} = \boxed{1.08 \times 10^{-34} \, m}$$

This wavelength is far too short to give any measurable effects. Recall that atomic diameters are in the order of 10^{-10} m, which is 24 powers of 10 greater than the baseball "wavelength."

You should now work Exercise 76.

© MARKA/Alamy
A modern electron microscope.

As you can see from the results of Example 4-7, the particles of the subatomic world behave very differently from the macroscopic objects with which we are familiar. To talk about the behavior of atoms and their particles, we must give up many of our long-held views about the behavior of matter. We must be willing to visualize a world of new and unfamiliar properties, such as the ability to act in some ways like a particle and in other ways like a wave.

The wave behavior of electrons is exploited in the electron microscope. This instrument allows magnification of objects far too small to be seen with an ordinary light microscope.

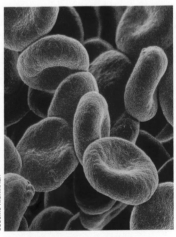
SUSUMU NISHINAGA
A color-enhanced scanning electron micrograph of human red blood cells, magnified 1200X.

4-15 The Quantum Mechanical Picture of the Atom

Through the work of de Broglie, Davisson and Germer, and others, we now know that electrons in atoms can be treated as waves more effectively than as small compact particles traveling in circular or elliptical orbits. Large objects such as golf balls and moving automobiles obey the laws of classical mechanics (Isaac Newton's laws), but very small particles such as electrons, atoms, and molecules do not. A different kind of mechanics, called **quantum mechanics**, which is based on the *wave* properties of matter, describes the behavior of very small particles much better. Quantization of energy is a consequence of these properties.

One of the underlying principles of quantum mechanics is that we cannot determine precisely the paths that electrons follow as they move about atomic nuclei. The **Heisenberg Uncertainty Principle**, stated in 1927 by Werner Heisenberg (1901–1976), is a theoretical assertion that is consistent with all experimental observations.

> It is impossible to determine accurately both the momentum and the position of an electron (or any other very small particle) simultaneously.

Momentum is mass times velocity, mv. Because electrons are so small and move so rapidly, their motion is usually detected by electromagnetic radiation. Photons that interact with electrons have about the same energies as the electrons. Consequently, the interaction of a photon with an electron severely disturbs the motion of the electron. It is not possible to determine simultaneously both the position and the velocity of an electron, so we use a statistical approach to describe the *probability* of finding an electron within specified regions in space.

▶ This is like trying to locate the position of a moving automobile by driving another automobile into it.

With these ideas in mind, we list some basic ideas of quantum mechanics.

1. Atoms and molecules can exist only in certain energy states. In each energy state, the atom or molecule has a definite energy. When an atom or molecule changes its energy state, it must emit or absorb just enough energy to bring it to the new energy state (the quantum condition).

Atoms and molecules possess various forms of energy. Let's focus our attention on their *electronic energies*.

2. When atoms or molecules emit or absorb radiation (light), they change their energies. The energy change in the atom or molecule is related to the frequency or wavelength of the light emitted or absorbed by the equations:

▶ Recall that $\lambda \nu = c$, so $\nu = c/\lambda$.

$$\Delta E = h\nu \qquad \text{or} \qquad \Delta E = hc/\lambda$$

This gives a relationship between the energy change, ΔE, and the wavelength, λ, of the radiation emitted or absorbed. *The energy lost (or gained) by an atom as it goes from higher to lower (or lower to higher) energy states is equal to the energy of the photon emitted (or absorbed) during the transition.*

3. The allowed energy states of atoms and molecules can be described by sets of numbers called *quantum numbers*.

The mathematical approach of quantum mechanics involves treating the electron in an atom as a *standing wave*. A standing wave is a wave that does not travel and therefore has at least one point at which it has zero amplitude, called a node. As an example, consider the various ways that a guitar string can vibrate when it is plucked (Figure 4-20). Because both ends are fixed (nodes), the string can vibrate only in ways in which there is a whole number of *half-wavelengths* in the length of the string (Figure 4-20a). Any possible motion of the string can be described as some combination of these allowed vibrations. In a similar way, we can imagine that the electron in the hydrogen atom behaves as a wave (recall the de Broglie relationship in the last section). The electron can be described by the same kind of standing-wave mathematics that is applied to a vibrating string. In this approach, the electron is characterized by a three-dimensional wave function, ψ. In a given space around the nucleus, only certain "waves" can exist. Each "allowed wave" is called an **orbital** and corresponds to a stable energy state for the electron and is described by a particular set of quantum numbers.

The quantum mechanical treatment of atoms and molecules is highly mathematical. The important point is that each solution of the Schrödinger wave equation (see the following Enrichment section) describes a possible energy state for the electrons in the atom. Each solution is described by a set of **quantum numbers**. These numbers are in accord with those deduced from experiment and from empirical equations such as the Balmer–Rydberg equation. Solutions of the Schrödinger equation also tell us about the shapes and orientations of the probability distributions of the electrons. (The Heisenberg Principle implies that this is how we must describe the positions of the electrons.) These *atomic orbitals* (which are described in Section 4-17) are deduced from the solutions of the Schrödinger equation. The orbitals are defined by the quantum numbers.

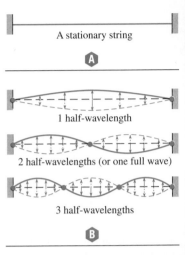

A stationary string

Ⓐ

1 half-wavelength

2 half-wavelengths (or one full wave)

3 half-wavelengths

Ⓑ

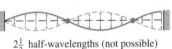

$2\frac{1}{2}$ half-wavelengths (not possible)

● = node

Ⓒ

Figure 4-20 When a stationary string that is fixed at both ends, such as a guitar or piano string (a) is plucked or struck, it has a number of natural patterns of vibration, called normal modes. Because the string is fixed at both ends, the ends must be stationary. Each different possible vibration is a standing wave and can be described by a wave function. The only waves that are possible are those in which a whole number of half-wavelengths fits into the string length. These allowed waves constitute a harmonic series. Any total motion of the string is some combination of these allowed harmonics. (b) Some of the ways in which a plucked string can vibrate. The position of the string at one extreme of each vibration is shown as a solid line, and at the other extreme as a dashed line. (c) An example of vibration that is *not* possible for a plucked string. In such a vibration, an end of the string would move; this is not possible because the ends are fixed.

ENRICHMENT

The Schrödinger Equation

In 1926 Erwin Schrödinger (1887–1961) modified an existing equation that described a three-dimensional standing wave by imposing wavelength restrictions suggested by de Broglie's ideas. The modified equation allowed him to calculate the energy levels in the hydrogen atom. It is a differential equation that need not be memorized or even understood to read this book. A knowledge of differential calculus would be necessary to solve it.

$$-\frac{h^2}{8\pi^2 m}\left(\frac{\partial^2\psi}{\partial x^2} + \frac{\partial^2\psi}{\partial y^2} + \frac{\partial^2\psi}{\partial z^2}\right) + V\psi = E\psi$$

This equation has been solved exactly only for one-electron species such as the hydrogen atom and the ions He^+ and Li^{2+}. Simplifying assumptions are necessary to solve the equation for more complex atoms and molecules. Chemists and physicists have used their intuition and ingenuity (and modern computers), however, to apply this equation to more complex systems.

In 1928 Paul A. M. Dirac (1902–1984) reformulated electron quantum mechanics to take into account the effects of relativity. This gave rise to an additional quantum number.

4-16 Quantum Numbers

The solutions of the Schrödinger and Dirac equations for hydrogen atoms give wave functions, ψ, that describe the various states available to hydrogen's single electron. Each of these possible states is described by four quantum numbers. We can use these quantum numbers to designate the electronic arrangements in all atoms, their so-called **electron configurations**. These quantum numbers play important roles in describing the energy levels of electrons and the shapes of the orbitals that describe distributions of electrons in space. The interpretation will become clearer when we discuss atomic orbitals in the following section. For now, let's say that

an **atomic orbital** is a region of space in which the probability of finding an electron is high.

Let's define each quantum number and describe the range of values it may take.

1. The **principal quantum number**, n, describes the *main energy level*, or shell, that an electron occupies. It may be any positive integer:

$$n = 1, 2, 3, 4, \ldots$$

2. Within a shell (defined by the value of n, the principal quantum number), different sublevels or subshells are possible, each with a characteristic shape. The **angular momentum quantum number**, ℓ, designates a *sublevel*, or a specific *shape* of atomic orbital that an electron may occupy. This number, ℓ, may take integral values from 0 up to and including $(n - 1)$:

$$\ell = 0, 1, 2, \ldots, (n - 1)$$

Thus, the maximum value of ℓ is $(n - 1)$. We give a letter notation to each value of ℓ. Each letter corresponds to a different sublevel (subshell) and a differently shaped orbital:

$$\ell = 0, 1, 2, 3, \ldots, (n - 1)$$
$$s \quad p \quad d \quad f$$

▶ The *s, p, d, f* designations arise from the characteristics of spectral emission lines produced by electrons occupying the orbitals: *s* (sharp), *p* (principal), *d* (diffuse), and *f* (fundamental).

In the first shell, the maximum value of ℓ is zero, which tells us that there is only an *s* subshell and no *p* subshell. In the second shell, the permissible values of ℓ are 0 and 1, which tells us that there are only *s* and *p* subshells.

3. Orbitals within a given subshell differ in their orientations in space, but not in their energies. The **magnetic quantum number**, m_ℓ, designates a specific orbital within a subshell. Within each subshell, m_ℓ may take any integral values from $-\ell$ through zero up to and including $+\ell$:

$$m_\ell = (-\ell), \ldots, 0, \ldots, (+\ell)$$

The maximum value of m_ℓ depends on the value of ℓ. For example, when $\ell = 1$, which designates the *p* subshell, there are three permissible values of m_ℓ: -1, 0, and $+1$. Thus, three distinct regions of space, called atomic orbitals, are associated with a *p* subshell. We refer to these orbitals as the p_x, p_y, and p_z orbitals (see Section 4-17).

▶ The subscripts *x, y,* and *z* refer to the axes on a Cartesian coordinate system. The p_x orbital, for example, lies along the positive and negative directions of the *x* axis with the nucleus located at the origin (see Figure 4-25).

4. The **spin quantum number**, m_s, refers to the spin of an electron and the orientation of the magnetic field produced by this spin. For every set of n, ℓ, and m_ℓ values, m_s can take the value $+\frac{1}{2}$ or $-\frac{1}{2}$:

$$m_s = \pm\frac{1}{2}$$

The values of n, ℓ, and m_ℓ describe a particular atomic orbital. Each atomic orbital can accommodate no more than two electrons, one with $m_s = +\frac{1}{2}$ and another with $m_s = -\frac{1}{2}$.

Table 4-8 summarizes some permissible values for the four quantum numbers. Spectroscopic evidence confirms the quantum mechanical predictions about the number of atomic orbitals in each shell.

4-17 Atomic Orbitals

Let's now describe the distributions of electrons in atoms. For each neutral atom, we must account for a number of electrons equal to the number of protons in the nucleus, that is, the atomic number of the atom. Each electron is said to occupy an atomic orbital defined by a set of quantum numbers n, ℓ, and m_ℓ. In any atom, each orbital can hold a maximum of two electrons (m_s values of $+\frac{1}{2}$ and $-\frac{1}{2}$). Within each atom, these atomic orbitals, taken together, can be represented as a diffuse cloud of electrons (Figure 4-21).

The main shell of each atomic orbital in an atom is indicated by the principal quantum number n (from the Schrödinger equation). As we have seen, the principal quantum number takes integral values: $n = 1, 2, 3, 4, \ldots$. The value $n = 1$ describes the first, or innermost, shell. These shells have been referred to as electron energy levels. Successive shells

Table 4-8 Permissible Values of the Quantum Numbers Through $n = 4$

n	ℓ	m_ℓ	m_s	Electron Capacity of Subshell $= 4\ell + 2$	Electron Capacity of Shell $= 2n^2$
1	$0(1s)$	0	$+\frac{1}{2}, -\frac{1}{2}$	2	2
2	$0(2s)$	0	$+\frac{1}{2}, -\frac{1}{2}$	2	8
	$1(2p)$	$-1, 0, +1$	$\pm\frac{1}{2}$ for each value of m_ℓ	6	
3	$0(3s)$	0	$+\frac{1}{2}, -\frac{1}{2}$	2	18
	$1(3p)$	$-1, 0, +1$	$\pm\frac{1}{2}$ for each value of m_ℓ	6	
	$2(3d)$	$-2, -1, 0, +1, +2$	$\pm\frac{1}{2}$ for each value of m_ℓ	10	
4	$0(4s)$	0	$+\frac{1}{2}, -\frac{1}{2}$	2	32
	$1(4p)$	$-1, 0, +1$	$\pm\frac{1}{2}$ for each value of m_ℓ	6	
	$2(4d)$	$-2, -1, 0, +1, +2$	$\pm\frac{1}{2}$ for each value of m_ℓ	10	
	$3(4f)$	$-3, -2, -1, 0, +1, +2, +3$	$\pm\frac{1}{2}$ for each value of m_ℓ	14	

are at increasingly greater distances from the nucleus. For example, the $n = 2$ shell is farther from the nucleus than the $n = 1$ shell. The electron capacity of each shell is indicated in the right-hand column of Table 4-8. For a given n, the capacity is $2n^2$.

By the rules given in Section 4-16, each shell has an s subshell (defined by $\ell = 0$) consisting of one s atomic orbital (defined by $m_\ell = 0$). We distinguish among orbitals in different principal shells (main energy levels) by using the principal quantum number as a coefficient; $1s$ indicates the s orbital in the first shell, $2s$ is the s orbital in the second shell, $2p$ is a p orbital in the second shell, and so on (see Table 4-8).

For each solution to the quantum mechanical equation, we can calculate the electron probability density (sometimes just called the electron density) at each point in the atom. This is the probability of finding an electron at that point. It can be shown that this electron density is proportional to $r^2\psi^2$, where r is the distance from the nucleus.

In the graphs in Figure 4-22, the electron probability density at a given distance from the nucleus is plotted against distance from the nucleus, for s orbitals. It is found that the electron probability density curve is the same regardless of the direction in the atom. We describe an s orbital as *spherically symmetrical*; that is, it is round like a basketball (Figure 4-23). The electron clouds (electron densities) associated with the $1s$, $2s$, and $3s$ atomic orbitals are shown just below the plots in Figure 4-22. The electron clouds are three-dimensional, and only cross sections are shown here. The regions shown in some figures (Figures 4-23 through 4-27) appear to have surfaces or skins only because they are arbitrarily "cut off" so that there is a 90% probability of finding an electron occupying the orbital somewhere within the volume defined by the surface.

▶ As you study the next two sections, keep in mind that the wave function, ψ, for an orbital characterizes two features of an electron in that orbital: (1) *where* (the region in space) the probability of finding the electron is high and (2) *how stable* that electron is (its energy).

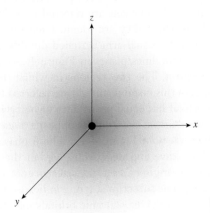

Figure 4-21 An electron cloud surrounding an atomic nucleus. The electron density drops off rapidly but smoothly as distance from the nucleus increases.

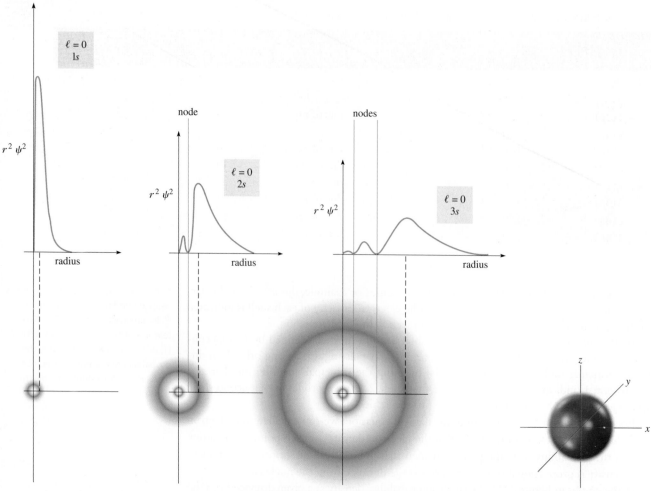

Figure 4-22 Plots of the electron density distributions associated with s orbitals. For any s orbital, this plot is the same in any direction (orbital is spherically symmetrical). The sketch below each plot shows a cross section, in the plane of the atomic nucleus, of the electron cloud associated with that orbital. Electron density is proportional to $r^2\psi^2$. s orbitals with $n > 1$ have $n - 1$ regions where the electron density drops to zero. These are indicated by blue vertical lines on the plots, indicating where the electron density drops to zero (nodes), and by the white regions on the cross section.

Figure 4-23 The shape of an s orbital.

Beginning with the second shell, each shell also contains a p subshell, defined by $\ell = 1$. Each of these subshells consists of a set of *three* p atomic orbitals, corresponding to the three allowed values of m_ℓ (-1, 0, and $+1$) when $\ell = 1$. The sets are referred to as 2p, 3p, 4p, 5p, … orbitals to indicate the main shells in which they are found. Each set of atomic p orbitals resembles three mutually perpendicular equal-arm flattened dumbbells (see Figure 4-24). Each p orbital has a nodal plane (blue lines/planes in Figure 4-24) in which there is zero probability of finding the electron. The two regions in which the electron probability is nonzero are on opposite sides of this nodal plane and are referred to as the *lobes* of the p orbital. Each electron in a p orbital has equal probability of being in either lobe. In the two lobes, the wave ψ represents that the electron has opposite *phases*, corresponding to the crests and troughs of water waves in Figure 4-12. These phases correspond to mathematical wave functions with positive and negative signs, but these signs *do not* represent charges. The nucleus defines the origin of a set of Cartesian coordinates with the usual x, y, and z axes (see Figure 4-25a). The subscript x, y, or z indicates the axis along which each of the orbitals is directed. A set of three p atomic orbitals may be represented as in Figure 4-25b.

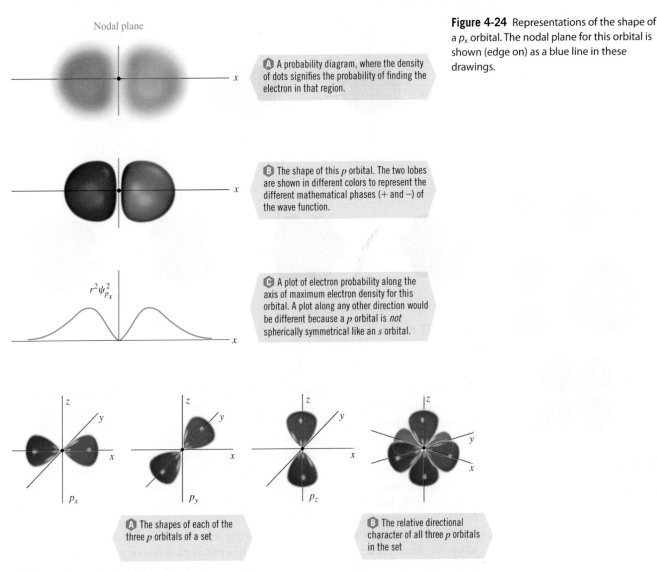

Nodal plane

Figure 4-24 Representations of the shape of a p_x orbital. The nodal plane for this orbital is shown (edge on) as a blue line in these drawings.

A A probability diagram, where the density of dots signifies the probability of finding the electron in that region.

B The shape of this p orbital. The two lobes are shown in different colors to represent the different mathematical phases (+ and −) of the wave function.

$r^2 \psi_{p_x}^2$

C A plot of electron probability along the axis of maximum electron density for this orbital. A plot along any other direction would be different because a p orbital is *not* spherically symmetrical like an s orbital.

p_x p_y p_z

A The shapes of each of the three p orbitals of a set

B The relative directional character of all three p orbitals in the set

Figure 4-25 Representation of p orbitals.

Beginning at the third shell, each shell also contains a third subshell ($\ell = 2$) composed of a set of *five d* atomic orbitals ($m_\ell = -2, -1, 0, +1, +2$). They are designated $3d$, $4d$, $5d$, ... to indicate the shell in which they are found. The shapes of the members of a set are indicated in Figure 4-26.

▶ Some excellent visual representations of orbital shapes can be seen at **www.winter.group.shef .ac.uk/orbitron**

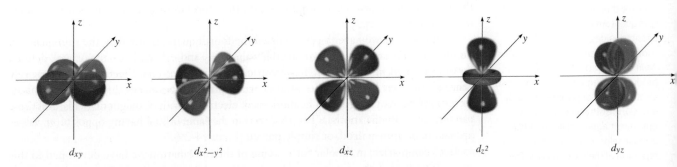

d_{xy} $d_{x^2-y^2}$ d_{xz} d_{z^2} d_{yz}

Figure 4-26 Spatial orientation of d orbitals. Note that the lobes of the $d_{x^2-y^2}$ and d_{z^2} orbitals lie along the axes, whereas the lobes of the others lie along diagonals between the axes.

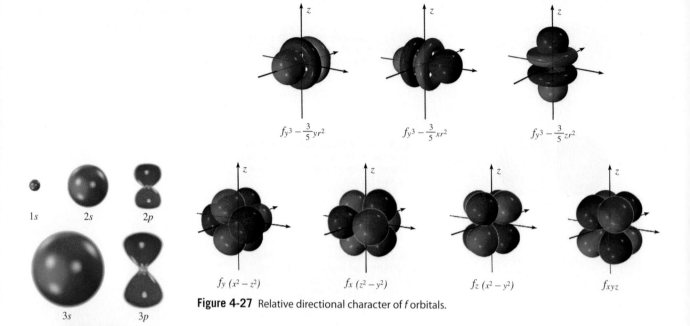

$$f_{y^3-\frac{3}{5}yr^2}$$ $$f_{y^3-\frac{3}{5}xr^2}$$ $$f_{y^3-\frac{3}{5}zr^2}$$

$$f_y\,(x^2-z^2)$$ $$f_x\,(z^2-y^2)$$ $$f_z\,(x^2-y^2)$$ $$f_{xyz}$$

Figure 4-27 Relative directional character of *f* orbitals.

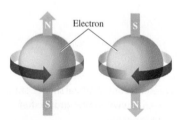

1*s*   2*s*   2*p*

3*s*   3*p*

3*d*

Figure 4-28 Shapes and approximate relative sizes of several orbitals in an atom.

Electron

Figure 4-29 Electron spin. Electrons act as though they spin about an axis through their centers. Electrons may spin in either of two directions, so the spin quantum number has two possible values, $+\frac{1}{2}$ and $-\frac{1}{2}$, sometimes referred to as "spin up" or "spin down." Each electron spin produces a magnetic field. When two electrons have opposite spins (*gray arrows*), the attraction due to their opposite magnetic fields (*red/blue arrows*) helps to overcome the repulsion of their like charges. This permits two electrons to occupy the same region (orbital).

In each of the fourth and larger shells, there is also a fourth subshell, containing a set of *seven f* atomic orbitals ($\ell = 3$, $m_\ell = -3, -2, -1, 0, +1, +2, +3$). These are shown in Figure 4-27. No elements are known in which *g* orbitals ($l = 4$) are occupied in their ground states. However, these orbitals may be populated in some excited states.

Thus, we see the first shell contains only the 1*s* orbital; the second shell contains the 2*s* and three 2*p* orbitals; the third shell contains the 3*s*, three 3*p*, and five 3*d* orbitals; and the fourth shell consists of a 4*s*, three 4*p*, five 4*d*, and seven 4*f* orbitals. All subsequent shells contain *s*, *p*, *d*, and *f* subshells as well as others that are not occupied in any presently known elements in their lowest energy states.

The sizes of orbitals increase with increasing *n*, as shown in Figure 4-28. How do we know the sizes of orbitals and the relationship between the value of *n* and orbital size? Experiments such as density measurements provide information about atomic radii, and thus about the sizes of the outermost orbitals. In addition, calculations and models of the orbitals enable us to make correct predictions. Figure 4-28 shows an example of the relationship between *n* and the size of the orbitals. We will find the following generalizations about orbital sizes useful:

1. In any atom, all orbitals with the same principal quantum number *n* are similar in size.

2. In an atom, larger values of *n* correspond to larger orbital size.

3. Each orbital with a given *n* value becomes smaller as nuclear charge increases.

The directions of *p*, *d*, and *f* orbitals, however, are easier to visualize in drawings such as those shown for *p* orbitals in Figure 4-25b; therefore, most chemists use such "slenderized" representations.

In this section, we haven't yet discussed the fourth quantum number, the spin quantum number, m_s. Because m_s has two possible values, $+\frac{1}{2}$ and $-\frac{1}{2}$, each atomic orbital, defined by the values of *n*, ℓ, and m_ℓ, has a capacity of two electrons. Electrons are negatively charged, and they behave as though they were spinning about axes through their centers, so they act like tiny magnets. The motions of electrons produce magnetic fields, and these can interact with one another. Two electrons in the same orbital having opposite m_s values are said to be **spin-paired**, or simply **paired** (Figure 4-29).

Let's summarize, in tabular form, some of the information we have developed to this point. The principal quantum number *n* indicates the main shell. The number of subshells per shell is equal to *n*, the number of atomic orbitals per shell is n^2, and the maximum number of electrons per shell is $2n^2$, because each atomic orbital can hold two electrons.

Shell n	Number of Subshells per Shell n	Number of Atomic Orbitals n^2	Maximum Number of Electrons $2n^2$
1	1	$1(1s)$	2
2	2	$4(2s, 2p_x, 2p_y, 2p_z)$	8
3	3	9 ($3s$, three $3p$'s, five $3d$'s)	18
4	4	16	32
5	5	25	50

4-18 Electron Configurations

The wave function for an atom simultaneously depends on (describes) all the electrons in the atom. The Schrödinger equation is much more complicated for atoms with more than one electron than for a one-electron species such as a hydrogen atom, and an explicit solution to this equation is not possible even for helium, let alone for more complicated atoms. We must therefore rely on approximations to solutions of the many-electron Schrödinger equation. One of the most common and useful of these is the *orbital approximation*. In this approximation, the electron cloud of an atom is assumed to be the superposition of charge clouds, or orbitals, arising from the individual electrons; these orbitals resemble the atomic orbitals of hydrogen (for which exact solutions are known), which we described in some detail in the previous section. Each electron is described by the same allowed combinations of quantum numbers (n, ℓ, m_ℓ, and m_s) that we used for the hydrogen atom; however, the order of energies of the orbitals is often different from that in hydrogen.

▶ The great power of modern computers has allowed scientists to make numerical approximations to this solution to very high accuracy for simple atoms such as helium. As the number of electrons increases, however, even such numerical approaches become more difficult to apply and interpret. For multielectron atoms, more qualitative approximations are used.

Let us now examine the electronic structures of atoms of different elements. The electronic arrangement that we will describe for each atom is called the **ground state** electron configuration. This corresponds to the isolated atom in its lowest energy, or unexcited, state. Electron configurations for the elements, as verified by experiment, are given in Appendix B. We will consider the elements in order of increasing atomic number, using the periodic table as our guide.

In describing a ground state electron configuration, the guiding idea is that the *total energy* of the atom is as low as possible. To determine these configurations, we use the **Aufbau Principle** as a guide:

▶ The German verb *aufbauen* means "to build up."

Each atom is "built up" by (1) adding the appropriate numbers of protons and neutrons in the nucleus as specified by the atomic number and the mass number, and (2) adding the necessary number of electrons into orbitals in the way that gives the lowest *total* energy for the atom.

As we apply this principle, we will focus on the difference in electronic arrangement between a given element and the element with an atomic number that is one lower. In doing this, we emphasize the particular electron that distinguishes each element from the previous one; however, we should remember that this distinction is artificial because electrons are not really distinguishable. Though we do not always point it out, we *must* keep in mind that the atomic number (the charge on the nucleus) also differs from one element to the next.

The orbitals increase in energy with increasing value of the quantum number n. For a given value of n, energy increases with increasing value of ℓ. In other words, within a particular main shell, the s subshell is lowest in energy, the p subshell is the next lowest, then the d, then the f, and so on. As a result of changes in the nuclear charge and interactions among the electrons in the atom, the order of energies of the orbitals can vary somewhat from atom to atom.

Two general rules help us to predict electron configurations.

> 1. Electrons are assigned to orbitals in order of increasing value of $(n + \ell)$.
> 2. For subshells with the same value of $(n + \ell)$, electrons are assigned first to the subshell with lower n.

For example, the 2s subshell has $(n + \ell = 2 + 0 = 2)$, and the 2p subshell has $(n + \ell = 2 + 1 = 3)$, so we would expect to fill the 2s subshell before the 2p subshell (Rule 1). This rule also predicts that the 4s subshell $(n + \ell = 4 + 0 = 4)$ will fill before the 3d subshell $(n + \ell = 3 + 2 = 5)$. Rule 2 reminds us to fill 2p $(n + \ell = 2 + 1 = 3)$ before 3s $(n + \ell = 3 + 0 = 3)$ because 2p has a lower value of n. The *usual* order of energies of orbitals of an atom and a helpful reminder of this order are shown in Figures 4-30 and 4-31.

But we should consider these rules as just a *guide* to predicting electron arrangements. The observed electron configurations of lowest total energy do not always match those predicted by the Aufbau guide, and we will see a number of exceptions, especially for elements in the B groups (transition metals) of the periodic table.

The electronic structures of atoms are governed by the **Pauli Exclusion Principle**:

> No two electrons in an atom may have identical sets of four quantum numbers.

An orbital is described by a particular allowed set of values for n, ℓ, and m_ℓ. Two electrons can occupy the same orbital only if they have opposite spins, m_s (see Figure 4-29). Two such electrons in the same orbital are said to be *spin-paired*, or simply *paired*. A single electron that occupies an orbital by itself is said to be *unpaired*. For simplicity, we shall indicate atomic orbitals as __ and show an unpaired electron as ↑ and paired electrons as ↑↓.

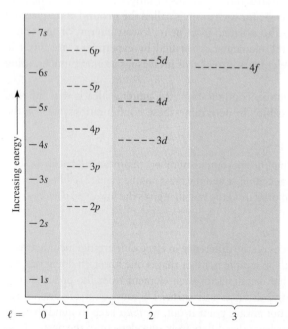

Figure 4-30 The usual order of filling (Aufbau order) of the orbitals of an atom, based on the two rules presented above. The relative energies are different for different elements, but the following main features should be noted: (1) The largest energy gap is between the 1s and 2s orbitals. (2) The energies of orbitals are generally closer together at higher energies. (3) The gap between np and $(n + 1)s$ (e.g., between 2p and 3s or between 3p and 4s) is fairly large. (4) The gap between $(n - 1)d$ and ns (e.g., between 3d and 4s) is quite small. (5) The gap between $(n - 2)f$ and ns (e.g., between 4f and 6s) is even smaller.

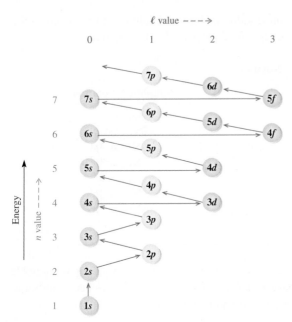

ℓ value - - - →

0   1   2   3

Figure 4-31 An aid to remembering the usual order of filling (Aufbau order) of atomic orbitals.

Row 1. The first shell consists of only one atomic orbital, 1s. This can hold a maximum of two electrons. Hydrogen, as we have already noted, contains just one electron. Helium, a noble gas, has a filled first main shell (two electrons) and is so stable that no chemical reactions of helium are known.

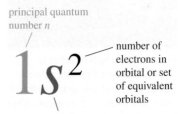

principal quantum number n

number of electrons in orbital or set of equivalent orbitals

angular momentum quantum number ℓ

In the simplified notation, we indicate with superscripts the number of electrons in each subshell.

	Orbital Notation	
	1s	**Simplified Notation**
${}_1$H	↑	$1s^1$
${}_2$He	↑↓	$1s^2$

Row 2. Elements of atomic numbers 3 through 10 occupy the second period, or horizontal row, in the periodic table. In neon atoms the second main shell is filled completely. Neon, a noble gas, is extremely stable. No reactions of it are known.

	1s	**2s**	**2p**	**Simplified Notation**	
Li	↑↓	↑		$1s^2 2s^1$ or	$[\text{He}] 2s^1$
Be	↑↓	↑↓		$1s^2 2s^2$	$[\text{He}] 2s^2$
B	↑↓	↑↓	↑ __ __	$1s^2 2s^2 2p^1$	$[\text{He}] 2s^2 2p^1$
C	↑↓	↑↓	↑ ↑ __	$1s^2 2s^2 2p^2$	$[\text{He}] 2s^2 2p^2$
N	↑↓	↑↓	↑ ↑ ↑	$1s^2 2s^2 2p^3$	$[\text{He}] 2s^2 2p^3$
O	↑↓	↑↓	↑↓ ↑ ↑	$1s^2 2s^2 2p^4$	$[\text{He}] 2s^2 2p^4$
F	↑↓	↑↓	↑↓ ↑↓ ↑	$1s^2 2s^2 2p^5$	$[\text{He}] 2s^2 2p^5$
Ne	↑↓	↑↓	↑↓ ↑↓ ↑↓	$1s^2 2s^2 2p^6$	$[\text{He}] 2s^2 2p^6$

Orbital Notation (header spanning 1s, 2s, 2p)

▶ In writing electron configurations of atoms, we frequently simplify the notations. The abbreviation $[\text{He}]$ indicates that the 1s orbital is completely filled, $1s^2$, as in helium.

We see that some atoms have unpaired electrons in the same set of energetically equivalent, or **degenerate**, orbitals. We have already seen that two electrons can occupy a given atomic orbital (with the same values of n, ℓ, and m_ℓ) *only* if their spins are paired (have opposite values of m_s). Even with pairing of spins, however, two electrons that are in the same orbital repel each other more strongly than do two electrons in different (but equal-energy) orbitals. Thus, both theory and experimental observations (see Section 4-18) lead to **Hund's Rule**:

Electrons occupy all the orbitals of a given subshell singly before pairing begins. These unpaired electrons have parallel spins.

Thus, carbon has two unpaired electrons in its $2p$ orbitals, and nitrogen has three.

Row 3. The next element beyond neon is sodium. Here we begin to add electrons to the third shell. Elements 11 through 18 occupy the third period in the periodic table.

	Orbital Notation		
	3s	**3p**	**Simplified Notation**
Na	[Ne] ↑		[Ne] $3s^1$
Mg	[Ne] ↑↓		[Ne] $3s^2$
Al	[Ne] ↑↓	↑ _ _	[Ne] $3s^2 3p^1$
Si	[Ne] ↑↓	↑ ↑ _	[Ne] $3s^2 3p^2$
P	[Ne] ↑↓	↑ ↑ ↑	[Ne] $3s^2 3p^3$
S	[Ne] ↑↓	↑↓ ↑ ↑	[Ne] $3s^2 3p^4$
Cl	[Ne] ↑↓	↑↓ ↑↓ ↑	[Ne] $3s^2 3p^5$
Ar	[Ne] ↑↓	↑↓ ↑↓ ↑↓	[Ne] $3s^2 3p^6$

Although the third shell is not yet filled (the *d* orbitals are still empty), argon is a noble gas. All noble gases except helium have ns^2np^6 electron configurations (where *n* indicates the largest occupied shell). The noble gases are quite unreactive.

Rows 4 and 5. It is observed experimentally that *each electron occupies the available orbital that gives the atom the lowest total energy.* It is observed that filling the 4s orbitals before electrons enter the 3d orbitals *usually* leads to a lower total energy for the atom than some other arrangements. We therefore fill the orbitals in this order (see Figure 4-30). According to the Aufbau order (recall Figures 4-30 and 4-31), 4s fills before 3d. In general, *the (n + 1)s orbital fills before the nd orbital.* This is sometimes referred to as the *(n + 1)s rule.*

After the 3d sublevel is filled to its capacity of 10 electrons, the 4p orbitals fill next, taking us to the noble gas krypton. Then the 5s orbital, the five 4d orbitals, and the three 5p orbitals fill to take us to xenon, a noble gas.

Let's now examine the electronic structure of the 18 elements in the fourth period in some detail. Some of these have electrons in *d* orbitals.

	Orbital Notation			
	3d	**4s**	**4p**	**Simplified Notation**
K	[Ar]	↑		[Ar] $4s^1$
Ca	[Ar]	↑↓		[Ar] $4s^2$
Sc	[Ar] ↑ _ _ _ _	↑↓		[Ar] $3d^1 4s^2$
Ti	[Ar] ↑ ↑ _ _ _	↑↓		[Ar] $3d^2 4s^2$
V	[Ar] ↑ ↑ ↑ _ _	↑↓		[Ar] $3d^3 4s^2$
Cr	[Ar] ↑ ↑ ↑ ↑ ↑	↑		[Ar] $3d^5 4s^1$
Mn	[Ar] ↑ ↑ ↑ ↑ ↑	↑↓		[Ar] $3d^5 4s^2$
Fe	[Ar] ↑↓ ↑ ↑ ↑ ↑	↑↓		[Ar] $3d^6 4s^2$
Co	[Ar] ↑↓ ↑↓ ↑ ↑ ↑	↑↓		[Ar] $3d^7 4s^2$
Ni	[Ar] ↑↓ ↑↓ ↑↓ ↑ ↑	↑↓		[Ar] $3d^8 4s^2$
Cu	[Ar] ↑↓ ↑↓ ↑↓ ↑↓ ↑↓	↑		[Ar] $3d^{10} 4s^1$
Zn	[Ar] ↑↓ ↑↓ ↑↓ ↑↓ ↑↓	↑↓		[Ar] $3d^{10} 4s^2$
Ga	[Ar] ↑↓ ↑↓ ↑↓ ↑↓ ↑↓	↑↓	↑ _ _	[Ar] $3d^{10} 4s^2 4p^1$
Ge	[Ar] ↑↓ ↑↓ ↑↓ ↑↓ ↑↓	↑↓	↑ ↑ _	[Ar] $3d^{10} 4s^2 4p^2$
As	[Ar] ↑↓ ↑↓ ↑↓ ↑↓ ↑↓	↑↓	↑ ↑ ↑	[Ar] $3d^{10} 4s^2 4p^3$
Se	[Ar] ↑↓ ↑↓ ↑↓ ↑↓ ↑↓	↑↓	↑↓ ↑ ↑	[Ar] $3d^{10} 4s^2 4p^4$
Br	[Ar] ↑↓ ↑↓ ↑↓ ↑↓ ↑↓	↑↓	↑↓ ↑↓ ↑	[Ar] $3d^{10} 4s^2 4p^5$
Kr	[Ar] ↑↓ ↑↓ ↑↓ ↑↓ ↑↓	↑↓	↑↓ ↑↓ ↑↓	[Ar] $3d^{10} 4s^2 4p^6$

The glow of these lights is emitted by electrons excited by high-voltage electric discharge. Different gases produce different colors; neon produces a red glow, so only red tubes are true "neon lights."

Photodisc Blue/Getty Images

As you study these electron configurations, you should be able to see how most of them are predicted from the Aufbau order. However, as we fill the $3d$ set of orbitals, from Sc to Zn, we see that these orbitals are not filled quite regularly. As the $3d$ orbitals are filled, their energies get closer to that of the $4s$ orbital and eventually become lower. If the order of filling of electrons on chromium gave the expected configuration, it would be: $[Ar] 4s^2 3d^4$. Chemical and spectroscopic evidence indicates, however, that the configuration of Cr has only one electron in the $4s$ orbital, $[Ar] 4s^1 3d^5$. For this element, the $4s$ and $3d$ orbitals are nearly equal in energy. Six electrons in these six orbitals of nearly the same energy are more stable with the electrons all unpaired, $[Ar] 3d \uparrow \uparrow \uparrow \uparrow \uparrow 4s \uparrow$ rather than the predicted order $[Ar] 3d \uparrow \uparrow \uparrow \uparrow \_ 4s \uparrow\downarrow$.

The next elements, Mn to Ni, have configurations as predicted by the Aufbau order, presumably because forming a pair of electrons in the larger $4s$ orbital is easier than in a smaller, less diffuse $3d$ orbital. By the time Cu is reached, the energy of $3d$ is sufficiently lower than that of $4s$ so that the total energy of the configuration $[Ar] 4s^1 3d^{10}$ is lower than that of $[Ar] 4s^2 3d^9$.

We notice that the exceptions for Cr and Cu give half-filled or filled sets of equivalent orbitals (d^5 and d^{10}, respectively), and this is also true for several other exceptions to the Aufbau order. You may wonder why such an exception does not occur in, for example, Si or Ge, where we could have an $s^1 p^3$ configuration that would have half-filled sets of s and p orbitals. It does not occur because of the very large energy gap between ns and np orbitals. There is some evidence that does, however, suggest an enhanced stability of half-filled sets of p orbitals.

The electron configurations for the transition metals discussed here and in Appendix B are for individual metal atoms in the gas phase. Most chemists work with the transition metals either in the metallic state or as coordination compounds (see Chapter 25). A solid transition metal has a band structure of overlapping d and s orbital levels (see Section 13-7). When transition metal atoms have other types of atoms or molecules bonded to them, however, the electronic configuration usually becomes simpler in that the d orbitals fill first, followed by the next higher s orbital. This is illustrated by Cr, which has a $4s^1 3d^5$ electronic configuration as a free atom in the gas phase. But in the compound $Cr(CO)_6$, chromium hexacarbonyl, which contains a central Cr atom surrounded by six neutral carbon monoxide (or carbonyl) groups, the chromium atom has a $3d^6$ electronic configuration.

▶ End-of-chapter Exercises 95–129 provide much valuable practice in writing electron configurations.

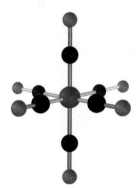

Ball-and-stick model of $Cr(CO)_6$ (Cr = purple, C = black, O = red)

⚙ Problem-Solving Tip Exceptions to the Aufbau Order

In Appendix B, you will find a number of exceptions to the electron configurations predicted from the Aufbau Principle. You should realize that statements such as the Aufbau Principle and the $(n + 1)$ rule merely represent general guidelines and should not be viewed as hard-and-fast rules; exceptions occur to make the *total energy* of the atom as low as possible. Some of the reasons for exceptions are

1. The Aufbau order of orbital energies is based on calculations for the hydrogen atom, which contains only one electron. The orbital energies also depend on additional factors such as the nuclear charge and interactions of electrons in different occupied orbitals.

2. The energy scale varies with the atomic number.

3. Some orbitals are very close together, so their order can change, depending on the occupancies of other orbitals.

Some types of exceptions to the Aufbau order are general enough to remember easily, for example, those based on the special stability of filled or half-filled sets of orbitals. Other exceptions are quite unpredictable. Your instructor may expect you to remember some of the exceptions.

Let us now write the quantum numbers to describe each electron in an atom of nitrogen. Keep in mind the fact that Hund's Rule must be obeyed. Thus, there is only one (unpaired) electron in each $2p$ orbital in a nitrogen atom.

EXAMPLE 4-8 Electron Configurations and Quantum Numbers

Write an acceptable set of four quantum numbers for each electron in a nitrogen atom.

Plan

Nitrogen has seven electrons, which occupy the lowest energy orbitals available. Two electrons can occupy the first shell, $n = 1$, in which there is only one s orbital; when $n = 1$, then, ℓ must be zero, and therefore $m_\ell = 0$. The two electrons differ only in spin quantum number, m_s. The next five electrons can all fit into the second shell, for which $n = 2$ and ℓ may be either 0 or 1. The $\ell = 0$ (s) subshell fills first, and the $\ell = 1$ (p) subshell is occupied next.

Solution

▶ Electrons are indistinguishable. We have numbered them 1, 2, 3, and so on as an aid to counting them.

▶ In the lowest energy configurations, the three $2p$ electrons either have $m_s = +\frac{1}{2}$ or all have $m_s = -\frac{1}{2}$.

Electron	n	ℓ	m_ℓ	m_s	e^- Configuration
1, 2	$\begin{cases} 1 \\ 1 \end{cases}$	0 0	0 0	$\left.\begin{matrix} +\frac{1}{2} \\ -\frac{1}{2} \end{matrix}\right\}$	$1s^2$
3, 4	$\begin{cases} 2 \\ 2 \end{cases}$	0 0	0 0	$\left.\begin{matrix} +\frac{1}{2} \\ -\frac{1}{2} \end{matrix}\right\}$	$2s^2$
5, 6, 7	$\begin{cases} 2 \\ 2 \\ 2 \end{cases}$	1 1 1	-1 0 $+1$	$\left.\begin{matrix} +\frac{1}{2} \text{ or } -\frac{1}{2} \\ +\frac{1}{2} \text{ or } -\frac{1}{2} \\ +\frac{1}{2} \text{ or } -\frac{1}{2} \end{matrix}\right\}$	$\left.\begin{matrix} 2p_x^1 \\ 2p_y^1 \\ 2p_z^1 \end{matrix}\right\}$ or $2p^3$

EXAMPLE 4-9 Electron Configurations and Quantum Numbers

Write an acceptable set of four quantum numbers for each electron in a chlorine atom.

Plan

Chlorine is element number 17. Its first seven electrons have the same quantum numbers as those of nitrogen in Example 4-8. Electrons 8, 9, and 10 complete the filling of the $2p$ subshell ($n = 2$, $\ell = 1$) and therefore also the second energy level. Electrons 11 through 17 fill the $3s$ subshell ($n = 3$, $\ell = 0$) and partially fill the $3p$ subshell ($n = 3$, $\ell = 1$).

S TOP & THINK

Apply the rules for quantum numbers (see Section 4-16), and remember the Aufbau order of energies (see Figures 4-30 and 4-31).

Solution

Electron	n	ℓ	m_ℓ	m_s	e^- Configuration
1, 2	1	0	0	$\pm\frac{1}{2}$	$1s^2$
3, 4	2	0	0	$\pm\frac{1}{2}$	$2s^2$
5–10	$\begin{cases} 2 \\ 2 \\ 2 \end{cases}$	1 1 1	-1 0 $+1$	$\left.\begin{matrix} \pm\frac{1}{2} \\ \pm\frac{1}{2} \\ \pm\frac{1}{2} \end{matrix}\right\}$	$2p^6$
11, 12	3	0	0	$\pm\frac{1}{2}$	$3s^2$
13–17	$\begin{cases} 3 \\ 3 \\ 3 \end{cases}$	1 1 1	-1 0 $+1$	$\left.\begin{matrix} \pm\frac{1}{2} \\ \pm\frac{1}{2} \\ +\frac{1}{2} \text{ or } -\frac{1}{2}* \end{matrix}\right\}$	$3p^5$

*The $3p$ orbital with only a single electron can be any one of the set, not necessarily the one with $m_\ell = +1$.

You should now work Exercises 118 and 122.

4-19 The Periodic Table and Electron Configurations

In this section, we will view the *periodic table* (see Section 4-10) from a modern, much more useful perspective—as a systematic representation of the electron configurations of the elements. In the periodic table, elements are arranged in blocks based on the kinds of atomic orbitals that are being filled (Figure 4-32). The periodic tables in this text are divided into "A" and "B" groups. The A groups contain elements in which *s* and *p* orbitals are being filled. Elements within any particular A group have similar electron configurations and chemical properties, as we shall see in the next chapter. The B groups include the transition metals in which there are one or two electrons in the *s* orbital of the outermost occupied shell, and the *d* orbitals, one shell smaller, are being filled.

Lithium, sodium, and potassium, elements of the leftmost column of the periodic table (Group 1A), have a single electron in their outermost *s* orbital (ns^1). Beryllium and magnesium, of Group 2A, have two electrons in their outermost shell, ns^2, while boron and aluminum (Group 3A) have three electrons in their outermost shell, ns^2np^1. Similar observations can be made for other A group elements.

The electron configurations of the A group elements and the noble gases can be predicted reliably from Figures 4-30 and 4-31. However, there are some more pronounced irregularities in the B groups below the fourth period. In the heavier B group elements, the higher energy subshells in different principal shells have energies that are very nearly equal (see Figure 4-31). It is easy for an electron to jump from one orbital to another of nearly the same energy, even in a different set. This is because the orbital energies are *perturbed* (changed slightly) as the nuclear charge changes, and an extra electron is added in

▶ A newer IUPAC system numbers the columns in the periodic table from 1 to 18 for the *s*-, *d*-, and *p*-block elements. This is shown in most of the periodic tables in this book in parentheses under the older system, which uses a number plus A or B. Some chemists use the still older system of a Roman numeral plus A or B.

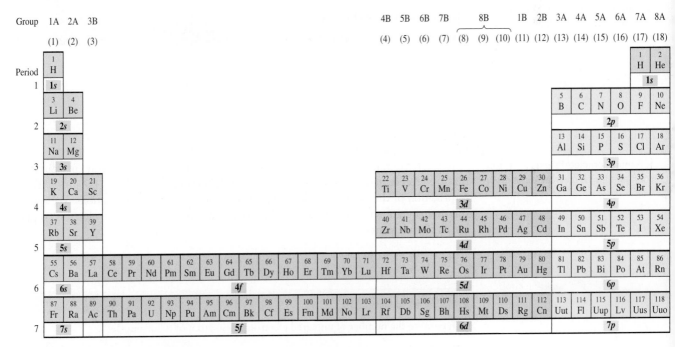

Figure 4-32 A periodic table colored to show the kinds of atomic orbitals (subshells) being filled and the symbols of blocks of elements. The electronic structures of the A group elements are quite regular and can be predicted from their positions in the periodic table, but many exceptions occur in the *d* and *f* blocks. The colors in this figure are the same as those in Figure 4-29.

Hydrogen and helium are shown here in their usual positions in the periodic table. These may seem somewhat unusual based just on their electron configurations. We should remember, however, that the first shell ($n = 1$) can hold a maximum of only two electrons. This shell is entirely filled in helium, so He behaves as a noble gas, and we put it in the column with the other noble gases (Group 8A). Hydrogen has one electron that is easily lost, like the alkali metals (Group 1A), so we put it in Group 1A even though it is not a metal. Furthermore, hydrogen is one electron short of a noble gas configuration (He), so we could also place it with the other such elements in Group 7A.

EXAMPLE 4-10 Electron Configurations

Use Table 4-9 to determine the electron configurations of (a) magnesium, Mg; (b) germanium, Ge; and (c) molybdenum, Mo.

Plan

We will use the electron configurations indicated in Table 4-9 for each group. Each *period* (row) begins filling a new shell (new value of n). Elements to the right of the d orbital block have the d orbitals in the $(n - 1)$ shell already filled. We often find it convenient to collect all sets of orbitals with the same value of n together, to emphasize the number of electrons in the *outermost* shell, that is, the shell with the highest value of n.

Solution

(a) Magnesium, Mg, is in Group 2A, which has the general configuration s^2; it is in Period 3 (third row). The last filled noble gas configuration is that of neon, or [Ne]. The electron configuration of Mg is $[\text{Ne}] \, 3s^2$.

(b) Germanium, Ge, is in Group 4A, for which Table 4-9 shows the general configuration s^2p^2. It is in Period 4 (the fourth row), so we interpret this as $4s^2 4p^2$. The last filled noble gas configuration is that of argon, Ar, accounting for 18 electrons. In addition, Ge lies beyond the d orbital block, so we know that the $3d$ orbitals are completely filled. The electron configuration of Ge is $[\text{Ar}] \, 4s^2 3d^{10} 4p^2$ or $[\text{Ar}] \, 3d^{10} 4s^2 4p^2$.

(c) Molybdenum, Mo, is in Group 6B, with the general configuration $d^5 s^1$; it is in Period 5, which begins with $5s$ and is beyond the noble gas krypton. The electron configuration of Mo is $[\text{Kr}] \, 5s^1 4d^5$ or $[\text{Kr}] \, 4d^5 5s^1$. The electron configuration of molybdenum is analogous to that of chromium, Cr, the element just above it. The configuration of Cr was discussed in Section 4-18 as one of the exceptions to the Aufbau order of filling.

You should now work Exercise 120.

▶ Although the 4s orbital usually fills before the 3d, most chemists will understand and accept either of the answers shown for the electron configurations of Ge and Mo. The same holds for the configurations of other elements.

▶ A more complete listing of electron configurations is given in Appendix B.

going from one element to the next. This phenomenon gives rise to other irregularities that are analogous to those seen for Cr and Cu, described earlier.

We can extend the information in Figure 4-32 to indicate the electron configurations that are represented by each *group* (column) of the periodic table. Table 4-9 shows this interpretation of the periodic table, along with the most important exceptions. We can use this interpretation of the periodic table to write, quickly and reliably, the electron configurations for elements.

EXAMPLE 4-11 Unpaired Electrons

Determine the number of unpaired electrons in an atom of tellurium, Te.

Plan

Te is in Group 6A in the periodic table, which tells us that its configuration is s^2p^4. All other shells are completely filled, so they contain only paired electrons. We need only to find out how many unpaired electrons are represented by s^2p^4.

Solution

The notation s^2p^4 is a short representation for $s \, \uparrow\downarrow \, p \, \uparrow\downarrow \, \uparrow \, \uparrow$. This shows that an atom of Te contains two unpaired electrons.

You should now work Exercises 126 and 128.

Ⓢ TOP & THINK
Remember that electrons occupy a set of equivalent orbitals (a given subshell) *singly* before they pair (Hund's Rule).

Table 4-9 The *s, p, d,* and *f* Blocks of the Periodic Table*

GROUPS

1A	2A	3B		4B	5B	6B	7B		8B		1B	2B	3A	4A	5A	6A	7A	8A
(1)	(2)	(3)		(4)	(5)	(6)	(7)	(8)	(9)	(10)	(11)	(12)	(13)	(14)	(15)	(16)	(17)	(18)

s orbital block

p orbital block

f orbital block

d orbital block

	s^1	s^2		d^1s^2	d^2s^2	d^3s^2	d^5s^1	d^5s^2	d^6s^2	d^7s^2	d^8s^2	$d^{10}s^1$	$d^{10}s^2$	s^2p^1	s^2p^2	s^2p^3	s^2p^4	s^2p^5	s^2p^6
$n=1$	1 H																		s^2 2 He
$n=2$	3 Li	4 Be												5 B	6 C	7 N	8 O	9 F	10 Ne
$n=3$	11 Na	12 Mg												13 Al	14 Si	15 P	16 S	17 Cl	18 Ar
$n=4$	19 K	20 Ca	21 Sc		22 Ti	23 V	24 Cr	25 Mn	26 Fe	27 Co	28 Ni	29 Cu	30 Zn	31 Ga	32 Ge	33 As	34 Se	35 Br	36 Kr
$n=5$	37 Rb	38 Sr	39 Y		40 Zr	41 Nb d^4s^1	42 Mo	43 Tc	44 Ru d^7s^1	45 Rh d^8s^1	46 Pd $d^{10}s^0$	47 Ag	48 Cd	49 In	50 Sn	51 Sb	52 Te	53 I	54 Xe
$n=6$	55 Cs	56 Ba	57 La	58 Ce→71 Lu	72 Hf	73 Ta	74 W d^4s^2	75 Re	76 Os	77 Ir	78 Pt d^9s^1	79 Au	80 Hg	81 Tl	82 Pb	83 Bi	84 Po	85 At	86 Rn
$n=7$	87 Fr	88 Ra	89 Ac	90 Th→103 Lr	104 Rf	105 Db	106 Sg	107 Bh	108 Hs	109 Mt	110 Ds	111 Rg	112 Cn	113 Uut	114 Fl	115 Uup	116 Lv	117 Uus	118 Uuo

$n=6$ Lanthanide Series	58 Ce	59 Pr	60 Nd	61 Pm	62 Sm	63 Eu	64 Gd	65 Tb	66 Dy	67 Ho	68 Er	69 Tm	70 Yb	71 Lu	*4f* subshell
$n=7$ Actinide Series	90 Th	91 Pa	92 U	93 Np	94 Pu	95 Am	96 Cm	97 Bk	98 Cf	99 Es	100 Fm	101 Md	102 No	103 Lr	*5f* subshell

*n is the principal quantum number. The d^1s^2, d^2s^2, ... designations represent *known* configurations. They refer to $(n-1)d$ and ns orbitals. Several exceptions to the *d*-block configurations are indicated.

The periodic table has been described as "the chemist's best friend." Chemical reactions involve loss, gain, or sharing of electrons. In this chapter, we have seen that the fundamental basis of the periodic table is that it reflects similarities and trends in electron configurations. It is easy to use the periodic table to determine many important aspects of electron configurations of atoms. Practice until you can use the periodic table with confidence to answer many questions about electron configurations. As we continue our study, we will learn many other useful ways to interpret the periodic table. We should always keep in mind that the many trends in chemical and physical properties that we correlate with the periodic table are ultimately based on the trends in electron configurations.

4-20 Paramagnetism and Diamagnetism

Substances that contain unpaired electrons are weakly *attracted* into magnetic fields and are said to be **paramagnetic**. By contrast, those in which all electrons are paired are very weakly repelled by magnetic fields and are called **diamagnetic**. The magnetic effect can be measured by hanging a test tube full of a substance on a balance by a long thread and suspending it above the gap of an electromagnet (Figure 4-33). When the current is switched on, a paramagnetic substance such as copper(II) sulfate is pulled into the strong field. The

▶ Both paramagnetism and diamagnetism are hundreds to thousands of times weaker than *ferromagnetism*, the effect seen in iron bar magnets.

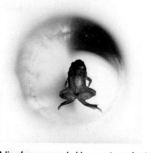

A live frog suspended in an extremely strong magnetic field (16 tesla) demonstrating the diamagnetic repulsion effect.

paramagnetic attraction per mole of substance can be measured by weighing the sample before and after energizing the magnet. The paramagnetism per mole increases with increasing number of unpaired electrons per formula unit. Many transition metals and ions have one or more unpaired electrons and are paramagnetic.

Iron, cobalt, and nickel are the only *free* elements that exhibit **ferromagnetism**. This property is much stronger than paramagnetism; it allows a substance to become permanently magnetized when placed in a magnetic field. This happens as randomly oriented electron spins align themselves with an applied field. To exhibit ferromagnetism, the atoms must be within the proper range of sizes so that unpaired electrons on adjacent atoms can interact cooperatively with one another, but not to the extent that they pair. Experimental evidence suggests that in ferromagnets, atoms cluster together into *domains* that contain large numbers of atoms in fairly small volumes. The atoms within each domain interact cooperatively with one another to generate ferromagnetism.

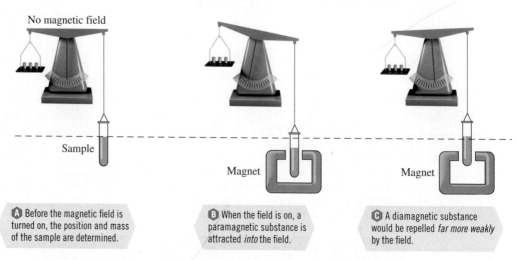

No magnetic field

Sample

Magnet

Magnet

A Before the magnetic field is turned on, the position and mass of the sample are determined.

B When the field is on, a paramagnetic substance is attracted *into* the field.

C A diamagnetic substance would be repelled *far more weakly* by the field.

Figure 4-33 Diagram of an apparatus for measuring the paramagnetism of a substance. The tube contains a measured amount of the substance, often in solution.

KEY TERMS

Absorption spectrum   The spectrum associated with absorption of electromagnetic radiation by atoms (or other species) resulting from transitions from lower to higher electronic energy states.

Alkali metals   Elements of Group 1A in the periodic table, except hydrogen.

Alkaline earth metals   Group 2A elements in the periodic table.

Alpha- (α-) particle   A helium ion with a 2+ charge; an assembly of two protons and two neutrons.

amu   See *Atomic mass unit*.

Angular momentum quantum number (ℓ)   The quantum mechanical solution to a wave equation that designates the subshell, or set of orbitals (s, p, d, f), within a given main shell in which an electron resides.

Anode   In a cathode-ray tube, the positive electrode.

Atomic mass unit (amu)   An arbitrary mass unit defined to be exactly one twelfth the mass of the carbon-12 isotope.

Atomic mass (weight)   Weighted average of the masses of the constituent isotopes of an element; the relative mass of atoms of different elements.

Atomic number   The integral number of protons in the nucleus; defines the identity of an element.

Atomic orbital   The region or volume in space in which the probability of finding electrons is highest.

Aufbau ("building up") Principle   A guide for predicting the order in which electrons fill subshells and shells in atoms.

Balmer–Rydberg equation   An empirical equation that relates wavelengths in the hydrogen emission spectrum to simple integers.

Canal ray   A stream of positively charged particles (cations) that moves toward the negative electrode in a cathode-ray tube; observed to pass through canals (holes) in the negative electrode.

Cathode   In a cathode-ray tube, the negative electrode.

Cathode ray   The beam of electrons going from the negative electrode toward the positive electrode in a cathode-ray tube.

Cathode-ray tube   A closed glass tube containing a gas under low pressure, with electrodes near the ends and a luminescent screen at the end near the positive electrode; produces cathode rays when high voltage is applied.

Chemical periodicity   The variation in properties of elements with their positions in the periodic table.

Continuous spectrum   A spectrum that contains all wavelengths in a specified region of the electromagnetic spectrum.

d orbitals   Beginning in the third shell, a set of five degenerate orbitals per shell, higher in energy than *s* and *p* orbitals in the same shell.

Degenerate orbitals   Two or more orbitals that have the same energy.

Diamagnetism   *Weak* repulsion by a magnetic field; associated with all electrons in an atom, molecule, or substance being paired.

Electromagnetic radiation   Energy that is propagated by means of electric and magnetic fields that oscillate in directions perpendicular to the direction of travel of the energy.

Electron   A subatomic particle having a mass of 0.00054858 amu and a charge of 1−.

Electron configuration   The specific distribution of electrons in the atomic orbitals of atoms and ions.

Electron transition   The transfer of an electron from one energy level to another.

Emission spectrum   The spectrum associated with emission of electromagnetic radiation by atoms (or other species) resulting from electron transitions from higher to lower energy states.

Excited state   Any energy state other than the ground state of an atom, ion, or molecule.

f orbitals   Beginning in the fourth shell, a set of seven degenerate orbitals per shell, higher in energy than *s*, *p*, and *d* orbitals in the same shell.

Ferromagnetism   The property that allows a substance to become permanently magnetized when placed in a magnetic field; exhibited by iron, cobalt, and nickel and some of their alloys.

Frequency (ν)   The number of crests of a wave that pass a given point per unit time.

Fundamental particles   Subatomic particles of which all matter is composed; protons, electrons, and neutrons are fundamental particles.

Ground state   The lowest energy state or most stable state of an atom, molecule, or ion.

Group (family)   The elements in a vertical column of the periodic table.

Halogens   Elements of Group 7A in the periodic table.

Heisenberg Uncertainty Principle   It is impossible to determine accurately both the momentum and position of an electron simultaneously.

Hund's Rule   Each orbital of a given subshell is occupied by a single electron before pairing begins. See *Aufbau Principle*.

Isotopes   Two or more forms of atoms of the same element with different masses; that is, atoms containing the same number of protons but different numbers of neutrons.

Line spectrum   An atomic emission or absorption spectrum.

Magnetic quantum number (m_ℓ)   Quantum mechanical solution to a wave equation that designates the particular orbital within a given subshell (s, p, d, f) in which an electron resides. The p_x, p_y, and p_z orbitals have different magnetic quantum numbers.

Mass number   The integral sum of the numbers of protons and neutrons in an atom.

Mass spectrometer   An instrument that measures the charge-to-mass ratios of charged particles.

Metal   An element below and to the left of the stepwise division (metalloids) of the periodic table; about 80% of the known elements are metals.

Metalloids   Elements with properties intermediate between metals and nonmetals: B, Si, Ge, As, Sb, Te, and At.

Natural radioactivity   Spontaneous decomposition of an atom.

Neutron   A subatomic nuclear particle having a mass of 1.0087 amu and no charge.

Noble (rare) gases   Elements of Group 8A in the periodic table.

Nonmetals   Elements above and to the right of the metalloids in the periodic table.

Nucleus   The very small, very dense, positively charged center of an atom, consisting of protons and neutrons (except for $_1^1$H, which has no neutrons).

Nuclide symbol   The symbol for an atom, $_Z^A$E, in which E is the symbol for an element, Z is its atomic number, and A is its mass number.

Orbital   Each allowed wave description of a stable state for an electron in an atom; a region of space in which the probability of finding an electron is high.

p orbitals   Beginning with the second shell, a set of three degenerate, mutually perpendicular, equal-arm, dumbbell-shaped atomic orbitals per shell.

Paired electrons   Two electrons with opposite m_s values in the same orbital (↑↓). Also known as *spin-paired electrons*.

Paramagnetism   Attraction toward a magnetic field, stronger than diamagnetism, but still very weak compared with ferromagnetism; due to presence of unpaired electrons.

Pauli Exclusion Principle   No two electrons in the same atom may have identical sets of four quantum numbers.

Period   The elements in a horizontal row of the periodic table.

Periodic law   The properties of the elements are periodic functions of their atomic numbers.

Periodic table   An arrangement of elements in order of increasing atomic number that also emphasizes periodicity.

Periodicity   Regular periodic variations of properties of elements with atomic number (and position in the periodic table).

Photoelectric effect   Emission of an electron from the surface of a metal, caused by impinging electromagnetic radiation of certain minimum energy; the resulting current increases with increasing intensity of radiation.

Photon   A "packet" of light or electromagnetic radiation; also called a quantum of light.

Principal quantum number (n)   The quantum mechanical solution to a wave equation that designates the main shell, or energy level, in which an electron resides.

Proton   A subatomic particle having a mass of 1.0073 amu and a charge of 1+, found in the nuclei of atoms.

Quantum   A "packet" of energy. See *Photon*.

Quantum mechanics   A mathematical method of treating particles on the basis of quantum theory, which assumes that energy (of small particles) is not infinitely divisible.

Quantum numbers   Numbers that describe the energies of electrons in atoms; they are derived from quantum mechanical treatment.

Radiant energy   See *Electromagnetic radiation*.

s orbital   A spherically symmetrical atomic orbital; one per shell.

Spectral line   Any of a number of lines corresponding to definite wavelengths in an atomic emission or absorption spectrum; these lines represent the energy difference between two energy levels.

Spectrum   Display of component wavelengths of electromagnetic radiation.

Spin quantum number (m_s)   The quantum mechanical solution to a wave equation that indicates the relative spins of electrons ("spin up" and "spin down").

Wavelength (λ)   The distance between two identical points of a wave.

EXERCISES

🔵 **Molecular Reasoning** exercises

▲ **More Challenging** exercises

Blue-Numbered exercises are solved in the Student Solutions Manual

Particles and the Nuclear Atom

1. List the three fundamental particles of atoms, and indicate the mass and charge associated with each.
2. In the oil-drop experiment, how did Millikan know that none of the oil droplets he observed were ones that had a deficiency of electrons rather than an excess?
3. 🔵 How many electrons carry a total charge of 1.00 coulomb?
4. (a) How do we know that canal rays have charges opposite in sign to cathode rays? What are canal rays? (b) Why are cathode rays from all samples of gases identical, whereas canal rays are not?
5. ▲ The following data are measurements of the charges on oil droplets using an apparatus similar to that used by Millikan:

13.458×10^{-19} C 15.373×10^{-19} C
17.303×10^{-19} C 15.378×10^{-19} C
17.308×10^{-19} C 28.844×10^{-19} C
11.545×10^{-19} C 19.214×10^{-19} C

   Each should be a whole-number ratio of some fundamental charge. Using these data, determine the largest possible value of the fundamental charge.
6. ▲ Suppose we discover a new positively charged particle, which we call the "whizatron." We want to determine its charge. (a) What modifications would we have to make to the Millikan oil-drop apparatus to carry out the corresponding experiment on whizatrons? (b) In such an experiment, we observe the following charges on five different droplets:

4.88×10^{-19} C 8.53×10^{-19} C
6.10×10^{-19} C 7.32×10^{-19} C
2.44×10^{-19} C

   What is the largest possible value of the charge on the whizatron?
7. Outline Rutherford's contribution to understanding the nature of atoms.
8. Why was Rutherford so surprised that some of the α-particles were scattered backward in the gold foil experiment?
9. Summarize Moseley's contribution to our knowledge of the structure of atoms.
10. The approximate radius of a hydrogen atom is 0.0529 nm, and that of a proton is 1.5×10^{-15} m. Assuming both the hydrogen atom and the proton to be spherical, calculate the fraction of the space in an atom of hydrogen that is occupied by the nucleus. $V = (4/3)\pi r^3$ for a sphere.
11. The approximate radius of a neutron is 1.5×10^{-15} m, and the mass is 1.675×10^{-27} kg. Calculate the density of a neutron. $V = (4/3)\pi r^3$ for a sphere.

Atomic Composition, Isotopes, and Atomic Weights

12. 🔵 Arrange the following in order of increasing ratio of charge to mass: $^{12}C^+$, $^{12}C^{2+}$, $^{14}N^+$, $^{14}N^{2+}$.
13. 🔵 ▲ Refer to Exercise 12. Suppose all of these high-energy ions are present in a mass spectrometer. For which one will its path be changed (a) the most and (b) the least by increasing the external magnetic field? Which of the ions would take (c) the longest time and (d) the shortest time to travel a given distance in a time-of-flight mass spectrometer?
14. 🔵 Estimate the percentage of the total mass of a ^{58}Ni atom that is due to (a) electrons, (b) protons, and (c) neutrons by *assuming* that the mass of the atom is simply the sum of the masses of the appropriate numbers of subatomic particles.
15. 🔵 (a) How are isotopic abundances determined experimentally? (b) How do the isotopes of a given element differ?
16. 🔵 Clearly define and provide examples that illustrate the meaning of each: (a) atomic number; (b) isotope; (c) mass number; (d) nuclear charge.
17. 🔵 Write the composition of one atom of each of the three isotopes of silicon: ^{28}Si, ^{29}Si, ^{30}Si.
18. 🔵 Write the composition of one atom of each of the four isotopes of strontium: ^{84}Sr, ^{86}Sr, ^{87}Sr, ^{88}Sr.
19. 🔵 Complete Chart A on the next page for neutral atoms.
20. 🔵 Complete Chart B on the next page for neutral atoms.
21. ▲ Prior to 1962, the atomic weight scale was based on the assignment of an atomic weight of exactly 16 amu to the *naturally occurring* mixture of oxygen. The atomic weight of nickel is 58.6934 amu on the carbon-12 scale. What would it have been on the older scale?
22. 🔵 Determine the number of protons, neutrons, and electrons in each of the following species: (a) ^{24}Mg; (b) ^{51}V; (c) ^{91}Zr; (d) ^{27}Al; (e) $^{65}Zn^{2+}$; (f) $^{108}Ag^+$.
23. 🔵 Determine the number of protons, neutrons, and electrons in each of the following species: (a) ^{52}Cr; (b) ^{112}Cd; (c) $^{137}Ba^{2+}$; (d) $^{63}Cu^+$; (e) $^{56}Fe^{2+}$; (f) $^{55}Fe^{3+}$.
24. 🔵 What is the symbol of the species composed of each of the following sets of subatomic particles? (a) 24p, 28n, 24e; (b) 20p, 20n, 20e; (c) 33p, 42n, 33e; (d) 53p, 74n, 53e.
25. 🔵 What is the symbol of the species composed of each of the following sets of subatomic particles? (a) 94p, 150n, 94e; (b) 79p, 118n, 76e; (c) 34p, 45n, 34e; (d) 56p, 80n, 56e.
26. The listed atomic weight of gallium is 69.723 amu. Gallium has two stable isotopes, both of which are used in nuclear medicine. These two stable isotopes have the following masses: ^{69}Ga, 68.925580; ^{71}Ga, 70.9247005. Calculate the percent of each isotope in naturally occurring gallium.

Chart A

Kind of Atom	Atomic Number	Mass Number	Isotope	Number of Protons	Number of Electrons	Number of Neutrons
_____	_____	_____	^{21}Ne	_____	_____	_____
potassium	_____	39		_____	_____	_____
_____	14	28		_____	_____	_____
_____	_____	202		80	_____	_____

Chart B

Kind of Atom	Atomic Number	Mass Number	Isotope	Number of Protons	Number of Electrons	Number of Neutrons
cobalt	_____	_____		_____	_____	32
_____	_____	_____	^{11}B	_____	_____	_____
_____	_____	_____		_____	25	30
_____	_____	182		_____	78	_____

27. The atomic weight of rubidium is 85.4678 amu. The two naturally occurring isotopes of rubidium have the following masses: ^{85}Rb, 84.9118 amu; ^{87}Rb, 86.9092 amu. Calculate the percent of each isotope in naturally occurring rubidium.

28. Strontium has four isotopes with the following masses: 83.9134 amu (0.56%), 85.9094 amu (9.86%), 86.9089 amu (7.00%), and 87.9056 (82.58%). Calculate the atomic mass of strontium.

29. What is the atomic weight of a hypothetical element that consists of the following isotopes in the indicated relative abundances?

Isotope	Isotopic Mass (amu)	% Natural Abundance
1	94.9	12.4
2	95.9	73.6
3	97.9	14.0

30. Naturally occurring iron consists of four isotopes with the abundances indicated here. From the masses and relative abundances of these isotopes, calculate the atomic weight of naturally occurring iron.

Isotope	Isotopic Mass (amu)	% Natural Abundance
^{54}Fe	53.9396	5.82
^{56}Fe	55.9349	91.66
^{57}Fe	56.9354	2.19
^{58}Fe	57.9333	0.33

31. Calculate the atomic weight of nickel from the following information.

Isotope	Isotopic Mass (amu)	% Natural Abundance
^{58}Ni	57.9353	68.08
^{60}Ni	59.9308	26.22
^{61}Ni	60.9311	1.14
^{62}Ni	61.9283	3.63
^{64}Ni	63.9280	0.93

32. The atomic weight of copper is 63.546 amu. The two naturally occurring isotopes of copper have the following masses: ^{63}Cu, 62.9298 amu; ^{65}Cu, 64.9278 amu. Calculate the percent of ^{63}Cu in naturally occurring copper.

Charles D. Winters

Native copper

33. Silver consists of two naturally occurring isotopes: ^{107}Ag, which has a mass of 106.90509 amu, and ^{109}Ag, which has a mass of 108.9047 amu. The atomic weight of silver is 107.8682 amu. Determine the percent abundance of each isotope in naturally occurring silver.

34. Refer to Table 4-3 *only* and calculate the atomic weights of oxygen and chlorine. Do your answers agree with the atomic weights given in that table?

35. The following is a mass spectrum of the 1+ charged ions of an element. Calculate the atomic weight of the element. What is the element?

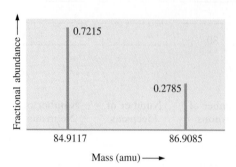

36. 💰 Suppose you measure the mass spectrum of the 1+ charged ions of germanium, atomic weight 72.61 amu. Unfortunately, the mass spectrometer malfunctions at the beginning and again at the end of your experiment. You obtain only the following spectrum, which *may or may not be complete*. From the information given here, can you tell whether one of the germanium isotopes is missing? If one is missing, at which end of the plot should it appear?

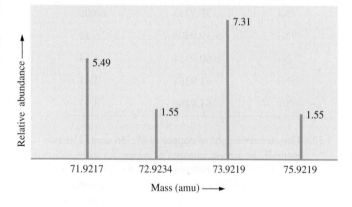

37. Calculate the atomic weight of silicon using the following data for the percent natural abundance and mass of each isotope: 92.23% ^{28}Si (27.9769 amu); 4.67% ^{29}Si (28.9765 amu); 3.10% ^{30}Si (29.9738 amu).

Silicon

38. Calculate the atomic weight of chromium using the following data for the percent natural abundance and mass of each isotope: 4.35% ^{50}Cr (49.9461 amu); 83.79% ^{52}Cr (51.9405 amu); 9.50% ^{53}Cr (52.9406 amu); 2.36% ^{54}Cr (53.9389 amu).

The Periodic Table

39. State the periodic law. What does it mean?

40. What was Mendeleev's contribution to the construction of the modern periodic table?

41. Consult a handbook of chemistry or a suitable website, and look up melting points of the elements of Periods 2 and 3. Show that melting point is a property that varies periodically for these elements.

42. ▲ Mendeleev's periodic table was based on increasing atomic weight. Argon has a higher atomic weight than potassium, yet in the modern table argon appears before potassium. Explain how this can be.

43. Estimate the density of antimony from the following densities (g/cm³): As, 5.72; Bi, 9.8; Sn, 7.30; Te, 6.24. Show how you arrived at your answer. Using a reference other than your textbook, look up the density of antimony. How does your predicted value compare with the reported value?

Antimony is used to harden the lead in lead storage batteries.

44. Estimate the density of selenium from the following densities (g/cm³): S, 2.07; Te, 6.24; As, 5.72; Br, 3.12. Show how you arrived at your answer. Using a reference other than your textbook, look up the density of selenium. How does your predicted value compare with the reported value?

45. Estimate the specific heat of antimony from the following specific heats (J/g · °C): As, 0.34; Bi, 0.14; Sn, 0.23; Te, 0.20. Show how you arrived at your answer.

46. Given the following melting points in °C, estimate the value for CBr₄: CF₄, −184; CCl₄, −23; CI₄, 171 (decomposes). Using a reference other than your textbook, look up the melting point of CBr₄. How does your predicted value compare with the reported value?

47. Calcium and magnesium form the following compounds: $CaCl_2$, $MgCl_2$, CaO, MgO, Ca_3N_2, and Mg_3N_2. Predict the formula for a compound of (a) magnesium and sulfur, (b) barium and bromine.

💰 **Molecular Reasoning** exercises   ▲ **More Challenging** exercises   Blue-Numbered exercises solved in Student Solutions Manual

48. The formulas of some hydrides of second-period representative elements are as follows: BeH_2, BH_3, CH_4, NH_3, H_2O, HF. A famous test in criminology laboratories for the presence of arsenic (As) involves the formation of arsine, the hydride of arsenic. Predict the formula of arsine.

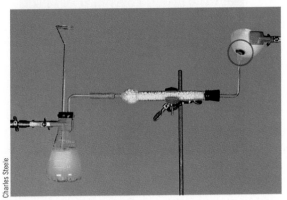

Arsine burns to form a dark spot.

49. Clearly distinguish between the following terms and provide specific examples of each: groups (families) of elements and periods of elements.
50. Write names and symbols for (a) the alkaline earth metals; (b) the Group 4A elements; (c) the Group 2B elements.
51. Write names and symbols for (a) the alkali metals; (b) the noble gases; (c) the Group 4A elements.
52. Clearly and concisely define the following terms and provide examples of each: (a) metals; (b) nonmetals; (c) halogens.

Electromagnetic Radiation

53. Calculate the wavelengths, in meters, of radiation of the following frequencies: (a) $4.80 \times 10^{15}\,s^{-1}$; (b) $1.18 \times 10^{14}\,s^{-1}$; (c) $5.44 \times 10^{12}\,s^{-1}$.
54. Calculate the frequency of radiation of each of the following wavelengths: (a) 8973Å; (b) 442 nm; (c) 4.92 cm; (d) 4.55×10^{-9} cm.
55. What is the energy of a photon of each of the radiations in Exercise 53? Express your answer in joules per photon. In which regions of the electromagnetic spectrum do these radiations fall?
56. Excited lithium ions emit radiation at a wavelength of 670.8 nm in the visible range of the spectrum. (This characteristic color is often used as a qualitative analysis test for the presence of Li^+.) Calculate (a) the frequency and (b) the energy of a photon of this radiation. (c) What color is this light?
57. Calculate the energy, in joules per photon, of the red line, 6573 Å, in the discharge spectrum of atomic calcium.
58. Ozone in the upper atmosphere absorbs ultraviolet radiation, which induces the following chemical reaction:

$$O_3(g) \rightarrow O_2 + O$$

What is the energy of a 3400-Å photon that is absorbed? What is the energy of a mole of these photons?

59. ▲ During photosynthesis, chlorophyll-α absorbs light of wavelength 440 nm and emits light of wavelength 670 nm. How much energy is available for photosynthesis from the absorption–emission of a mole of photons?

Photosynthesis

60. Alpha Centauri is the star closest to our solar system. It is 4.3 light-years away. How many miles is this? A light year is the distance that light travels (in a vacuum) in one year. Assume that space is essentially a vacuum.

The Photoelectric Effect

61. What evidence supports the idea that electromagnetic radiation is (a) wave-like; (b) particle-like?
62. Describe the influence of frequency and intensity of electromagnetic radiation on the current in the photoelectric effect.
63. ♣ ▲ Cesium is often used in "electric eyes" for self-opening doors in an application of the photoelectric effect. The amount of energy required to ionize (remove an electron from) a cesium atom is 3.89 electron volts (1 eV = 1.60×10^{-19} J). Show by calculation whether a beam of yellow light with wavelength 5830 Å would ionize a cesium atom.
64. ▲ Refer to Exercise 63. What would be the wavelength, in nanometers, of light with just sufficient energy to ionize a cesium atom? What color would this light be?

Atomic Spectra and the Bohr Theory

65. (a) Distinguish between an atomic emission spectrum and an atomic absorption spectrum. (b) Distinguish between a continuous spectrum and a line spectrum.

♣ **Molecular Reasoning** exercises   ▲ **More Challenging** exercises   Blue-Numbered exercises solved in Student Solutions Manual

Unless otherwise noted, all content on this page is © Cengage Learning.

66. 🔵 ▲ Prepare a sketch similar to Figure 4-18b that shows a ground energy state and three excited energy states. Using vertical arrows, indicate the transitions that would correspond to the absorption spectrum for this system.

67. 🔵 Why is the Bohr model of the hydrogen atom referred to as the solar system model?

68. 🔵 ▲ If each atom in one mole of atoms emits a photon of wavelength 5.50×10^3 Å, how much energy is lost? Express the answer in kJ/mol. As a reference point, burning one mole (16 g) of CH_4 produces 819 kJ of heat.

69. What is the Balmer–Rydberg equation? Why is it called an empirical equation?

70. Hydrogen atoms absorb energy so that the electrons are excited to the energy level $n = 7$. Electrons then undergo these transitions: (1) $n = 7 \rightarrow n = 1$; (2) $n = 7 \rightarrow n = 2$; (3) $n = 2 \rightarrow n = 1$. Which of these transitions will produce the photon with (a) the smallest energy; (b) the highest frequency; (c) the shortest wavelength? (d) What is the frequency of a photon resulting from the transition $n = 6 \rightarrow n = 1$?

71. ▲ Five energy levels of the He atom are given in joules per atom above an *arbitrary* reference energy: (1) 6.000×10^{-19}; (2) 8.812×10^{-19}; (3) 9.381×10^{-19}; (4) 10.443×10^{-19}; (5) 10.934×10^{-19}. Construct an energy level diagram for He, and find the energy of the photon (a) absorbed for the electron transition from level 1 to level 5 and (b) emitted for the electron transition from level 4 to level 1.

72. The following are prominent lines in the visible region of the emission spectra of the elements listed. The lines can be used to identify the elements. What color is the light responsible for each line? (a) lithium, 4603 Å; (b) neon, 540.0 nm; (c) calcium, 6573 Å; (d) potassium, $\nu = 3.90 \times 10^{14}$ Hz.

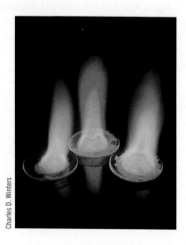

73. Hydrogen atoms have an absorption line at 1026 Å. What is the frequency of the photons absorbed, and what is the energy difference, in joules, between the ground state and this excited state of the atom?

74. An argon laser emits blue light with a wavelength of 488.0 nm. How many photons are emitted by this laser in 2.00 seconds, operating at a power of 515 milliwatts? One watt (a unit of power) is equal to 1 joule/second.

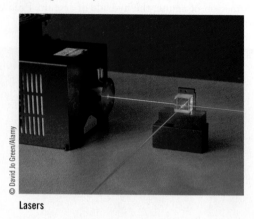

Lasers

The Wave–Particle View of Matter

75. (a) What evidence supports the idea that electrons are particle-like? (b) What evidence supports the idea that electrons are wave-like?

76. (a) What is the de Broglie wavelength of a proton moving at a speed of 2.50×10^7 m/s? The proton mass is 1.67×10^{-24} g. (b) What is the de Broglie wavelength of a stone with a mass of 30.0 g moving at 2.00×10^5 m/h (≈ 100 mph)? (c) How do the wavelengths in parts (a) and (b) compare with the typical radii of atoms? (See the atomic radii in Figure 5-1.)

77. What is the wavelength corresponding to a neutron of mass 1.67×10^{-27} kg moving at 2360 m/s?

78. What is the velocity of an α-particle (a helium nucleus) that has a de Broglie wavelength of 0.529 Å?

Quantum Numbers and Atomic Orbitals

79. (a) What is a quantum number? What is an atomic orbital? (b) How many quantum numbers are required to specify a single atomic orbital? What are they?

80. How are the possible values for the angular momentum quantum number for a given electron restricted by the value of n?

81. Without giving the ranges of possible values of the four quantum numbers, n, ℓ, m_ℓ, and m_s, describe briefly what information each one gives.

82. Draw an orbital that has the following quantum numbers: $n = 3$, $\ell = 1$, $m_\ell = -1$, and $m_s = -\frac{1}{2}$.

83. What is the maximum number of electrons in an atom that can have the following quantum numbers? (a) $n = 2$; (b) $n = 3$ and $\ell = 1$; (c) $n = 3$, $\ell = 1$, and $m_\ell = 0$; (d) $n = 3$, $\ell = 1$, $m_\ell = -1$, and $m_s = -\frac{1}{2}$.

84. What is the maximum number of electrons in an atom that can have the following quantum numbers? (a) $n = 3$ and $\ell = 1$; (b) $n = 3$ and $\ell = 2$; (c) $n = 3$, $\ell = 0$ and $m_\ell = -1$; (d) $n = 3$, $\ell = 1$, and $m_\ell = -1$; (e) $n = 3$, $\ell = 1$, $m_\ell = 0$, and $m_s = -\frac{1}{2}$.

85. What are the values of n and ℓ for the following subshells? (a) $1s$; (b) $3s$; (c) $5p$; (d) $3d$; (e) $4f$.

86. 🔵 (a) How many sublevels are in the third main energy level? (b) Which, if any, of these sublevels contain a set of equivalent orbitals? (c) Sketch, on the same relative scale, at least one orbital from each of these sublevels.

87. 🔵 (a) How many sublevels are in the second main energy level? (b) Which, if any, of these sublevels contain a set of equivalent orbitals? (c) Sketch, on the same relative scale, at least one orbital from each of these sublevels.

88. How many individual orbitals are there in the third shell? Write out n, ℓ, and m_ℓ quantum numbers for each one, and label each set by the s, p, d, f designations.

89. (a) Write the possible values of ℓ when $n = 4$. (b) Write the allowed number of orbitals (1) with the quantum numbers $n = 3$, $\ell = 1$; (2) with the quantum numbers $n = 2$, $\ell = 1$; (3) with the quantum numbers $n = 3$, $\ell = 1$, $m_l = -1$; (4) with the quantum number $n = 1$.

90. What are the possible values for m_ℓ for (a) the p sublevel? (b) the f sublevel? (c) all sublevels where $n = 3$?

91. Write a complete set of quantum numbers (n, ℓ, and m_ℓ) for each of the following orbitals: (a) $5f$; (b) $4d$; and (c) $2s$.

92. How many orbitals correspond to each of the following designations? (a) $3p$; (b) $4p$; (c) $4p_x$; (d) $6d$; (e) $5d$; (f) $5f$; (g) $n = 5$; (h) $7s$

93. The following incorrect sets of quantum numbers in the order n, ℓ, m_ℓ, m_s are written for paired electrons or for one electron in an orbital. Correct them, assuming the n values are correct. (a) $1, 0, 0, +\frac{1}{2}, +\frac{1}{2}$; (b) $2, 2, 1, \frac{1}{2}$; (c) $3, 2, 3, \pm\frac{1}{2}$; (d) $3, 1, 2, +\frac{1}{2}$; (e) $2, 1, -1, 0$; (f) $3, -0, -1, -\frac{1}{2}$.

94. (a) How are a $1s$ orbital and a $2s$ orbital in an atom similar? How do they differ? (b) How are a $3p_x$ orbital and a $2p_y$ orbital in an atom similar? How do they differ?

Electron Configurations and the Periodic Table

You should be able to use the positions of elements in the periodic table to answer the exercises in this section.

95. Draw representations of ground state electron configurations using the orbital notation ($\uparrow\downarrow$) for the following elements. (a) F; (b) V; (c) Br; (d) Rh.

96. Draw representations of ground state electron configurations using the orbital notation ($\uparrow\downarrow$) for the following elements. (a) P; (b) Ni; (c) Ga; (d) Cd.

97. Determine the number of electrons in the outer occupied shell of each of the following elements, and indicate the principal quantum number of that shell. (a) Na; (b) S; (c) Si; (d) Sr; (e) Ba; (f) Br.

98. Explain why each of the following ground state configurations is incorrect, and correct it.

(a) Si $1s\,\uparrow\downarrow\ 2s\,\uparrow\downarrow\ 2p\,\uparrow\downarrow\ \uparrow\ \uparrow\ 3s\,\uparrow\ 3p\,\uparrow\ \uparrow\ \uparrow$
(b) Ni   [Ar] $4s\,\uparrow\ 3d\,\uparrow\downarrow\ \uparrow\downarrow\ \uparrow\downarrow\ \uparrow\downarrow\ \uparrow$
(c) S   [Ne] $3s\,\uparrow\downarrow\ 3p\,\uparrow\downarrow\ \uparrow\downarrow$

99. Explain why each of the following ground state configurations is incorrect, and correct it.

(a) Ca $1s\,\uparrow\downarrow\ 2s\,\uparrow\downarrow\ 2p\,\uparrow\downarrow\ \uparrow\downarrow\ \uparrow\downarrow\ 3s\,\uparrow\ 3p\,\uparrow$
(b) V   [Ar] $3d\,\uparrow\ \uparrow\ \uparrow\ \uparrow\ \uparrow$
(c) F $1s\,\uparrow\downarrow\ 2s\,\uparrow\ 2p\,\uparrow\downarrow\ \uparrow\downarrow\ \uparrow\downarrow$

100. 🔵 A neutral atom has two electrons with $n = 1$, eight electrons with $n = 2$, eight electrons with $n = 3$, and two electrons with $n = 4$. Assume this element is in its ground state configuration.

(a) What are the atomic number, symbol, and name of this element?
(b) In which period of the periodic table does this element appear?
(c) In which group of the periodic table does this element appear?
(d) What is the total number of s electrons in this atom?
(e) What is the total number of p electrons in this atom?
(f) What is the total number of d electrons in this atom?

101. 🔵 A neutral atom has two electrons with $n = 1$, eight electrons with $n = 2$, sixteen electrons with $n = 3$, and two electrons with $n = 4$. Assume this element is in its ground state configuration.

(a) What are the atomic number, symbol, and name of this element?
(b) In which period of the periodic table does this element appear?
(c) In which group of the periodic table does this element appear?
(d) What is the total number of s electrons in this atom?
(e) What is the total number of p electrons in this atom?

102. With the help of Appendix B, list the symbols for the first five elements, by atomic number, that have an unpaired electron in an s orbital. Identify the group in which most of these are found in the periodic table.

103. List the elements having an atomic number of 20 or less that have one or more unpaired p orbital electrons. Indicate the group to which each of these elements belongs in the periodic table.

104. Identify the element or elements possible, given only the number of electrons in the outermost shell and the principal quantum number of that shell. (a) 1 electron, first shell; (b) 3 electrons, second shell; (c) 3 electrons, third shell; (d) 2 electrons, seventh shell; (e) 4 electrons, third shell; (f) 8 electrons, fifth shell.

105. 🔵 Give the ground state electron configurations for the elements of Exercise 95 using shorthand notation—that is, [He] $2s^2 2p^6$, and so on.

106. 🔵 Give the ground state electron configurations for the elements of Exercise 96 using shorthand notation—that is, [He] $2s^2 2p^6$, and so on.

🔵 **Molecular Reasoning** exercises   ▲ **More Challenging** exercises   Blue-Numbered exercises solved in Student Solutions Manual

Unless otherwise noted, all content on this page is © Cengage Learning.

107. State the Pauli Exclusion Principle. Would any of the following ground state electron configurations violate this rule: (a) $1s^3$; (b) $1s^22s^22p_x^2 2p_y^3$; (c) $1s^22s^22p_x^2$; (d) $1s^22s^23s^2$? Explain.

108. State Hund's Rule. Would any of the following ground state electron configurations violate this rule: (a) $1s^2$; (b) $1s^22s^22p_x^2$; (c) $1s^22s^22p_x^1 2p_y^1$; (d) $1s^22s^12p_x^1 2p_z^1$; (e) $1s^22s^12p_x^2 2p_y^1 2p_z^1$? Explain.

109. ▲ Classify each of the following atomic electron configurations as (i) a ground state, (ii) an excited state, or (iii) a forbidden state: (a) $1s^22p^3$; (b) $[Kr]\ 4d^{10}5s^3$; (c) $1s^22s^22p^63s^23p^63d^{12}4s^2$; (d) $1s^22s^22p^63s^23p^62d^1$; (e) $1s^22s^22p^83s^23p^5$.

110. Which of the elements with atomic numbers of 11 or less are paramagnetic when in the ground atomic state?

111. Semiconductor industries depend on such elements as Si, Ga, As, Ge, B, Cd, and S. Write the predicted electron configuration of each element.

112. The manufacture of high-temperature ceramic superconductors depends on such elements as Cu, O, La, Y, Ba, Tl, and Bi. Write the predicted electron configuration of each element. (Consult Appendix B if necessary.)

113. In nature, potassium and sodium are often found together. (a) Write the electron configurations for potassium and for sodium. (b) How are they similar? (c) How do they differ?

Metallic potassium

Metallic sodium

114. Which elements are represented by the following electron configurations?

(a) $1s^22s^22p^63s^23p^63d^{10}4s^24p^3$
(b) $[Kr]\ 4d^{10}4f^{14}5s^25p^65d^{10}6s^26p^3$
(c) $[Kr]\ 4d^{10}4f^{14}5s^25p^65d^{10}5f^{14}6s^26p^67s^2$
(d) $[Kr]\ 4d^55s^2$
(e) $1s^22s^22p^63s^23p^63d^24s^2$

115. Repeat Exercise 114 for

(a) $1s^22s^22p^63s^23p^63d^{10}4s^1$
(b) $[Kr]\ 4d^{10}4f^{14}5s^25p^65d^{10}6s^26p^4$
(c) $1s^22s^22p^63s^23p^5$
(d) $[Kr]\ 4d^{10}4f^{14}5s^25p^65d^{10}6s^26p^67s^2$

116. Find the total number of s, p, and d electrons in each of the following: (a) P; (b) Kr; (c) Ni; (d) Zn; (e) Ti.

117. Write the electron configurations of the Group 2A elements Be, Mg, and Ca (see inside front cover). What similarities do you observe?

118. Construct a table in which you list a possible set of values for the four quantum numbers for each electron in the following atoms in their ground states. (a) Na; (b) O; (c) Ca.

119. Construct a table in which you list a possible set of values for the four quantum numbers for each electron in the following atoms in their ground states. (a) Mg; (b) S; (c) Sc.

120. Draw general electron structures for the A group elements using the ↑↓ notation, where n is the principal quantum number for the highest occupied energy level.

	ns	np
1A	—	— — —
2A	—	— — —

and so on

121. Repeat Exercise 120 using $ns^x np^y$ notation.

122. List n, ℓ, and m_ℓ quantum numbers for the highest energy electron (or one of the highest energy electrons if there are more than one) in the following atoms in their ground states. (a) Si; (b) Ac; (c) Cl; (d) Pr.

123. List n, ℓ, and m_ℓ quantum numbers for the highest energy electron (or one of the highest energy electrons if there are more than one) in the following atoms in their ground states. (a) Se; (b) Zn; (c) Mg; (d) Pu.

124. ♣ Write the ground state electron configurations for elements A–E.

		E															
																F	
					G				A				H				C
J			B							I		D					

125. ♣ Repeat Exercise 124 for elements F–J.

126. How many unpaired electrons are in atoms of Na, Ne, Al, Be, Br, As, and Ti?

127. (a) Distinguish between the terms "diamagnetic" and "paramagnetic," and provide an example that illustrates the meaning of each. (b) How is paramagnetism measured experimentally?

128. Which of the following ions or atoms possess paramagnetic properties? (a) Br; (b) Kr; (c) Ne^+; (d) Fe; (e) Br^-.

129. Which of the following ions or atoms possess paramagnetic properties? (a) Cl^-; (b) Ca^{2+}; (c) Ca; (d) Ar^-; (e) Si.

♣ **Molecular Reasoning** exercises   ▲ **More Challenging** exercises   Blue-Numbered exercises solved in Student Solutions Manual

Unless otherwise noted, all content on this page is © Cengage Learning.

Conceptual Exercises

130. 🌑 The atomic mass of chlorine is reported to be 35.5, yet no atom of chlorine has the mass of 35.5 amu. Explain.

131. Chemists often use the terms "atomic weight" and "atomic mass" interchangeably. Explain why it would be more accurate if, in place of either of these terms, we used the phrase "average atomic mass."

132. The diameter of an atom is about 100,000 times larger than the diameter of the nucleus of the atom. Suppose an atom is enlarged until its nucleus is the size of a basketball, which has a diameter of 9.39 inches. What would be the diameter of this enlarged atom?

133. Using the electron configurations of the elements, given in Appendix B, and Hund's Rule, determine which elements have a pair of electrons in every occupied orbital (no singles). Are they about half of the elements, rather small in number, or rather large in number? To what groups of elements do they belong?

134. Draw a three-dimensional representation of each of the following orbitals: (a) $3p_x$; (b) $2s$; (c) $3d_{xy}$; (d) $3d_{z^2}$.

135. 🌑 We often show the shapes of orbitals as drawings. What are some of the limitations of these drawings?

136. An atom in its ground state contains 18 electrons. How many of these electrons are in orbitals with $\ell = 0$ values?

137. Suppose that scientists were to discover a new element, one that has the chemical properties of the noble gases, and positioned directly below radon on the periodic table. Assuming that the g orbitals of the elements preceding it in the period had not yet begun to fill, what would be the atomic number and ground state electron configuration of this new element?

138. For a lithium atom, give (a) its ground state electron configuration; (b) the electron configuration for one of its lowest energy excited states; and (c) an electron configuration for a forbidden or impossible state.

139. Suppose we could excite all of the electrons in a sample of hydrogen atoms to the $n = 6$ level. They would then emit light as they relaxed to lower energy states. Some atoms might undergo the transition $n = 6$ to $n = 1$, and others might go from $n = 6$ to $n = 5$, then from $n = 5$ to $n = 4$, and so on. How many lines would we expect to observe in the resulting emission spectrum?

140. Examine each of the following statements. What is incorrect about each statement? How can each statement be changed to make it a correct statement?

(a) A hydrogen atom has one energy level.

(b) A lithium atom has three electrons, two in the $1s$ sublevel and one in the $2p$ sublevel.

(c) The angular momentum quantum number, ℓ, of an electron in a p sublevel has a value of 2.

(d) Three electrons in a p sublevel will occupy separate orbitals, so one will be positive $(+1)$, one will be neutral (0), and one will be negative (-1).

(e) Two electrons in the same orbital must have the same spin.

141. Antimatter is composed of antiparticles in the same way that normal matter is composed of particles. For every subatomic particle there exists an antiparticle with the same mass but opposite charge. The antielectron (or positron) has a positive charge, and the antiproton has a negative charge. In 1995 the European Organization for Nuclear Research (commonly known as CERN) announced that it had successfully created nine antihydrogen atoms using these antiparticles. Describe the composition of an antihydrogen atom. What's in the nucleus and what's outside the nucleus?

Building Your Knowledge

142. 🌑 Two isotopes of hydrogen occur naturally (^{1}H, > 99%, and ^{2}H, < 1%) and two of chlorine occur naturally (^{35}Cl, 76%, and ^{37}Cl, 24%). (a) How many different masses of HCl molecules can be formed from these isotopes? (b) What is the approximate mass of each of the molecules, expressed in atomic mass units? (Use atomic weights rounded to the nearest whole number.) (c) List these HCl molecules in order of decreasing relative abundance.

143. 🌑 CH$_4$ is methane. If ^{1}H, ^{2}H, ^{12}C, and ^{13}C were the only isotopes present in a given sample of methane, show the different formulas and formula weights that might exist in that sample. (Use atomic weights rounded to the nearest whole number.)

144. Sodium is easily identified in a solution by its strong emission at $\lambda = 589$ nm. According to Einstein's equation, $E = mc^2$ (where m is mass), this amount of energy can be converted into mass. What is the mass equivalent of one photon emitted by an excited sodium atom? ($1 \text{ J} = 1 \text{ kg} \cdot \text{m}^2/\text{s}^2$)

145. A student was asked to calculate the wavelength and frequency of light emitted for an electron in an excited state H atom making the following transitions: (a) $n = 6 \rightarrow n = 2$, and (b) $n = 6 \rightarrow n = 3$. She was asked to determine whether she would be able to visually detect either of these electron transitions. Are her responses below correct? If not, make the necessary corrections.

(a) $1/\lambda = (1.097 \times 10^7/\text{m})(1/2^2 - 1/6^2) = 2.44 \times 10^6/\text{m}; \ \lambda = 244$ nm

(b) $1/\lambda = (1.907 \times 10^7/\text{m})(1/3^2 - 1/6^2) = 9.14 \times 10^5/\text{m}; \ \lambda = 1090$ nm

She concluded that she couldn't see either of the transitions because neither is in the visible region of the spectrum.

146. When compounds of barium are heated in a flame, green light of wavelength 554 nm is emitted. How much energy is lost when one mole of barium atoms each emit one photon of this wavelength?

🌑 **Molecular Reasoning** exercises ▲ **More Challenging** exercises Blue-Numbered exercises solved in Student Solutions Manual

147. A 60-watt incandescent light bulb consumes energy at the rate of $60\,J \cdot s^{-1}$. Much of the light is emitted in the infrared region, and less than 5% of the energy appears as visible light. Calculate the number of visible photons emitted per second. Make the simplifying assumptions that 5.0% of the light is visible and that all visible light has a wavelength of 550 nm (yellow-green).

An incandescent light bulb

Charles D. Winters

148. Classical music radio station KMFA in Austin broadcasts at a frequency of 89.5 MHz. What is the wavelength of its signal in meters?

149. ♣ (a) How many electrons are in 25.0 g of copper? (b) How many electrons are in one mole of nitrogen molecules?

150. ♣ (a) How many electrons are in one mole of nitrogen molecules? (b) How many electrons are in 30.0 g of water?

Beyond the Textbook

NOTE: *Whenever the answer to an exercise depends on information obtained from a source other than this textbook, the source must be included as an essential part of the answer.*

151. At **www.chemsoc.org/viselements, www.webelements .com.** or another suitable website, locate information on scandium, vanadium, chromium, and copper that will assist you in answering the following questions.

(a) Which of the four elements listed was first isolated in a laboratory in Mexico?
(b) Which was discovered first?
(c) Which of the four elements are (is) not essential in our diet?
(d) Which has only two known nonzero oxidation states?

152. Use an internet search engine (such as **http://www .google.com**) to locate a table of isotopes found in naturally occurring samples of nickel. From these data, calculate the atomic mass of nickel. How does your answer compare to the value found on the periodic table? How do the values you found compare to those in Exercise 31?

153. Use an internet search engine (such as **http://www .google.com**) to locate a table of isotopes found in naturally occurring samples of chromium. How many neutrons are present in an atom of each stable isotope of chromium? How does the data you found compare to that in Exercise 38?

154. Use an internet search engine (such as **http://www.google .com**) to locate a biography of Sir Isaac Newton. How old was he when he entered college? How old was he when he died?

155. Go to **http://numericana.com/answer/humor .htm#units.** (a) Locate the value for microcentury expressed in minutes. (b) Locate the so-called "New Scientific Units" and give your favorite one.

Chemical Periodicity

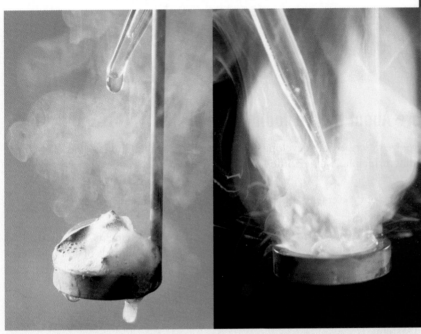

The reaction of H_2O and Li (*left*) to produce LiOH and $H_2(g)$ is much slower than the analogous reaction between H_2O and Na (*right*). The higher reactivity of sodium relative to lithium is one of the many predictions and trends from chemical periodicity discussed in this chapter.

Charles D. Winters

OBJECTIVES

After you have studied this chapter, you should be able to

▶ Understand and effectively use the periodic table

▶ Discuss chemical periodicity of the following physical properties:

  Atomic radii

  Ionization energy

  Electron affinity

  Ionic radii

  Electronegativity

  Oxidation state

▶ Assign oxidation states to elements when they are free, in compounds, or ions

▶ Describe chemical periodicity in the reactions of

  Hydrogen

  Oxygen

▶ Describe chemical periodicity in the compounds of

  Hydrogen

  Oxygen

5-1 More About the Periodic Table

In Chapter 4 we described the development of the periodic table, some terminology for it, and its guiding principle, the **periodic law**.

> The properties of the elements are periodic functions of their atomic numbers.

In Chapter 4 we also described electron configurations of the elements. In the long form of the periodic table, elements are arranged in blocks based on the kinds of atomic orbitals being filled. (Please review Table 4-9 and Figure 4-32 carefully.) We saw that electron configurations of all elements in the A groups can be predicted from their positions in the periodic table. We also noted, however, that some irregularities occur within the B groups.

Now we can classify the elements according to their electron configurations, which is a very useful system.

Noble Gases. For many years the Group 8A elements—the noble gases—were called inert gases because no chemical reactions were known for them. We now know that the heavier members do form compounds, mostly with fluorine and oxygen. Except for helium, each of these elements has eight electrons in its outermost occupied shell. Their outer shell may be represented as having the electron configuration . . . ns^2np^6.

Representative Elements. The A group elements in the periodic table are called representative elements. Their "last" electron is assigned to an outer shell s or p orbital. These elements show distinct and fairly regular variations in their properties with changes in atomic number.

▶ The properties of elements are correlated with their positions in the periodic table. Chemists use the periodic table as an invaluable guide in their search for new, useful materials.

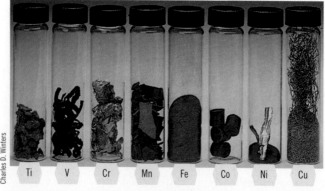

Some transition metals (*left to right*): Ti, V, Cr, Mn, Fe, Co, Ni, Cu.

Charles D. Winters

The Periodic Table

The periodic table is one of the first things a student of chemistry encounters. It appears invariably in textbooks, in lecture halls, and in laboratories. Scientists consider it an indispensable reference. And yet, less than 150 years ago, the idea of arranging the elements by atomic weight or number was considered absurd. At an 1866 meeting of the Chemical Society at Burlington House, England, J. A. R. Newlands (1837–1898) presented a theory he called the law of octaves. It stated that when the known elements were listed by increasing atomic weights, those that were eight places apart would be similar, much like notes on a piano keyboard. His colleagues' reactions are probably summed up best by the remark of a Professor Foster: "Have you thought of arranging the elements according to their initial letters? Maybe some better connections would come to light that way."

It is not surprising that poor Newlands was not taken seriously. In the 1860s, little information was available to illustrate relationships among the elements. Only 62 of them had been distinguished from more complex substances when Mendeleev first announced his discovery of the periodic law in 1869.

Mendeleev's discovery was the result of many years of hard work. He gathered information on the elements from all corners of the earth—by corresponding with colleagues, studying books and papers, and redoing experiments to confirm data. He put the statistics of each element on a small card and pinned the cards to his laboratory wall, where he arranged and rearranged them many times until he was sure that they were in the right order. One especially farsighted feature of Mendeleev's accomplishment was his realization that some elements were missing from the table. He predicted the properties of these substances (gallium, scandium, and germanium).

Since its birth in 1869, the periodic table has been discussed and revised many times. Spectroscopic and other discoveries have filled in the blanks left by Mendeleev and added a new column consisting of the noble gases. As scientists learned more about atomic structure, the basis for ordering was changed from atomic weight to atomic number. The perplexing *f*-transition elements were sorted out and given a special place, along with many of the radioactive elements created by atomic bombardment. Even the form of the table has been experimented with, resulting in everything from spiral and circular tables to exotic shapes such as the one suggested by Charles Janet (shown here).

During the past century, chemistry has become a fast-moving science in which methods and instruments are often outdated within a few years. But it is doubtful that our old friend, the periodic table, will ever become obsolete. It may be modified, but it will always stand as a statement of basic relationships in chemistry and as a monument to the wisdom and insight of its creator, Dmitri Mendeleev.

Joseph Wright of Derby/Getty Images

The Alchymist in Search of the Philosophers' Stone Discovers Phosphorus, by Joseph Wright (1771).

The Discovery of Phosphorus

Technology and its impact on society have always been intriguing subjects for artists. This was particularly true during the Industrial Revolution, when chemistry was on the verge of transforming itself from alchemical "magic" into a scientific discipline. It is easy to see how the scientist, toiling away in a laboratory full of strange equipment and trying to make sense of the natural world, held a certain heroic appeal to artists.

One of the more romantic accounts of chemical activity during that period is *The Alchymist in Search of the Philosophers' Stone Discovers Phosphorus* (1771) by the English painter Joseph Wright of Derby (1734–1797). In Wright's depiction, a stately, bearded alchemist has just isolated a new element by distillation. As the substance collects in the flask it begins to glow in the dark, illuminating the laboratory with an eerie white light and bringing the imaginary scientist to his knees in wonder. The element phosphorus was in fact named for this property—*phosphorescence*—with both words deriving from the Greek *phosphoros*, or "giving light."

The actual discovery of elemental phosphorus was probably not quite as dramatic as Joseph Wright envisioned. It was first isolated from urine by the German chemist Henning Brand in 1669, by a much more laborious process than the one represented by the tidy distillation apparatus in Wright's painting. The first step of the preparation, as described in a 1726 treatise entitled "Phosphoros Elementalis," involved steeping 50 or 60 pails of urine in tubs for two weeks " . . . till it putrify and breed Worms"—hardly a fitting subject for 18th-century artwork!

Expecting a bigger reward later, Brand gave two scientific contemporaries the recipe for phosphorus in exchange for some small gifts. However, one man instead claimed the discovery for himself after repeating Brand's work in his own laboratory. Through the other, Brand did receive a contract with the Duke of Hanover for the preparation of phosphorus; however, he was dissatisfied with his pay, and it was only after writing a number of complaint letters (and enlisting his wife to do the same) that he finally received what he felt was fair compensation for his discovery.

LISA SAUNDERS BAUGH

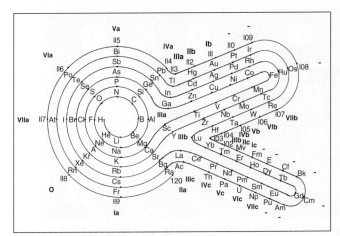

An alternative representation of the periodic table, as proposed by Charles Janet, 1928.

***d*-Transition Elements.** Elements in the B groups in the periodic table are known as the *d*-transition elements or, more simply, as transition elements or transition metals. The elements of the four transition series are all metals and are characterized by electrons filling the *d* orbitals. Stated differently, the *d*-transition elements contain electrons in both the *ns* and $(n - 1)d$ orbitals, but not in the *np* orbitals. The first transition series, Sc through Zn, has electrons in the 4*s* and 3*d* orbitals, but not in the 4*p* orbitals. They are referred to as

First transition series (4*s* and 3*d* orbitals occupied): $_{21}$Sc through $_{30}$Zn

Second transition series (5*s* and 4*d* orbitals occupied): $_{39}$Y through $_{48}$Cd

Third transition series (6*s* and 5*d* orbitals occupied): $_{57}$La and $_{72}$Hf through $_{80}$Hg

Fourth transition series (7*s* and 6*d* orbitals occupied): $_{89}$Ac and $_{104}$Rf through element 112

***f*-Transition Elements.** Sometimes known as **inner transition elements**, these are elements in which electrons are being added to *f* orbitals. In these elements, the second from the outermost occupied shell is building from 18 to 32 electrons. All are metals. The *f*-transition elements are located between Groups 3B and 4B in the periodic table. They are

First *f*-transition series (lanthanides, 4*f* orbitals occupied): $_{58}$Ce through $_{71}$Lu

Second *f*-transition series (actinides, 5*f* orbitals occupied): $_{90}$Th through $_{103}$Lr

The A and B designations for groups of elements in the periodic table are somewhat arbitrary, and they may be reversed in some periodic tables. In another standard designation, the groups are numbered 1 through 18. The system used in this text is the one commonly used in the United States. Elements with the same group numbers, but with different letters, have only a few similar properties. The origin of the A and B designations is the fact that some compounds of elements with the same group numbers have similar formulas but quite different properties, for example, NaCl (1A) and AgCl (1B), $MgCl_2$(2A) and $ZnCl_2$(2B). As we shall see, variations in the properties of the B groups across a row are not nearly as regular and dramatic as the variations observed across a row of A group elements.

> The *outermost* or *valence* electrons have the greatest influence on the properties of elements. Adding an electron to an *s* or *p* orbital usually causes dramatic changes in the physical and chemical properties. Adding an electron to a *d* or *f* orbital typically has a smaller effect on properties.

▶ The lanthanides are also known as the **rare earths**. They are not especially rare relative to gold and platinum, for example, but are spread out rather evenly through the earth's crust. They are also difficult to separate and purify due to their similar chemical properties. The largest concentrated deposits are in China, which has recently reduced exports, causing a dramatic increase in their prices.

▶ The B group elements are the transition metals.

▶ In any atom the *outermost* electrons are those that have the highest value of the principal quantum number, *n*.

The elements of Period 3. Properties progress (*left to right*) from solids (Na, Mg, Al, Si, P, S) to gases (Cl, Ar) and from the most metallic (Na) to the most nonmetallic (Ar). The sticks of white phosphorus are in a beaker of water because they would ignite and burn in air (O_2).

Charles Steele

Periodic Properties of the Elements

Now we investigate the nature of periodicity. Knowledge of periodicity is valuable in understanding bonding in simple compounds. Many physical properties, such as melting points, boiling points, and atomic volumes, show periodic variations. For now, we describe the variations that are most useful in predicting chemical behavior. The changes in these properties depend on electron configurations, especially the configurations in the outermost occupied shell, and on how far away that shell is from the nucleus.

5-2 Atomic Radii

In Section 4-17 we described individual atomic orbitals in terms of probabilities of distributions of electrons over certain regions in space. Similarly, we can visualize the total electron cloud that surrounds an atomic nucleus as somewhat indefinite with no distinct edge or boundary. We cannot easily isolate a single atom and measure its diameter the way we can measure the diameter of a golf ball. For all practical purposes, the size of an individual atom cannot be uniquely defined. An indirect approach is required. The size of an atom is determined by its immediate environment, especially its interaction with surrounding atoms. By analogy, suppose we arrange some golf balls in an orderly array in a box. If we know how the balls are positioned, the number of balls, and the dimensions of the box, we can calculate the diameter of an individual ball. Application of this reasoning to solids and their densities allows us to calculate values for the atomic sizes of many elements. In other cases, we derive atomic radii from the observed distances between atoms that are combined with one another. For example, the distance between atomic centers (nuclei) in the Cl_2 molecule is measured to be 2.00 Å. This suggests that the radius of *each* Cl atom is half the interatomic distance, or 1.00 Å. We collect the data obtained from many such measurements to indicate the *relative* sizes of individual atoms.

Figure 5-1 displays the relative sizes of atoms of the representative elements and the noble gases. It shows the periodicity in atomic radii.

The **effective nuclear charge**, Z_{eff}, experienced by an electron in an outer shell is less than the actual nuclear charge, Z. This is because the *attraction* of outer-shell electrons by the nucleus is partly counterbalanced by the repulsion of the outer-shell electrons by electrons in inner shells. We say that the electrons in inner shells *screen*, or *shield*, electrons in outer shells from the full effect of the nuclear charge. This concept of a **screening**, or **shielding, effect** helps us understand many periodic trends in atomic properties.

Consider an atom of lithium. It has two electrons in a filled shell, $1s^2$, and one electron in the 2s orbital, $2s^1$. The electron in the 2s orbital is fairly effectively screened from the nucleus by the two electrons in the filled 1s orbital, so the 2s electron does not "feel" the full 3+ charge of the nucleus. The effective nuclear charge, Z_{eff}, experienced by the electron in the 2s orbital, however, is not 1 (3 minus 2) either. The electron in the outer shell of lithium has some probability of being found close to the nucleus (see Figure 4-22). We say that, to some extent, it *penetrates* the region of the 1s electrons; that is, the 1s electrons do not completely shield the outer-shell electrons from the nucleus. The electron in the 2s shell "feels" an effective nuclear charge a little larger than 1+.

Sodium, element number 11, has ten electrons in inner shells, $1s^2 2s^2 2p^6$, and one electron in an outer shell, $3s^1$. The ten inner-shell electrons of the sodium atom screen (shield) the outer-shell electron from most of the 11+ nuclear charge. Recall from Chapter 4 that the third shell ($n = 3$) is farther from the nucleus than the second shell ($n = 2$). Thus, we see why sodium atoms are larger than lithium atoms. Similar reasoning explains why potassium atoms are larger than sodium atoms and why the sizes of the elements in each column of the periodic table are related in a similar way.

> Within a family (vertical group on the periodic table) of representative elements, atomic radii increase from top to bottom as electrons are added to shells farther from the nucleus.

▶ Atomic radii are often stated in **angstroms** ($1 \text{ Å} = 10^{-10}$ m) or in the SI units *nanometers* ($1 \text{ nm} = 10^{-9}$ m) or *picometers* ($1 \text{ pm} = 10^{-12}$ m). To convert from Å to nm, move the decimal point to the left one place ($1 \text{ Å} = 0.1$ nm). For example, the atomic radius of Li is 1.52 Å, or 0.152 nm. To convert from Å to pm, move the decimal place to the right two places, thus 1.52 Å would be 152 pm. Many European chemistry journals use pm as the standard atomic distance unit.

The radius of an atom, *r*, is taken as half the distance between nuclei in *homonuclear* molecules such as Cl_2.

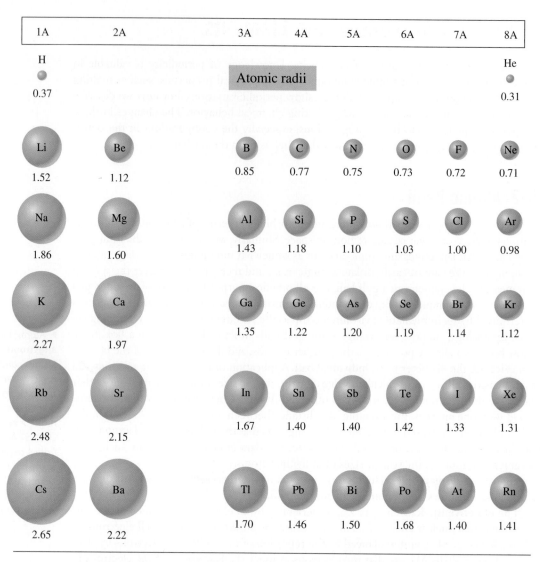

Figure 5-1 Atomic radii of the A group (representative) elements and the noble gases, in angstroms, Å (see Section 5-2). Atomic radii *increase going down a group* because a number of electrons (8, 18, or 32 depending on the row and the presence of filled *d* and *f* orbitals) are being added to shells farther from the nucleus. Atomic radii generally *decrease from left to right within a given period* due to increasing effective nuclear charge. Hydrogen atoms are the smallest and cesium atoms are the largest naturally occurring atoms.

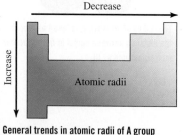

General trends in atomic radii of A group elements with position in the periodic table.

As we move *across* the periodic table, atoms become smaller due to increasing effective nuclear charges even though more electrons are being added. Consider the elements B ($Z = 5$, $1s^2 2s^2 2p^1$) to Ne ($Z = 10$, $1s^2 2s^2 2p^6$). In B there are two electrons in a noble gas configuration, $1s^2$, and three electrons in the second shell, $2s^2 2p^1$. The two core electrons effectively screen out most of the effect of two of the five protons in the boron nucleus. So the three electrons in the outermost orbitals only "feel" the attraction of just over three protons. Carbon ($Z = 6$, $1s^2 2s^2 2p^2$) has the same number of inner electrons ($1s^2$) to screen as boron, but the extra proton present in the nucleus provides additional attraction to pull the four outermost electrons in closer to the nucleus, making C smaller than B. This same effect continues as one moves to the right. Ne ($Z = 10$, $1s^2 2s^2 2p^6$) still has only two core electrons, but it has ten protons in the nucleus to pull the outermost electrons in even closer. Thus, even though neon has the most electrons of any element in the second row it has the smallest atomic radius. Neon is smaller, however, by only a small amount relative to fluorine because of the electron–electron repulsions that partially counter the increased effective nuclear charge.

As we move from left to right *across a period* in the periodic table, atomic radii of representative elements *decrease* as a proton is added to the nucleus and an electron is added to a particular shell.

For the transition elements, the variations are not so regular because electrons are being added to an inner shell, but the general trend of decreasing radii certainly continues as one moves across the *d*- or *f*-block metals. All transition elements have smaller radii than the preceding Group 1A and 2A elements in the same period.

Careful examination of Figure 5-1 reveals two exceptions to the decreasing atomic radius as one moves to the right in a row. The heavier main group elements Te and Po both are larger than the preceding elements. The increase in size is caused by a variety of factors, some of which are beyond the scope of a general chemistry book. One reason is the increased electron–electron repulsions caused when a fourth *p* electron is added to that shell and forced to spin-pair with one of the three unpaired *p* electrons. This leaves only two unpaired electrons available for bonding. The *s* electrons in these heavier elements are also rather "inert" and generally do not engage in any bonding interactions. Finally, the filled *d* orbitals are higher in energy due to much weaker attraction of their electrons by the nuclear charges. This causes more significant electron–electron repulsions between Te or Po atoms. These factors all work together to weaken the Te–Te and Po–Po bonds in their elemental forms, from which these radii are calculated.

EXAMPLE 5-1 Trends in Atomic Radii   MOLECULAR REASONING

Arrange the following elements in order of increasing atomic radii. Justify your order.

$$Cs, \quad F, \quad K, \quad Cl$$

Plan

Both K and Cs are Group 1A metals, whereas F and Cl are halogens (7A nonmetals). Figure 5-1 shows that atomic radii increase as we descend a group, so K < Cs and F < Cl. Atomic radii decrease from left to right.

Solution

The order of increasing atomic radii is F < Cl < K < Cs.

You should now work Exercise 16.

> **S**TOP & THINK
> Remember the trends in atomic size—across within a row and vertically within a column.

5-3 Ionization Energy

The *first* **ionization energy** (IE_1), also called the *first ionization potential*, is

the minimum amount of energy required to remove the most loosely bound electron from an isolated gaseous atom to form an ion with a 1+ charge.

For calcium, for example, the first ionization energy, IE_1, is 599 kJ/mol:

$$Ca(g) + 599 \text{ kJ} \longrightarrow Ca^+(g) + e^-$$

The *second* **ionization energy** (IE_2) is the amount of energy required to remove the second electron. For calcium, it may be represented as

$$Ca^+(g) + 1145 \text{ kJ} \longrightarrow Ca^{2+}(g) + e^-$$

For a given element, IE_2 *is always greater than* IE_1 because it is always more difficult to remove a negatively charged electron from a positively charged ion than from the corresponding neutral atom. Table 5-1 gives first ionization energies.

Ionization energies measure how tightly electrons are bound to atoms. Ionization always requires energy to remove an electron from the attractive force of the nucleus. Low

Table 5-1 First Ionization Energies (kJ/mol of atoms) of Some Elements

H 1312																	He 2372
Li 520	Be 899											B 801	C 1086	N 1402	O 1314	F 1681	Ne 2081
Na 496	Mg 738											Al 578	Si 786	P 1012	S 1000	Cl 1251	Ar 1521
K 419	Ca 599	Sc 631	Ti 658	V 650	Cr 652	Mn 717	Fe 759	Co 758	Ni 757	Cu 745	Zn 906	Ga 579	Ge 762	As 947	Se 941	Br 1140	Kr 1351
Rb 403	Sr 550	Y 617	Zr 661	Nb 664	Mo 685	Tc 702	Ru 711	Rh 720	Pd 804	Ag 731	Cd 868	In 558	Sn 709	Sb 834	Te 869	I 1008	Xe 1170
Cs 377	Ba 503	La 538	Hf 681	Ta 761	W 770	Re 760	Os 840	Ir 880	Pt 870	Au 890	Hg 1007	Tl 589	Pb 715	Bi 703	Po 812	At 890	Rn 1037

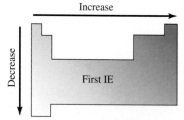

Increase
Decrease
First IE

General trends in first ionization energies of A group elements with position in the periodic table. Exceptions occur at Groups 3A and 6A.

▶ By Coulomb's Law, $F \propto \dfrac{(q^{+})(q^{-})}{d^{2}}$, the attraction for the outer shell electrons is directly proportional to the *effective* charges and inversely proportional to the *square* of the distance between the charges. Even though the effective nuclear charge increases going down a group, the greatly increased size causes a weaker net attraction for the outer electrons and thus results in a lower first ionization energy.

ionization energies indicate easy removal of electrons, and hence easy positive ion (cation) formation. Figure 5-2 shows a plot of first ionization energy versus atomic number for several elements.

Elements with low ionization energies (IE) easily lose electrons to form cations.

Figure 5-2 shows that each noble gas has the highest first ionization energy in its period. This should not be surprising because the noble gases are known to be very unreactive elements. It requires more energy to remove an electron from a helium atom (slightly less than 4.0×10^{-18} J/atom, or 2372 kJ/mol) than to remove one from a neutral atom of any other element.

$$He(g) + 2372\ kJ \longrightarrow He^{+}(g) + e^{-}$$

The Group 1A metals (Li, Na, K, Rb, Cs) have very low first ionization energies. Each of these elements has only one electron in its outermost shell (. . . ns^{1}), and they are the largest atoms in their periods. The first electron added to a shell is easily removed to form a noble gas configuration. As we move down the group, the first ionization energies become smaller. The force of attraction of the positively charged nucleus for electrons decreases as the square of the distance between them increases. So as atomic radii increase in a given group, first ionization energies decrease because the outermost electrons are farther from the nucleus.

Effective nuclear charge, Z_{eff}, increases going from left to right across a period. The increase in effective nuclear charge causes the outermost electrons to be held more tightly, making them harder to remove. The first ionization energies therefore generally *increase* from left to right across the periodic table. The reason for the trend in first ionization ener-

Figure 5-2 A plot of first ionization energies for the first 38 elements versus atomic number. The noble gases have very high first ionization energies, and the 1A metals have low first ionization energies. Note the similarities in the variations for the Period 2 elements, 3 through 10, to those for the Period 3 elements, 11 through 18, as well as for the later A group elements. Variations for B group elements are not nearly so pronounced as those for A group elements.

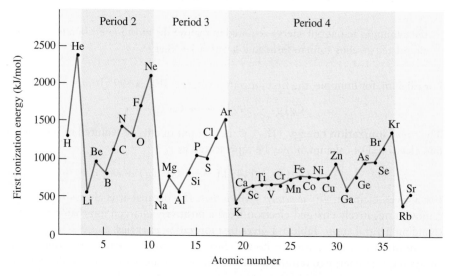

gies is the same as that used in Section 5-2 to explain trends in atomic radii. The first ionization energies of the Group 2A elements (Be, Mg, Ca, Sr, Ba) are significantly higher than those of the Group 1A elements in the same periods. This is because the Group 2A elements have higher Z_{eff} values and smaller atomic radii. Thus, their outermost electrons are held more tightly than those of the neighboring 1A metals. It is harder to remove an electron from a pair in the filled outermost s orbitals of the Group 2A elements than to remove the single electron from the half-filled outermost s orbitals of the Group 1A elements.

The first ionization energies for the Group 3A elements (B, Al, Ga, In, Tl) are exceptions to the general horizontal trends. They are *lower* than those of the 2A elements in the same periods because the 3A elements have only a single electron in their outermost p orbitals. Less energy is required to remove the first p electron than the second s electron from the outermost shell because the p orbital is at a higher energy (less stable) than an s orbital within the same shell (n value).

Going from Groups 3A to 5A, electrons are going singly into separate np orbitals, where they do not shield one another significantly. The general left-to-right increase in IE_1 for each period is interrupted by a dip between Groups 5A (N, P, As, Sb, Bi) and 6A elements (O, S, Se, Te, Po). Presumably, this behavior is because the fourth np electron in the Group 6A elements is paired with another electron in the same orbital, so it experiences greater repulsion than it would in an orbital by itself. This increased repulsion outweighs the increase in Z_{eff}, so the fourth np electron in an outer shell (Group 6A elements) is somewhat easier to remove (lower ionization energy) than is the third np electron in an outer shell (Group 5A elements). After the dip between Groups 5A and 6A, the importance of the increasing Z_{eff} outweighs the repulsion of electrons needing to be paired, and the general left-to-right increases in first ionization energies resume.

▶ As one goes across a period on the periodic table, the slight breaks in the increasing ionization energies occur between Groups 2A and 3A (electrons first enter the np subshell) and again between Groups 5A and 6A (electrons are first paired in the np subshell).

Knowledge of the relative values of ionization energies assists us in predicting whether an element is likely to form ionic or molecular (covalent) compounds. Elements with low ionization energies form ionic compounds by losing electrons to form *cations* (positively charged ions). Elements with intermediate ionization energies generally form molecular compounds by sharing electrons with other elements. Elements with very high ionization energies, such as Groups 6A and 7A, often gain electrons to form *anions* (negatively charged ions) with closed shell (noble gas) electron configurations.

▶ Here is one reason why trends in ionization energies are important.

One factor that favors an atom of a *representative* element forming a monatomic ion in a compound is the formation of a stable noble gas electron configuration. Energy considerations are consistent with this observation. For example, as 1 mol Li from Group 1A forms 1 mol Li^+ ions, it absorbs 520 kJ/mol. The IE_2 value is 14 times greater, 7298 kJ/mol, and is prohibitively large for the formation of Li^{2+} ions under ordinary conditions. For Li^{2+} ions to form, an electron would have to be removed from the filled first shell, which is very unlikely. The other alkali metals behave in the same way, for similar reasons.

▶ Noble gas electron configurations are stable only for ions in *compounds*. In fact, $Li^+(g)$ is less stable than $Li(g)$ by 520 kJ/mol.

The first two ionization energies of Be (Group 2A) are 899 and 1757 kJ/mol, but IE_3 is more than eight times larger, 14,849 kJ/mol. So Be forms Be^{2+} ions, but not Be^{3+} ions. The other alkaline earth metals—Mg, Ca, Sr, Ba, and Ra—behave in a similar way. Only the lower members of Group 3A, beginning with Al, form $3+$ ions. Bi and some d- and f-transition metals do so, too. We see that the magnitudes of successive ionization energies support the ideas of electron configurations discussed in Chapter 4.

Due to the high energy required, *simple monatomic cations with charges greater than 3+ do not form under ordinary circumstances.*

EXAMPLE 5-2 Trends in First IEs

Arrange the following elements in order of increasing first ionization energy. Justify your order.

Na,   Mg,   Al,   Si

Plan

The first ionization energies generally increase from left to right in the same period, but there are exceptions at Groups 3A and 6A. Al is a 3A element with only one electron in its outer p orbitals, $1s^2 2s^2 2p^6 3s^2 3p^1$, which makes the first ionization energy lower than one might normally expect.

Solution

There is a slight dip at Group 3A in the plot of first IE versus atomic number (see Figure 5-2). The order of increasing first ionization energy is $Na < Al < Mg < Si$.

You should now work Exercise 24.

5-4 Electron Affinity

The **electron affinity (EA)** of an element may be defined as

> the energy change when an electron is added to an isolated gaseous atom to form an ion with a 1− charge.

▶ This is consistent with thermodynamic convention.

The convention is to assign a negative value when energy is released and a positive value when energy is absorbed. Most elements have no affinity for an additional electron and thus have an electron affinity equal to zero. We can represent the electron affinities of helium and chlorine as

$$He(g) + e^- \nrightarrow He^-(g) \qquad EA = 0 \text{ kJ/mol}$$
$$Cl(g) + e^- \longrightarrow Cl^-(g) + 349 \text{ kJ} \qquad EA = -349 \text{ kJ/mol}$$

▶ The value of EA for Cl can also be represented as -5.79×10^{-19} J/atom or -3.61 eV/atom. The electron volt (eV) is a unit of energy ($1 \text{ eV} = 1.6022 \times 10^{-19}$ J).

The first equation tells us that helium will not add an electron. The second equation tells us that when one mole of gaseous chlorine atoms gain one electron each to form gaseous chloride ions, 349 kJ of energy is *released* (*exothermic*). Figure 5-3 shows a plot of electron affinity versus atomic number for several elements.

Electron affinity involves the *addition* of an electron to a neutral gaseous atom. The process by which a neutral atom X gains an electron

$$X(g) + e^- \longrightarrow X^-(g) \qquad \text{(EA)}$$

is *not* the reverse of the ionization process

$$X^+(g) + e^- \longrightarrow X(g) \qquad \text{(reverse of IE}_1\text{)}$$

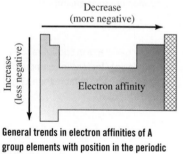

General trends in electron affinities of A group elements with position in the periodic table. There are many exceptions.

The first process begins with a neutral atom, whereas the second begins with a positive ion. Thus, IE_1 and EA are *not* simply equal in value with the signs reversed. We see from Figure 5-3 that electron affinities generally become more negative from left to right across

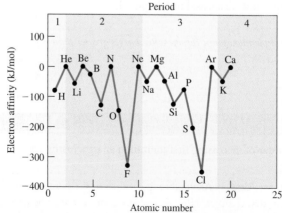

Figure 5-3 A plot of electron affinity versus atomic number for the first 20 elements. The *general* horizontal trend is that electron affinities become more negative (more energy is released as an extra electron is added) from Group 1A through Group 7A for a given period. Exceptions occur at the 2A and 5A elements.

a row in the periodic table (excluding the noble gases). This means that most representative elements in Groups 1A to 7A show a greater attraction for an extra electron from left to right. Halogen atoms, which have the outer electron configuration ns^2np^5, have the most negative electron affinities. They form stable anions with noble gas configurations, . . . ns^2np^6, by gaining one electron.

> Elements with very negative electron affinities gain electrons easily to form negative ions (anions).

"Electron affinity" is a precise and quantitative term, like "ionization energy," but it is difficult to measure. Table 5-2 shows electron affinities for several elements.

For many reasons, the variations in electron affinities are not regular across a period. The general trend is: the electron affinities of the elements become more negative from left to right in each period. Noteworthy exceptions are the elements of Groups 2A and 5A, which have less negative values than the trends suggest (see Figure 5-3). It is very difficult to add an electron to a 2A metal atom because its outer s subshell is filled. The values for the 5A elements are slightly less negative than expected because they apply to the addition of an electron to a half-filled set of np orbitals ($ns^2np^3 \rightarrow ns^2np^4$), which requires pairing. The resulting repulsion overcomes the increased attractive force of the nucleus.

▶ This reasoning is similar to that used to explain the low IE_1 values for Group 6A elements.

EXAMPLE 5-3 Trends in EAs

MOLECULAR REASONING

Arrange the following elements from most negative to least negative electron affinity.

$$K, \quad Br, \quad Cs, \quad Cl$$

Plan

Electron affinity values generally become more negative from left to right across a period, with major exceptions at Groups 2A (Be) and 5A (N). They generally become more negative from bottom to top.

Solution

The order of electron affinities from most negative to least negative is

(most negative EA) $Cl < Br < K < Cs$ (least negative EA)

This means that Cl most readily forms a 1− ion, while Cs is least able to do so.

You should now work Exercises 30 and 31.

▶ In fact, K and Cs readily form 1+ cations.

Table 5-2 Electron Affinity Values (kJ/mol) of Some Elements*

1	H −73									He 0
2	Li −60	Be (~0)		B −29	C −122	N 0	O −141	F −328	Ne 0
3	Na −53	Mg (~0)		Al −43	Si −134	P −72	S −200	Cl −349	Ar 0
4	K −48	Ca (~0)	Cu −118	Ga −29	Ge −119	As −78	Se −195	Br −324	Kr 0
5	Rb −47	Sr (~0)	Ag −125	In −29	Sn −107	Sb −101	Te −190	I −295	Xe 0
6	Cs −45	Ba (~0)	Au −282	Tl −19	Pb −35	Bi −91			

*Estimated values are in parentheses.

Energy is always required to bring a negative charge (electron) closer to another negative charge (anion). So the addition of a second electron to a 1− anion to form an ion with a 2− charge is always endothermic. Thus, electron affinities of *anions* are always positive.

5-5 Ionic Radii

Many elements on the left side of the periodic table react with other elements by *losing* electrons to form positively charged ions. Each of the Group 1A elements (Li, Na, K, Rb, Cs) has only one electron in its outermost shell (electron configuration . . . ns^1). These elements react with other elements by losing one electron to form the ions Li^+, Na^+, K^+, Rb^+, and Cs^+, thus attaining noble gas configurations. A neutral lithium atom, Li, contains three protons in its nucleus and three electrons, with its outermost electron in the $2s$ orbital. A lithium ion, Li^+, however, contains three protons in its nucleus but only two electrons, both in the $1s$ orbital. So a Li^+ ion is much smaller than a neutral Li atom (Figure 5-4). Likewise, a sodium ion, Na^+, is considerably smaller than a sodium atom, Na. The relative sizes of atoms and common ions of some representative elements are shown in Figure 5-4.

▶ The nuclear charge remains constant when the ion is formed.

Isoelectronic species have the same number of electrons. The radius of the Li^+ ion is 0.90 Å, whereas the radius of the Be^{2+} ion is only 0.59 Å. This is what we should expect. A beryllium ion, Be^{2+}, is formed when a beryllium atom, Be, loses both of its $2s$ electrons, while the 4+ nuclear charge remains constant. We expect the 4+ nuclear charge in Be^{2+} to attract the remaining two electrons quite strongly. Comparison of the ionic radii of the 2A elements with their atomic radii indicates the validity of our reasoning. We see that the ions formed by the Group 2A elements (Be^{2+}, Mg^{2+}, Ca^{2+}, Sr^{2+}, Ba^{2+}) are significantly smaller than the *isoelectronic* ions formed by the Group 1A elements in the same period. Similar reasoning indicates that the ions of the Group 3A metals (Al^{3+}, Ga^{3+}, In^{3+}, Tl^{3+}) should be even smaller than the ions of Group 1A and Group 2A elements in the same periods.

Now consider the Group 7A elements (F, Cl, Br, I). These have the outermost electron configuration . . . ns^2np^5. These elements can completely fill their outermost p orbitals by *gaining* one electron to attain noble gas configurations. Thus, when a fluorine atom (with seven electrons in its outer shell) gains one electron, it becomes a fluoride ion, F^-, with eight electrons in its outer shell. These eight electrons repel one another more strongly than the original seven, so the electron cloud expands. The F^- ion is, therefore, much larger than the

Comparison of Atomic and Ionic Radii

	1A		2A		3A		5A		6A		7A	
	Li 1.52	Li^+ 0.90	Be 1.12	Be^{2+} 0.59			N 0.75	N^{3-} 1.71	O 0.73	O^{2-} 1.26	F 0.72	F^- 1.19
	Na 1.86	Na^+ 1.16	Mg 1.60	Mg^{2+} 0.85	Al 1.43	Al^{3+} 0.68			S 1.03	S^{2-} 1.70	Cl 1.00	Cl^- 1.67
	K 2.27	K^+ 1.52	Ca 1.97	Ca^{2+} 1.14	Ga 1.35	Ga^{3+} 0.76			Se 1.19	Se^{2-} 1.84	Br 1.14	Br^- 1.82
	Rb 2.48	Rb^+ 1.66	Sr 2.15	Sr^{2+} 1.32	In 1.67	In^{3+} 0.94			Te 1.42	Te^{2-} 2.07	I 1.33	I^- 2.06
	Cs 2.65	Cs^+ 1.81	Ba 2.22	Ba^{2+} 1.49	Tl 1.70	Tl^{3+} 1.03						

Figure 5-4 Sizes of ions of the A group representative elements, in angstroms (Å), compared to the neutral covalent atoms (*green*). Positive ions (cations, *blue*) are always smaller than the neutral atoms from which they are formed. Negative ions (anions, *red*) are always larger than the neutral atoms from which they are formed.

neutral F atom (see Figure 5-4). Similar reasoning indicates that a chloride ion, Cl^-, should be larger than a neutral chlorine atom, Cl. Observed ionic radii verify these predictions.

Comparing the sizes of an oxygen atom (Group 6A) and an oxide ion, O^{2-}, again we find that the negatively charged ion is larger than the neutral atom. The oxide ion is also larger than the isoelectronic fluoride ion because the oxide ion contains ten electrons held by a nuclear charge of only 8+, whereas the fluoride ion has ten electrons held by a nuclear charge of 9+. Comparison of radii is not a simple issue when we try to compare atoms, positive and negative ions, and ions with varying charge. Sometimes we compare atoms to their ions, atoms or ions that are vertically positioned on the periodic table, or isoelectronic species. The following guidelines are often considered.

1. Simple positively charged ions (cations) are always smaller than the neutral atoms from which they are formed.

2. Simple negatively charged ions (anions) are always larger than the neutral atoms from which they are formed.

3. Both cation and anion sizes increase going down a group.

4. Within an isoelectronic series, radii decrease with increasing atomic number because of increasing nuclear charge.

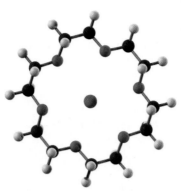

Large ring compounds can selectively trap ions based on the ability of various ions to fit within a cavity in the large compound. This ball-and-stick model is an example of this with a sodium cation, Na^+, in the middle (magenta atom). The partial negative charges on the oxygen atoms (*red*) attract and help hold the Na^+ within the ring. This results in selectivity such as occurs in transport across membranes in biological systems.

An isoelectronic series of ions

	N^{3-}	O^{2-}	F^-	Na^+	Mg^{2+}	Al^{3+}
Ionic radius (Å)	1.71	1.26	1.19	1.16	0.85	0.68
No. of electrons	10	10	10	10	10	10
Nuclear charge	7+	8+	9+	11+	12+	13+

EXAMPLE 5-4 Trends in Ionic Radii   MOLECULAR REASONING

Arrange the following ions in order of increasing ionic radii: (a) Ca^{2+}, K^+, Al^{3+}; (b) Se^{2-}, Br^-, Te^{2-}.

Plan

Some of the ions are isoelectronic, so we can compare their sizes on the basis of nuclear charges. Other comparisons can be made based on the outermost occupied shell (highest value of n).

Solution

(a) Ca^{2+} and K^+ are isoelectronic (18 electrons each) with an outer-shell electron configuration of $3s^2 3p^6$. Because Ca^{2+} has a higher nuclear charge (20+) than K^+ (19+), Ca^{2+} holds its 18 electrons more tightly, and Ca^{2+} is smaller than K^+. Al^{3+} has electrons only in the second main shell (outer-shell electron configuration of $2s^2 2p^6$), so it is smaller than either of the other two ions.

$$Al^{3+} < Ca^{2+} + K^+$$

(b) Br^- and Se^{2-} are isoelectronic (36 electrons each) with an outer-shell electron configuration of $4s^2 4p^6$. Because Br^- has a higher nuclear charge (35+) than Se^{2-} (34+), Br^- holds its 36 electrons more tightly, and Br^- is smaller than Se^{2-}. Te^{2-} has electrons in the fifth main shell (outer configuration of $5s^2 5p^6$), so it is larger than either of the other two ions.

$$Br^- < Se^{2-} < Te^{2-}$$

You should now work Exercises 36 and 38.

S TOP & THINK
Isoelectronic species have the same number of electrons. Comparing such species, the higher the nuclear charge, the smaller the radius.

5-6 Electronegativity

▶ Because the noble gases form few compounds, they are not included in this discussion.

The **electronegativity (EN)** of an element is a measure of the relative tendency of an atom to attract electrons to itself *when it is chemically combined with another atom.*

> Elements with high electronegativities (nonmetals) often gain electrons to form anions. The higher the electronegativity, the more stable the anions that are formed.

> Elements with low electronegativities (metals) often lose electrons to form cations. The lower the electronegativity, the more stable the cations that are formed.

Electronegativities of the elements are expressed on a somewhat arbitrary scale, called the Pauling scale (Table 5-3). The electronegativity of fluorine (4.0) is higher than that of any other element. This tells us that when fluorine is chemically bonded to other elements, it has a greater tendency to attract electron density to itself than does any other element. Fluorine atoms, for example, have such a strong tendency for adding an electron to generate the fluoride anion (F^-) that they can remove an electron from any other atom or compound. The high electronegativity of fluorine also means that fluoride anions are very stable and do not readily lose an electron. Oxygen is the second most electronegative element and also has a strong tendency to remove electrons from other elements and compounds that have lower electronegativities.

> For the representative elements, electronegativities usually increase from left to right across periods and decrease from top to bottom within groups.

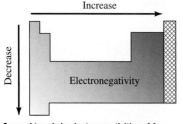

General trends in electronegativities of A group elements with position in the periodic table.

Variations among the transition metals are not as regular, but they follow the same trends as the other elements. Although the electronegativities of the transition metals all appear to be quite similar, there are considerable differences in the tendency of a transition metal to lose electrons as one proceeds from the left to the right. For example, Ti, which only

Table 5-3 Electronegativity Values of the Elements

	1A	2A	3B	4B	5B	6B	7B	8B			1B	2B	3A	4A	5A	6A	7A	8A
1	H 2.1																	He
2	Li 1.0	Be 1.5											B 2.0	C 2.5	N 3.0	O 3.5	F 4.0	Ne
3	Na 1.0	Mg 1.2											Al 1.5	Si 1.8	P 2.1	S 2.5	Cl 3.0	Ar
4	K 0.9	Ca 1.0	Sc 1.3	Ti 1.4	V 1.5	Cr 1.6	Mn 1.6	Fe 1.7	Co 1.7	Ni 1.8	Cu 1.8	Zn 1.6	Ga 1.7	Ge 1.9	As 2.1	Se 2.4	Br 2.8	Kr
5	Rb 0.9	Sr 1.0	Y 1.2	Zr 1.3	Nb 1.5	Mo 1.6	Tc 1.7	Ru 1.8	Rh 1.8	Pd 1.8	Ag 1.6	Cd 1.6	In 1.6	Sn 1.8	Sb 1.9	Te 2.1	I 2.5	Xe
6	Cs 0.8	Ba 1.0	La 1.1 *	Hf 1.3	Ta 1.4	W 1.5	Re 1.7	Os 1.9	Ir 1.9	Pt 1.8	Au 1.9	Hg 1.7	Tl 1.6	Pb 1.7	Bi 1.8	Po 1.9	At 2.1	Rn
7	Fr 0.8	Ra 1.0	Ac 1.1 †															

Metals / Nonmetals / Metalloids

*	Ce 1.1	Pr 1.1	Nd 1.1	Pm 1.1	Sm 1.1	Eu 1.1	Gd 1.1	Tb 1.1	Dy 1.1	Ho 1.1	Er 1.1	Tm 1.1	Yb 1.0	Lu 1.2
†	Th 1.2	Pa 1.3	U 1.5	Np 1.3	Pu 1.3	Am 1.3	Cm 1.3	Bk 1.3	Cf 1.3	Es 1.3	Fm 1.3	Md 1.3	No 1.3	Lr 1.5

has four outermost electrons, readily loses all four to form Ti^{4+} cations. Nickel, on the other hand, has 10 outermost electrons, but rarely loses more than two of these. In general, both ionization energies and electronegativities are low for elements at the lower left of the periodic table and high for those at the upper right.

EXAMPLE 5-5 Trends in ENs

Arrange the following elements in order of increasing electronegativity.

$$B, \quad Na, \quad F, \quad O$$

Plan

Electronegativities increase from left to right across a period and decrease from top to bottom within a group.

Solution

The order of increasing electronegativity is $Na < B < O < F$.

You should now work Exercise 42.

Although the electronegativity scale is somewhat arbitrary, we can use it with reasonable confidence to make predictions about bonding. Two elements with quite different electronegativities (a metal and a nonmetal) tend to react with each other to form ionic compounds. The less electronegative element gives up its electron(s) to the more electronegative element. Two nonmetals with similar electronegativities tend to form covalent bonds with each other. That is, they share their electrons. In this sharing, the more electronegative element attains a greater share. This is discussed in detail in Chapters 7 and 8.

5-7 Oxidation States

Many reactions involve the transfer of electrons from one species to another. We use oxidation states to keep track of electron transfers. The systematic naming of compounds (see Sections 6-3 and 6-4) also makes use of oxidation states.

The **oxidation state**, or **oxidation number**, of an element in a simple *binary* ionic compound is the number of electrons gained or lost by an atom of that element when it forms the compound. In the case of a single-atom ion, it corresponds to the actual charge on the ion. In molecular compounds, oxidation states do not have the same significance they have in binary ionic compounds. Oxidation states, however, are very useful aids in writing formulas and in balancing equations. In molecular species, the oxidation states are assigned according to an arbitrary set of rules. The most electronegative element (farther to the right and higher up in the periodic table) is assigned a negative oxidation state, and the element farther to the left and lower down in the periodic table is assigned a positive oxidation state.

Some rules for assigning oxidation states follow. These rules are not comprehensive, but they cover most cases. In applying these rules, keep in mind two important points. First, oxidation states are always assigned on a per atom basis; second, treat the rules in order of *decreasing* importance—the first rule that applies takes precedence over any subsequent rules that seem to apply.

1. The oxidation state of the atoms in any free, uncombined element is zero. This includes polyatomic elements such as H_2, O_2, H_2S, P_4, and S_8.

2. The oxidation state of an element in a simple (monatomic) ion is equal to the charge on the ion.

3. The *sum* of the oxidation states of all atoms in a neutral compound is zero.

4. In a polyatomic ion, the *sum* of the oxidation states of the constituent atoms is equal to the charge on the ion.

5. Fluorine, the most electronegative element, has an oxidation state of -1 in all its compounds.

STOP & THINK

Electronegativity is a critical concept used throughout chemistry. You do not have to memorize the Pauling electronegativity values. Just remember that fluorine is the most electronegative element, followed by oxygen, chlorine, and nitrogen. Although Cl and N have the same Pauling electronegativity values, Cl is almost always considered by chemists to be more electronegative than N. This fluorine "corner club" defines the elements with the highest electronegativity. Cs and Fr, in the opposite corner of the periodic table, are the elements with the lowest electronegativity.

▶ Ionization energy (see Section 5-3) and electron affinity (see Section 5-4) are precise quantitative concepts. We find, however, that the more qualitative concept of *electronegativity* is more useful in describing chemical bonding and properties. Most chemists do not use electron affinities because it often seems to conflict with the more commonly accepted electronegativity concepts. For example, although fluorine is the most electronegative element, it has a lower electron affinity than chlorine.

▶ Binary means two. Binary compounds contain only two elements.

▶ Oxidation state and oxidation number are interchangeable terms.

▶ Polyatomic elements have two or more atoms per molecule.

STOP & THINK
Note that these oxidation state rules are mainly based on electronegativity trends. The most electronegative atom in a compound is assigned a negative oxidation state, while the less electronegative atom(s) lose electrons and have positive oxidation states.

▶ Group 5A elements have oxidation states of −3 with less electronegative elements such as H, C, or metals. When Group 5A elements are combined with more electronegative elements, positive oxidation states up to +5 are found.

6. Hydrogen has an oxidation state of +1 in compounds unless it is combined with metals, in which case it has an oxidation state of −1. Examples of these exceptions are NaH and CaH_2.

7. Oxygen, the second most electronegative element, usually has an oxidation state of −2 in its compounds. There are just a few exceptions:

   (a) Oxygen has an oxidation state of −1 in hydrogen peroxide, H_2O_2, and in peroxides, which contain the O_2^{2-} ion; examples are CaO_2 and Na_2O_2.

   (b) Oxygen has an oxidation state of $-\frac{1}{2}$ in superoxides, which contain the O_2^- ion; examples are KO_2 and RbO_2.

   (c) When combined with the more electronegative fluorine in OF_2, oxygen has an oxidation state of +2.

8. The position of the element in the periodic table helps to assign its oxidation state:

   (a) Group 1A elements have oxidation states of +1 in all of their compounds.

   (b) Group 2A elements have oxidation states of +2 in all of their compounds.

   (c) Group 3A elements have oxidation states of +3 in all of their compounds, with a few rare exceptions.

   (d) Group 5A elements have oxidation numbers of −3 in *binary* compounds with metals, with H, or with NH_4^+. Exceptions are compounds with a Group 5A element combined with an element to its right in the periodic table; in this case, their oxidation states can be found by using rules 3 and 4.

   (e) Group 6A elements below oxygen have oxidation numbers of −2 in *binary* compounds with metals, with H, or with NH_4^+. When these elements are

Table 5-4 Common Oxidation States for Group A Elements in Compounds and Ions

Element(s)	Common Oxidation States	Examples	Other Oxidation States
H	+1	H_2O, CH_4, NH_4Cl	−1 in metal hydrides, e.g., NaH, CaH_2
Group 1A	+1	KCl, NaH, $RbNO_3$, K_2SO_4	None
Group 2A	+2	$CaCl_2$, MgH_2, $Ba(NO_3)_2$, $SrSO_4$	None
Group 3A	+3	$AlCl_3$, BF_3, $Al(NO_3)_3$, GaI_3	None in common compounds
Group 4A	+2 +4	CO, PbO, $SnCl_2$, $Pb(NO_3)_2$ CCl_4, SiO_2, SiO_3^{2-}, $SnCl_4$	Many others are also seen for C and Si
Group 5A	−3 in binary compounds with metals −3 in NH_4^+, binary compounds with H	Mg_3N_2, Na_3P, Cs_3As NH_3, PH_3, AsH_3, NH_4^+	+3, e.g., NO_2^-, PCl_3 +5, e.g., NO_3^-, PO_4^{3-}, AsF_5, P_4O_{10}
O	−2	H_2O, P_4O_{10}, Fe_2O_3, CaO, ClO_3^-	+2 in OF_2 −1 in peroxides, e.g., H_2O_2, Na_2O_2 $-\frac{1}{2}$ in superoxides, e.g., KO_2, RbO_2
Group 6A (other than O)	−2 in binary compounds with metals and H −2 in binary compounds with NH_4^+	H_2S, CaS, Fe_2S_3, Na_2Se $(NH_4)_2S$, $(NH_4)_2Se$	+4 with O and the more electronegative halogens, e.g., SO_2, SeO_2, Na_2SO_3, SO_3^{2-}, SF_4 +6 with O and the more electronegative halogens, e.g., SO_3, TeO_3, H_2SO_4, SO_4^{2-}, SF_6
Group 7A	−1 in binary compounds with metals and H −1 in binary compounds with NH_4^+	MgF_2, KI, $ZnCl_2$, $FeBr_3$ NH_4Cl, NH_4Br	Cl, Br, or I with O or with a more electronegative halogen +1, e.g., BrF, ClO^-, BrO^- +3, e.g., ICl_3, ClO_2^-, BrO_2^- +5, e.g., BrF_5, ClO_3^-, BrO_3^- +7, e.g., IF_7, ClO_4^-, BrO_4^-

combined with oxygen or with a lighter halogen, their oxidation states can be found by using rules 3 and 4.

(f) Group 7A elements (halogens) have oxidation states of -1 in *binary* compounds with metals, with H, with NH_4^+, or with a heavier halogen. When these elements, except fluorine (i.e., Cl, Br, I), are combined with oxygen or with a lighter halogen, their oxidation numbers can be found by using rules 3 and 4.

Table 5-4 summarizes rules 5 through 8, with many examples.

If you use element electronegativity to guide the assignment of oxidation state, you may wonder how to proceed when two elements have the same electronegativity. Take, for example, NCl_3, PH_3, and CS_2. For each of these binary compounds the elements have the same electronegativities. The periodic table is our guide, with the element that is closest to fluorine being assigned the negative oxidation state: $NCl_3 (Cl = -1, N = +3)$, $PH_3 (P = -3, H = +1)$, and $CS_2 (S = -2, C = +4)$. It is important to remember that oxidation states do not necessarily reflect reality.

> Group 6A elements below oxygen have oxidation states of -2 with less electronegative elements such as H, C, or metals. When Group 6A elements are combined with more electronegative elements, positive oxidation states are found.

EXAMPLE 5-6 Oxidation States

Determine the oxidation states of nitrogen in the following species: (a) N_2O_4, (b) NH_3, (c) HNO_3, (d) NO_3^-, (e) N_2.

Plan

We first assign oxidation states to elements that exhibit a single common oxidation number (see Table 5-4). We recall that (1) oxidation states are represented *per atom*, (2) the sum of the oxidation states in a neutral compound is zero, and (3) the sum of the oxidation states in an ion equals the charge on the ion.

Solution

(a) The oxidation state of O is -2. The sum of the oxidation states for all atoms in a neutral compound must be zero:

ox. no./atom: Ⓧ ⊖2
$$N_2O_4$$

total ox. no.: $2x + 4(-2) = 0$ or $x = +4$

We see that oxygen, the more electronegative element, has a negative oxidation state, while nitrogen, the less electronegative element, has the positive oxidation state.

(b) The oxidation state of H is then $+1$:

ox. no./atom: Ⓧ ⊕1
$$NH_3$$

total ox. no.: $x + 3(1) = 0$ or $x = -3$

Nitrogen is more electronegative than H, so N is in the -3 oxidation state and hydrogen is in the $+1$ state.

(c) The oxidation state of H is $+1$ and the oxidation state of O is -2.

ox. no./atom: ⊕1 Ⓧ ⊖2
$$HNO_3$$

total ox. no.: $1 + x + 3(-2) = 0$ or $x = +5$

Oxygen, the most electronegative element present, has an oxidation state of -2, while nitrogen, being less electronegative, has a positive oxidation state.

(d) The sum of the oxidation states for all atoms in an ion equals the charge on the ion:

ox. no./atom: Ⓧ ⊖2
$$NO_3^-$$

total ox. no.: $x + 3(-2) = -1$ or $x = +5$

(e) The oxidation state of any free element is zero.

You should now work Exercise 46.

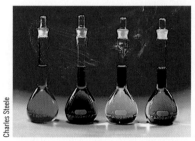
Charles Steele

Aqueous solutions of some compounds that contain chromium. *Left to right*: chromium(II) chloride, $CrCl_2$, is blue; chromium(III) chloride, $CrCl_3$ is green; potassium chromate, K_2CrO_4 is yellowish; potassium dichromate, $K_2Cr_2O_7$ is orangish.

> By convention, *oxidation states* are represented as $+n$ and $-n$, but ionic charges are represented as $n+$ and $n-$. We shall circle oxidation states associated with formulas and show them in colored circles indicating positive (blue), negative (red), or neutral (gray) oxidation states. Both oxidation states and ionic charges can be combined algebraically.

> Usually the element with the positive oxidation state is written first. For historic reasons, however, in compounds containing nitrogen and hydrogen, such as NH_3, and many compounds containing carbon and hydrogen, such as CH_4, hydrogen is written last, although it has a positive oxidation state.

Chemical Reactions and Periodicity

Now we will illustrate the periodicity of chemical properties by considering some reactions of hydrogen, oxygen, and their compounds. We choose to discuss hydrogen and oxygen because, of all the elements, they form the most kinds of compounds with other elements. Additionally, compounds of hydrogen and oxygen are very important in such diverse phenomena as all life processes and most corrosion.

5-8 Hydrogen and the Hydrides

Hydrogen

▶ The name "hydrogen" means *water former*.

Elemental hydrogen is a colorless, odorless, tasteless diatomic gas with the lowest molecular weight and density of any known substance. Discovery of the element is attributed to the Englishman Henry Cavendish (1731–1810), who prepared it in 1766 by passing steam through a red-hot gun barrel (mostly iron) and by the reaction of acids with reactive metals. The latter is still the method commonly used for the preparation of small amounts of H_2 in the laboratory.

$$3Fe(s) + 4H_2O(g) \xrightarrow{heat} Fe_3O_4(s) + 4H_2(g)$$

$$Zn(s) + 2HCl(aq) \longrightarrow ZnCl_2(aq) + H_2(g)$$

Hydrogen also can be prepared by electrolysis of water.

$$2H_2O(\ell) \xrightarrow{electricity} 2H_2(g) + O_2(g)$$

In the future, if it becomes economical to convert solar energy into electrical energy that can be used to electrolyze water, H_2 could become an important fuel (although the dangers of storage and transportation would have to be overcome). The *combustion* of H_2 liberates a great deal of heat. **Combustion** is the highly exothermic combination of a substance with oxygen, usually with a flame (see Section 5-9, Combustion Reactions).

▶ This is the reverse of the decomposition of H_2O.

$$2H_2(g) + O_2(g) \xrightarrow[\text{or heat}]{\text{spark}} 2H_2O(\ell) + energy$$

Hydrogen is very flammable; it was responsible for the *Hindenburg* airship disaster in 1937. A spark is all it takes to initiate the **combustion reaction**, which is exothermic enough to provide the heat necessary to sustain the reaction.

▶ Hydrogen is no longer used in blimps and dirigibles. It has been replaced by helium, which is slightly denser, nonflammable, and much safer.

Hydrogen is prepared by the "water gas reaction," which results from the passage of steam over white-hot coke (impure carbon, a nonmetal) at 1500°C. The mixture of products commonly called "water gas" is used industrially as a fuel. Both components, CO and H_2, undergo combustion.

$$\underset{\text{in coke}}{C(s)} + \underset{\text{steam}}{H_2O(g)} \longrightarrow \underbrace{CO(g) + H_2(g)}_{\text{"water gas"}}$$

Vast quantities of hydrogen are produced commercially each year by a process called *steam cracking*. Methane reacts with steam at 830°C in the presence of a nickel catalyst.

$$CH_4(g) + H_2O(g) \xrightarrow[\text{Ni}]{\text{heat}} CO(g) + 3H_2(g)$$

The mixture of H_2 and CO gases is also referred to as "synthesis gas." It can be used to produce a wide variety of organic chemicals like methanol (CH_3OH) and hydrocarbon mixtures for gasoline, kerosene, and related fuels.

Reactions of Hydrogen and Hydrides

Atomic hydrogen has the $1s^1$ electron configuration. It reacts with metals and with other nonmetals to form binary compounds. When hydrogen reacts with an active metal, it gains one electron per atom to form the hydride ion, H^-; the resulting compounds are called

ionic hydrides. In combination of hydrogen with nonmetals or metalloids, hydrogen shares electrons to form *molecular* compounds.

The ionic or molecular character of the binary compounds of hydrogen depends on the position of the other element in the periodic table (Figure 5-5). The reactions of H_2 with the *alkali* (1A) and the heavier (more active) *alkaline earth* (2A) *metals* result in solid *ionic hydrides*. The reaction with the molten (liquid) 1A metals may be represented in general terms as

$$2M(\ell) + H_2(g) \xrightarrow[\text{high pressures}]{\text{high temperatures}} 2(M^+, H^-)(s) \qquad M = Li, Na, K, Rb, Cs$$

▶ The use of the term "hydride" does not necessarily imply the presence of the hydride ion, H^-.

Thus, hydrogen combines with lithium to form lithium hydride and with sodium to form sodium hydride.

$$2Li(\ell) + H_2(g) \longrightarrow 2LiH(s) \qquad \text{lithium hydride (mp 680°C)}$$

$$2Na(\ell) + H_2(g) \longrightarrow 2NaH(s) \qquad \text{sodium hydride (mp 800°C)}$$

▶ The ionic hydrides are named by naming the metal first, followed by "hydride."

In general terms, the reactions of the heavier (more active) 2A metals may be represented as

$$M(\ell) + H_2(g) \longrightarrow (M^{2+}, 2H^-)(s) \qquad M = Ca, Sr, Ba$$

Thus, calcium combines with hydrogen to form calcium hydride:

$$Ca(\ell) + H_2(g) \longrightarrow CaH_2(s) \qquad \text{calcium hydride (mp 816°C)}$$

These *ionic hydrides are all basic* because they react with water to form hydroxide ions. When water is added by drops to lithium hydride, for example, lithium hydroxide and hydrogen are produced. The reaction of calcium hydride is similar.

▶ Ionic hydrides can serve as sources of hydrogen. They must be stored in environments free of moisture and O_2.

$$LiH(s) + H_2O(\ell) \longrightarrow LiOH(s) + H_2(g)$$

$$CaH_2(s) + 2H_2O(\ell) \longrightarrow Ca(OH)_2(s) + 2H_2(g)$$

▶ We show LiOH and Ca(OH)$_2$ as solids here because not enough water is available to act as a solvent.

Hydrogen reacts with *nonmetals* to form binary *molecular compounds*. The nonmetals have higher (or equal) electronegativity relative to hydrogen, so the nonmetal takes on a negative oxidation state while hydrogen goes into the +1 oxidation state. For example, H_2 combines with the halogens to form colorless, gaseous hydrogen halides (Figure 5-6):

▶ The hydrogen halides are named by the word "hydrogen" followed by the stem for the halogen with an "-ide" ending.

$$H_2(g) + X_2 \longrightarrow \underset{\text{hydrogen halides}}{2HX(g)} \qquad X = F, Cl, Br, I$$

Specifically, hydrogen reacts with fluorine to form hydrogen fluoride and with chlorine to form hydrogen chloride:

$$H_2(g) + F_2(g) \longrightarrow 2HF(g) \qquad \text{hydrogen fluoride}$$

$$H_2(g) + Cl_2(g) \longrightarrow 2HCl(g) \qquad \text{hydrogen chloride}$$

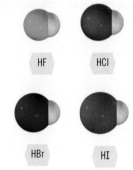

HF   HCl

HBr   HI

1A	2A	3A	4A	5A	6A	7A
LiH	BeH$_2$	B$_2$H$_6$	CH$_4$	NH$_3$	H$_2$O	HF
NaH	MgH$_2$	(AlH$_3$)$_x$	SiH$_4$	PH$_3$	H$_2$S	HCl
KH	CaH$_2$	Ga$_2$H$_6$	GeH$_4$	AsH$_3$	H$_2$Se	HBr
RbH	SrH$_2$	InH$_3$	SnH$_4$	SbH$_3$	H$_2$Te	HI
CsH	BaH$_2$	TlH	PbH$_4$	BiH$_3$	H$_2$Po	HAt

▶ When the other element has similar or higher electronegativity than hydrogen, the compound with hydrogen has more molecular character. When the other element is considerably less electronegative than hydrogen, ionic hydrides containing H^- are formed (e.g., CsH).

Figure 5-5 Common compounds of hydrogen with the representative elements. The ionic hydrides are shaded pink, molecular compounds of hydrogen are shaded green, those of intermediate character are shaded purple, and the ones in blue are acidic. The gray shaded hydrides are unstable and have not been isolated. The green and blue shaded compounds do not use hydride in their names.

▶ The compounds with Group 6A are named:

H$_2$O, hydrogen oxide (water)
H$_2$S, hydrogen sulfide
H$_2$Se, hydrogen selenide
H$_2$Te, hydrogen telluride

All except H$_2$O are *very* toxic.

Hydrogen combines with oxygen to form molecular compounds with a 2:1 stoichiometry:

$$2H_2(g) + O_2(g) \xrightarrow{\text{heat}} 2H_2O(g)$$

The heavier members of the Group 6A family also combine with hydrogen to form binary compounds that are gases at room temperature. Their formulas resemble that of water.

The primary industrial use of H$_2$ is in the synthesis of ammonia, NH$_3$, by the Haber process (see Section 17-7). Most of the NH$_3$ is used in liquid form as a fertilizer (Figure 5-7) or to make other fertilizers, such as ammonium nitrate, NH$_4$NO$_3$, and ammonium sulfate, (NH$_4$)$_2$SO$_4$:

$$N_2(g) + 3H_2(g) \xrightarrow[\text{heat, high pressure}]{\text{catalysts}} 2NH_3(g)$$

The molecular compounds of hydrogen with Groups 6A and 7A are acidic; their aqueous solutions contain hydrogen cations (H$^+$). These include HF, HCl, HBr, HI, H$_2$S, H$_2$Se, and H$_2$Te. Acids and bases will be discussed in more detail in Chapters 6 and 10.

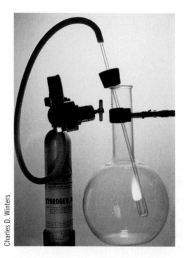

Figure 5-6 Hydrogen, H$_2$ burns in an atmosphere of pure chlorine, Cl$_2$ to produce hydrogen chloride.

$$H_2 + Cl_2 \longrightarrow 2HCl$$

Figure 5-7 Ammonia may be applied directly to the soil as a fertilizer.

EXAMPLE 5-7 Predicting Products of Reactions

Predict the products of the reactions involving the reactants shown. Write a balanced formula unit equation for each.

(a) H$_2$(g) + I$_2$(g) $\xrightarrow{\text{heat}}$

(b) K(ℓ) + H$_2$(g) $\xrightarrow{\text{heat}}$

(c) NaH(s) + H$_2$O(ℓ) (excess) $\longrightarrow$

Plan

(a) Hydrogen reacts with the halogens (Group 7A) to form hydrogen halides—in this example, HI.

(b) Hydrogen reacts with active metals to produce hydrides—in this case, KH.

(c) Active metal hydrides react with water to produce a metal hydroxide and H$_2$.

Solution

▶ Remember that hydride ions, H$^-$, react with water to produce OH$^-$ ions and H$_2$(g).

(a) H$_2$(g) + I$_2$(g) $\xrightarrow{\text{heat}}$ 2HI(g)

(b) K(ℓ) + H$_2$(g) $\xrightarrow{\text{heat}}$ 2KH(s)

(c) NaH(s) + H$_2$O(ℓ) $\longrightarrow$ NaOH(aq) + H$_2$(g)

Charles D. Winters

© Phil Degginger/Alamy

NH$_3$

EXAMPLE 5-8 Ionic and Molecular Properties

Predict the ionic or molecular character of the products in Example 5-7.

Plan

We refer to Figure 5-5, which displays the nature of binary compounds with hydrogen.

Solution

Reaction (a) is a reaction between hydrogen and another nonmetal. The product, HI, must be molecular. Reaction (b) is the reaction of hydrogen with an active Group 1A metal. Thus, KH must be ionic. The products of reaction (c) are molecular $H_2(g)$ and the strong base, NaOH, which is ionic.

You should now work Exercises 54 and 55.

5-9 Oxygen and the Oxides

Oxygen and Ozone

Oxygen was discovered in 1774 by an English minister and scientist, Joseph Priestley (1733–1804). He observed the thermal decomposition of mercury(II) oxide, a red powder, to form liquid Hg and a colorless gas:

$$2HgO(s) \xrightarrow{\text{heat}} 2Hg(\ell) + O_2(g)$$

That part of the earth we see—land, water, and air—is approximately 50% oxygen by mass. About two-thirds of the mass of the human body is due to oxygen in H_2O. Elemental oxygen, O_2, is an odorless and colorless gas that makes up about 21% by volume of dry air. In the liquid (bp = $-183°C$) and solid (mp = $-218°C$) states, it is pale blue. Oxygen is only slightly soluble in water; only about 0.04 g dissolves in 1 L water at 25°C (0.001 M solutions). This is sufficient to sustain fish and other marine organisms. Oxygen is obtained commercially by cooling air until it liquefies and then separating N_2, O_2, Ar, and other gaseous components. The greatest single industrial use of O_2 is for oxygen enrichment in blast furnaces for the conversion of pig iron (reduced, high-carbon iron) to steel.

Oxygen also exists in a second allotropic form, called ozone, O_3. Ozone is an unstable, pale blue gas at room temperature. It is formed by passing an electrical discharge through gaseous oxygen. Its unique, pungent odor is often noticed during electrical storms and in the vicinity of electrical equipment. Not surprisingly, its density is about $1\frac{1}{2}$ times that of O_2. At $-112°C$, it condenses to a deep blue liquid. It is a very strong oxidizing agent. As a concentrated gas or a liquid, ozone can easily decompose explosively:

$$2O_3(g) \longrightarrow 3O_2(g)$$

Oxygen atoms, or **radicals**, are intermediates in this exothermic decomposition of O_3 to O_2. They act as strong oxidizing agents in such applications as destroying bacteria in water purification.

The ozone molecule is angular and has two oxygen–oxygen bond lengths (1.28 Å) that are identical. This is intermediate between typical single and double bond lengths between oxygen atoms.

Reactions of Oxygen and the Oxides

Oxygen forms oxides by direct combination with all other elements except the noble gases and noble (unreactive) metals (Au, Pd, Pt). **Oxides** are binary compounds that contain oxygen. Although such reactions are generally very exothermic, many proceed quite slowly and require heating to supply the energy necessary to break the strong bonds in O_2 mol-

▶ The name "oxygen" means "acid former."

▶ Liquid O_2 is used as an oxidizer for rocket fuels. O_2 also is used in the health fields for oxygen-enriched air.

▶ *Allotropes* are different structural forms of the same element (see Section 2-1).

▶ A *radical* is a species containing one or more unpaired electrons; many radicals are very reactive.

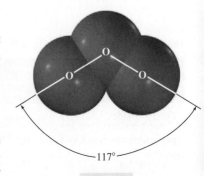

O_3 molecule

ecules. After these reactions are initiated, most release more than enough energy to be self-sustaining, and some become "red hot."

Reactions of O$_2$ with Metals. Metals can combine with oxygen to form three kinds of solid ionic products called oxides, peroxides, and superoxides. You can recognize these classes of compounds as

Class	Contains Ions	Oxidation No. of Oxygen
normal oxides	O^{2-}	-2
peroxides	O_2^{2-}	-1
superoxides	O_2^{-}	$-\frac{1}{2}$

In general, metallic oxides (including peroxides and superoxides) are ionic solids.

The Group 1A metals combine with oxygen to form all three kinds of solid ionic products called oxides, peroxides, and superoxides. Lithium combines with oxygen to form lithium oxide.

$$4Li(s) + O_2(g) \longrightarrow 2Li_2O(s) \qquad \text{lithium oxide (mp} > 1700°C)$$

By contrast, sodium reacts with an excess of oxygen to form sodium peroxide, Na_2O_2, as the major product, rather than sodium oxide, Na_2O.

$$2Na(s) + O_2(g) \longrightarrow Na_2O_2(g) \qquad \text{sodium peroxide (decomposes at 460°C)}$$

Peroxides contain the $O-O^{2-}$ ion (O_2^{2-}), in which the oxidation number of each oxygen is -1, whereas **normal oxides** such as lithium oxide, Li_2O, contain oxide ions, O^{2-}. The heavier members of the family (K, Rb, Cs) react with excess oxygen to form *superoxides*. These contain the **superoxide** ion, O_2^{-}, in which the oxidation number of each oxygen is $-\frac{1}{2}$. The reaction with K is

$$K(s) + O_2(g) \longrightarrow KO_2(s) \qquad \text{potassium superoxide (mp 430°C)}$$

▶ The larger K^+, Rb^+, and Cs^+ cations prefer the larger O_2^- and O_2^{2-} anions owing to more efficient solid-state packing, which results from better size matching of the ions.

The tendency of the Group 1A metals to form oxygen-rich compounds increases going down the group. This is because cation radii increase going down the group.

The Group 2A metals react with oxygen to form normal ionic oxides, MO, but at high pressures of oxygen the heavier ones form ionic peroxides, MO_2 (Table 5-5).

▶ Beryllium reacts with oxygen only at elevated temperatures and forms only the normal oxide, BeO. The other Group 2A metals form normal oxides at moderate temperatures.

$$2M(s) + O_2(g) \longrightarrow 2(M^{2+}, O^{2-})(s) \qquad M = Be, Mg, Ca, Sr, Ba$$

$$M(s) + O_2(g) \longrightarrow (M^{2+}, O_2^{2-})(s) \qquad M = Ca, Sr, Ba$$

For example, the equations for the reactions of calcium and oxygen are

$$2Ca(s) + O_2(g) \longrightarrow 2CaO(s) \qquad \text{calcium oxide (mp 2580°C)}$$

$$Ca(s) + O_2(g) \longrightarrow CaO_2(s) \qquad \text{calcium peroxide (decomposes at 275°C)}$$

Table 5-5 Oxygen Compounds of the 1A and 2A Metals*

	1A					2A				
	Li	Na	K	Rb	Cs	Be	Mg	Ca	Sr	Ba
normal oxides	Li_2O	Na_2O	K_2O	Rb_2O	Cs_2O	BeO	MgO	CaO	SrO	BaO
peroxides	Li_2O_2	Na_2O_2	K_2O_2	Rb_2O_2	Cs_2O_2			CaO_2	SrO_2	BaO_2
superoxides		NaO_2	KO_2	RbO_2	CsO_2					

*The shaded compounds represent the principal products of the direct reaction of the metal with oxygen.

The other metals, with the exceptions noted previously (Au, Pd, and Pt), react with oxygen to form solid metal oxides. Many metals to the right of Group 2A show variable oxidation states, so they may form several oxides. For example, iron combines with oxygen in the following series of reactions to form three different oxides (Figure 5-8).

$$2Fe(s) + O_2(g) \longrightarrow 2FeO(s) \qquad \text{iron(II) oxide}$$

$$6FeO(s) + O_2(g) \longrightarrow 2Fe_3O_4(s) \qquad \text{magnetic iron oxide (a mixed oxide)}$$

$$4Fe_3O_4(s) + O_2(g) \longrightarrow 6Fe_2O_3(s) \qquad \text{iron(III) oxide}$$

Copper reacts with a limited amount of oxygen to form red Cu_2O, whereas with excess oxygen it forms black CuO.

$$4Cu(s) + O_2(g) \xrightarrow{\text{heat}} 2Cu_2O(s) \qquad \text{copper(I) oxide}$$

$$2Cu(s) + O_2(g) \xrightarrow{\text{heat}} 2CuO(s) \qquad \text{copper(II) oxide}$$

Metals that exhibit variable oxidation states react with a limited amount of oxygen to give oxides with lower oxidation states (such as FeO and Cu_2O). They react with an excess of oxygen to give oxides with higher oxidation states (such as Fe_2O_3 and CuO).

Figure 5-8 Steel wool burns brilliantly to form iron(III) oxide, Fe_2O_3.

Reactions of Metal Oxides with Water. Oxides of metals are called **basic anhydrides** (or **basic oxides**) because many of them combine with water to form bases with no change in oxidation state of the metal (Figure 5-9). "Anhydride" means "without water," and in a sense, the metal oxide is a hydroxide base with the water "removed." Metal oxides that are soluble in water react to produce the corresponding hydroxides.

	Metal Oxide	+	Water	$\longrightarrow$	Metal Hydroxide (base)	
sodium oxide	$Na_2O(s)$	+	$H_2O(\ell)$	$\longrightarrow$	$2NaOH(aq)$	sodium hydroxide
calcium oxide	$CaO(s)$	+	$H_2O(\ell)$	$\longrightarrow$	$Ca(OH)_2(aq)$	calcium hydroxide
barium oxide	$BaO(s)$	+	$H_2O(\ell)$	$\longrightarrow$	$Ba(OH)_2(aq)$	barium hydroxide

The oxides of the Group 1A metals and the heavier Group 2A metals dissolve in water to give solutions of strong bases. Most other metal oxides are relatively insoluble in water.

Reactions of O_2 with Nonmetals. *Oxygen combines with many nonmetals to form molecular oxides.* For example, carbon burns in oxygen to form carbon monoxide or carbon dioxide, depending on the relative amounts of carbon and oxygen.

	Increasing acidic character ⟶						
	1A	2A	3A	4A	5A	6A	7A
	Li_2O	BeO	B_2O_3	CO_2	N_2O_5		OF_2
	Na_2O	MgO	Al_2O_3	SiO_2	P_4O_{10}	SO_3	Cl_2O_7
	K_2O	CaO	Ga_2O_3	GeO_2	As_2O_5	SeO_3	Br_2O_7
	Rb_2O	SrO	In_2O_3	SnO_2	Sb_2O_5	TeO_3	I_2O_7
	Cs_2O	BaO	Tl_2O_3	PbO_2	Bi_2O_5	PoO_3	At_2O_7

Increasing base character (vertical label, left side)

Figure 5-9 The normal oxides of the representative elements in their maximum oxidation states. Acidic oxides (acid anhydrides) are shaded blue, amphoteric oxides are shaded purple, and basic oxides (basic anhydrides) are shaded pink. An **amphoteric oxide** is one that shows some acidic and some basic properties.

CO   CO₂

H₂CO₃

P₄O₆

P₄O₁₀

▶ The production of SO_3 at a reasonable rate requires the presence of a catalyst.

$$2C(s) + O_2(g) \longrightarrow \overset{+2}{2CO}(s) \qquad \text{(excess C and limited O}_2\text{)}$$

$$C(s) + O_2(g) \longrightarrow \overset{+4}{CO_2}(s) \qquad \text{(limited C and excess O}_2\text{)}$$

Carbon monoxide is a very poisonous gas because it forms a stronger bond with the iron atom in hemoglobin than does an oxygen molecule. Attachment of the CO molecule to the iron atom destroys the ability of hemoglobin to pick up oxygen in the lungs and carry it to the brain and muscle tissue. Carbon monoxide poisoning is particularly insidious because the gas has no odor and because the victim first becomes drowsy.

Unlike carbon monoxide, carbon dioxide is not toxic. It is one of the products of the respiratory process. It is used to make carbonated beverages, which are mostly saturated solutions of carbon dioxide in water; a small amount of the carbon dioxide combines with the water to form carbonic acid (H_2CO_3), a very weak acid.

Phosphorus reacts with a limited amount of oxygen to form tetraphosphorus hexoxide, P_4O_6:

$$P_4(s) + 3O_2(g) \longrightarrow \overset{+3}{P_4O_6}(s) \qquad \text{tetraphosphorus hexoxide}$$

whereas reaction with an excess of oxygen gives tetraphosphorus decoxide, P_4O_{10}:

$$P_4(s) + 5O_2(g) \longrightarrow \overset{+5}{P_4O_{10}}(s) \qquad \text{tetraphosphorus decoxide}$$

Sulfur burns in oxygen to form primarily sulfur dioxide (Figure 5-10) and only very small amounts of sulfur trioxide.

$$S_8(s) + 8O_2(g) \longrightarrow \overset{+4}{8SO_2}(g) \qquad \text{sulfur dioxide (bp } = -10.0°C)$$

$$S_8(s) + 12O_2(g) \longrightarrow \overset{+6}{8SO_3}(\ell) \qquad \text{sulfur trioxide (bp } = 43.4°C)$$

The reactions of nonmetals with a limited amount of oxygen usually give products that contain the nonmetals (other than oxygen) in lower oxidation states. Reactions with excess oxygen give products in which the nonmetals exhibit higher oxidation states. The examples we have cited are CO and CO_2, P_4O_6 and P_4O_{10}, and SO_2 and SO_3. The molecular formulas of the oxides are sometimes not easily predictable, but the *simplest* formulas are. For example, the two most common oxidation states of phosphorus in molecular compounds are +3 and +5. The simplest formulas for the corresponding phosphorus oxides therefore are P_2O_3 and P_2O_5, respectively. The molecular (true) formulas are twice these, P_4O_6 and P_4O_{10}.

Charles Steele

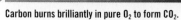

Carbon burns brilliantly in pure O_2 to form CO_2.

Reactions of Nonmetal Oxides with Water. *Nonmetal oxides* are called **acid anhydrides** (or **acidic oxides**) because many of them dissolve in water to form acids *with no change in oxidation state of the nonmetal* (see Figure 5-9). Several **ternary acids** can be prepared by reaction of the appropriate nonmetal oxides with water. Ternary acids contain three elements, usually H, O, and another nonmetal.

	Nonmetal Oxide	+ Water	⟶ Ternary Acid	
carbon dioxide	$\overset{+4}{C}O_2(g)$	$+ H_2O(\ell)$	$\longrightarrow H_2\overset{+4}{C}O_3(aq)$	carbonic acid
sulfur dioxide	$\overset{+4}{S}O_2(g)$	$+ H_2O(\ell)$	$\longrightarrow H_2\overset{+4}{S}O_3(aq)$	sulfurous acid
sulfur trioxide	$\overset{+6}{S}O_3(\ell)$	$+ H_2O(\ell)$	$\longrightarrow H_2\overset{+6}{S}O_4(aq)$	sulfuric acid
dinitrogen pentoxide	$\overset{+5}{N}_2O_5(s)$	$+ H_2O(\ell)$	$\longrightarrow 2H\overset{+5}{N}O_3(aq)$	nitric acid
tetraphosphorus decoxide	$\overset{+5}{P}_4O_{10}(s)$	$+ 6H_2O(\ell)$	$\longrightarrow 4H_3\overset{+5}{P}O_4(aq)$	phosphoric acid

Nearly all oxides of nonmetals and metalloids react with water to give solutions of ternary acids. The oxides of boron and silicon, which are insoluble, are two exceptions.

Reactions of Metal Oxides with Nonmetal Oxides. Another common kind of reaction of oxides is the *combination of metal oxides (basic anhydrides) with nonmetal oxides (acid anhydrides), with no change in oxidation states, to form salts.*

	Metal Oxide	+ Nonmetal Oxide	⟶ Salt	
calcium oxide + sulfur trioxide	$\overset{+2}{Ca}O(s)$	$+ \overset{+6}{S}O_3(\ell)$	$\longrightarrow \overset{+2}{Ca}\overset{+6}{S}O_4(s)$	calcium sulfate
magnesium oxide + carbon dioxide	$\overset{+2}{Mg}O(s)$	$+ \overset{+4}{C}O_2(g)$	$\longrightarrow \overset{+2}{Mg}\overset{+4}{C}O_3(s)$	magnesium carbonate
sodium oxide + tetraphosphorus decoxide	$6\overset{+1}{Na}_2O(s)$	$+ \overset{+5}{P}_4O_{10}(s)$	$\longrightarrow 4\overset{+1}{Na}_3\overset{+5}{P}O_4(s)$	sodium phosphate

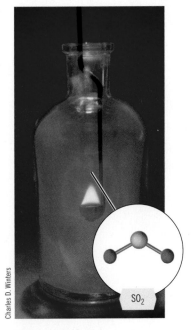

Figure 5-10 Sulfur burns in oxygen to form sulfur dioxide.

▶ More information on strong and weak acids will appear in Chapter 6.

EXAMPLE 5-9 Acidic Character of Oxides   🔵 MOLECULAR REASONING

Arrange the following oxides in order of increasing molecular (acidic) character: SO_3, Cl_2O_7, CaO, and PbO_2.

Plan

Molecular (acidic) character of oxides increases as nonmetallic character of the element that is combined with oxygen increases (see Figure 5-9).

increasing nonmetallic character ⟶

$$Ca < Pb < S < Cl$$

Periodic group: 2A   4A   6A   7A

Solution

increasing molecular character ⟶

Thus, the order is $CaO < PbO_2 < SO_3 < Cl_2O_7$

🅢 **TOP & THINK**
Be sure you can relate properties such as metallic character of elements and oxide character to the periodic table.

EXAMPLE 5-10 Basic Character of Oxides

Arrange the oxides in Example 6-8 in order of increasing basicity.

Plan

The greater the molecular character of an oxide, the more acidic it is. Thus, the most basic oxides have the least molecular (most ionic) character (see Figure 5-9).

Solution

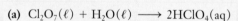

increasing basic character

molecular $Cl_2O_7 < SO_3 < PbO_2 < CaO$ ionic

EXAMPLE 5-11 Predicting Reaction Products

Predict the products of the following pairs of reactants. Write a balanced equation for each reaction.

(a) $Cl_2O_7(\ell) + H_2O(\ell) \longrightarrow$

(b) $As_4(s) + O_2(g)$ (excess) $\xrightarrow{\text{heat}}$

(c) $Mg(s) + O_2(g) \xrightarrow{\text{heat}}$

Plan

(a) The reaction of a nonmetal oxide (acid anhydride) with water forms a ternary acid in which the nonmetal (Cl) has the same oxidation state ($+7$) as in the oxide. Thus, the acid is perchloric acid, $HClO_4$.

(b) Arsenic, a Group 5A metalloid, exhibits common oxidation states of $+5$ and $+5 - 2 = +3$. Reaction of arsenic with *excess* oxygen produces the higher-oxidation-state oxide, As_2O_5. By analogy with the oxide of phosphorus in the $+5$ oxidation state, P_4O_{10}, we might write the formula as As_4O_{10}, but this oxide exists as As_2O_5.

(c) The reaction of a Group 2A metal with oxygen produces the normal metal oxide—MgO in this case.

Solution

(a) $Cl_2O_7(\ell) + H_2O(\ell) \longrightarrow 2HClO_4(aq)$

(b) $As_4(s) + 5O_2(g) \xrightarrow{\text{heat}} 2As_2O_5(s)$

(c) $2Mg(s) + O_2(g) \xrightarrow{\text{heat}} 2MgO(s)$

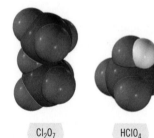

Cl_2O_7 $HClO_4$

CAUTION!
Perchloric acid is an especially dangerous strong acid because it is also a very strong oxidizing acid. The perchlorate salts produced from its reactions with bases are prone to explosions if they are touched or disturbed when dry.

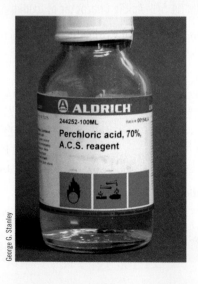

George G. Stanley

EXAMPLE 5-12 Predicting Reaction Products

Predict the products of the following pairs of reactants. Write a balanced equation for each reaction.

(a) $CaO(s) + H_2O(\ell) \longrightarrow$

(b) $Li_2O(s) + SO_3(\ell) \longrightarrow$

Plan

(a) The reaction of a metal oxide with water produces the metal hydroxide.

(b) The reaction of a metal oxide with a nonmetal oxide produces a salt containing the cation of the metal oxide and the anion of the acid for which the nonmetal oxide is the anhydride. SO_3 is the acid anhydride of sulfuric acid, H_2SO_4.

Solution

(a) Calcium oxide reacts with water to form calcium hydroxide.

$$CaO(s) + H_2O(\ell) \longrightarrow Ca(OH)_2(aq)$$

(b) Lithium oxide reacts with sulfur trioxide to form lithium sulfate.

$$Li_2O(s) + SO_3(\ell) \longrightarrow Li_2SO_4(s)$$

You should now work Exercises 66–69.

▶ CaO is called quicklime. $Ca(OH)_2$ is called slaked lime. Both are sometimes just called lime.

Combustion Reactions

Combustion, or burning, is an oxidation–reduction reaction in which oxygen combines rapidly with oxidizable materials in highly exothermic reactions, usually with a visible flame. The complete combustion of *hydrocarbons*, in fossil fuels for example, produces carbon dioxide and water (steam) as the major products:

▶ Hydrocarbons are compounds that contain only hydrogen and carbon.

$$\overset{-4}{\underset{}{}}\overset{+1}{\underset{}{}}CH_4(g) + \overset{0}{\underset{excess}{2O_2(g)}} \xrightarrow{\text{heat}} \overset{+4}{\underset{}{}}\overset{-2}{\underset{}{}}CO_2(g) + \overset{+1}{\underset{}{}}\overset{-2}{\underset{}{}}2H_2O(g) + \text{heat}$$

$$\overset{-2}{\underset{}{}}\overset{+1}{\underset{cyclohexane}{}}C_6H_{12}(g) + \overset{0}{\underset{excess}{9O_2(g)}} \xrightarrow{\text{heat}} \overset{+4}{\underset{}{}}\overset{-2}{\underset{}{}}6CO_2(g) + \overset{+1}{\underset{}{}}\overset{-2}{\underset{}{}}6H_2O(g) + \text{heat}$$

▶ Recall that oxidation states are indicated by numbers in colored circles (blue for positive oxidation states, red for negative oxidations states, and gray for 0).

As we have seen, the origin of the term "oxidation" lies in just such reactions, in which oxygen "oxidizes" another species.

Combustion of Fossil Fuels and Air Pollution

Fossil fuels are mixtures of variable composition that consist primarily of hydrocarbons. We burn them to use the energy that is released rather than to obtain chemical products (Figure 5-11). For example, burning octane, C_8H_{18}, in an excess of oxygen (plenty of air) produces carbon dioxide and water. There are many similar compounds in gasoline and diesel fuels.

$$2C_8H_{18}(\ell) + \underset{excess}{25O_2(g)} \longrightarrow 16CO_2(g) + 18H_2O(\ell)$$

Carbon monoxide is produced by the incomplete burning of carbon-containing compounds in a limited amount of oxygen.

$$2C_8H_{18}(\ell) + \underset{\text{limited amount}}{17O_2(g)} \longrightarrow 16CO(g) + 18H_2O(\ell)$$

Figure 5-11 Plants such as this one burn more than 10^7 tons of coal and produce over 2×10^8 megawatt-hours of electricity each year.

▶ Carbon in the form of soot is one of the many kinds of *particulate matter* in polluted air.

In very limited oxygen, carbon (soot) is produced by partially burning hydrocarbons. For octane, the reaction is

$$2C_8H_{18}(\ell) + 9O_2(g) \longrightarrow 16C(s) + 18H_2O(\ell)$$
very limited amount

When you see blue or black smoke (carbon) coming from an internal combustion engine (or smell unburned fuel in the air), you may be quite sure that lots of toxic carbon monoxide is also being produced and released into the air.

We see that the incomplete combustion of hydrocarbons yields undesirable products—carbon monoxide and elemental carbon (soot), which pollute the air. Unfortunately, all fossil fuels—natural gas, coal, gasoline, kerosene, oil, and so on—also have undesirable nonhydrocarbon impurities that burn to produce oxides that act as additional air pollutants. At this time it is not economically feasible to remove all of these impurities from the fuels before burning them.

Fossil fuels result from the decay of animal and vegetable matter (Figure 5-12). All living matter contains some sulfur and nitrogen, so fossil fuels also contain sulfur and nitrogen impurities to varying degrees. Table 5-6 gives composition data for some common kinds of coal.

Combustion of sulfur produces sulfur dioxide, SO_2, probably the single most harmful pollutant.

Figure 5-12 The luxuriant growth of vegetation that occurred during the carboniferous age is the source of our coal deposits.

$$\overset{0}{S_8}(s) + 8O_2(g) \xrightarrow{\text{heat}} 8\overset{+4}{S}O_2(g)$$

Large amounts of SO_2 are produced by the burning of sulfur-containing coal.

Many metals occur in nature as sulfides. The process of extracting the free (elemental) metals involves **roasting**—heating an ore in the presence of air. For many metal sulfides this produces a metal oxide and SO_2. The metal oxides are then reduced to the free metals. Consider lead sulfide, PbS, as an example:

$$2PbS(s) + 3O_2(g) \longrightarrow 2PbO(s) + 2SO_2(g)$$

Sulfur dioxide is corrosive; it damages plants, structural materials, and humans. It is a nasal, throat, and lung irritant. Sulfur dioxide is slowly oxidized to sulfur trioxide, SO_3, by oxygen in air:

$$2SO_2(g) + O_2(g) \longrightarrow 2SO_3(\ell)$$

Table 5-6 Some Typical Coal Compositions in Percent (dry, ash-free)

	C	H	O	N	S
lignite	70.59	4.47	23.13	1.04	0.74
subbituminous	77.2	5.01	15.92	1.30	0.51
bituminous	80.2	5.80	7.53	1.39	5.11
anthracite	92.7	2.80	2.70	1.00	0.90

The Blue Ridge Mountain next to Palmerton, Pennsylvania, was decimated by SO_2 pollution from the zinc refinery located there. The roasting of the ZnS ore to produce ZnO (used to produce Zn metal) also made SO_2 most of which was captured to generate sulfuric acid. But cumulative SO_2 releases over many years killed most of the vegetation on the mountain next to the refinery. The refinery is now shut down, and the Environmental Protection Agency (EPA) is doing extensive remediation of the mountain with acid- and zinc-resistant plants.

Sulfur trioxide readily combines with moisture in the air to form the strong, corrosive acid, sulfuric acid:

$$SO_3(\ell) + H_2O(\ell) \longrightarrow H_2SO_4(\ell)$$

Oxides of sulfur are the main cause of acid rain.

Compounds of nitrogen are also impurities in fossil fuels; they burn to form nitric oxide, NO. Most of the nitrogen in the NO in exhaust gases from furnaces, automobiles, airplanes, and so on, however, comes from the air that is mixed with the fuel.

$$\overset{0}{N_2}(g) + O_2(g) \longrightarrow 2\overset{+2}{N}O(g)$$

NO can be further oxidized by oxygen to nitrogen dioxide, NO_2; this reaction is enhanced in the presence of ultraviolet light from the sun.

$$2\overset{+2}{N}O(g) + O_2(g) \xrightarrow[\text{light}]{UV} 2\overset{+4}{N}O_2(g) \qquad \text{(a reddish-brown gas)}$$

NO_2 is responsible for the reddish-brown haze that hangs over many cities on sunny afternoons (Figure 5-13) and probably for most of the respiratory problems associated with this kind of air pollution. It can react to produce other oxides of nitrogen and other secondary pollutants.

In addition to being a pollutant itself, nitrogen dioxide reacts with water in the air to form nitric acid, another major contributor to acid rain:

$$3NO_2(g) + H_2O(\ell) \longrightarrow 2HNO_3(aq) + NO(g)$$

▶ Remember that "clean air" is *about* 80% N_2 and 20% O_2 by mass. This reaction does *not* occur at room temperature but does occur at the high temperatures of furnaces, internal combustion engines, and jet engines.

National Center for Atmospheric Research/ National Science Foundation

Figure 5-13 Photochemical pollution (a brown haze) enveloping a city.

KEY TERMS

Acid anhydride   A nonmetal oxide that reacts with water to form an acid.

Acidic oxide   See *Acid anhydride.*

Actinides   Elements 90 through 103 (after *actinium*).

Amphoteric oxide   An oxide that shows some acidic and some basic properties.

Amphoterism   The ability of a substance to react with both acids and bases.

Angstrom (Å) 10^{-10} meter, 10^{-1} nm, or 100 pm.

Atomic radius   The radius of an atom.

Basic anhydride   A metal oxide that reacts with water to form a base.

Basic oxide   See *Basic anhydride.*

Catalyst   A substance that speeds up a chemical reaction without itself being consumed in the reaction.

Combustion reaction   The rapid oxidation–reduction reaction of an oxidizable substance with oxygen in a highly exothermic reaction, usually with a visible flame.

d-Transition elements (metals)   The B group elements in the periodic table; sometimes called simply transition elements.

Effective nuclear charge (Z_{eff})   The nuclear charge experienced by the outermost electrons of an atom; the actual nuclear charge minus the effects of shielding due to inner shell electrons.

Electron affinity (EA)   The amount of energy absorbed in the process in which an electron is added to a neutral isolated gaseous atom to form a gaseous ion with a $1-$ charge; has a negative value if energy is released.

Electronegativity (EN)   A measure of the relative tendency of an atom to attract electrons to itself when chemically combined with another atom.

f-Transition elements (metals)   Elements 58 through 71 and 90 through 103; also called inner transition elements (metals).

Inner transition elements   See *f-Transition elements.*

Ionic hydride   An ionic compound that contains the hydride ion, H^-.

Ionic radius   The radius of an ion.

Ionization energy   The amount of energy required to remove the most loosely held electron of an isolated gaseous atom or ion.

Isoelectronic   Having the same number of electrons.

Lanthanides   Elements 58 through 71 (after *lanthanum*); also known as *rare earth elements.*

Noble gas configuration   The stable electron configuration of a noble gas.

Noble gases   Elements of periodic Group 8A; also called rare gases; formerly called inert gases.

Normal oxide   A metal oxide containing the oxide ion, O^{2-} (oxygen in the -2 oxidation state).

Oxidation states (numbers)   Arbitrary numbers that can be used as aids in writing formulas and balancing equations; for single-atom ions they correspond to the charge on the ion; less metallic elements are assigned negative oxidation states in compounds and ions.

Oxide   A binary compound of oxygen.

Periodicity   Regular periodic variations of properties of elements with atomic number and position in the periodic table.

Periodic law   The properties of the elements are periodic functions of their atomic numbers.

Peroxide   A compound containing oxygen in the -1 oxidation state. Metal peroxides contain the peroxide ion, O_2^{2-}.

Radical   A species containing one or more unpaired electrons; many radicals are very reactive.

Representative elements   The A group elements in the periodic table.

Roasting   Heating an ore of an element in the presence of air.

Shielding effect   Electrons in filled sets of s and p orbitals between the nucleus and outer shell electrons shield the outer shell electrons somewhat from the effect of protons in the nucleus; also called screening effect.

Superoxide   A compound containing the superoxide ion, O_2^- (oxygen in the $-\frac{1}{2}$ oxidation state).

Ternary acid   An acid containing three elements: H, O, and (usually) another nonmetal.

EXERCISES

⬤ **Molecular Reasoning** exercises

▲ **More Challenging** exercises

Blue-Numbered exercises are solved in the Student Solutions Manual

Classification of the Elements

1. Define and illustrate the following terms clearly and concisely: (a) representative elements; (b) d-transition elements; (c) inner transition elements.
2. The third shell ($n = 3$) has $s, p,$ and d subshells. Why does Period 3 contain only eight elements?
3. Account for the number of elements in Period 5.
4. ▲ What would be the atomic number of the as-yet undiscovered alkali metal of Period 8?
5. Identify the group, family, or other periodic table location of each element with the outer electron configuration (a) ns^2np^3; (b) ns^2; (c) $ns^2(n-1)d^{0-2}(n-2)f^{1-14}$.
6. Repeat Exercise 5 for (a) ns^2np^5; (b) ns^1; (c) $ns^2(n-1)d^{1-10}$; (d) ns^2np^1.
7. Write the outer electron configurations for the (a) alkaline earth metals; (b) first column of d-transition metals; and (c) alkali metals.
8. Which of the elements in the following periodic table is (are) (a) alkali metals; (b) an element with the outer configuration of d^7s^2; (c) lanthanides; (d) p-block representative elements; (e) elements with partially filled f-subshells; (f) halogens; (g) s-block representative elements; (h) actinides; (i) d-transition elements; (j) noble gases; (k) alkaline earth elements?

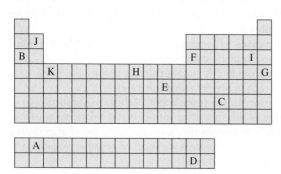

9. Identify the elements and the part of the periodic table in which the elements with the following configurations are found. (a) $1s^22s^22p^63s^23p^64s^2$; (b) [Kr] $4d^85s^2$; (c) [Xe] $4f^{14}5d^56s^1$; (d) [Xe] $4f^96s^2$; (e) [Kr] $4d^{10}5s^25p^4$; (f) [Kr] $4d^{10}4f^{14}5s^25p^65d^{10}6s^26p^1$

10. (a) Which ions in this list are likely to be formed: K^{2+}, Cs^+, Al^{4+}, F^{2-}, Se^{2-}? (b) Which, if any, of these ions have a noble gas configuration?
11. Give the electron configurations of these ions, and indicate which ones are isoelectronic. (a) Ca^{2+}; (b) K^+; (c) O^{2-}

Atomic Radii

12. ⬤ What is meant by nuclear shielding? What effect does it have on trends in atomic radii?
13. ⬤ Why do atomic radii decrease from left to right within a period in the periodic table?
14. ⬤ Consider the elements in Group 6A. Even though it has not been isolated or synthesized, what can be predicted about the atomic radius of element number 116?
15. ⬤ Variations in the atomic radii of the transition elements are not as pronounced as those of the representative elements. Why?
16. ⬤ Arrange each of the following sets of atoms in order of increasing atomic radii: (a) the alkaline earth elements; (b) the noble gases; (c) the representative elements in the third period; (d) C, Si, Sn, and Pb.

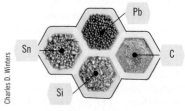

Carbon (*right*), silicon (*bottom*), tin (*left*) and lead (*top*)

17. ⬤ Arrange the following species in order of decreasing radius: S, Cl^-, Ar, K^+. Explain your answer.

Ionization Energy

18. Define (a) first ionization energy and (b) second ionization energy.
19. Why is the second ionization energy for a given element always greater than the first ionization energy?

20. What is the usual relationship between atomic radius and first ionization energy, other factors being equal?

21. What is the usual relationship between nuclear charge and first ionization energy, other factors being equal?

22. Going across a period on the periodic table, what is the relationship between shielding and first ionization energy?

23. Within a group on the periodic table, what is the relationship between shielding and first ionization energy?

24. Arrange the members of each of the following sets of elements in order of increasing first ionization energies: (a) the alkali metals; (b) the halogens; (c) the elements in the second period; (d) Br, F, B, Ga, Cs, and H.

25. The following series of five ionization energies pertains to an element in the second period: $IE_1 = 1.33 \times 10^{-21}$ kJ/atom; $IE_2 = 4.03 \times 10^{-21}$ kJ/atom; $IE_3 = 6.08 \times 10^{-21}$ kJ/atom; $IE_4 = 4.16 \times 10^{-20}$ kJ/atom; $IE_5 = 5.45 \times 10^{-20}$ kJ/atom. Identify the element, and explain why you selected that element.

26. What is the general relationship between the sizes of the atoms of Period 2 and their first ionization energies? Rationalize the relationship.

27. In a plot of first ionization energy versus atomic number for Periods 2 and 3, "dips" occur at the 3A and 6A elements. Account for these dips.

28. On the basis of electron configurations, would you expect a Li^{2+} ion to exist in compounds? Why or why not? How about Be^{2+}?

29. How much energy, in kilojoules, must be absorbed by 1.25 mol of gaseous lithium atoms to convert all of them to gaseous Li^+ ions?

Lithium

30. Arrange the following elements in order of increasing negative values of electron affinity: P, S, Cl, and Br.

31. Arrange the members of each of the following sets of elements in order of increasingly negative electron affinities: (a) the Group 1A metals; (b) the Group 4A elements; (c) the elements in the second period; (d) Li, K, C, F, and Cl.

Some uses of Group 4A elements

32. The electron affinities of the halogens are much more negative than those of the Group 6A elements. Why is this so?

33. The addition of a second electron to form an ion with a 2− charge is always endothermic. Why is this so?

34. Write the equation for the change described by each of the following, and write the electron configuration for each atom or ion shown: (a) the electron affinity of oxygen; (b) the electron affinity of chlorine; (c) the electron affinity of magnesium.

Ionic Radii

35. Select the smaller member of each pair. (a) N and N^{3-}; (b) Ba and Ba^{2+}; (c) Se and Se^{2-}; (d) Co^{2+} and Co^{3+}

36. Arrange the members of each of the following sets of cations in order of increasing ionic radii: (a) K^+, Ca^{2+}, Ga^{3+}; (b) Ca^{2+}, Be^{2+}, Ba^{2+}, Mg^{2+}; (c) Al^{3+}, Sr^{2+}, Rb^+, K^+; (d) K^+, Ca^{2+}, Rb^+.

37. ♣ Study the radii of Cl and Cl^- in Figure 5-4. Why is one larger than the other?

38. Arrange the following sets of anions in order of increasing ionic radii: (a) Cl^-, S^{2-}, P^{3-}; (b) O^{2-}, S^{2-}, Se^{2-}; (c) N^{3-}, S^{2-}, Br^-, P^{3-}; (d) Cl^-, Br^-, I^-.

39. Select the atom or ion in each pair that has the smaller radius. (a) Cs or Rb; (b) O^{2-} or O; (c) Br or As; (d) Ba or Ba^{2+}; (e) Cl^- or Ca^{2+}

40. Most transition metals can form more than one simple positive ion. For example, iron forms both Fe^{2+} and Fe^{3+} ions, and tin forms both Sn^{2+} and Sn^{4+} ions. Which is the smaller ion of each pair, and why?

Electronegativity

41. What is electronegativity?

42. Arrange the members of each of the following sets of elements in order of increasing electronegativities: (a) Pb, C, Sn, Ge; (b) S, Na, Mg, Cl; (c) P, N, Sb, Bi; (d) Se, Ba, F, Si, Sc.

43. Which of the following statements is better? Why? (a) Magnesium has a weak attraction for electrons in a chemical bond because it has a low electronegativity. (b) The electronegativity of magnesium is low because magnesium has a weak attraction for electrons in a chemical bond.

44. Arrange the elements Na, Si, and S in order of (a) increasing atomic radius; (b) increasing first ionization energy; (c) decreasing electronegativity.

45. One element takes on only a negative oxidation number when combined with other elements. From the table of electronegativity values, determine which element this is.

Oxidation States

46. Assign oxidation states to the element specified in each group of compounds. (a) P in PCl_3, P_2O_5, P_4O_{10}, HPO_3, H_3PO_3, $POCl_3$, $H_4P_2O_7$, $Mg_3(PO_4)_2$; (b) Br in Br^-, BrO^-, BrO_2^-, BrO_3^-, BrO_4^-; (c) Mn in MnO, MnO_2, $Mn(OH)_2$, K_2MnO_4, $KMnO_4$, Mn_2O_7; (d) O in OF_2, Na_2O, Na_2O_2, KO_2.

47. Assign oxidation states to the element specified in each group of compounds. (a) N in NO, N_2O_3, N_2O_4, NH_4Cl,

♣ **Molecular Reasoning** exercises   ▲ **More Challenging** exercises   Blue-Numbered exercises solved in Student Solutions Manual

Unless otherwise noted, all content on this page is © Cengage Learning.

N_2H_4, NH_2OH, HNO_2, HNO_3; (b) C in CO, CO_2, CH_2O, CH_4O, C_2H_6O, Na_2CO_3, C_6H_6; (c) S in S^{2-}, SO_3^{2-}, SO_4^{2-}, $S_2O_3^{2-}$, $S_4O_6^{2-}$, H_2S.

48. Assign oxidation states to the element specified in each group of ions. (a) N in N^{3-}, NO_2^-, NO_3^-, N_3^-, NH_4^+; (b) Cl in Cl_2, HCl, HClO, $HClO_2$, $KClO_3$, Cl_2O_7, $Ca(ClO_4)_2$, PCl_5.

49. Assign oxidation states to the element specified in each group. (a) S in S_8, H_2S, SO_2, SO_3, Na_2SO_3, H_2SO_4, K_2SO_4; (b) Cr in CrO_2^-, $Cr(OH)_4^-$, CrO_4^{2-}, $Cr_2O_7^{2-}$; (c) B in BO_2^-, BO_3^{3-}, $B_4O_7^{2-}$.

Periodic Properties

50. Compare the respective values of the first ionization energy (see Table 5-1) and electron affinity (see Table 5-2) for several elements. Which energy is greater? Why?

51. Compare the respective values of the first ionization energy (see Table 5-1) and electron affinity (see Table 5-2) for nitrogen to those for carbon and oxygen. Explain why the nitrogen values are considerably different.

Hydrogen and the Hydrides

52. Summarize the physical properties of hydrogen.

53. Write balanced equations for (a) the reaction of iron with steam, (b) the reaction of calcium with hydrochloric acid, (c) the electrolysis of water, and (d) the "water gas" reaction.

54. Write a balanced equation for the preparation of (a) an ionic hydride and (b) a binary molecular compound of hydrogen.

55. Classify the following compounds as molecular or ionic: (a) NaH; (b) H_2S; (c) AlH_3; (d) RbH; (e) NH_3.

56. Explain why NaH and H_2S have different degrees of ionic character.

57. Write balanced equations for the reactions with water of (a) CaH_2, (b) AlH_3, and (c) NaH.

Charles D. Winters

58. Name the following (pure) compounds: (a) H_2S; (b) HCl; (c) KH; (d) NH_3; (e) H_2Se; (f) MgH_2; (g) AlH_3.

59. Write a balanced equation for the reaction of an ionic hydride with water. What products are always formed during these reactions?

Oxygen and the Oxides

60. Briefly compare and contrast the properties of oxygen with those of hydrogen.

61. Write molecular equations to show how oxygen can be prepared from (a) mercury(II) oxide, HgO; (b) hydrogen peroxide, H_2O_2; and (c) potassium chlorate, $KClO_3$.

62. ▲ Which of the following elements form normal oxides as the *major* products of reactions with oxygen? (a) Li; (b) Ba; (c) Rb; (d) Mg; (e) Zn (exhibits only one common oxidation state); (f) Al.

63. Oxygen has a positive oxidation number when combined with which element? Compare the electronegativity values of oxygen and that element.

64. Write balanced equations for the reactions of the following elements with a *limited* amount of oxygen: (a) C; (b) As_4; (c) Ge.

65. Write balanced equations for the reactions of the following elements with an *excess* of oxygen: (a) C; (b) As_4; (c) Ge.

66. Distinguish among normal oxides, peroxides, and superoxides. What is the oxidation state of oxygen in each case?

67. ▲ Which of the following can be classified as basic anhydrides? (a) CO_2; (b) Li_2O; (c) SeO_3; (d) CaO; (e) N_2O_5.

68. Write balanced equations for the following reactions and name the products: (a) carbon dioxide, CO_2, with water; (b) sulfur trioxide, SO_3, with water; (c) selenium trioxide, SeO_3, with water; (d) dinitrogen pentoxide, N_2O_5, with water; and (e) dichlorine heptoxide, Cl_2O_7, with water.

69. Write balanced equations for the following reactions and name the products: (a) sodium oxide, Na_2O, with water; (b) calcium oxide, CaO, with water; (c) lithium oxide, Li_2O, with water; (d) magnesium oxide, MgO, with sulfur dioxide, SO_2; and (e) calcium oxide, CaO, with carbon dioxide, CO_2.

70. ▲ Identify the acid anhydrides of the following ternary acids: (a) H_2SO_4; (b) H_2CO_3; (c) H_2SO_3; (d) H_3PO_4; (e) HNO_2.

71. Identify the basic anhydrides of the following metal hydroxides: (a) NaOH; (b) $Mg(OH)_2$; (c) $Fe(OH)_2$; (d) $Al(OH)_3$.

Combustion Reactions

72. ● Define combustion. Write a balanced equation for the combustion of diatomic hydrogen.

73. ● Write equations for the complete combustion of the following compounds: (a) methane, $CH_4(g)$; (b) propane, $C_3H_8(g)$; (c) ethanol, $C_2H_5OH(\ell)$.

Charles D. Winters

74. Write equations for the *incomplete* combustion of the following compounds to produce carbon monoxide: (a) methane, $CH_4(g)$; (b) propane, $C_3H_8(g)$. As we have seen, two substances may react to form different products when they are mixed in different proportions under different conditions.

In Exercises 75 and 76, draw molecular representations of the materials before and after reaction as described in the quantitative descriptions.

75. ● Ethane, C_2H_6, burns in excess oxygen to form carbon dioxide and water. To illustrate this reaction, two molecules of ethane will react in the presence of nine molecules of oxygen, O_2, to yield four molecules of carbon dioxide, six molecules of water, and two molecules of excess oxygen left unreacted.

Ethane, C_2H_6

76. ● Propane, C_3H_8, burns in excess oxygen to form carbon dioxide and water. To illustrate this reaction, a molecule of propane reacts in the presence of seven molecules of oxygen, O_2, to yield three molecules of carbon dioxide, four molecules of water, and two molecules of excess oxygen left unreacted.

Propane, C_3H_8

77. ▲ (a) How much SO_2 would be formed by burning 1.00 kg of bituminous coal that is 5.15% sulfur by mass? Assume that all of the sulfur is converted to SO_2. (b) If 19.0% of the SO_2 escaped into the atmosphere and 75.0% of the escaped SO_2 were converted to H_2SO_4, how many grams of H_2SO_4 would be produced in the atmosphere?

78. ▲ Write equations for the complete combustion of the following compounds. Assume that sulfur is converted to SO_2 and nitrogen is converted to NO. (a) $C_6H_5NH_2(\ell)$; (b) $C_2H_5SH(\ell)$; (c) $C_7H_{10}NO_2S(\ell)$.

Conceptual Exercises

79. Write the electron configuration for the product of the second ionization of the third largest alkaline earth metal.

80. You are given the atomic radii of 110 pm, 118 pm, 120 pm, 122 pm, and 135 pm, but do not know to which element

(As, Ga, Ge, P, and Si) these values correspond. Which must be the value of Ge?

81. ● Which is larger, Na^+ or F^-? For each of these ions, draw a representation of the shape of the highest energy occupied orbital.

82. ● Write the electron configurations of beryllium and magnesium. What similarities in their chemical properties can you predict on the basis of their electron configurations? Compare the sizes of their most stable ions.

83. Dolostone is often more porous than limestone. One explanation of the origin of dolostone is that it results from partial replacement of calcium by magnesium in an original limestone sediment. Is this explanation reasonable, given what you know of the ionic radii of magnesium and calcium ions?

84. On an outline of the periodic table like the one below, label the areas in which the "last" electron assigned in the electron configuration is in a filled orbital of each of the following types: 1s, 2s, 2p, 3s, 3p, 3d, 4s, 4p, 4d, 4f, 5s, 5p, 5d, 5f, 6s, 6p, 6d, 7s, and 7p.

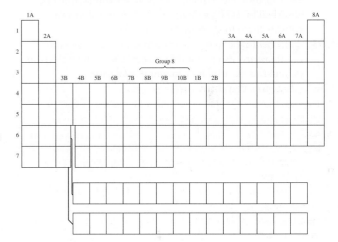

85. Generally, elements with very negative electron affinities gain electrons easily to form negative ions. Which group of elements tends to form anions most easily?

86. Identify all the elements that have an electronegativity of 3.0 or greater. Where are they located on the periodic table? Identify all the elements that have an electronegativity of 1.0 or less. Except for Yb, where are they located on the periodic table?

87. Figure 5-9 includes the formulas of the normal oxides of the representative elements in their maximum oxidation states. Use these formulas to determine the oxidation state of each element, assuming an oxidation state of −2 for oxygen. What is the oxidation state of every element in Groups 1A, 2A, 3A, 4A, 5A, and 6A? What is the oxidation state of most elements in Group 7A? Which element is the exception?

Building Your Knowledge

88. Hydrogen can be obtained from water by electrolysis. Hydrogen may someday be an important replacement for current fuels. Describe some of the problems that you would predict if hydrogen were used in today's motor vehicles.

● **Molecular Reasoning** exercises   ▲ **More Challenging** exercises   Blue-Numbered exercises solved in Student Solutions Manual

Unless otherwise noted, all content on this page is © Cengage Learning.

89. The only chemically stable ion of rubidium is Rb^+. The most stable monoatomic ion of bromine is Br^-. Krypton (Kr) is among the least reactive of all elements. Compare the electron configurations of Rb^+, Br^-, and Kr. Then predict the most stable monatomic ions of strontium (Sr) and selenium (Se).

90. The first ionization energy of potassium, K, is 419 kJ/mol. What is the minimum frequency of light required to ionize gaseous potassium atoms?

91. Potassium and argon would be anomalies in a periodic table in which elements are arranged in order of increasing atomic weights. Identify two other elements among the transition elements whose positions in the periodic table would have been reversed in a "weight-sequence" arrangement. Which pair of elements would most obviously be out of place on the basis of their chemical behavior? Explain your answer in terms of the current atomic model, showing electron configurations for these elements.

92. ▲ The second ionization energy for magnesium is 1451 kJ/mol. How much energy, in kilojoules, must be absorbed by 1.75 g of gaseous magnesium atoms to convert them to gaseous Mg^{2+} ions?

93. The chemical reactivities of carbon and lead are similar, but there are also major differences. Using their electron configurations, explain why these similarities and differences may exist.

Beyond the Textbook

NOTE: *Whenever the answer to an exercise depends on information obtained from a source other than this textbook, the source must be included as an essential part of the answer.*

94. Go to the web and locate "MSDS Data Sheets." Find the MSDS for sodium nitrate. (a) What does LDLo stand for? (b) What does mus stand for?

95. While at the MSDS sheet for sodium nitrate required for Exercise 94, answer the following: (a) What does the Risk Phrase "R8" indicate? (b) What does the Safety Phrase "S39" indicate?

96. Go to **http://www.nist.gov/pml/data/ion_energy.cfm** and locate values given for the first ionization energies for Al and P. Are the values different than those given in Table 5-1? Explain.

97. ▲ Use the *Handbook of Chemistry and Physics* or a suitable website to find the Crystal Ionic Radii of the Elements. Plot atomic number versus radius of the 2+ ions of the first *d*-transition series. Is there a trend? Is a minimum size formed during the transition from Sc^{2+} to Zn^{2+}? Do the values for the second and third *d*-transition series appear to form a similar minimum at about the same group number?

Some Types of Chemical Reactions

6

Pouring a solution of silver nitrate, $AgNO_3$, into a solution of potassium iodide, KI, produces an immediate precipitate of silver iodide, AgI. The potassium nitrate, KNO_3, is soluble and remains in solution.

George G. Stanley

OBJECTIVES

After you have studied this chapter, you should be able to

▶ Recognize and describe nonelectrolytes, strong electrolytes, and weak electrolytes

▶ Recognize and classify acids (strong, weak), bases (strong, weak, insoluble), and salts (soluble, insoluble); use the solubility guidelines

▶ Describe reactions in aqueous solutions by writing formula unit equations, total ionic equations, and net ionic equations

▶ Name and write formulas for common binary and ternary inorganic compounds

▶ Recognize oxidation–reduction reactions and identify which species are oxidized, reduced, oxidizing agents, and reducing agents

▶ Recognize and describe classes of reactions: decomposition reactions, displacement reactions, various types of metathesis reactions, and gas-formation reactions

In this chapter we examine some types of chemical reactions. Millions of reactions are known, so it is useful to group them into classes, or types, so that we can deal systematically with them. We describe whether or not compounds dissolve in water to make aqueous solutions and how these solutions behave, including how well they conduct electricity. We introduce several ways to represent chemical reactions in aqueous solution—formula unit equations, total ionic equations, and net ionic equations—and the advantages and disadvantages of these methods. We also introduce systematic ways to describe chemical reactions, as well as their reactants and their products.

6-1 Aqueous Solutions: An Introduction

Approximately three-fourths of the earth's surface is covered with water. The body fluids of all plants and animals are mainly water. Thus we can see that many important chemical reactions occur in aqueous (water) solutions or in contact with water. In Chapter 3, we introduced solutions and methods of expressing concentrations of solutions. It is useful to know the kinds of substances that are soluble in water, and the forms in which they exist, before we begin our systematic study of chemical reactions.

Many substances that interact with water are classified as acids, bases, and salts. An **acid** can be defined as a substance that produces hydrogen ions, H^+, in aqueous solutions. We usually write the formulas of inorganic acids with hydrogen written first. Organic acids can often be recognized by the presence of the COOH group in the formula. Many properties of aqueous solutions of acids are due to $H^+(aq)$ ions. These are described in Section 10-4. A **base** is a substance that produces hydroxide ions, OH^-, in aqueous solutions. Acids and bases are further identified in Subsections 2, 3, and 4. A **salt** is an ionic compound that contains a cation other than H^+ and an anion other than hydroxide ion, OH^-, or oxide ion, O^{2-} (see Table 2-2). As we will see later in this chapter, salts are formed when acids react with bases.

▶ Positively charged ions are called *cations*, and negatively charged ions are called *anions* (see Section 2-2). The formula for a salt may include H or OH, but it *must* contain another cation *and* another anion. For example, $NaHSO_4$ and $Al(OH)_2Cl$ are salts, but NaOH and Na_2O are not.

1 Electrolytes and Extent of Ionization

Dissociation refers to the process in which a solid *ionic compound*, such as NaCl, separates into its ions in solution:

▶ To give a more complete description of reactions, we indicate the physical states of reactants and products: (g) for gases, (ℓ) for liquids, and (s) for solids. The notation (aq) following ions indicates that they are hydrated in aqueous solution; that is, they interact with water molecules in solution. The complete ionization of a strong electrolyte is indicated by a single arrow (⟶).

$$NaCl(s) \xrightarrow{H_2O} Na^+(aq) + Cl^-(aq)$$

Molecular compounds, for example *pure* HCl, exist as discrete molecules and do not contain ions; however, many such compounds form ions in solution. **Ionization** refers to the process in which a *molecular compound* separates or reacts with water to form ions in solution:

$$HCl(g) \xrightarrow{H_2O} H^+(aq) + Cl^-(aq)$$

Solutes that are water-soluble can be classified as either electrolytes or nonelectrolytes.

> **Electrolytes** are substances whose aqueous solutions conduct electric current. **Strong electrolytes** are substances that conduct electricity well in dilute aqueous solution. **Weak electrolytes** conduct electricity poorly in dilute aqueous solution. Aqueous solutions of **nonelectrolytes** do not conduct electricity.

Electric current is carried through aqueous solution by the movement of ions. The strength of an electrolyte depends on the number of ions in solution and also on the charges on these ions (Figure 6-1).

> Three major classes of solutes are strong electrolytes: (1) strong acids, (2) strong bases, and (3) most soluble salts. *These compounds are completely or nearly completely ionized or dissociated in aqueous solution.*

▶ Pure water does not conduct electricity; it is an electrical insulator.

▶ Recall that ions are charged particles. The movement of charged particles conducts electricity.

2 Strong and Weak Acids

As a matter of convenience we place acids into two classes: strong acids and weak acids. **Strong acids** ionize (separate into hydrogen ions and stable anions) completely, or very nearly completely, in dilute aqueous solution. Seven strong acids and their anions are listed in Table 6-1. Please learn this short list; you can then assume that other acids you encounter are weak.

Because strong acids ionize completely or very nearly completely in dilute solutions, their solutions contain predominantly ions rather than acid molecules. Consider the ionization of hydrochloric acid. Pure hydrogen chloride, HCl, is a molecular compound that is a gas at

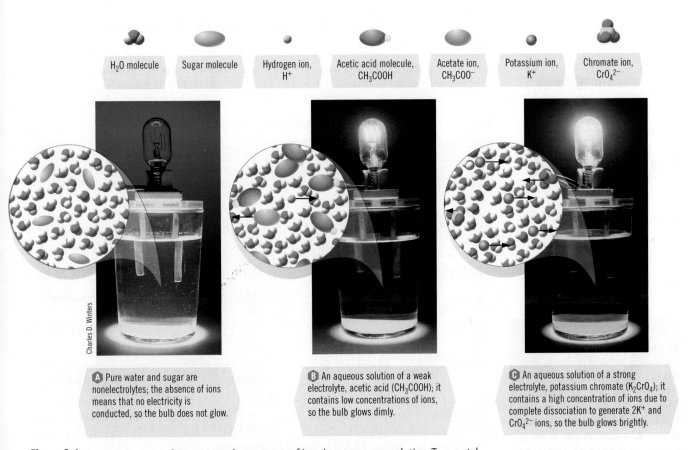

| H_2O molecule | Sugar molecule | Hydrogen ion, H^+ | Acetic acid molecule, CH_3COOH | Acetate ion, CH_3COO^- | Potassium ion, K^+ | Chromate ion, CrO_4^{2-} |

Charles D. Winters

Ⓐ Pure water and sugar are nonelectrolytes; the absence of ions means that no electricity is conducted, so the bulb does not glow.

Ⓑ An aqueous solution of a weak electrolyte, acetic acid (CH_3COOH); it contains low concentrations of ions, so the bulb glows dimly.

Ⓒ An aqueous solution of a strong electrolyte, potassium chromate (K_2CrO_4); it contains a high concentration of ions due to complete dissociation to generate $2K^+$ and CrO_4^{2-} ions, so the bulb glows brightly.

Figure 6-1 An experiment to demonstrate the presence of ions in an aqueous solution. Two metal electrodes are dipped into a liquid in a beaker. When the liquid contains significant concentrations of ions, the ions move between the electrodes to complete the circuit (which includes a light bulb).

Table 6-1 The Common Strong Acids and Their Anions

Common Strong Acids		Anions of These Strong Acids	
Formula	Name	Formula	Name
HCl	hydrochloric acid	Cl^-	chloride ion
HBr	hydrobromic acid	Br^-	bromide ion
HI	hydroiodic acid	I^-	iodide ion
HNO_3	nitric acid	NO_3^-	nitrate ion
$HClO_4$	perchloric acid	ClO_4^-	perchlorate ion
$HClO_3$	chloric acid	ClO_3^-	chlorate ion
H_2SO_4	sulfuric acid	$\begin{cases} HSO_4^- \\ SO_4^{2-} \end{cases}$	hydrogen sulfate ion sulfate ion

▶ Chloric acid is sometimes not listed with the common strong acids since it is not commonly encountered. However, its anion is much more common. So we have included both the acid and its anion in this table.

room temperature and atmospheric pressure. When it dissolves in water, it reacts essentially completely to produce a solution that contains hydrogen ions and chloride ions:

$$HCl(g) \xrightarrow{H_2O} H^+(aq) + Cl^-(aq) \qquad \text{(to completion)}$$

Similar equations can be written for all strong acids.

Weak acids ionize only slightly (usually less than 5%) in dilute aqueous solution. Some common weak acids are listed in Appendix F. Several of them and their anions are given in Table 6-2.

The equation for the ionization of acetic acid, CH_3COOH, in water is typical of weak acids:

$$CH_3COOH(aq) \rightleftharpoons H^+(aq) + CH_3COO^-(aq) \qquad \text{(reversible)}$$

▶ Acetic acid is the most familiar organic acid.

▶ The names given in Table 6-2 correspond to the aqueous solutions.

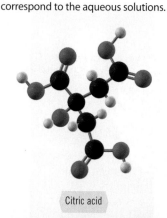

Citric acid

Table 6-2 Some Common Weak Acids and Their Anions

Common Weak Acids		Anions of These Weak Acids	
Formula	Name	Formula	Name
HF*	hydrofluoric acid	F^-	fluoride ion
CH_3COOH	acetic acid	CH_3OO^-	acetate ion
HCN	hydrocyanic acid	CN^-	cyanide ion
HNO_2†	nitrous acid	NO_2^-	nitrite ion
H_2CO_3†	carbonic acid	HCO_3^- CO_3^{2-}	hydrogen carbonate ion carbonate ion
H_2SO_3†	sulfurous acid	HSO_3^- SO_3^{2-}	hydrogen sulfite ion sulfite ion
H_3PO_4	phosphoric acid	$H_2PO_4^-$ HPO_4^{2-} PO_4^{3-}	dihydrogen phosphate ion hydrogen phosphate ion phosphate ion
$(COOH)_2$	oxalic acid	$H(COO)_2^-$ $(COO)_2^{2-}$	hydrogen oxalate ion oxalate ion

Charles Steele

Citrus fruits contain citric acid, so their juices are acidic. This is shown here by the red colors on the indicator paper. Acids taste sour.

*HF is a weak acid, whereas HCl, HBr, and HI are strong acids.

†Free acid molecules exist only in dilute aqueous solution or not at all. Many salts of these acids are common, stable compounds, however.

The double arrow $\rightleftharpoons$ generally signifies that the reaction occurs in *both* directions; the longer arrow indicates the direction in which the reaction is favored (in this case the reactants). All of us are familiar with solutions of acetic acid. Vinegar is 5% acetic acid by mass. Our use of oil and vinegar as a salad dressing suggests that acetic acid is a weak acid; we could not safely drink a 5% solution of any strong acid. To be specific, acetic acid is 0.5% ionized (and 99.5% nonionized) in 5% solution.

A multitude of organic acids occur in living systems. Organic acids contain the carboxyl grouping of atoms, $-COOH$. Most common organic acids are weak. They can ionize slightly by breaking the $O-H$ bond to form the carboxylate group, $-COO^-$, as shown for acetic acid:

$$H_3C-C\overset{O}{\underset{O-H}{\big<}}\ (aq) \rightleftharpoons H_3C-C\overset{O}{\underset{O^-}{\big<}}\ (aq) + H^+(aq)$$

Organic acids are discussed in Chapter 23. Some naturally occurring organic weak acids are tartaric acid (grapes), lactic acid (sour milk), and formic acid (ants). Carbonic acid, H_2CO_3, and hydrocyanic acid, $HCN(aq)$, are two common acids that contain carbon but that are considered to be *inorganic* acids. Inorganic acids are often called **mineral acids** because they are obtained primarily from nonliving sources.

▶ We will learn more about acids in Chapter 10. There we will see that it is appropriate to represent $H^+(aq)$ as H_3O^+ to emphasize its interaction with water.

▶ Our stomachs have linings that are much more resistant to attack by acids than are our other tissues.

▶ The carboxyl group $-COOH$ is

$$-C\overset{O}{\underset{O-H}{\big<}}$$

▶ Other organic acids have different groups in the position of the H_3C- group in acetic acid. The double line linking C to one O represents a double bond, which is stronger than a single bond.

EXAMPLE 6-1 Strong and Weak Acids

In the following lists of common acids, which are strong and which are weak? (a) H_3PO_4, HCl, H_2CO_3, HNO_3; (b) $HClO_4$, H_2SO_4, HClO, HF.

Plan

We recall that Table 6-1 lists some common strong acids. Other *common* acids are assumed to be weak.

Solution

(a) HCl and HNO_3 are strong acids; H_3PO_4 and H_2CO_3 are weak acids.

(b) $HClO_4$ and H_2SO_4 are strong acids; HClO and HF are weak acids.

You should now work Exercises 5 and 7.

▶ Inorganic acids may be strong or weak.

Charles D. Winters

Many common food and household products are acidic (orange juice, vinegar, soft drinks, citrus fruits) or basic (cleaning preparations, baking soda).

---

3 Reversible Reactions

Reactions that occur in both directions are **reversible reactions**. We use a double arrow $\rightleftharpoons$ to indicate that a reaction is *reversible*. Chemists often qualitatively indicate the favored direction of a reversible reaction by using a longer arrow. Equal length arrows, however, do not mean that there are equal amounts of reactant and product. The favored direction and extent of the reaction is described quantitatively by the equilibrium constant (see Chapter 17). What is the fundamental difference between reactions that go to completion and those that are reversible? We have seen that HCl ionizes completely in water. Suppose we dissolve some table salt, NaCl, in water and then add some dilute nitric acid to it. The resulting solution contains Na^+ and Cl^- ions (from the dissociation of NaCl) as well as H^+ and NO_3^- (from the ionization of HNO_3). The H^+ and Cl^- ions do *not* react significantly to form nonionized HCl molecules; this would be the reverse of the ionization of HCl.

$$H^+(aq) + Cl^-(aq) \longrightarrow \text{no reaction}$$

▶ Na$^+$ and NO$_3^-$ ions do not combine because NaNO$_3$ is a soluble ionic compound.

In contrast, when a sample of sodium acetate, NaCH$_3$COO, is dissolved in H$_2$O and mixed with nitric acid, the resulting solution initially contains Na$^+$, CH$_3$COO$^-$, H$^+$, and NO$_3^-$ ions. But most of the H$^+$ and CH$_3$COO$^-$ ions combine to produce nonionized molecules of acetic acid, the reverse of the ionization of the acid. Thus, the ionization of acetic acid, like that of any other weak electrolyte, is reversible.

$$H^+(aq) + CH_3COO^-(aq) \rightleftharpoons CH_3COOH(aq) \qquad \text{(reversible)}$$

4 Strong Bases, Insoluble Bases, and Weak Bases

▶ Solutions of bases have a set of common properties due to the OH$^-$ ion. These are described in Section 10-4.

Most common bases are *ionic* metal hydroxides. **Strong bases** are soluble in water and are dissociated completely in dilute aqueous solution. The common strong bases are listed in Table 6-3. They are the hydroxides of the Group 1A metals and the heavier members of Group 2A. The equation for the dissociation of sodium hydroxide in water is typical. Similar equations can be written for other strong bases.

▶ Strong bases are ionic compounds in the solid state.

$$NaOH(s) \xrightarrow{H_2O} Na^+(aq) + OH^-(aq) \qquad \text{(to completion)}$$

Other metals form ionic hydroxides, but these are so sparingly soluble in water that they cannot produce strongly basic solutions. They are called **insoluble bases** or sometimes sparingly soluble bases. Typical examples include Cu(OH)$_2$, Zn(OH)$_2$, Fe(OH)$_2$, and Fe(OH)$_3$.

▶ The weak bases are *molecular* substances that dissolve in water to give slightly basic solutions; they are sometimes called molecular bases.

Common **weak bases** are molecular substances that are soluble in water but form only low concentrations of ions in solution. The most common weak base is ammonia, NH$_3$.

$$NH_3(aq) + H_2O(\ell) \rightleftharpoons NH_4^+(aq) + OH^-(aq) \qquad \text{(reversible)}$$

Closely related N-containing compounds, the *amines*, such as methylamine, CH$_3$NH$_2$, and aniline, C$_6$H$_5$NH$_2$, are also weak bases. Nicotine (found in tobacco) and caffeine (found in coffee, tea, and cola drinks) are naturally occurring amines.

Ammonia, NH$_3$

EXAMPLE 6-2 Classifying Bases

From the following lists, choose (i) the strong bases, (ii) the insoluble bases, and (iii) the weak bases. (a) NaOH, Cu(OH)$_2$, Pb(OH)$_2$, Ba(OH)$_2$; (b) Fe(OH)$_3$, KOH, Mg(OH)$_2$, Sr(OH)$_2$, NH$_3$.

Plan

(i) We recall that Table 6-3 lists the *common strong bases*. (ii) Other common metal hydroxides are assumed to be *insoluble bases*. (iii) Ammonia and closely related nitrogen-containing compounds, the amines, are the common *weak bases*.

Solution

(a) (i)   The strong bases are NaOH and Ba(OH)$_2$, so
   (ii) The insoluble bases are Cu(OH)$_2$ and Pb(OH)$_2$.

(b) (i)   The strong bases are KOH and Sr(OH)$_2$, so
   (ii) The insoluble bases are Fe(OH)$_3$ and Mg(OH)$_2$, and
   (iii) The weak base is NH$_3$.

You should now work Exercises 8 and 10.

Table 6-3 The Common Strong Bases

Group 1A		Group 2A	
LiOH	lithium hydroxide		
NaOH	sodium hydroxide		
KOH	potassium hydroxide	$Ca(OH)_2$	calcium hydroxide
RbOH	rubidium hydroxide	$Sr(OH)_2$	strontium hydroxide
CsOH	cesium hydroxide	$Ba(OH)_2$	barium hydroxide

5 Solubility Guidelines for Compounds in Aqueous Solution

Solubility is a complex phenomenon, and it is not possible to give a complete summary of all our observations. The following brief summary for solutes in aqueous solutions will be very useful. These generalizations are often called the *solubility guidelines*. Compounds whose solubility in water is less than about 0.02 mol/L are usually classified as insoluble compounds, whereas those that are more soluble are classified as soluble compounds. No gaseous or solid substances are infinitely soluble in water. You may wish to review Tables 2-2, 6-1, and 6-2. They list some common ions. Table 6-6 contains a more comprehensive list.

▶ There is no sharp dividing line between "soluble" and "insoluble" compounds. Compounds whose solubilities fall near the arbitrary division are called "moderately soluble" compounds.

1. The common inorganic acids are soluble in water. Low-molecular-weight organic acids are also soluble.

2. All common compounds of the Group 1A metal ions $(Li^+, Na^+, K^+, Rb^+, Cs^+)$ and the ammonium ion, NH_4^+, are soluble in water.

3. The common nitrates, NO_3^-; acetates, CH_3COO^-; chlorates, ClO_3^-; and perchlorates, ClO_4^-, are soluble in water.

4. (a) The common chlorides, Cl^-, are soluble in water except $AgCl$, Hg_2Cl_2, and $PbCl_2$.

   (b) The common bromides, Br^-, and iodides, I^-, show approximately the same solubility behavior as chlorides, but there are some exceptions. As these halide ions (Cl^-, Br^-, I^-) increase in size, the solubilities of their slightly soluble compounds decrease.

   (c) The common fluorides, F^-, are soluble in water except MgF_2, CaF_2, SrF_2, BaF_2, and PbF_2.

5. The common sulfates, SO_4^{2-}, are soluble in water except $PbSO_4$, $BaSO_4$, and $HgSO_4$; $CaSO_4$, $SrSO_4$, and Ag_2SO_4 are moderately soluble.

6. The common metal hydroxides, OH^-, are *insoluble* in water except those of the Group 1A metals and the heavier members of the Group 2A metals, beginning with $Ca(OH)_2$.

7. The common carbonates, CO_3^{2-}, phosphates, PO_4^{3-}, and arsenates, AsO_4^{3-}, are *insoluble* in water except those of the Group 1A metals and NH_4^+. $MgCO_3$ is moderately soluble.

8. The common sulfides, S^{2-}, are *insoluble* in water except those of the Group 1A and Group 2A metals and the ammonium ion.

Table 6-4 summarizes much of the information about the solubility guidelines.

The White Cliffs of Dover, England, are composed mainly of calcium carbonate ($CaCO_3$).

Table 6-4 Solubility Guidelines for Common Ionic Compounds in Water

Generally Soluble	Exceptions
Na^+, K^+, NH_4^+ compounds	No common exceptions
fluorides (F^-)	Insoluble: MgF_2, CaF_2, SrF_2, BaF_2, PbF_2
chlorides (Cl^-)	Insoluble: $AgCl$, Hg_2Cl_2 Soluble in hot water: $PbCl_2$
bromides (Br^-)	Insoluble: $AgBr$, Hg_2Br_2, $PbBr_2$ Moderately soluble: $HgBr_2$
iodides (I^-)	Insoluble: many heavy-metal iodides
sulfates (SO_4^{2-})	Insoluble: $BaSO_4$, $PbSO_4$, $HgSO_4$ Moderately soluble: $CaSO_4$, $SrSO_4$, Ag_2SO_4
nitrates (NO_3^-), nitrites (NO_2^-)	Moderately soluble: $AgNO_2$
chlorates (ClO_3^-), perchlorates (ClO_4^-)	No common exceptions
acetates (CH_3COO^-)	Moderately soluble: $AgCH_3COO$
Generally Insoluble	**Exceptions**
sulfides (S^{2-})	Soluble[†]: those of NH_4^+, Na^+, K^+, Mg^{2+}, Ca^{2+}
oxides (O^{2-}), hydroxides (OH^-)	Soluble: Li_2O*, $LiOH$, Na_2O*, $NaOH$, K_2O*, KOH, BaO*, $Ba(OH)_2$ Moderately soluble: CaO*, $Ca(OH)_2$, SrO*, $Sr(OH)_2$
carbonates (CO_3^{2-}), phosphates (PO_4^{3-}), arsenates (AsO_4^{3-})	Soluble: those of NH_4^+, Na^+, K^+

*Dissolves with evolution of heat and formation of hydroxides.
[†]Dissolves with formation of HS^- and H_2S.

EXAMPLE 6-3 **Solubility of Some Common Ionic Compounds**

From the following compounds, choose (a) those that are likely to be soluble in water and (b) those that are likely to be insoluble: $NaBr$, $Cu(OH)_2$, $PbCl_2$, AgI, Fe_2O_3, $Mg(NO_3)_2$, $(NH_4)_2SO_4$.

Plan

We recall from the guidelines and Table 6-4 that all Na^+, K^+, and NH_4^+ salts are soluble. Therefore, we predict that $NaBr$ and $(NH_4)_2SO_4$ will be soluble. Similarly, NO_3^- salts are soluble, so $Mg(NO_3)_2$ should also be soluble. All other compounds listed in this example should be insoluble.

Solution

(a) The soluble compounds are $NaBr$, $(NH_4)_2SO_4$, and $Mg(NO_3)_2$.

(b) The insoluble compounds are $Cu(OH)_2$, $PbCl_2$, AgI, and Fe_2O_3.

You should now work Exercises 14 and 16.

 Problem-Solving Tip Solubility Guidelines and Charges on Ions

To help understand the solubility rules for ionic compounds, think about the magnitudes of the charges on the cation and anion. The higher the charges are, the more strongly the anion and cation attract one another and the less soluble the salt is likely to be. For example, almost all salts composed of 1+ cations and 1− anions are soluble (Ag^+ salts are a notable exception). Almost all salts composed of 2+/2− and 3+/3− ion pairs are insoluble (or only slightly soluble).

The situation is a little more complicated with mixed charge combinations, but you can always estimate the force of ionic attraction between the anion and cation by multiplying the absolute values of their charges. Larger numbers indicate stronger attractive forces and suggest lower solubility.

For example, Na_3PO_4 has a 1+ charged cation and a 3− charged anion giving a relative ionic attractive force of 3 (you use only *one* Na^+ in this multiplication, not the three needed to balance the charge on the anion). $CaSO_4$ (2+/2− combination) has a relative ionic attractive force of 4, while $Ca_3(PO_4)_2$ (2+/3− combination) has a relative attractive force of 6. The solubility of these compounds is as follows (greatest to least soluble): $Na_3PO_4 > CaSO_4 > Ca_3(PO_4)_2$.

The size of the ions is also a factor, with smaller ions able to get closer to one another and thus increase the ionic attractive force. This is why larger anions with low negative charges almost always give soluble salts (e.g., NO_3^- or ClO_4^-). These ionic charge and size considerations are based on Coulomb's Law (discussed in Chapter 13).

You may wonder about the trend for AgCl, AgBr, and AgI, where the solubility decreases despite the increasing size of the anions. Transition metal compounds often involve dative bonding (see Section 10-10 and Chapter 25), which is a weaker form of covalent bonding, between the cation and anion. Dative bonding generally increases with donor strength: $I^- > Br^- > Cl^-$.

STOP & THINK
This problem-solving tip is based on the simple fundamental concept that opposite charges attract. Higher and more concentrated charges have stronger attractive forces that can resist the solution process that pulls the ions apart. Further, transition metal and heavier main group metalloid cations form stronger bonds to most anions. You can use these concepts to explain most of the solubility trends.

We have distinguished between strong and weak electrolytes and between soluble and insoluble compounds. Let us now see how we can describe chemical reactions in aqueous solutions.

6-2 Reactions in Aqueous Solutions

Many important chemical reactions occur in aqueous solutions. In this chapter you will learn to describe such aqueous reactions and to predict the products of many reactions.

First, let's look at how we write chemical equations that describe reactions in aqueous solutions. We use three kinds of chemical equations. Table 6-5 shows the kinds of information about each substance that we use in writing equations for reactions in aqueous solutions. Some typical examples are included. Refer to Table 6-5 often as you study the following sections.

Table 6-5 Bonding, Solubility, Electrolyte Characteristics, and Predominant Forms of Solutes in Contact with Water

	Acids		Bases			Salts	
	Strong Acids	*Weak Acids*	*Strong Bases*	*Insoluble Bases*	*Weak Bases*	*Soluble Salts*	*Insoluble Salts*
Examples	HCl HNO_3	CH_3COOH HF	NaOH $Ca(OH)_2$	$Mg(OH)_2$ $Al(OH)_3$	NH_3 CH_3NH_2	KCl, $NaNO_3$, NH_4Br	$BaSO_4$, AgCl, $Ca_3(PO_4)_2$
Pure compound ionic or molecular?	Molecular	Molecular	Ionic	Ionic	Molecular	Ionic	Ionic
Water-soluble or insoluble?	Soluble*	Soluble*	Soluble	Insoluble	Soluble†	Soluble	Insoluble
≈ 100% ionized or dissociated in dilute aqueous solution?	Yes	No	Yes	(footnote‡)	No	Yes§	(footnote‡)
Written in ionic equations as	Separate ions	Molecules	Separate ions	Complete formulas	Molecules	Separate ions	Complete formulas

*Most common inorganic acids and the low-molecular-weight organic acids (—COOH) are water-soluble.

†The low-molecular-weight amines are water-soluble.

‡The *very small concentrations* of "insoluble" metal hydroxides and insoluble salts in saturated aqueous solutions are nearly completely dissociated.

§There are a few exceptions. A few soluble salts are molecular (and not ionic) compounds.

Charles Steele

Figure 6-2 Reaction of Cu(s) and Ag⁺(aq).

A Copper wire and a silver nitrate solution

B The copper wire has been placed in the solution and some finely divided silver has deposited on the wire. The solution is blue because it contains copper(II) nitrate.

1. In formula unit equations, we show complete formulas for all compounds. When metallic copper is added to a solution of (colorless) silver nitrate, the more active metal—copper—displaces silver ions from the solution. The resulting solution contains blue copper(II) nitrate, and metallic silver forms as a finely divided solid (Figure 6-2):

$$2AgNO_3(aq) + Cu(s) \longrightarrow 2Ag(s) + Cu(NO_3)_2(aq)$$

Both silver nitrate and copper(II) nitrate are soluble ionic compounds (for solubility guidelines see Table 6-4 and Section 6-1, Part 5).

▶ Because we have not studied periodic trends in properties of transition metals, you might not be able to predict that Cu is more active than Ag. The fact that this reaction occurs (see Figure 6-2) shows that it is.

2. In total ionic equations, formulas are written to show the (predominant) form in which each substance exists when it is in contact with aqueous solution. We sometimes use brackets in total ionic equations to show ions that have a common source or that remain in solution after the reaction is complete. The total ionic equation for this reaction is

$$2[Ag^+(aq) + NO_3^-(aq)] + Cu(s) \longrightarrow 2Ag(s) + [Cu^{2+}(aq) + 2NO_3^-(aq)]$$

▶ Ions that appear in the same form in solution on both sides of the total ionic equation are called **spectator ions**; they undergo no change in the chemical reaction.

Examination of the total ionic equation shows that NO_3^- ions do not participate in the reaction. Because they do not change, they are often called "spectator" ions.

3. In **net ionic equations**, we show only the species that react. The net ionic equation is obtained by eliminating the spectator ions and the brackets from the total ionic equation.

$$2Ag^+(aq) + Cu(s) \longrightarrow 2Ag(s) + Cu^{2+}(aq)$$

▶ Brackets are not used in net ionic equations.

▶ This is why it is important to know how and when to construct net ionic equations from formula unit equations.

Net ionic equations allow us to focus on the *essence* of a chemical reaction in aqueous solutions. On the other hand, if we are dealing with stoichiometric calculations, we frequently must deal with formula weights and therefore with the *complete* formulas of all species. In such cases, formula unit equations are more useful. Total ionic equations provide the bridge between the two.

STOP & THINK

The only common substances that should be written as ions in ionic equations are (1) strong acids, (2) strong bases, and (3) soluble salts. You must also remember the common polyatomic ions, their charges, and that they are units that do not typically dissociate further (e.g., PO_4^{3-}, SO_4^{2-}, CO_3^{2-}).

Problem-Solving Tip Writing Ionic Equations

The following chart will help in deciding which formula units are to be written as separate ions in the total ionic equation and which ones are to be written as unchanged formula units. You must answer two questions about a substance to determine whether it should be written in ionic form or as a formula unit in the total and net ionic equations.

1. Does it dissolve in water? If not, write the full formula.

2. (a) If it dissolves, does it ionize (a strong acid)?

   (b) If it dissolves, does it dissociate (a strong base or a soluble salt)?

If the answer to *either part* of the second question is yes, the substance is a soluble strong electrolyte, and its formula is written in ionic form.

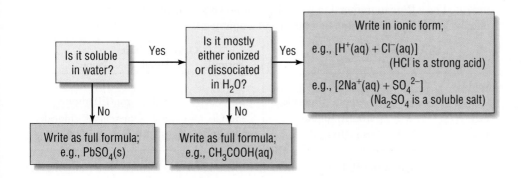

Recall the lists of strong acids (see Table 6-1) and strong bases (see Table 6-3). These acids and bases are completely or almost completely ionized or dissociated in dilute aqueous solutions. Other common acids and bases are either insoluble or only slightly ionized or dissociated. In addition, the solubility guidelines (see Table 6-4 and Section 6-1, Part 5) allow you to determine which salts are soluble in water. Most salts that are soluble in water are also strong electrolytes. Exceptions such as lead acetate, $Pb(CH_3COO)_2$, which is soluble but does not ionize appreciably, will be noted as they are encountered.

Naming Some Inorganic Compounds

The rules for naming compounds are determined by the Committee on Inorganic Nomenclature of the International Union of Pure and Applied Chemistry (IUPAC). The names and formulas of a few organic compounds were given in Table 2-1, and more systematic rules for naming them will appear in Chapter 23.

6-3 Naming Binary Compounds

A **binary compound** consists of two elements; it may be either ionic or molecular. The rule is to name the less electronegative element first and the more electronegative element second. The more electronegative element will have a negative oxidation state and is named by adding an "-ide" suffix to the element's *unambiguous* stem. Stems for the nonmetals follow.

▶ Millions of compounds are known, so it is important to be able to associate names and formulas in a systematic way.

3A		4A		5A		6A		7A	
								H	hydr
B	bor	C	carb	N	nitr	O	ox	F	fluor
		Si	silic	P	phosph	S	sulf	Cl	chlor
				As	arsen	Se	selen	Br	brom
				Sb	antimon	Te	tellur	I	iod

▶ The stem for each element is derived from the name of the element.

Binary ionic compounds contain metal cations and nonmetal anions. The cation is named first and the anion second.

Formula	Name	Formula	Name
KBr	potassium bromide	Rb_2S	rubidium sulfide
$CaCl_2$	calcium chloride	Ba_3N_2	barium nitride
NaH	sodium hydride	SrO	strontium oxide

▶ Notice that there is a space between the name of the cation and the name of the anion.

The preceding method is sufficient for naming binary ionic compounds containing metals that exhibit *only one oxidation state* other than zero (see Section 6-3). Most transition metals and the metals of Groups 3A (except Al), 4A, and 5A exhibit more than one oxidation state. These metals may form two or more binary compounds with the same nonmetal. To distinguish among all the possibilities, the oxidation state of the metal is

▶ Roman numerals are *not* necessary for metals that commonly exhibit only one oxidation state in their compounds.

indicated by a Roman numeral in parentheses following its name. This method can be applied to any binary compound of a metal and a nonmetal.

Formula	Oxidation State of Metal	Name	Formula	Oxidation State of Metal	Name
Cu_2O	+1	copper(I) oxide	$FeBr_2$	+2	iron(II) bromide
CuF_2	+2	copper(II) fluoride	$Fe(NO_3)_2$	+3	iron(III) nitrate
FeS	+2	iron(II) sulfide	Hg_2Cl_2	+1	mercury(I) chloride
Fe_2O_3	+3	iron(III) oxide	$HgCl_2$	+2	mercury(II) chloride

The advantage of the IUPAC system is that if you know the formula, you can write the exact and unambiguous name; if you are given the name, you can write the formula at once. An older method, still in use but not recommended by the IUPAC, uses "-ous" and "-ic" suffixes to indicate lower and higher oxidation states, respectively. This system can distinguish between only two different oxidation states for a metal. It is therefore not as useful as the Roman numeral system and we will use it rarely in this book.

▶ Familiarity with the older system is still necessary. It is still widely used in many scientific, engineering, and medical fields. The most commonly used older cation names are

Cation	IUPAC Name	Older Name
Fe^{2+}	iron(II)	ferrous
Fe^{3+}	iron(III)	ferric
Cu^+	copper(I)	cuprous
Cu^{2+}	copper(II)	cupric
Hg_2^{2+}	mercury(I)	mercurous
Hg^{2+}	mercury(II)	mercuric

Your instructor may require you to know this short list, as well as others to be specified.

Formula	Oxidation State of Metal	Name	Formula	Oxidation State of Metal	Name
$CuCl$	+1	cuprous chloride	$FeSO_4$	+2	ferrous sulfate
$CuCl_2$	+2	cupric chloride	$Fe(NO_3)_3$	+3	ferric nitrate
FeO	+2	ferrous oxide	Hg_2Cl_2	+1	mercurous chloride
$FeBr_3$	+3	ferric bromide	$HgCl_2$	+2	mercuric chloride

A list of common cations and anions appears in Table 6-6. It will enable you to name many of the ionic compounds you encounter.

Nearly all **binary molecular compounds** involve two *nonmetals* bonded together, such as PCl_3. Although many nonmetals can exhibit different oxidation states, their oxidation states are *not* properly indicated by Roman numerals or suffixes. Instead, elemental proportions in binary covalent compounds are indicated by using a *prefix* system for both elements. The Greek and Latin prefixes for one through ten are *mono-, di-, tri-, tetra-, penta-, hexa-, hepta-, octa-, nona-,* and *deca-*. The prefix "mono-" is omitted for both elements except in the common name for CO, carbon monoxide. We use the minimum number of prefixes needed to name a compound unambiguously. The final "a" in a prefix is omitted when the nonmetal stem begins with the letter "o"; we write "heptoxide," not "heptaoxide."

▶ If you don't already know them, you should learn these common prefixes.

Number	Prefix
2	di
3	tri
4	tetra
5	penta
6	hexa
7	hepta
8	octa
9	nona
10	deca

Formula	Name	Formula	Name
SO_2	sulfur dioxide	Cl_2O_7	dichlorine heptoxide
SO_3	sulfur trioxide	CS_2	carbon disulfide
N_2O_4	dinitrogen tetroxide	SF_4	sulfur tetrafluoride
As_4O_6	tetraarsenic hexoxide	SF_6	sulfur hexafluoride

Binary acids are compounds in which H is bonded to a Group 6A element other than O or to a Group 7A element; they act as acids when dissolved in water. *The pure compounds are named as typical binary compounds.* Their aqueous solutions are named by modifying the characteristic stem of the nonmetal with the prefix "hydro-" and the suffix "-ic" followed by the word "acid." The stem for sulfur in this instance is "sulfur" rather than "sulf."

Formula	Name of Compound	Name of Aqueous Solution
HCl	hydrogen chloride	hydrochloric acid, $HCl(aq)$
HF	hydrogen fluoride	hydrofluoric acid, $HF(aq)$
H_2S	hydrogen sulfide	hydrosulfuric acid, $H_2S(aq)$
HCN	hydrogen cyanide	hydrocyanic acid, $HCN(aq)$

In later chapters we will learn additional systematic rules for naming more complex compounds.

Table 6-6 Formulas and Names for Some Common Ions

Common Cations		Common Anions	
Formula	*Name*	*Formula*	*Name*
Li^+	lithium ion	F^-	fluoride ion
Na^+	sodium ion	Cl^-	chloride ion
K^+	potassium ion	Br^-	bromide ion
NH_4^+	ammonium ion	I^-	iodide ion
Ag^+	silver ion	OH^-	hydroxide ion
		CN^-	cyanide ion
Mg^{2+}	magnesium ion	ClO^-	hypochlorite ion
Ca^{2+}	calcium ion	ClO_2^-	chlorite ion
Ba^{2+}	barium ion	ClO_3^-	chlorate ion
Cd^{2+}	cadmium ion	ClO_4^-	perchlorate ion
Zn^{2+}	zinc ion	CH_3COO^-	acetate ion
Cu^{2+}	copper(II) ion or cupric ion	MnO_4^-	permanganate ion
Hg_2^{2+}	mercury(I) ion or mercurous ion	NO_2^-	nitrite ion
		NO_3^-	nitrate ion
Hg^{2+}	mercury(II) ion or mercuric ion	SCN^-	thiocyanate ion
Mn^{2+}	manganese(II) ion	O^{2-}	oxide ion
Co^{2+}	cobalt(II) ion	S^{2-}	sulfide ion
Ni^{2+}	nickel(II) ion	HSO_3^-	hydrogen sulfite ion or bisulfite ion
Pb^{2+}	lead(II) ion or plumbous ion	SO_3^{2-}	sulfite ion
Sn^{2+}	tin(II) ion or stannous ion	HSO_4^-	hydrogen sulfate ion or bisulfate ion
Fe^{2+}	iron(II) ion or ferrous ion	SO_4^{2-}	sulfate ion
Fe^{3+}	iron(III) ion or ferric ion	HCO_3^-	hydrogen carbonate ion or bicarbonate ion
Al^{3+}	aluminum ion	CO_3^{2-}	carbonate ion
Cr^{3+}	chromium(III) ion or chromic ion	CrO_4^{2-}	chromate ion
		$Cr_2O_7^{2-}$	dichromate ion
		PO_4^{3-}	phosphate ion
		AsO_4^{3-}	arsenate ion

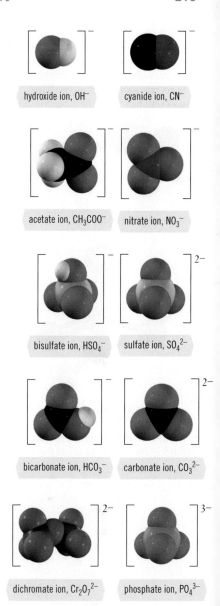

hydroxide ion, OH^- cyanide ion, CN^-

acetate ion, CH_3COO^- nitrate ion, NO_3^-

bisulfate ion, HSO_4^- sulfate ion, SO_4^{2-}

bicarbonate ion, HCO_3^- carbonate ion, CO_3^{2-}

dichromate ion, $Cr_2O_7^{2-}$ phosphate ion, PO_4^{3-}

6-4 Naming Ternary Acids and Their Salts

A **ternary compound** consists of three elements. **Ternary acids (oxoacids)** are compounds of hydrogen, oxygen, and (usually) a nonmetal. Nonmetals that exhibit more than one oxidation state form more than one ternary acid. These ternary acids differ in the number of oxygen atoms they contain. The suffixes "-ous" and "-ic" following the stem name of the central element indicate lower and higher oxidation states, respectively. One common ternary acid of each nonmetal is (somewhat arbitrarily) designated as the "-ic" acid. That is, it is named by putting the element stem before the "-ic" suffix. The common ternary "-ic

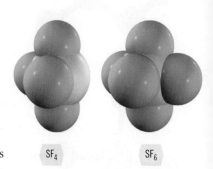

SF_4 SF_6

▶ The oxoacid with the central element in the highest oxidation state usually contains more O atoms. Oxoacids with their central elements in lower oxidation states usually have fewer O atoms.

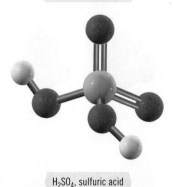

H_2SO_3, sulfurous acid

H_2SO_4, sulfuric acid

▶ Notice that $H_2N_2O_2$ has a 1:1 ratio of nitrogen to oxygen, as would the hypothetical HNO.

acids" are shown in Table 6-7. It is important to learn the names and formulas of these acids because the names of all other ternary acids and salts are derived from them. There are no common "-ic" ternary acids for the omitted nonmetals.

Acids containing *one fewer oxygen atom* per central atom are named in the same way except that the "-ic" suffix is changed to "-ous." The oxidation state of the central element is *lower by 2* in the "-ous" acid than in the "-ic" acid.

Formula	Oxidation State	Name	Formula	Oxidation State	Name
H_2SO_3	+4	sulfur*ous* acid	H_2SO_4	+6	sulfur*ic* acid
HNO_2	+3	nitr*ous* acid	HNO_3	+5	nitr*ic* acid
H_2SeO_3	+4	selen*ous* acid	H_2SeO_4	+6	selen*ic* acid
$HBrO_2$	+3	brom*ous* acid	$HBrO_3$	+5	brom*ic* acid

Ternary acids that have one fewer O atom than the "-ous" acids (two fewer O atoms than the "-ic" acids) are named using the prefix "hypo-" and the suffix "-ous." These are acids in which the oxidation state of the central nonmetal is *lower by 2* than that of the central nonmetal in the "-ous acids."

Formula	Oxidation State	Name
HClO	+1	*hypo*chlor*ous* acid
H_3PO_2	+1	*hypo*phosphor*ous* acid
HIO	+1	*hypo*iod*ous* acid
$H_2N_2O_2$	+1	*hypo*nitr*ous* acid

Acids containing *one more oxygen atom* per central nonmetal atom than the normal "-ic acid" are named "*per*stem*ic*" acids.

Formula	Oxidation State	Name
$HClO_4$	+7	*per*chlor*ic* acid
$HBrO_4$	+7	*per*brom*ic* acid
HIO_4	+7	*per*iod*ic* acid

HNO_3, nitric acid

H_3PO_4, phosphoric acid

Table 6-7 Formulas of Some "-ic" Acids

Periodic Group of Central Elements				
3A	4A	5A	6A	7A
+3 H_3BO_3 boric acid	+4 H_2CO_3 carbonic acid	+5 HNO_3 nitric acid		
	+4 H_4SiO_4 silicic acid	+5 H_3PO_4 phosphoric acid	+6 H_2SO_4 sulfuric acid	+5 $HClO_3$ chloric acid
		+5 H_3AsO_4 arsenic acid	+6 H_2SeO_4 selenic acid	+5 $HBrO_3$ bromic acid
			+6 H_6TeO_6 telluric acid	+5 HIO_3 iodic acid

Note that the oxidation state of the central atom is equal to its periodic group number, except for the halogens.

The oxoacids of chlorine can be summarized as follows:

Formula	Oxidation State	Name
HClO	+1	*hypo*chlor*ous* acid
HClO$_2$	+3	chlor*ous* acid
HClO$_3$	+5	chlor*ic* acid
HClO$_4$	+7	*per*chlor*ic* acid

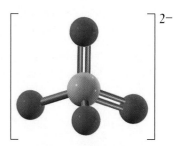

$SO_4{}^{2-}$, sulfate anion

Ternary salts are compounds that result from replacing the hydrogen in a ternary acid with another ion. They usually contain metal cations or the ammonium ion. As with binary compounds, the cation is named first. The name of the anion is based on the name of the ternary acid from which it is derived.

An anion derived from a ternary acid with an "-ic" ending is named by dropping the "-ic acid" and replacing it with "-ate." An anion derived from an "-ous acid" is named by replacing the suffix "-ous acid" with "-ite." The "per-" and "hypo-" prefixes are retained.

Formula	Name
(NH$_4$)$_2$SO$_4$	ammonium sulfate ($SO_4{}^{2-}$ from sulfuric acid, H_2SO_4)
KNO$_3$	potassium nitrate ($NO_3{}^-$ from nitric acid, HNO_3)
Ca(NO$_2$)$_2$	calcium nitrite ($NO_2{}^-$ from nitrous acid, HNO_2)
LiClO$_4$	lithium perchlorate ($ClO_4{}^-$ from perchloric acid, $HClO_4$)
FePO$_4$	iron(III) phosphate ($PO_4{}^{3-}$ from phosphoric acid, H_3PO_4)
NaClO	sodium hypochlorite (ClO^- from hypochlorous acid, $HClO$)

$HSO_4{}^-$, hydrogen sulfate anion

Acidic salts contain anions derived from ternary polyprotic acids in which one or more acidic hydrogen atoms remain. These salts are named as if they were the usual type of ternary salt, with the word "hydrogen" or "dihydrogen" inserted after the name of the cation to show the number of acidic hydrogen atoms.

Formula	Name	Formula	Name
NaHSO$_4$	sodium hydrogen sulfate	KH$_2$PO$_4$	potassium dihydrogen phosphate
NaHSO$_3$	sodium hydrogen sulfite	K$_2$HPO$_4$	potassium hydrogen phosphate
		NaHCO$_3$	sodium hydrogen carbonate

An older, commonly used method (which is not recommended by the IUPAC, but which is widely used in commerce) involves the use of the prefix "bi-" attached to the name of the anion to indicate the presence of an acidic hydrogen. According to this system, NaHSO$_4$ is called sodium bisulfate and NaHCO$_3$ is called sodium bicarbonate.

Problem-Solving Tip Naming Ternary Acids and Their Anions

The following table will help you to remember the names of the ternary acids and their ions. First learn the formulas of the acids mentioned earlier that end with "-ic acid." Then relate possible other acids to the following table. The stem (XXX) represents the stem of the name, for example, "nitr," "sulfur," or "chlor."

	Ternary Acid	Anion	
Decreasing number of oxygen atoms on central atom ↓	perXXXic acid	perXXXate	Decreasing oxidation number of central atom ↓
	XXXic acid	XXXate	
	XXXous acid	XXXite	
	hypoXXXous acid	hypoXXXite	

Classifying Chemical Reactions

We will now discuss chemical reactions in further detail. We classify them as oxidation–reduction reactions, combination reactions, decomposition reactions, displacement reactions, gas-formation reactions, and metathesis reactions. The last type can be further described as precipitation reactions and acid–base (neutralization) reactions. We will see that many reactions, especially oxidation–reduction reactions, fit into more than one category, and that some reactions do not fit neatly into any of them. As we study different kinds of chemical reactions, we will learn to predict the products of other similar reactions. In Chapter 5 we described typical reactions of hydrogen, oxygen, and their compounds. These reactions illustrate periodic relationships with respect to chemical properties. It should be emphasized that our system is not an attempt to transform nature so that it fits into small categories but rather an effort to give some order to our many observations of chemical reactions.

6-5 Oxidation–Reduction Reactions: Introduction

The term "oxidation" originally referred to the combination of a substance with oxygen. This results in an increase in the oxidation state of an element in that substance. According to the original definition, the following reactions involve oxidation of the substance shown on the far left of each equation. Oxidation states are shown for *one* atom of the indicated kind.

1. The formation of rust, Fe_2O_3, iron(III) oxide: oxidation state of Fe

$$4Fe(s) + 3O_2(g) \longrightarrow 2Fe_2O_3(s) \qquad\qquad 0 \longrightarrow +3$$

2. Combustion reactions: oxidation state of C

$$C(s) + O_2(g) \longrightarrow CO_2(g) \qquad\qquad 0 \longrightarrow +4$$
$$2CO(g) + O_2(g) \longrightarrow 2CO_2(g) \qquad\qquad +2 \longrightarrow +4$$
$$C_3H_8(g) + 5O_2(g) \longrightarrow 3CO_2(g) + 4H_2O(g) \qquad\qquad -8/3 \longrightarrow +4$$

▶ Oxidation state is a formal concept adopted for our convenience. The numbers are determined by relying on rules. These rules can result in a fractional oxidation state, as shown here. This does not mean that electronic charges are split.

Originally, *reduction* described the removal of oxygen from a compound. Oxide ores are reduced to metals (a very real reduction in mass). For example, tungsten for use in light bulb filaments can be prepared by reduction of tungsten(VI) oxide with hydrogen at 1200°C:

oxidation state of W

$$WO_3(s) + 3H_2(g) \longrightarrow W(s) + 3H_2O(g) \qquad +6 \longrightarrow 0$$

▶ The terms "oxidation number" and "oxidation state" are often used interchangeably.

Tungsten is reduced, and its oxidation state decreases from +6 to zero. Hydrogen is oxidized from zero to the +1 oxidation state. The terms "oxidation" and "reduction" are now applied much more broadly.

▶ In biological systems, *reduction* often corresponds to the addition of hydrogen to molecules or polyatomic ions and *oxidation* often corresponds to the removal of hydrogen.

> **Oxidation** is an increase in oxidation state and corresponds to the loss, or apparent loss, of electrons. **Reduction** is a decrease in oxidation state and corresponds to a gain, or apparent gain, of electrons.

Electrons are neither created nor destroyed in chemical reactions. So oxidation and reduction always occur simultaneously, and to the same extent, in ordinary chemical reactions. In the four equations cited previously as *examples of oxidation*, the oxidation states of iron and carbon atoms increase as they are oxidized. In each case oxygen is reduced as its oxidation state decreases from zero to -2.

Because oxidation and reduction occur simultaneously in all of these reactions, they are referred to as **oxidation–reduction reactions**. For brevity, we usually call them **redox reactions**. Redox reactions occur in nearly every area of chemistry and biochemistry. We need to be able to identify oxidizing agents and reducing agents and to balance oxidation–reduction equations. These skills are necessary for the study of electrochemistry in Chapter 21. Electrochemistry involves electron transfer between physically separated oxidizing and reducing agents and interconversions between chemical energy and electrical energy. These skills are also fundamental to the study of biology, biochemistry, environmental science, and materials science.

> **Oxidizing agents** are species that (1) oxidize other substances, (2) contain atoms that are reduced, and (3) gain (or appear to gain) electrons. **Reducing agents** are species that (1) reduce other substances, (2) contain atoms that are oxidized, and (3) lose (or appear to lose) electrons.

S TOP & THINK
Oxidation cannot occur without reduction (and vice versa). An *oxidizing agent* in a chemical reaction is *reduced,* while a *reducing agent* is *oxidized.* This can be very confusing, so take some extra time to understand these important relationships.

The following equations represent examples of redox reactions. Oxidation states are shown above the formulas, and oxidizing and reducing agents are indicated:

$$\overset{0}{2Fe(s)} + \overset{0}{3Cl_2(g)} \longrightarrow \overset{+3\ -1}{2FeCl_3(s)}$$
$$\text{red. agt.}\quad\text{ox. agt.}$$

$$\overset{+3\ -1}{2FeBr_3(aq)} + \overset{0}{3Cl_2(g)} \longrightarrow \overset{+3\ -1}{2FeCl_3(aq)} + \overset{0}{3Br_2(\ell)}$$
$$\text{red. agt.}\quad\text{ox. agt.}$$

▶ The following abbreviations are widely used:
  ox. no. = oxidation number
  ox. agt. = oxidizing agent
  red. agt. = reducing agent

Equations for redox reactions can also be written as total ionic and net ionic equations. For example, the second equation may also be written as:

$$2[Fe^{3+}(aq) + 3Br^-(aq)] + 3Cl_2(g) \longrightarrow 2[Fe^{3+}(aq) + 3Cl^-(aq)] + 3Br_2(\ell)$$

We distinguish between oxidation states and actual charges on ions by denoting oxidation numbers as $+n$ or $-n$ *in circles just above the symbols of the elements*, and actual charges as $n+$ or $n-$ above and to the right of formulas of ions. The spectator ions, Fe^{3+}, do not participate in electron transfer. Their cancellation allows us to focus on the oxidizing agent, $Cl_2(g)$, and the reducing agent, $Br^-(aq)$.

$$2Br^-(aq) + Cl_2(g) \longrightarrow 2Cl^-(aq) + Br_2(\ell)$$

A **disproportionation reaction** is a redox reaction in which the same element is oxidized and reduced. An example is:

$$\overset{0}{Cl_2} + H_2O \longrightarrow \overset{-1}{HCl} + \overset{+1}{HClO}$$

Iron reacts with chlorine to form iron(III) chloride.

EXAMPLE 6-4 Redox Reactions

Write each of the following formula unit equations as a net ionic equation if the two differ. Which ones are redox reactions? For the redox reactions, identify the oxidizing agent, the reducing agent, the species oxidized, and the species reduced.

(a) $2AgNO_3(aq) + Cu(s) \longrightarrow Cu(NO_3)_2(aq) + 2Ag(s)$

(b) $4KClO_3(s) \xrightarrow{heat} KCl(s) + 3KClO_4(s)$

(c) $3AgNO_3(aq) + K_3PO_4(aq) \longrightarrow Ag_3PO_4(s) + 3KNO_3(aq)$

Plan

To write ionic equations, we must recognize compounds that are (1) soluble in water and (2) ionized or dissociated in aqueous solutions. To determine which are oxidation–reduction reactions, we should assign an oxidation state to each element.

Metallic silver formed by immersing a spiral of copper wire in a silver nitrate solution (see Example 6-4a).

Solution

(a) According to the solubility guidelines (see Section 6-1, Part 5), both silver nitrate, $AgNO_3$, and copper(II) nitrate, $Cu(NO_3)_2$, are water-soluble ionic compounds. The total ionic equation and oxidation states are:

$$2[\overset{+1}{Ag^+}(aq) + \overset{+5}{N}\overset{-2}{O_3^-}(aq)] + \overset{0}{Cu}(s) \longrightarrow [\overset{+2}{Cu^{2+}}(aq) + 2\overset{+5}{N}\overset{-2}{O_3^-}(aq)] + 2\overset{0}{Ag}(s)$$

$$+2$$
$$-1$$

The nitrate ions, NO_3^-, are spectator ions. Canceling them from both sides gives the net ionic equation:

$$2\overset{+1}{Ag^+}(aq) + \overset{0}{Cu}(s) \longrightarrow \overset{+2}{Cu^{2+}}(aq) + 2\overset{0}{Ag}(s)$$

This is a redox equation. The oxidation state of silver decreases from $+1$ to zero; silver ion is reduced and is the oxidizing agent. The oxidation state of copper increases from zero to $+2$; copper is oxidized and is the reducing agent.

(b) This reaction involves only solids, so there are no ions in solution, and the formula unit and net ionic equations are identical. It is a redox reaction:

$$4\overset{+1}{K}\overset{+5}{Cl}\overset{-2}{O_3}(s) \longrightarrow \overset{+1}{K}\overset{-1}{Cl}(s) + 3\overset{+1}{K}\overset{+7}{Cl}\overset{-2}{O_4}(s)$$

$$-6$$
$$+2$$

Chlorine is reduced from $+5$ in $KClO_3$ to the -1 oxidation state in KCl; the oxidizing agent is $KClO_3$. Chlorine is oxidized from $+5$ in $KClO_3$ to the $+7$ oxidation state in $KClO_4$. $KClO_3$ is also the reducing agent. This is a disproportionation reaction. We see that $KClO_3$ is both the oxidizing agent and the reducing agent.

(c) The solubility guidelines indicate that all these salts are soluble except for silver phosphate, Ag_3PO_4. The total ionic equation is

$$3[Ag^+(aq) + NO_3^-(aq)] + [3K^+(aq) + PO_4^{3-}(aq)] \longrightarrow$$
$$Ag_3PO_4(s) + 3[K^+(aq) + NO_3^-(aq)]$$

Eliminating the spectator ions gives the net ionic equation:

$$3\overset{+1}{Ag^+}(aq) + \overset{+5}{P}\overset{-2}{O_4^{3-}}(aq) \longrightarrow \overset{+1}{Ag_3}\overset{+5}{P}\overset{-2}{O_4}(s)$$

There are no changes in oxidation states, so this is not a redox reaction.

You should now work Exercises 56 and 59.

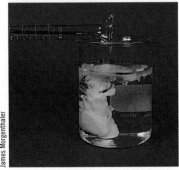

The reaction of $AgNO_3(aq)$ and $K_3PO_4(aq)$ is a precipitation reaction (see Example 6-4c).

Problem-Solving Tip: A Foolproof Way to Recognize a Redox Reaction

You can always recognize a redox reaction by analyzing oxidation states. First determine the oxidation state of each element wherever it appears in the reaction. If no elements change in oxidation states, the reaction is not an oxidation–reduction reaction. If changes do occur, the reaction is an oxidation–reduction reaction. Remember that oxidation and reduction must always occur together; if some elements increase in oxidation states, then others must decrease.

In Chapter 11 we will learn to balance redox equations and to carry out stoichiometric calculations using the balanced equations.

6-6 Combination Reactions

Reactions in which two or more substances combine to form a single compound are called **combination reactions**.

They may involve (1) the combination of two elements to form a compound, (2) the combination of an element and a compound to form a single new compound, or (3) the combination of two compounds to form a single new compound. Let's examine some of these reactions.

1 Element + Element ⟶ Compound

For this type of combination reaction, each element goes from an uncombined state, where its oxidation state is zero, to a combined state in a compound, where its oxidation state is not zero. Thus reactions of this type are oxidation–reduction reactions (see Section 6-5).

Metal + Nonmetal → Binary Ionic Compound

Most metals (low electronegativity) react with most nonmetals (higher electronegativity) to form binary ionic compounds. The Group 1A metals combine vigorously with the Group 7A nonmetals to form binary *ionic* compounds with the general formula MX (see Section 7-2):

$$2M(s) + X_2 \longrightarrow 2(M^+X^-)(s) \qquad M = \text{Li, Na, K, Rb, Cs}$$
$$X = \text{F, Cl, Br, I}$$

This general equation thus represents the 20 combination reactions that form the ionic compounds listed in Table 6-8. Sodium, a silvery-white metal, combines with chlorine, a pale green gas, to form sodium chloride, or ordinary table salt. All members of both families undergo similar reactions.

$$2Na(s) + Cl_2(g) \longrightarrow 2NaCl(s) \qquad \text{sodium chloride (mp} = 801°C)$$

As we might expect, the Group 2A metals also combine with the Group 7A nonmetals to form binary compounds. Except for $BeCl_2$, $BeBr_2$, and BeI_2, these are ionic compounds. In general terms these combination reactions may be represented as:

$$M(s) + X_2 \longrightarrow MX_2(s) \qquad M = \text{Be, Mg, Ca, Sr, Ba}$$
$$X = \text{F, Cl, Br, I}$$

Consider the reaction of magnesium with fluorine to form magnesium fluoride:

$$Mg(s) + F_2(g) \longrightarrow MgF_2(s) \qquad \text{magnesium fluoride (mp} = 1266°C)$$

Because all the 2A and 7A elements undergo similar reactions, the general equation, written above, represents 20 reactions. We omit radium and astatine, the rare and highly radioactive members of the families.

Nonmetal + Nonmetal ⟶ Binary Covalent Compound

When two nonmetals combine with each other, they form binary *covalent* compounds. In such reactions, the oxidation state of the element with the more positive oxidation state is often variable, depending on reaction conditions. For example, phosphorus (Group 5A) combines with a *limited amount* of chlorine to form phosphorus trichloride, in which phosphorus exhibits the +3 oxidation state.

$$P_4(s) + 6Cl_2(g) \overset{+3}{\longrightarrow} 4PCl_3(\ell) \qquad \text{(with limited } Cl_2) \qquad \text{(mp } -112°C)$$

Charles D. Winters

Potassium, a metal, reacts with chlorine, a nonmetal, to form potassium chloride, KCl. The reaction releases energy in the form of heat and light.

▶ Another important reaction of this kind is the formation of metal oxides (see Section 5-9).

Table 6-8 Alkali Metal Halides: Compounds Formed by Group 1A and 7A Elements

LiF	LiCl	LiBr	LiI
NaF	NaCl	NaBr	NaI
KF	KCl	KBr	KI
RbF	RbCl	RbBr	RbI
CsF	CsCl	CsBr	CsI

With an excess of chlorine, the product is phosphorus pentachloride, which contains phosphorus in the +5 oxidation state:

$$P_4(s) + 10Cl_2(g) \longrightarrow 4\overset{+5}{P}Cl_5(s) \quad \text{(with excess } Cl_2) \quad \text{(decomposes at 167°C)}$$

In general, *a higher oxidation state of a nonmetal is formed when it reacts with an excess of another more electronegative nonmetal.* There are many more reactions in which two elements combine to form a compound (see Sections 5-8 and 5-9).

2 Compound + Element ⟶ Compound

Phosphorus in the +3 oxidation state in PCl_3 molecules can be converted to the +5 state in PCl_5 by combination with chlorine:

$$\overset{+3}{P}Cl_3(\ell) + Cl_2(g) \longrightarrow \overset{+5}{P}Cl_5(s)$$

> ► Nonmetals in odd-numbered periodic groups favor odd oxidation states, whereas those in even-numbered groups favor even oxidation states in their compounds. The maximum oxidation state for a representative element is equal to its periodic group state. For example, sulfur (Group 6A) can form both SF_4 and SF_6.

Likewise, sulfur in the +4 state is converted to the +6 state when SF_4 reacts with fluorine to form SF_6:

$$\overset{+4}{S}F_4(g) + F_2(g) \longrightarrow \overset{+6}{S}F_6(g) \quad \text{sulfur hexafluoride (mp } -50.5°C)$$

Combination reactions of this type are also oxidation–reduction reactions.

3 Compound + Compound ⟶ Compound

> ► Because there is no change in oxidation states for any of the elements in these reactions, these are not redox reactions.

An example of reactions in this category is the combination of calcium oxide with carbon dioxide to produce calcium carbonate:

$$CaO(s) + CO_2(g) \longrightarrow CaCO_3(s)$$

Pyrosulfuric acid is produced by dissolving sulfur trioxide in concentrated sulfuric acid:

$$SO_3(g) + H_2SO_4(\ell) \longrightarrow H_2S_2O_7(\ell)$$

Pyrosulfuric acid, $H_2S_2O_7$, is then diluted with water to make H_2SO_4:

$$H_2S_2O_7(\ell) + H_2O(\ell) \longrightarrow 2H_2SO_4(\ell)$$

Oxides of the Group 1A and 2A metals react with water to form metal hydroxides, e.g.:

$$CaO(s) + H_2O(\ell) \longrightarrow Ca(OH)_2(aq)$$

6-7 Decomposition Reactions

Decomposition reactions are those in which a compound decomposes to produce (1) two elements, (2) one or more elements *and* one or more compounds, or (3) two or more compounds.

Examples of each type follow.

1 Compound ⟶ Element + Element

> ► Decomposition reactions can be considered as the opposite of combination reactions. A decomposition reaction may or may not also be an oxidation–reduction reaction. You can always identify a redox reaction by determining the oxidation state of each element in each occurrence in the reaction (see the Problem-Solving Tip in Section 6-5).

The electrolysis of water produces two elements by the decomposition of a compound. A compound that ionizes, such as H_2SO_4, is added to increase the conductivity of water and the rate of the reaction (see Figure 1-13), but it does not participate in the reaction:

$$2H_2O(\ell) \xrightarrow{\text{electrolysis}} 2H_2(g) + O_2(g)$$

Small amounts of oxygen can be prepared by the thermal decomposition of certain oxygen-containing compounds. Some metal oxides, such as mercury(II) oxide, HgO, decompose on heating to produce oxygen:

$$2HgO(s) \xrightarrow{\text{heat}} 2Hg(\ell) + O_2(g)$$
$$\text{mercury(II) oxide}$$

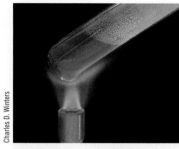

Mercury(II) oxide, a red compound, decomposes when heated into the two elements: mercury (a metal) and oxygen (a nonmetal).

2 Compound ⟶ Compound + Element

The alkali metal chlorates, such as $KClO_3$, decompose when heated to produce the corresponding chlorides and liberate oxygen. Potassium chlorate is a common laboratory source for small amounts of oxygen:

$$2KClO_3(s) \xrightarrow[\text{MnO}_2]{\text{heat}} 2KCl(s) + 3O_2(g)$$
$$\text{potassium chlorate} \qquad \text{potassium chloride}$$

▶ Manganese dioxide, MnO_2, is used as a catalyst, a substance that speeds up a chemical reaction but is not consumed. Here it allows the decomposition to occur at a lower temperature.

Nitrate salts of alkali metals or alkaline earth metals decompose to form metal nitrites and oxygen gas.

$$2NaNO_3(s) \longrightarrow 2NaNO_2(s) + O_2(g)$$

Hydrogen peroxide decomposes to form water and oxygen even at room temperature. H_2O_2 is usually stored in a refrigerator to slow down this decomposition reaction.

$$2H_2O_2(\ell) \longrightarrow 2H_2O(\ell) + O_2(g)$$

3 Compound ⟶ Compound + Compound

The thermal decomposition of calcium carbonate (limestone) and other carbonates produces two compounds, a metal oxide and carbon dioxide:

$$CaCO_3(s) \xrightarrow{\text{heat}} CaO(s) + CO_2(g)$$

This is an important reaction in the production of cement. Calcium oxide (commonly called lime) is also used as a base in industrial processes.

When some solid hydroxides are heated, they decompose to form a metal oxide and water vapor.

$$Mg(OH)_2(s) \xrightarrow{\text{heat}} MgO(s) + H_2O(g)$$

Magnesium oxide, MgO, is pressed into sheets for use as a thermal insulating material in oven walls.

Ammonium salts lose ammonia.

$$(NH_4)_2SO_4(s) \xrightarrow{\text{heat}} 2NH_3(g) + H_2SO_4(\ell)$$

If the ammonium salt contains an anion that is a strong oxidizing agent (e.g., nitrate, nitrite, or dichromate), its decomposition reaction produces an oxide, water (as vapor at high temperatures), and nitrogen gas. Such a reaction is a redox reaction.

$$(NH_4)_2Cr_2O_7(s) \xrightarrow{\text{heat}} Cr_2O_3(s) + 4H_2O(g) + N_2(g)$$

Solid ammonium dichromate, [$(NH_4)_2Cr_2O_7$, *orange*] decomposes when heated into chromium(III) oxide, (Cr_2O_3, *green*), nitrogen, and steam (water vapor). This reaction is sometimes demonstrated as the "classroom volcano," but it must be done with extreme caution due to the carcinogenic (cancer-causing) nature of $(NH_4)_2Cr_2O_7$.

6-8 Displacement Reactions

Reactions in which one element displaces another from a compound are called **displacement reactions**.

These reactions are always redox reactions. The lower the electronegativity of a metal, the more readily that metal undergoes oxidation, and the more active we say it is.

> More active (less electronegative) metals displace less active (more electronegative) metals or hydrogen from their compounds in aqueous solution to form the oxidized form of the more active metal and the reduced (free metal) form of the other metal or hydrogen gas.

In Table 6-9, the most active metals are listed at the top of the first column. These metals tend to react to form their oxidized forms (cations). Elements at the bottom of the activity series (the first column of Table 6-9) are the most electronegative and tend to remain in their reduced form. They are easily converted from their oxidized forms to their reduced forms.

$$1 \begin{bmatrix} \text{More Active Metal} + \\ \text{Salt of Less Active Metal} \end{bmatrix} \longrightarrow \begin{bmatrix} \text{Less Active Metal} + \\ \text{Salt of More Active Metal} \end{bmatrix}$$

The reaction of copper with silver nitrate that was described in detail in Section 6-2 is typical. Please refer to it.

EXAMPLE 6-5 Displacement Reaction

A large piece of zinc metal is placed in a copper(II) sulfate, $CuSO_4$, solution. The blue solution becomes colorless as finely divided copper metal falls to the bottom of the container. The resulting solution contains zinc sulfate, $ZnSO_4$. Write balanced formula unit, total ionic, and net ionic equations for the reaction.

Plan

The metals zinc and copper are *not* ionized or dissociated in contact with H_2O. Both $CuSO_4$ and $ZnSO_4$ are soluble salts (solubility guideline 5), so they are written in ionic form.

Solution

$$Zn(s) + CuSO_4(aq) \longrightarrow Cu(s) + ZnSO_4(aq)$$

$$Zn(s) + [Cu^{2+}(aq) + SO_4^{2-}(aq)] \longrightarrow Cu(s) + [Zn^{2+}(aq) + SO_4^{2-}(aq)]$$

$$Zn(s) + Cu^{2+}(aq) \longrightarrow Cu(s) + Zn^{2+}(aq)$$

In this *displacement reaction*, the more active metal, zinc, displaces the ions of the less active metal, copper, from aqueous solution.

You should now work Exercise 64.

2 [Active Metal + Nonoxidizing Acid] $\longrightarrow$ [Hydrogen + Salt of Acid]

A common method for preparing small amounts of hydrogen involves the reaction of active metals with nonoxidizing acids, such as HCl and H_2SO_4. For example, when zinc is dissolved in H_2SO_4, the reaction produces zinc sulfate; hydrogen is displaced from the acid, and it bubbles off as gaseous H_2. The formula unit equation for this reaction is

$$Zn(s) + H_2SO_4(aq) \longrightarrow ZnSO_4(aq) + H_2(g)$$
$$\quad\quad\quad \text{strong acid} \quad\quad \text{soluble salt}$$

Both sulfuric acid (in very dilute solution) and zinc sulfate exist primarily as ions, so the total ionic equation is

$$Zn(s) + [2H^+(aq) + SO_4^{2-}(aq)] \longrightarrow [Zn^{2+}(aq) + SO_4^{2-}(aq)] + H_2(g)$$

Elimination of spectator ions from the total ionic equation gives the net ionic equation:

$$Zn(s) + 2H^+(aq) \longrightarrow Zn^{2+}(aq) + H_2(g)$$

A strip of zinc metal was placed in a blue solution of copper(II) sulfate, $CuSO_4$. The copper has been displaced from solution and has fallen to the bottom of the beaker. The resulting zinc sulfate, $ZnSO_4$, solution is colorless.

Zinc reacts with dilute H_2SO_4 to produce H_2 and a solution that contains $ZnSO_4$. This is a displacement reaction.

Table 6-9 Activity Series of Some Elements

Element	Displace hydrogen from nonoxidizing acids	Displace hydrogen from steam	Displace hydrogen from cold water	Common Reduced Form	Common Oxidized Forms
Li				Li	Li^+
K				K	K^+
Ca				Ca	Ca^{2+}
Na				Na	Na^+
Mg				Mg	Mg^{2+}
Al				Al	Al^{3+}
Mn				Mn	Mn^{2+}
Zn				Zn	Zn^{2+}
Cr				Cr	Cr^{3+}, Cr^{6+}
Fe				Fe	Fe^{2+}, Fe^{3+}
Cd				Cd	Cd^{2+}
Co				Co	Co^{2+}
Ni				Ni	Ni^{2+}
Sn				Sn	Sn^{2+}, Sn^{4+}
Pb				Pb	Pb^{2+}, Pb^{4+}
H (a nonmetal)				H_2	H^+
Sb (a metalloid)				Sb	Sb^{3+}
Cu				Cu	Cu^+, Cu^{2+}
Hg				Hg	Hg_2^{2+}, Hg^{2+}
Ag				Ag	Ag^+
Pt				Pt	Pt^{2+}, Pt^{4+}
Au				Au	Au^+, Au^{3+}

Increasing Activity (Oxidized Form Favored) ↑

Table 6-9 lists the **activity series**. When any metal listed above hydrogen in this series is added to a solution of a *nonoxidizing* acid such as hydrochloric acid, HCl, or sulfuric acid, H_2SO_4, the metal dissolves to produce hydrogen, and a salt is formed. HNO_3 is the common *oxidizing acid*. It reacts with active metals to produce oxides of nitrogen, but *not* hydrogen, H_2.

EXAMPLE 6-6 Displacement Reaction

Which of the following metals can displace hydrogen from hydrochloric acid solution? Write balanced formula unit, total ionic, and net ionic equations for reactions that can occur.

$$Al, \quad Cu, \quad Ag$$

Plan

The activity series of the metals, Table 6-9, tells us that copper and silver *do not* displace hydrogen from solutions of nonoxidizing acids. Aluminum is an active metal that can displace H_2 from HCl and form aluminum chloride.

Solution

$$2Al(s) + 6HCl(aq) \longrightarrow 3H_2(g) + 2AlCl_3(aq)$$
$$2Al(s) + 6[H^+(aq) + Cl^-(aq)] \longrightarrow 3H_2(g) + 2[Al^{3+}(aq) + 3Cl^-(aq)]$$
$$2Al(s) + 6H^+(aq) \longrightarrow 3H_2(g) + 2Al^{3+}(aq)$$

You should now work Exercise 63.

Charles Steele

Aluminum displaces H_2 from a hydrochloric acid solution.

CHEMISTRY IN USE

Troublesome Displacement Reactions

The deterioration of the Statue of Liberty and the damage done at the Three Mile Island and Chernobyl nuclear facilities are just a few of the major problems that have resulted from ignorance about chemical reactivity.

When originally constructed over one hundred years ago the Statue of Liberty had a 200,000-pound outer copper skin supported by a framework of 2000 iron bars. First, oxygen in the air oxidized the copper skin to form copper oxide. In a series of reactions, iron (the more active metal) then reduced the Cu^{2+} ions in copper oxide.

$$2Fe + 3Cu^{2+} \longrightarrow 2Fe^{3+} + 3Cu$$

Over the years, the supporting iron frame was reduced to less than half its original thickness; this made necessary the repairs done to the statue before the celebration of its 100th birthday on July 4, 1986.

Two major nuclear power plant accidents, one at Three Mile Island near Harrisburg, Pennsylvania, in 1979 and the other at Chernobyl in Ukraine in 1986, were also unexpected consequences of chemical reactivity. In each case, cooling pump failures sent temperatures soaring above 340°C. Like aluminum, zirconium (used in building the reactors) forms an oxide coating that shields it from further reactions. However, that protective coating breaks down at high temperatures. Without its protective coating, zirconium reacts with steam.

$$Zr(s) + 2H_2O(g) \longrightarrow ZrO_2(s) + 2H_2(g)$$

At Three Mile Island, this displacement reaction produced a 1000-cubic foot bubble of hydrogen gas. Because hydrogen is easily ignited by a spark, the nuclear power plant was in real danger of a complete meltdown until the hydrogen could be removed.

During the Middle Ages (~AD 400–1400), another displacement reaction completely misled alchemists into foolishly pursuing a philosophers' stone that was believed to have the power to turn base metals such as iron and lead into more precious metals such as silver and gold. The alchemists' ignorance of relative activities of metals led them to believe that they had turned iron into a more precious metal when they inserted an iron rod into a blue copper(II) sulfate solution. In fact, the following displacement reaction had occurred, plating shiny copper metal onto the iron rod:

$$2Fe(s) + 3Cu^{2+}(aq) \longrightarrow 2Fe^{3+}(aq) + 3Cu(s)$$

In the 1960s and 1970s, some automobile manufacturers showed their ignorance of chemical reactivity by building cars with aluminum water pumps and aluminum engine heads attached to cast-iron engine blocks. These water pumps often

Fuse/Jupiterimages

leaked and the engine heads quickly deteriorated. These problems occurred as the more active aluminum reacted with iron(III) oxide (formed when the iron engine reacted with atmospheric oxygen).

$$2Al(s) + Fe_2O_3(s) \longrightarrow Al_2O_3(s) + 2Fe(s)$$

Some dentists have made similar mistakes by placing gold caps over teeth that are adjacent to existing fillings. The slightly oxidized gold can react with a dental amalgam filling (an alloy of silver, tin, copper, and mercury). As the dental amalgam is oxidized, it dissolves in saliva to produce a persistent metallic taste in the patient's mouth.

When plumbers connect galvanized pipes (iron pipes coated with zinc) to copper pipes, copper ions oxidize the zinc coating and expose the underlying iron, allowing it to rust. The displacement reaction that occurs is

$$Zn + Cu^{2+} \longrightarrow Zn^{2+} + Cu$$

Once the zinc coating has been punctured on an iron pipe, oxidation of the iron pipes occurs rapidly because iron is a more active metal than copper.

It is important to keep in mind that a variety of reactions other than the displacement reactions discussed here probably take place. For example, less active metals (such as copper) can conduct electrons from the metals being oxidized to oxidizing agents (such as oxygen or the oxide of nitrogen and sulfur) that are present in the atmosphere. Oxygen plays an important role in all these displacement examples.

RONALD DELORENZO

MIDDLE GEORGIA COLLEGE

Very active metals can even displace hydrogen from water. The reaction of potassium, or another metal of Group 1A, with water is also a *displacement reaction*:

$$2K(s) + 2H_2O(\ell) \longrightarrow 2[K^+(aq) + OH^-(aq)] + H_2(g)$$

Such reactions of very active metals of Group 1A are dangerous, however, because they generate enough heat to cause explosive ignition of the hydrogen.

EXAMPLE 6-7 Displacement Reaction

Which of the following metals can displace hydrogen from water at room temperature? Write balanced formula unit, total ionic, and net ionic equations for reactions that can occur.

Sn,   Ca,   Hg

Plan

The activity series, Table 6-9, tells us that tin and mercury *cannot* displace hydrogen from water. Calcium is a very active metal (see Table 6-9) that displaces hydrogen from cold water (Figure 6-3) and forms calcium hydroxide, a strong base.

Solution

$$Ca(s) + 2H_2O(\ell) \longrightarrow H_2(g) + Ca(OH)_2(aq)$$

$$Ca(s) + 2H_2O(\ell) \longrightarrow H_2(g) + [Ca^{2+}(aq) + 2OH^-(aq)]$$

$$Ca(s) + 2H_2O(\ell) \longrightarrow H_2(g) + Ca^{2+}(aq) + 2OH^-(aq)$$

You should now work Exercise 71.

Figure 6-3 The displacement reaction of calcium with water at room temperature produces bubbles of hydrogen.

$$3 \begin{bmatrix} \text{Active Nonmetal} + \\ \text{Salt of Less Active Nonmetal} \end{bmatrix} \longrightarrow \begin{bmatrix} \text{Less Active Nonmetal} + \\ \text{Salt of More Active Nonmetal} \end{bmatrix}$$

Many *nonmetals* displace less active nonmetals from combination with a metal or other cation. For example, when chlorine is bubbled through a solution containing bromide ions (derived from a soluble salt such as sodium bromide, NaBr), chlorine displaces bromide ions to form elemental bromine and chloride ions (as aqueous sodium chloride):

$$Cl_2(g) + 2[Na^+(aq) + Br^-(aq)] \longrightarrow 2[Na^+(aq) + Cl^-(aq)] + Br_2(\ell)$$
chlorine   sodium bromide   sodium chloride   bromine

Similarly, when bromine is added to a solution containing iodide ions, the iodide ions are displaced by bromine to form iodine and bromide ions:

$$Br_2(\ell) + 2[Na^+(aq) + I^-(aq)] \longrightarrow 2[Na^+(aq) + Br^-(aq)] + I_2(s)$$
bromine   sodium iodide   sodium bromide   iodine

Each halogen will displace less active (less electronegative) halogens from their binary salts; that is, the order of decreasing activities is

$$F_2 > Cl_2 > Br_2 > I_2$$

Conversely, a halogen will *not* displace more active (more electronegative) members from their salts:

$$I_2(s) + 2F^- \longrightarrow \text{no reaction}$$

EXAMPLE 6-8 Displacement Reaction

Which of the following combinations would result in a displacement reaction? Write balanced formula unit, total ionic, and net ionic equations for reactions that occur.

(a) $I_2(s) + NaBr(aq) \longrightarrow$

(b) $Cl_2(g) + NaI(aq) \longrightarrow$

(c) $Br_2(\ell) + NaCl(aq) \longrightarrow$

Plan

▶ Activity of the halogens decreases going down the group in the periodic table.

The activity of the halogens decreases as their electronegativity decreases from top to bottom in the periodic table. We see (a) that Br is above I and (c) that Cl is above Br in the periodic table; therefore, neither combination (a) nor combination (c) could result in reaction. Cl is above I in the periodic table, and so combination (b) results in a displacement reaction.

Solution

The more active halogen, Cl_2, displaces the less active halogen, I_2, from its compounds.

$$Cl_2(g) + 2NaI(aq) \longrightarrow I_2(s) + 2NaCl(aq)$$

$$Cl_2(g) + 2[Na^+(aq) + I^-(aq)] \longrightarrow I_2(s) + 2[Na^+(aq) + Cl^-(aq)]$$

$$Cl_2(g) + 2I^-(aq) \longrightarrow I_2(s) + 2Cl^-(aq)$$

You should now work Exercise 72.

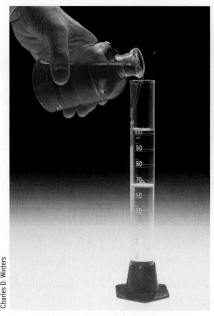

Charles D. Winters

Ⓐ Bromine, Br_2, in water (*pale orange*) is poured into an aqueous solution of NaI, the top layer in the cylinder.

Ⓑ Br_2 displaces I^- from solution and forms solid iodine, I_2. The I_2 dissolves in water to give a brown solution but is more soluble in many organic liquids (*purple bottom layer*).

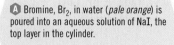

A nonmetal-nonmetal displacement reaction.

6-9 Metathesis Reactions

In many reactions between two compounds in aqueous solution, the positive and negative ions appear to "change partners" to form two new compounds, with *no change in oxidation numbers*. Such reactions are called **metathesis reactions**.

We can represent such reactions by the following general equation, where A and B represent positive ions (cations) and X and Y represent negative ions (anions):

$$AX + BY \longrightarrow AY + BX$$

For example, when we mix silver nitrate and sodium chloride solutions, solid silver chloride is formed and sodium nitrate remains dissolved in water:

$$AgNO_3(aq) + NaCl(aq) \longrightarrow AgCl(s) + NaNO_3(aq)$$

Metathesis reactions result in the removal of ions from solution; this removal of ions can be thought of as the *driving force* for the reaction—the reason it occurs. The removal of ions can occur in various ways, which can be used to classify types of metathesis reactions:

▶ Pronounced "meh-tath-uh-sis." Metathesis reactions are sometimes referred to as **double displacement reactions**.

1. Formation of predominantly nonionized molecules (weak or nonelectrolytes) in solution; the most common such nonelectrolyte product is water

2. Formation of an insoluble solid, called a precipitate (which separates from the solution)

1 Acid–Base (Neutralization) Reactions: Formation of a Nonelectrolyte

Acid–base reactions are among the most important kinds of chemical reactions. Many acid–base reactions occur in nature in both plants and animals. Many acids and bases are essential compounds in an industrialized society (Table 6-10). For example, approximately 300 pounds of sulfuric acid, H_2SO_4, and approximately 100 pounds of ammonia, NH_3, are required to support the lifestyle of an average American for one year.

The reaction of an acid with a metal hydroxide base produces a salt and water. Such reactions are called **neutralization reactions** because the typical properties of acids and bases are neutralized.

▶ The manufacture of fertilizers consumes more H_2SO_4 *and* more NH_3 than any other single use.

In nearly all neutralization reactions, the driving force is the combination of $H^+(aq)$ from an acid and $OH^-(aq)$ from a base (or a base plus water) to form water molecules.

▶ When a base such as ammonia or an amine reacts with an acid, a salt, but no water, is formed. This is still called an acid–base, or neutralization, reaction.

Consider the reaction of hydrochloric acid, HCl(aq), with aqueous sodium hydroxide, NaOH. Table 6-1 tells us that HCl is a strong acid, and Table 6-3 tells us that NaOH is a

Table 6-10 2009 Production of Inorganic Acids, Bases, and Salts in the United States

Formula	Name	Billions of Pounds	Major Uses
H_2SO_4	sulfuric acid	64.25	Manufacture of fertilizers and other chemicals
CaO, $Ca(OH)_2$	lime (calcium oxide and calcium hydroxide)	40.67	Manufacture of other chemicals, steelmaking, water treatment
Na_2CO_3	sodium carbonate (soda ash)	20.91	Manufacture of glass, other chemicals, detergents, pulp, and paper
NH_3	ammonia	20.66	Fertilizer; manufacture of fertilizers and other chemicals
H_3PO_4	phosphoric acid	19.08	Manufacture of fertilizers
NaOH	sodium hydroxide	14.48	Manufacture of other chemicals, pulp and paper, soap and detergents, aluminum, textiles
NH_4NO_3	ammonium nitrate	13.88	Fertilizer and explosives
HNO_3	nitric acid	13.06	Manufacture of fertilizers, explosives, plastics, and lacquers
HCl	hydrochloric acid	7.16	Manufacture of other chemicals and rubber; metal cleaning
$(NH_4)_2SO_4$	ammonium sulfate	5.00	Fertilizer
KOH, K_2CO_3	potash	2.25	Manufacture of fertilizers
$Al_2(SO_4)_3$	aluminum sulfate	1.66	Water treatment, dyeing textiles
$NaClO_3$	sodium chlorate	1.04	Manufacture of other chemicals, explosives, plastics
Na_2SO_4	sodium sulfate	0.83	Manufacture of paper, glass, and detergents

strong base. The salt sodium chloride, NaCl, is formed in this reaction. It contains the cation of its parent base, Na^+, and the anion of its parent acid, Cl^-. Solubility guidelines 2 and 4 (see page 213) tell us that NaCl is a soluble salt.

$$HCl(aq) + NaOH(aq) \longrightarrow H_2O(\ell) + NaCl(aq)$$

$$[H^+(aq) + Cl^-(aq)] + [Na^+(aq) + OH^-(aq)] \longrightarrow H_2O(\ell) + [Na^+(aq) + Cl^-(aq)]$$

$$H^+(aq) + OH^-(aq) \longrightarrow H_2O(\ell)$$

The net ionic equation for *all* reactions of strong acids with strong bases that form soluble salts and water is

$$H^+(aq) + OH^-(aq) \longrightarrow H_2O(\ell)$$

Problem-Solving Tip Salt Formation

The salt that is formed in a neutralization reaction is composed of the cation of the base and the anion of the acid. The salt may be soluble or insoluble. If our goal were to obtain the salt from the reaction of aqueous HCl with aqueous NaOH, we could evaporate the water and obtain solid NaCl.

EXAMPLE 6-9 Neutralization Reactions

Predict the products of the reaction between $HI(aq)$ and $Ca(OH)_2(aq)$. Write balanced formula unit, total ionic, and net ionic equations.

Plan

This is an acid–base neutralization reaction; the products are H_2O and the salt that contains the cation of the base, Ca^{2+}, and the anion of the acid, I^-; CaI_2 is a soluble salt (solubility guideline 4). HI is a strong acid (see Table 6-1), $Ca(OH)_2$ is a strong base (see Table 6-3), and CaI_2 is a soluble salt, so all are written in ionic form.

Solution

$$2HI(aq) + Ca(OH)_2(aq) \longrightarrow CaI_2(aq) + 2H_2O(\ell)$$

$$2[H^+(aq) + I^-(aq)] + [Ca^{2+}(aq) + 2OH^-(aq)] \longrightarrow [Ca^{2+}(aq) + 2I^-(aq)] + 2H_2O(\ell)$$

We cancel the spectator ions.

$$2H^+(aq) + 2OH^-(aq) \longrightarrow 2H_2O(\ell)$$

▶ Recall that in balanced equations we show the smallest whole-number coefficients possible.

Dividing by 2 gives the net ionic equation:

$$H^+(aq) + OH^-(aq) \longrightarrow H_2O(\ell)$$

You should now work Exercise 77.

Reactions of *weak* acids with strong bases also produce salts and water, but there is a significant difference in the balanced ionic equations because weak acids are only *slightly* ionized.

▶ A *monoprotic acid* contains one acidic H per formula unit.

The reactions of *weak monoprotic acids* with *strong bases* that form *soluble salts* can be represented in general terms as

$$HA(aq) + OH^-(aq) \longrightarrow A^-(aq) + H_2O(\ell)$$

where HA represents the weak acid and A^- represents its anion.

EXAMPLE 6-10 Neutralization Reactions

Write balanced formula unit, total ionic, and net ionic equations for the reaction of acetic acid with potassium hydroxide.

Plan

Neutralization reactions involving metal hydroxide bases produce a salt and water. CH_3COOH is a weak acid (see Table 6-2), so it is written as formula units. KOH is a strong base (see Table 6-3) and KCH_3COO is a soluble salt (solubility guidelines 2 and 3), so both are written in ionic form.

Solution

$$CH_3COOH(aq) + KOH(aq) \longrightarrow KCH_3COO(aq) + H_2O(\ell)$$
$$CH_3COOH(aq) + [K^+(aq) + OH^-(aq)] \longrightarrow [K^+(aq) + CH_3COO^-(aq)] + H_2O(\ell)$$

The spectator ion is K^+, the cation of the strong base, KOH.

$$CH_3COOH(aq) + OH^-(aq) \longrightarrow CH_3COO^-(aq) + H_2O(\ell)$$

Thus, we see that *this* net ionic equation includes *molecules* of the weak acid and *anions* of the weak acid.

You should now work Exercise 78.

EXAMPLE 6-11 Salt Formation

Write balanced formula unit, total ionic, and net ionic equations for an acid–base reaction that will produce the salt, barium chloride.

Plan

Neutralization reactions produce a salt. The salt contains the cation from the base and the anion from the acid. The base must therefore contain Ba^{2+}, that is, $Ba(OH)_2$, and the acid must contain Cl^-, that is, HCl. We write equations that represent the reaction between the strong base, $Ba(OH)_2$, and the strong acid, HCl.

Solution

$$2HCl(aq) + Ba(OH)_2(aq) \longrightarrow BaCl_2(aq) + 2H_2O(\ell)$$
$$2[H^+(aq) + Cl^-(aq)] + [Ba^{2+}(aq) + 2OH^-(aq)] \longrightarrow [Ba^{2+}(aq) + 2Cl^-(aq)] + 2H_2O(\ell)$$

We cancel the spectator ions.

$$2H^+(aq) + 2OH^-(aq) \longrightarrow 2H_2O(\ell)$$

Dividing by 2 gives the net ionic equation:

$$H^+(aq) + OH^-(aq) \longrightarrow H_2O(\ell)$$

You should now work Exercise 86.

▶ The net ionic equation shows the driving force for this reaction. The formula unit equation shows the salt formed or that could be isolated if the water were evaporated.

2 Precipitation Reactions

In **precipitation reactions** an insoluble solid, a **precipitate**, forms and then settles out of solution. The driving force for these reactions is the strong attraction between cations and anions. This results in the removal of ions from solution by the formation of a precipitate. Our teeth and bones were formed by very slow precipitation reactions in which mostly calcium phosphate $Ca_3(PO_4)_2$ was deposited in the correct geometric arrangements.

▶ To understand the discussion of precipitation reactions, you must know the solubility guidelines, Table 6-4.

An example of a precipitation reaction is the formation of bright yellow insoluble lead(II) chromate when we mix solutions of the soluble ionic compounds lead(II) nitrate and potassium chromate (Figure 6-4). The other product of the reaction is KNO_3, a soluble salt.

The balanced formula unit, total ionic, and net ionic equations for this reaction follow:

$$Pb(NO_3)_2(aq) + K_2CrO_4(aq) \longrightarrow PbCrO_4(s) + 2KNO_3(aq)$$

$$[Pb^{2+}(aq) + 2NO_3^-(aq)] + [2K^+(aq) + CrO_4^{2-}(aq)] \longrightarrow$$
$$PbCrO_4(s) + 2[K^+(aq) + NO_3^-(aq)]$$

$$Pb^{2+}(aq) + CrO_4^{2-}(aq) \longrightarrow PbCrO_4(s)$$

Another important precipitation reaction involves the formation of insoluble carbonates (solubility guideline 7). Limestone deposits are mostly calcium carbonate, $CaCO_3$, although many also contain significant amounts of magnesium carbonate, $MgCO_3$.

Suppose we mix together aqueous solutions of sodium carbonate, Na_2CO_3, and calcium chloride, $CaCl_2$. We recognize that *both* Na_2CO_3 and $CaCl_2$ (solubility guidelines 2, 4a, and 7) are soluble ionic compounds. At the instant of mixing, the resulting solution contains four ions:

$$Na^+(aq), \qquad CO_3^{2-}(aq), \qquad Ca^{2+}(aq), \qquad Cl^-(aq)$$

One pair of ions, Na^- and Cl^-, *cannot* form an insoluble compound (solubility guidelines 2 and 4). We look for a pair of ions that could form an insoluble compound. Ca^{2+} ions and CO_3^{2-} ions are such a combination; they form insoluble $CaCO_3$ (solubility guideline 7). The equations for the reaction follow:

$$CaCl_2(aq) + Na_2CO_3(aq) \longrightarrow CaCO_3(s) + 2NaCl(aq)$$

$$[Ca^{2+}(aq) + 2Cl^-(aq)] + [2Na^+(aq) + CO_3^{2-}(aq)] \longrightarrow$$
$$CaCO_3(s) + 2[Na^+(aq) + Cl^-(aq)]$$

$$Ca^{2+}(aq) + CO_3^{2-}(aq) \longrightarrow CaCO_3(s)$$

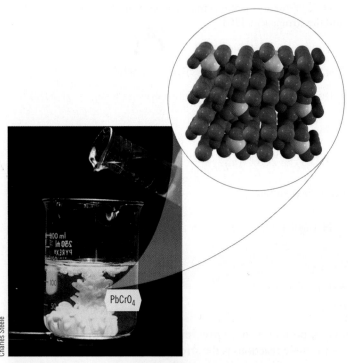

Figure 6-4 A precipitation reaction. When K_2CrO_4 solution is added to aqueous $Pb(NO_3)_2$ solution, the yellow compound $PbCrO_4$ precipitates. The resulting solution contains K^+ and NO_3^- ions, the ions of KNO_3.

EXAMPLE 6-12 Solubility Guidelines and Precipitation Reactions

Will a precipitate form when aqueous solutions of $Ca(NO_3)_2$ and $NaCl$ are mixed in reasonable concentrations? Write balanced formula unit, total ionic, and net ionic equations for any reaction.

Plan

We recognize that both $Ca(NO_3)_2$ (solubility guideline 3) and $NaCl$ (solubility guidelines 2 and 4) are soluble compounds. We use the solubility guidelines to determine whether any of the possible products are insoluble.

Solution

At the instant of mixing, the resulting solution contains four ions:

$$Ca^{2+}(aq), \qquad NO_3^-(aq), \qquad Na^+(aq), \qquad Cl^-(aq)$$

New combinations of ions *could* be $CaCl_2$ and $NaNO_3$. But solubility guideline 4 tells us that $CaCl_2$ is a soluble compound, and solubility guidelines 2 and 3 tell us that $NaNO_3$ is a soluble compound. Therefore, no precipitate forms in this solution.

You should now work Exercise 90.

Seashells, which are formed in very slow precipitation reactions, are mostly calcium carbonate ($CaCO_3$) a white compound. Traces of transition metal ions give them color.

EXAMPLE 6-13 Solubility Guidelines and Precipitation Reactions

Will a precipitate form when aqueous solutions of $CaCl_2$ and K_3PO_4 are mixed in reasonable concentrations? Write balanced formula unit, total ionic, and net ionic equations for any reaction.

Plan

We recognize that both $CaCl_2$ (solubility guideline 4) and K_3PO_4 (solubility guideline 2) are soluble compounds. We use the solubility guidelines to determine whether any of the possible products are insoluble.

Solution

At the instant of mixing, the resulting solution contains four ions:

$$Ca^{2+}(aq), \qquad Cl^-(aq), \qquad K^+(aq), \qquad PO_4^{3-}(aq)$$

New combinations of ions *could* be KCl and $Ca_3(PO_4)_2$. Solubility guidelines 2 and 4 tell us that KCl is a soluble compound; solubility guideline 7 tells us that $Ca_3(PO_4)_2$ is an insoluble compound, so a precipitate of $Ca_3(PO_4)_2$ forms in this solution.

The equations for the formation of calcium phosphate follow:

$$3CaCl_2(aq) + 2K_3PO_4(aq) \longrightarrow Ca_3(PO_4)_2(s) + 6KCl(aq)$$
$$3[Ca^{2+}(aq) + 2Cl^-(aq)] + 2[3K^+(aq) + PO_4^{3-}(aq)] \longrightarrow$$
$$Ca_3(PO_4)_2(s) + 6[K^+(aq) + Cl^-(aq)]$$
$$3Ca^{2+}(aq) + 2PO_4^{3-}(aq) \longrightarrow Ca_3(PO_4)_2(s)$$

You should now work Exercise 96.

6-10 Gas-Formation Reactions

When there are *no gaseous reactants*, the formation of an insoluble or slightly soluble gas provides a driving force for a type of reaction that we call a **gas-formation reaction**. The only common gases that are very soluble in water are $HCl(g)$ and $NH_3(g)$. The low solubility of other gases can force a reaction to proceed if they are formed as a reaction product.

When an acid—for example, hydrochloric acid—is added to solid calcium carbonate, a reaction occurs in which carbonic acid, a weak acid, is produced.

A gas-formation causes muffins or biscuits to rise. When the sodium bicarbonate, $NaHCO_3$, in baking powder reacts with an acid, carbon dioxide gas is formed. Baking powders contain acidic salts such as a $CaHPO_4$ or weak organic acids such as tartaric acid, $C_2H_2(OH)_2(COOH)_2$.

▶ Hydrogen sulfide, H_2S, is responsible for the smell of rotten eggs. This gas-formation reaction is also a metathesis reaction.

Blackboard chalk is mostly calcium carbonate, $CaCO_3$. Bubbles of carbon dioxide, CO_2, are clearly visible in this photograph of $CaCO_3$ reacting with HCl in a gas-forming metathesis reaction.

$$2HCl(aq) + CaCO_3(s) \longrightarrow H_2CO_3(aq) + CaCl_2(aq)$$
$$2[H^+(aq) + Cl^-(aq)] + CaCO_3(s) \longrightarrow H_2CO_3(aq) + [Ca^{2+}(aq) + 2Cl^-(aq)]$$
$$2H^+(aq) + CaCO_3(s) \longrightarrow H_2CO_3(aq) + Ca^{2+}(aq)$$

The heat generated in the reaction causes thermal decomposition of carbonic acid to gaseous carbon dioxide and water:

$$H_2CO_3(aq) \longrightarrow CO_2(g) + H_2O(\ell)$$

Most of the CO_2 bubbles off, and the reaction goes to completion (with respect to the limiting reactant). The net effect is the conversion of ionic species into nonionized molecules of a gas (CO_2) and water.

$$2HCl(aq) + CaCO_3(s) \longrightarrow CO_2(g) + H_2O(\ell) + CaCl_2(aq)$$

Salts containing the sulfite ion, SO_3^{2-}, react with acids in a similar manner to form sulfur dioxide gas, $SO_2(g)$.

$$SO_3^{2-}(aq) + 2H^+(aq) \longrightarrow SO_2(g) + H_2O(\ell)$$

Many sulfide salts react with acids to form gaseous hydrogen sulfide, H_2S. The low solubility of H_2S in water helps the reaction to proceed.

$$MnS(s) + 2HCl(aq) \longrightarrow MnCl_2(aq) + H_2S(g)$$

Displacement reactions in which an active metal displaces hydrogen from an acid or from water (see Section 6-8, Part 2) are gas-formation reactions, but they are *not* metathesis reactions.

6-11 Summary of Reaction Types

Table 6-11 summarizes the reaction types we have presented. Remember that a reaction might be classified in more than one category.

EXAMPLE 6-14 Classifying Reactions

Classify each of the following reactions.

(a) $Zn(s) + 2AgNO_3(aq) \longrightarrow Zn(NO_3)_2(aq) + 2Ag(s)$
(b) $Ca(OH)_2(s) \xrightarrow{heat} CaO(s) + H_2O(g)$
(c) $2HI(g) \xrightarrow{heat} H_2(g) + I_2(g)$
(d) $Cu(NO_3)_2(aq) + Na_2S(aq) \longrightarrow CuS(s) + 2NaNO_3(aq)$
(e) $SO_2(g) + H_2O(\ell) \longrightarrow H_2SO_3(aq)$
(f) $H_2SO_3(aq) + 2KOH(aq) \longrightarrow K_2SO_3(aq) + 2H_2O(\ell)$

Plan

We identify each reaction type by its characteristics, using Table 6-11 and the appropriate sections as a guide.

Solution

(a) One element, Zn, displaces another, Ag, from a compound; this is a displacement reaction. Zn is oxidized and Ag is reduced. So this is also an oxidation–reduction (redox) reaction.

(b) A single compound breaks apart into two compounds; this is a decomposition reaction.

(c) A single compound breaks apart into two elements; this is another decomposition reaction. However, now there are changes in oxidation numbers; H changes from +1 in HI to 0 in H_2, and I changes from −1 in HI to 0 in I_2. So this is also an oxidation–reduction (redox) reaction.

(d) The positive and negative ions in the two reactant compounds change partners; this is a metathesis reaction. An insoluble product, CuS(s), is formed, so the reaction is a precipitation reaction.

(e) Two compounds combine to form a single product; this is a combination reaction.

(f) The positive and negative ions change partners; this is a metathesis reaction. An acid and a base react to form a salt and water; this is an acid–base (neutralization) reaction.

You should now work Exercises 99 through 109.

Table 6-11 Summary and Examples of Reaction Types

Section Reaction Type, Examples	Characteristics
6-5 Oxidation–reduction (redox)	Oxidation states (see Section 5-7) of some elements change; at least one element must increase and at least one must decrease in oxidation states
6-6 Combination 1. element + element $\longrightarrow$ compound $2Al(s) + 3Cl_2(g) \longrightarrow 2AlCl_3(s)^*$ $P_4(s) + 10Cl_2(g) \longrightarrow 4PCl_5(s)^*$ 2. compound + element $\longrightarrow$ compound $SF_4(g) + F_2(g) \longrightarrow SF_6(g)^*$ $2SO_2(g) + O_2(g) \longrightarrow 2SO_3(\ell)^*$ 3. compound + compound $\longrightarrow$ compound $CaO(s) + CO_2(g) \longrightarrow CaCO_3(s)$ $Na_2O(s) + H_2O(\ell) \longrightarrow 2NaOH(aq)$	More than one reactant, single product
6-7 Decomposition 1. compound $\longrightarrow$ element + element $2HgO(s) \longrightarrow 2Hg(\ell) + O_2(g)^*$ $2H_2O(\ell) \longrightarrow 2H_2(g) + O_2(g)^*$ 2. compound $\longrightarrow$ compound + element $2NaNO_3(s) \longrightarrow 2NaNO_2(s) + O_2(g)^*$ $2H_2O_2(\ell) \longrightarrow 2H_2O(\ell) + O_2(g)^*$ 3. compound $\longrightarrow$ compound + compound $CaCO_3(s) \longrightarrow CaO(s) + CO_2(g)$ $Mg(OH)_2(s) \longrightarrow MgO(s) + H_2O(\ell)$	Single reactant, more than one product
6-8 Displacement $Zn(s) + CuSO_4(aq) \longrightarrow Cu(s) + ZnSO_4(aq)^*$ $Zn(s) + H_2SO_4(aq) \longrightarrow H_2(g) + ZnSO_4(aq)^*$ $Cl_2(g) + 2NaI(aq) \longrightarrow I_2(s) + 2NaCl(aq)^*$	One element displaces another from a compound: Element + compound $\longrightarrow$ element + compound Activity series (see Table 6-9) summarizes metals and hydrogen; halogen activities (Group 7A) decrease going down the group
6-9 Metathesis	Positive and negative ions in two compounds appear to "change partners" to form two new compounds; no change in oxidation numbers
1. acid–base neutralization $HCl(aq) + NaOH(aq) \longrightarrow NaCl(aq) + H_2O(\ell)$ $CH_3COOH(aq) + KOH(aq) \longrightarrow KCH_3COO(aq) + H_2O(\ell)$ $HCl(aq) + NH_3(aq) \longrightarrow NH_4Cl(aq)$ $2H_3PO_4(aq) + 3Ca(OH)_2(aq) \longrightarrow Ca_3(PO_4)_2(s) + 6H_2O(\ell)^\dagger$	Product is a salt; water is often formed
2. precipitation $CaCl_2(aq) + Na_2CO_3(aq) \longrightarrow CaCO_3(s) + 2NaCl(aq)$ $Pb(NO_3)_2(aq) + K_2CrO_4(aq) \longrightarrow PbCrO_4(s) + 2KNO_3(aq)$ $2H_3PO_4(aq) + 3Ca(OH)_2(aq) \longrightarrow Ca_3(PO_4)_2(s) + 6H_2O(\ell)^\dagger$	Products include an insoluble substance, which precipitates from solution as a solid; solubility guidelines assist in predicting, recognizing
6-10 Gas-formation $2HCl(aq) + CaCO_3(s) \longrightarrow CO_2(g) + H_2O(\ell) + CaCl_2(aq)$ $MnS(s) + 2HCl(aq) \longrightarrow MnCl_2(aq) + H_2S(g)$ $Mg(s) + 2HNO_3(aq) \longrightarrow H_2(g) + Mg(NO_3)_2(aq)$	Products include an insoluble or slightly soluble gas, which escapes from solution

*These examples are also oxidation–reduction (redox) reactions.

†This reaction is both an acid–base neutralization reaction and a precipitation reaction.

KEY TERMS

Acid   A substance that produces $H^+(aq)$ ions in aqueous solution. Strong acids ionize completely or almost completely in dilute aqueous solution. Weak acids ionize only slightly.

Acid–base reaction   See *Neutralization reaction.*

Active metal   A metal that readily loses electrons to form cations.

Activity series   A listing of metals (and hydrogen) in order of decreasing activity.

Alkali metals   Elements of Group 1A in the periodic table, except hydrogen.

Alkaline earth metals   Group 2A elements in the periodic table.

Atomic number   The number of protons in the nucleus of an atom of an element.

Base   A substance that produces $OH^-(aq)$ ions in aqueous solution. Strong bases are soluble in water and are completely *dissociated.* Weak bases ionize only slightly.

Binary acid   A binary compound in which H is bonded to a nonmetal in Group 7A or a nonmetal other than oxygen in Group 6A.

Binary compound   A compound consisting of two elements; may be ionic or molecular.

Combination reaction   Reaction in which two substances (elements or compounds) combine to form one compound.

Decomposition reaction   Reaction in which a compound decomposes to form two or more products (elements, compounds, or some combination of these).

Displacement reaction   A reaction in which one element displaces another from a compound.

Disproportionation reaction   A redox reaction in which the oxidizing agent and the reducing agent are the same element.

Dissociation   In aqueous solution, the process in which a solid *ionic compound* separates into its ions.

Electrolyte   A substance whose aqueous solutions conduct electricity due to ions in solution. Acids, bases, and soluble salts are electrolytes.

Formula unit equation   An equation for a chemical reaction in which all formulas are written as complete formulas.

Gas-formation reaction   A reaction in which an insoluble or slightly soluble gas is formed as a product.

Group (family)   The elements in a vertical column of the periodic table.

Halogens   Elements of Group 7A in the periodic table.

Ionization   In aqueous solution, the process in which a *molecular compound* separates to form ions.

Metal   An element below and to the left of the stepwise division (metalloids) of the periodic table; about 80% of the known elements are metals.

Metalloids   Elements with properties intermediate between metals and nonmetals: B, Si, Ge, As, Sb, Te, Po, and At.

Metathesis reaction   A reaction in which the positive and negative ions in two compounds "change partners," with no change in oxidation numbers, to form two new compounds; also referred to as a *double displacement reaction.*

Net ionic equation   An equation that results from canceling spectator ions from a total ionic equation.

Neutralization reaction   The reaction of an acid with a base to form a salt. Often, the reaction of hydrogen ions with hydroxide ions to form water molecules.

Noble (rare) gases   Elements of Group 8A in the periodic table.

Nonelectrolyte   A substance whose aqueous solutions do not conduct electricity.

Nonmetals   Elements above and to the right of the metalloids in the periodic table.

Oxidation   An increase in oxidation number; corresponds to a loss of electrons.

Oxidation numbers   See *Oxidation states.*

Oxidation–reduction reaction   A reaction in which oxidation and reduction occur; also known as a redox reaction.

Oxidation states   Arbitrary numbers that can be used as mechanical aids in writing formulas and balancing equations; for single-atom ions they correspond to the charge on the ion; less metallic atoms are assigned negative oxidation states in compounds and polyatomic ions.

Oxidizing agent   The substance that oxidizes another substance and is reduced.

Oxoacid   See *Ternary acid.*

Precipitate   An insoluble solid that forms and separates from a solution.

Precipitation reaction   A reaction in which a solid (precipitate) forms.

Redox reaction   See *Oxidation–reduction reaction.*

Reducing agent   The substance that reduces another substance and is oxidized.

Reduction   A decrease in oxidation number; corresponds to a gain of electrons.

Reversible reaction   A reaction that occurs in both directions; described with double arrows ($\rightleftharpoons$). The equal-length arrows do not indicate equal amounts of reactants and products, just that some of each are present. Chemists sometimes indicate the favored direction of a reversible reaction by using a longer arrow on top or bottom ($\underrightarrow{} \overleftarrow{}$, $\overrightarrow{} \underleftarrow{}$).

Salt   An ionic compound that contains a cation other than H^+ and an anion other than OH^- or O^{2-}.

Semiconductor   A substance that does not conduct electricity at low temperatures but does so at higher temperatures.

Spectator ions   Ions that appear in solution on both sides of the total ionic equation; they undergo no change in the chemical reaction.

Strong acid   An acid that ionizes (separates into ions) completely, or very nearly completely, in dilute aqueous solution.

Strong base   Metal hydroxide that is soluble in water and dissociates completely in dilute aqueous solution.

Strong electrolyte   A substance that conducts electricity well in dilute aqueous solution due to nearly complete ionization or dissociation.

Ternary acid   A ternary compound containing H, O, and another element, usually a nonmetal; also known as an *oxoacid.*

Ternary compound   A compound consisting of three elements; may be ionic or molecular.

Ternary salt   A salt resulting from replacing the hydrogen in a ternary acid with another ion.

Total ionic equation   An equation for a chemical reaction written to show the predominant form of all species in aqueous solution or in contact with water.

Weak acid   An acid that ionizes only slightly in dilute aqueous solution.

Weak base A molecular substance that ionizes only slightly in water to produce an alkaline (base) solution.

Weak electrolyte A substance that conducts electricity poorly in dilute aqueous solution due to very limited ionization or dissociation.

EXERCISES

🔵 **Molecular Reasoning** exercises

▲ **More Challenging** exercises

Blue-Numbered exercises are solved in the Student Solutions Manual

Aqueous Solutions

1. 🔵 Similar to the inserts in Figure 6-1, draw molecular representations of a solution of a strong electrolyte, of a weak electrolyte, and of a nonelectrolyte.

2. Three common classes of compounds are electrolytes. Name them and give an example of each.

3. Define (a) acids, (b) bases, (c) salts, and (d) molecular compounds.

4. How can a salt be related to a particular acid and a particular base?

5. List the names and formulas of three common strong acids.

6. Write equations for the ionization of the following acids: (a) hydrochloric acid; (b) nitric acid; (c) chlorous acid; (d) carbonic acid.

7. List the names and formulas of five weak acids.

8. List the names and formulas of the common strong bases.

9. Write equations for the ionization of the following acids. Which ones ionize only slightly? (a) HF; (b) HCN; (c) CH_3COOH; (d) $HClO_3$; (e) HBr.

10. The most common weak base is present in a common household chemical. Write the equation for the ionization of this weak base.

11. Summarize the electrical properties of strong electrolytes, weak electrolytes, and nonelectrolytes.

12. What is the difference between ionization and dissociation in aqueous solution?

13. Predict whether each of these compounds is likely to be water-soluble. Indicate which ions are present in solution for the water-soluble compounds.
(a) $Fe(ClO_4)_2$; (b) Na_2SO_4; (c) KBr; (d) Na_2CO_3.

14. Which of the following are strong electrolytes? weak electrolytes? nonelectrolytes? (a) Na_2S; (b) $Ba(OH)_2$; (c) CH_3OH; (d) HCN; (e) $Al(NO_3)_3$. Write equations that show the dissociation of the strong electrolytes.

15. Classify the following as strong electrolytes, weak electrolytes, or nonelectrolytes: (a) $NaClO_4$; (b) $HClO_2$; (c) CH_3CH_2OH; (d) CH_3COOH; (e) HNO_3. Write equations that show the dissociation of the strong electrolytes.

16. Write the formulas of two soluble and two insoluble chlorides, sulfates, and hydroxides.

17. Describe an experiment for classifying each of these compounds as a strong electrolyte, a weak electrolyte, or a nonelectrolyte: Na_2CO_3, HCN, CH_3OH, H_2S, H_2SO_4, NH_3. Predict and explain the expected results.

18. Classify the following compounds as acids or bases, weak or strong: (a) perchloric acid; (b) cesium hydroxide; (c) carbonic acid; H_2CO_3; (d) ethylamine, $C_2H_5NH_2$.

19. ▲ Classify each substance as either an electrolyte or a nonelectrolyte: NH_4Cl, HCl, C_6H_6, $Zn(CH_3COO)_2$, $Cu(NO_3)_2$, CH_3CH_2OH, $C_{12}H_{22}O_{11}$ (sugar), LiOH, $KHCO_3$, CCl_4, K_2SO_4, I_2.

20. What is an electrolyte? How can you differentiate experimentally between a weak electrolyte and a strong electrolyte? Give an example of each.

21. Classify each substance as soluble, moderately soluble, or insoluble: Ag_2SO_4, $(NH_4)_2CO_3$, AgCl, $HgBr_2$, $AgNO_3$.

22. Classify each substance as soluble, moderately soluble, or insoluble: $Ca(CH_3COO)_2$, NH_4Cl, $AgNO_3$, $PbCl_2$, $(NH_4)_3PO_4$.

23. 🔵 What are reversible reactions? Give some examples that illustrate reversible reactions at the molecular level.

24. Many household "chemicals" are acidic or basic. List a few of each kind.

25. 🔵 Some chemical reactions reach an equilibrium rather than going to completion. What is "equal" in such an equilibrium? Use equations to illustrate "equal" at the molecular level in an equilibrium reaction.

26. Vinegar is 5% acetic acid, an organic acid, by mass. Many organic acids occur in living systems. What conclusion can be drawn from this information as to the strengths of organic acids?

Naming Compounds

27. Name the following common anions using the IUPAC system of nomenclature: (a) NO_3^-; (b) SO_4^{2-}; (c) ClO_3^-; (d) CH_3COO^-; (e) PO_4^{3-}.

28. Name the following monatomic cations using the IUPAC system of nomenclature: (a) Li^+; (b) Au^{3+}; (c) Ca^{2+}; (d) Zn^{2+}; (e) Ag^+.

29. Write the chemical symbol for each of the following: (a) sodium ion; (b) iron(II) ion; (c) silver ion; (d) mercury(II) ion; (e) bismuth(III) ion.

30. Write the chemical formula for each of the following: (a) chloride ion; (b) hydrogen sulfide ion; (c) telluride ion; (d) hydroxide ion; (e) nitrite ion.

31. Name the following compounds: (a) Li_2S; (b) SnO_2; (c) RbBr; (d) K_2O; (e) Ba_3N_2.

32. Name the following compounds: (a) CuI_2; (b) Hg_2Cl_2; (c) Li_3N; (d) $MnCl_2$; (e) $CuCO_3$; (f) FeO.

33. Write the chemical formula for each of the following compounds: (a) lithium fluoride; (b) zinc oxide; (c) barium hydroxide; (d) magnesium bromide; (e) hydrogen cyanide; (f) copper(I) chloride.

34. Write the chemical formula for each of the following compounds: (a) copper(II) chlorite; (b) potassium nitrate; (c) barium phosphate; (d) copper(I) sulfate; (e) sodium sulfite.

35. 🔵 What is the name of the acid with the formula H_2CO_3? Write the formulas of the two anions derived from it and name these ions.

36. What is the name of the acid with the formula H_3PO_4? What are the names of the ions: $H_2PO_4^-$; HPO_4^{2-}; PO_4^{3-}?

37. Name the following binary molecular compounds: (a) NO_2; (b) CO_2; (c) SF_6; (d) $SiCl_4$; (e) IF.

38. Name the following binary molecular compounds: (a) AF_3; (b) Br_2O; (c) BrF_5; (d) CSe_2; (e) N_2O_4.

39. Write the chemical formula for each of the following compounds: (a) iodine bromide; (b) silicon dioxide; (c) phosphorus trichloride; (d) tetrasulfur dinitride; (e) bromine trifluoride; (f) hydrogen telluride; (g) xenon tetrafluoride.

40. Write the chemical formula for each of the following compounds: (a) diboron trioxide; (b) dinitrogen pentasulfide; (c) phosphorus triiodide; (d) sulfur tetrafluoride; (e) silicon sulfide; (f) hydrogen sulfide; (g) tetraphosphorus hexoxide.

In Exercises 41 through 44, write the name and the formula of the compound or ion represented by each model. Black = C, white = H, red = O, and blue 5 nitrogen.

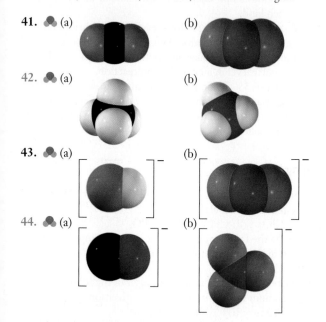

41. 🔵 (a)   (b)

42. 🔵 (a)   (b)

43. 🔵 (a)   (b)

44. 🔵 (a)   (b)

45. Write formulas for the compounds that are expected to be formed by the following pairs of ions:

	A. Br^-	B. OH^-	C. SO_4^{2-}	D. PO_4^{3-}	E. NO_3^-
1. NH_4^+		Omit – see note			
2. Na^+					
3. Mg^{2+}					
4. Cu^{2+}					
5. Fe^{3+}					
6. Ag^+					

Note: The compound NH_4OH does not exist. The solution commonly labeled "NH_4OH" is aqueous ammonia, $NH_3(aq)$.

46. Write the names for the compounds of Exercise 45.

47. Write balanced chemical equations for each of the following processes: (a) Calcium phosphate reacts with sulfuric acid to produce calcium sulfate and phosphoric acid. (b) Calcium phosphate reacts with water containing dissolved carbon dioxide to produce calcium hydrogen carbonate and calcium hydrogen phosphate.

48. ▲ Write balanced chemical equations for each of the following processes: (a) When heated, nitrogen and oxygen combine to form nitrogen oxide. (b) Heating a mixture of lead(II) sulfide and lead(II) sulfate produces metallic lead and sulfur dioxide.

Oxidation–Reduction Reactions

49. Define and provide examples of the following terms: (a) oxidation; (b) reduction; (c) oxidizing agent; (d) reducing agent.

50. Why must oxidation and reduction always occur simultaneously in chemical reactions?

51. Determine which of the following are oxidation–reduction reactions. For those that are, identify the oxidizing and reducing agents.

(a) $3Zn(s) + 2CoCl_3(aq) \longrightarrow 3ZnCl_2(aq) + 2Co(s)$
(b) $ICl(s) + H_2O(\ell) \longrightarrow HCl(aq) + HIO(aq)$
(c) $3HCl(aq) + HNO_3(aq) \longrightarrow Cl_2(g) + NOCl(g) + 2H_2O(\ell)$
(d) $Fe_2O_3(s) + 3CO(g) \xrightarrow{\text{heat}} 2Fe(s) + 3CO_2(g)$

52. Determine which of the following are oxidation–reduction reactions. For those that are, identify the oxidizing and reducing agents.

(a) $HgCl_2(aq) + 2KI(aq) \longrightarrow HgI_2(s) + 2KCl(aq)$
(b) $4NH_3(g) + 3O_2(g) \longrightarrow 2N_2(g) + 6H_2O(g)$
(c) $CaCO_3(s) + 2HNO_3(aq) \longrightarrow Ca(NO_3)_2(aq) + CO_2(g) + H_2O(\ell)$
(d) $PCl_3(\ell) + 3H_2O(\ell) \longrightarrow 3HCl(aq) + H_3PO_3(aq)$

🔵 **Molecular Reasoning** exercises   ▲ **More Challenging** exercises   Blue-Numbered exercises solved in Student Solutions Manual

Unless otherwise noted, all content on this page is © Cengage Learning.

53. Write balanced formula unit equations for the following redox reactions:

  (a) aluminum reacts with sulfuric acid, H_2SO_4, to produce aluminum sulfate, $Al_2(SO_4)_3$, and hydrogen;

  (b) nitrogen, N_2, reacts with hydrogen, H_2, to form ammonia, NH_3;

  (c) zinc sulfide, ZnS, reacts with oxygen, O_2, to form zinc oxide, ZnO, and sulfur dioxide, SO_2;

  (d) carbon reacts with nitric acid, HNO_3, to produce nitrogen dioxide, NO_2, carbon dioxide, CO_2, and water;

  (e) sulfuric acid reacts with hydrogen iodide, HI, to produce sulfur dioxide, SO_2, iodine, I_2, and water.

54. Identify the oxidizing agents and reducing agents in the oxidation–reduction reactions given in Exercise 53.

55. Write total ionic and net ionic equations for the following redox reactions occurring in aqueous solution or in contact with water:

  (a) $Fe + 2HCl \longrightarrow FeCl_2 + H_2$

  (b) $2KMnO_4 + 16HCl \longrightarrow 2MnCl_2 + 2KCl$
  $\qquad\qquad\qquad\qquad + 5Cl_2 + 8H_2O$

  (*Note*: $MnCl_2$ is water-soluble.)

  (c) $4Zn + 10HNO_3 \longrightarrow 4Zn(NO_3)_2 + NH_4NO_3 +$
  $\qquad\qquad\qquad\qquad\qquad\qquad 3H_2O$

56. Balance each of these equations, and then write the complete ionic and net ionic equations.

  (a) $Zn(s) + HCl(aq) \longrightarrow H_2(g) + ZnCl_2(aq)$

  (b) $Mg(OH)_2(s) + HCl(aq) \longrightarrow MgCl_2(aq) + H_2O(\ell)$

  (c) $HNO_3(aq) + CaCO_3(s) \longrightarrow Ca(NO_3)_2(aq)$
  $\qquad\qquad\qquad\qquad\qquad + H_2O(\ell) + CO_2(g)$

  (d) $HCl(aq) + MnO_2(s) \longrightarrow MnCl_2(aq)$
  $\qquad\qquad\qquad\qquad\qquad + Cl_2(g) + H_2O(\ell)$

Combination Reactions

57. Write balanced equations that show the combination reactions of the following Group 1A metals combining with the Group 7A nonmetals. (a) Li and Cl_2; (b) K and F_2; (c) Na and I_2.

58. Write balanced equations that show the combination reactions of the following Group 2A metals and Group 7A nonmetals. (a) Be and F_2; (b) Ca and Br_2; (c) Ba and Cl_2.

In Exercises 59 and 60, some combination reactions are described by words. Write the balanced chemical equation for each, and assign oxidation states to elements other than H and O.

59. (a) Antimony reacts with a limited amount of chlorine to form antimony(III) chloride. (b) Antimony(III) chloride reacts with excess chlorine to form antimony(V) chloride. (c) Carbon burns in a limited amount of oxygen to form carbon monoxide.

60. (a) Sulfur trioxide reacts with aluminum oxide to form aluminum sulfate. (b) Dichlorine heptoxide reacts with water to form perchloric acid. (c) When cement "sets," the main reaction is the combination of calcium oxide with silicon dioxide to form calcium silicate, $CaSiO_3$.

Decomposition Reactions

In Exercises 61 and 62, write balanced formula unit equations for the reactions described by words. Assign oxidation states to all elements.

61. (a) Hydrogen peroxide, H_2O_2, is used as an antiseptic. Blood causes it to decompose into water and oxygen.
(b) When heated, ammonium nitrate can decompose explosively to form dinitrogen oxide and steam.

Models of hydrogen peroxide

62. (a) A "classroom volcano" is made by heating solid ammonium dichromate, $(NH_4)_2Cr_2O_7$, which decomposes into nitrogen, chromium(III) oxide, and steam. (b) At high temperatures, sodium nitrate (a fertilizer) forms sodium nitrite and oxygen.

Charles D. Winters

Ammonium dichromate volcano

Displacement Reactions

63. Which of the following would displace hydrogen when a piece of the metal is dropped into dilute HCl solution? Write balanced total ionic and net ionic equations for the reactions: Zn, Cu, Sn, Al.

64. Which of the following metals would displace copper from an aqueous solution of copper(II) sulfate? Write balanced total ionic and net ionic equations for the reactions: Hg, Zn, Fe, Ni.

65. Arrange the metals listed in Exercise 63 in order of increasing activity.

66. Arrange the metals listed in Exercise 64 in order of increasing activity.

67. Which of the following metals would displace hydrogen from cold water? Write balanced net ionic equations for the reactions: Ag, Na, Ca, Cr.

68. Arrange the metals listed in Exercise 67 in order of increasing activity.

● **Molecular Reasoning** exercises   ▲ **More Challenging** exercises   Blue-Numbered exercises solved in Student Solutions Manual

Unless otherwise noted, all content on this page is © Cengage Learning.

69. What is the order of decreasing activity of the halogens?

70. Name five elements that will react with steam but not with cold water.

71. (a) Name two common metals: one that *does not* displace hydrogen from water, and one that *does not* displace hydrogen from water or acid solutions. (b) Name two common metals: one that *does* displace hydrogen from water, and one that displaces hydrogen from acid solutions but not from water. Write net ionic equations for the reactions that occur.

72. Of the possible displacement reactions shown, which one(s) could occur?

(a) $2Cl^-(aq) + Br_2(\ell) \longrightarrow 2Br^-(aq) + Cl_2(g)$
(b) $2Br^-(aq) + F_2(g) \longrightarrow 2F^-(aq) + Br_2(\ell)$
(c) $2I^-(aq) + Cl_2(g) \longrightarrow 2Cl^-(aq) + I_2(s)$
(d) $2Br^-(aq) + I_2(s) \longrightarrow 2I^-(aq) + Br_2(\ell)$

73. Use the activity series to predict whether or not the following reactions will occur:

(a) $Cu(s) + Pt^{2+} \longrightarrow Pt(s) + Cu^{2+}$
(b) $Ni(s) + Cu^{2+} \longrightarrow Ni^{2+} + Cu(s)$
(c) $Cu(s) + 2H^+ \longrightarrow Cu^{2+} + H_2(g)$
(d) $Ni(s) + H_2O(g) \longrightarrow NiO(s) + H_2(g)$

74. Repeat Exercise 73 for

(a) $Cd(s) + Ca^{2+} \longrightarrow Cd^{2+} + Ca(s)$
(b) $Al_2O_3(s) + 3H_2(g) \longrightarrow 2Al(s) + 3H_2O(g)$
(c) $Zn(s) + 2H^+ \longrightarrow Zn^{2+} + H_2(g)$
(d) $Zn(s) + Pb^{2+} \longrightarrow Zn^{2+} + Pb(s)$

Metathesis Reactions

Exercises 75 and 76 describe precipitation reactions *in aqueous solutions*. For each, write balanced (i) formula unit, (ii) total ionic, and (iii) net ionic equations. Refer to the solubility guidelines as necessary.

75. (a) Black-and-white photographic film contains some silver bromide, which can be formed by the reaction of sodium bromide with silver nitrate. (b) Barium sulfate is used when X-rays of the gastrointestinal tract are made. Barium sulfate can be prepared by reacting barium chloride with dilute sulfuric acid. (c) In water purification systems small solid particles are often "trapped" as aluminum hydroxide precipitates and fall to the bottom of the sedimentation pool. Aluminum sulfate reacts with calcium hydroxide (from lime) to form aluminum hydroxide and calcium sulfate.

76. (a) Our bones are mostly calcium phosphate. Calcium chloride reacts with potassium phosphate to form calcium phosphate and potassium chloride. (b) Mercury compounds are very poisonous. Mercury(II) nitrate reacts with sodium sulfide to form mercury(II) sulfide, which is very insoluble, and sodium nitrate. (c) Chromium(III) ions are very poisonous. They can be removed from solution by precipitating very insoluble chromium(III) hydroxide. Chromium(III) chloride reacts with calcium hydroxide to form chromium(III) hydroxide and calcium chloride.

In Exercises 77 through 80, write balanced (i) formula unit, (ii) total ionic, and (iii) net ionic equations for the reactions that occur between the acid and the base. Assume that all reactions occur in water or in contact with water.

77. (a) hydrochloric acid + calcium hydroxide
(b) dilute sulfuric acid + strontium hydroxide
(c) perchloric acid + aqueous ammonia

78. (a) acetic acid + potassium hydroxide
(b) sulfurous acid + sodium hydroxide
(c) hydrofluoric acid + sodium hydroxide

79. ▲ (a) potassium hydroxide + hydrosulfuric acid
(b) potassium hydroxide + hydrochloric acid
(c) lead(II) hydroxide + hydrosulfuric acid

80. (a) lithium hydroxide + sulfuric acid
(b) calcium hydroxide + phosphoric acid
(c) copper(II) hydroxide + nitric acid

In Exercises 81 through 84, write balanced (i) formula unit, (ii) total ionic, and (iii) net ionic equations for the reaction of an acid and a base that will produce the indicated salts.

81. (a) potassium chloride; (b) sodium nitrate; (c) barium sulfate

82. (a) calcium perchlorate; (b) ammonium sulfate; (c) copper(II) acetate

83. ▲ (a) sodium carbonate; (b) barium carbonate; (c) nickel(II) acetate

84. ▲ (a) sodium sulfide; (b) aluminum phosphate; (c) lead(II) carbonate

85. (a) Propose a definition for salts, as a class of compounds, on the basis of how they are formed. (b) Provide an example, in the form of a chemical reaction, to illustrate your definition of salts.

86. We can tell from the formula of a salt how it can be produced. Write a balanced chemical equation for the production of each of the following salts: (a) magnesium nitrate; (b) aluminum sulfite; (c) potassium carbonate; (d) zinc chlorate; (e) lithium acetate.

87. Magnesium hydroxide is a gelatinous material that forms during the water purification process in some water treatment plants because of magnesium ions in the water. (a) Write the chemical equation for the reaction of hydrochloric acid with magnesium hydroxide. (b) Explain what drives this reaction to completion.

Precipitation Reactions

88. A common test for the presence of chloride ions is the formation of a heavy, white precipitate when a solution of silver nitrate is added. (a) Write the balanced chemical equation for the production of silver chloride from silver nitrate solution and calcium chloride solution. (b) Explain why this reaction goes to completion.

89. Based on the solubility guidelines given in Table 6-4, how would you write the formulas for the following substances in a total ionic equation? (a) $PbSO_4$; (b) $Na(CH_3COO)$; (c) Na_2CO_3; (d) MnS; (e) $BaCl_2$.

🔹 **Molecular Reasoning** exercises   ▲ **More Challenging** exercises   Blue-Numbered exercises solved in Student Solutions Manual

Unless otherwise noted, all content on this page is © Cengage Learning.

90. Repeat Exercise 89 for the following: (a) $(NH_4)_2SO_4$; (b) NaBr; (c) $SrCl_2$; (d) MgF_2; (e) Na_2CO_3.

Refer to the solubility guidelines given in Table 6-4. Classify the compounds in Exercises 91 through 94 as soluble, moderately soluble, or insoluble in water.

91. (a) $NaClO_4$, (b) AgCl, (c) $Pb(NO_3)_2$, (d) KOH, (e) $CaSO_4$

92. (a) $BaSO_4$, (b) $Al(NO_3)_3$, (c) CuS, (d) Na_3AsO_4, (e) $Ca(CH_3COO)_2$

93. (a) $Fe(NO_3)_3$, (b) $Hg(CH_3COO)_2$, (c) $BeCl_2$, (d) $CuSO_4$, (e) $CaCO_3$

94. (a) $KClO_3$, (b) NH_4Cl, (c) NH_3, (d) HNO_2, (e) PbS

In Exercises 95 and 96, write balanced (i) formula unit, (ii) total ionic, and (iii) net ionic equations for the reactions that occur when *aqueous solutions* of the compounds are mixed.

95. (a) $Ba(NO_3)_2 + K_2CO_3 \longrightarrow$
    (b) $NaOH + NiCl_2 \longrightarrow$
    (c) $Al_2(SO_4)_3 + NaOH \longrightarrow$

96. (a) $Cu(NO_3)_2 + Na_2S \longrightarrow$
    (b) $CdSO_4 + H_2S \longrightarrow$
    (c) $Bi_2(SO_4)_3 + (NH_4)_2S \longrightarrow$

97. In each of the following, both compounds are water-soluble. Predict whether a precipitate will form when solutions of the two are mixed, and, if so, identify the compound that precipitates. (a) $Pb(NO_3)_2$, NaI; (b) $Ba(NO_3)_2$, KCl; (c) $(NH_4)_2S$, $AgNO_3$.

98. Classify each of these exchange reactions as an acid-base reaction, a precipitation reaction, or a gas-forming reaction. Predict the products of the reaction, and then balance the completed equation.
    (a) $MnCl_2(aq) + Na_2S(aq) \longrightarrow$
    (b) $Na_2CO_3(aq) + ZnCl_2(aq) \longrightarrow$
    (c) $K_2CO_3(aq) + HClO_4(aq) \longrightarrow$

Identifying Reaction Types

The following reactions apply to Exercises 99 through 109.

(a) $H_2SO_4(aq) + 2KOH(aq) \longrightarrow K_2SO_4(aq) + 2H_2O(\ell)$
(b) $2Rb(s) + Br_2(\ell) \xrightarrow{heat} 2RbBr(s)$
(c) $2KI(aq) + F_2(g) \longrightarrow 2KF(aq) + I_2(s)$
(d) $CaO(s) + SiO_2(s) \xrightarrow{heat} CaSiO_3(s)$
(e) $S(s) + O_2(g) \xrightarrow{heat} SO_2(g)$
(f) $BaCO_3(s) \xrightarrow{heat} BaO(s) + CO_2(g)$
(g) $HgS(s) + O_2(g) \xrightarrow{heat} Hg(\ell) + SO_2(g)$
(h) $AgNO_3(aq) + HCl(aq) \longrightarrow AgCl(s) + HNO_3(aq)$
(i) $Pb(s) + 2HBr(aq) \longrightarrow PbBr_2(s) + H_2(g)$
(j) $2HI(aq) + H_2O_2(aq) \longrightarrow I_2(s) + 2H_2O(\ell)$
(k) $RbOH(aq) + HNO_3(aq) \longrightarrow RbNO_3(aq) + H_2O(\ell)$
(l) $N_2O_5(s) + H_2O(\ell) \longrightarrow 2HNO_3(aq)$
(m) $H_2O(g) + CO(g) \xrightarrow{heat} H_2(g) + CO_2(g)$
(n) $MgO(s) + H_2O(\ell) \longrightarrow Mg(OH)_2(s)$
(o) $PbSO_4(s) + PbS(s) \xrightarrow{heat} 2Pb(s) + 2SO_2(g)$

99. Identify the precipitation reactions.
100. Identify the acid–base reactions.
101. Identify the oxidation–reduction reactions.
102. Identify the oxidizing agent and reducing agent for each oxidation–reduction reaction.
103. Identify the displacement reactions.
104. Identify the metathesis reactions.
105. Identify the combination reactions.
106. Identify the decomposition reactions.
107. Identify the gas-formation reactions.
108. (a) Identify the oxidation–reduction reactions that form gaseous products, whether or not they can be classified as gas-formation reactions. (b) Which of these also fit the definition of gas-formation reactions? Why?
109. (a) Do any of these reactions fit into more than one class? Which ones? (b) Do any of these reactions not fit into any of our classes of reactions? Which ones?
110. Predict whether or not a solid is formed when we mix the following; identify any solid product by name and identify the reaction type: (a) copper(II) nitrate solution and magnesium metal; (b) barium nitrate and sodium phosphate solutions; (c) calcium acetate solution and aluminum metal; (d) silver nitrate and sodium iodide solutions.
111. Predict whether or not a solid is formed when we mix the following; identify any solid product by formula and by name: (a) potassium permanganate and sodium phosphate solutions; (b) lithium carbonate and cadmium nitrate solutions; (c) stannous fluoride and bismuth chloride solutions; (d) strontium sulfate and barium chloride solutions.

Conceptual Exercises

112. Each of the following statements is incorrect. Explain why. (a) A 1.2 M CH_3COOH solution is a stronger acid than a 0.12 M CH_3COOH solution. (b) The salt produced during the neutralization of nitric acid with potassium hydroxide is KNO_4. (c) Nickel will react with a HCl solution but not with steam to produce hydrogen and nickel ion solution. Magnesium will react with steam to produce hydrogen and magnesium ions. Therefore, nickel is more reactive than magnesium.
113. Determine the oxidation state of bromine in each of the following: (a) Br_2; (b) Br^-; (c) KBr; (d) BrCl; (e) PBr_5; (f) BrO_3^-. In which of these species is the charge on the bromine actually the same as its oxidation state?
114. Which of the following types of reactions is *always* an oxidation–reduction reaction: combination, decomposition, displacement, and metathesis? Which of these types of reactions is *never* an oxidation–reduction reaction?

As we have seen, two substances may react to form different products when they are mixed in different proportions under different conditions. In Exercises 115 and 116, write balanced equations for the reactions described by words. Assign oxidation states.

115. (a) Ethane burns in excess air to form carbon dioxide and water. (b) Ethane burns in a limited amount of air to form carbon monoxide and water. (c) Ethane burns (poorly) in a very limited amount of air to form elemental carbon and water.

🐾 **Molecular Reasoning** exercises   ▲ **More Challenging** exercises   Blue-Numbered exercises solved in Student Solutions Manual

Unless otherwise noted, all content on this page is © Cengage Learning.

116. (a) Butane (C_4H_{10}) burns in excess air to form carbon dioxide and water. (b) Butane burns in a limited amount of air to form carbon monoxide and water. (c) When heated in the presence of *very little* air, butane "cracks" to form acetylene, C_2H_2, carbon monoxide, and hydrogen.

117. Calcium phosphate is the component of human bone that provides rigidity. Fallout from a nuclear bomb can contain radioactive strontium-90. These two facts are closely tied together when one considers human health. Explain.

118. Limestone consists mainly of the mineral calcite, which is calcium carbonate. A very similar deposit called dolostone is composed primarily of the mineral dolomite, an ionic substance that contains carbonate ions and a mixture of magnesium and calcium ions. (a) Is this a surprising mixture of ions? Explain, based on the periodic table. (b) A test for limestone is to apply cold dilute hydrochloric acid, which causes the rapid formation of bubbles. What causes these bubbles?

The Dolomite Alps of Italy

119. Chemical equations can be interpreted on either a particulate level (atoms, molecules, ions) or a mole level (moles of reactants and products). Write word statements to describe the combustion of propane on a particulate level and a mole level.

$$2C_3H_8(g) + 10O_2(g) \longrightarrow 6CO_2(g) + 8H_2O(\ell)$$

120. Write word statements to describe the following reaction on a particulate level and a mole level:

$$P_4(s) + 6Cl_2(g) \longrightarrow 4PCl_3(\ell).$$

121. When the following pairs of reactants are combined in a beaker: (a) describe in words what the contents of the beaker would look like before and after any reaction that might occur; (b) use different circles for different types of atoms, molecules, and ions to draw a nanoscale (particulate-level) diagram of what the contents would look like; and (c) write a chemical equation for any reactions that might occur.

LiCl(aq)	and	$AgNO_3$(aq)
NaOH(aq)	and	HCl(aq)
$CaCO_3$(s)	and	HCl(aq)
Na_2CO_3(aq)	and	$Ca(OH)_2$(aq)

122. Nitric acid reacts with strontium hydroxide producing soluble strontium nitrate and water. Write the balanced formula unit equation, the total ionic equation, and the net ionic equation for this reaction. Sulfuric acid reacts with rubidium hydroxide producing soluble rubidium sulfate and water. Write the balanced formula unit equation, the total ionic equation, and the net ionic equation for this reaction. What do the net ionic equations for these two reactions have in common?

123. Suppose solutions of magnesium acetate and potassium sulfide were mixed. If a reaction occurred, the products would be magnesium sulfide and potassium acetate, both of which are soluble. Write the balanced formula unit equation, the total ionic equation, and the net ionic equation for this reaction. Did you get the same net ionic equation as you obtained in Exercise 122? Explain your finding.

124. Explain how you could prepare barium sulfate by (a) an acid–base reaction, (b) a precipitation reaction, and (c) a gas-forming reaction. The materials you have to start with are $BaCO_3$, $Ba(OH)_2$, Na_2SO_4, and H_2SO_4.

125. When acetic acid, CH_3COOH, is dissolved in water, 0.5% of the acetic acid molecules ionize:

$$CH_3COOH(aq) \rightleftharpoons H^+(aq) + CH_3COO^-(aq)$$

Standard vinegar is 5.0% acetic acid by mass. Draw models illustrating the components in vinegar (include a model for water). Given that the density of the vinegar is about 1.01 g/mL, calculate the mass of 1.0 L of vinegar. What masses of the acetic acid and water are present? Convert the mass of the acetic acid to moles. Given that 0.50% of the acetic acid ionizes, how many moles each of hydrogen ion and acetate ion are produced? Calculate the molarity of the acid and of each of the ions. Convert the mass of the water to moles. What is the molar concentration of the water? Which component of the solution has the largest concentration?

126. Some types of chemical reactions are sometimes represented by general equations that don't represent any specific substances or reactions but illustrate key characteristics that are common to that type of reaction. What type of reaction might be represented by each of the following general equations:
(a) $AB + CD \longrightarrow AD + CB$, (b) $AB \longrightarrow A + B$,
(c) $A + BC \longrightarrow AC + B$, and (d) $A + B \longrightarrow AB$?

Building Your Knowledge

127. Magnesium oxide, marketed as tablets or as an aqueous slurry called "milk of magnesia," is a common commercial antacid. What volume, in milliliters, of fresh gastric juice, corresponding in acidity to 0.17 M HCl, could be neutralized by 104 mg of magnesium oxide?

$$MgO(s) + 2HCl(aq) \longrightarrow MgCl_2(aq) + H_2O(\ell)$$

Milk of magnesia

♣ **Molecular Reasoning** exercises   ▲ **More Challenging** exercises   Blue-Numbered exercises solved in Student Solutions Manual

Unless otherwise noted, all content on this page is © Cengage Learning.

128. How many moles of oxygen can be obtained by the decomposition of 24.0 grams of reactant in each of the following reactions?

(a) $2KClO_3(s) \xrightarrow{\text{heat}} 2KCl(s) + 3O_2(g)$

(b) $2H_2O_2(aq) \longrightarrow 2H_2O(\ell) + O_2(g)$

(c) $2HgO(s) \xrightarrow{\text{heat}} 2Hg(\ell) + O_2(g)$

Beyond the Textbook

NOTE: *Whenever the answer to an exercise depends on information obtained from a source other than this textbook, the source must be included as an essential part of the answer.*

129. Go to **www.nist.gov**, then click on "General Information."
(a) What does NIST stand for?
(b) What is the mission of NIST?

130. Go to **www.nrc.gov**, then click on "who we are."
(a) What does NRC stand for?
(b) What is the mission of NRC?

131. In *The Merck Index* and at various sites on the web one can find descriptions of small and large compounds that utilize terms not normally found in general chemistry textbooks. These terms include acidulant, astringent, diuretic, and expectorant. Describe each of these four properties.

Chemical Bonding

7

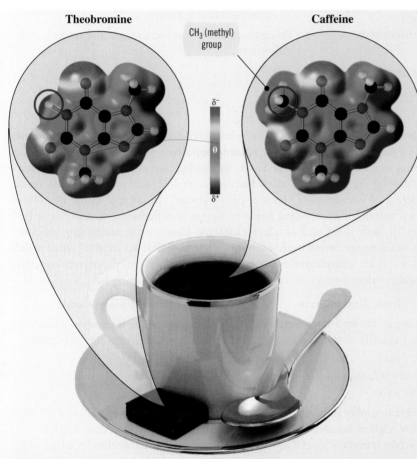

Theobromine

Caffeine

CH₃ (methyl) group

δ⁻

0

δ⁺

The main stimulants in chocolate and coffee are closely related chemicals—theobromine and caffeine, respectively. The structural difference is circled in the two molecular drawings. Theobromine is a milder stimulant that lasts longer than caffeine and has a mood improving effect.

© Iconotec/Alamy

OBJECTIVES

After you have studied this chapter, you should be able to

▶ Write Lewis dot representations of atoms

▶ Predict whether bonding between specified elements will be primarily ionic, nonpolar covalent, or polar covalent

▶ Compare and contrast characteristics of ionic and covalent compounds

▶ Describe how the properties of compounds depend on their bonding

▶ Describe how the elements bond by electron transfer (ionic bonding)

▶ Describe energy relationships in ionic compounds

▶ Predict the formulas of ionic compounds

▶ Describe how elements bond by sharing electrons (covalent bonding)

▶ Write Lewis dot and dash formulas for molecules and polyatomic ions

▶ Recognize exceptions to the octet rule

▶ Write formal charges for atoms in covalent structures

▶ Describe resonance, and know when to write resonance structures and how to do so

▶ Relate the nature of bonding to electronegativity differences

Chemical bonding refers to the attractive forces that hold atoms together in compounds. There are two major classes of bonding. (1) **Ionic bonding** results from the net *transfer* of electrons from one atom or group of atoms to another and the attractive electrostatic interactions among the *cations* and *anions* that are formed. (2) **Covalent bonding** results from the *sharing* of one or more electron pairs between two atoms. These two classes represent two extremes; all bonding between atoms of different elements has at least some degree of both ionic and covalent character. Compounds containing predominantly ionic bonding are called **ionic compounds**. Those that are held together mainly by covalent bonds are called **covalent compounds**. Some general properties associated with ionic and covalent compounds are summarized in the following list.

Ionic Compounds	Covalent Compounds
1. They are solids with high melting points (typically >400°C).	1. They are gases, liquids, or solids with low melting points (typically <300°C).
2. Many are soluble in polar solvents such as water.	2. Many are insoluble in polar solvents.
3. Most are insoluble in nonpolar solvents, such as hexane, C_6H_{14}, and carbon tetrachloride, CCl_4.	3. Most are soluble in nonpolar solvents, such as hexane, C_6H_{14}, and carbon tetrachloride, CCl_4.
4. Ionic liquids conduct electricity well because they contain mobile charged particles (ions).	4. Covalent liquids do not conduct electricity.
5. Aqueous solutions conduct electricity well because they contain mobile charged particles (ions).	5. Aqueous solutions are *usually* poor conductors of electricity because most do not contain charged particles.
6. They are often formed between two elements with quite different electronegativities, usually a metal and a nonmetal.	6. They are often formed between two elements with similar electronegativities, usually nonmetals.

▶ As you study Chapters 7 and 8, keep in mind the periodic similarities that you learned in Chapters 5 and 6. What you learn about the bonding of an element usually applies to the other elements in the same column of the periodic table, with minor variations.

▶ The distinction between polar and nonpolar molecules is discussed in Section 7-10.

▶ As we saw in Section 6-1, aqueous solutions of some covalent compounds do conduct electricity, because they react with water to some extent to form ions.

7-1 Lewis Dot Formulas of Atoms

The number and arrangements of electrons in the outermost shells of atoms determine the chemical and physical properties of the elements as well as the kinds of chemical bonds they form. We write **Lewis formulas** (sometimes called **Lewis dot formulas** or

Table 7-1 Lewis Dot Formulas for Atoms of Representative Elements

Group	1A	2A	3A	4A	5A	6A	7A	8A
Number of electrons in valence shell	1	2	3	4	5	6	7	8 (except He)
Period 1	H·							He :
Period 2	Li·	Be :	B·	C·	·N·	·O:	·F:	:Ne :
Period 3	Na·	Mg :	Al·	Si·	·P·	·S:	·Cl:	:Ar :
Period 4	K·	Ca :	Ga·	Ge·	·As·	·Se:	·Br:	:Kr :
Period 5	Rb·	Sr :	In·	Sn·	·Sb·	·Te:	·I:	:Xe :
Period 6	Cs·	Ba :	Tl·	Pb·	·Bi·	·Po:	·At:	:Rn :
Period 7	Fr·	Ra :						

▶ For the Group A elements, the number of valence electrons (dots in the Lewis formula) for the *neutral* atom is equal to the group number. Exception: He (two valence electrons).

Lewis dot representations) as a convenient bookkeeping method for keeping track of these "chemically important electrons." We now introduce this method for atoms of elements; in our discussion of chemical bonding we will frequently use such formulas for atoms, molecules, and ions.

Chemical bonding involves only the **valence electrons**, which are usually the electrons in the outermost occupied shells. In Lewis dot representations, only the electrons in the outermost occupied s and p orbitals are shown as dots. Table 7-1 shows Lewis dot formulas for atoms of the representative elements. All elements in a given group have the same outer-shell electron configuration. It is somewhat arbitrary on which side of the atom symbol we write the electron dots. We do, however, represent an electron pair as a pair of dots and an unpaired electron as a single dot. Because of the large numbers of dots, such formulas are not as useful for compounds of the transition metals, lanthanides, and actinides.

▶ For example, Al has the electron configuration [Ar] $3s^2 3p^1$. The three dots in the Lewis dot formula for Al represent the two s electrons (the pair of dots) and the p electron (the single dot) beyond the noble gas configuration.

Ionic Bonding

7-2 Formation of Ionic Compounds

The first kind of chemical bonding we will describe is ionic bonding. We recall (see Section 2-2) that an **ion** is an atom or a group of atoms that carries an electrical charge. An ion in which the atom or group of atoms has fewer electrons than protons is positively charged and is called a **cation**; one that has more electrons than protons is negatively charged and is called an **anion**. An ion that consists of only one atom is described as a **monatomic ion**. Examples include the chloride ion, Cl^-, and the magnesium ion, Mg^{2+}. An ion that contains more than one atom is called a **polyatomic ion**. Examples include the ammonium ion, NH_4^+; the hydroxide ion, OH^-; and the sulfate ion, SO_4^{2-}. The atoms within a polyatomic ion are held to one another by covalent bonds. In this section we shall discuss how ions can be formed from individual atoms; polyatomic ions will be discussed later, along with other covalently bonded species.

> **Ionic bonding** is the attraction of oppositely charged ions (cations and anions) in large numbers to form a solid. Such a solid compound is called an *ionic solid*.

As our previous discussions of ionization energy, electronegativity, and electron affinity would suggest, ionic bonding can occur easily when elements that have low

S TOP & THINK
The chemical and physical properties of an ion are quite different from those of the atom from which the ion is derived. For example, an atom of Na and an Na^+ ion have extremely different chemical properties. It is important to keep track of charges and oxidation states.

Freshly cut sodium has a metallic luster. A little while after being cut, the sodium metal surface turns white as it reacts with the air.

electronegativities and low ionization energies (metals) react with elements that have high electronegativities and very negative electron affinities (nonmetals). Many metals are easily *oxidized*—that is, they lose electrons to form cations; and many nonmetals are readily *reduced*—that is, they gain electrons to form anions.

> When the electronegativity difference, $\Delta(EN)$, between two elements is large, as between a metal and a nonmetal, the elements are likely to form a compound by ionic bonding (transfer of electrons).

Let's describe some combinations of metals with nonmetals to form ionic compounds.

Group 1A Metals (Alkali Metals) and Group 7A Nonmetals (Halogens)

Consider the reaction of sodium (a Group 1A metal) with chlorine (a Group 7A nonmetal). Sodium is a soft silvery metal (mp = 98°C), and chlorine is a yellowish green corrosive gas at room temperature. Both sodium and chlorine react with water; sodium reacts vigorously.

By contrast, sodium chloride is a white solid (mp = 801°C) that dissolves in water with no reaction and with the mild absorption of heat. We can represent the reaction for its formation as

$$2Na(s) + Cl_2(g) \longrightarrow 2NaCl(s)$$
$$\text{sodium} \qquad \text{chlorine} \qquad \text{sodium chloride}$$

We can understand this reaction better by showing electron configurations for all species. We represent chlorine as individual atoms rather than molecules, for simplicity.

▶ *Isoelectronic* species have the same number of electrons (see Section 5-5). Some isoelectronic species:

O^{2-}	8 protons	10 electrons
F^-	9 protons	10 electrons
Ne	10 protons	10 electrons
Na^+	11 protons	10 electrons
Mg^{2+}	12 protons	10 electrons

$$
\begin{array}{ll}
Na & [Ne] \quad \underset{3s}{\uparrow} \\[2mm]
Cl & [Ne] \quad \underset{3s}{\uparrow\downarrow}\ \underset{\ \ 3p}{\uparrow\downarrow\ \uparrow\downarrow\ \uparrow}
\end{array}
\Biggr\} \longrightarrow
\begin{cases}
Na^+ & [Ne] & 1e^- \text{ lost} \\[2mm]
Cl^- & [Ne] \quad \underset{3s}{\uparrow\downarrow}\ \underset{\ \ 3p}{\uparrow\downarrow\ \uparrow\downarrow\ \uparrow\downarrow} & 1e^- \text{ gained}
\end{cases}
$$

In this reaction, Na atoms lose one electron each to form Na^+ ions, which contain only ten electrons, the same number as the *preceding* noble gas, neon. We say that sodium ions have the noble gas electronic structure of neon: Na^+ is *isoelectronic* with Ne. In contrast, Cl atoms gain one electron each to form Cl^- ions, which contain 18 electrons. This is the same number as the *following* noble gas, argon; Cl^- is *isoelectronic* with Ar. These processes can be represented compactly as

$$Na \longrightarrow Na^+ + e^- \qquad \text{and} \qquad Cl + e^- \longrightarrow Cl^-$$

The loss of electrons is *oxidation* (see Section 6-5). Na atoms are *oxidized* to form Na^+ ions. The gain of electrons is *reduction* (see Section 6-5). Cl atoms are *reduced* to form Cl^- ions.

Some ionic compounds. Clockwise from front right: sodium chloride (NaCl, *white*); copper(II) sulfate pentahydrate (CuSO₄ · 5H₂O, *blue*); nickel(II) chloride hexahydrate (NiCl₂ · 6H₂O, *green*); potassium dichromate (K₂Cr₂O₇, *orange*); and cobalt(II) chloride hexahydrate (CoCl₂ · 6H₂O, *red*). One mole of each substance is shown.

Similar observations apply to most ionic compounds formed by reactions between *metals and nonmetals*.

We can use Lewis dot formulas (see Section 7-1) to represent the reaction.

$$\text{Na} \cdot + \ddot{:Cl} \cdot \longrightarrow \text{Na}^+ \left[\ddot{:Cl:} \right]^-$$

The Na^+ and Cl^- ions can be present only in a 1:1 ratio in the compound sodium chloride, so the formula must be NaCl. We predict the same formula based on the fact that each Na atom can lose only one electron from its outermost occupied shell and each Cl atom needs only one electron to fill completely its outermost p orbitals.

The chemical formula NaCl does not explicitly indicate the ionic nature of the compound, only the ratio of ions. Furthermore, values of electronegativities are not always available. We must learn to use the positions of elements in the periodic table and their trends in electronegativity to help recognize when the difference in electronegativity is large enough to favor ionic bonding.

> The farther apart *across* the periodic table two elements are, the more ionic their bonding will be.

▶ The noble gases and hydrogen are excluded from this generalization.

The greatest difference in electronegativity occurs from the lower left to upper right, so CsF ($\Delta[\text{EN}] = 3.2$) is more ionic than LiI ($\Delta[\text{EN}] = 1.5$).

All the Group 1A metals (Li, Na, K, Rb, Cs) will react with the Group 7A elements (F, Cl, Br, I) to form ionic compounds of the same general formula, MX. All the resulting ions, M^+ and X^-, have noble gas configurations. Once we understand the bonding of one member of a group (column) in the periodic table, we know a great deal about the others in the family. Combining each of the five common alkali metals with each of the four common halogens gives $5 \times 4 = 20$ possible compounds. The discussion of NaCl presented here applies also to the other 19 such compounds.

▶ Formulas for some of these are

LiF	LiCl	LiBr	LiI
NaF	NaCl	NaBr	NaI
KF	KCl	KBr	KI

The collection of isolated positive and negative ions occurs at a higher energy than the elements from which they are formed. The ion formation alone is not sufficient to account for the formation of ionic compounds. Some other favorable factor must account for the observed stability of these compounds. Because of the opposite charges on Na^+ and Cl^-, an attractive force is developed. According to Coulomb's Law, the force of attraction, F, between two oppositely charged particles of charge magnitudes q^+ and q^- is directly proportional to the product of the charges and inversely proportional to the square of the distance separating their centers, d.

> Coulomb's Law is $F \propto \dfrac{q^+ q^-}{d^2}$.

▶ The symbol $\propto$ means "is proportional to."

Thus, the greater the charges on the ions and the smaller the ions are, the stronger the resulting ionic bonding. Of course, ions with the same charge repel each other, so the distances separating the ions in ionic solids are those at which the attractions exceed the repulsions by the greatest amount.

The energy associated with the attraction of separated gaseous positive and negative ions to form an ionic solid is the *crystal lattice energy* of the solid. For NaCl, this energy is -789 kJ/mol; that is, one mole of NaCl solid is 789 kJ lower in energy (*more stable*) than one mole of isolated Na^+ ions and one mole of isolated Cl^- ions. We could also say that it would require 789 kJ of energy to separate one mole of NaCl solid into isolated gaseous ions. The stability of ionic compounds is thus due to the interplay of the energy cost of ion formation and the energy repaid by the crystal lattice energy. The best trade-off usually comes when the monatomic ions of representative elements have noble gas configurations. For more on these ideas, see the Enrichment feature "Introduction to Energy Relationships in Ionic Bonding" on page 256.

▶ Although the common name for NaCl is "salt," many chemists use the term salt in a more generic way to refer to ionic compounds.

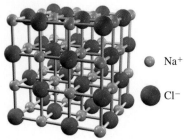

Figure 7-1 A representation of the crystal structure of NaCl. Each Cl⁻ ion (*green*) is surrounded by six sodium ions, and each Na⁺ ion (*gray*) is surrounded by six chloride ions. Any NaCl crystal includes billions of ions in the pattern shown. Adjacent ions actually are in contact with one another; in this drawing, the structure has been expanded to show the spatial arrangement of ions. The lines *do not* represent covalent bonds. Compare with Figure 2-2, a space-filling drawing of the NaCl structure.

▶ Although the oxides of the other Group 1A metals are prepared by different methods, similar descriptions apply to compounds between the Group 1A metals (Li, Na, K, Rb, Cs) and the Group 6A nonmetals (O, S, Se, Te, Po).

▶ Each Li atom has 1 e^- in its valence shell, one more e^- than a noble gas configuration, [He]. Each O atom has 6 e^- in its valence shell and needs 2 e^- more to attain a noble gas configuration [Ne]. The Li⁺ ions are formed by oxidation of Li atoms, and the O^{2-} ions are formed by reduction of O atoms.

The structure of common table salt, sodium chloride (NaCl), is shown in Figure 7-1. Like other simple ionic compounds, NaCl(s) exists in a regular, extended array of positive and negative ions, Na⁺ and Cl⁻. Distinct molecules of solid ionic substances do not exist, so we must refer to *formula units* (see Section 2-2) instead of molecules. The forces that hold all the particles together in an ionic solid are quite strong. This explains why such substances have quite high melting and boiling points (a topic that we will discuss more fully in Chapter 13). When an ionic compound is melted or dissolved in water, its charged particles are free to move in an electric field, so such a liquid shows high electrical conductivity (Section 6-1, Part 1).

We can represent the general reaction of the 1A metals with the 7A elements as follows:

$$2M(s) + X_2 \rightarrow 2MX(s) \qquad M = Li, Na, K, Rb, Cs; \ X = F, Cl, Br, I$$

The Lewis dot representation for the generalized reaction is

$$2M\cdot + :\overset{..}{\underset{..}{X}}:\overset{..}{\underset{..}{X}}: \longrightarrow 2\left(M^+\left[:\overset{..}{\underset{..}{X}}:\right]^-\right)$$

Group 1A Metals (Alkali Metals) and Group 6A Nonmetals

Next, consider the reaction of lithium (Group 1A) with oxygen (Group 6A) to form lithium oxide, a solid ionic compound (mp > 1700°C). We may represent the reaction as

$$4Li(s) + O_2(g) \longrightarrow 2Li_2O(s)$$
$$\text{lithium} \qquad \text{oxygen} \qquad \text{lithium oxide}$$

The formula for lithium oxide, Li_2O, indicates that two atoms of lithium combine with one atom of oxygen. If we examine the structures of the atoms before reaction, we can see the reason for this ratio.

In a compact representation,

$$2[Li \longrightarrow Li^+ + e^-] \qquad \text{and} \qquad O + 2e^- \longrightarrow O^{2-}$$

The Lewis dot formulas for the atoms and ions are

$$2Li\cdot + :\overset{..}{O}\cdot \longrightarrow 2Li^+\left[:\overset{..}{\underset{..}{O}}:\right]^{2-}$$

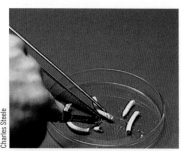

Lithium is a metal, as the shiny surface of freshly cut Li shows. Where it has been exposed to air, the surface is covered with lithium oxide.

Lithium ions, Li⁺, are isoelectronic with helium atoms $(2e^-)$. Oxide ions, O^{2-}, are isoelectronic with neon atoms $(10e^-)$.

The very small size of the Li⁺ ion gives it a much higher *charge density* (ratio of charge to size) than that of the larger Na⁺ ion (see Figure 5-4). Similarly, the O^{2-} ion is smaller than the Cl⁻ ion, so its smaller size and double negative charge give it a much higher charge density. These more concentrated charges and smaller sizes bring the Li⁺ and O^{2-} ions closer together in Li_2O than the Na⁺ and Cl⁻ ions are in NaCl. Consequently, the q^+q^- product in the numerator of Coulomb's Law is greater in Li_2O, and the d^2 term in the denominator is smaller. The net result is that the ionic bonding is much stronger (the lattice energy is much more negative) in Li_2O than in NaCl. This is consistent with the higher melting temperature of Li_2O (>1700°C) compared to NaCl (801°C).

Group 2A Metals (Alkaline Earth Metals) and Group 6A Nonmetals

As our final illustration of ionic bonding, consider the reaction of calcium (Group 2A) with oxygen (Group 6A). This reaction forms calcium oxide, a white solid ionic compound with a very high melting point, 2580°C.

$$2Ca(s) + O_2(g) \longrightarrow 2CaO(s)$$
$$\text{calcium} \qquad \text{oxygen} \qquad \text{calcium oxide}$$

Again, we show the electronic structure of the atoms and ions, representing the inner electrons by the symbol of the preceding noble gas.

► This discussion also applies to other ionic compounds between any Group 2A metal (Be, Mg, Ca, Sr, Ba) and any Group 6A nonmetal (O, S, Se, Te).

$$
\begin{array}{ll}
Ca & [Ar] \; \underset{4s}{\boxed{\uparrow\downarrow}} \\[2ex]
O & [He] \; \underset{2s}{\boxed{\uparrow\downarrow}} \; \underset{2p}{\boxed{\uparrow\downarrow}\,\boxed{\uparrow}\,\boxed{\uparrow}}
\end{array}
\Bigg\}
\longrightarrow
\begin{cases}
Ca^{2+} & [Ar] \; \underset{4s}{\boxed{}} & 2e^- \text{ lost} \\[2ex]
O^{2-} & [He] \; \underset{2s}{\boxed{\uparrow\downarrow}} \; \underset{2p}{\boxed{\uparrow\downarrow}\,\boxed{\uparrow\downarrow}\,\boxed{\uparrow\downarrow}} & 2e^- \text{ gained}
\end{cases}
$$

► Chemists do not ordinarily represent transition metals or their ions as Lewis dot formulas.

The Lewis dot notation for the reacting atoms and the resulting ions is

$$\text{Ca:} + :\ddot{\text{O}}\cdot \longrightarrow Ca^{2+}\left[:\ddot{\text{O}}:\right]^{2-}$$

Calcium ions, Ca^{2+}, are isoelectronic with argon $(18\,e^-)$, the preceding noble gas. Oxide ions, O^{2-}, are isoelectronic with neon $(10\,e^-)$, the following noble gas.

Ca^{2+} is about the same size as Na^+ (see Figure 5-4) but carries twice the charge, so its charge density is higher. Because the attraction between the two small, highly charged ions Ca^{2+} and O^{2-} is quite high, the ionic bonding is very strong, accounting for the very high melting point of CaO, 2580°C.

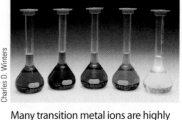

Many transition metal ions are highly colored. These flasks contain (*left to right*), aqueous solutions of $Fe(NO_3)_3$, $Co(NO_3)_2$, $Ni(NO_3)_2$, $Cu(NO_3)_2$, and $Zn(NO_3)_2$. Colorless Zn^{2+} ions differ from the others by having completely filled $3d$ orbitals.

d-Transition Metal Ions

Electron configurations of the *d*-transition metal atoms include the *s* electrons in the outermost occupied shell and the *d* electrons one energy level lower (e.g., $3d4s$ for the first transition series in Period 4). The outer *s* electrons lie outside the *d* electrons and are *always* the first ones lost when transition metals form simple ions. In the first transition series, scandium and zinc each form only one type of cation. Scandium loses its two $4s$ electrons and its only $3d$ electron to form Sc^{3+}. Zinc loses its two $4s$ electrons to form Zn^{2+}.

$$
\begin{array}{lll}
 & & \overset{3d}{\rule{3cm}{0.4pt}} \quad \overset{4s}{\rule{0.8cm}{0.4pt}} \\
Sc & [Ar] & \boxed{\uparrow}\,\rule{2cm}{0.4pt} \quad \boxed{\uparrow\downarrow} \\[1ex]
Zn & [Ar] & \boxed{\uparrow\downarrow}\,\boxed{\uparrow\downarrow}\,\boxed{\uparrow\downarrow}\,\boxed{\uparrow\downarrow}\,\boxed{\uparrow\downarrow} \quad \boxed{\uparrow\downarrow}
\end{array}
\Bigg\}
\longrightarrow
\begin{cases}
Sc^{3+} & [Ar] & \rule{2.5cm}{0.4pt}\;\rule{0.8cm}{0.4pt} & 3e^- \text{ lost} \\[1ex]
Zn^{2+} & [Ar] & \boxed{\uparrow\downarrow}\,\boxed{\uparrow\downarrow}\,\boxed{\uparrow\downarrow}\,\boxed{\uparrow\downarrow}\,\boxed{\uparrow\downarrow}\;\rule{0.8cm}{0.4pt} & 2e^- \text{ lost}
\end{cases}
$$

Most other $3d$-transition metals can form at least two differently charged cations in their compounds. For example, cobalt commonly forms Co^{2+} and Co^{3+} ions.

$$
\begin{array}{lll}
 & & \overset{3d}{\rule{3cm}{0.4pt}} \quad \overset{4s}{\rule{0.8cm}{0.4pt}} \\
Co & [Ar] & \boxed{\uparrow\downarrow}\,\boxed{\uparrow\downarrow}\,\boxed{\uparrow}\,\boxed{\uparrow}\,\boxed{\uparrow} \quad \boxed{\uparrow\downarrow} \\[1ex]
Co & [Ar] & \boxed{\uparrow\downarrow}\,\boxed{\uparrow\downarrow}\,\boxed{\uparrow}\,\boxed{\uparrow}\,\boxed{\uparrow} \quad \boxed{\uparrow\downarrow}
\end{array}
\Bigg\}
\longrightarrow
\begin{cases}
Co^{2+} & [Ar] & \boxed{\uparrow\downarrow}\,\boxed{\uparrow\downarrow}\,\boxed{\uparrow}\,\boxed{\uparrow}\,\boxed{\uparrow}\;\rule{0.8cm}{0.4pt} & 2e^- \text{ lost} \\[1ex]
Co^{3+} & [Ar] & \boxed{\uparrow\downarrow}\,\boxed{\uparrow}\,\boxed{\uparrow}\,\boxed{\uparrow}\,\boxed{\uparrow}\;\rule{0.8cm}{0.4pt} & 3e^- \text{ lost}
\end{cases}
$$

Binary Ionic Compounds: A Summary

Table 7-2 summarizes the general formulas of binary ionic compounds formed by the representative elements. "M" represents metals, and "X" represents nonmetals from the indicated groups. In these examples of ionic bonding, each of the metal atoms has lost one, two, or

► **Binary compounds** contain *two* elements.

Table 7-2 Simple Binary Ionic Compounds

Metal		Nonmetal		General Formula	Ions Present	Example	mp (°C)
1A*	+	7A	$\longrightarrow$	MX	(M^+, X^-)	LiBr	547
2A	+	7A	$\longrightarrow$	MX_2	$(M^{2+}, 2X^-)$	$MgCl_2$	708
3A	+	7A	$\longrightarrow$	MX_3	$(M^{3+}, 3X^-)$	GaF_3	800 (subl)
1A*†	+	6A	$\longrightarrow$	M_2X	$(2M^+, X^{2-})$	Li_2O	>1700
2A	+	6A	$\longrightarrow$	MX	(M^{2+}, X^{2-})	CaO	2580
3A	+	6A	$\longrightarrow$	M_2X_3	$(2M^{3+}, 3X^{2-})$	Al_2O_3	2045
1A*	+	5A	$\longrightarrow$	M_3X	$(3M^+, X^{3-})$	Li_3N	840
2A	+	5A	$\longrightarrow$	M_3X_2	$(3M^{2+}, 2X^{3-})$	Ca_3P_2	1600
3A	+	5A	$\longrightarrow$	MX	(M^{3+}, X^{3-})	AlP	

▶ "subl" stands for sublimes, that is, the solid transforms directly to the gas phase without forming a liquid state.

*Hydrogen is a nonmetal. All binary compounds of hydrogen are covalent, except for certain metal hydrides such as NaH and CaH_2, which contain hydride, H^-, ions.

†As we saw in Section 5-9, the metals in Groups 1A and 2A also commonly form peroxides (containing the O_2^{2-} ion) or superoxides (containing the O_2^- ion) (see Table 5-5). The peroxide and superoxide ions contain atoms that are covalently bonded to one another.

three electrons, and each of the nonmetal atoms has gained one, two, or three electrons. *Simple (monatomic) ions rarely have charges greater than* 3+ *or* 3−. Ions with greater charges interact strongly with the electron clouds of other ions. The electron clouds become very distorted, resulting in considerable covalent character in the bonds. Distinct molecules of solid ionic substances do not exist. The sum of the attractive forces of all the interactions in an ionic solid is substantial. Therefore, binary ionic compounds have high melting and boiling points.

▶ The distortion of the electron cloud of an anion by a small, highly charged cation is called *polarization*.

All common monatomic anions have noble gas configurations. Most monatomic cations of the representative elements (A groups) have noble gas configurations. The *d-* and *f*-transition elements form many compounds that are essentially ionic in character. Most *d-* and *f*-transition metal cations do not have noble gas configurations.

ENRICHMENT

Introduction to Energy Relationships in Ionic Bonding

The following discussion may help you to understand why ionic bonding occurs between elements with low ionization energies and those with high electronegativities. There is a general tendency in nature to achieve stability. One way to do this is by lowering potential energy; *lower* energies generally represent *more stable* arrangements.

Let's use energy relationships to describe why the ionic solid NaCl is more stable than a mixture of individual Na and Cl atoms. Consider a gaseous mixture of one mole of sodium atoms and one mole of chlorine atoms, $Na(g) + Cl(g)$. The energy change associated with the loss of one mole of electrons by one mole of Na atoms to form one mole of Na^+ ions (Step 1 in Figure 7-2) is given by the *first ionization energy* of Na (see Section 5-3).

$$Na(g) \longrightarrow Na^+(g) + e^- \qquad \text{first ionization energy} = 496 \text{ kJ/mol}$$

This is a positive value, so the mixture $Na^+(g) + e^- + Cl(g)$ is 496 kJ/mol higher in energy than the original mixture of atoms (the mixture $Na^+ + e^- + Cl$ is *less stable* than the mixture of atoms).

The energy change for the gain of one mole of electrons by one mole of Cl atoms to form one mole of Cl^- ions (Step 2) is given by the *electron affinity* of Cl (see Section 5-4).

$$Cl(g) + e^- \longrightarrow Cl^-(g) \qquad \text{electron affinity} = -349 \text{ kJ/mol}$$

This negative value, -349 kJ/mol, lowers the energy of the mixture, but the mixture of separated ions, $Na^+ + Cl^-$, is still *higher* in energy (*less stable*) by $(496 - 349)$ kJ/mol = 147 kJ/mol than the original mixture of atoms (the red arrow in Figure 7–2). Thus, just the formation of ions does not explain why the process occurs. The strong attractive force between ions of opposite charge draws the ions together into the regular array shown in Figure 7–1. The energy associated with this attraction (Step 3) is the *crystal lattice energy* of NaCl, -789 kJ/mol.

$$Na^+(g) + Cl^-(g) \longrightarrow NaCl(s) \qquad \text{crystal lattice energy} = -789 \text{ kJ/mol}$$

The crystal (solid) formation thus further *lowers* the energy to $(147 - 789)$ kJ/mol = -642 kJ/mol. The overall result is that one mole of NaCl(s) is 642 kJ/mol lower in energy (more stable) than the original mixture of atoms (the blue arrow in Figure 7-2). The very large electrostatic stabilization due to the attraction of the ionic charges (Step 3) is a major driving force for the formation of ionic compounds.

In this discussion we have not taken into account the fact that sodium is a solid metal or that chlorine gas exists as diatomic molecules. The additional energy changes involved when these are changed to gaseous Na and Cl atoms, respectively, are small enough that the overall energy change starting from Na(s) and $Cl_2(g)$ is still negative.

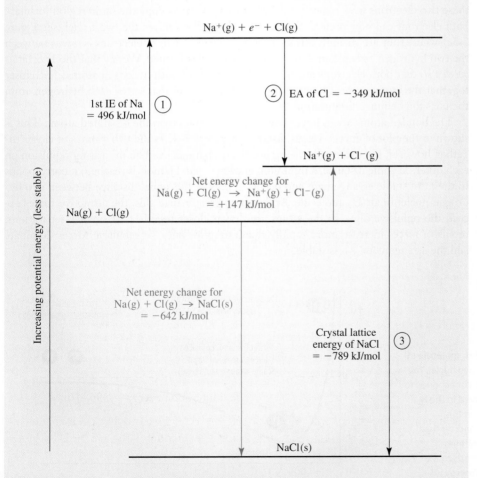

Figure 7-2 A schematic representation of the energy changes that accompany the process

$$Na(g) + Cl(g) \rightarrow NaCl(s).$$

The red arrow represents the *positive* energy change (unfavorable) for the process of ion formation,

$$Na(g) + Cl(g) \rightarrow$$
$$Na^+(g) + Cl^-(g).$$

The blue arrow represents the *negative* energy change (favorable) for the overall process, including the formation of the ionic solid.

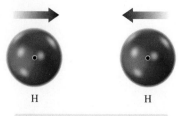

A Two hydrogen atoms separated by a large distance

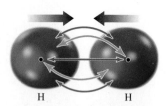

B As the atoms approach each other, the electron of each atom is attracted by the positively charged nucleus of the other atom (*blue arrows*), so the electron density begins to shift. At the same time, the electron clouds of the two atoms repel one another, and so do the nuclei of the two atoms (*red arrows*).

H_2

C The two electrons can both be in the region where the two $1s$ orbitals overlap; the electron density is highest in the region between the nuclei of the two atoms.

Figure 7-3 A representation of the formation of a covalent bond between two hydrogen atoms. The position of each positively charged nucleus is represented by a black dot.

Covalent Bonding

Ionic bonding cannot result from a reaction between two atoms with similar electronegativities, because their electronegativity difference is not great enough for electron transfer to take place. Instead, these reactions, typically between nonmetals, result in *covalent bonding*.

> A **covalent bond** is formed when two atoms share one or more pairs of electrons. Covalent bonding occurs when the electronegativity difference, $\Delta(EN)$, between elements (atoms) is zero or relatively small.

In predominantly covalent compounds the bonds between atoms *within* a molecule (*intra*molecular bonds) are relatively strong, but the forces of attraction *between* molecules (*inter*molecular forces) are relatively weak. As a result, covalent compounds have lower melting and boiling points than ionic compounds. The relation of bonding types to physical properties of liquids and solids will be developed more fully in Chapter 13.

7-3 Formation of Covalent Bonds

Let's look at the simplest case of covalent bonding, the reaction of two hydrogen atoms to form the diatomic molecule H_2. As you recall, an isolated hydrogen atom has the ground state electron configuration $1s^1$, with the probability density for this one electron spherically distributed about the hydrogen nucleus (Figure 7-3a). As two hydrogen atoms approach each other from large distances, the electron of each hydrogen atom is attracted by the nucleus of the *other* hydrogen atom as well as by its own nucleus (see Figure 7-3b). If these two electrons have opposite spins so that they can occupy the same region (orbital), both electrons can now preferentially occupy the region *between* the two nuclei (see Figure 7-3c), where they are strongly attracted by *both* nuclei. A pair of electrons is *shared* between the two hydrogen atoms, and a single covalent bond is formed. We say that the $1s$ orbitals *overlap* so that both electrons are now in the orbitals of both hydrogen atoms. The closer together the atoms come, the more nearly this is true. In that sense, each hydrogen atom then has the helium configuration $1s^2$.

The bonded atoms are at lower energy (more stable) than the separated atoms. This is shown in the plot of energy versus distance in Figure 7-4. As the two atoms get closer together, however, the two nuclei, being positively charged, exert an increasing repulsion on each other. At some distance, a minimum energy, -436 kJ/mol, is reached; it corresponds to the most stable arrangement and occurs at 0.74 Å, the actual distance between two hydrogen nuclei in an H_2 molecule. At distances greater than this, the attractive forces exceed the repulsive ones, so the atoms are drawn closer together. At smaller separations, repulsive forces increase more rapidly than attractive ones, so repulsive forces dominate and the arrangement is less stable.

Figure 7-4 The potential energy of the H_2 molecule as a function of the distance between the two nuclei. The lowest point in the curve, -436 kJ/mol, corresponds to the internuclear distance actually observed in the H_2 molecule, 0.74 Å. At distances longer than this, attractive forces dominate; at distances shorter than this, repulsive forces dominate. (The minimum potential energy, -436 kJ/mol, corresponds to the value of -7.23×10^{-19} J/H_2 molecule.) Energy is compared with that of two separated hydrogen atoms.

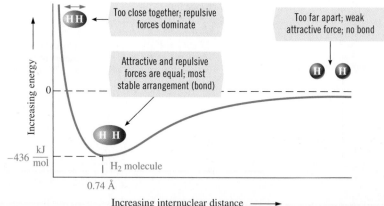

Too close together; repulsive forces dominate

Too far apart; weak attractive force; no bond

Attractive and repulsive forces are equal; most stable arrangement (bond)

Increasing energy

0

$-436 \frac{kJ}{mol}$

H_2 molecule

0.74 Å

Increasing internuclear distance

Other pairs of nonmetal atoms share electron pairs to form covalent bonds. The result of this sharing is that each atom attains a more stable electron configuration—frequently the same as that of the nearest noble gas. This results in a more stable arrangement for the bonded atoms. (This is discussed in Section 7-6.) Most covalent bonds involve sharing of two, four, or six electrons—that is, one, two, or three *pairs* of electrons. Two atoms form a **single covalent bond** when they share one pair of electrons, a **double covalent bond** when they share two electron pairs, and a **triple covalent bond** when they share three electron pairs. These are usually called simply *single*, *double*, and *triple* bonds. Covalent bonds that involve sharing of one and three electrons are known but are relatively rare.

In our discussion, we have described how covalent bonds form by the *overlap* of two atomic orbitals. This is the essence of the *valence bond theory*, which we will describe in more detail in the next chapter. Another description, the *molecular orbital theory*, is discussed in Chapter 9. For the rest of this chapter, we concentrate on the *number* of electron pairs shared and defer the discussion of *which* orbitals are involved in the sharing until the next chapter.

7-4 Bond Lengths and Bond Energies

We have seen that for any covalent bond there is some internuclear distance at which the attractive and repulsive forces balance and the bond is most stable; this distance is called the **bond length** of that covalent bond. At that distance, the combination of bonded atoms is more stable than the separated atoms by some energy; this energy difference is called the **bond dissociation energy**, or just the **bond energy**. This can be viewed as the stabilization of the bond compared to the separated atoms. It can also be described as the energy that must be supplied to separate the atoms, breaking the covalent bond.

Higher energy H· + ·H

436 kJ/mol released

436 kJ/mol absorbed

H–H Lower energy

Similar bonds between the same pairs of atoms usually have similar bond lengths and bond energies. Thus, we can develop tables of typical bond energies (Table 7-3) and bond lengths (Table 7-4) for each type of covalent bond.

Let's compare some typical carbon–carbon bond lengths and energies:

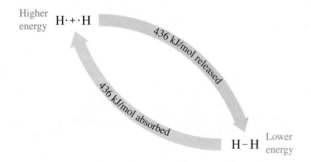

	Single Bond	Double Bond	Triple Bond
Bond length (Å)	1.54 Å	1.34 Å	1.21 Å
		Shorter Bonds →	
Bond energy (kJ/mol)	346	602	835
		Stronger Bonds →	

▶ Note that a C═C double bond is not twice as strong as a single bond. Similarly, a triple bond is not three times as strong as a single bond.

Table 7-3 Selected Average Bond Dissociation Energies (kJ/mol)

	Single Bonds						Double Bonds	Triple Bonds
	H	C	N	O	F	S		
H	436	413	391	463	563	347		
C		346	305	358	485	272	C＝C 602	C≡C 835
N			163	201	283	—	C＝N 615	C≡N 887
O				146	190	—	C＝O 732 (except	C≡O 1072
F					155	284	in CO_2, where it	
S						226	is 799)	

Table 7-4 Selected Average Bond Lengths (Å)

	Single Bonds						Double Bonds	Triple Bonds
	H	C	N	O	F	S		
H	0.74	1.10	0.98	0.94	0.92	1.32		
C		1.54	1.47	1.43	1.41	1.81	C＝C 1.34	C≡C 1.21
N			1.40	1.36	1.34	1.74	C＝N 1.27	C≡N 1.15
O				1.32	1.30	1.70	C＝O 1.22	C≡O 1.13
F					1.28	1.68		
S						2.08		

▶ Although multiple bonds are stronger than single bonds, they are often more reactive, especially for C — C double and triple bonds.

We see that the more bonds there are between atoms of the same two elements (i.e., the more electron pairs are shared), the closer together those atoms are (the shorter the bond length is) and the harder it is to break the bonding (increasing bond energy). Similar patterns can be seen for any other pairs of elements. Bond dissociation energies will be discussed in more rigorous detail in Section 15-9.

7-5 Lewis Formulas for Molecules and Polyatomic Ions

In Sections 7-1 and 7-2 we drew *Lewis dot formulas* for atoms and monatomic ions. We can use Lewis formulas to show the *valence electrons* in molecules and polyatomic ions.

In a Lewis formula, we represent a covalent bond by writing *each shared electron pair* either as a pair of two dots between the two atom symbols or as a dash connecting them. Thus, the formation of H_2 from H atoms could be represented as

$$H\cdot \ + \ \cdot H \longrightarrow H:H \quad \text{or} \quad H—H$$

where the dash represents a single bond. Similarly, the combination of two fluorine atoms to form a molecule of fluorine, F_2, can be shown as

▶ The bonding in the other halogens, Cl_2, Br_2, and I_2, is analogous to that in F_2.

$$:\!\ddot{F}\cdot \ + \ \cdot\ddot{F}\!: \longrightarrow :\!\ddot{F}\!:\!\ddot{F}\!: \quad \text{or} \quad :\!\ddot{F}\!—\!\ddot{F}\!:$$

The formation of a hydrogen fluoride molecule, HF, from a hydrogen atom and a fluorine atom can be shown as

▶ The bonding in gaseous HCl, HBr, and HI is analogous to that in HF.

$$H\cdot \ + \ \cdot\ddot{F}\!: \longrightarrow H:\!\ddot{F}\!: \quad \text{or} \quad H—\!\ddot{F}\!:$$

A water molecule can be represented by either of the following diagrams.

H:O: or   H—O:
 H   H

dot formula   dash formula

An H_2O molecule has two shared electron pairs, that is, two single covalent bonds. The O atom also has two unshared pairs.

▶ In H_2O, two of the six valence electrons of an oxygen atom are used in covalent bonding; the one valence electron of each hydrogen atom is used in covalent bonding.

In *dash formulas*, a shared pair of electrons is indicated by a dash. The following diagrams show the two *double* bonds in carbon dioxide and its Lewis formula.

:O::C::O: or   :O=C=O:

dot formula   dash formula

A CO_2 molecule has four shared electron pairs in two double bonds. The central atom (C) has no unshared pairs.

▶ In CO_2, the four valence electrons of a carbon atom are used in covalent bonding; two of the six valence electrons of each oxygen atom are used in covalent bonding.

▶ A polyatomic ion is an ion that contains more than one atom.

The covalent bonds in a polyatomic ion can be represented in the same way. The Lewis formula for the ammonium ion, NH_4^+, shows only eight electrons, even though the N atom has five electrons in its valence shell and each H atom has one, for a total of $5 + 4(1) = 9$ electrons. The NH_4^+ ion, with a charge of 1+, has one fewer electron than the original atoms.

▶ The NH_3 molecule, like the NH_4^+ ion, has eight valence electrons about the N atom. As we will see in Chapter 8, the three-dimensional shapes of the NH_3 molecule and the NH_4^+ ion are:

$$\begin{bmatrix} H \\ H:N:H \\ H \end{bmatrix}^+ \quad \begin{bmatrix} H \\ | \\ H-N-H \\ | \\ H \end{bmatrix}^+$$

dot formula   dash formula

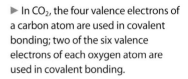

The writing of Lewis formulas is an electron bookkeeping method that is useful as a first approximation to suggest bonding schemes. It is important to remember that Lewis dot formulas only show the number of valence electrons, the number and kinds of bonds, and the order in which the atoms are connected. *They are not intended to show the three-dimensional shapes of molecules and polyatomic ions.* We will see in Chapter 8, however, that the three-dimensional geometry of a molecule can be predicted from its Lewis formula.

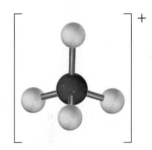

7-6 Writing Lewis Formulas: The Octet Rule

Representative elements usually attain stable noble gas electron configurations when they share electrons. In the water molecule eight electrons are in the outer shell of the O atom, and it has the neon electron configuration; two electrons are in the valence shell of each H atom, and each has the helium electron configuration. Likewise, the C and O of CO_2 and the N of NH_3 and the NH_4^+ ion each have a share in eight electrons in their outer shells. The H atoms in NH_3 and NH_4^+ each share two electrons. Many Lewis formulas are based on the idea that

in *most* of their compounds, the representative elements achieve noble gas configurations.

▶ In some compounds, the central atom does not achieve a noble gas configuration. Such exceptions to the octet rule are discussed in Section 7-8.

This statement is usually called the **octet rule** because the noble gas configurations have $8e^-$ in their outermost shells (except for He, which has $2e^-$).

For now, we restrict our discussion to compounds of the *representative elements*. The octet rule alone does not let us write Lewis formulas. We still must decide how to place the electrons around the bonded atoms—that is, how many of the available valence electrons are present as **bonding pairs** (shared) and how many are as **unshared pairs** (associated with only one atom). A pair of unshared electrons in the same orbital is called a **lone pair**. A simple mathematical relationship is helpful here:

▶ The representative elements are those in the A groups of the periodic table.

$$S = N - A$$

where S is the total number of electrons *shared* in the molecule or polyatomic ion.

N is the total number of valence shell electrons *needed* by all the atoms in the molecule or ion to achieve noble gas configurations ($N = 8 \times$ number of atoms that are not H, plus $2 \times$ number of H atoms).

A is the total number of electrons *available* in the valence shells of all of the (representative) atoms. This is equal to the sum of their periodic group numbers. If necessary, adjust A for ionic charges. To do this, we add electrons to account for negative charges and subtract electrons to account for positive charges.

Let's see how this relationship applies to some species whose Lewis formulas we have already shown.

For F_2,

$$N = 2 \times 8 \text{ (for two F atoms)} = 16e^- \text{ needed}$$

$$A = 2 \times 7 \text{ (for two F atoms)} = 14e^- \text{ available}$$

$$S = N - A = 16 - 14 = 2e^- \text{ shared}$$

:F̈· + ·F̈:
↓
:F̈:F̈:

The Lewis formula for F_2 shows 14 valence electrons total, with $2e^-$ shared in a single bond. An alternative way of approaching this is to focus on the unpaired electrons on each atom and pair them to form a covalent bond.

For HF,

$$N = 1 \times 2 \text{ (for one H atom)} + 1 \times 8 \text{ (for one F atom)} = 10e^- \text{ needed}$$

$$A = 1 \times 1 \text{ (for one H atom)} + 1 \times 7 \text{ (for one F atom)} = 8e^- \text{ available}$$

$$S = N - A = 10 - 8 = 2e^- \text{ shared}$$

H· + ·F̈:
↓
H:F̈:

The Lewis formula for HF shows 8 valence electrons total, with $2e^-$ shared in a single bond. Once again, focusing on the unpaired electrons and pairing them to form a covalent bond gets the same answer.

For H_2O,

$$N = 2 \times 2 \text{ (for two H atoms)} + 1 \times 8 \text{ (for one O atom)} = 12e^- \text{ needed}$$

$$A = 2 \times 1 \text{ (for two H atoms)} + 1 \times 6 \text{ (for one O atom)} = 8e^- \text{ available}$$

$$S = N - A = 12 - 8 = 4e^- \text{ shared}$$

2H· + ·Ö:
↓
H:Ö:
H

The Lewis formula for H_2O shows 8 valence electrons total, with a total of $4\,e^-$ shared, $2\,e^-$ in each single bond. Once again, focusing on the unpaired electrons and pairing them to form two covalent bonds gets the same answer.

For CO_2,

$$N = 1 \times 8 \text{ (for one C atom)} + 2 \times 8 \text{ (for two O atoms)} = 24e^- \text{ needed}$$

$$A = 1 \times 4 \text{ (for one C atom)} + 2 \times 6 \text{ (for two O atoms)} = 16e^- \text{ available}$$

$$S = N - A = 24 - 16 = 8e^- \text{ shared}$$

2Ö: + ·C·
↓
:Ö::C::Ö:

The Lewis formula for CO_2 shows 16 valence electrons total, with a total of $8\,e^-$ shared, $4\,e^-$ in each double bond. For this example, pairing the unpaired electrons is not quite as obvious. The margin diagram shows the O atom with all electrons paired. But if you unpair the electrons on O as shown for the water example above, it becomes more clear that the two unpaired electrons on each oxygen atom can pair with two of the unpaired electrons on each carbon to make two C=O double bonds. Then check to verify that each O and C atom has an octet of electrons in the final Lewis dot structure.

For NH_4^+,

$N = 1 \times 8$ (for one N atom) $+ 4 \times 2$ (for four H atoms) $= 16e^-$ needed

$A = 1 \times 5$ (for one N atom) $+ 4 \times 1$ (for four H atoms) $- 1$ (for 1+ charge) $= 8e^-$ available

$S = N - A = 16 - 8 = 8e^-$ shared

The Lewis formula for NH_4^+ shows 8 valence electrons total, with all 8 e^- shared, 2 e^- in each single bond.

The following general steps describe the use of the $S = N - A$ relationship in constructing dot formulas for molecules and polyatomic ions.

▶ The 1+ ionic charge is due to a *deficiency* of one e^- relative to the neutral atoms.

$$\left[\begin{array}{c} H \\ \cdot\cdot \\ H : N : H \\ \cdot\cdot \\ H \end{array} \right]^+$$

A Guide to Writing Lewis Formulas

1. Select a reasonable (symmetrical) "skeleton" for the molecule or polyatomic ion.

   a. The *least electronegative element* is usually the central element, except that H is never the central element, because it forms only one bond. The least electronegative element is usually the one that needs the most electrons to fill its octet. Example: CS_2 has the skeleton S   C   S.

   b. Carbon bonds to two, three, or four atoms, but *never* more than four. Nitrogen bonds to one (rarely), two, three (most commonly), or four atoms. Oxygen bonds to one, two (most commonly), or three atoms.

   c. Oxygen atoms do not bond to each other except in (1) O_2 and O_3 molecules; (2) hydrogen peroxide, H_2O_2, and its derivatives, the peroxides, which contain the O_2^{2-} group; and (3) the rare superoxides, which contain the O_2^- group. Example: The nitrate ion, NO_3^-, has the skeleton

$$\left[\begin{array}{ccc} & O & \\ & N & \\ O & & O \end{array} \right]^-$$

   d. In *ternary oxoacids*, hydrogen usually bonds to an O atom, *not* to the central atom. Example: Nitrous acid, HNO_2, has the skeleton H   O   N   O. There are a few exceptions to this guideline, such as H_3PO_3 and H_3PO_2.

   e. For ions or molecules that have more than one central atom, the most symmetrical skeletons possible are used. Examples: C_2H_4 and $P_2O_7^{4-}$ have the following skeletons:

▶ A ternary oxoacid contains *three* elements—H, O, and another element, often a nonmetal.

$$\begin{array}{cc} H & H \\ C & C \\ H & H \end{array} \quad \text{and} \quad \left[\begin{array}{ccccc} & O & & O & \\ O & P & O & P & O \\ & O & & O & \end{array} \right]^{4-}$$

2. Calculate N, *the number of valence (outer) shell electrons* needed by all atoms in the molecule or ion to achieve noble gas configurations. Examples:

   For PF_3,

$$N = 1 \times 8 \text{ (P atom)} + 3 \times 8 \text{ (F atoms)} = 32e^- \text{needed}$$

   For CH_3OH,

$$N = 1 \times 8 \text{ (C atom)} + 4 \times 2 \text{ (H atoms)} + 1 \times 8 \text{ (O atom)} = 24e^- \text{needed}$$

   For NO_3^-,

$$N = 1 \times 8 \text{ (N atom)} + 3 \times 8 \text{ (O atoms)} = 32e^- \text{needed}$$

▶ For compounds containing only representative elements, N is equal to 8 × number of atoms that are *not* H, plus 2 × number of H atoms.

▶ For the representative elements, the number of valence shell electrons in an atom is equal to its periodic group number. Exceptions: 1 for an H atom and 2 for He.

Calculate A, *the number of electrons available* in the valence (outer) shells of all the atoms. For negatively charged ions, add to this total the number of electrons equal to the charge on the anion; for positively charged ions, subtract the number of electrons equal to the charge on the cation. Examples:

For PF_3,

$$A = 1 \times 5 \text{ (P atom)} + 3 \times 7 \text{ (F atoms)} = 26 e^- \text{ available}$$

For CH_3OH,

$$A = 1 \times 4 \text{ (C atom)} + 4 \times 1 \text{ (H atoms)} + 1 \times 6 \text{ (O atom)} = 14 e^- \text{ available}$$

For NO_3^-,

$$A = 1 \times 5 \text{ (N atom)} + 3 \times 6 \text{ (O atoms)} + 1 \text{ (for } 1- \text{ charge)} = 5 + 18 + 1$$

$$= 24 e^- \text{ available}$$

Calculate S, *total number of electrons shared* in the molecule or ion, using the relationship $S = N - A$. Examples:

For PF_3,

$$S = N - A = 32 - 26$$

$$= 6 \text{ electrons shared (3 pairs of } e^- \text{ shared)}$$

For CH_3OH,

$$S = N - A = 24 - 14$$

$$= 10 \text{ electrons shared (5 pairs of } e^- \text{ shared)}$$

For NO_3^-,

$$S = N - A = 32 - 24 = 8 e^- \text{ shared (4 pairs of } e^- \text{ shared)}$$

▶ C, N, and O often form double and triple bonds. S can form double bonds with C, N, and O.

3. Place the S electrons into the skeleton as shared pairs. Use double and triple bonds only when necessary. Lewis formulas may be shown as either dot formulas or dash formulas.

▶ Formulas are sometimes written to give clues about which atoms are bonded together. In this format, the H atoms are bonded to the atom preceding them; in CH_3OH the first three H atoms are bonded to C, and the last H atom is bonded to O. Unfortunately, oxoacids rarely follow this guideline. In H_2SO_4, HNO_3, and H_3PO_4, the hydrogen atoms are attached to the oxygen atoms.

Formula	Skeleton	Dot Formula ("bonds" in place, but incomplete)	Dash Formula ("bonds" in place, but incomplete)
PF_3	F P F F	F : P : F .. F	F —P— F | F
CH_3OH	H H C O H H	H .. H : C : O : H .. H	H | H— C —O—H | H
NO_3^-	$\left[\begin{array}{c} O \\ N \\ O \quad O \end{array}\right]^-$	$\left[\begin{array}{c} O \\ ..N.. \\ O \quad O \end{array}\right]^-$	$\left[\begin{array}{c} O \\ \| \\ N \\ O \quad O \end{array}\right]^-$

4. Place the additional electrons into the skeleton as *unshared (lone) pairs* to fill the octet of every A group element (except H, which can share only $2 e^-$). Check that the total number of valence electrons is equal to A, from Step 2. Examples:

For PF_3,

$$: \ddot{F} : \ddot{P} : \ddot{F} : \qquad \text{or} \qquad : \ddot{F} — P — \ddot{F} :$$
$$: \ddot{F} : \qquad\qquad\qquad : \ddot{F} :$$

Check: 13 pairs of e^- have been used and all octets are satisfied. $2 \times 13 = 26\,e^-$ available.

For CH_3OH,

$$
\begin{array}{ccc}
& \text{H} & \\
& \ddot{} & \\
\text{H} : \ddot{\text{C}} : \ddot{\text{O}} : \text{H} & \quad\text{or}\quad & \text{H}-\overset{\displaystyle \text{H}}{\underset{\displaystyle \text{H}}{\text{C}}}-\ddot{\text{O}}-\text{H} \\
& \text{H} &
\end{array}
$$

Check: 7 pairs of e^- have been used and all octets are satisfied. $2 \times 7 = 14\,e^-$ available.

For NO_3^-,

$$
\left[\;\ddot{\underset{..}{\text{O}}}\;\atop{\underset{..}{\ddot{\text{O}}} \; \text{N} \; \underset{..}{\ddot{\text{O}}}}\right]^- \quad\text{or}\quad \left[\;\overset{\text{O}}{\underset{..}{\ddot{\text{O}} \; \text{N} \; \ddot{\text{O}}}}\;\right]^-
$$

Check: 12 pairs of e^- have been used and all octets are satisfied. $2 \times 12 = 24\,e^-$ available.

EXAMPLE 7-1 Writing Lewis Formulas

Write the Lewis formula for the nitrogen molecule, N_2.

Plan

We follow the stepwise procedure that was just presented for writing Lewis formulas.

Solution

Step 1: The skeleton is N N.

Step 2: $N = 2 \times 8 = 16\,e^-$ needed (total) by both atoms

$A = 2 \times 5 = 10\,e^-$ available (total) for both atoms

$S = N - A = 16\,e^- - 10\,e^- = 6\,e^-$ shared

Step 3: $\text{N} ::: \text{N}$ $6\,e^-$ (3 pairs) are shared; a *triple* bond.

Step 4: The additional $4\,e^-$ are accounted for by a lone pair on each N. The complete Lewis formula is

$$:\text{N} ::: \text{N}: \quad\text{or}\quad :\text{N} \equiv \text{N}:$$

▶ We see that each N forms three bonds.

Check: $10\,e^-$ (5 pairs) have been used.

You should now work Exercise 30.

EXAMPLE 7-2 Writing Lewis Formulas

Write the Lewis formula for carbon disulfide, CS_2, a foul-smelling liquid.

Plan

Again, we follow the stepwise procedure to apply the relationship $S = N - A$.

Solution

Step 1: The skeleton is S   C   S.

Step 2: $N = 1 \times 8$ (for C) $+ 2 \times 8$ (for S) $= 24e^-$ needed by all atoms

$A = 1 \times 4$ (for C) $+ 2 \times 6$ (for S) $= 16e^-$ available

$S = N - A = 24e^- - 16e^- = 8e^-$ shared

Step 3: S::C::S $8e^-$ (4 pairs) are shared; two *double* bonds.

▶ C is the central atom, or the element in the middle of the molecule. It needs four more electrons to acquire an octet, and forms four bonds. Each S atom needs only two more electrons.

Step 4: C already has an octet, so the remaining $8\,e^-$ are distributed as lone pairs on the S atoms to give each S an octet. The complete Lewis formula is

$$\ddot{\text{S}}::\text{C}::\ddot{\text{S}} \qquad \text{or} \qquad \ddot{\text{S}}=\text{C}=\ddot{\text{S}}$$

Check: $16\,e^-$ (8 pairs) have been used. The bonding picture is similar to that of CO_2; this is not surprising, because S is below O in Group 6A.

You should now work Exercise 32.

EXAMPLE 7-3 Writing Lewis Formulas   MOLECULAR REASONING

Write the Lewis formula for the carbonate ion, CO_3^{2-}.

Plan

The same stepwise procedure can be applied to ions. We must remember to adjust A, the total number of electrons, to account for the charge shown on the ion.

Solution

Step 1: The skeleton is $\left[\begin{array}{c} \text{O} \\ \text{O} \quad \text{C} \quad \text{O} \end{array} \right]^{2-}$

Step 2: $N = 1 \times 8$ (for C) $+ 3 \times 8$ (for O) $= 8 + 24 = 32\,e^-$ needed by all atoms

$A = 1 \times 4$ (for C) $+ 3 \times 6$ (for O) $+ 2$ (for the $2-$ charge)

$= 4 + 18 + 2 = 24\,e^-$ available

$S = N - A = 32\,e^- - 24\,e^- = 8\,e^-$ (4 pairs) shared

Step 3: $\left[\begin{array}{c} \text{O} \\ \text{O} \quad \text{C} \quad \text{O} \end{array} \right]^{2-}$ (Four pairs are shared. At this point it doesn't matter which O is doubly bonded.)

Step 4: The Lewis formula is

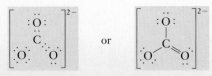

or

Check: $24\,e^-$ (12 pairs) have been used.

You should now work Exercises 36 and 38.

Calcium carbonate, $CaCO_3$, occurs in several forms in nature. The mineral calcite forms very large clear crystals (*right*); in microcrystalline form it is the main constituent of limestone (*top left*). Seashells (*bottom*) are largely calcium carbonate.

▶ We see that carbon forms four bonds.

You should practice writing many Lewis formulas. A few common types of organic compounds and their Lewis formulas are shown here. Each follows the octet rule. Methane, CH_4, is the simplest of a huge family of organic compounds called *hydrocarbons* (composed solely of hydrogen and carbon). Ethane, C_2H_6, is another hydrocarbon that contains only single bonds. Ethylene, C_2H_4, has a carbon–carbon double bond, and acetylene, C_2H_2, contains a carbon–carbon triple bond.

$$
\begin{array}{cccc}
\underset{\text{methane, } CH_4}{\overset{\displaystyle H}{\underset{\displaystyle H}{H-\underset{|}{\overset{|}{C}}-H}}}
&
\underset{\text{ethane, } C_2H_6}{\overset{\displaystyle H \quad H}{\underset{\displaystyle H \quad H}{H-\underset{|}{\overset{|}{C}}-\underset{|}{\overset{|}{C}}-H}}}
&
\underset{\text{ethylene, } C_2H_4}{\overset{H}{\underset{H}{}}\!\!C=C\!\!\overset{H}{\underset{H}{}}}
&
\underset{\text{acetylene, } C_2H_2}{H-C\equiv C-H}
\end{array}
$$

▶ For practice, apply the methods of this section to write these Lewis formulas. In each of these, carbon forms four bonds.

Halogen atoms can appear in place of hydrogen atoms in many organic compounds because hydrogen and halogen atoms each need one more electron to attain noble gas configurations. An example is chloroform, $CHCl_3$. Alcohols contain the group $C-O-H$; the most common alcohol is ethanol, CH_3CH_2OH. An organic compound that contains a carbon–oxygen double bond is formaldehyde, H_2CO.

$$
\begin{array}{ccc}
\underset{\text{chloroform, } CHCl_3}{\ddot{\underset{\displaystyle :\ddot{C}l:}{:\ddot{C}l-\underset{|}{\overset{|}{C}}-\ddot{C}l:}}}
&
\underset{\text{ethanol, } CH_3CH_2OH}{\overset{\displaystyle H \quad H}{\underset{\displaystyle H \quad H}{H-\underset{|}{\overset{|}{C}}-\underset{|}{\overset{|}{C}}-\ddot{O}-H}}}
&
\underset{\text{formaldehyde, } H_2CO}{\overset{\displaystyle \ddot{\overset{..}{O}}}{\underset{H\qquad H}{\overset{\|}{C}}}}
\end{array}
$$

Problem-Solving Tip Drawing Lewis Formulas

The following guidelines might help you draw Lewis formulas.

1. In most of their covalent compounds, the representative elements follow the octet rule, except that hydrogen always shares only two electrons.

2. Hydrogen forms only one bond to another element; thus hydrogen can never be a central atom.

3. Carbon forms four bonds (carbon monoxide, $:C\equiv O:$, and cyanide ion, $:C\equiv N:^-$, are prominent exceptions). This can be accomplished as:

   a. four single bonds

   b. two double bonds

   c. two single bonds and one double bond or

   d. one single bond and one triple bond

4. In neutral (uncharged) species, nitrogen forms three bonds, and oxygen forms two bonds.

5. In positive ions, nitrogen can form four bonds (e.g., NH_4^+) and oxygen can form three bonds (e.g., H_3O^+).

6. Nonmetals can form single, double, or triple bonds, but never quadruple bonds.

7. Carbon forms double or triple bonds to C, N, O, or S atoms; oxygen can form double bonds with many other elements.

8. Carbon is the only element that has a high tendency to form stable bonds with itself in compounds with other elements.

▶ C, N, and O often form double and triple bonds. S can form double bonds with C, N, and O.

7-7 Formal Charges

Formal charge is the hypothetical charge on an atom *in a molecule or polyatomic ion*; to find the formal charge, we count bonding electrons as though they were equally shared between the two bonded atoms. The concept of formal charges helps us to write correct Lewis formulas in most cases. The most energetically favorable formula for a molecule is usually one in which the formal charge on each atom is zero or as near zero as possible.

► The H^+ ion has a vacant orbital, which accepts a share in the lone pair on nitrogen. The formation of a covalent bond by the sharing of an electron pair that is provided by one atom is called *coordinate covalent bond formation*. This type of bond formation is discussed again in Chapters 10 and 25.

Consider the reaction of NH_3 with hydrogen ion, H^+, to form the ammonium ion, NH_4^+.

$$H-\overset{..}{\underset{|}{N}}-H + H^+ \longrightarrow \left[H-\overset{\overset{H}{|}}{\underset{\underset{H}{|}}{N}}-H \right]^+$$

The previously unshared pair of electrons on the N atom in the NH_3 molecule is shared with the H^+ ion to form the NH_4^+ ion, in which the N atom has four covalent bonds. Because N is a Group 5A element, we expect it to form three covalent bonds to complete its octet. How can we describe the fact that N has four covalent bonds in species like NH_4^+? The answer is obtained by calculating the *formal charge* on each atom in NH_4^+ by the following rules.

Rules for Assigning Formal Charges to Atoms of Group A Elements

1. The formal charge, abbreviated FC, on an atom in a Lewis formula is given by the relationship

    FC = (group number) − [(number of bonds) + (number of unshared e^-)]

    Formal charges are represented by ⊕ and ⊖ to distinguish them from real charges on ions.

2. In a Lewis formula, an atom that has the same number of bonds plus unshared electrons as its periodic group number has a formal charge of zero.

3. **a.** In a molecule, the sum of the formal charges is zero.

    b. In a polyatomic ion, the sum of the formal charges is equal to the charge on the ion.

Let us apply these rules to the ammonia molecule, NH_3, and to the ammonium ion, NH_4^+. Because N is a Group 5A element, its group number is 5.

$$H-\overset{..}{\underset{\underset{H}{|}}{N}}-H \qquad \left[H-\overset{\overset{H}{|}}{\underset{\underset{H}{|}}{N}}-H \right]^+$$

In NH_3 the N atom has 3 bonds and 2 unshared e^-, and so for N,

    FC = (group number) − [(number of bonds) + (number of unshared e^-)]
    　　 = 5 − (3 + 2) = 0 (for N)

For H,

    FC = (group number) − [(number of bonds) + (number of unshared e^-)]
    　　 = 1 − (1 + 0) = 0 (for H)

The formal charges of N and H are both zero in NH_3, so the sum of the formal charges is $0 + 3(0) = 0$, consistent with Rule 3a.

In NH_4^+ the atom has four bonds and no unshared e^-, and so for N,

    FC = (group number) − [(number of bonds) + (number of unshared e^-)]
    　　 = 5 − (4 + 0) = +1 (for N)

Calculation of the FC for H atoms gives zero, as shown previously. The sum of the formal charges in NH_4^+ is $(+1) + 4(0) = +1$. This is consistent with Rule 3b.

► FCs are indicated by ⊕ and ⊖. The sum of the formal charges in a polyatomic ion is equal to the charge on the ion: $+1$ in NH_4^+.

$$\left[H-\overset{\overset{H}{|}}{\underset{\underset{H}{|}}{\overset{\oplus}{N}}}-H \right]^+$$

Thus, we see the octet rule is obeyed in both NH_3 and NH_4^+. The sum of the formal charges in each case is that predicted by Rule 3, even though nitrogen has four covalent bonds in the NH_4^+ ion.

This bookkeeping system helps us to choose among various Lewis formulas for a molecule or ion, according to the following guidelines.

> **a.** The most likely formula for a molecule or ion is usually one in which the formal charge on each atom is zero or as near zero as possible.
> **b.** Negative formal charges are more likely to occur on the more electronegative elements.
> **c.** Lewis formulas in which adjacent atoms have formal charges of the same sign are usually *not* accurate representations (the *adjacent charge rule*).

Now let's write some Lewis formulas for, and assign formal charges to, the atoms in nitrosyl chloride, NOCl, a compound often used in organic synthesis. The Cl atom and the O atom are both bonded to the N atom. Two Lewis formulas that satisfy the octet rule are

(i) $:\!\overset{\oplus}{Cl}\!=\!N\!-\!\overset{..}{\underset{..}{O}}\!:^{\ominus}$ (ii) $:\!\overset{..}{\underset{..}{Cl}}\!-\!N\!=\!\overset{..}{O}\!:$

For Cl, FC $= 7 - (2 + 4) = +1$ For Cl, FC $= 7 - (1 + 6) = 0$

For N, FC $= 5 - (3 + 2) = 0$ For N, FC $= 5 - (3 + 2) = 0$

For O, FC $= 6 - (1 + 6) = -1$ For O, FC $= 6 - (2 + 4) = 0$

We believe that (ii) is a preferable Lewis formula because it has smaller formal charges than (i). We see that a double-bonded terminal Cl atom would have its electrons arranged as $:\!\overset{.}{Cl}\!=\!X$, with the formal charge of Cl equal to $7 - (2 + 4) = +1$. A positive formal charge on such an electronegative element is quite unlikely, and double bonding to chlorine does not occur. The same reasoning would apply to the other halogens.

Problem-Solving Tip Calculating Formal Charges

A quick way to calculate formal charges for C, N, O, or F (and that generally holds for Cl, Br, and I as well) is to note the number of covalent bonds to that atom when it has an octet of electrons. The normal numbers of covalent bonds are: C $= 4$, N $= 3$, O $= 2$, and F $= 1$. For each bond that exceeds the normal number of covalent bonds, add a formal positive charge to that atom. For each atom that has fewer covalent bonds, add a formal negative charge for each missing covalent bond.

For example, consider carbon monoxide:

$$:\!C\!\equiv\!O\!:$$

Each atom has an octet of electrons. The C atom, however, has only three covalent bonds, one fewer than usual, so it is assigned a formal charge of -1. The O atom has three covalent bonds when it normally should have only two, so it is assigned a formal charge of $+1$.

In structure (i) of the previous example, $:\!\overset{.}{Cl}\!=\!N\!-\!\overset{..}{O}\!:$, the Cl has two covalent bonds (normal $= 1$), so it is assigned a formal charge of $+1$. The O atom has only a single covalent bond (normal $= 2$), so it is assigned a formal charge of -1. The N atom has three covalent bonds (normal $= 3$), so it has a formal charge of 0.

7-8 Writing Lewis Formulas: Limitations of the Octet Rule

Recall that representative elements achieve noble gas electron configurations in *most* of their compounds. But when the octet rule is not applicable, the relationship $S = N - A$ will not work without modification. The following are general cases for which the procedure in Section 7-6 *must be modified*—that is, there are four types of limitations of the octet rule.

A. Most covalent compounds of beryllium, Be. Because Be contains only two valence shell electrons, it usually forms only two covalent bonds when it bonds to two other atoms. We therefore use *four electrons* as the number *needed* by Be in Step 2. In Steps 3 and 4 we use only two pairs of electrons for Be.

B. Most covalent compounds of the Group 3A elements, especially boron, B. The 3A elements contain only three valence shell electrons, so they often form three covalent bonds when they bond to three other atoms. We therefore use *six electrons* as the number *needed* by the 3A elements in Step 2. In Steps 3 and 4 we use only three pairs of electrons for the 3A elements.

C. Compounds or ions containing an odd number of electrons. Examples are NO, with 11 valence shell electrons, and NO_2, with 17 valence shell electrons.

D. Compounds or ions in which the central element needs a share in more than eight valence shell electrons to hold all the available electrons, *A*. We say that the central atom in such species has an **expanded valence shell**. Extra rules are added to Steps 2 and 4 when this is encountered.

> ▶ An atom cannot share in more than eight electrons using only *s* and *p* orbitals. To do so, it must have *d* or *f* valence shell orbitals. Thus, Limitation D can occur only for elements beyond Period 2.

> ▶ Lewis formulas are not normally written for compounds containing *d*- and *f*-transition metals. The *d*- and *f*-transition metals utilize *d* or *f* orbitals (or both) in bonding as well as *s* and *p* orbitals. Thus, they can accommodate more than eight valence electrons.

Step 2a: If S, the number of electrons shared, is less than the number needed to bond all atoms to the central atom, then S is increased to the number of electrons needed.

Step 4a: If S must be increased in Step 2a, then the octets of all the atoms might be satisfied before all of the electrons (*A*) have been added. Place the extra electrons on the central element.

Many species that violate the octet rule are quite reactive. For instance, compounds containing atoms with only four valence shell electrons (limitation type A) or six valence shell electrons (limitation type B) frequently react with other species that supply electron pairs. A compound that accepts a share in a pair of electrons is called a **Lewis acid**; a **Lewis base** is a species that makes available a share in a pair of electrons. (This kind of behavior will be discussed in detail in Section 10-10.) Molecules with an odd number of electrons often *dimerize* (combine in pairs) to give products that do satisfy the octet rule. Examples are the dimerization of NO to form N_2O_2 (Section 28-15) and NO_2 to form N_2O_4 (Section 28-15). Examples 7-4 through 7-8 illustrate some limitations and show how such Lewis formulas are constructed.

EXAMPLE 7-4   **Limitation A of the Octet Rule**

Write the Lewis formula for gaseous beryllium chloride, $BeCl_2$, a covalent compound.

Plan

This is an example of limitation type A. So, as we follow the steps in writing the Lewis formula, we must remember to use *four electrons* as the number *needed* by Be in Step 2. Steps 3 and 4 should show only two pairs of electrons for Be.

Solution

Step 1: The skeleton is Cl Be Cl

                                     see limitation type A
                                           ↓

Step 2: $N = 2 \times 8$ (for Cl) $+ 1 \times 4$ (for Be) $= 20e^-$ needed

         $A = 2 \times 7$ (for Cl) $+ 1 \times 2$ (for Be) $= 16e^-$ available

         $S = N - A = 20e^- - 16e^- = 4e^-$ shared

Step 3: Cl: Be: Cl

Step 4: $:\!\overset{..}{Cl}\!:Be:\overset{..}{Cl}\!:$ or $:\!\overset{..}{Cl}\!—Be—\overset{..}{Cl}\!:$

Calculation of formal charges shows that

       for Be, FC $= 2 - (2 + 0) = 0$ and   for Cl, FC $= 7 - (1 + 6) = 0$

In $BeCl_2$, the chlorine atoms achieve the argon configuration, [Ar], but the beryllium atom has a share of only four electrons. Compounds such as $BeCl_2$, in which the central atom shares fewer than $8\,e^-$, are sometimes referred to as **electron-deficient compounds**. This "deficiency" refers only to satisfying the octet rule for the central atom. The term does not imply that there are fewer electrons than there are protons in the nuclei, as in the case of a cation, because the molecule is neutral.

A Lewis formula can be written for $BeCl_2$ that *does* satisfy the octet rule

$$\ddot{\text{C}}\text{l}=\text{Be}=\text{Cl}\!:\!$$

Let us evaluate the formal charges for that formula:

for Be, FC $= 2 - (4 + 0) = -2$ and for Cl, FC $= 7 - (2 + 4) = +1$

We have said that the most favorable structure for a molecule is one in which the formal charge on each atom is as near zero as possible. In case some atoms did have nonzero formal charges, we would expect that the more electronegative atoms (Cl) would be the ones with lowest formal charge. Thus, we prefer the Lewis structure shown in Example 7-4 over the double-bonded one above.

One might expect a similar situation for compounds of the other 2A metals, Mg, Ca, Sr, Ba, and Ra. These elements, however, have *lower ionization energies*, *lower electronegativities*, and *larger radii* than Be, so they usually form ions by losing two electrons. Mg, Ca, Sr, Ba, and Ra, therefore, form ionic compounds.

BF$_3$ and BCl$_3$ are gases at room temperature. Liquid BBr$_3$ and solid BI$_3$ are shown here.

Charles D. Winters

EXAMPLE 7-5 Limitation B of the Octet Rule

MOLECULAR REASONING

Write the Lewis formula for boron trichloride, BCl_3, a covalent compound.

Plan

This covalent compound of boron is an example of limitation type B. As we follow the steps in writing the Lewis formula, we use *six electrons* as the number *needed* by boron in Step 2. Steps 3 and 4 should show only three pairs of electrons for boron.

Solution

$$\text{Cl}$$

Step 1: The skeleton is Cl B Cl

see limitation type B

Step 2: $N = 3 \times 8$ (for Cl) $+ 1 \times 6$ (for B) $= 30e^-$ needed

$A = 3 \times 7$ (for Cl) $+ 1 \times 3$ (for B) $= 24e^-$ available

$S = N - A = 30e^- - 24e^- = 6e^-$ shared

Step 3:
$$\begin{array}{c} \text{Cl} \\ \text{Cl} : \ddot{\text{B}} : \text{Cl} \end{array}$$

Step 4:
$$:\ddot{\text{C}}\text{l}: \\ :\ddot{\text{C}}\text{l} : \ddot{\text{B}} : \ddot{\text{C}}\text{l}: \quad \text{or} \quad :\ddot{\text{C}}\text{l} - \ddot{\text{B}} - \ddot{\text{C}}\text{l}:$$

Each chlorine atom achieves the Ne configuration. The boron (central) atom acquires a share of only six valence shell electrons. Calculation of formal charges shows that

for B, FC $= 3 - (3 + 0) = 0$ and   for Cl, FC $= 7 - (1 + 6) = 0$

You should now work Exercise 52.

EXAMPLE 7-6 Limitation D of the Octet Rule

Write the Lewis formula for phosphorus pentafluoride, PF_5, a covalent compound.

Plan

We apply the usual stepwise procedure to write the Lewis formula. In PF_5, all five F atoms are bonded to P. This requires the sharing of a minimum of $10\ e^-$, so this is an example of limitation type D. We therefore add Step 2a, and increase S from the calculated value of $8\ e^-$ to $10\ e^-$.

Solution

Step 1: The skeleton is

$$
\begin{matrix}
 & & F & & \\
 & F & P & F & \\
 & & F & F &
\end{matrix}
$$

Step 2: $N = 5 \times 8$ (for F) $+ 1 \times 8$ (for P) $= 48 e^-$ needed

$A = 5 \times 7$ (for F) $+ 1 \times 5$ (for P) $= 40 e^-$ available

$S = N - A = 8 e^-$ shared

Five F atoms are bonded to P. This requires the sharing of a minimum of $10 e^-$. But only $8 e^-$ have been calculated. This is therefore an example of limitation type D.

Step 2a: Increase S from $8 e^-$ to $10 e^-$, the number required to bond five F atoms to one P atom. The number of electrons available, 40, does not change.

Step 3:

$$
\begin{matrix}
 & & \ddot{F} & & \\
 & F\!:\! & P & \!:\!F & \\
 & & F & F &
\end{matrix}
$$

Step 4:

$$
\begin{matrix}
 & \ddot{\ddot{F}}\!: & \\
:\ddot{F}\!\cdot & P & \cdot\ddot{F}: \\
 & \dot{F}\!: \ \!:\dot{F} &
\end{matrix}
\qquad \text{or} \qquad
\begin{matrix}
 & :\ddot{F}: & \\
:\ddot{F}\!-\! & P & \!-\!\ddot{F}: \\
 & :\ddot{F}\ \ \ddot{F}: &
\end{matrix}
$$

When the octets of the five F atoms have been satisfied, all 40 of the available electrons have been added. The phosphorus (central) atom has a share of 10 electrons.

Calculation of formal charges shows that

for P, FC $= 5 - (5 + 0) = 0$ and for F, FC $= 7 - (1 + 6) = 0$

You should now work Exercise 56.

▶ An atom that exhibits an expanded valence shell is said to be **hypervalent**.

We see that P in PF_5 exhibits an expanded valence shell. The electronic basis of the octet rule is that one s and three p orbitals in the valence shell of an atom can accommodate a maximum of eight electrons. The valence shell of phosphorus has $n = 3$, so it also has $3d$ orbitals available that can be involved in bonding. The availability of valence shell d orbitals allows phosphorus (and many other representative elements of Period 3 and beyond) to exhibit an expanded valence shell. By contrast, elements in the *second row* of the periodic table can *never* exceed eight electrons in their valence shells because each atom has only one s and three p orbitals in that shell. Thus, we understand why PF_5 can exist but NF_5 cannot.

EXAMPLE 7-7 Limitation D of the Octet Rule

Write the Lewis formula for sulfur tetrafluoride, SF_4.

Plan

We apply the usual stepwise procedure. The calculation of $S = N - A$ in Step 2 shows only $6e^-$ shared, but a minimum of $8e^-$ are required to bond four F atoms to the central S atom. Limitation type D applies, and we proceed accordingly.

Solution

Step 1: The skeleton is $\begin{matrix} F & & F \\ & S & \\ F & & F \end{matrix}$

Step 2: $N = 1 \times 8$ (S atom) $+ 4 \times 8$ (F atom) $= 40e^-$ needed

$A = 1 \times 6$ (S atom) $+ 4 \times 7$ (F atom) $= 34e^-$ available

$S = N - A = 40 - 34 = 6e^-$ shared. Four F atoms are bonded to the central S. This requires a minimum of $8e^-$, but only $6e^-$ have been calculated in Step 2. This is therefore an example of limitation type D.

Step 2a: We increase S from $6e^-$ to $8e^-$.

Step 3: $\begin{matrix} F: & & :F \\ & S & \\ F & & F \end{matrix}$

Step 4: $\begin{matrix} :\!\ddot F: & & :\!\ddot F: \\ & S & \\ :\!\ddot F: & & :\!\ddot F: \end{matrix}$ We first complete octets on the atoms around the central atom.

Step 4a: Now we have satisfied the octet rule, but we have used only 32 of the $34e^-$ available. We place the other two electrons on the central S atom.

▶ The availability of valence shell *d* orbitals allows sulfur to have an expanded valence shell in SF_4.

Calculation of the formal charge shows that

for S, FC $= 6 - (4 + 2) = 0$

for F, FC $= 7 - (1 + 6) = 0$

You should now work Exercise 51.

EXAMPLE 7-8 Limitation D of the Octet Rule

Write the Lewis formula for the triiodide ion, I_3^-.

Plan

We apply the usual stepwise procedure. The calculation of $S = N - A$ in Step 2 shows only $2e^-$ shared, but at least $4e^-$ are required to bond two I atoms to the central I. Limitation type D applies, and we proceed accordingly.

Solution

Step 1: The skeleton is $[\text{I I I}]^-$

Step 2: $N = 3 \times 8$ (for I) $= 24\,e^-$ needed

$A = 3 \times 7$ (for I) $+ 1$ (for the $1-$ charge) $= 22\,e^-$ available

$S = N - A = 2\,e^-$ shared. Two I atoms are bonded to the central I. This requires a minimum of $4\,e^-$, but only $2\,e^-$ have been calculated in Step 4. This is therefore an example of limitation type D.

Step 2a: Increase S from $2\,e^-$ to $4\,e^-$.

Step 3: $[\text{I:I:I}]^-$

Step 4: $\left[:\!\ddot{\text{I}}:\!\ddot{\text{I}}:\!\ddot{\text{I}}:\right]^-$

Step 4a: Now we have satisfied the octets of all atoms using only 20 of the $22\,e^-$ available. We place the other two electrons on the central I atom.

$$\left[:\!\ddot{\ddot{\text{I}}}:\!\ddot{\text{I}}:\!\ddot{\ddot{\text{I}}}:\right]^- \qquad \text{or} \qquad \left[:\!\ddot{\ddot{\text{I}}}\!-\!\ddot{\text{I}}\!-\!\ddot{\ddot{\text{I}}}:\right]^-$$

Calculation of the formal charge shows that

for I on ends, FC $= 7 - (1 + 6) = 0$

for I in middle, FC $= 7 - (2 + 6) = -1$

You should now work Exercise 55.

▶ The central iodine atom in I_3^- has an expanded valence shell.

A Lewis formula for sulfuric acid, H_2SO_4, can be written that follows the octet rule. This Lewis formula and the formal charges are

$$\begin{array}{c} :\!\ddot{\text{O}}: \\ | \\ \text{H}-\ddot{\text{O}}-\text{S}-\ddot{\text{O}}-\text{H} \\ | \\ :\!\ddot{\text{O}}: \end{array}$$

for S, FC $= 6 - (4 + 0) = +2$

for H, FC $= 1 - (1 + 0) = 0$

for O (in –OH), FC $= 6 - (2 + 4) = 0$

for other O, FC $= 6 - (1 + 6) = -1$

As we saw in Example 7-7, the availability of d orbitals in its valence shell permits sulfur to have an expanded valence shell. A different Lewis formula that does *not* follow the octet rule is

$$\begin{array}{c} \cdot\ddot{\text{O}}\cdot \\ \| \\ \text{H}-\ddot{\text{O}}-\text{S}-\ddot{\text{O}}-\text{H} \\ \| \\ \cdot\ddot{\text{O}}\cdot \end{array}$$

for S, FC $= 6 - (6 + 0) = 0$

for H, FC $= 1 - (1 + 0) = 0$

for O (in –OH), FC $= 6 - (2 + 4) = 0$

for other O, FC $= 6 - (2 + 4) = 0$

Many chemists prefer this formula because it has more favorable formal charges.

We have seen that *atoms attached to the central atom nearly always attain noble gas configurations*, even when the central atom does not.

7-9 Resonance

In addition to the Lewis formula shown in Example 7-3, two other Lewis formulas with the same skeleton for the CO_3^{2-} ion are equally acceptable. In these formulas, the double bond could be between the carbon atom and either of the other two oxygen atoms.

$$\left[\begin{array}{c} \ddot{O} \\ \ddot{O} \diagdown C \diagup \ddot{O} \end{array}\right]^{2-} \longleftrightarrow \left[\begin{array}{c} \ddot{O} \\ \ddot{O} \diagdown C \diagup \ddot{O} \end{array}\right]^{2-} \longleftrightarrow \left[\begin{array}{c} O \\ \diagdown C \diagup \\ \ddot{O} \qquad \ddot{O} \end{array}\right]^{2-}$$

A molecule or polyatomic ion for which two or more Lewis formulas *with the same arrangements of atoms* can be drawn to describe the bonding is said to exhibit **resonance**. The three structures shown here are *resonance structures* of the carbonate ion. The relationship among them is indicated by the double-headed arrows, ↔. This symbol *does not mean* that the ion flips back and forth among these three structures. The true structure can be described as an average, or hybrid, of the three.

Experiments show that the C—O bonds in CO_3^{2-} are *neither* double nor single bonds but are intermediate in bond length and strength. Based on measurements in many compounds, the typical C—O single bond length is 1.43 Å, and the typical C=O double bond length is 1.22 Å. The C—O bond length for each bond in the CO_3^{2-} ion is intermediate at 1.29 Å. Another way to represent this situation is by **delocalization** of bonding electrons:

$$\left[\begin{array}{c} O \\ \| \\ O \diagup C \diagdown O \end{array}\right]^{2-} \quad \text{(lone pairs on O atoms not shown)}$$

▶ When electrons are shared among more than two atoms, the electrons are said to be *delocalized*. The concept of delocalization is important in molecular orbital theory (see Chapter 9).

The dashed lines indicate that some of the electrons shared between C and O atoms are *delocalized* among all four atoms; that is, the four pairs of shared electrons are equally distributed among three C—O bonds.

EXAMPLE 7-9 Lewis Formulas, Resonance

MOLECULAR REASONING

Draw two resonance structures for the sulfur dioxide molecule, SO_2.

Plan

The stepwise procedure (see Section 7–6) can be used to write each resonance structure.

Solution

$$\begin{array}{cc} S & O \\ \searrow & \searrow \end{array}$$

$$N = 1(8) + 2(8) = 24e^-$$

$$A = 1(6) + 2(6) = 18e^-$$

$$\overline{S = N - A \qquad\quad = 6e^- \text{ shared}}$$

The resonance structures are

or

$$\ddot{O}=\ddot{S}-\ddot{O}\colon \longleftrightarrow \colon\ddot{O}-\ddot{S}=\ddot{O}$$

We could show delocalization of electrons as follows:

$$O = \ddot{S} = O \quad \text{(lone pairs on O not shown)}$$

Remember that Lewis formulas *do not necessarily show shapes*. SO_2 molecules are angular, not linear.

You should now work Exercises 60 and 62.

The rose on the left is in an atmosphere of sulfur dioxide, SO_2. Gaseous SO_2 and its aqueous solutions are used as bleaching agents. A similar process is used to bleach wood pulp before it is converted to paper.

Charles D. Winters

7-10 Polar and Nonpolar Covalent Bonds

Covalent bonds may be either *polar* or *nonpolar*. In a **nonpolar bond** such as that in the hydrogen molecule, H_2 (H:H or H — H), the electron pair is *shared equally* between the two hydrogen nuclei. We defined electronegativity as the tendency of an atom to attract electrons to itself in a chemical bond (see Section 5-6). Both H atoms have the same electronegativity. This means that the shared electrons are equally attracted to both hydrogen nuclei and therefore spend equal amounts of time near each nucleus. In this nonpolar covalent bond, the *electron density* is symmetrical about a plane that is perpendicular to a line between the two nuclei. This is true for all homonuclear *diatomic molecules*, such as H_2, O_2, N_2, F_2, and Cl_2, because the two identical atoms have identical electronegativities. We can generalize:

▶ A **homonuclear** molecule contains only one kind of atom. A molecule that contains two or more kinds of atoms is described as **heteronuclear**.

The covalent bonds in all homonuclear diatomic molecules must be nonpolar.

Let us now consider *heteronuclear diatomic molecules*. Start with the fact that hydrogen fluoride, HF, is a gas at room temperature. This tells us that it is a covalent compound because ionic compounds are solids at room temperature. We also know that the H — F bond has some degree of polarity because H and F are not identical atoms and therefore do not attract the electrons equally. But how polar will this bond be?

The electronegativity of hydrogen is 2.1, and that of fluorine is 4.0 (see Table 5-3). The F atom, with its higher electronegativity, attracts the shared electron pair much more strongly than does the H atom. We can represent the structure of HF as shown in the margin. The electron density is distorted in the direction of the more electronegative fluorine atom, making F more negative. This small shift of electron density leaves H somewhat positive.

Covalent bonds, such as the one in HF, in which the *electron pairs are shared unequally* are called **polar covalent bonds**. Two kinds of notation used to indicate polar bonds are shown in the margin.

The $\delta-$ over the F atom indicates a "partial negative charge." This means that the F end of the molecule is somewhat more negative than the H end. The $\delta+$ over the H atom indicates a "partial positive charge," or that the H end of the molecule is positive *with respect to* the F end. We are *not* saying that H has a charge of 1+ or that F has a charge of 1−! A second way to indicate the polarity is to draw an arrow so that the head points toward the negative end (F) of the bond and the crossed tail, which resembles a positive sign, indicates the positive end (H).

The separation of charge in a polar covalent bond creates an electric **dipole**. We expect the dipoles in the covalent molecules HF, HCl, HBr, and HI to be different because F, Cl, Br, and I have different electronegativities. This tells us that atoms of these elements have different tendencies to attract an electron pair that they share with hydrogen. We indicate this difference as shown here, where $\Delta(EN)$ is the difference in electronegativity between two atoms that are bonded together.

H:F:

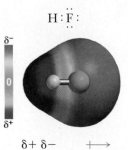

$\delta+\ \delta-$ $\longmapsto$
H—F or H—F

▶ The word "dipole" means "two poles." Here it refers to the positive and negative poles that result from the separation of charge within a molecule. In physics the dipole arrow has the opposite definition, with the crossed tail indicating the negative charge and the arrow head the positive charge. We will use the standard chemistry notation where the arrow points from the positive charge toward the negative charge.

Most polar   Least polar

H — F   H — Cl   H — Br   H — I
EN: 2.1   4.0   2.1   3.0   2.1   2.8   2.1   2.5
Δ(EN)   1.9   0.9   0.7   0.4

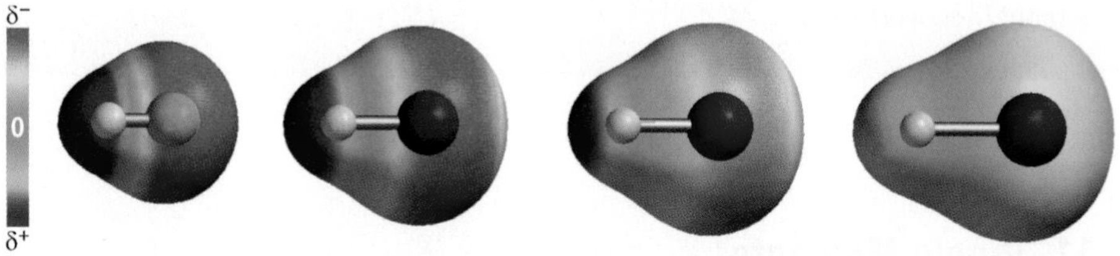

▶ The values of electronegativity are obtained from Table 5-3.

δ⁻

0

δ⁺

The longest arrow indicates the largest dipole, or greatest separation of electron density in the molecule (Table 7-5). For comparison, the Δ(EN) values for some typical 1:1 ionic compounds are RbCl, 2.1; NaF, 3.0; and KCl, 2.1.

EXAMPLE 7-10 Polar Bonds

 MOLECULAR REASONING

Each halogen can form single covalent bonds with other halogens, to form compounds called *interhalogens*; some examples are ClF and BrF. Use the electronegativity values in Table 5-3 to rank the following single bonds from most polar to least polar: F — F, F — Cl, F — Br, Cl — Br, Cl — I, and Cl — Cl.

Plan

The bond polarity decreases as the electronegativity difference between the two atoms decreases. We can calculate Δ(EN) for each bond and then arrange them according to decreasing Δ(EN) value.

Solution

We know that two F atoms have the same electronegativity, so Δ(EN) for F — F must be zero, and the F — F bond is nonpolar; the same reasoning applies to Cl — Cl. We use the values from Table 5-3 to calculate Δ(EN) for each of the other pairs, always subtracting the smaller from the larger value:

Elements	Δ(EN)
F, Cl	$4.0 - 3.0 = 1.0$
F, Br	$4.0 - 2.8 = 1.2$
Cl, Br	$3.0 - 2.8 = 0.2$
Cl, I	$3.0 - 2.5 = 0.5$

The bonds, arranged from most polar to least polar, are

F — Br   F — Cl   Cl — I   Cl — Br   Cl — Cl   F — F
EN: 4.0   2.8   4.0   3.0   3.0   2.5   3.0   2.8   3.0   3.0   4.0   4.0
Δ(EN)   1.2   1.0   0.5   0.2   0   0

δ⁻

0

δ⁺

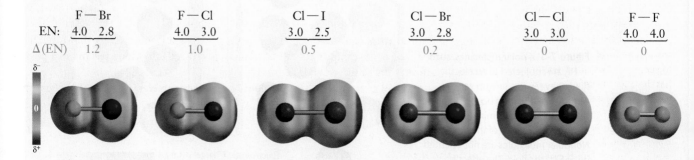

We know that the halogens, like the elements in any column in the periodic table, decrease in electronegativity going down the group. In this example, F and Br are the two halogens with the greatest separation in the column, so they have the biggest electronegativity difference. Thus the F — Br bond is the most polar bond in this example, more polar than F — Cl. Two like atoms have equal attraction for the shared electrons, so any X — X bond such as Cl — Cl or F — F must be nonpolar. (Your instructor may require you to predict some relative bond polarities from reasoning such as this, even without numerical values of electronegativity.)

You should now work Exercise 74.

7-11 Dipole Moments

It is convenient to express bond polarities on a numerical scale. We indicate the polarity of a molecule by its dipole moment, which measures the separation of charge within the molecule. The **dipole moment**, μ, is defined as the product of the distance, d, separating charges of equal magnitude and opposite sign, and the magnitude of the charge, q. A dipole moment is measured by placing a sample of the substance between two plates and applying a voltage. This causes a small shift in electron density of any molecule, so the applied voltage is diminished very slightly. Diatomic molecules that contain polar bonds, however, such as HF, HCl, and CO, tend to orient themselves in the electric field (Figure 7-5). This causes the measured voltage between the plates to decrease more markedly for these substances, and we say that these molecules are *polar*. Molecules such as F_2 or N_2 do not reorient, so the change in voltage between the plates remains slight; we say that these molecules are *nonpolar*.

▶ $\mu = d \times q$

Generally, as electronegativity differences increase in diatomic molecules, the measured dipole moments increase. This can be seen clearly from the data for the hydrogen halides (see Table 7-5).

Unfortunately, the dipole moments associated with *individual bonds* can be measured only in simple diatomic molecules. *Entire molecules* rather than selected pairs of atoms must be used for experimental measurement. Measured values of dipole moments thus reflect the *overall* polarities of molecules. For polyatomic molecules they are the result of all the bond dipoles in the molecules. In Chapter 8, we will see that structural features, such as molecular geometry and the presence of lone (unshared) pairs of electrons, also affect the polarity of a molecule.

Table 7-5 Δ(EN) Values and Dipole Moments for Some Pure (Gaseous) Substances

Substance	Δ (EN)	Dipole Moment $(\mu)^*$
HF	1.9	1.91 D
HCl	0.9	1.03 D
HBr	0.7	0.79 D
HI	0.4	0.38 D
H_2	0.0	0.00 D

*Molecular dipole moments are usually expressed in debyes (D).

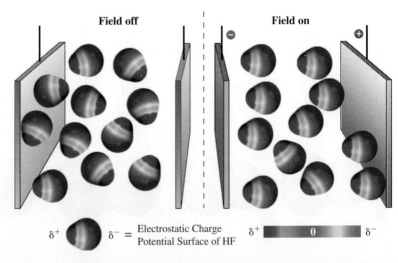

Figure 7-5 If polar molecules, such as HF, are subjected to an electric field, they tend to line up very slightly in a direction opposite to that of the field. This minimizes the electrostatic energy of the molecules. Nonpolar molecules are not oriented by an electric field. The effect is greatly exaggerated in this drawing.

Field off   Field on

δ^+ δ^- = Electrostatic Charge Potential Surface of HF δ^+ 0 δ^-

7-12 The Continuous Range of Bonding Types

Now let's clarify our classification of bonding types. The degree of electron sharing or transfer depends on the electronegativity difference between the bonding atoms. Nonpolar covalent bonding (involving *equal sharing* of electron pairs) is one extreme, occurring when the atoms are identical ($\Delta[EN]$ is zero). Ionic bonding (involving *complete transfer* of electrons) represents the other extreme, and occurs when two elements with very different electronegativities interact ($\Delta[EN]$ is large).

Polar covalent bonds may be thought of as intermediate between pure (nonpolar) covalent bonds and pure ionic bonds. In fact, bond polarity is sometimes described in terms of *partial ionic character*. This usually increases with increasing difference in electronegativity between bonded atoms. Calculations based on the measured dipole moment of gaseous HCl indicate about 17% "ionic character."

When cations and anions interact strongly, some amount of electron sharing takes place; in such cases we can consider the ionic compound as having some *partial covalent character*. For instance, the high charge density of the very small Li^+ ion causes it to distort large anions that it approaches. The distortion attracts electron density from the anion to the region between it and the Li^+ ion, giving lithium compounds a higher degree of covalent character than in other alkali metal compounds.

Almost all bonds have both ionic and covalent character. By experimental means, a given type of bond usually can be identified as being "closer" to one or the other extreme type. We find it useful and convenient to use the labels for the major classes of bonds to describe simple substances, keeping in mind that they represent ranges of behavior.

Above all, we must recognize that any classification of a compound that we might suggest based on electronic properties *must* be consistent with the physical properties of ionic and covalent substances described at the beginning of the chapter. For instance, HCl has a rather large electronegativity difference (0.9), and its aqueous solutions conduct electricity. But we know that we cannot view it as an ionic compound because it is a gas, and not a solid, at room temperature. Liquid HCl is a nonconductor.

▶ HCl *ionizes* in aqueous solution. We will study more about this behavior in Chapter 10.

Let us point out another aspect of the classification of compounds as ionic or covalent. Not all ions consist of single charged atoms. Many are small groups of atoms that are covalently bonded together, yet they still have excess positive or negative charge. Examples of such *polyatomic ions* are ammonium ion, NH_4^+, sulfate ion, SO_4^{2-}, and nitrate ion, NO_3^-. A compound such as potassium sulfate, K_2SO_4, contains potassium ions, K^+, and sulfate ions, SO_4^{2-}, in a 2:1 ratio. We should recognize that this compound contains both covalent bonding (electron sharing *within* each sulfate ion) and ionic bonding (electrostatic attractions *between* potassium and sulfate ions). We classify this compound as *ionic*, however, because it is a high-melting solid (mp = 1069°C), it conducts electricity both in molten form and in aqueous solution, and it displays other properties that we generally associate with ionic compounds. Put another way, covalent bonding holds each sulfate ion together, but the forces that hold the *entire* substance together are ionic, so the compound is classified as ionic.

In summary, we can describe chemical bonding as a continuum that may be represented as

$\Delta(EN)$ for the bonding atoms	zero	$\longrightarrow$	intermediate	$\longrightarrow$	large
Bonding types	nonpolar covalent	$\longrightarrow$	polar covalent	$\longrightarrow$	ionic

Ionic character increases

Covalent character increases

KEY TERMS

Anion   A negatively charged ion; that is, an ion in which the atom or group of atoms has more electrons than protons.

Binary compound   A compound consisting of two elements; may be ionic or covalent.

Bond dissociation energy   The stabilization of a bonded pair of atoms compared to the same atoms when separated; the energy required to break the bonding between a pair of atoms; also known as *bond energy*.

Bond energy   See *Bond dissociation energy*.

Bonding pair   A pair of electrons involved in a covalent bond; also known as *shared pair*.

Bond length   The distance between the centers (nuclei) of two bonded atoms.

Cation   A positively charged ion; that is, an ion in which the atom or group of atoms has fewer electrons than protons.

Chemical bonds   Attractive forces that hold atoms together in elements and compounds.

Covalent bond   A chemical bond formed by the sharing of one or more electron pairs between two atoms.

Covalent compound   A compound containing predominantly covalent bonds.

Debye   The unit used to express dipole moments.

Delocalization of electrons   Refers to bonding electrons distributed among more than two atoms that are bonded together; occurs in species that exhibit resonance.

Dipole   Refers to the separation of charge between two covalently bonded atoms.

Dipole moment (μ)   The product of the distance separating opposite charges of equal magnitude and the magnitude of the charge; a measure of the polarity of a bond or molecule. A measured dipole moment refers to the dipole moment of an entire molecule.

Double bond   A covalent bond resulting from the sharing of four electrons (two pairs) between two atoms.

Electron-deficient compound   A compound containing at least one atom (other than H) that has fewer than eight valence shell electrons.

Expanded valence shell   Describes a Group A (representative) atom that contains more than eight valence shell electrons.

Formal charge   The hypothetical charge on an atom in a co-valently bonded molecule or ion; bonding electrons are counted as though they were shared equally between the two bonded atoms.

Heteronuclear   Consisting of different elements.

Homonuclear   Consisting of only one element.

Hypervalent   See *Expanded valence shell*.

Ion   An atom or a group of atoms that carries an electrical charge.

Ionic bonding   The attraction of oppositely charged ions (cations and anions) in large numbers to form a solid. Ions result from the transfer of one or more electrons from one atom or group of atoms to another.

Ionic compound   A compound containing predominantly ionic bonding.

Lewis acid   A substance that accepts a share in a pair of electrons from another species.

Lewis base   A substance that makes available a share in an electron pair.

Lewis formula   The representation of a molecule, ion, or formula unit by showing atomic symbols and only outer-shell electrons; does not represent the shape of the molecule or ion. Each bonding electron pair can be represented by a pair of dots (the Lewis dot formula) or by a dash (the Lewis dash formula).

Lone pair   A pair of electrons residing on one atom and not shared by other atoms; also known as *unshared pair*.

Monatomic ion   An ion that consists of only one atom.

Nonpolar bond   A covalent bond between two atoms with the same electronegativity so that the electron density is symmetrically distributed.

Octet rule   Many representative elements attain at least a share of eight electrons in their valence shells when they form molecular or ionic compounds; this rule has some limitations.

Polar bond   A covalent bond between two atoms with different electronegativities so that the electron density is unsymmetrically distributed.

Polyatomic ion   An ion that consists of more than one atom.

Resonance   A concept in which two or more Lewis formulas for the same arrangement of atoms (resonance structures) are used to describe the bonding in a molecule or ion.

Single bond   A covalent bond resulting from the sharing of two electrons (one pair) between two atoms.

Triple bond   A covalent bond resulting from the sharing of six electrons (three pairs) between two atoms.

Unshared pair   See *Lone pair*.

Valence electrons   The electrons in the outermost shell of an atom.

EXERCISES

🌰 **Molecular Reasoning** exercises

▲ **More Challenging** exercises

Blue-Numbered exercises are solved in the Student Solutions Manual

Chemical Bonding: Basic Ideas

1. 🌰 What type of force is responsible for chemical bonding? Explain the differences between ionic bonding and covalent bonding.

2. 🌰 What kind of bonding (ionic or covalent) would you predict for the products resulting from the following combination of elements? (a) $K + Cl_2$; (b) $C + O_2$; (c) $N_2 + O_2$; (d) $S + O_2$.

3. Why are covalent bonds called directional bonds, whereas ionic bonding is termed nondirectional?

4. (a) What do Lewis dot formulas for atoms show? (b) Write Lewis dot formulas for the following atoms: He, Si, P, Ne, Mg, I.

5. Write Lewis dot formulas for the following atoms: B, C, S, Ar, Ge, Te.

6. 🌰 Describe the types of bonding in sodium chlorate, $NaClO_3$.

$$Na^+ \quad \left[\begin{array}{c} \ddot{\underset{..}{O}} \\ :\ddot{O}-\overset{..}{\underset{..}{Cl}}-\ddot{O}: \end{array} \right]^-$$

7. 🌰 Describe the types of bonding in ammonium chloride, NH_4Cl.

$$\left[\begin{array}{c} H \\ | \\ H-N-H \\ | \\ H \end{array} \right]^+ \quad :\ddot{\underset{..}{Cl}}:^-$$

8. 🌰 Based on the positions in the periodic table of the following pairs of elements, predict whether bonding between the two would be primarily ionic or covalent. Justify your answers. (a) Ca and Cl; (b) P and O; (c) Br and I; (d) Na and I; (e) Si and Br; (f) Ba and F.

9. 🌰 Predict whether the bonding between the following pairs of elements would be primarily ionic or covalent. Justify your answers. (a) Rb and Cl; (b) N and O; (c) Ca and F; (d) N and S; (e) C and F; (f) K and O.

10. 🌰 Classify the following compounds as ionic or covalent: (a) $Ca(NO_3)_2$; (b) H_2Se; (c) KNO_3; (d) $CaCl_2$; (e) H_2CO_3; (f) NCl_3; (g) Li_2O; (h) N_2H_4; (i) $SOCl_2$.

Ionic Bonding

11. Describe what happens to the valence electron(s) as a metal atom and a nonmetal atom combine to form an ionic compound.

12. ▲ Describe an ionic crystal. What factors might determine the geometrical arrangement of the ions?

13. 🌰 Why are solid ionic compounds rather poor conductors of electricity? Why does conductivity increase when an ionic compound is melted or dissolved in water?

14. Write the formula for the ionic compound that forms between each of the following pairs of elements: (a) Li and O_2; (b) K and Se; (c) Mg and Br_2.

15. Write the formula for the ionic compound that forms between each of the following pairs of elements: (a) Li and O_2; (b) K and Se; (c) Mg and Br_2.

16. When a d-transition metal ionizes, it loses its outer s electrons before it loses any d electrons. Using [noble gas] $(n-1)\,d^x$ representations, write the outer-electron configurations for the following ions: (a) Cr^{3+}; (b) Mn^{2+}; (c) Ag^+; (d) Fe^{3+}; (e) Cu^{2+}; (f) Sc^{2+}; (g) Fe^{2+}.

17. 🌰 Which of the following do not accurately represent stable binary ionic compounds? Why? $MgBr_3$, NaS, AlF_4, SrS_2, Ca_2O_3, $NaBr_2$, NCl_4, $LiSe_2$, NaO.

18. 🌰 Which of the following do not accurately represent stable binary ionic compounds? Why? MgI, $Al(OH)_2$, InF_2, CO_4, $RbCl_2$, CsS, Be_3O.

19. 🌰 (a) Write Lewis formulas for the positive and negative ions in these compounds: $SrBr_2$, K_2O, Ca_3P_2, GaF_3, Bi_2O_3. (b) Which ions do not have a noble gas configuration?

20. Write formulas for two cations that have the following valence shell electron configuration: (a) $3s^23p^6$; (b) $6s^26p^6$.

21. Write formulas for two anions that have each of the electron configurations listed in Exercise 20.

Covalent Bonding: General Concepts

22. 🌰 What does Figure 7-4 tell us about the attractive and repulsive forces in a hydrogen molecule?

23. 🌰 Distinguish between heteronuclear and homonuclear diatomic molecules.

24. How many electrons are shared between two atoms in (a) a single covalent bond, (b) a double covalent bond, and (c) a triple covalent bond?

25. What is the maximum number of covalent bonds that a second-period element could form? How can the representative elements beyond the second period form more than this number of covalent bonds?

26. 🌰 Complete the following chart using data found in Tables 7-3 and 7-4. Compare the energies and lengths of single, double, and triple bonds of carbon to oxygen. Then compare the changes between single-, double-, and triple-

● ●

🌰 **Molecular Reasoning** exercises   ▲ **More Challenging** exercises   Blue-Numbered exercises solved in Student Solutions Manual

Unless otherwise noted, all content on this page is © Cengage Learning.

bonded carbon to oxygen to the similar changes in carbon bonded to carbon.

	Single Bond C—O	Double Bond C=O	Triple Bond C≡O
Bond energy (kJ/mol)	—	—	—
Bond length (Å)	—	—	—

27. 🐾 Complete the following chart using data found in Tables 7-3 and 7-4. Compare the energies and lengths of single, double, and triple bonds of carbon to nitrogen. Then compare the changes between single-, double-, and triple-bonded carbon to nitrogen to the similar changes in carbon bonded to carbon.

	Single Bond C—N	Double Bond C=N	Triple Bond C≡N
Bond energy (kJ/mol)	—	—	—
Bond length (Å)	—	—	—

Lewis Formulas for Molecules and Polyatomic Ions

28. What information about chemical bonding can a Lewis formula give for a compound or ion? What information about bonding is not directly represented by a Lewis formula?

29. 🐾 Write Lewis formulas for the following: H_2, N_2, I_2, HCl, HI.

30. 🐾 Write Lewis formulas for the following: H_2O, NH_3, OH^-, Br^-.

31. 🐾 Use Lewis formulas to represent the covalent molecules formed by these pairs of elements. Write only structures that satisfy the octet rule. (a) P and H; (b) As and Br; (c) N and Cl; (d) Si and Cl.

32. 🐾 Use Lewis formulas to represent the covalent molecules formed by these pairs of elements. Write only structures that satisfy the octet rule. (a) S and Cl; (b) As and F; (c) I and Cl; (d) Se and Cl.

33. 🐾 Find the total number of valence electrons in each of the following molecules or ions: (a) NH_2^-; (b) ClO_2^-; (c) HCN; (d) $SnCl_4$.

34. How many valence electrons does each of these molecules or ions have? (a) H_2Se; (b) PCl_3; (c) ClO_4^-; (d) OH^-.

35. 🐾 Write Lewis structures for the molecules or ions in Exercise 33.

36. 🐾 Write Lewis structures for the molecules or ions in Exercise 34.

37. 🐾 Write Lewis structures for the following molecules or ions: (a) ClO_3^-; (b) C_2H_6O (two possibilities); (c) HOCl; (d) SO_3^{2-}.

38. 🐾 Write Lewis structures for the following molecules or ions: (a) H_2CO; (b) ClBr; (c) BF_4^-; (d) PO_4^{3-}; (e) $HClO_3$.

39. 🐾 ▲ Name an element with which nitrogen would form: (a) a mostly ionic bond, (b) a polar covalent bond, and (c) a nonpolar covalent bond (other than another nitrogen atom). How did you determine which elements would form each type of bond with nitrogen? Does the element that forms a polar covalent bond with nitrogen form a polar covalent bond with every element?

40. 🐾 ▲ Why do atoms of two nonmetals generally form a compound by sharing valence electrons, rather than by transferring electrons, as in the formation of ionic compounds?

41. Write Lewis structures for these molecules or ions. (a) ClF; (b) H_2Se; (c) BF_4^-; (d) PO_4^{3-}.

42. 🐾 Write Lewis formulas for CCl_4, SiF_4, and PbI_4. Explain the similarity.

Formal Charges

43. 🐾 Assign a formal charge to each atom in the following:

(a) :Cl—O:
    :Cl:

(b) :O—S=O:

(c) :O: :O:
    :O—Cl—O—Cl—O:
    :O: :O:

(d) [:O=C—O:]²⁻
        :O:

(e) [:O:
    :O—Cl—O:
        :O:]⁻

44. 🐾 Assign a formal charge to each atom in the following:

(a) :F—As—F:
        :F:

(b) F   F
      \ /
       P
      /|\
    F | F
       :F:

(c) :O=C=O:

(d) [:O=N=O:]⁺

(e) [:Cl:
    :Cl—Al—Cl:
        :Cl:]⁻

45. 🐾 What is the formal charge on the indicated atom in each of the following species? (a) sulfur in SO_2; (b) nitrogen in N_2H_4; (c) each oxygen atom in ozone, O_3.

46. 🐾 Write Lewis formulas for six different resonance forms of the sulfate ion, SO_4^{2-}. Indicate all formal charges. Predict which arrangement is likely to be the least stable and justify your selection. (*Hint:* The answer must include resonance structures that have more than an octet of electrons about the sulfur atom.)

47. 🐾 The formula of the thiocyanate ion is SCN^-. Draw two Lewis formulas for this ion, one with two double bonds and one with a single bond and a triple bond.

🐾 **Molecular Reasoning** exercises   ▲ **More Challenging** exercises   Blue-Numbered exercises solved in Student Solutions Manual

Unless otherwise noted, all content on this page is © Cengage Learning.

Calculate the formal charges on each atom in each Lewis formula. Which structure is more likely?

More Lewis Formulas

48. 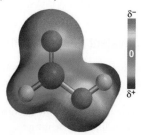 Write Lewis formulas for butane, $CH_3CH_2CH_2CH_3$, and propane, $CH_3CH_2CH_3$. Describe the nature of the bond indicated: $CH_3CH_2 — CH_2CH_3$ and $CH_3 — CH_2CH_3$.

49. Write Lewis structures for the following molecules:

(a) formic acid, HCOOH, in which the ECP plot is:

(b) acetonitrile, CH_3CN;

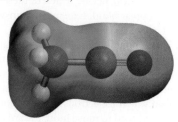

(c) vinyl chloride, CH_2CHCl, the molecule from which PVC plastics are made.

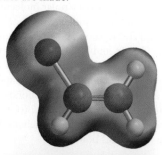

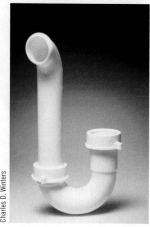

PVC Pipe

Charles D. Winters

50. 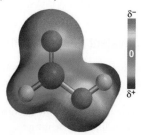 Write Lewis structures for the following molecules: (a) tetrafluoroethylene, C_2F_4, the molecule from which Teflon is made; (b) acrylonitrile, CH_2CHCN, the molecule from which Orlon is made.

Charles D. Winters

Teflon-coated pan

Limitation of the Octet Rule

51. Draw Lewis formulas for sulfur difluoride (SF_2) and sulfur hexafluoride (SF_6). Is either one an exception to the octet rule?

52. Write the Lewis formula for each of the following covalent compounds. Which ones contain at least one atom with a share in less than an octet of valence electrons? (a) $BeBr_2$; (b) BBr_3; (c) NCl_3; (d) $AlCl_3$.

53. Which of the following species contain at least one atom that is an exception to the octet rule?

(a) $:\ddot{F}—\ddot{Cl}:$ (b) $:\ddot{O}—\ddot{Cl}—\ddot{O}:$ (c) $:\ddot{F}—\ddot{Xe}—\ddot{F}:$

(d)
$$\left[\begin{array}{c} :\ddot{O}: \\ :\ddot{O}—\overset{}{Cl}—\ddot{O}: \\ :\ddot{O}: \end{array} \right]^-$$

54. Write the Lewis formula for each of the following molecules or ions. Which ones contain at least one atom with a share in less than an octet of valence electrons? (a) CH_2Cl_2; (b) BF_3; (c) BCl_4^-; (d) AlF_4^-.

55. ▲ None of the following is known to exist. What is wrong with each one?

(a) $:\ddot{Cl}—\ddot{S}=\ddot{O}:$

(b) $H—H—\ddot{O}—\overset{\displaystyle :\ddot{Cl}:}{\underset{}{P}}—\ddot{Cl}:$

(c) $:O≡N—\ddot{O}:^-$

(d) $Na—\ddot{O}: \\ \quad\quad\quad Na$

(e) $:\ddot{O}:\ddot{O}:\ddot{Cl}:^-$

56. In which of the following does the central atom obey the octet rule: NO_2, SF_4, NH_3, SO_3, ClO_2, and ClO_2^-? Are any of these species odd-electron molecules or ions?

 Molecular Reasoning exercises   ▲ **More Challenging** exercises   Blue-Numbered exercises solved in Student Solutions Manual

Unless otherwise noted, all content on this page is © Cengage Learning.

Resonance Structures

57. What do we mean by the term "resonance"? Do the resonance structures that we draw actually represent the bonding in the substance? Explain your answer.

58. 🔮 Careful examination of the ozone molecule indicates that the two outer oxygens are the same distance from the central oxygen. Write Lewis formulas or resonance structures that are consistent with this finding.

59. Draw resonance structures for (a) NO_2^-; (b) NNO; (c) HCO_2^-.

60. ▲ We can write two resonance structures for toluene, $C_6H_5CH_3$:

$$
\begin{array}{c}
H \\
| \\
C \\
H-C \quad C-H \\
H-C \quad C-H \\
C \\
| \\
H-C-H \\
| \\
H
\end{array}
\longleftrightarrow
\begin{array}{c}
H \\
| \\
C \\
H-C \quad C-H \\
H-C \quad C-H \\
C \\
| \\
H-C-H \\
| \\
H
\end{array}
$$

How would you expect the carbon–carbon bond lengths in the six-membered ring of toluene to compare with the carbon–carbon bond length between the CH_3 group and the carbon atom on the ring?

61. Write resonance structures for the acetate ion, CH_3COO^-.

62. 🔮 Write resonance structures for each of the following ions. (a) NO_2^-; (b) BrO_3^-; (c) PO_4^{3-}. (*Hint*: Consider both the Br and the P to share more than an octet of electrons in order for them to also form at least one double bond.)

Mixed Exercises

63. 🔮 ▲ Suppose that "El" is the general symbol for a representative element. In each case, in which periodic group is El located? Justify your answers and cite a specific example for each one.

(a) $\left[\overset{..}{\underset{..}{O}} - El - \overset{..}{\underset{..}{O}} \right]^-$
$\quad \begin{array}{c} | \\ \overset{..}{\underset{..}{O}} \end{array}$

(c) $H - \overset{..}{\underset{..}{O}} - El = \overset{..}{O}$

(b) $\left[\begin{array}{c} \overset{..}{\underset{..}{O}} \\ | \\ \overset{..}{\underset{..}{O}} - El - \overset{..}{\underset{..}{O}} \\ | \\ \overset{..}{\underset{..}{O}} \end{array} \right]^{2-}$

(d) $H - \overset{..}{\underset{..}{O}} - El - H$
$\qquad \begin{array}{c} | \\ H \end{array}$

64. 🔮 ▲ Suppose that "El" is the general symbol for a representative element. In each case, in which periodic group is El located? Justify your answers and cite a specific example for each one.

(a) $\overset{..}{\underset{..}{:}} Br - El - \overset{..}{\underset{..}{Br}} :$
$\quad \begin{array}{c} | \\ \overset{..}{\underset{..}{Br}} : \end{array}$

(b) $\left[\begin{array}{c} H \\ | \\ H - El - H \\ | \\ H \end{array} \right]^+$

(c) $\overset{..}{\underset{..}{:}} O :: El :: \overset{..}{\underset{..}{O}} \overset{..}{:}$

(d) $\left[\begin{array}{c} H : \overset{..}{El} : H \\ | \\ H \end{array} \right]^+$

65. 🔮 Many common stains, such as those of chocolate and other fatty foods, can be removed by dry-cleaning solvents such as tetrachloroethylene, C_2Cl_4. Is C_2Cl_4 ionic or covalent? Write its Lewis formula.

66. 🔮 ▲ Write acceptable Lewis formulas for the following common air pollutants: (a) SO_2; (b) NO_2; (c) CO; (d) O_3 (ozone); (e) SO_3; (f) $(NH_4)_2SO_4$. Which one is a solid? Which ones exhibit resonance? Which ones violate the octet rule?

Ionic Versus Covalent Character and Bond Polarities

67. Distinguish between polar and nonpolar covalent bonds.

68. 🔮 Why is an HCl molecule polar but a Cl_2 molecule is nonpolar?

69. How does one predict that the chemical bonding between two elements is likely to be ionic?

70. Using just a periodic table (not a table of electronegativities), decide which of these is likely to be the most polar bond. Explain your answer. (a) C—F; (b) S—F; (c) Si—F; (d) O—F.

71. 🔮 Ionic compounds generally have a higher melting point than covalent compounds. What is the major difference in the structures of ionic and covalent compounds that explains the difference in melting points?

72. 🔮 Explain why the electrons in the carbon–fluorine covalent bond tend to move more toward the halogen atom than do the electrons in the carbon–bromine covalent bond.

73. 🔮 Why do we show only partial charges, and not full charges, on the atoms of a polar molecule?

74. In each pair of bonds, indicate the more polar bond, and use $\delta+$ and $\delta-$ to show the direction of polarity in each bond. (a) C—O and C—N; (b) N—Cl and C—S; (c) P—H and P—N; (d) B—H and B—I.

75. 🔮 The molecule below is urea, a compound used in plastics and fertilizers. (a) Which bonds in this molecule are polar and which are nonpolar? (b) Which is the most polar bond in the molecule? Which atom is the partial negative end of this bond?

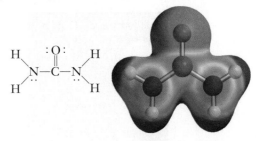

$$
\begin{array}{c}
\qquad \overset{..}{\underset{..}{O}} : \\
\qquad || \\
H \qquad \qquad H \\
\diagdown \qquad \qquad \diagup \\
N - C - N \\
\diagup \qquad \qquad \diagdown \\
H \qquad \qquad H
\end{array}
$$

76. (a) Which two of the following pairs of elements are most likely to form ionic bonds? I and H; C and F; Ba and F; N and F; K and O. (b) Of the remaining three pairs, which one forms the least polar, and which the most polar covalent bond?

🔮 **Molecular Reasoning** exercises   ▲ **More Challenging** exercises   Blue-Numbered exercises solved in Student Solutions Manual

Unless otherwise noted, all content on this page is © Cengage Learning.

77. ✿ (a) List three reasonably nonpolar covalent bonds between dissimilar atoms. (b) List three pairs of elements whose compounds should exhibit extreme ionic character.

78. Classify the bonding between the following pairs of atoms as ionic, polar covalent, or nonpolar covalent. (a) K and O; (b) Br and I; (c) Na and H; (d) O and O; (e) H and O.

79. ✿ For each of the following, tell whether the bonding is primarily ionic or covalent. (a) sodium and iodine in sodium iodide; (b) beryllium and the nitrate ion in beryllium nitrate; (c) the carbon–carbon bond in CH_3CH_3; (d) carbon and oxygen in carbon monoxide; (e) phosphorus and oxygen in the phosphate ion.

80. ✿ Identify the bond in each of the following bonded pairs that is likely to have the greater proportion of "ionic character." (a) Na — Cl or Mg — Cl; (b) Ca — S or Fe — S; (c) Al — Br or O — Br; (d) Ra — H or C — H.

81. ✿ Identify the bond in each of the following bonded pairs that is likely to have the greater proportion of "covalent character." (a) K — Br or Cr — Br; (b) Li — O or H — O; (c) Al — Cl or C — Cl; (d) As — S or O — S.

Conceptual Exercises

82. When asked to give an example of resonance structures, a student drew the following. Why is this example incorrect?

$$H-\overset{\overset{\displaystyle O}{\|}}{C}-\overset{\overset{\displaystyle H}{|}}{\underset{\underset{\displaystyle H}{|}}{C}}-H \longleftrightarrow H-\overset{\overset{\displaystyle OH}{|}}{C}=C\overset{H}{\underset{H}{\big\langle}}$$

83. Why is the following not an example of resonance structures?

$$:\overset{..}{\underset{..}{S}}-C\equiv N: \longleftrightarrow :\overset{..}{\underset{..}{S}}-N\equiv C:$$

84. Describe the circumstances under which one would expect a bond to exhibit 100% "covalent character" and 0% "ionic character." Give an example of two bonded atoms that would be predicted to exhibit 0% "ionic character."

85. ✿ Select one of the electrostatic charge potential (ECP) plots of a heteronuclear, diatomic molecule found in this chapter. Does the ECP plot that you selected reflect what you have learned thus far in this textbook about atomic size and electronegativity?

86. ✿ Below are electrostatic charge potential (ECP) plots for Cl_2 and F_2. Which one is for Cl_2? How can you tell?

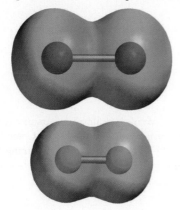

87. If one uses the atomic radii given in Figure 5-1 to calculate the bond length of H — C, H — N, and H — O bonds, do the calculated values agree with those found in Table 7-4? Is the trend for bond length consistent with the location of the elements in the periodic table?

88. Within Table 7-4 is there any indication that there is a trend of bond lengths becoming longer as the group members become larger as one moves down in the periodic table?

89. A monatomic cation most often has a charge of $1+$, $2+$, or $3+$. A monatomic anion most often has a charge of $1-$, $2-$, or $3-$. Consider all the possible combinations of a monatomic cation (M^+, M^{2+}, or M^{3+}) with a monatomic anion (X^-, X^{2-}, or X^{3-}). How many possible combinations are there? What would be the simplest formula for a neutral compound made by each of these combinations? Are any of the formulas the same? Altogether, how many different simplest formulas, produced from these combinations, are there?

90. It is often assumed that when a metal combines with a nonmetal, the compound produced is ionic. Alternately, if the electronegativity difference between two elements is large, the compound they form is likely to be ionic. But the ultimate test is to experimentally examine the properties of the compound produced: Does it *behave* like an ionic compound? Compare the general characteristics of ionic and covalent compounds with the specific properties of the following metal/nonmetal compounds. Do they appear to be ionic or covalent?

	Color	Density (g/cm³)	Melting point (°C)	Boiling point (°C)	Solubility in H_2O (g/100 cm³)
$SnCl_2$	white	3.95	246	623	83.9
$SnCl_4$	colorless	2.23	−33	114	decomposes
$SnBr_2$	yellow	5.12	216	620	85
$SnBr_4$	white	3.34	31	202	very soluble
SnI_2	red	5.28	320	714	0.99
SnI_4	red-orange	4.56	143	364	decomposes
$PbCl_2$	white	5.85	501	950	0.99
$PbCl_4$	yellow	3.18	−15	50	decomposes

What difference does the charge on the metal ion appear to have on the type of compound formed?

Building Your Knowledge

91. (a) How many moles of electrons are transferred when 10.0 g of magnesium react as completely as possible with 10.0 g of fluorine to form MgF_2? (b) How many electrons is this? (c) Look up the charge on the electron in coulombs. What is the total charge, in coulombs, that is transferred?

---

92. 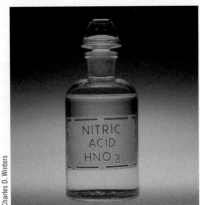 Write the formula for the compound that forms between (a) calcium and nitrogen; (b) aluminum and oxygen; (c) potassium and selenium; and (d) strontium and bromine. Classify each compound as covalent or ionic.

93. 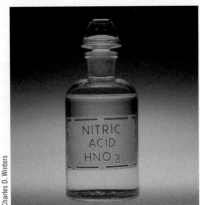 ▲ Write the Lewis formulas for the nitric acid molecule (HNO_3) that are consistent with the following bond length data: 1.405 Å for the bond between the nitrogen atom and the oxygen atom that is attached to the hydrogen atom; 1.206 Å for the bonds between the nitrogen atom and each of the other oxygen atoms.

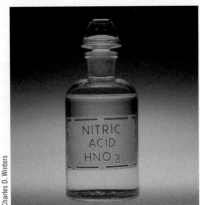

Aqueous nitric acid solution

Charles D. Winters

94. Write the total ionic and net ionic equations for the reaction between each of the following pairs of compounds in aqueous solution. Then give the Lewis formula for each species in these equations. (a) HCN and NaOH; (b) HCl and NaOH; (c) $CaCl_2$ and Na_2CO_3.

95. 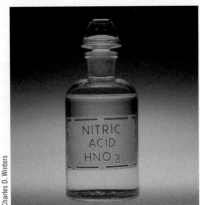 Sketch a portion of an aqueous solution of NaCl. Show the Lewis formulas of the solute and solvent species. Suggest the relative location of each species with respect to the others.

96. 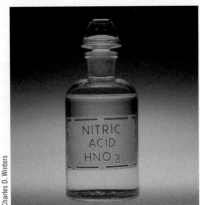 Sketch a portion of an aqueous solution of CH_3COOH. Show the Lewis formulas of the solute

and solvent species. Suggest the relative location of each species with respect to the others.

97. The following properties can be found in the *Handbook of Chemistry and Physics*:
Camphor, $C_{10}H_{16}O$ — colorless crystals; specific gravity, 0.990 at 25 °C; sublimes, 204 °C; insoluble in water; very soluble in alcohol and ether.
Praseodymium chloride, $PrCl_3$ — blue-green needle crystals; specific gravity, 4.02; melting point, 786 °C; boiling point, 1700 °C; solubility in cold water, 103.9 g/100 mL H_2O; very soluble in hot water. Would you describe each of these as ionic or covalent? Why?

Beyond the Textbook

NOTE: *Whenever the answer to an exercise depends on information obtained from a source other than this textbook, the source must be included as an essential part of the answer.*

98. Look up the properties of NaCl and PCl_3 in the *Handbook of Chemistry and Physics*. Why do we describe NaCl as an ionic compound and PCl_3 as a covalent compound?

99. Look up the dipole moment for CO (carbon monoxide). How does it compare to the formal charges calculated from the Lewis dot structure? What does that tell you about the physical meaning of formal charges for this molecule? How does the dipole moment fit with electronegativity values for the atoms?

100. CO_2 does not have a dipole moment and is considered a nonpolar molecule. CO_2 readily reacts with water and hydroxide ions. What two compounds are formed? Sketch out Lewis dot structures for these two compounds.

101. Use the *Handbook of Chemistry and Physics* or a suitable web page to find dipole moments. Do the values for HF, HCl, and HI agree with what you also know about electronegativity?

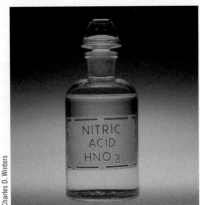 **Molecular Reasoning** exercises　　　▲ **More Challenging** exercises　　　Blue-Numbered exercises solved in Student Solutions Manual

Unless otherwise noted, all content on this page is © Cengage Learning.

Molecular Structure and Covalent Bonding Theories

8

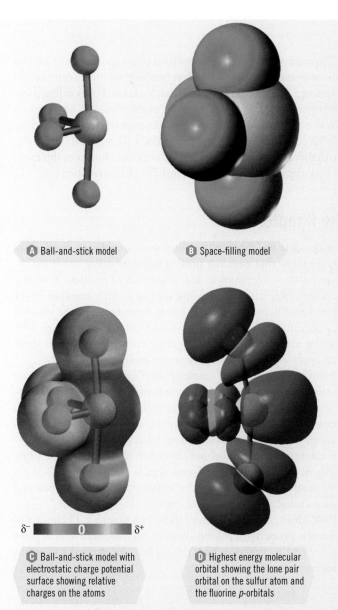

A Ball-and-stick model

B Space-filling model

δ^- ▬▬▬ 0 ▬▬▬ δ^+

C Ball-and-stick model with electrostatic charge potential surface showing relative charges on the atoms

D Highest energy molecular orbital showing the lone pair orbital on the sulfur atom and the fluorine p-orbitals

Some representations of the structure and bonding in SF_4. Refer to Example 7-7 for Lewis formula.

OBJECTIVES

After you have studied this chapter, you should be able to

▶ Describe the basic ideas of the valence shell electron pair repulsion (VSEPR) theory

▶ Use the VSEPR theory to predict the electronic geometry and the molecular geometry of polyatomic molecules and ions

▶ Describe the relationships between molecular shapes and polarities

▶ Predict whether a molecule is polar or nonpolar

▶ Describe the basic ideas of the valence bond (VB) theory

▶ Describe the hybrid orbitals used in bonding in polyatomic molecules and ions

▶ Use the theory of hybrid orbitals to describe the bonding in double and triple bonds

We know a great deal about the molecular structures of millions of compounds, all based on reliable experiments. In our discussion of theories of covalent bonding, we must keep in mind that the theories represent *an attempt to explain and organize* what we know. For bonding theories to be valid, they must be consistent with the large body of experimental observations about molecular structure. In this chapter we will study two theories of covalent bonding. These theories allow us to predict correct structures and properties. Like any simplified theories, they are not entirely satisfactory in describing *every* known structure; however, their successful application to the vast majority of structures studied justifies their continued use.

8-1 A Preview of the Chapter

The electrons responsible for bonding are those in the outer shell, or **valence shell**, of an atom. Valence shell electrons are those that were not present in the *preceding* noble gas orbitals. We will focus attention on these electrons in our discussion of covalent bonding. The electrons in the lower energy noble gas configuration are not directly involved in covalent bonding and are often referred to as *core electrons*. Lewis formulas show the number of valence shell electrons in a polyatomic molecule or ion (see Sections 7-5 through 7-9). We will write Lewis formulas for each molecule or polyatomic ion we discuss. The theories introduced in this chapter apply equally well to polyatomic molecules and to ions.

Two theories go hand in hand in a discussion of covalent bonding. The *valence shell electron pair repulsion (VSEPR) theory* predicts the spatial arrangement of atoms in a polyatomic molecule or ion. It shows *where* the bonding occurs and where lone (unshared) pairs of valence shell electrons are directed, but it does not explain *how* the bonding occurs. The *valence bond (VB) theory* describes *how* the bonding takes place, in terms of *overlapping atomic orbitals*. In this theory, the atomic orbitals discussed in Chapter 4 are often "mixed," or *hybridized*, to form new orbitals with different spatial orientations. Used together, these two simple ideas enable us to understand the bonding, molecular shapes, and properties of a wide variety of polyatomic molecules and ions.

We will first discuss the basic ideas and application of these two theories. Then we will learn how the important molecular property of *polarity* depends on molecular shape. Most of this chapter will then be devoted to studying how these ideas are applied to various types of polyatomic molecules and ions.

▶ Lone pairs are sometimes called unshared pairs.

▶ In Chapter 7 we used valence bond terminology to discuss the bonding in H_2, although we did not name the theory there.

Important Note

Different instructors prefer to cover these two theories in different ways. Your instructor will tell you the order in which you should study the material in this chapter. Regardless of how you study this chapter, Tables 8-1, 8-2, 8-3, and 8-4 are important summaries, and you should refer to them often.

1. One approach is to discuss both the VSEPR theory and the VB theory together, emphasizing how they complement each other. If your instructor prefers this parallel approach, you should study the chapter in the order in which it is presented.

2. An alternative approach is to first master the VSEPR theory and the related topic of molecular polarity for different structures, and then learn how the VB theory describes the overlap of bonding orbitals in these structures. If your instructor takes this approach, you should study this chapter in the following order:

    a. Read the summary material under the main heading "Molecular Shapes and Bonding" preceding Section 8-5.

    b. *VSEPR theory, molecular polarity.* Study Sections 8-2 and 8-3; then in Sections 8-5 through 8-12, study only the subsections marked A and B.

    c. *VB theory.* Study Section 8-4; then in Sections 8-5 through 8-13, study the Valence Bond Theory subsections, marked C; then study Sections 8-14 and 8-15.

No matter which order your instructor prefers, the following procedure will help you analyze the structure and bonding in any compound.

1. Write the Lewis formula for the molecule or polyatomic ion, and identify a *central atom*—an atom that is bonded to more than one other atom (Section 8-2).

2. Count the *number of electron groups* (bonded atoms and lone pairs) on the central atom (Section 8-2).

3. Apply the VSEPR theory to determine the arrangement of the *electron groups* (the *electronic geometry*) about the central atom (Section 8-2; Tables 8-1 and 8-4).

4. Using the Lewis formula as a guide, determine the arrangement of the *bonded atoms* (the *molecular geometry*) about the central atom, as well as the location of the lone pairs on that atom (Parts B of Sections 8-5 through 8-12; Tables 8-3 and 8-4). This description includes ideal bond angles.

5. If there are lone pairs of valence shell electrons on the central atom, consider how their presence might modify somewhat the *ideal* molecular geometry and bond angles deduced in Step 4 (Section 8-2; Parts B of Sections 8-8 and 8-9; Parts D of Sections 8-11 and 8-12).

6. Use the VB theory to determine the *hybrid orbitals* utilized by the central atom; describe the overlap of these orbitals to form bonds; describe the orbitals that contain lone pairs of valence shell electrons on the central atom (Parts C of Sections 8-5 through 8-12; Sections 8-14 and 8-15; Tables 8-2, 8-3, and 8-4).

7. If more than one atom can be identified as a central atom (as in many organic molecules), repeat Steps 2 through 6 for each central atom, to build up a picture of the geometry and bonding in the entire molecule or ion.

8. When all central atoms in the molecule or ion have been accounted for, use the entire molecular geometry, electronegativity differences, and the presence of lone pairs of valence shell electrons on the central atom to predict *molecular polarity* (Section 8-3; Parts B of Sections 8-5 through 8-12; Section 8.13).

STOP & THINK
Never skip to Step 4 until you have done Step 3. The electronic geometry and the molecular geometry may or may not be the same; knowing the electronic geometry first will enable you to determine the correct molecular geometry.

The following diagram summarizes this procedure.

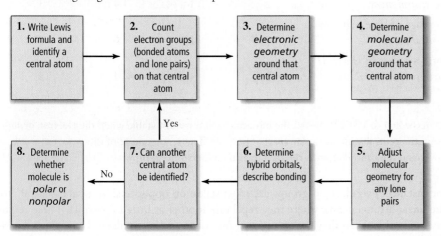

STOP & THINK
Learn this procedure, and use it as a mental "checklist." Trying to do this reasoning in a different order often leads to confusion or wrong answers.

In Section 7-5 we showed that Lewis formulas of polyatomic ions can be constructed in the same way as those of neutral molecules. Once the Lewis formula of an ion is known, we use the VSEPR and VB theories to deduce its electronic geometry, shape, and hybridization, just as for neutral molecules.

8-2 Valence Shell Electron Pair Repulsion Theory

The basic ideas of the **valence shell electron pair repulsion (VSEPR) theory** are:

> Each region of high electron density in the valence shell of a central atom is significant. Such a region is referred to as an *electron group*. The groups of valence shell electrons on the *central atom* repel one another. They are arranged about the *central atom* so that the repulsions among them are as small as possible. This results in maximum separation of the electron groups about the central atom.

▶ The VSEPR theory assumes that the electron groups (which are regions of high electron density on the central atom) will be as far from one another as possible.

A **central atom** is any atom that is bonded to more than one other atom. We first count the number of **electron groups** around the *central atom*, as follows:

1. Each bonded atom is counted as *one electron group* for VSEPR, *regardless of whether the bonding is single, double, or triple.*

2. Each lone pair of valence electrons on the central atom is counted as *one electron group for* VSEPR.

The number of electron groups then determines their arrangement around that central atom. In some molecules, more than one central atom may be present. In such a case, we determine the arrangement around each central atom in turn, to build up a picture of the overall shape of the entire molecule or ion.

Consider the following molecules and polyatomic ions as examples.

Formula:	CO_2	NH_3	CH_4	NO_3^-
Lewis formula:	$\ddot{O}=C=\ddot{O}$	H $\mid$ $:N-H$ $\mid$ H	H $\mid$ $H-C-H$ $\mid$ H	$\left[\begin{array}{c}\ddot{O}\\ \parallel\\ N\\ \diagup \diagdown \\ \ddot{O} \quad \ddot{O}\end{array}\right]^-$
Central atom:	C	N	C	N
Number of atoms bonded to *central atom*:	2	3	4	3
Number of lone pairs on *central atom*:	0	1	0	0
Total number of electron groups on *central atom*:	2	4	4	3

> According to VSEPR theory, the molecule or ion is most stable when the electron groups on the central atom are as far apart as possible. The arrangement of these *electron groups* around the central atom is referred to as the **electronic geometry** of the central atom.

For instance, two electron groups are most stable on opposite sides of the central atom (the linear arrangement), where they repel one another as little as possible. Three regions are most stable when they are arranged at the corners of an equilateral triangle. Table 8-1

Table 8-1 Electronic Geometry versus Number of Electron Groups (*eg*) on Central Atom

Electron Groups on Central Atom	Electronic Geometry*			Ball-and-Stick Model
	Orientation of Electron Groups	Description; Angles†	Line Drawing‡	
2		linear; 180°		
3		trigonal planar; 120°	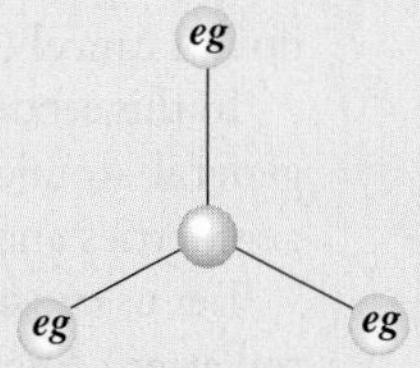	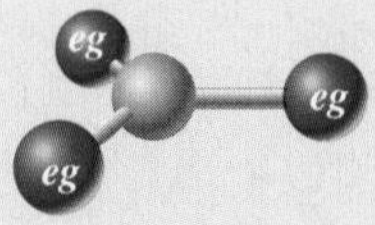
4		tetrahedral; 109.5°	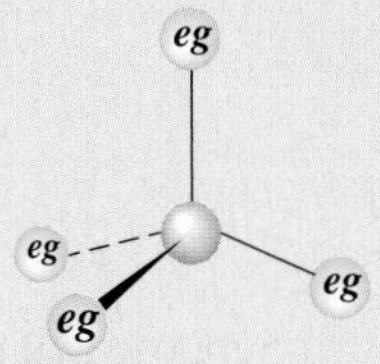	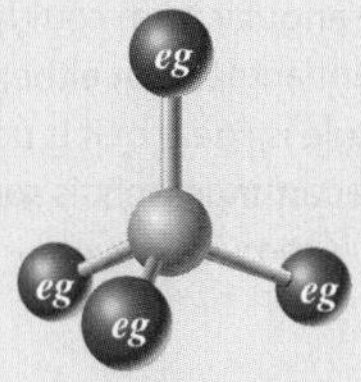
5		trigonal bipyramidal; 90°, 120°, 180°	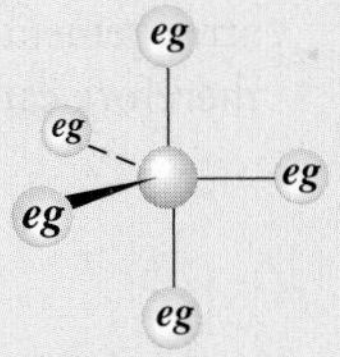	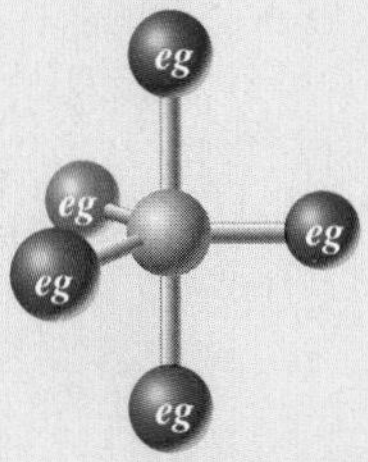
6		octahedral; 90°, 180°	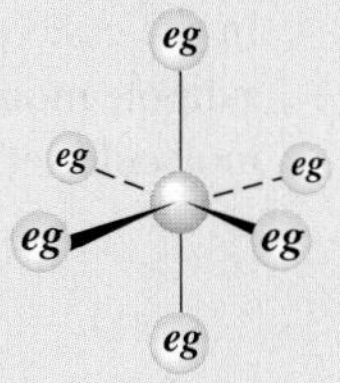	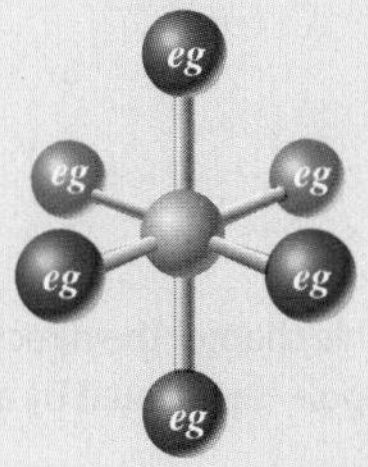

*Electronic geometries are illustrated here using electron groups ("eg") that represent lone pairs or bonded atoms about the central atom (gray sphere). In the ball-and-stick models the electron groups are located at the end of the silver sticks (atoms) or in the region of space around the silver stick (lone pairs).

†Angles made by imaginary lines through the nucleus and the electron groups.

‡By convention, a line in the plane of the drawing is represented by a solid line ——, a line behind this plane is shown as a dashed line ----, and a line in front of this plane is shown as a wedge ➤ with the fat end of the wedge nearest the viewer. Chemists also use a dashed wedge (⫶⫶⫶) to indicate an atom oriented behind the plane or atom to which it is bonded.

shows the relationship between the common numbers of electron groups and their corresponding electronic geometries. After we know the electronic geometry (and *only then*), we can use the bonding electron groups on the central atom to attach the remaining atoms. This lets us deduce the arrangement of *atoms* around the central atom, called the **molecular geometry**. If necessary, we repeat this procedure for each central atom in the molecule or ion. These procedures are illustrated in Parts B of Sections 8-5 through 8-12.

▶ You *must* know the electronic geometry before you can deduce the molecular geometry.

8-3 Polar Molecules: The Influence of Molecular Geometry

In Chapter 7 we saw that the unequal sharing of electrons between two atoms with different electronegativities, $\Delta(EN) > 0$, results in a *polar bond*. For heteronuclear diatomic molecules such as HF, this bond polarity results in a *polar molecule*. Then the entire molecule acts as a dipole, and we would find that the molecule has a measurable *dipole moment*, that is, it is greater than zero.

When a molecule consists of more than two atoms joined by polar bonds, we must also take into account the *arrangement* of the resulting bond dipoles to decide whether or not a molecule is polar. For such a case, we first use the VSEPR theory to deduce the molecular geometry (arrangement of atoms), as described in the preceding section and exemplified in Parts A and B of Sections 8-5 through 8-12. Then we determine whether the bond dipoles are arranged in such a way that they cancel (so that the resulting molecule is *nonpolar*) or do not cancel (so that the resulting molecule is *polar*).

In this section we will discuss the ideas of cancellation of dipoles in general terms, using general atomic symbols A and B. Then we will apply these ideas to specific molecular geometries and molecular polarities in Parts B of Sections 8-5 through 8-12.

Let us consider a heteronuclear triatomic molecule with the formula AB_2 (A is the central atom). Such a molecule must have one of the following two molecular geometries:

▶ The angular form could have different angles, but either the molecule is linear or it is not. The angular arrangement is sometimes called *V-shaped* or *bent*.

$$B\text{—}A\text{—}B \quad \text{or} \quad B\text{—}A$$
$$\phantom{B\text{—}A\text{—}B \quad \text{or} \quad B\text{—}A}\diagdown$$
$$\phantom{B\text{—}A\text{—}B \quad \text{or} \quad B\text{—}A\diagdown}B$$

$$\text{linear} \qquad\qquad \text{angular}$$

Suppose that atom B has a higher electronegativity than atom A. Then each $A\text{—}B$ bond is polar, with the negative end of the bond dipole pointing toward B. We can view each bond dipole as an *electronic vector*, with a *magnitude* and a *direction*. In the linear AB_2 arrangement, the two bond dipoles are *equal* in magnitude and *opposite* in direction. They therefore cancel to give a nonpolar molecule (dipole moment equal to zero).

$$\overset{\longleftarrow + \;+\longrightarrow}{B\text{—}A\text{—}B}$$
net dipole = 0
(nonpolar molecule)

In the case of the angular arrangement, the two equal dipoles *do not cancel*, but add to give a dipole moment greater than zero. The angular molecular arrangement represents a polar molecule.

▶ In this chapter the direction of the net dipole is indicated by a shaded arrow:

➡

The arrow head indicates the area of partial negative charge and the tail (without a cross) represents the region of partial positive charge.

$$\overset{\longleftarrow +}{B\text{—}A}$$
$$\phantom{B\text{—}A}\diagdown B$$
net dipole > 0
(polar molecule)

If the electronegativity differences were reversed in the $B\text{—}A\text{—}B$ molecule—that is, if A were more electronegative than B—the directions of all bond polarities would be reversed. But the bond polarities would still cancel in the linear arrangement to give a nonpolar molecule. In the angular arrangement, bond polarities would still add to give a polar molecule, but with the net dipole pointing in the opposite direction from that described earlier.

We can make similar arguments based on addition of bond dipoles for other arrangements. As we will see in Section 8-8, lone pairs on the central atom can also affect the direction and the magnitude of the net molecular dipole, so the presence of lone pairs on the central atom must always be taken into account.

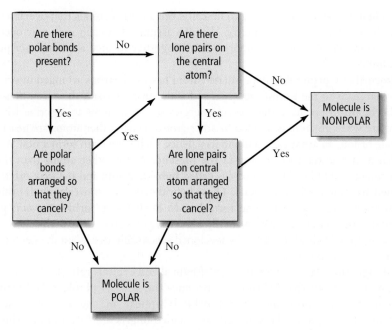

Figure 8-1 A guide to determining whether a polyatomic molecule is polar or nonpolar. Study the more detailed presentation in the text.

For a molecule to be polar, *two* conditions must *both* be met:

1. There must be at least one polar bond or one lone pair on the central atom.
   and
2. **a.** The polar bonds, if there are more than one, must be arranged so that their polarities (bond dipoles) *do not cancel*.
   or
   b. If there are two or more lone pairs on the central atom, they must be arranged so that their polarities *do not cancel*.

Put another way, if there are no polar bonds or lone pairs of electrons on the central atom, the molecule *cannot* be polar. Even if polar bonds or lone pairs are present, they may be arranged so that their polarities cancel one another, resulting in a nonpolar molecule.

Carbon dioxide, CO_2, is a three-atom molecule in which each carbon-oxygen bond is *polar* because of the electronegativity difference between C and O. But the molecule *as a whole* is shown by experiment (dipole moment measurement) to be nonpolar. This tells us that the polar bonds are arranged in such a way that the bond polarities cancel. Water, H_2O, on the other hand, is a very polar molecule; this tells us that the H—O bond polarities do not cancel one another. Molecular shapes clearly play a crucial role in determining molecular dipole moments. We will develop a better understanding of molecular shapes in order to understand molecular polarities.

The logic used to predict whether a molecule is polar or nonpolar is outlined in Figure 8-1. The approach described in this section will be applied to various electronic and molecular geometries in Parts B of Sections 8-5 through 8-12.

linear molecule;
bond dipoles cancel;
molecule is nonpolar

angular molecule;
bond dipoles do not cancel;
molecule is polar

8-4 Valence Bond Theory

In Chapter 7 we described covalent bonding as electron pair sharing that results from the overlap of orbitals from two atoms. This is the basic idea of the **valence bond (VB) theory**—it describes *how* bonding occurs. In many examples throughout this chapter, we first use the VSEPR theory to describe the *orientations* of the electron

We can describe hybridization as the mathematical combination of the waves that represent the orbitals of the atom. This is analogous to the formation of new waves on the surface of water when different waves interact.

▶ Although the terminology is not as precise as we might wish, we use "molecular geometry" to describe the arrangement of atoms in *polyatomic ions* as well as in molecules.

S **TOP & THINK**
See the "Important Note" on page 288 in Section 8-1; consult your instructor for guidance on the order in which you should study Sections 8-5 through 8-12.

groups. Then we use the VB theory to describe the atomic orbitals that overlap to produce the bonding with that geometry. We also assume that each lone pair occupies a separate orbital. Thus, the two theories work together to give a fuller description of the bonding.

We learned in Chapter 4 that an isolated atom has its electrons arranged in orbitals in the way that leads to the lowest total energy for the atom. Usually, however, these "pure atomic" orbitals do not have the correct energies or orientations to describe where the electrons are when an atom is bonded to other atoms. When other atoms are nearby as in a molecule or ion, an atom can combine its valence shell orbitals to form a new set of orbitals that is at a lower total energy in the presence of the other atoms than the pure atomic orbitals would be. This process is called **hybridization**, and the new orbitals that are formed are called **hybrid orbitals**. These hybrid orbitals can overlap with orbitals on other atoms to share electrons and form bonds. Such hybrid orbitals *usually* give an improved description of the experimentally observed geometry of the molecule or ion. In fact, the concept of hybrid orbitals was developed specifically to explain the geometries of polyatomic ions and molecules.

The designation (label) given to a set of hybridized orbitals reflects the *number and kind* of atomic orbitals that hybridize to produce the new set (Table 8-2). Further details about hybridization and hybrid orbitals appear in the following sections. Throughout the chapter, hybrid orbitals are shaded in green, while atomic orbitals are colored blue.

Molecular Shapes and Bonding

We are now ready to study the structures of some simple molecules. We often refer to generalized chemical formulas in which "A" represents the central atom and "B" represents an atom bonded to A. We follow the eight steps of analysis outlined in Section 8-1. We first give the known (experimentally determined) facts about the polarity and the shape of the molecule. We then write the Lewis formula (Part A of each section). Then we explain these facts in terms of the VSEPR and VB theories. The simpler VSEPR theory will be used to explain (or predict) first the *electronic geometry* (all the electron groups) and then the *molecular geometry* (just the bonded atoms) in the molecule (Part B). We then show how the molecular polarity of a molecule is a result of bond polarities, lone pairs, and molecular geometry. Finally, we use the VB theory to describe the bonding in molecules in more detail, usually using hybrid orbitals (Part C). As you study each section, refer frequently to the summaries that appear in Table 8-4.

Table 8-2 Relation Between Electronic Geometries and Hybridization

Electron Groups on Central Atom	Electronic Geometry	Atomic Orbitals Mixed from Valence Shell of Central Atom	Hybridization
2	linear	one s, one p	sp
3	trigonal planar	one s, two p's	sp^2
4	tetrahedral	one s, three p's	sp^3
5	trigonal bipyramidal	one s, three p's, one d	sp^3d
6	octahedral	one s, three p's, two d's	sp^3d^2

8-5 Linear Electronic Geometry: AB₂ Species (No Lone Pairs on A)

A. Experimental Facts and Lewis Formulas

Several linear molecules consist of a central atom plus two atoms of another element, abbreviated as AB_2. These compounds include $BeCl_2$, $BeBr_2$, and BeI_2 (in their gaseous state), as well as CdX_2 and HgX_2, where $X = Cl$, Br, or I. All of these are known to be linear (bond angle = 180°), nonpolar, covalent compounds.

Let's focus on *gaseous* $BeCl_2$ molecules. We wrote the Lewis formula for $BeCl_2$ in Example 7-4. It shows two single covalent bonds, with Be and Cl each contributing one electron to each bond.

In many of its compounds, Be does not satisfy the octet rule (see Section 7-8).

$$: \ddot{C}l : Be : \ddot{C}l : \quad \text{or} \quad : \ddot{C}l - Be - \ddot{C}l :$$

Another linear, nonpolar AB_2 molecule is carbon dioxide, CO_2.

$$: \ddot{O} :: C :: \ddot{O} : \quad \text{or} \quad : \ddot{O} = C = \ddot{O} :$$

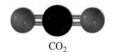

A model of gaseous BeCl₂, a linear AB₂ molecule.

CO_2

B. VSEPR Theory

Valence shell electron pair repulsion theory places the two electron pairs on Be 180° apart, that is, with **linear** *electronic geometry*. Both electron pairs are bonding pairs, so VSEPR also predicts a linear atomic arrangement, or *linear molecular geometry*, for $BeCl_2$.

▶ The VSEPR theory describes the locations of bonded atoms around the central atom, as well as where its lone pairs of valence shell electrons are directed.

$$\overset{180°}{: \ddot{C}l - Be - \ddot{C}l :}$$

If we examine the bond dipoles, we see that the electronegativity difference (see Table 5-3) is large (1.5 units) and each bond is quite polar:

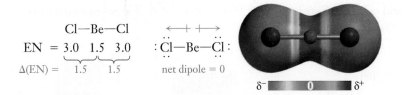

$$\begin{array}{c} Cl - Be - Cl \\ EN = \underbrace{3.0 \quad 1.5}_{} \underbrace{\quad 3.0}_{} \\ \Delta(EN) = \quad 1.5 \quad \quad 1.5 \end{array}$$

$: \ddot{C}l - Be - \ddot{C}l :$

net dipole = 0

$\delta^- \quad \blacksquare \quad 0 \quad \blacksquare \quad \delta^+$

STOP & THINK

It is important to distinguish between *nonpolar bonds* and *nonpolar molecules*. Polar bonds do not necessarily produce a polar molecule.

The two bond dipoles are *equal* in magnitude and *opposite* in direction. They therefore cancel to give a nonpolar molecule.

The difference in electronegativity between Be and Cl is so large that we might expect ionic bonding. The radius of Be^{2+} is so small (0.59 Å) and its *charge density* (ratio of charge to size) is so high, however, that most simple beryllium compounds are covalent rather than ionic. The high charge density of Be^{2+} causes it to attract and distort the electron cloud of monatomic anions of all but the most electronegative elements. As a result, the bonds in $BeCl_2$ are polar covalent rather than ionic. Two exceptions are BeF_2 and BeO. They are ionic compounds because they contain the two most electronegative elements bonded to Be.

▶ We say that the Be^{2+} ion *polarizes* the anions, Cl^-.

Similarly, VSEPR theory counts two electron groups on the carbon atom in CO_2. Thus, C in CO_2 has linear electronic geometry with both electron groups attached to O atoms. The molecular geometry of CO_2 is linear. Each $C=O$ bond is polar, but these

S TOP & THINK
Remember that a double
bond counts as only one
electron group.

bond dipoles point in opposite directions (180°), so they cancel, making CO_2 a nonpolar
molecule.

$$O=C=O$$
$$EN = \underbrace{3.5 \quad 2.5 \quad 3.5}$$
$$\Delta(EN) = \underbrace{1.0} \quad \underbrace{1.0}$$

$$\overset{\longleftarrow + \quad + \longrightarrow}{\ddot{\text{O}}=\text{C}=\ddot{\text{O}}}$$
net dipole = 0

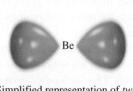

δ^- ▬▬▬▬▬ **0** ▬▬▬▬▬ δ^+

C. Valence Bond Theory

Consider the ground state electron configuration of Be. There are two electrons in the $1s$
orbital, but these nonvalence (inner or *core*) electrons are *not* involved in bonding. Two
more electrons are *paired* in the $2s$ orbital. How, then, will a Be atom bond to two Cl atoms? The Be atom must somehow make available one orbital for each bonding Cl electron (the unpaired p electrons). The following *ground state* electron configuration for Be is
the configuration for an isolated Be atom. Another configuration may be more stable when
the Be atom is covalently bonded. Suppose that the Be atom "promoted" one of the paired
$2s$ electrons to one of the $2p$ orbitals, the next higher energy orbitals.

▶ Cl ground state configuration:

[Ne] $\underset{3s}{\underline{\uparrow\downarrow}} \quad \underset{3p}{\underline{\uparrow\downarrow} \ \underline{\uparrow\downarrow} \ \underline{\uparrow}}$

Be [He] $\underset{2s}{\underline{\uparrow\downarrow}}$ $\overset{\overbrace{}}{\underline{\quad}\ \underline{\quad}\ \underline{\quad}}_{2p}$ $\xrightarrow{\text{promote}}$ Be [He] $\underset{2s}{\underline{\uparrow}}$ $\overset{\overbrace{}}{\underline{\uparrow}\ \underline{\quad}\ \underline{\quad}}_{2p}$

Then there would be two Be orbitals available for bonding. This description, however, is
still not fully consistent with experimental fact. The Be $2s$ and $2p$ orbitals could not overlap a Cl $3p$ orbital with equal effectiveness; that is, this "promoted pure atomic" arrangement would predict two *nonequivalent* Be — Cl bonds. Yet we observe experimentally that
the Be — Cl bonds are *identical* in bond length and strength.

For these two different orbitals on Be to become equivalent, they must *hybridize* to give
two new orbitals that reflect the equal contribution of the s and p orbitals. These are called
***sp* hybrid orbitals**. Consistent with Hund's Rule, each of these equivalent hybrid orbitals
on Be would contain one electron.

▶ Hund's Rule is discussed in
Section 4-18.

Be [He] $\underset{2s}{\underline{\uparrow\downarrow}}$ $\overset{\overbrace{}}{\underline{\quad}\ \underline{\quad}}_{2p}$ $\xrightarrow{\text{Hybridize}}$ Be [He] $\underset{sp}{\underline{\uparrow}\ \underline{\uparrow}}$ $\overset{\overbrace{}}{\underline{\quad}\ \underline{\quad}}_{2p}$

The sp hybrid orbitals are described as *linear orbitals*, and we say that Be has *linear electronic
geometry*.

▶ In this chapter, pure atomic
orbitals are shown in blue, and
hybrid orbitals are shown in green.
As we did for pure atomic orbitals,
we often draw hybrid orbitals more
slender than they actually are. Such
drawings are intended to remind us
of the orientations and general shapes
of orbitals.

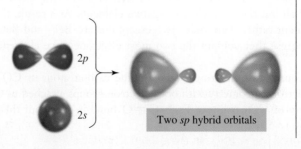

Two sp hybrid orbitals

Simplified representation of *two*
sp hybrid orbitals on a Be atom

We can imagine that there is one electron in each of these hybrid orbitals on the Be atom. Recall that each Cl atom has a half-filled $3p$ orbital that can overlap with a half-filled sp hybrid of Be. We picture the bonding in $BeCl_2$ in the following diagram, in which only the bonding electrons are represented.

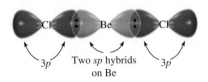

$3p$ Two sp hybrids $3p$
on Be

▶ Lone pairs of electrons on Cl atoms are not shown. The hybrid orbitals on the central atom are shown in green in this and subsequent drawings. The atomic orbitals are shown all in blue without different phase colors.

Thus, the Be and two Cl nuclei would lie on a straight line. *This is consistent with the experimental observation that the molecule is linear.*

The structures of beryllium bromide, $BeBr_2$, and beryllium iodide, BeI_2, are similar to that of $BeCl_2$. The chlorides, bromides, and iodides of cadmium, CdX_2, and mercury, HgX_2, are also linear covalent molecules (where X = Cl, Br, or I).

▶ The two X's within one structure are identical.

When there are two electron groups around the central atom, it is sp hybridized. AB_2 molecules and ions with no lone pairs on the central atom have linear electronic geometry, linear molecular geometry, and sp hybridization on the central atom.

The linear geometry of carbon in CO_2 tells us that the hybridization on the carbon is sp. We will postpone a detailed discussion of the double bonds until Section 8-14.

Problem-Solving Tip Number and Kind of Hybrid Orbitals

One additional idea about hybridization is worth special emphasis:

The number of hybrid orbitals is always equal to the number of atomic orbitals that hybridize.

Hybrid orbitals are named by indicating the *number and kind* of atomic orbitals hybridized. Hybridization of *one s* orbital and *one p* orbital gives *two sp hybrid orbitals*. We shall see presently that hybridization of *one s* and *two p* orbitals gives *three sp²* hybrid orbitals; hybridization of *one s* orbital and *three p* orbitals gives *four sp³* hybrids, and so on (see Table 8-2).

▶ Hybridization usually involves orbitals from the same main shell (same *n*).

8-6 Trigonal Planar Electronic Geometry: AB₃ Species (No Lone Pairs on A)

A. Experimental Facts and Lewis Formulas

Boron is a Group 3A element that forms many covalent compounds by bonding to three other atoms. Typical examples include boron trifluoride, BF_3 (mp = $-127°C$); boron trichloride, BCl_3 (mp = $-107°C$); boron tribromide, BBr_3 (mp = $-46°C$); and boron triiodide, BI_3 (mp = $50°C$). All are trigonal planar nonpolar molecules.

▶ A trigonal planar molecule is a flat molecule in which all three bond angles are 120°.

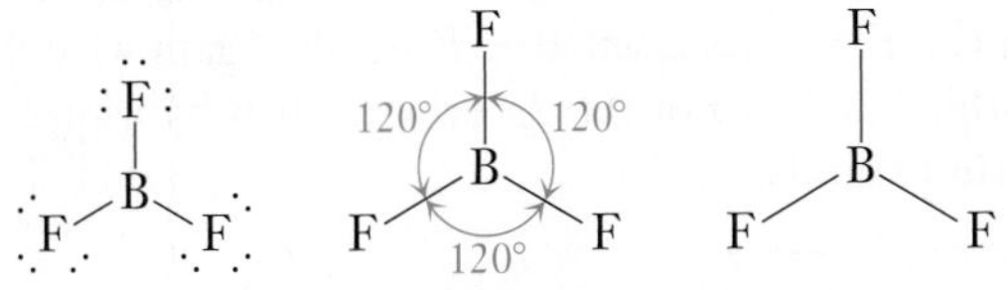

The Lewis formula for BF_3 is derived from the following: (a) each B atom has three electrons in its valence shell and (b) each B atom is bonded to three F (or Cl, Br, I) atoms. In Example 7-5 we wrote the Lewis formula for BCl_3. Both F and Cl are members of Group 7A, and so the Lewis formulas for BF_3 and BCl_3 should be similar.

A model of BF₃, a trigonal planar AB₃ molecule.

formaldehyde, H₂C = O

▶ Trigonal planar geometry is sometimes called *plane triangular* or simply *triangular*.

▶ The B^{3+} ion is so small (radius = 0.20 Å) that boron does not form simple ionic compounds.

We see that BF_3 and other similar molecules have a central element that does *not* satisfy the octet rule. Boron shares only six electrons (as do most of the Group 3A elements).

Another trigonal AB_3 molecule is formaldehyde, H_2C=O, one of the simplest organic compounds.

B. VSEPR Theory

Boron, the central atom, has three electron groups (three bonded atoms, no lone pairs on B). The VSEPR theory predicts **trigonal planar** *electronic geometry* for molecules such as BF_3 because this structure gives maximum separation among the three electron groups. There are no lone pairs of electrons associated with the boron atom, so a fluorine atom is at each corner of the equilateral triangle, and the *molecular geometry* is also trigonal planar. The maximum separation of any three items (electron groups) around a fourth item (B atom) is at 120° angles in a single plane. All four atoms are in the same plane. The three F atoms are at the corners of an equilateral triangle, with the B atom in the center. The structures of BCl_3, BBr_3, and BI_3 are similar.

Examination of the bond dipoles of BF_3 shows that the electronegativity difference (see Table 5-3) is very large (2.0 units) and that the bonds are very polar.

$$\underbrace{\begin{matrix} B\text{—}F \\ EN = 2.0 \quad 4.0 \end{matrix}}_{}$$
$$\Delta(EN) = \quad 2.0$$

net molecular dipole = 0

However, the three bond dipoles are symmetrically distributed, so they cancel to give a nonpolar molecule.

Similarly, VSEPR theory counts three electron groups on the carbon atom in H_2C=O. Therefore, C in H_2C=O has trigonal planar electronic geometry with the three electron groups bonded to one oxygen and two hydrogen atoms. The molecular geometry of H_2C=O is thus trigonal planar. The C=O bond is far more polar than the C=H bonds and is the biggest factor in defining the overall dipole of formaldehyde.

$$\underbrace{\begin{matrix} C\text{=}O \\ EN = 2.5 \quad 3.5 \end{matrix}}_{} \qquad \underbrace{\begin{matrix} H\text{—}C \\ EN = 2.1 \quad 2.5 \end{matrix}}_{}$$
$$\Delta(EN) = \quad 1.0 \qquad\qquad \Delta(EN) = \quad 0.4$$

net molecular dipole > 0

C. Valence Bond Theory

To be consistent with experimental findings and the predictions of the VSEPR theory, the VB theory must explain three *equivalent* B—F bonds. Again we use the idea of hybridization. Now the $2s$ orbital and two of the $2p$ orbitals of B hybridize to form a set of three equivalent sp^2 **hybrid orbitals**.

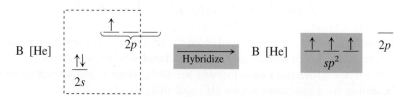

Three sp^2 hybrid orbitals point toward the corners of an equilateral triangle:

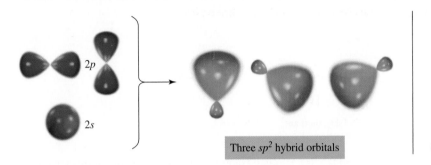

	Three sp^2 hybrid orbitals	Simplified representation of *three* sp^2 hybrid orbitals on a B atom

The B atom supplies one electron in each of these hybrid orbitals. Each of the three F atoms has a $2p$ orbital with one unpaired electron. The $2p$ orbitals can overlap the three sp^2 hybrid orbitals on B. Three electron pairs are shared among one B and three F atoms:

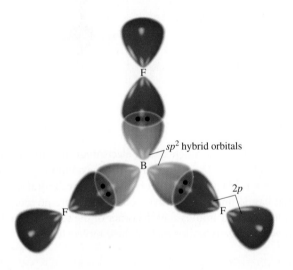

▶ Lone pairs of electrons are not shown for the F atoms.

> When there are three electron groups around the central atom, it is sp^2 hybridized. AB₃ molecules and ions with no lone pairs on the central atom have trigonal planar electronic geometry, trigonal planar molecular geometry, and sp^2 hybridization on the central atom.

In H_2C=O the trigonal planar geometry on carbon tells us that the hybridization on the carbon is sp^2. As with CO_2, we will postpone a detailed discussion of the double bonds until Section 8-14.

8-7 Tetrahedral Electronic Geometry: AB₄ Species (No Lone Pairs on A)

A. Experimental Facts and Lewis Formulas

Each Group 4A element has four electrons in its highest occupied energy level. The Group 4A elements form many covalent compounds by sharing those four electrons with four other atoms. Typical examples include CH_4 (mp = $-182°C$), CF_4 (mp = $-184°C$), CCl_4 (mp = $-23°C$), SiH_4 (mp = $-185°C$), and SiF_4 (mp = $-90°C$). All are tetrahedral, nonpolar molecules (bond angles = $109.5°$). In each, the Group 4A atom is located in the center of a regular tetrahedron. The other four atoms are located at the four corners of the tetrahedron.

▶ The names of many solid figures are based on the numbers of plane faces they have. A *regular* **tetrahedron** is a three-dimensional figure with four equal-sized equilateral triangular faces (the prefix *tetra-* means "four").

The Group 4A atom contributes four electrons to the bonding in a tetrahedral AB_4 molecule, and the other four atoms contribute one electron each. The Lewis formulas for methane, CH_4, and carbon tetrafluoride, CF_4, are typical.

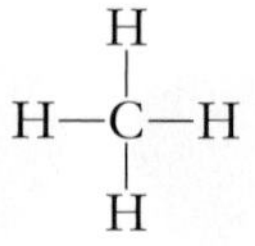

CH$_4$, methane 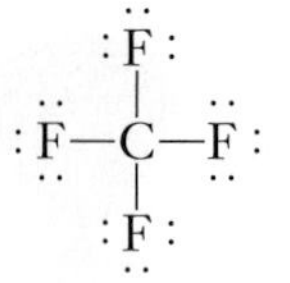   CF$_4$, carbon tetrafluoride

The ammonium ion, NH_4^+, is a familiar example of a polyatomic ion of this type. In an ammonium ion, the central atom is located at the center of a regular tetrahedron with the other atoms at the corners (H—N—H bond angles = 109.5°).

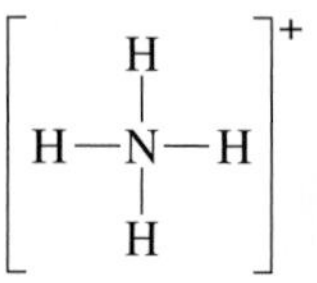

NH$_4^+$, ammonium ion

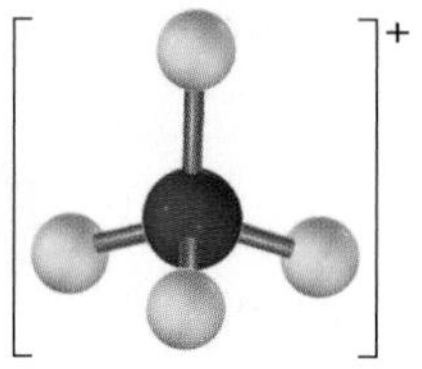

B. VSEPR Theory

VSEPR theory predicts that four valence shell electron groups are directed toward the corners of a regular tetrahedron. That shape gives the maximum separation for four electron groups around one atom. Thus, VSEPR theory predicts **tetrahedral** *electronic geometry* for an AB_4 molecule that has no unshared electrons on A. There are no lone pairs of electrons on the central atom, so a bonded atom is at each corner of the tetrahedron. VSEPR theory predicts a *tetrahedral molecular geometry* for each of these molecules.

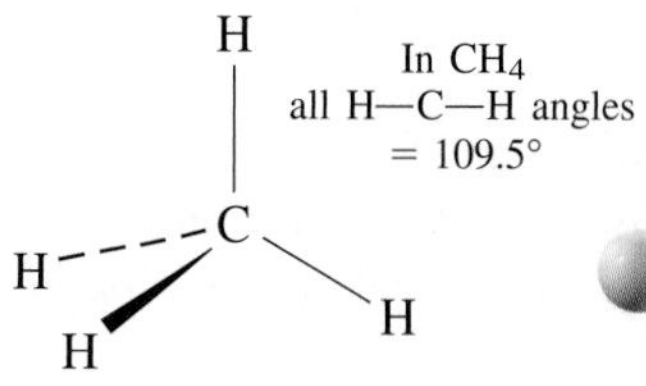

In CH$_4$
all H—C—H angles
= 109.5°

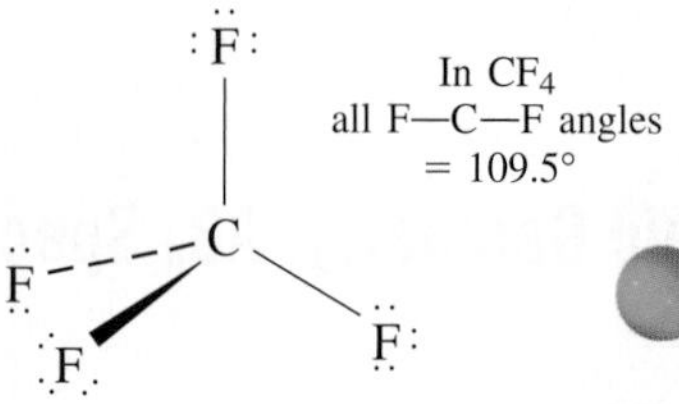

In CF$_4$
all F—C—F angles
= 109.5°

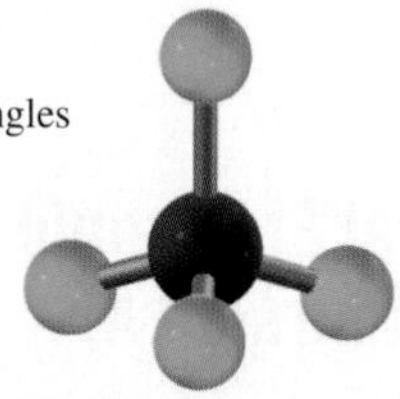

The results that we discussed in Sections 8-5 (BeX_2, CdX_2, and HgX_2, where $X = Cl$, Br, or I), and 8-6 (BX_3, where $X = F$, Cl, Br, or I), and in this section (CH_4, CF_4, CCl_4, SiH_4, SiF_4, and NH_4^+) illustrate an important generalization:

STOP & THINK

This is a good generalization to remember.

When a molecule or polyatomic ion has no lone pairs of valence electrons on the central atom, the *molecular geometry is the same as the electronic geometry.*

Examination of bond dipoles shows that in CH_4 the individual bonds are only slightly polar, whereas in CF_4 the bonds are quite polar. In CH_4 the bond dipoles are directed toward carbon, but in CF_4 they are directed away from carbon. Both molecules are very symmetrical, so the bond dipoles cancel, and both molecules are nonpolar. This is true for all AB_4 molecules in which there are *no unshared electron pairs on the central element* and all four B atoms are identical.

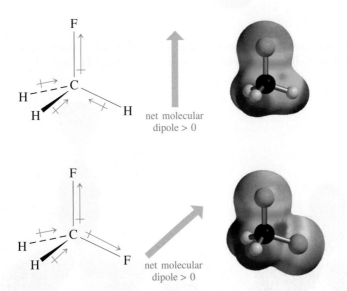

In some tetrahedral molecules, the atoms bonded to the central atom are not all the same. Such molecules are usually polar, with the degree of polarity depending on the relative sizes of the bond dipoles present. In CH_3F or CH_2F_2, for example, the addition of unequal dipoles makes the molecule polar.

The VSEPR theory also predicts that the NH_4^+ ion has tetrahedral electronic geometry. Each region of high electron density bonds the central atom to another atom (H in NH_4^+) at the corner of the tetrahedral arrangement. We describe the molecular geometry of this ion as tetrahedral.

You may wonder whether square planar AB_4 molecules exist. We will discuss some examples of square planar AB_4 species in Section 8-12. The bond angles in square planar molecules are only 90°. Most AB_4 molecules are tetrahedral, however, with larger bond angles (109.5°) and greater separation of valence electron pairs around A.

C. Valence Bond Theory

According to VB theory, each Group 4A atom (e.g., C in CH_4) must make four equivalent orbitals available for bonding. To do this, C forms four *sp*³ **hybrid orbitals** by mixing the *s* and all three *p* orbitals in its outer ($n = 2$) shell. This results in four unpaired electrons.

These *sp*³ hybrid orbitals are directed toward the corners of a regular tetrahedron, which has a 109.5° angle from any corner to the center to any other corner.

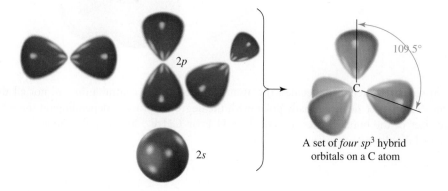

A set of *four sp*³ hybrid orbitals on a C atom

Each of the four atoms that bond to C has a half-filled atomic orbital; these can overlap the half-filled *sp*³ hybrid orbitals on C, as is illustrated for CH_4 and CF_4.

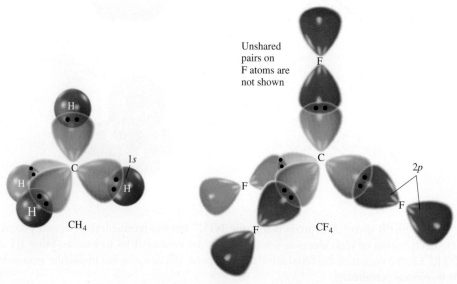

Unshared pairs on F atoms are not shown

CH_4 CF_4

Problem-Solving Tip Use Periodic Relationships

Because F, Cl, Br, and I are all in the same group of the periodic table, we know that their compounds will be similar. We expect that the detailed descriptions we have seen for CF_4 will also apply to CCl_4, CBr_4, and CI_4, and we do not need to go through the entire reasoning for each one. Thus, we can say that each of the CX_4 molecules ($X = F$, Cl, Br, or I) also has tetrahedral electronic geometry, tetrahedral molecular geometry, sp^3 hybridization on the carbon atom, zero dipole moment, and so on.

We can give the same VB description for the hybridization of the central atoms in polyatomic ions. In NH_4^+ the N atom forms four sp^3 hybrid orbitals directed toward the corners of a regular tetrahedron. Each of these sp^3 hybrid orbitals overlaps with an orbital on a neighboring atom (H in NH_4^+) to form a bond.

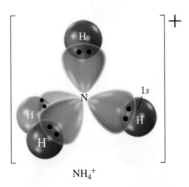

NH_4^+

When there are four electron groups around the central atom, it is sp^3 hybridized. AB₄ molecules and ions with no lone pairs on the central atom have tetrahedral electronic geometry, tetrahedral molecular geometry, and sp^3 hybridization on the central atom.

Problem-Solving Tip Often There Is More Than One Central Atom

Many molecules contain more than one central atom, that is, there is more than one atom that is bonded to several other atoms. We can analyze such molecules one central atom at a time, to build up a picture of the three-dimensional aspects of the molecule. An example is ethane, C_2H_6; its Lewis formula is

$$
\begin{array}{ccc}
& H & H \\
& | & | \\
H- & C- & C-H \\
& | & | \\
& H & H
\end{array}
$$

Let us first consider the left-hand carbon atom. The arrangement of its electron groups allows us to locate the other C and three H atoms with respect to that C atom (the atoms outlined in red below). Then we carry out a similar analysis for the right-hand C atom to deduce the arrangements of *its* neighbors (outlined in blue).

Each C atom in C_2H_6 has four electron groups. The VSEPR theory tells us that each C atom has tetrahedral electronic geometry; the resulting atomic arrangement around each C atom has one C and three H atoms at the corners of this tetrahedral arrangement. The VB interpretation is that each C atom is sp^3 hybridized. The C—C bond is formed by overlap of a half-filled sp^3 hybrid orbital of one C atom with a half-filled sp^3 hybrid orbital of the other C atom. Each C—H bond is formed by the overlap of a half-filled sp^3 hybrid orbital on C with the half-filled $1s$ orbital of an H atom.

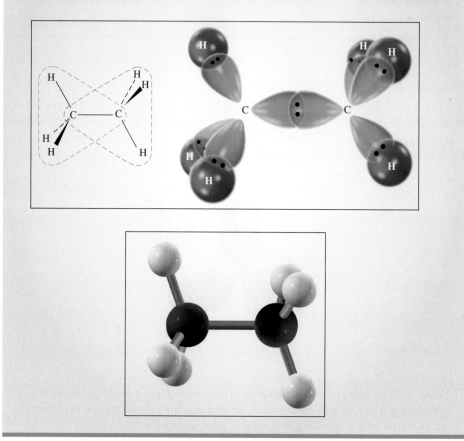

8-8 Tetrahedral Electronic Geometry: AB_3U Species (One Lone Pair on A)

We are now ready to study the structures of some simple molecules with lone pairs on the central atom. In this and subsequent sections, we use generalized chemical formulas in which "A" represents the central atom, "B" represents an atom bonded to A, and "U" represents a lone (unshared) pair on the central atom A. For instance, AB_3U would represent any molecule with three B atoms bonded to a central atom A, with one lone pair on A.

A. Experimental Facts and Lewis Formulas

Each Group 5A element has five electrons in its valence shell. The Group 5A elements form some covalent compounds by sharing three of those electrons with three other atoms. Let us describe two examples: ammonia, NH_3, and nitrogen trifluoride, NF_3. Each is a trigonal pyramidal, polar molecule with a lone pair on the nitrogen atom. Each has a nitrogen atom at the apex and the other three atoms at the corners of the triangular base of the pyramid.

The Lewis formulas for NH_3 and NF_3 are

$$H-\overset{\cdot\cdot}{N}-H \qquad :\overset{\cdot\cdot}{\underset{\cdot\cdot}{F}}-\overset{\cdot\cdot}{N}-\overset{\cdot\cdot}{\underset{\cdot\cdot}{F}}:$$
$$\mid \qquad \mid$$
$$H \qquad :\overset{\cdot\cdot}{\underset{\cdot\cdot}{F}}:$$

$$NH_3 \qquad NF_3$$

B. VSEPR Theory

As in Section 8-7, VSEPR theory predicts that the *four* electron groups around a central atom will be directed toward the corners of a tetrahedron because this gives maximum separation. So N has tetrahedral electronic geometry in NH_3 and NF_3. We must reemphasize the distinction between electronic geometry and molecular geometry. *Electronic geometry* refers to the geometric arrangement of the *electron groups* around the central atom. But the *molecular geometry* excludes the lone pairs on the central atom, and describes only the arrangement of *atoms* (i.e., nuclei) around the central atom. We can represent the tetrahedral *electronic geometry* around N in NH_3 or NF_3 as follows.

We then use the Lewis formula as a guide to arrange the bonded atoms and the lone pairs in these tetrahedral sites around the nitrogen atom to give the molecular geometry.

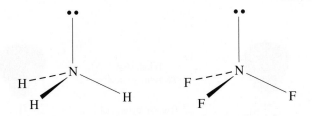

Then we describe the *molecular geometry* as the arrangement of the *atoms*. In each of these molecules, the N atom is at the apex of a (shallow) trigonal pyramidal arrangement and the other three atoms are at the corners of the triangular base of the pyramid. Thus, the molecular geometry of each molecule is described as **trigonal pyramidal**.

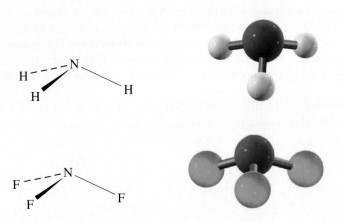

> **S**TOP & THINK
> When there are lone pairs on the central atom the molecular geometry is *not* the same as the electronic geometry, because lone pairs must occupy space of their own.

We have seen that CH_4, CF_4, NH_3, and NF_3 all have tetrahedral electronic geometry. But CH_4 and CF_4 (AB_4) have tetrahedral molecular geometry, whereas NH_3 and NF_3 (AB_3U) have trigonal pyramidal molecular geometry.

> In molecules or polyatomic ions that contain lone (unshared) pairs of valence electrons on the central atom, the *electronic geometry* and the *molecular geometry* cannot be the same.

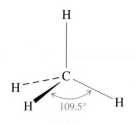

Because this trigonal pyramidal molecular geometry is a fragment of tetrahedral electronic geometry, we expect that the H—N—H angle would be close to the tetrahedral value, 109.5°. In CH_4 (a tetrahedral AB_4 molecule), all H—C—H bond angles are observed to be this ideal value, 109.5°. In NH_3, however, the H—N—H bond angles are observed to be less than this, 107.3°. How can we explain this deviation?

A lone pair is a pair of valence electrons that is associated with only one nucleus in contrast to a bonded pair, which is associated with two nuclei. The known geometries of many molecules and polyatomic ions, based on measurements of bond angles, show that *lone pairs of electrons occupy more space than bonding pairs*. A lone pair has only one atom exerting strong attractive forces on it, so it can spread out and take up more space than bonding electrons. The relative magnitudes of the repulsive forces between pairs of electrons on an atom are

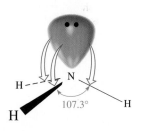

$$lp/lp \gg lp/bp > bp/bp$$

where *lp* refers to lone pairs and *bp* refers to bonding pairs of electrons. We are most concerned with the repulsions among the electrons in the valence shell of the *central atom* of a molecule or polyatomic ion. The angles at which repulsive forces among electron pairs are minimized are the angles at which the bonding pairs and lone pairs are found in covalently bonded molecules and polyatomic ions. Due to *lp/bp* repulsions in NH_3 and NF_3, their bond angles are *less* than the angles of 109.5° we observed in CH_4 and CF_4 molecules.

A model of NH_3, a trigonal pyramidal AB_3U molecule, showing the lone pair.

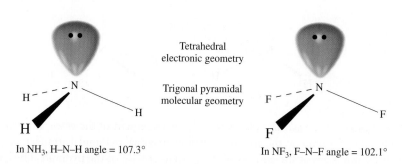

Tetrahedral electronic geometry

Trigonal pyramidal molecular geometry

In NH_3, H–N–H angle = 107.3°

In NF_3, F–N–F angle = 102.1°

The formulas are frequently written as :NH_3 and :NF_3 to emphasize the lone pairs of electrons. The lone pairs must be considered when the polarities of these molecules are examined; they are extremely important in chemical reactions. This is why NH_3 is a base, as we saw in Section 6-1.4 and as we shall discuss more fully in Chapter 10. The contribution of each lone pair to polarity can be depicted as shown below and discussed in the margin.

The electronegativity differences in NH_3 and NF_3 are nearly equal, *but* the resulting nearly equal bond polarities are in opposite directions.

$$\begin{array}{cc} & \text{N—H} \\ \text{EN} = & \underbrace{3.0 \quad 2.1} \\ \Delta(\text{EN}) = & 0.9 \end{array} \qquad \overset{\longleftarrow +}{\text{N—H}} \qquad \begin{array}{cc} & \text{N—F} \\ \text{EN} = & \underbrace{3.0 \quad 4.0} \\ \Delta(\text{EN}) = & 1.0 \end{array} \qquad \overset{+ \longrightarrow}{\text{N—F}}$$

Thus, we have

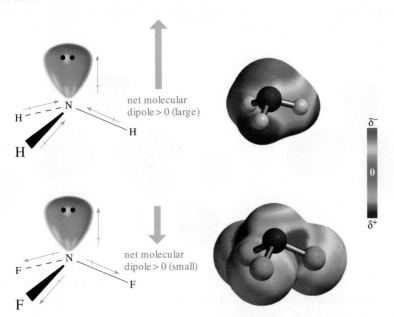

net molecular
dipole > 0 (large)

net molecular
dipole > 0 (small)

▶ In NH_3 the bond dipoles *reinforce* the effect of the lone pair, so NH_3 is very polar ($\mu = 1.47$ D).

▶ In NF_3 the bond dipoles *oppose* the effect of the unshared pair, so NF_3 is only slightly polar ($\mu = 0.23$ D).

We can now use this information to explain the bond angles observed in NF_3 and NH_3. Because of the direction of the bond dipoles in NH_3, the electron-rich end of each N—H bond is at the central atom, N. On the other hand, the fluorine end of each bond in NF_3 is the electron-rich end. As a result, the lone pair can more closely approach the N in NF_3 than in NH_3. In NF_3 the lone pair therefore exerts greater repulsion toward the bonded pairs than in NH_3. In addition, the longer N—F bond length makes the *bp–bp* distance greater in NF_3 than in NH_3, so that the *bp/bp* repulsion in NF_3 is less than that in NH_3. The net effect is that the bond angles are reduced more in NF_3. We can represent this situation as:

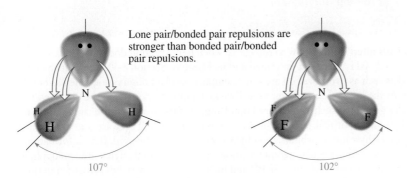

Lone pair/bonded pair repulsions are stronger than bonded pair/bonded pair repulsions.

107°

102°

Bonded pair/bonded pair repulsions are weaker in NF_3 than in NH_3 due to the longer N—F bond.

▶ We might expect the larger F atoms ($r = 0.75$ Å) to repel each other more strongly than the H atoms ($r = 0.37$ Å), leading to larger bond angles in NF_3 than in NH_3. This is not the case, however, because the N—F bond is longer than the N—H bond. The N—F bond density is farther from the N than the N—H bond density.

C. Valence Bond Theory

Experimental results suggest four nearly equivalent orbitals (three involved in bonding, a fourth to accommodate the lone pair), so we again need four sp^3 hybrid orbitals.

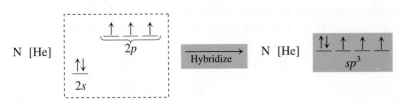

In both NH_3 and NF_3 the lone pair of electrons occupies one of the sp^3 hybrid orbitals. Each of the other three sp^3 orbitals participates in bonding by sharing electrons with another atom. They overlap with half-filled H $1s$ orbitals and F $2p$ orbitals in NH_3 and NF_3, respectively.

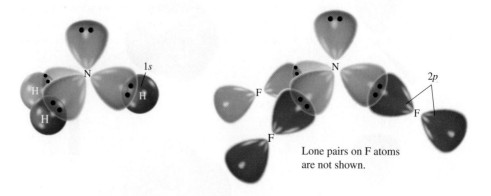

AB$_3$U molecules and ions, each having four electron groups around the central atom, *usually* have tetrahedral electronic geometry, trigonal pyramidal molecular geometry, and sp^3 hybridization on the central atom.

We must remember that *theory* (and its application) depends on fact, not the other way around. Sometimes the experimental facts are not consistent with the existence of hybrid orbitals. In PH_3 and AsH_3, each H — P — H bond angle is 93.7°, and each H — As — H bond angle is 91.8°. These angles very nearly correspond to three p orbitals at 90° to each other. Thus, there appears to be no need to use the VSEPR theory or hybridization to describe the bonding in these molecules. In such cases, we just use the "pure" atomic orbitals rather than hybrid orbitals to describe the bonding.

Problem-Solving Tip When Do We Not Need to Describe Hybrid Orbitals?

Students often wonder how to recognize when hybridization does not apply, as in the PH_3 and AsH_3 cases just described and in H_2S (see Section 8-9). Remember that models such as hybridization are our attempts to explain observations such as bond angles. At the level of our studies, we will be given information about the observed molecular geometry, such as measured bond angles. If these are near the angles of pure (unhybridized) orbitals, then hybridization is not needed; if they are near the predicted angles for hybridized orbitals, then hybridization should be used. If no information about observed molecular geometry (molecular shape, bond angles, etc.) is supplied, you should assume that the VSEPR and hybridization approaches presented in this chapter should be used.

8-9 Tetrahedral Electronic Geometry: AB$_2$U$_2$ Species (Two Lone Pairs on A)

A. Experimental Facts and Lewis Formulas

Each Group 6A element has six electrons in its valence shell. The Group 6A elements form many covalent compounds by sharing a pair of electrons with each of two other atoms. Typical examples are H_2O, H_2S, and Cl_2O. The Lewis formulas for these molecules are

$$H\text{—}\overset{\displaystyle ..}{\underset{\displaystyle H}{O}}:\qquad H\text{—}\overset{\displaystyle ..}{\underset{\displaystyle H}{S}}:\qquad :\overset{\displaystyle ..}{\underset{\displaystyle :Cl:}{Cl}}\text{—}\overset{\displaystyle ..}{O}:$$

All are angular, polar molecules. The bond angle in water, for example, is 104.5°, and the molecule is very polar with a dipole moment of 1.85 D.

B. VSEPR Theory

The VSEPR theory predicts that the four electron pairs around the oxygen atom in H_2O should be 109.5° apart in a tetrahedral arrangement. The observed $H—O—H$ bond angle is 104.5°. The two lone pairs strongly repel each other and the bonding pairs of electrons. These repulsions force the bonding pairs closer together and result in the decreased bond angle. The decrease in the $H—O—H$ bond angle (from 109.5° to 104.5°) is greater than the corresponding decrease in the $H—N—H$ bond angles in ammonia (from 109.5° to 107.3°) because of the stronger *lp/lp* repulsion in H_2O.

The electronegativity difference is large (1.4 units), so each $O—H$ bond is quite polar. Additionally, the bond dipoles *reinforce* the effect of the two lone pairs, so the H_2O molecule is very polar. Its dipole moment is 1.8 D. The unusual properties of water can be explained in large part by its high polarity.

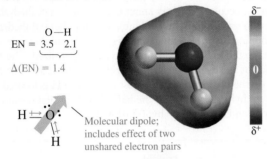

$$O—H$$
$$EN = 3.5 \quad 2.1$$
$$\Delta(EN) = 1.4$$

Molecular dipole; includes effect of two unshared electron pairs

C. Valence Bond Theory

The bond angle in H_2O (104.5°) is closer to the tetrahedral value (109.5°) than to the 90° angle that would result from bonding by pure $2p$ atomic orbitals on O. Valence bond theory therefore postulates four sp^3 hybrid orbitals centered on the O atom: two that participate in bonding and two that hold the two lone pairs.

> AB_2U_2 molecules and ions, each having four electron groups around the central atom, *usually* have tetrahedral electronic geometry, angular molecular geometry, and sp^3 hybridization on the central atom.

Hydrogen sulfide, H_2S, is also an angular molecule, but the $H—S—H$ bond angle is 92.2°. This is very close to the 90° angles between two unhybridized $3p$ orbitals of S. We therefore *do not* need to propose hybrid orbitals to describe the bonding in H_2S. The two H atoms are able to exist at approximately right angles to each other when they are bonded to the larger S atom. The bond angles in H_2Se and H_2Te are 91° and 89.5°, respectively, indicating that they also use pure p orbitals for bonding.

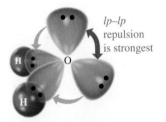

lp–lp repulsion is strongest

There are now *two* lone pairs that repel the bonded pairs.

▶ Sulfur is in Group 6A, directly below oxygen.

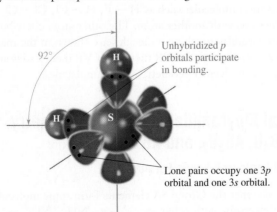

92°

Unhybridized p orbitals participate in bonding.

Lone pairs occupy one $3p$ orbital and one $3s$ orbital.

Problem-Solving Tip Some Molecules Have Two Central Atoms and Lone Pairs

Methanol, CH_3OH, is a simple molecule that has more than one central atom *and* two lone pairs. It is the simplest member of a family of organic molecules called *alcohols*; all alcohols contain the atom grouping $C—O—H$. The Lewis formula for methanol is

$$H—\overset{\displaystyle H}{\underset{\displaystyle H}{C}}—\overset{\displaystyle ..}{\underset{\displaystyle ..}{O}}—H$$

Again, we consider the arrangements around two central atoms in sequence. The carbon atom has four electron groups (outlined below in red). VSEPR theory tells us that this atom has tetrahedral *electronic* geometry; the resulting atomic arrangement around the C atom has four atoms (O and three H) at the corners of this tetrahedral arrangement, so the molecular geometry about the C atom is tetrahedral. The oxygen atom has four electron groups (outlined in blue), so it, too, has tetrahedral *electronic* geometry. Thus, the $C—O—H$ arrangement is angular, and there are two lone pairs on O. The VB interpretation is that both atoms are sp^3 hybridized. The $C—O$ bond is formed by overlap of a half-filled sp^3 hybrid orbital on the C atom with a half-filled sp^3 hybrid orbital on the O atom. Each covalent bond to an H is formed by the overlap of a half-filled sp^3 hybrid orbital with the half-filled $1s$ orbital on an H atom. Each lone pair of electrons on O is in an sp^3 hybrid orbital.

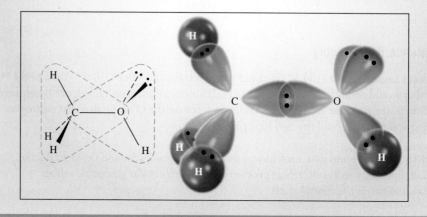

8-10 Tetrahedral Electronic Geometry: ABU_3 Species (Three Lone Pairs on A)

Each Group 7A element has seven electrons in its highest occupied energy level. The Group 7A elements form molecules such as $H—F$, $H—Cl$, $Cl—Cl$, and $I—I$ by sharing one of their electrons with another atom. The other atom contributes one electron to the bonding. Lewis formulas for these molecules are shown in the margin. Any diatomic molecule must be linear. Neither VSEPR theory nor VB theory adds anything to what we already know about the molecular geometry of such molecules.

8-11 Trigonal Bipyramidal Electronic Geometry: AB_5, AB_4U, AB_3U_2, and AB_2U_3

A. Experimental Facts and Lewis Formulas

In Section 8-8 we saw that the Group 5A elements form some molecules by sharing only three of their five electrons with other atoms (e.g., NH_3, NF_3, and PCl_3). Group 5A

▶ We represent the halogen as X.

HX, $H:\overset{..}{\underset{..}{X}}:$ X_2, $:\overset{..}{\underset{..}{X}}:\overset{..}{\underset{..}{X}}:$

In the latter case, either halogen may be considered the A atom of AB.

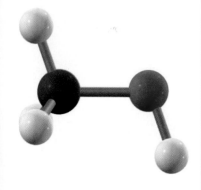

elements (P, As, and Sb) beyond the second period also form some covalent compounds by sharing all five of their valence electrons with five other atoms (see Section 7-8). Phosphorus pentafluoride, PF_5 (mp = $-83°C$), is such a compound. Each P atom has five valence electrons to share with five F atoms. The Lewis formula for PF_5 (see Example 7-6) is shown in the margin. PF_5 molecules are **trigonal bipyramidal** nonpolar molecules. A **trigonal bipyramid** is a six-sided polyhedron consisting of two pyramids joined at a common triangular (trigonal) base.

B. VSEPR Theory

The VSEPR theory predicts that the five electron groups around the phosphorus atom in PF_5 should be as far apart as possible. Maximum separation of five electron groups around a central atom is achieved when the five electron groups (bonding pairs) are placed at the corners and the central atom (P) is placed in the center of a trigonal (or triangular) bipyramid. This is in agreement with experimental observation.

▶ A trigonal bipyramid.

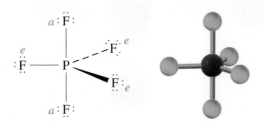

The three F atoms marked *e* are at the corners of the common base, in the same plane as the P atom. These are called *equatorial* F atoms (*e*). The other two F atoms, one above and one below the plane, are called *axial* F atoms (*a*). The F—P—F bond angles are 90° (axial to equatorial), 120° (equatorial to equatorial), and 180° (axial to axial).

The large electronegativity difference between P and F (1.9) suggests very polar bonds. Let's consider the bond dipoles in two groups, because there are two different kinds of P—F bonds in PF_5 molecules, axial and equatorial.

▶ Are there other ways that five fluorine atoms could be arranged *symmetrically* around a phosphorus atom? Compare the hypothetical bond angles in such arrangements with those in a trigonal bipyramidal arrangement.

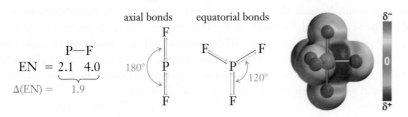

▶ The two axial bonds are in a linear arrangement, like the two bonds in $BeCl_2$ (see Section 8-5); the three equatorial bonds are in a trigonal planar arrangement, like the three bonds in BF_3 (see Section 8-6).

The two axial bond dipoles cancel each other, and the three equatorial bond dipoles cancel, so PF_5 molecules are nonpolar.

C. Valence Bond Theory

Because phosphorus is the central atom in a PF_5 molecule, it must have available five orbitals to form bonds with five F atoms. Hybridization involves one *d* orbital from the vacant set of $3d$ orbitals along with the $3s$ and $3p$ orbitals of the P atom.

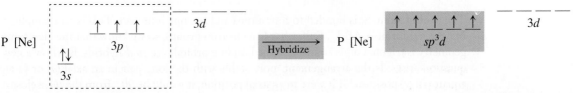

The five *sp³d* **hybrid orbitals** on P point toward the corners of a trigonal bipyramid. Each of these half-filled orbitals is overlapped by a singly occupied 2p orbital of an F atom. The resulting pairing of P and F electrons forms five covalent bonds.

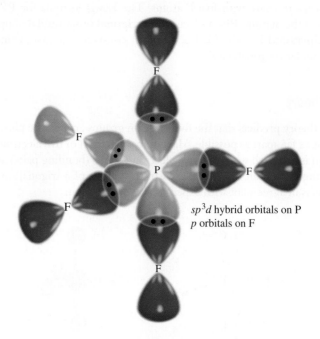

sp³d hybrid orbitals on P
p orbitals on F

> When there are five electron groups around the central atom, it is *sp³d* hybridized. AB₅ molecules and ions with no lone pairs on the central atom have trigonal bipyramidal electronic geometry, trigonal bipyramidal molecular geometry, and *sp³d* hybridization on the central atom.

▶ The P atom is said to have an *expanded valence shell* (see Section 7-8).

We see that *sp³d* hybridization uses an available *d* orbital in the outermost occupied shell of the central atom. The heavier Group 5A elements—P, As, and Sb—can form five covalent bonds using this hybridization. But nitrogen, also in Group 5A, cannot form five covalent bonds because the valence shell of N has no *d* orbitals (only one *s* and three *p* orbitals). The set of *s* and *p* orbitals in a given energy level (and therefore any set of hybrids composed only of *s* and *p* orbitals) can accommodate a *maximum* of eight electrons and participate in a *maximum* of four covalent bonds. The same is true of all elements of the second period because they have only *s* and *p* orbitals in their valence shells. No atoms in the first and second periods can exhibit expanded valence.

D. Lone Pairs in Trigonal Bipyramidal Electronic Geometry

▶ Reminder: The relative magnitudes of repulsive forces are:

$$lp/lp \gg lp/bp > bp/bp$$

As we saw in Parts B of Sections 8-8 and 8-9, lone pairs of electrons occupy more space than bonding pairs, resulting in increased repulsions from lone pairs. What happens when one or more of the five electron groups on the central atom are lone pairs? Let us first consider a molecule such as SF_4, for which the Lewis formula is

$$\ddot{F}\!:\!\!\!\overset{\displaystyle \ddot{F}:}{\underset{\displaystyle :\ddot{F}}{S}}\!\!\!\ddot{F}:$$

The central atom, S, is bonded to four atoms and has one lone pair. This is an example of the general formula AB₄U. Sulfur has five electron groups, so we know that the electronic geometry is trigonal bipyramidal and the bonding orbitals are *sp³d* hybrids. But now a new question arises: Is the arrangement more stable with the lone pair in an axial (*a*) or in an equatorial (*e*) position? If it were in an axial position, it would be 90° from the *three* closest other pairs (the pairs bonding three F atoms in equatorial positions) and 180° from the other axial pair. If it were in an equatorial position, only the *two* axial pairs would be at 90° from the lone pair, and the two equatorial pairs would be farther away, at 120°. The lone pair would therefore be less crowded in an *equatorial* position.

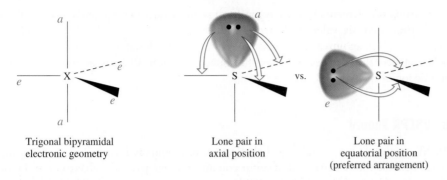

| Trigonal bipyramidal electronic geometry | Lone pair in axial position | Lone pair in equatorial position (preferred arrangement) |

The four F atoms then occupy the remaining four positions. We describe the resulting arrangement of *atoms* as a **seesaw arrangement**. Imagine rotating the arrangement so that the line joining the two axial positions is the board on which the two seesaw riders sit, and the two bonded equatorial positions are the pivot of the seesaw.

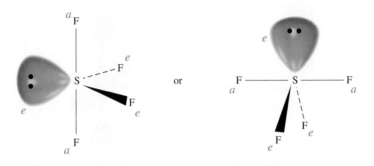

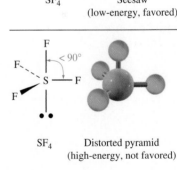

SF₄   Seesaw (low-energy, favored)

SF₄   Distorted pyramid (high-energy, not favored)

As we saw in Sections 8-8 and 8-9, the differing magnitudes of repulsions involving lone pairs and bonding pairs often result in observed bond angles that are slightly different from idealized values. For instance, *lp/bp* repulsion in the seesaw molecule SF₄ causes distortion of the axial S—F bonds away from the lone pair, to an angle of 177°; the two equatorial S—F bonds, ideally at 120°, move much closer together to an angle of 101.6°.

By the same reasoning, we understand why additional lone pairs also take equatorial positions (AB₃U₂ with both lone pairs equatorial or AB₂U₃ with all three lone pairs equatorial). These arrangements are summarized in Figure 8-2.

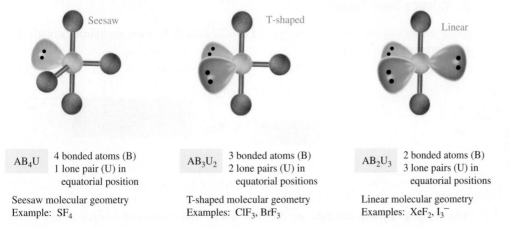

| AB₄U | 4 bonded atoms (B) 1 lone pair (U) in equatorial position | AB₃U₂ | 3 bonded atoms (B) 2 lone pairs (U) in equatorial positions | AB₂U₃ | 2 bonded atoms (B) 3 lone pairs (U) in equatorial positions |

Seesaw molecular geometry
Example: SF₄

T-shaped molecular geometry
Examples: ClF₃, BrF₃

Linear molecular geometry
Examples: XeF₂, I₃⁻

Figure 8-2 Arrangements of bonded atoms and lone pairs (five electron groups—trigonal pyramidal electronic geometry).

8-12 Octahedral Electronic Geometry: AB_6, AB_5U, and AB_4U_2

A. Experimental Facts and Lewis Formulas

The Group 6A elements below oxygen form some covalent compounds of the AB_6 type by sharing their six valence electrons with six other atoms. Sulfur hexafluoride, SF_6 (mp = $-51°C$), an unreactive gas, is an example. Sulfur hexafluoride molecules are nonpolar octahedral molecules. The hexafluorophosphate ion, PF_6^-, is an example of a polyatomic ion of the type AB_6.

▶ In a *regular* **octahedron**, each of the eight faces is an equilateral triangle.

B. VSEPR Theory

An SF_6 molecule has six valence shell electron pairs and six F atoms surrounding one S atom. Because the valence shell of sulfur contains no lone pairs, the electronic and molecular geometries in SF_6 are identical. The maximum separation possible for six electron groups around one S atom is achieved when the electron groups are at the corners and the S atom is at the center of a regular octahedron. Thus, VSEPR theory is consistent with the observation that SF_6 molecules are **octahedral**.

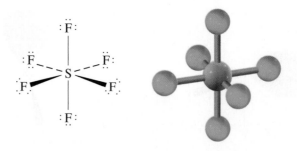

In this octahedral molecule the F—S—F bond angles are 90° and 180°. Each S—F bond is quite polar, but each bond dipole is canceled by an equal dipole 180° from it. So the large bond dipoles cancel and the SF_6 molecule is nonpolar.

By similar reasoning, VSEPR theory predicts octahedral electronic geometry and octahedral molecular geometry for the PF_6^- ion, which has six valence shell electron pairs and six F atoms surrounding one P atom.

C. Valence Bond Theory

Sulfur atoms can use one $3s$, three $3p$, and two $3d$ orbitals to form six hybrid orbitals that accommodate six electron pairs:

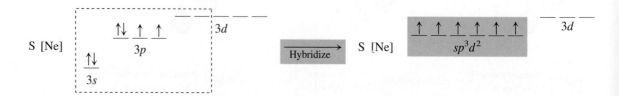

The six sp^3d^2 **hybrid orbitals** are directed toward the corners of a regular octahedron. Each sp^3d^2 hybrid orbital is overlapped by a half-filled $2p$ orbital from fluorine to form a total of six covalent bonds.

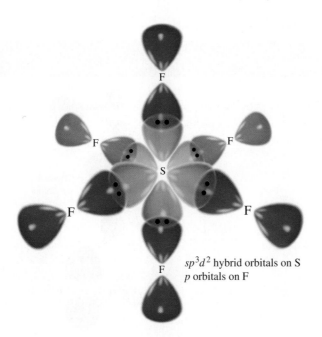

sp^3d^2 hybrid orbitals on S
p orbitals on F

> ▶ Se and Te, in the same group, form analogous compounds. O cannot do so, because it does not have low-energy d orbitals available with which the s and p orbitals can hybridize.

An analogous picture could be drawn for the PF_6^- ion.

> When there are six electron groups around the central atom, it is sp^3d^2 hybridized. AB_6 molecules and ions with no lone pairs on the central atom have octahedral electronic geometry, octahedral molecular geometry, and sp^3d^2 hybridization on the central atom.

D. Lone Pairs in Octahedral Electronic Geometry

We can reason along the lines used in Part D of Section 8-11 to predict the preferred locations of lone pairs on the central atom in octahedral electronic geometry. Because of the high symmetry of the octahedral arrangement, all six positions are equivalent, so it does not matter in which position in the drawing we put the first lone pair. AB_5U molecules and ions are described as having **square pyramidal** molecular geometry. When a second lone pair is present, the most stable arrangement has the two lone pairs in two octahedral positions at $180°$ angles from each other. This leads to a **square planar** molecular geometry for AB_4U_2 species. These arrangements are shown in Figure 8-3.

> ▶ Two lone pairs at $90°$ from each other would be much more crowded.

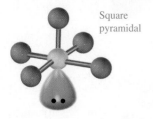

Square pyramidal

Square planar

AB_5U	5 bonded atoms (B) 1 lone pair (U)

Square pyramidal molecular geometry
Examples: IF_5, BrF_5

AB_4U_2	4 bonded atoms (B) 2 lone pairs (U)

Square planar molecular geometry
Examples: XeF_4, IF_4^-

Figure 8-3 Arrangements of bonded atoms and lone pairs (six electron groups—octahedral electronic geometry).

8-13 Lone Pairs on the Central Atom—A Summary

Table 8-3 summarizes a great deal of information about molecules and ions with lone pairs on the central atom. You should study this table carefully.

Table 8-3 Molecular Geometry of Species with Lone Pairs (U) on the Central Atom

General Formula	Electron Groups[a]	Electronic Geometry	Hybridization at Central Atom	Lone Pairs	Molecular Geometry	Examples
AB_2U	3	trigonal planar	sp^2	1	Angular	O_3, NO_2^-, SO_2
AB_3U	4	tetrahedral	sp^3	1	Trigonal pyramidal	NH_3, SO_3^{2-}
AB_2U_2	4	tetrahedral	sp^3	2	Angular	H_2O, NH_2^-
AB_4U	5	trigonal bipyramidal	sp^3d	1	Seesaw	SF_4
AB_3U_2	5	trigonal bipyramidal	sp^3d	2	T-shaped	ICl_3, ClF_3
AB_2U_3	5	trigonal bipyramidal	sp^3d	3	Linear	XeF_2, I_3^-
AB_5U	6	octahedral	sp^3d^2	1	Square pyramidal	IF_5, BrF_5
AB_4U_2	6	octahedral	sp^3d^2	2	Square planar	XeF_4, IF_4^-

[a]Remember that double and triple bonds are treated as one electron group for determining VSEPR geometries.

Problem-Solving Tip Placing Lone Pairs on the Central Atom

Remember that lone pairs occupy more space than bonded pairs, so the lone pairs are always put in positions where they will be least crowded.

If the Lewis formula for a molecule or ion shows only one lone pair: In linear, trigonal planar, tetrahedral, or octahedral electronic geometry, all positions are equivalent, so it doesn't matter where we place the lone pair. In trigonal bipyramidal electronic geometry, place the lone pair in the equatorial position where it is least crowded, and put the bonded atoms in the other positions.

If the Lewis formula shows two lone pairs: In trigonal planar or tetrahedral electronic geometry, we can place the lone pairs in any two positions and the bonded atoms in the other position(s). In trigonal bipyramidal electronic geometry, place the two lone pairs in two equatorial positions (120° apart) where they are least crowded, and put the bonded atoms in the other positions. In octahedral electronic geometry, place the two lone pairs in two positions *across* (180°) from each other, and put the bonded atoms in the other positions (square planar molecular geometry).

8-14 Compounds Containing Double Bonds

In Chapter 7 we constructed Lewis formulas for some molecules and polyatomic ions that contain double and triple bonds. We have not yet considered bonding and shapes for such species. Let us consider ethylene (ethene), C_2H_4, as a specific example. Its Lewis formula is

$$S = N - A$$
$$= 24 - 12 = \underline{12e^-} \text{ shared}$$

$$\begin{array}{cc} H & H \\ {}^{\diagdown}C{=}C^{\diagup} \\ H^{\diagup} & {}^{\diagdown}H \end{array}$$

Each atom has three electron groups. The VSEPR theory tells us that each C atom is at the center of a trigonal plane.

► Here each C atom is considered a central atom. Remember that each bonded atom counts as *one* electron group.

Valence bond theory describes each doubly bonded carbon atom as sp^2 hybridized, with one electron in each sp^2 hybrid orbital and one electron in the unhybridized $2p$ orbital. This $2p$ orbital is perpendicular to the plane of the three sp^2 hybrid orbitals:

$$
\text{C [He]} \quad
\begin{array}{c}
\uparrow \ \uparrow \quad \underline{} \\
2p \\
\uparrow\downarrow \\
2s
\end{array}
\quad \xrightarrow{\text{Hybridize}} \quad
\text{C [He]} \quad
\begin{array}{cc}
\boxed{\uparrow \quad \uparrow \quad \uparrow} & \uparrow \\
sp^2 & 2p_z
\end{array}
$$

Recall that sp^2 hybrid orbitals are directed toward the corners of an equilateral triangle. Figure 8-4 shows top and side views of these hybrid orbitals.

The two C atoms interact by head-on (end-to-end) overlap of sp^2 hybrids pointing toward each other to form a *sigma (σ) bond* and by side-on overlap of the unhybridized $2p$ orbitals to form a *pi (π) bond*.

A **sigma bond** is a bond resulting from head-on overlap of atomic orbitals. *The region of electron sharing is along and cylindrically around an imaginary line connecting the bonded atoms.*

All single bonds are sigma bonds. Many kinds of pure atomic orbitals and hybridized orbitals can be involved in sigma bond formation.

A **pi bond** is a bond resulting from side-on overlap of atomic orbitals. *The regions of electron sharing are on opposite sides of an imaginary line connecting the bonded atoms and parallel to this line.*

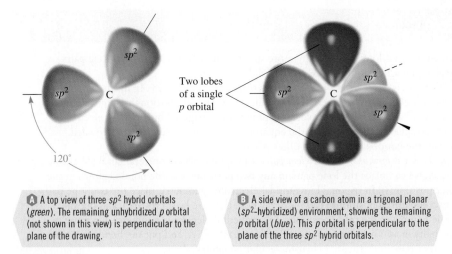

A A top view of three sp^2 hybrid orbitals (*green*). The remaining unhybridized p orbital (not shown in this view) is perpendicular to the plane of the drawing.

B A side view of a carbon atom in a trigonal planar (sp^2-hybridized) environment, showing the remaining p orbital (*blue*). This p orbital is perpendicular to the plane of the three sp^2 hybrid orbitals.

Figure 8-4 Orbitals on a sp^2-hybridized carbon atom.

A pi bond can form *only* if there is *also* a sigma bond between the same two atoms. One sigma and one pi bond together make a double bond (Figure 8-5). The $1s$ orbitals (with one e^- each) of four hydrogen atoms overlap the remaining four sp^2 orbitals (with one e^- each) on the carbon atoms to form four C—H sigma bonds (Figure 8-6).

A double bond consists of one sigma bond and one pi bond.

As a consequence of the sp^2 hybridization of C atoms in carbon–carbon double bonds, each carbon atom is at the center of a trigonal plane. The p orbitals that overlap to form the π bond must be parallel to each other for effective overlap to occur. This adds the further restriction that these trigonal planes (sharing a common corner) must also be *coplanar*.

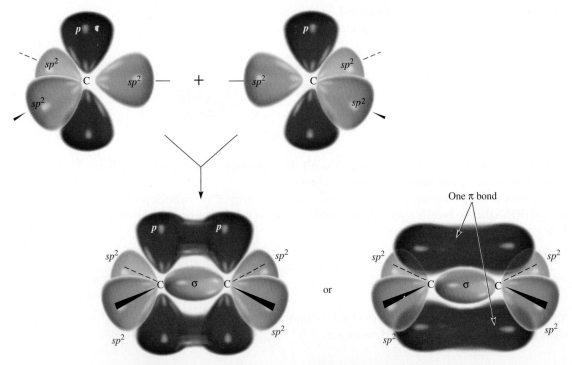

Figure 8-5 A schematic representation of the formation of a carbon–carbon double bond. Two sp^2-hybridized carbon atoms form a sigma (σ) bond by overlap of two sp^2 orbitals (*green*) and a pi (π) bond by overlap of properly aligned p orbitals (*blue*). All orbitals are fatter than shown here.

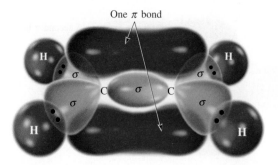

Figure 8-6 Four C—H σ bonds, one C—C σ bond (*green*), and one C—C π bond (*blue*) in the planar C_2H_4 molecule.

An important use of ethylene, C_2H_4, is in the manufacture of polyethylene, a nonbreakable, nonreactive plastic.

▶ The three *p* orbitals in a set are indistinguishable. We can label the one involved in hybridization as "p_x" to help us visualize the orientations of the two unhybridized *p* orbitals on carbon.

Thus, all four atoms attached to the doubly bonded C atoms lie in the same plane (see Figure 8-6). Many other important organic compounds contain carbon–carbon double bonds. Several are described in Chapter 23.

8-15 Compounds Containing Triple Bonds

One compound that contains a triple bond is ethyne (acetylene), C_2H_2. Its Lewis formula is

$$S = N - A$$
$$= 20 - 10 = \underline{10e^- \text{ shared}}$$

$$H:C::C:H \qquad H-C\equiv C-H$$

The VSEPR theory predicts that the two electron groups around each carbon atom are 180° apart.

Each triple-bonded carbon atom has two electron groups, so valence bond theory postulates that each is *sp* hybridized (see Section 8-5). Let us designate the p_x orbitals as the ones involved in hybridization. Carbon has one electron in each *sp* hybrid orbital and one electron in each of the $2p_y$ and $2p_z$ orbitals (before bonding is considered) (Figure 8-7).

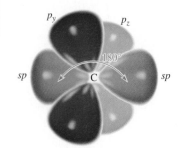

Figure 8-7 Diagram of the two linear hybridized *sp* orbitals (*green*) of an atom. These line in a straight line, and the two unhybridized *p* orbitals p_y and p_z (*blue*) line in the perpendicular plane and are perpendicular to each other.

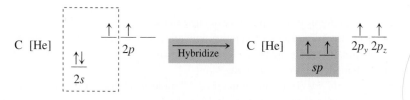

The two carbon atoms form one sigma bond by head-on overlap of the *sp* hybrid orbitals; each C atom also forms a sigma bond with one H atom. The *sp* hybrids on each atom are 180° apart. Thus, the entire molecule must be linear.

The unhybridized atomic $2p_y$ and $2p_z$ orbitals are perpendicular to each other and to the line through the centers of the two *sp* hybrid orbitals (Figure 8-8). The side-on overlap of the $2p_y$ orbitals on the two C atoms forms one pi bond; the side-on overlap of the $2p_z$ orbitals forms another pi bond.

A triple bond consists of one sigma bond and two pi bonds.

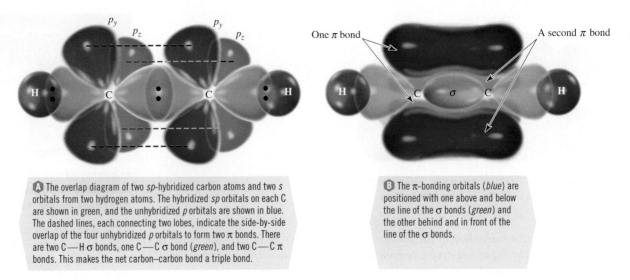

A The overlap diagram of two *sp*-hybridized carbon atoms and two *s* orbitals from two hydrogen atoms. The hybridized *sp* orbitals on each C are shown in green, and the unhybridized *p* orbitals are shown in blue. The dashed lines, each connecting two lobes, indicate the side-by-side overlap of the four unhybridized *p* orbitals to form two π bonds. There are two C—H σ bonds, one C—C σ bond (*green*), and two C—C π bonds. This makes the net carbon–carbon bond a triple bond.

B The π-bonding orbitals (*blue*) are positioned with one above and below the line of the σ bonds (*green*) and the other behind and in front of the line of the σ bonds.

Figure 8-8 The acetylene molecule, C_2H_2.

▶ In propyne, the C atom in the CH$_3$ group is *sp^3* hybridized and at the center of a tetrahedral arrangement.

Some other molecules containing triply bonded atoms are nitrogen, $:N≡N:$, hydrogen cyanide, $H—C≡N$, and propyne, $CH_3—C≡C—H$. In each case, both atoms involved in the triple bonds are *sp* hybridized. In the triple bond, each atom participates in one sigma and two pi bonds. The C atom in carbon dioxide, $:O=C=O:$, must participate in two pi bonds (to two different O atoms) and also participates in two sigma bonds, so it is also *sp* hybridized, and the molecule is linear.

8-16 A Summary of Electronic and Molecular Geometries

We have discussed several common types of polyatomic molecules and ions, and provided a reasonable explanation for the observed structures and polarities of these species. Table 8-4 provides a summation.

Our discussion of covalent bonding illustrates some important points:

1. Molecules and polyatomic ions have definite shapes.
2. The properties of molecules and polyatomic ions are determined to a great extent by their shapes. Incompletely filled electron shells and lone pairs of electrons on the central element are very important.
3. There are only *five* electronic geometries. All molecular geometries are simply special cases of these five basic geometries (Table 8-4).

Our ideas about chemical bonding have developed over many years. As experimental techniques for determining the *structures* of molecules have improved, our understanding of chemical bonding has also improved. Experimental observations on molecular geometry support our ideas about chemical bonding. The ultimate test for any theory is this: Can it correctly predict the results of experiments before they are performed? When the answer is yes, we have confidence in the theory. When the answer is no, the theory must be modified. Current theories of chemical bonding enable us to make predictions that are usually accurate.

Table 8-4 A Summary of Electronic and Molecular Geometries of Polyatomic Molecules and Ions

Electron Groups $(eg)^a$	Electronic Geometry	Hybridization at Central Atom (Angles)	Hybridized Orbital Orientation	Examples	Molecular Geometry
2	eg—A—eg linear	sp (180°)	A	$BeCl_2$ $HgBr_2$ CdI_2 $CO_2{}^b$ $C_2H_2{}^c$	linear linear linear linear linear
3	trigonal planar	sp^2 (120°)	A	BF_3 BCl_3 $NO_3{}^{-\ e}$ $SO_2{}^{d,e}$ $NO_2{}^{-\ d,e}$ $C_2H_4{}^f$	trigonal planar trigonal planar trigonal planar angular (AB_2U) angular (AB_2U) planar (trig. planar at each C)
4	tetrahedral	sp^3 (109.5°)	A	CH_4 CCl_4 $NH_4{}^+$ $SO_4{}^{2-}$ $CHCl_3$ $NH_3{}^d$ $SO_3{}^{2-\ d}$ $H_3O^{+\ d}$ H_2O^d	tetrahedral tetrahedral tetrahedral tetrahedral distorted tetrahedral pyramidal (AB_3U) pyramidal (AB_3U) pyramidal (AB_3U) angular (AB_2U_2)
5	trigonal bipyramidal	sp^3d (90°, 120°, 180°)	A	PF_5 $SbCl_5$ $SF_4{}^d$ $ClF_3{}^d$ $XeF_2{}^d$ $I_3{}^{-\ d}$	trigonal bipyramidal trigonal bipyramidal seesaw (AB_4U) T-shaped (AB_3U_2) linear (AB_2U_3) linear (AB_2U_3)
6	octahedral	sp^3d^2 (90°, 180°)	A	SF_6 SeF_6 $PF_6{}^-$ $BrF_5{}^d$ $XeF_4{}^d$	octahedral octahedral octahedral square pyramidal (AB_5U) square planar (AB_4U_2)

^{a}The number of electron groups around the central atom. An electron group may be a single bond, a double bond, a triple bond, or a lone pair. These determine the electronic geometry, and thus the hybridization of the central atom.

^{b}Contains two double bonds.

^{c}Contains a triple bond.

^{d}Central atom in molecule or ion has lone pair(s) of electrons.

^{e}Bonding involves resonance.

^{f}Contains one double bond.

KEY TERMS

Angular A term used to describe the molecular geometry of a molecule that has two atoms bonded to a central atom and one or more lone pairs on the central atom (AB_2U or AB_2U_2); also called *V-shaped* or *bent*.

Central atom An atom in a molecule or polyatomic ion that is bonded to more than one other atom.

Electron group A group of valence shell electrons that determines the electronic geometry on a central atom. Can be a single bond, double bond, triple bond, or lone pair.

Electronic geometry The geometric arrangement of the bonding and lone pair (unshared pair) electron groups around the central atom of a molecule or polyatomic ion. This arrangement minimizes the repulsions among the electron groups. Each electronic geometry implies a particular hybridization on the central atom.

Hybridization The mixing of a set of atomic orbitals on an atom to form a new set of hybrid orbitals with the same total electron capacity and with properties and energies intermediate between those of the original unhybridized orbitals.

Hybrid orbitals Orbitals formed on an atom by the process of hybridization.

Lewis formula A method of representing a molecule or formula unit by showing atoms and only outer-shell electrons; does not show shape.

Linear A term used to describe the electronic geometry around a central atom that has two electron groups. Also used to describe the molecular geometry of a molecule or polyatomic ion that has one atom in the center bonded to two atoms on opposite sides (180°) of the central atom (AB_2 or AB_2U_3).

Molecular geometry The arrangement of atoms (not electron groups) around a central atom of a molecule or polyatomic ion.

Octahedral A term used to describe the electronic geometry around a central atom that has six electron groups. Also used to describe the molecular geometry of a molecule or polyatomic ion that has one atom in the center bonded to six atoms at the corners of an octahedron (AB_6).

Octahedron (regular) A polyhedron with eight equal-sized, equilateral triangular faces and six apices (corners).

Overlap of orbitals The interaction of orbitals on different atoms in the same region of space.

Pi (π) bond A bond resulting from the side-on overlap of atomic orbitals, in which the regions of electron sharing are on opposite sides of and parallel to an imaginary line connecting the bonded atoms.

Seesaw A term used to describe the molecular geometry of a molecule or polyatomic ion that has four atoms bonded to a central atom and one lone pair on the central atom (AB_4U).

Sigma (σ) bond A bond resulting from the head-on overlap of atomic orbitals, in which the region of electron sharing is

along and (cylindrically) symmetrical to an imaginary line connecting the bonded atoms.

Square planar A term used to describe molecules and polyatomic ions that have one atom in the center and four atoms at the corners of a square.

Square pyramidal A term used to describe the molecular geometry of a molecule or polyatomic ion that has five atoms bonded to a central atom and one lone pair on the central atom (AB_5U).

Tetrahedral A term used to describe the electronic geometry around a central atom that has four electron groups. Also used to describe the molecular geometry of a molecule or polyatomic ion that has one atom in the center bonded to four atoms at the corners of a tetrahedron (AB_4).

Tetrahedron (regular) A polyhedron with four equal-sized, equilateral triangular faces and four apices (corners).

Trigonal bipyramid A six-sided polyhedron with five apices (corners), consisting of two pyramids sharing a common triangular base.

Trigonal bipyramidal A term used to describe the electronic geometry around a central atom that has five electron groups. Also used to describe the molecular geometry of a molecule or polyatomic ion that has one atom in the center bonded to five atoms at the corners of a trigonal bipyramid (AB_5).

Trigonal planar (also plane triangular) A term used to describe the electronic geometry around a central atom that has three electron groups. Also used to describe the molecular geometry of a molecule or polyatomic ion that has one atom in the center bonded to three atoms at the corners of an equilateral triangle (AB_3).

Trigonal pyramidal A term used to describe the molecular geometry of a molecule or polyatomic ion that has three atoms bonded to a central atom and one lone pair on the central atom (AB_3U).

T-shaped A term used to describe the molecular geometry of a molecule or polyatomic ion that has three atoms bonded to a central atom and two lone pairs on the central atom (AB_3U_2).

Valence bond (VB) theory Assumes that covalent bonds are formed when atomic orbitals on different atoms overlap and electrons are shared.

Valence shell The outermost occupied electron shell of an atom.

Valence shell electron pair repulsion (VSEPR) theory Assumes that valence electron pairs are arranged around the central element of a molecule or polyatomic ion so that there is maximum separation (and minimum repulsion) among electron groups.

EXERCISES

VSEPR Theory: General Concepts

1. State in your own words the basic idea of the VSEPR theory.
2. (a) Distinguish between "lone pairs" and "bonding pairs" of electrons. (b) Which has the greater spatial requirement? How do we know this? (c) Indicate the order of increasing repulsions among lone pairs and bonding pairs of electrons.
3. 🔴 What two shapes could a triatomic species have? How would the electronic geometries for the two shapes differ?
4. ▲ How are double and triple bonds treated when the VSEPR theory is used to predict molecular geometry? How is a single unshared electron treated?
5. 🔴 Sketch the three different possible arrangements of the three B atoms around the central atom A for the molecule AB_3U_2. Which of these structures correctly describes the molecular geometry? Why? What are the predicted ideal bond angles? How would observed bond angles deviate from these values?
6. 🔴 Sketch the three different possible arrangements of the two B atoms around the central atom A for the molecule AB_2U_3. Which of these arrangements predicts the most likely molecular geometry? Why?

Valence Bond Theory: General Concepts

7. What are hybridized atomic orbitals? How is the theory of hybridized orbitals useful?
8. (a) What is the relationship between the electron groups on an atom and the number of its pure atomic orbitals that hybridize? (b) What is the relationship between the number of atomic orbitals that hybridize and the number of hybrid orbitals formed?
9. 🔴 What hybridization is associated with these electronic geometries: trigonal planar, linear, tetrahedral, octahedral, trigonal bipyramidal?
10. Prepare sketches of the orbitals around atoms that are (a) sp, (b) sp^2, (c) sp^3, (d) sp^3d, and (e) sp^3d^2 hybridized. Show in the sketches any unhybridized p orbitals that might participate in multiple bonding.
11. 🔴 What types of hybridization would you predict for molecules having the following general formulas? (a) AB_4; (b) AB_2U_3; (c) AB_3U; (d) ABU_4; (e) ABU_3.
12. 🔴 Repeat Exercise 11 for (a) ABU_5; (b) AB_2U_4; (c) AB_3; (d) AB_3U_2; (e) AB_5.
13. 🔴 (a) What is the maximum number of bonds that an atom can form without expanding its valence shell? (b) What must be true of the electron configuration of an element for it to be able to expand its valence shell? (c) Which of the following elements can expand its valence shell? N, O, F, P, S, Cl, Xe.
14. The formation of what set of hybrid orbitals is being shown in the following incomplete sketch? Complete the sketch by drawing the hybrid orbitals formed.

15. The formation of what set of hybrid orbitals is being shown in the following incomplete sketches? Complete the sketch by drawing the hybrid orbitals formed.

16. What angles are associated with orbitals in the following sets of hybrid orbitals? (a) sp; (b) sp^2; (c) sp^3; (d) sp^3d; (e) sp^3d^2. Sketch each set.
17. 🔴 What are the primary factors on which we base a decision on whether the bonding in a molecule is better described in terms of overlap of pure atomic orbitals or overlap involving hybridized atomic orbitals?
18. 🔴 The elements in Group 2A form compounds, such as Cl — Be — Cl, that are linear and, therefore, nonpolar. What is the hybridization at the central atoms?
19. 🔴 The elements in Group 3A form compounds, such as $AlCl_3$, that are planar and, therefore, nonpolar. What is the hybridization at the central atoms?

Electronic and Molecular Geometry

20. Under what conditions is molecular (or ionic) geometry identical to electronic geometry about a central atom?
21. Distinguish between electronic geometry and molecular geometry.
22. 🔴 Identify the central atom (or atoms) in each of the following compounds or ions: (a) HCO_3^-; (b) SiO_2; (c) SO_3; (d) $Al(OH)_4^-$; (e) $BeBr_2$; (f) $(CH_3)_4Pb$.

🔴 *Molecular Reasoning* exercises   ▲ *More Challenging* exercises   Blue-Numbered exercises solved in Student Solutions Manual

Unless otherwise noted, all content on this page is © Cengage Learning.

23. 🔴 Identify the central atom in each of the following compounds or ions: (a) SO_4^{2-}; (b) NH_3; (c) NH_4^+; (d) $AlCl_3$; (e) CH_3NH_2; (f) $CdCl_2$.

24. 🔴 Write a Lewis formula for each of the following species. Indicate the number of electron groups and the electronic and molecular or ionic geometries. (a) $CdCl_2$; (b) $SnCl_4$; (c) BrF_3; (d) SbF_6^-.

25. 🔴 Write a Lewis formula for each of the following species. Indicate the number of electron groups and the electronic and molecular or ionic geometries. (a) BF_3; (b) SO_2; (c) IO_3^-; (d) $SiCl_4$; (e) SeF_6.

26. 🔴 (a) What would be the ideal bond angles in each molecule or ion in Exercise 24? (b) How do these differ, if at all, from the actual values? Why?

27. (a) What would be the ideal bond angles in each molecule or ion in Exercise 25? (b) Are these values greater than, less than, or equal to the actual values? Why?

28. Write the Lewis formula and identify the electronic geometry and molecular geometry for each polyatomic species in the following equations:
    (a) $H^+ + H_2O \longrightarrow H_3O^+$
    (b) $NH_3 + H^+ \longrightarrow NH_4^+$

29. 🔴 Pick the member of each pair that you would expect to have the smaller bond angles, if different, and explain why.
    (a) SF_2 and SO_2; (b) BF_3 and BCl_3; (c) SiF_4 and SF_4; (d) NF_3 and OF_2.

30. 🔴 Draw a Lewis formula, sketch the three-dimensional shape, and name the electronic and ionic geometries for the following polyatomic ions. (a) H_3O^+; (b) PCl_6^-; (c) PCl_4^-; (d) $SbCl_4^+$.

31. 🔴 As the name implies, the interhalogens are compounds that contain two halogens. Write Lewis formulas and three-dimensional structures for the following. Name the electronic and molecular geometries of each. (a) BrF_3; (b) BrF; (c) BrF_5.

32. 🔴 ▲ (a) Write a Lewis formula for each of the following molecules: SiF_4, SF_4, XeF_4. (b) Contrast the molecular geometries of these three molecules. Account for differences in terms of the VSEPR theory.

33. 🔴 Draw a Lewis structure for each of the following molecules or ions: (a) BrF_5; (b) IF_3; (c) IBr_2^-; (d) BrF_2^+.

34. 🔴 Write the Lewis formulas and predict the shapes of (a) I_3^-; (b) $TeCl_4$; (c) XeO_3; (d) $NOBr$ (N is the central atom); (e) NO_2Cl (N is the central atom); (f) $SOCl_2$ (S is the central atom).

35. Describe the shapes of these polyatomic ions: (a) BO_3^{3-}; (b) AsO_4^{3-}; (c) SO_3^{2-}; (d) NO_3^-.

36. Would you predict a nitrogen–oxygen bond to have the same magnitude of bond polarity as a hydrogen–oxygen bond? Explain your answer.

37. 🔴 Which of the following molecules are polar? Why? (a) CH_4; (b) CH_3Br; (c) CH_2Br_2; (d) $CHBr_3$; (e) CBr_4.

38. 🔴 Which of the following molecules are polar? Why? (a) CdI_2; (b) BCl_3; (c) $AsCl_3$; (d) H_2O; (e) SF_6.

39. 🔴 Which of the following molecules are nonpolar? Justify your answer. (a) SO_3; (b) IF; (c) Cl_2O; (d) NF_3; (e) $CHCl_3$.

40. 🔴 Each of these molecules has fluorine atoms attached to an atom from Group 1A or 3A to 6A. Draw the Lewis structure for each one and then describe the electron-pair geometry and the molecular geometry. Comment on similarities and differences in the series. (a) BF_3; (b) CF_4; (c) NF_3; (d) OF_2; (e) HF.

41. 🔴 ▲ In what two major ways does the presence of lone pairs of valence electrons affect the polarity of a molecule? Describe two molecules for which the presence of lone pairs on the central atom helps to make the molecules polar. Can you think of a bonding arrangement that has lone pairs of valence electrons on the central atom but that is nonpolar? Describe a molecule with this arrangement.

42. 🔴 Is the phosphorus–chlorine bond in phosphorus trichloride a polar bond? Is phosphorus trichloride a polar molecule? Explain.

43. 🔴 Is the phosphorus–chlorine bond in phosphorus pentachloride a polar bond? Is phosphorus pentachloride a polar molecule? Explain.

44. 🔴 Write the Lewis formula for each of the following. Indicate which bonds are polar. (See Table 5-3.) Indicate which molecules are polar. (a) CS_2; (b) AlF_3; (c) H_2S; (d) SnF_2.

45. 🔴 Write the Lewis formula for each of the following. Indicate which bonds are polar. (See Table 5-3.) Indicate which molecules are polar. (a) OF_2; (b) CH_4; (c) H_2SO_4; (d) SnF_4.

Valence Bond Theory

46. Describe the orbital overlap model of covalent bonding.

47. Briefly summarize the reasoning by which we might have predicted that the formula of the simplest stable hydrocarbon would be CH_2, if we did not consider hybridization. Would this species satisfy the octet rule?

48. What is the hybridization of the central atom in each of the following? (a) NCl_3; (b) molecular $AlCl_3$; (c) CF_4; (d) SF_6; (e) IO_4^-.

49. What is the hybridization of the central atom in each of the following? (a) IF_4^-; (b) SiO_4^{4-}; (c) AlH_4^-; (d) NH_4^+; (e) PCl_3; (f) ClO_3^-.

50. (a) Describe the hybridization of the central atom in each of these covalent species. (i) $CHCl_3$; (ii) CH_2Cl_2; (iii) NF_3; (iv) PO_4^{3-}; (v) IF_6^+; (vi) SiF_6^{2-}. (b) Give the shape of each species.

51. Describe the hybridization of the underlined atoms in $\underline{C}_2F_6$, $\underline{C}_2F_4$, and $(H_2N)_2\underline{C}O$.

52. 🔴 ▲ Prepare a sketch of the molecule $CH_3CCl = CH_2$ showing orbital overlaps. Identify the type of hybridization of atomic orbitals on each carbon atom.

53. 🔴 ▲ What is the maximum number of hybrid orbitals that a carbon atom may form? What is the minimum number? Explain briefly.

🔴 **Molecular Reasoning** exercises   ▲ **More Challenging** exercises   Blue-Numbered exercises solved in Student Solutions Manual

Unless otherwise noted, all content on this page is © Cengage Learning.

54. 🔵 ▲ Predict the hybridization at each carbon atom in each of the following molecules.

(a) acetone (a common solvent)

(b) glycine (an amino acid)

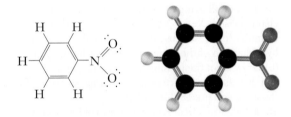

(c) nitrobenzene[1]

(d) chloroprene (used to make neoprene, a synthetic rubber)

(e) 4-penten-1-yne

55. 🔵 ▲ Predict the hybridization at the numbered atoms (①, ② and so on) in the following molecules and predict the approximate bond angles at those atoms.

(a) diethyl ether, an anesthetic

(b) caffeine, a stimulant in coffee and in many over-the-counter medicinals[1]

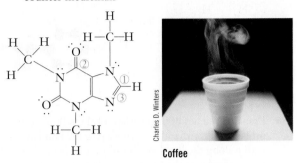

Coffee

(c) acetylsalicylic acid (aspirin)[1]

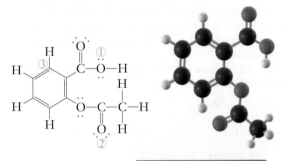

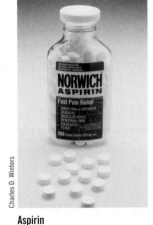

Aspirin

(d) nicotine[1]

[1]In these kinds of structural drawings, each intersection of lines represents a C atom.

🔵 **Molecular Reasoning** exercises   ▲ **More Challenging** exercises   Blue-Numbered exercises solved in Student Solutions Manual

Unless otherwise noted, all content on this page is © Cengage Learning.

(e) ephedrine, a nasal decongestant[1]

56. Prepare sketches of the overlaps of the following atomic orbitals: (a) *s* with *s*; (b) *s* with *p* along the bond axis; (c) *p* with *p* along the bond axis (head-on overlap); (d) *p* with *p* perpendicular to the bond axis (side-on overlap).

57. Prepare a sketch of the cross section (through the atomic centers) taken between two atoms that have formed (a) a single σ bond; (b) a double bond consisting of a σ bond and a π bond; and (c) a triple bond consisting of a σ bond and two π bonds.

58. ☙ How many sigma and how many pi bonds are there in each of the following molecules?

(a) H—C—C=C—C—H   (b)

(c) H—C—C   (d) H—C=C—C≡C—H

59. ☙ ▲ How many sigma bonds and how many pi bonds are there in each of the following molecules?

(a) H—C—C—C=C   (b) H—C—C

(c)   (d) CH₂CHCH₂OCH₂CH₃

60. In each of these ions, three oxygen atoms are attached to a central atom. Draw the Lewis structure for each one, and then describe the electron-pair geometry and the ionic geometry. Comment on similarities and differences in the series. (a) BO_3^{3-}; (b) CO_3^{2-}; (c) SO_3^{2-}; (d) ClO_3^{-}.

61. Write Lewis formulas for molecular oxygen and ozone. Assuming that all of the valence electrons in the oxygen atoms are in hybrid orbitals, what would be the hybridization of the oxygen atoms in each substance? Prepare sketches of the molecules.

[1]In these kinds of structural drawings, each intersection of lines represents a C atom.

62. ☙ ▲ Draw a Lewis formula and a three-dimensional structure for each of the following polycentered molecules. Indicate hybridizations and bond angles at each carbon atom. (a) butane, C_4H_{10}; (b) propene, $H_2C=CHCH_3$; (c) 1-butyne, $HC≡CCH_2CH_3$; (d) acetaldehyde, CH_3CHO.

63. How many σ bonds and how many π bonds are there in each of the molecules of Exercise 62?

64. (a) Describe the hybridization of N in each of these species. (i) $:NH_3$; (ii) NH_4^+; (iii) $HN=NH$; (iv) $:N≡HC$; (v) $H_2N—NH_2$. (b) Give an orbital description for each species, specifying the location of any lone pairs and the orbitals used for the multiple bonds.

65. ☙ Write the Lewis formulas and predict the hybrid orbitals and the shapes of these polyatomic ions and covalent molecules: (a) $HgCl_2$; (b) BF_3; (c) BF_4^-; (d) $SbCl_5$; (e) SbF_6^-.

66. ☙ (a) What is the hybridization of each C in these molecules? (i) $H_2C=O$; (ii) $HC≡N$; (iii) $CH_3CH_2CH_3$; (iv) ketene, $H_2C=C=O$. (b) Describe the shape of each molecule.

67. ☙ ▲ The following fluorides of xenon have been well characterized: XeF_2, XeF_4, and XeF_6. (a) Write Lewis formulas for these substances, and decide what type of hybridization of the Xe atomic orbitals has taken place. (b) Draw all of the possible atomic arrangements of XeF_2, and discuss your choice of molecular geometry. (c) What shape do you predict for XeF_4?

68. ☙ ▲ Iodine and fluorine form a series of interhalogen molecules and ions. Among these are IF (minute quantities observed spectroscopically), IF_3, IF_4^-, IF_5, IF_6^-, and IF_7. (a) Write Lewis formulas for each of these species. (b) Identify the type of hybridization that the orbitals of the iodine atom have undergone in the first four substances. (c) Identify the shape of the molecule or ion represented by the first four formulas.

Mixed Exercises

69. ☙ In the pyrophosphate ion, $P_2O_7^{4-}$, one oxygen atom is bonded to both phosphorus atoms.

Write a Lewis formula, and sketch the three-dimensional shape of the ion. Describe the electronic and molecular geometries with respect to the central O atom and with respect to each P atom.

☙ **Molecular Reasoning** exercises   ▲ **More Challenging** exercises   Blue-Numbered exercises solved in Student Solutions Manual

Unless otherwise noted, all content on this page is © Cengage Learning.

70. ♠ Briefly discuss the bond angles in the hydroxylamine molecule in terms of the ideal geometry and the small changes caused by electron-pair repulsions.

$$H-\overset{..}{\underset{|}{N}}-\overset{..}{\underset{..}{O}}-H$$
$$\quad\;\; H$$

71. ♠ Repeat Exercise 70 for the nitrite ion.

$$\left[\overset{\overset{..}{O}}{\underset{..}{\overset{||}{\underset{..}{O}-N}}}\right]^{-} \longleftrightarrow \left[\overset{:\overset{..}{O}:}{\underset{..}{\overset{}{\underset{..}{O}=N}}}\right]^{-}$$

72. ♠ ▲ The methyl free radical ·CH₃ has bond angles of about 120°, whereas the methyl carbanion :CH₃⁻ has bond angles of about 109°. What can you infer from these facts about the repulsive force exerted by an unpaired, unshared electron as compared with that exerted by an unshared pair of electrons?

73. ♠ ▲ Two Lewis structures can be written for the square planar molecule $PtCl_2Br_2$.

$$\underset{Br}{\overset{Br}{\diagdown}}Pt\underset{Cl}{\overset{Cl}{\diagup}} \quad \text{and} \quad \underset{Cl}{\overset{Br}{\diagdown}}Pt\underset{Br}{\overset{Cl}{\diagup}}$$

Show how a difference in dipole moments can distinguish between these two possible structures.

74. (a) Describe the hybridization of N in NO_2^+ and NO_2^-. (b) Predict the bond angle in each case.

75. ♠ ▲ The skeleton and a ball-and-stick model for the nitrous acid molecule, HNO_2, are shown here. Draw the Lewis formula. What are the hybridizations at the middle O and N atoms?

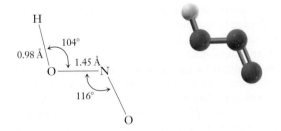

76. ♠ Describe the change in hybridization that occurs at the central atom of the reactant at the left in each of the following reactions.
(a) $PF_5 + F^- \longrightarrow PF_6^-$
(b) $2CO + O_2 \longrightarrow 2CO_2$
(c) $AlI_3 + I^- \longrightarrow AlI_4^-$
(d) What change in hybridization occurs in the following reaction? $:NH_3 + BF_3 \longrightarrow H_3N:BF_3$

77. ♠ ▲ Predict the geometry of the following species: (a) NNO; (b) ONCl; (c) NH_4^+; (d) O_3.

78. ♠ What hybridizations are predicted for the central atoms in molecules having the formulas AB_2U_2 and AB_3U? What are the predicted bond angles for these molecules? The observed bond angles for representative substances are:

H_2O 104.5°	NH_3 106.7°
H_2S 92.2°	PH_3 93.7°
H_2Se 91.0°	AsH_3 91.8°
H_2Te 89.5°	SbH_3 91.3°

What would be the predicted bond angle if no hybridization occurred? What conclusion can you draw concerning the importance of hybridization for molecules of compounds involving elements with higher atomic numbers?

Conceptual Exercises

79. ♠ Draw and explain the difference in the three-dimensional shapes of $CH_3CH_2CH_3$ and CH_3COCH_3.

80. ♠ Complete the following table.

Molecule or Ion	Electronic Geometry	Molecular Geometry	Hybridization of the Sulfur Atom
SO_2			
SCl_2			
SO_3			
SO_3^{2-}			
SF_4			
SO_4^{2-}			
SF_5^+			
SF_6			

81. ♠ Compare the shapes of the following pairs of molecules: (a) H_2CO and CH_4; (b) $PbCl_4$ and PbO_2; (c) CH_4 and $PbCl_4$.

82. ♠ (a) Why is trifluoromethane (HCF_3) polar and tetrafluoromethane (CF_4) nonpolar? (b) Give an example of a linear triatomic molecule that is polar. (c) What can be said about the distribution of valence electrons in a polar molecule?

♠ **Molecular Reasoning** exercises   ▲ **More Challenging** exercises   Blue-Numbered exercises solved in Student Solutions Manual

Unless otherwise noted, all content on this page is © Cengage Learning.

83. 🔵 Complete the following table regarding hybridized orbitals:

Hybridized Atomic Orbitals	*p* Orbitals Not Hybridized	Hybridization	Electronic Geometry
one *s*, three *p*'s	–	sp^3	tetrahedral
one *s*, two *p*'s		sp^2	
	2 *p*		linear
one *s*, three *p*'s, one *d*	–		
		sp^3d^2	octahedral

84. 🔵 (a) What are the five different electronic geometries? (b) How many molecular geometries are described in this chapter? (c) An ion or molecule having the following would lead one to predict what molecular geometry of each combination?

> 2 bonded atoms, 1 lone pair
> 3 bonded atoms, 1 lone pair
> 2 bonded atoms, 2 lone pairs
> 4 bonded atoms, 1 lone pair
> 3 bonded atoms, 2 lone pairs
> 2 bonded atoms, 3 lone pairs
> 5 bonded atoms, 1 lone pair
> 4 bonded atoms, 2 lone pairs

85. 🔵 What advantages does the VSEPR model of chemical bonding have compared with Lewis formulas?

86. 🔵 What evidence could you present to show that two carbon atoms joined by a single sigma bond are able to rotate about an axis that coincides with the bond, but two carbon atoms bonded by a double bond cannot rotate about an axis along the double bond?

Building Your Knowledge

87. 🔵 Sketch three-dimensional representations of the following molecules and indicate the direction of any net dipole for each molecule: (a) CH_4; (b) CH_3Cl; (c) CH_2Cl_2; (d) $CHCl_3$; (e) CCl_4.

88. 🔵 Carbon forms two common oxides, CO and CO_2. It also forms a third (very uncommon) oxide, carbon suboxide, C_3O_2, which is linear. The structure has terminal oxygen atoms on both ends. Write the Lewis formula for C_3O_2. How many electron groups are there about each of the three carbon atoms?

89. 🔵 Draw the Lewis formula of an ammonium ion. Describe the formation of the ammonium ion from ammonia plus H^+. Does the hybridization of orbitals on nitrogen change during the formation of the ammonium ion? Do the bond angles change?

90. 🔵 The following is an incomplete Lewis formula for a molecule. This formula has all the atoms at the correct places, but it is missing several valence electrons. Complete this Lewis formula, including lone pairs.

$$
\begin{array}{ccccc}
 & Cl & H & Br & \\
 & | & | & | & \\
H— & C & C—C & & O \\
\end{array}
$$

91. The following is an incomplete Lewis formula for a molecule. This formula has all the atoms at the correct places, but it is missing several valence electrons. Complete this Lewis formula, including lone pairs.

$$
\begin{array}{ccccc}
H—O & H & & & \\
| & | & & & \\
O & C & C & C & C & N—H \\
& | & & | & | & \\
& H & & Br & H & H \\
\end{array}
$$

Beyond the Textbook

NOTE: *Whenever the answer to an exercise depends on information obtained from a source other than this textbook, the source must be included as an essential part of the answer.*

92. Open **www.winter.group.shef.ac.uk/orbitron** or a site that describes atomic orbitals. (a) Click on 2*p*. What is said to be wrong with the "figure-of-eight" style of drawing of *p* orbitals that is found in most textbooks? (b) What is the difference between 2*p* and 3*p* orbitals? (c) Click on 4*f*. Draw one of the 4*f* orbitals that contains eight easily distinguished lobes. (d) Click on 5*g*. How many lobes does the $5g_{zy^3}$ orbital contain?

93. 🔵 Use the *Handbook of Chemistry and Physics* or a suitable web page to find dipole moments. What do the dipole moments for SnI_4 and $TiCl_4$ tell us about the shapes of these compounds?

94. 🔵 Predict whether the dipole moment of each of the following molecules should be zero, nearly zero, or significantly larger than zero. Then use the *Handbook of Chemistry and Physics* to find their correct dipole moment values. Compare your predictions with the values found in the Handbook or at a suitable website. (a) acetylene; (b) trichloromethane (chloroform); (c) dibromomethane; (d) methanol (CH_3OH); (e) ethanol (CH_3CH_2OH).

🔵 **Molecular Reasoning** exercises   ▲ **More Challenging** exercises   Blue-Numbered exercises solved in Student Solutions Manual

Unless otherwise noted, all content on this page is © Cengage Learning.

Molecular Orbitals in Chemical Bonding

9

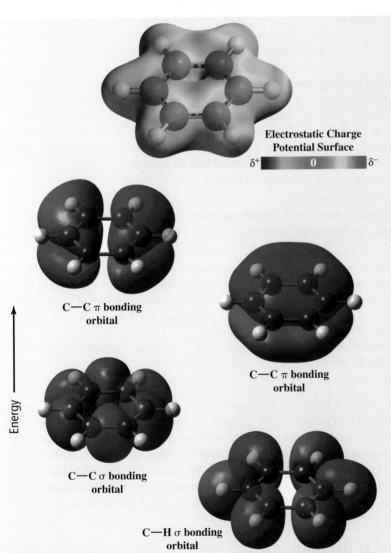

Electrostatic Charge Potential Surface

δ^+ 0 δ^-

C—C π bonding orbital

C—C π bonding orbital

C—C σ bonding orbital

C—H σ bonding orbital

Energy →

The lower part of the figure shows some of the molecular orbitals for benzene (C_6H_6) that contribute to the various C—H and C—C σ- and π-bonding interactions. The purple and blue colors represent the different phases (+ or −) for the wave functions that define the orbitals. The top image is a ball-and-stick model of benzene superimposed on an electrostatic charge potential surface showing relative charges. These images were all generated from a computer program (Gaussian 09) that calculates the electronic structure of molecules and plots the molecular orbitals.

OBJECTIVES

After you have studied this chapter, you should be able to

▶ Describe the basic concepts of molecular orbital theory

▶ Relate the shapes and overlap of atomic orbitals to the shapes and energies of the resulting molecular orbitals

▶ Distinguish among bonding, antibonding, and nonbonding orbitals

▶ Apply the Aufbau Principle to find molecular orbital descriptions for homonuclear diatomic molecules and ions

▶ Apply the Aufbau Principle to find molecular orbital descriptions for heteronuclear diatomic molecules and ions with small Δ(EN) values

▶ Find the bond order in diatomic molecules and ions

▶ Relate bond order to bond stability

▶ Use the MO concept of delocalization for molecules for which valence bond theory would postulate resonance

We have described bonding and molecular geometry in terms of valence bond (VB) theory. In valence bond theory, we postulate that bonds result from the sharing of electrons in overlapping orbitals of different atoms. We describe electrons in overlapping orbitals of different atoms as being localized in the bonds between the two atoms involved. We use hybridization to help account for the geometry of a molecule. In valence bond theory, however, we view each orbital as belonging to an individual atom.

In **molecular orbital** (MO) **theory**, we postulate that

> the combination of atomic orbitals on different atoms forms **molecular orbitals** (MOs) so that electrons in them belong to the molecule as a whole.

Valence bond and molecular orbital theories are alternative descriptions of chemical bonding. They have strengths and weaknesses, so they are complementary. Valence bond theory is descriptively attractive, and it lends itself well to visualization. Molecular orbital theory gives better descriptions of electron cloud distributions, bond energies, and magnetic properties, but its results are not as easy to visualize.

The valence bond description of bonding in the O_2 molecule involves a double bond.

$$\overset{..}{O} :: \overset{..}{\underset{..}{O}}$$

▶ In some polyatomic molecules, a molecular orbital may extend over only a fraction of the molecule.

▶ Polyatomic ions such as $CO_3{}^{2-}$, $SO_4{}^{2-}$, and $NH_4{}^+$ can be described by the molecular orbital approach.

▶ Species with all electrons paired are diamagnetic; species that contain any unpaired electrons are paramagnetic (see Section 4-20).

This shows no unpaired electrons, so it predicts that O_2 is diamagnetic. Experiments show, however, that O_2 is paramagnetic; therefore, it must have unpaired electrons. Thus, the valence bond description is not consistent with experimental fact, so it cannot be accepted as a description of the bonding in O_2. Molecular orbital theory accounts for the fact that O_2 has two unpaired electrons. This ability of MO theory to explain the paramagnetism of O_2 helped to establish it as a major theory of bonding. We will develop some of the ideas of MO theory and apply them to some molecules and polyatomic ions.

9-1 Molecular Orbitals

We learned in Chapter 4 that each solution to the Schrödinger equation, called a wave function, represents an atomic orbital. In valence bond theory (see Chapter 5), the mathematical picture of a hybrid orbital can be generated by combining the wave functions that describe two or more atomic orbitals (AOs) on a *single* atom. Similarly, combining wave functions that describe atomic orbitals on *separate* atoms generates mathematical descriptions of molecular orbitals.

An orbital has physical meaning only when we square its wave function to describe the electron density. Thus, the overall sign on the wave function that describes a *single* atomic orbital is not important, but when we *combine* two orbitals, the signs of the wave functions become very significant. When waves are combined, they may interact either constructively or destructively (Figure 9-1). Likewise, when two atomic orbitals overlap, they can

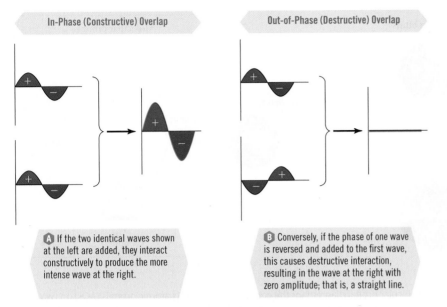

In-Phase (Constructive) Overlap

Out-of-Phase (Destructive) Overlap

A If the two identical waves shown at the left are added, they interact constructively to produce the more intense wave at the right.

B Conversely, if the phase of one wave is reversed and added to the first wave, this causes destructive interaction, resulting in the wave at the right with zero amplitude; that is, a straight line.

Figure 9-1 An illustration of constructive and destructive interference of waves.

Leon Lewandowski

Liquid oxygen is attracted to the poles of a powerful magnet, indicating that it is paramagnetic. An early triumph of molecular orbital theory was its ability to account for the observed paramagnetism of oxygen, O_2. According to earlier theories, O_2 was expected to be diamagnetic, that is, to have only paired electrons.

be in phase or out of phase. When they overlap in phase, constructive interaction occurs in the region between the nuclei, and a **bonding molecular orbital** is produced. The energy of the bonding orbital is always lower (more stable) than the energies of the combining orbitals. When the orbitals overlap out of phase, destructive interaction reduces the probability of finding electrons in the region between the nuclei, and an **antibonding molecular orbital** is produced. This is higher in energy (less stable) than the original atomic orbitals, leading to a repulsion between the two atoms. The overlap of two atomic orbitals always produces two MOs: one bonding and one antibonding.

In a bonding molecular orbital, the electron density is high *between* the two atoms, where it stabilizes the arrangement by attracting both nuclei. Electrons are *more* stable (have lower energy) in bonding molecular orbitals than in the individual atoms. By contrast, an antibonding orbital has a node (a region of zero electron density) between the nuclei; this causes the nuclei to repel one another more strongly, which makes the arrangement less stable. Placing electrons in antibonding orbitals requires an increase in their energy, which makes them *less* stable than in the individual atoms.

To summarize, electrons in *bonding* orbitals tend to *stabilize* a molecule or ion; electrons in *antibonding* orbitals tend to *destabilize* a molecule or ion. The relative number of electrons in bonding versus antibonding orbitals determines the *overall stability* of the molecule or ion.

We can illustrate this basic principle by considering the combination of the $1s$ atomic orbitals *on two different atoms* (Figure 9-2). When these orbitals are occupied by electrons, the shapes of the orbitals are plots of electron density. These plots show the regions in molecules where the probabilities of finding electrons are the greatest.

In the bonding orbital, the two $1s$ orbitals have reinforced each other in the region between the two nuclei by in-phase (constructive) overlap of their electron waves. In the antibonding orbital, they have canceled each other in this region by out-of-phase (destructive) overlap of their electron waves. We designate both molecular orbitals as **sigma (σ) molecular orbitals** (which indicates that they are cylindrically symmetrical about the internuclear axis). We use subscripts to indicate the atomic orbitals that have been combined. The asterisk (*) denotes an antibonding orbital. Thus, two $1s$ orbitals produce a σ_{1s} (read "sigma-1s") bonding orbital and a σ_{1s}^* (read "sigma-1s-star") antibonding orbital. The right-hand side of Figure 9-2 shows the relative energy levels of these orbitals. All sigma antibonding orbitals have nodal planes bisecting the internuclear axis. A **node**, or **nodal plane,** is a region in which the probability of finding electrons is zero.

For any two sets of p orbitals on two different atoms, corresponding orbitals such as p_x orbitals can overlap *head-on*. This gives σ_p and σ_p^* orbitals, as shown in Figure 9-3 for the

► How we name the axes is arbitrary. Here we designate the internuclear axis as the *x* direction.

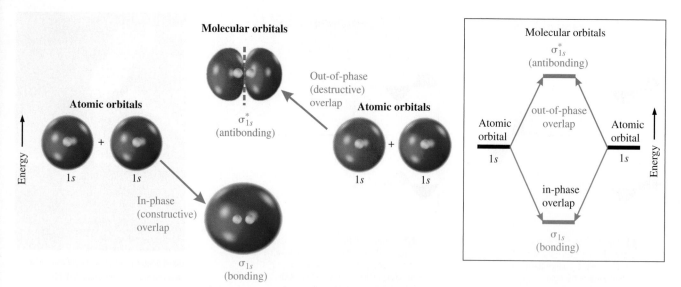

Figure 9-2 Molecular orbital diagram for the combination of the 1s atomic orbitals (AOs) on two identical atoms to form two new molecular orbitals (MOs). One is a *bonding* orbital, σ_{1s}, resulting from the constructive (in-phase) overlap of 1s wave functions that have the same mathematical sign (both + or both −, represented here by the same color). The other is an *antibonding* orbital, σ_{1s}^*, at higher energy resulting from the destructive (out-of-phase) overlap of 1s wave functions with opposite signs (represented here by different orbital colors), resulting in a repulsive force between the atoms. In all σ-type MOs, the electron density is symmetrical about an imaginary line connecting the two nuclei. The nodal plane between the atoms in the σ_{1s}^* is indicated by a dashed red line.

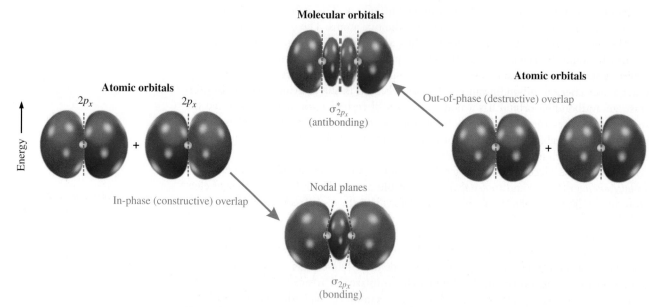

Figure 9-3 Production of σ_{2p_x} and $\sigma_{2p_x}^*$ molecular orbitals by overlap of $2p_x$ atomic orbitals on two atoms.

head-on overlap of $2p_x$ orbitals on the two atoms. If the remaining p orbitals overlap (p_y with p_y and p_z with p_z), they must do so sideways, or *side-on*, forming **pi (π) molecular orbitals**. Depending on whether all p orbitals overlap, there can be as many as two π_p and two π_p^* orbitals. Figure 9-4 illustrates the overlap of two corresponding p orbitals on two atoms to form π_p and π_p^* molecular orbitals. There is a nodal plane along the internuclear axis for all pi molecular orbitals. If one views a sigma molecular orbital along the internuclear axis, it appears to be symmetrical around the axis like a pure s atomic orbital. A similar cross-sectional view of a pi molecular orbital looks like a pure p atomic orbital, with a node along the internuclear axis.

▶ This would involve rotating Figures 9-2, 9-3, and 9-4 by 90° so that the internuclear axes are perpendicular to the plane of the pages.

Molecular orbitals

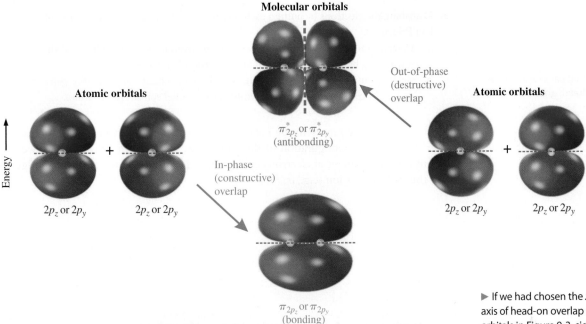

Out-of-phase
(destructive)
overlap

$\pi^*_{2p_z}$ or $\pi^*_{2p_y}$
(antibonding)

In-phase
(constructive)
overlap

Atomic orbitals

$2p_z$ or $2p_y$ $2p_z$ or $2p_y$

Atomic orbitals

$2p_z$ or $2p_y$ $2p_z$ or $2p_y$

Energy

π_{2p_z} or π_{2p_y}
(bonding)

Figure 9-4 The π_{2p} and π^*_{2p} molecular orbitals from overlap of one pair of 2p atomic orbitals (for instance, $2p_y$ orbitals). There can be an identical pair of molecular orbitals at right angles to these, formed by another pair of p orbitals on the same two atoms (in this case, $2p_z$ orbitals).

▶ If we had chosen the z axis as the axis of head-on overlap of the 2p orbitals in Figure 9-3, side-on overlap of the $2p_x$–$2p_x$ and $2p_y$–$2p_y$ orbitals would form the π-type molecular orbitals.

The number of molecular orbitals formed is equal to the number of atomic orbitals that are combined. When two atomic orbitals are combined, one of the resulting MOs is at a *lower* energy than the original atomic orbitals; this is a *bonding* orbital. The other MO is at a *higher* energy than the original atomic orbitals; this is an *antibonding* orbital.

9-2 Molecular Orbital Energy Level Diagrams

A molecular orbital energy level diagram (MO diagram for short) shows the MOs resulting from combination of the valence atomic orbitals of all atoms of the molecule, arranged in order of increasing energy. Figure 9-5 shows molecular orbital energy level diagrams for homonuclear diatomic molecules of elements in the first and second periods. Each diagram is an extension of the right-hand diagram in Figure 9-2, to which we have added the molecular orbitals formed from 2s and 2p atomic orbitals.

For the diatomic species shown in Figure 9-5a, the two π_{2p} orbitals are lower in energy than the σ_{2p} orbital. Molecular orbital calculations indicate, however, that for O_2, F_2, and hypothetical Ne_2 molecules, the σ_{2p} orbital is lower in energy than the π_{2p} orbitals (see Figure 9-5b).

Diagrams such as these are used to describe the bonding in a molecule in MO terms. Electrons occupy MOs according to the same rules developed for atomic orbitals; they follow the Aufbau Principle, the Pauli Exclusion Principle, and Hund's Rule (see Section 4-18). To obtain the molecular orbital description of the bonding in a molecule or ion, follow these steps:

1. Select (or draw) the appropriate molecular orbital energy level diagram.

2. Determine the *total* number of electrons in the molecule or ion. Note that in applying MO theory, we will account for *all* electrons. This includes both the inner-shell electrons and the valence electrons.

▶ "Homonuclear" means consisting only of atoms of the same element. "Diatomic" means consisting of two atoms.

▶ Spectroscopic data support these orders.

3. Distribute the electrons by putting each into the lowest energy level available (Aufbau Principle).

    a. A maximum of *two* electrons can occupy any given molecular orbital, and then only if they have opposite spin (Pauli Exclusion Principle).

    b. Electrons must occupy all the orbitals of the same energy singly before pairing begins. These unpaired electrons must have parallel spins (Hund's Rule).

▶ Remember that paramagnetism is an indication that unpaired electrons are present.

For isolated atoms, we represent the resulting arrangement of electrons in the atomic orbitals as the electron configuration of the atom (e.g., $1s^2\ 2s^2$). In the same way, we can represent the arrangement of electrons in the molecular orbitals as the electron configuration of the molecule or ion (e.g., $\sigma_{1s}^2\ \sigma_{1s}^{*2}\ \sigma_{2s}^2\ \sigma_{2s}^{*2}$).

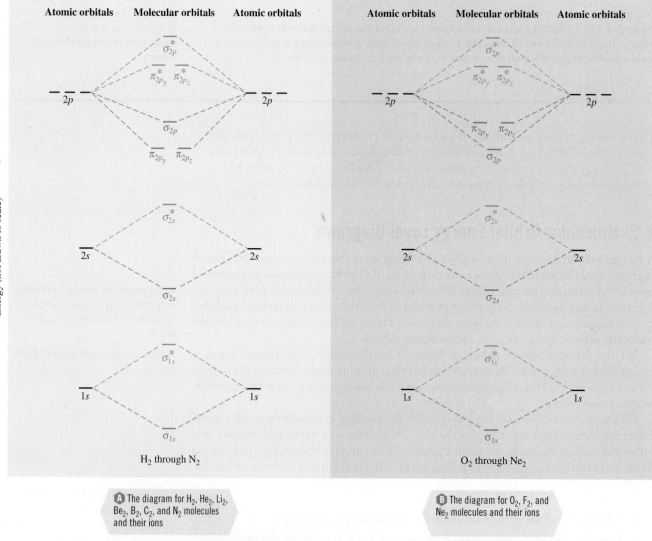

Energy (not drawn to scale) ⟶

Ⓐ The diagram for H_2, He_2, Li_2, Be_2, B_2, C_2, and N_2 molecules and their ions

Ⓑ The diagram for O_2, F_2, and Ne_2 molecules and their ions

Figure 9-5 Energy level diagrams for first- and second-period homonuclear diatomic molecules and ions (not drawn to scale). The solid lines represent the relative energies of the indicated atomic and molecular orbitals.

9-3 Bond Order and Bond Stability

Now we need a way to judge the stability of a molecule or ion once its energy level diagram has been filled with the appropriate number of electrons. This criterion is the **bond order**:

$$\text{bond order} = \frac{(\text{number of bonding electrons}) - (\text{number of antibonding electrons})}{2}$$

▶ Electrons in bonding orbitals are often called **bonding electrons**, and electrons in antibonding orbitals are called **antibonding electrons**.

The bond order usually corresponds to the number of bonds described by the valence bond theory. Fractional bond orders exist in species that contain an odd number of electrons, such as the nitrogen oxide molecule, NO (15 electrons), and the superoxide ion, O_2^- (17 electrons).

A bond order *equal to zero* means that the molecule has equal numbers of electrons in bonding MOs (more stable than in separate atoms) and in antibonding MOs (less stable than in separate atoms). Such a molecule would be no more stable than separate atoms, so it would not exist. A bond order *greater than zero* means that more electrons occupy bonding MOs (stabilizing) than antibonding MOs (destabilizing). Such a molecule would be more stable than the separate atoms, and we predict that its existence is possible. But such a molecule could still be quite reactive.

> The greater the bond order of a diatomic molecule or ion, the more stable we predict it to be. Likewise, for a bond between two given atoms, the greater the bond order, the shorter is the bond length and the greater is the bond energy.

The **bond energy** is the amount of energy necessary to break a mole of bonds (see Section 15-9); therefore, bond energy is a measure of bond strength.

Problem-Solving Tip Working with MO Theory

MO theory is often the best model to predict the bond order, bond stability, or magnetic properties of a molecule or ion. The procedure is as follows:

1. Select (or draw) the appropriate MO energy level diagram.
2. Count the total number of electrons in the molecule or ion.
3. As each electron is placed in an available orbital having the lowest energy, the Pauli Exclusion Principle and Hund's Rule must be followed.
4. Calculate the bond order $= \left(\dfrac{\text{bonding } e\text{'s} - \text{antibonding } e\text{'s}}{2} \right)$.
5. Use the bond order to evaluate stability.
6. Look for the presence of unpaired electrons to determine if a species is paramagnetic.

9-4 Homonuclear Diatomic Molecules

The electron configurations for the homonuclear diatomic molecules of the first and second periods are shown in Table 9-1 together with their bond orders, bond lengths, and bond energies. You can derive these electron configurations by putting the required numbers of electrons into the appropriate diagram of Figure 9-5. This procedure is illustrated by the following cases.

▶ This is just like the Aufbau process we used in Chapter 4 to develop the electron configurations of isolated atoms. There we put electrons into the atomic orbitals of isolated atoms; here we put them into the molecular orbitals of a collection of atoms.

The Hydrogen Molecule, H_2

The overlap of the $1s$ orbitals of two hydrogen atoms produces σ_{1s} and σ_{1s}^* molecular orbitals. The two electrons of the molecule occupy the lower energy σ_{1s} orbital (Figure 9-6a).

▶ H_2 bond order $= \dfrac{2-0}{2} = 1$

Because the only two electrons in an H_2 molecule are in a bonding orbital, the bond order is one. We conclude that the H_2 molecule would be stable, and we know it is. The energy associated with two electrons in the H_2 molecule is lower than that associated with the same two electrons in separate $1s$ atomic orbitals. The lower the energy of a system, the more stable it is.

The Helium Molecule (Hypothetical), He_2

The energy level diagram for He_2 is similar to that for H_2 except that it has two more electrons. These occupy the antibonding σ_{1s}^* orbital (see Figures 9-5a and 9-6b and Table 9-1), giving He_2 a bond order of zero. That is, the two electrons in the bonding orbital of He_2 would make the molecule *more stable* than the separate atoms. But the two electrons in the antibonding orbital would make the molecule *less stable* than the separate atoms. These effects cancel, so the molecule would be no more stable than the separate atoms. The bond order is zero, and the molecule would not exist. In fact, He_2 is unknown.

▶ He_2 bond order $= \dfrac{2-2}{2} = 0$

The Boron Molecule, B_2

The boron atom has the configuration $1s^2\,2s^2\,2p^1$. Here p electrons participate in the bonding. Figure 9-5a and Table 9-1 show that the π_{p_y} and π_{p_z} molecular orbitals are lower in energy than the σ_{2p} for B_2. Thus, the electron configuration is

▶ B_2 bond order $= \dfrac{6-4}{2} = 1$

$$\sigma_{1s}^2 \quad \sigma_{1s}^{*2} \quad \sigma_{2s}^2 \quad \sigma_{2s}^{*2} \quad \pi_{2p_y}^1 \quad \pi_{2p_z}^1$$

Table 9-1 Molecular Orbitals for First- and Second-Period (Row) Diatomic Molecules[a]

	H_2	$He_2{}^c$	$Li_2{}^b$	$Be_2{}^c$	$B_2{}^b$	$C_2{}^b$	N_2			O_2	F_2	$Ne_2{}^c$
σ_{2p}^*	—	—	—	—	—	—	—			—	—	⇅
$\pi_{2p_y}^*, \pi_{2p_z}^*$	— —	— —	— —	— —	— —	— —	— —			↑ ↑	⇅ ⇅	⇅ ⇅
σ_{2p}	—	—	—	—	—	—	⇅	π_{2p_y}, π_{2p_z}		⇅ ⇅	⇅ ⇅	⇅ ⇅
π_{2p_y}, π_{2p_z}	— —	— —	— —	— —	↑ ↑	⇅ ⇅	⇅ ⇅	σ_{2p}		⇅	⇅	⇅
σ_{2s}^*	—	—	⇅	⇅	⇅	⇅	⇅			⇅	⇅	⇅
σ_{2s}	—	—	⇅	⇅	⇅	⇅	⇅			⇅	⇅	⇅
σ_{1s}^*	—	⇅	⇅	⇅	⇅	⇅	⇅			⇅	⇅	⇅
σ_{1s}	⇅	⇅	⇅	⇅	⇅	⇅	⇅			⇅	⇅	⇅
Paramagnetic?	no	no	no	no	yes	no	no			yes	no	no
Bond order	1	0	1	0	1	2	3			2	1	0
Observed bond length (Å)	0.74	—	2.67	—	1.59	1.31	1.09			1.21	1.43	—
Observed bond energy (kJ/mol)	436	—	110	9	≈ 270	602	945			498	155	—

Increasing energy (not to scale) →

[a] Electron distribution in molecular orbitals, bond order, bond length, and bond energy of homonuclear diatomic molecules of the first- and second-period elements. Note that nitrogen molecules, N_2, have the highest bond energies listed; they have a bond order of three. The species C_2 and O_2, with a bond order of two, have the next highest bond energies.

[b] Exists only in the vapor state at elevated temperatures.

[c] Unknown species.

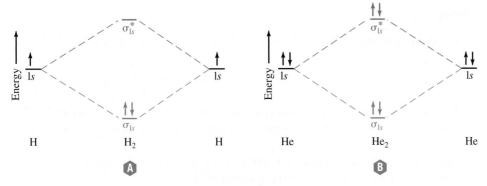

Figure 9-6 Molecular orbital diagrams for (a) H_2 and (b) He_2.

The unpaired electrons are consistent with the observed paramagnetism of B_2. Here we illustrate Hund's Rule in molecular orbital theory. The π_{2p_y} and π_{2p_z} orbitals are equal in energy and contain a total of two electrons. Accordingly, one electron occupies each orbital. The bond order is one. Experiments verify that B_2 molecules exist in the vapor state.

▶ Orbitals of equal energy are called **degenerate orbitals**. Hund's Rule for filling degenerate orbitals was discussed in Section 4-18.

The Nitrogen Molecule, N_2

Experimental thermodynamic data show that the N_2 molecule is stable, is diamagnetic, and has a very high bond energy, 946 kJ/mol. This is consistent with molecular orbital theory. Each nitrogen atom has 7 electrons, so the diamagnetic N_2 molecule has 14 electrons.

$$\sigma_{1s}^2 \quad \sigma_{1s}^{*2} \quad \sigma_{2s}^2 \quad \sigma_{2s}^{*2} \quad \pi_{2p_y}^2 \quad \pi_{2p_z}^2 \quad \sigma_{2p}^2$$

▶ N_2 bond order $= \dfrac{10-4}{2} = 3$

Six more electrons occur in bonding orbitals than in antibonding orbitals, so the bond order is three. We see (Table 9-1) that N_2 has a very short bond length, only 1.09 Å, the shortest of any diatomic species except H_2.

▶ In the valence bond representation, N_2 is shown as $:N \equiv N:$, with a triple bond.

The Oxygen Molecule, O_2

Among the homonuclear diatomic molecules, only N_2 and the very small H_2 have shorter bond lengths than O_2, 1.21 Å. Recall that valence bond (VB) theory predicts that O_2 is diamagnetic. Experiments show, however, that it is paramagnetic, with two unpaired electrons. MO theory predicts a structure consistent with this observation. For O_2, the σ_{2p} orbital is lower in energy than the π_{2p_y} and π_{2p_z} orbitals. Each oxygen atom has 8 electrons, so the O_2 molecule has 16 electrons.

$$\sigma_{1s}^2 \quad \sigma_{1s}^{*2} \quad \sigma_{2s}^2 \quad \sigma_{2s}^{*2} \quad \sigma_{2p}^2 \quad \pi_{2p_y}^2 \quad \pi_{2p_z}^2 \quad \pi_{2p_y}^{*1} \quad \pi_{2p_z}^{*1}$$

The two unpaired electrons reside in the *degenerate* antibonding orbitals, $\pi_{2p_y}^*$ and $\pi_{2p_z}^*$. Because there are four more electrons in bonding orbitals than in antibonding orbitals, the bond order is two (see Figure 9-5b and Table 9-1). We see why the molecule is much more stable than two free O atoms.

▶ O_2 bond order $= \dfrac{10-6}{2} = 2$

Similarly, MO theory can be used to predict the structures and stabilities of ions, as Example 9-1 shows.

EXAMPLE 9-1 Predicting Stabilities and Bond Orders

Predict the stabilities and bond orders of the ions (a) O_2^+ and (b) O_2^-.

Plan

(a) The O_2^+ ion is formed by removing one electron from the O_2 molecule. The electrons that are withdrawn most easily are those in the highest energy orbitals.

(b) The superoxide ion, O_2^-, results from adding an electron to the O_2 molecule.

Solution

(a) We remove one of the π^*_{2p} electrons of O_2 to find the configuration of O_2^+:

$$\sigma_{1s}^2 \quad \sigma_{1s}^{*2} \quad \sigma_{2s}^2 \quad \sigma_{2s}^{*2} \quad \sigma_{2p}^2 \quad \pi_{2p_y}^2 \quad \pi_{2p_z}^2 \quad \pi_{2p_y}^{*1}$$

There are five more electrons in bonding orbitals than in antibonding orbitals, so the bond order is 2.5. We conclude that the ion would be reasonably stable, and it does exist.

In fact, the unusual ionic compound $[O_2^+][PtF_6^-]$ played an important role in the discovery of the first noble gas compound, $XePtF_6$ (see Section 28-2).

(b) We add one electron to the appropriate orbital of O_2 to find the configuration of O_2^-. Following Hund's Rule, we add this electron into the $\pi^*_{2p_y}$ orbital to form a pair:

$$\sigma_{1s}^2 \quad \sigma_{1s}^{*2} \quad \sigma_{2s}^2 \quad \sigma_{2s}^{*2} \quad \sigma_{2p}^2 \quad \pi_{2p_y}^2 \quad \pi_{2p_z}^2 \quad \pi_{2p_y}^{*2} \quad \pi_{2p_z}^{*1}$$

There are three more bonding electrons than antibonding electrons, so the bond order is 1.5. We conclude that the ion should exist but be less stable than O_2.

The known superoxides of the heavier Group 1A elements—KO_2, RbO_2, and CsO_2—contain the superoxide ion, O_2^-. These compounds are formed by combination of the free metals with oxygen (see Section 5-9, second subsection).

You should now work Exercises 20 and 22.

S **TOP & THINK**

Remember the steps for assessing the stability of a molecule or ion. First, determine the configuration of electrons in its molecular orbitals, as outlined in Section 9-1. Then find the bond order as shown above. The higher the bond order, the more stable we expect the molecule or ion to be.

The Fluorine Molecule, F_2

Each fluorine atom has 9 electrons, so there are 18 electrons in F_2.

$$\sigma_{1s}^2 \quad \sigma_{1s}^{*2} \quad \sigma_{2s}^2 \quad \sigma_{2s}^{*2} \quad \sigma_{2p}^2 \quad \pi_{2p_y}^2 \quad \pi_{2p_z}^2 \quad \pi_{2p_y}^{*2} \quad \pi_{2p_z}^{*2}$$

The bond order is one. As you know, F_2 exists. The F—F bond distance is longer (1.43 Å) than the bond distances in O_2 (1.21 Å) or N_2 (1.09 Å) molecules. The bond order in F_2 (one) is less than that in O_2 (two) or N_2 (three). The bond energy of the F_2 molecules is lower than that of either O_2 or N_2 (see Table 9-1). As a result, F_2 molecules are the most reactive of the three.

▶ F_2 bond order $= \dfrac{10-8}{2} = 1$

Heavier Homonuclear Diatomic Molecules

It might appear reasonable to use the same types of molecular orbital diagrams to predict the stability or existence of homonuclear diatomic molecules of the third and subsequent periods. However, the heavier halogens, Cl_2, Br_2, and I_2, which contain only sigma (single) bonds, are the only well-characterized examples at room temperature. We would predict from both molecular orbital theory and valence bond theory that the other (nonhalogen) homonuclear diatomic molecules from below the second period would exhibit pi bonding and therefore multiple bonding.

Some heavier elements, such as S_2, exist as diatomic species in the vapor phase at elevated temperatures. These species are neither common nor very stable. The instability is related to the inability of atoms of the heavier elements to form strong pi bonds *with each other*. For larger atoms, the sigma bond length is too great to allow the atomic *p* orbitals on different atoms to overlap very effectively. The strength of pi bonding therefore decreases rapidly with increasing atomic size. For example, N_2 is *much* more stable than P_2. This is because the 3*p* orbitals on one P atom do not overlap side by side in a pi-bonding manner with corresponding 3*p* orbitals on another P atom nearly as effectively as do the corresponding 2*p* orbitals on the smaller N atoms. MO theory does not predict multiple bonding for Cl_2, Br_2, or I_2, each of which has a bond order of one.

9-5 Heteronuclear Diatomic Molecules

Heteronuclear Diatomic Molecules of Second-Period Elements

Corresponding atomic orbitals of two different elements, such as the $2s$ orbitals of nitrogen and oxygen atoms, have different energies because their nuclei have different charges and therefore different attractions for electrons. Atomic orbitals of the *more electronegative element* are *lower* in energy than the corresponding orbitals of the less electronegative element. Accordingly, a molecular orbital diagram such as Figure 9-5 is inappropriate for *heteronuclear* diatomic molecules. If the two elements are similar (as in NO or CN molecules, for example), we can modify the diagram of Figure 9-5 by skewing it slightly. Figure 9-7 shows the energy level diagram and electron configuration for nitrogen oxide, NO, also known as nitric oxide.

▶ Note: CN is a reactive molecule, not the stable cyanide ion, CN^-.

The closer the energy of a molecular orbital is to the energy of one of the atomic orbitals from which it is formed, the more of the character of that atomic orbital it shows. Thus, as we see in Figure 9-7, the bonding MOs in the NO molecule have more oxygen-like atomic orbital character, and the antibonding orbitals have more nitrogen-like atomic orbital character.

In general the energy differences ΔE_1, ΔE_2, and ΔE_3 (*orange backgrounds* in Figure 9-7) depend on the difference in electronegativities between the two atoms. The greater these energy differences, the more polar is the bond joining the atoms and the greater is its ionic character. On the other hand, the energy differences reflect the degree of overlap between

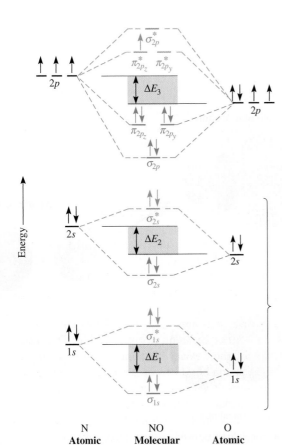

Figure 9-7 MO energy level diagram for nitrogen oxide, NO, a slightly polar heteronuclear diatomic molecule ($\mu = 0.15$ D). The atomic orbitals of oxygen, the more electronegative element, are a little lower in energy than the corresponding atomic orbitals of nitrogen, the less electronegative element. For this molecule, the energy differences ΔE_1, ΔE_2, and ΔE_3 are not very large; the molecule is not very polar.

atomic orbitals; the smaller these differences are, the more the orbitals can overlap, and the greater the covalent character of the bond is.

We see that NO has a total of 15 electrons, making it isoelectronic with the N_2^- ion. The distribution of electrons is therefore the same in NO as in N_2^-, although we expect the energy levels of the MOs to be different. In accord with our predictions, nitrogen oxide is a stable molecule. It has a bond order of 2.5, a short nitrogen–oxygen bond length of 1.15 Å, a low dipole moment of 0.15 D, and a high bond energy of 891 kJ/mol.

The Hydrogen Fluoride Molecule, HF

The electronegativity difference between hydrogen (EN = 2.1) and fluorine (EN = 4.0) is very large [(Δ(EN) = 1.9)]. The hydrogen fluoride molecule contains a very polar bond (μ = 1.91 D). The bond in HF involves the $1s$ electron of H and an unpaired electron from a $2p$ orbital of F. Figure 9-8 shows the overlap of the $1s$ orbital of H with a $2p$ orbital of F to form σ_{sp} and σ_{sp}^* molecular orbitals. The remaining two $2p$ orbitals of F have no net overlap with H orbitals. They are called **nonbonding molecular orbitals**. The same is true for the F $2s$ and $1s$ orbitals. These nonbonding orbitals retain the characteristics of the F atomic orbitals from which they are formed. The MO diagram of HF is shown in Figure 9-9.

Other Diatomic Species with Large Δ(EN) Values

If the energies of the atomic orbitals of the two atoms of a diatomic molecule or ion are quite different, the MO diagram may be unlike that known for any homonuclear species. Its unique MO diagram is constructed by combining the Schrödinger equations for the two atoms. Construction of the MO diagram for CO is a complex case, beyond the coverage in this textbook.

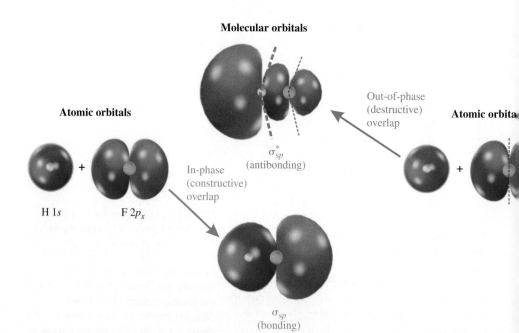

Figure 9-8 Formation of σ_{sp} and σ_{sp}^* molecular orbitals in HF by overlap of the $1s$ orbital of H with a $2p$ orbital of F.

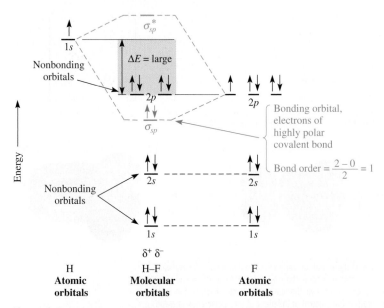

Figure 9-9 MO energy level diagram for hydrogen fluoride, HF, a very polar molecule ($\mu = 1.91$ D). ΔE is large because the electronegativity difference is large.

9-6 Delocalization and the Shapes of Molecular Orbitals

In Section 7-9 we described resonance formulas for molecules and polyatomic ions. Resonance is said to exist when two or more equivalent Lewis formulas can be written for the same species and a single such formula does not account for the properties of a substance. In molecular orbital terminology, a more appropriate description involves delocalization of electrons. The shapes of molecular orbitals for species in which electron **delocalization** occurs can be predicted by combining all the contributing atomic orbitals.

▶ This section includes pictorial representations of molecular orbitals. The details of the corresponding molecular orbital diagrams are too complicated to present here.

The Carbonate Ion, CO_3^{2-}

Consider the trigonal planar carbonate ion, CO_3^{2-} as an example. All the carbon–oxygen bonds in the ion have the same bond length and the same energy, intermediate between those of typical C—O and C=O bonds. Valence bond theory describes the ion in terms of three contributing resonance structures (Figure 9-10a). No one of the three resonance forms adequately describes the bonding.

▶ The average carbon–oxygen bond order in the CO_3^{2-} ion is $1\frac{1}{3}$.

According to valence bond theory, the C atom is described as sp^2 hybridized, and it forms one sigma bond with each of the three O atoms. This leaves one unhybridized $2p$ atomic orbital on the C atom, say the $2p_z$ orbital. This orbital is capable of overlapping and mixing with the $2p_z$ orbital of any of the three O atoms. The sharing of two electrons in the resulting localized pi orbital would form a pi bond. Thus, three equivalent resonance structures can be drawn in valence bond terms (see Figure 9-10b). We emphasize that there is *no evidence* for the existence of these separate resonance structures.

The MO description of the pi bonding involves the simultaneous overlap and mixing of the carbon $2p_z$ orbital with the $2p_z$ orbitals of all three oxygen atoms. This forms a delocalized bonding pi molecular orbital lying above and below the plane of the sigma system, as well as an antibonding pi orbital. The electron pair that occupies this delocalized bonding pi MO is spread over all four atoms, as depicted in Figure 9-10c. The bonding in such species as nitrate ion, NO_3^-, and ozone, O_3, can be described similarly.

▶ In a polyatomic molecule or ion, MOs can be formed by overlap of the AOs of more than two atoms.

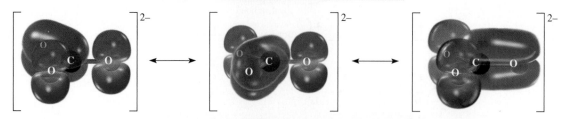

A Lewis formulas of the three valence bond resonance structures

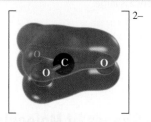

B Representation of the *p*-orbital overlap in the valence bond resonance structures. In each resonance form, the *p* orbitals on two atoms would overlap to form the π components of the hypothetical double bonds. Each O atom has two additional sp^2 orbitals (not shown) in the plane of the nuclei. Each of these additional sp^2 orbitals contains an oxygen unshared pair.

C In the MO description, the electrons in the π-bonded region are spread out, or *delocalized*, over all four atoms of the CO_3^{2-} ion. This MO description is more consistent with the experimental observation of equal bond lengths and energies than are the valence bond pictures in (a) and (b).

Figure 9-10 Alternative representations of the bonding in the carbonate ion, CO_3^{2-}.

The Benzene Molecule, C_6H_6

▶ There is no evidence for the existence of either of these forms of benzene. The MO description of benzene is far better than the valence bond description.

Now let us consider the benzene molecule, C_6H_6, whose two valence bond resonance forms are shown in Figure 9-11a. The valence bond description involves sp^2 hybridization at each C atom. Each C atom is at the center of a trigonal plane, and the entire molecule is known to be planar. There are sigma bonds from each C atom to the two adjacent C atoms and to one H atom. This leaves one unhybridized $2p_z$ orbital on each C atom and one remaining valence electron for each. According to valence bond theory, adjacent pairs of $2p_z$ orbitals and the six remaining electrons occupy the regions of overlap to form a total of three pi bonds in either of the two ways shown in Figure 9-11b.

Experimental studies of the C_6H_6 structure prove that it does *not* contain alternating single and double carbon–carbon bonds. The usual C — C single bond length is 1.54 Å, and the usual C = C double bond length is 1.34 Å. All six of the carbon–carbon bonds in benzene are observed to be the same length, 1.39 Å, intermediate between those of single and double bonds.

This is well explained by the MO theory, which predicts that the six $2p_z$ orbitals of the C atoms overlap and mix to form three pi-bonding and three pi-antibonding molecular orbitals. The delocalized bonding pi molecular orbitals of benzene are shown in Figure 9-11c. The six pi electrons occupy these three bonding MOs. Thus, they are distributed throughout the molecule as a whole, above and below the plane of the sigma-bonded framework. This results in identical character for all carbon–carbon bonds in benzene. The MO representation of the extended pi system is the same as that obtained by averaging the two contributing valence bond resonance structures.

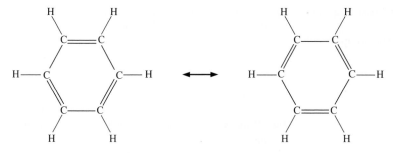

Ⓐ Lewis formulas of the two valence bond resonance structures

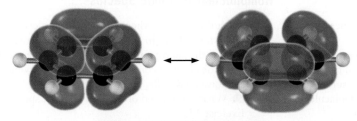

Ⓑ The six *p* orbitals of the benzene ring, shown overlapping to form the (hypothetical) double bonds of the two resonance forms of valence bond theory

Ⓒ In the MO description, each bonding π MO is *delocalized*, meaning that it occupies an extended π-bonding region above and below the plane of the six C atoms. Each of these bonding π MOs contains a pair of electrons.

Figure 9-11 Representations of the bonding in the benzene molecule, C_6H_6.

KEY TERMS

Antibonding electrons   Electrons in antibonding orbitals.

Antibonding molecular orbital   A molecular orbital higher in energy than any of the atomic orbitals from which it is derived; when populated with electrons, lends instability to a molecule or ion. Denoted with an asterisk (*) superscript on its symbol.

Bond energy   The amount of energy necessary to break one mole of bonds of a given kind (in the gas phase).

Bond order   Half the number of electrons in bonding orbitals minus half the number of electrons in antibonding orbitals.

Bonding electrons   Electrons in bonding orbitals.

Bonding molecular orbital   A molecular orbital lower in energy than any of the atomic orbitals from which it is derived; when populated with electrons, lends stability to a molecule or ion.

Degenerate orbitals   Orbitals of the same energy.

Delocalization   The formation of a set of molecular orbitals that extend over more than two atoms; important in species

that valence bond theory describes in terms of resonance (see Section 7-6).

Heteronuclear   Consisting of different elements.

Homonuclear   Consisting of only one element.

Molecular orbital (MO)   An orbital resulting from overlap and mixing of atomic orbitals on different atoms. An MO belongs to the molecule as a whole.

Molecular orbital theory   A theory of chemical bonding based on the postulated existence of molecular orbitals.

Nodal plane   A region in which the probability of finding an electron is zero; also known as a *node*.

Nonbonding molecular orbital   A molecular orbital derived only from an atomic orbital of one atom; lends neither stability nor instability to a molecule or ion when populated with electrons.

Pi (π) bond   A bond resulting from electron occupancy of a pi molecular orbital.

Pi (π) molecular orbital A molecular orbital resulting from side-on overlap of atomic orbitals.

Sigma (σ) bond A bond resulting from electron occupancy of a sigma molecular orbital.

Sigma (σ) molecular orbital A molecular orbital resulting from head-on overlap of two atomic orbitals.

EXERCISES

· ·

🔵 **Molecular Reasoning** exercises

▲ **More Challenging** exercises

Blue-Numbered exercises are solved in the Student Solutions Manual

MO Theory: General Concepts

1. Describe the main differences between the valence bond theory and the molecular orbital theory.
2. In molecular orbital theory, what is a molecular orbital? What two types of information can be obtained from molecular orbital calculations? How do we use such information to describe the bonding within a molecule?
3. What is the relationship between the maximum number of electrons that can be accommodated by a set of molecular orbitals and the maximum number that can be accommodated by the atomic orbitals from which the MOs are formed? What is the maximum number of electrons that one MO can hold?
4. Answer Exercise 3 after replacing "molecular orbitals" or "MO" with "hybridized atomic orbitals."
5. What differences and similarities exist among (a) atomic orbitals, (b) localized hybridized atomic orbitals according to valence bond theory, and (c) molecular orbitals?
6. Describe the shapes, including the locations of the nuclei, of σ and σ^* orbitals.
7. Describe the shapes, including the locations of the nuclei, of π and π^* orbitals.
8. State the three rules for placing electrons in molecular orbitals.
9. What is meant by the term "bond order"? How is the value of the bond order calculated?
10. Compare and illustrate the differences between (a) atomic orbitals and molecular orbitals, (b) bonding and antibonding molecular orbitals, (c) σ orbitals and π orbitals, and (d) localized and delocalized molecular orbitals.
11. 🔵 Is it possible for a molecule or polyatomic ion in its ground state to have a negative bond order? Why?
12. What is the relationship between the energy of a bonding molecular orbital and the energies of the original atomic orbitals? What is the relationship between the energy of an antibonding molecular orbital and the energies of the original atomic orbitals?
13. Compare and contrast the following three concepts: (a) bonding orbitals; (b) antibonding orbitals; (c) nonbonding orbitals.

Homonuclear Diatomic Species

14. What do we mean when we say that a molecule or ion is (a) homonuclear, (b) heteronuclear, or (c) diatomic?
15. 🔵 Use the appropriate molecular orbital energy diagram to write the electron configurations of the following molecules and ions: (a) Be_2, Be_2^+, Be_2^-; (b) B_2, B_2^+, B_2^-.
16. 🔵 What is the bond order of each of the species in Exercise 15?
17. 🔵 Which of the species in Exercise 15 are diamagnetic and which are paramagnetic? How many unpaired electrons are indicated by the MO description of each species?
18. Use MO theory to predict relative stabilities of the species in Exercise 15. Comment on the validity of these predictions. What else *must* be considered in addition to electron occupancy of MOs?
19. 🔵 Use the appropriate molecular orbital energy diagram to write the electron configuration for each of the following; calculate the bond order of each, and predict which would exist. (a) H_2^+; (b) H_2; (c) H_2^-; (d) H_2^{2-}.
20. 🔵 Repeat Exercise 19 for (a) Ne_2^+; (b) Ne_2; (c) Ne_2^{2+}.
21. 🔵 Repeat Exercise 19 for (a) N_2; (b) He_2; (c) C_2^{2-}.
22. 🔵 Repeat Exercise 19 for (a) Li_2; (b) Li_2^+; (c) O_2^{2-}.
23. 🔵 ▲ Which homonuclear diatomic molecules or ions of the second period have the following electron distributions in MOs? In other words, identify X in each.

    (a) X_2 $\quad \sigma_{1s}^2 \ \sigma_{1s}^{*2} \ \sigma_{2s}^2 \ \sigma_{2s}^{*2} \ \pi_{2p_y}^2 \ \pi_{2p_z}^2 \ \sigma_{2p}^2$

    (b) X_2 $\quad \sigma_{1s}^2 \ \sigma_{1s}^{*2} \ \sigma_{2s}^2 \ \sigma_{2s}^{*2} \ \sigma_{2p}^2 \ \pi_{2p_y}^2 \ \pi_{2p_z}^2 \ \pi_{2p_y}^{*1} \ \pi_{2p_z}^{*1}$

    (c) X_2^- $\quad \sigma_{1s}^2 \ \sigma_{1s}^{*2} \ \sigma_{2s}^2 \ \sigma_{2s}^{*2} \ \pi_{2p_y}^2 \ \pi_{2p_z}^2 \ \sigma_{2p}^2 \ \pi_{2p_y}^{*1}$

24. 🔵 What is the bond order of each of the species in Exercise 23?
25. 🔵 Write MO electron configurations for (a) F_2, F_2^-, F_2^+; (b) C_2, C_2^+, C_2^-.
26. 🔵 (a) What is the bond order of each species in Exercise 25? (b) Are they diamagnetic or paramagnetic? (c) What would MO theory predict about the stabilities of these species?
27. 🔵 (a) Give the MO designations for O_2, O_2^-, O_2^{2-}, O_2^+, and O_2^{2+}. (b) Give the bond order in each case. (c) Match these species with the following observed bond lengths: 1.04 Å, 1.12 Å, 1.21 Å, 1.33 Å, and 1.49 Å.
28. 🔵 (a) Give the MO designations for N_2, N_2^-, and N_2^+. (b) Give the bond order in each case. (c) Rank these three species by increasing predicted bond length.

· ·

🔵 **Molecular Reasoning** exercises   ▲ **More Challenging** exercises   Blue-Numbered exercises solved in Student Solutions Manual

Heteronuclear Diatomic Species

The following is a molecular orbital energy level diagram for a heteronuclear diatomic molecule, XY, in which both X and Y are from Period 2 and Y is slightly more electronegative. This diagram may be used in answering questions in this section.

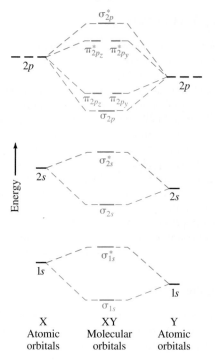

X
Atomic orbitals

XY
Molecular orbitals

Y
Atomic orbitals

29. ✿ Use the preceding diagram to fill in an MO diagram for NO⁻. What is the bond order of NO⁻? Is it paramagnetic? How would you assess its stability?

30. ✿ Repeat Exercise 29 for NO⁺.

31. ✿ Repeat Exercise 29 for CN⁻. Refer to the preceding diagram, but assume that the π_{2p_y} and π_{2p_z} MOs are lower in energy than the σ_{2p} MO.

32. ✿ Compare the MO descriptions for CN, CN⁺, CN²⁺, CN⁻, and CN²⁻. Refer to the preceding diagram but assume that the π_{2p_y} and π_{2p_z} MOs are lower in energy than the σ_{2p} MO. Which would be most stable? Which would you predict to be paramagnetic? Why? Determine the bond order of each.

33. ✿ Oxygen, O_2, can acquire one or two electrons to give O_2^- (superoxide ion) or O_2^{2-} (peroxide ion). Write the electron configuration for the ions in molecular orbital terms, and then compare them with the O_2 molecule on the following bases. (a) magnetic character; (b) net number of σ and π bonds; (c) bond order; (d) oxygen–oxygen bond length.

34. ✿ For each of the two species NF and NF⁺, (a) draw MO energy level diagrams; (b) write out electron configurations; (c) determine bond orders and predict relative stabilities; and (d) predict diamagnetism or paramagnetism.

35. ✿ The nitrosyl ion, NO⁺, has an interesting chemistry.

   (a) Is NO⁺ diamagnetic or paramagnetic? If paramagnetic, how many unpaired electrons does it have?

   (b) Assume the molecular orbital diagram for a homonuclear diatomic molecule (see Figure 9-5a) applies to NO⁺. What is the highest-energy molecular orbital occupied by electrons?

   (c) What is the nitrogen–oxygen bond order?

   (d) Is the N—O bond in NO⁺ stronger or weaker than the bond in NO?

36. To decrease the strength of the bonding in the hypothetical compound BC, would you add or subtract an electron? Explain your answer with the aid of an MO electron structure.

Delocalization

37. ✿ Use Lewis formulas to depict the resonance structures of the following species from the valence bond point of view, and then sketch MOs for the delocalized π systems: (a) NO_3^-, nitrate ion; (b) HCO_3^-, hydrogen carbonate ion (H is bonded to O); (c) NO_2^-, nitrite ion.

38. ✿ Use Lewis formulas to depict the resonance structures of the following species from the valence bond point of view, and then sketch MOs for the delocalized π systems: (a) SO_2, sulfur dioxide; (b) O_3, ozone; (c) HCO_2^-, formate ion (H is bonded to C).

Mixed Exercises

39. ✿ Draw and label the complete MO energy level diagrams for the following species. For each, determine the bond order, predict the stability of the species, and predict whether the species will be paramagnetic or diamagnetic. (a) He_2^+; (b) CN; (c) HeH^+.

A paramagnetic material is attracted toward a magnetic field.

40. ✿ Draw and label the complete MO energy level diagrams for the following species. For each, determine the bond order, predict the stability of the species, and predict whether the species will be paramagnetic or diamagnetic. (a) O_2^{2+}; (b) HO⁻; (c) HF.

41. ✿ Which of these species would you expect to be paramagnetic and which to be diamagnetic? (a) He_2^-; (b) N_2; (c) NO⁺; (d) N_2^{2+}; (e) F_2^+.

✿ **Molecular Reasoning** exercises   ▲ **More Challenging** exercises   Blue-Numbered exercises solved in Student Solutions Manual

Unless otherwise noted, all content on this page is © Cengage Learning.

Conceptual Exercises

42. ♣ Refer to the diagrams in Figure 9-5 as needed. (a) Can the bond order of a diatomic species having 20 or fewer electrons be greater than three? Why? (b) Can the bond order be a value that is not divisible by 0.5? Why?

43. ♣ As NO ionizes to form NO^+, does the nitrogen–oxygen bond become stronger or weaker?

$$NO \rightarrow NO^+ + e^-$$

44. Which of the homonuclear diatomic molecules of the second row of the periodic table (Li_2 to Ne_2) are predicted by MO theory to be paramagnetic? Which ones are predicted to have a bond order of one? Which ones are predicted to have a bond order of two? Which one is predicted to have the highest bond order?

45. ♣ ▲ Use valence bond and molecular orbital theory to describe the change in Cl — Cl bond length when Cl_2 loses an electron to form Cl_2^+. Would the cation be diamagnetic or paramagnetic? Explain.

46. ♣ ▲ Briefly explain the finding that the N — O bond is longer in NO^- than in NO. Should NO^- exist? If so, how would its bond length compare with those in NO^+ and NO? What is the bond order of each species?

47. The validity of molecular orbital theory is supported by its ability, unlike valence bond theory, to correctly predict certain properties of homonuclear diatomic molecules of elements in the first and second periods. What prediction would valence bond theory make about the paramagnetism of these molecules? For which molecules does molecular orbital theory make a different prediction?

48. For which of the molecules in Exercise 47 does molecular orbital theory allow us to make a prediction about the bond order that we might not make on the basis of valence bond theory? Describe the level of agreement between the bond order predicted by molecular orbital theory and the observed bond length and bond energy. (Also consider the atomic radii.)

49. ♣ ▲ For which of the homonuclear diatomic molecules or ions of elements in the first and second periods would the paramagnetism or the bond order actually be different if the incorrect energy level diagram (Figure 9-5a vs. Figure 9-5b) were used? (*Hint:* There are four or more correct answers.)

50. What effect does the addition of electrons to a bonding orbital have on the bond strength? What effect does the addition of electrons to an antibonding orbital have on the bond strength? What effect does the addition of electrons to a nonbonding orbital have on the bond strength?

Building Your Knowledge

51. ♣ When carbon vaporizes at extremely high temperatures, the diatomic molecule C_2 is among the species present in the vapor. Write a Lewis formula for C_2. Does your Lewis formula of C_2 obey the octet rule? (C_2 does not contain a quadruple bond.) Does C_2 contain a single, a double, or a triple bond? Is it paramagnetic or diamagnetic? Show how molecular orbital theory can be used to predict the answers to questions left unanswered by valence bond theory.

52. ♣ ▲ Rationalize the following observations in terms of the stabilities of σ and π bonds. (a) The most common form of nitrogen is N_2, whereas the most common form of phosphorus is P_4 (see the structure in Figure 1-4). (b) The most common forms of oxygen are O_2 and (less common) O_3, whereas the most common form of sulfur is S_8.

Beyond the Textbook

NOTE: *Whenever the answer to an exercise depends on information obtained from a source other than this textbook, the source must be included as an essential part of the answer.*

53. Use an internet search engine (such as **http://www.google.com**) to locate information on vision and molecular orbital theory. How are the two related?

54. ▲ Use an internet search engine (such as **http://www.google.com**) to locate information on the comparison of other bonding theories (such as valence bond theory, crystal field theory, band theory, and metallic bonding) to molecular orbital theory. How are they related?

55. Open **www.winter.group.shef.ac.uk/orbitron** or another suitable animated discussion of Molecular Orbital Theory. (a) Click on π_x and watch the animation. Describe the final product shown. (b) Click on π_x^* and watch the animation. Describe the final product shown.

Reactions in Aqueous Solutions I: Acids, Bases, and Salts

10

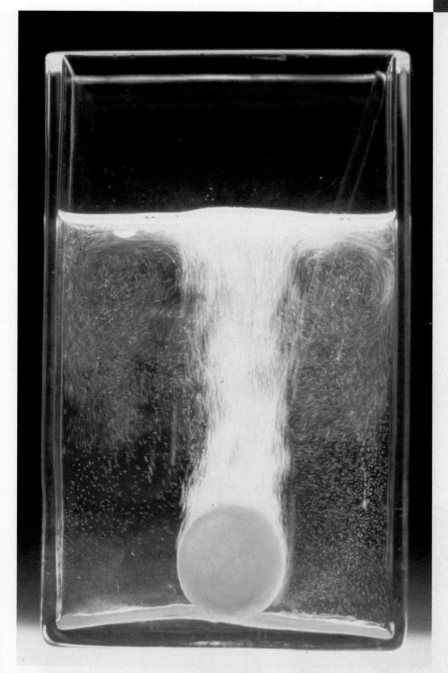

The acid-base reaction of citric acid and sodium bicarbonate (NaHCO₃) when placed into water produces carbon dioxide (CO₂) bubbles and the fizz in an Alka Seltzer™ tablet.

Charles D. Winters

OBJECTIVES

After you have studied this chapter, you should be able to

▶ Describe the Arrhenius theory of acids and bases

▶ Describe hydrated hydrogen ions

▶ Describe the Brønsted–Lowry theory of acids and bases

▶ List properties of aqueous solutions of acids

▶ List properties of aqueous solutions of bases

▶ Arrange binary acids in order of increasing strength

▶ Arrange ternary acids in order of increasing strength

▶ Describe the Lewis theory of acids and bases

▶ Complete and balance equations for acid–base reactions

▶ Define acidic and basic salts

▶ Explain amphoterism

▶ Describe methods for preparing acids

▶ You will encounter many of these in your laboratory work.

In technological societies, acids, bases, and salts are indispensable compounds. Table 6-10 lists the 14 such compounds that were included in the top 50 chemicals produced in the United States in 2009. The production of sulfuric acid (H_2SO_4, number 1) was more than three times as great as the production of ammonia (NH_3). Sixty-five percent of the H_2SO_4 is used in the production of fertilizers.

Many acids, bases, and salts occur in nature and serve a wide variety of purposes. For instance, your stomach "digestive juice" contains approximately 0.10 mole of hydrochloric acid (HCl) per liter. Human blood and the aqueous components of most cells are slightly basic. The liquid in your car battery is approximately 40% H_2SO_4 by mass. Baking soda ($NaHCO_3$) is a salt of carbonic acid (H_2CO_3). Sodium hydroxide (NaOH), a base, is used in the manufacture of soaps, paper, and many other chemicals. "Drano" is solid NaOH that contains some aluminum chips. Sodium chloride (NaCl) is used to season food and as a food preservative. Calcium chloride ($CaCl_2$) is used to melt ice on highways and in the emergency treatment of cardiac arrest. Several ammonium salts are used as fertilizers. Many organic acids (carboxylic acids) and their derivatives occur in nature. Acetic acid is present in vinegar; the sting of an ant bite is due to formic acid. Amino acids are carboxylic acids that also contain basic groups derived from ammonia. Amino acids are the building blocks of proteins, which are important materials in all forms of life. The pleasant odors and flavors of ripe fruit are due in large part to the presence of esters (see Chapter 23) that are formed from organic acids in unripe fruit.

(*Left*) Many common household liquids are acidic, including soft drinks, vinegar, and fruit juices. (*Right*) Most cleaning materials are basic.

10-1 Properties of Aqueous Solutions of Acids and Bases

Aqueous solutions of most **protic acids** (those containing acidic hydrogen atoms) exhibit certain properties, which are properties of hydrated hydrogen ions in aqueous solution.

1. Acids have a sour taste. Pickles are usually preserved in vinegar, a 5% solution of acetic acid. Many pickled condiments contain large amounts of sugar so that the taste of acetic acid is partially masked by the sweet taste of sugar. Lemons contain citric acid, which is responsible for their characteristic sour taste.

2. Acids change the colors of many indicators (highly colored dyes whose colors depend on the acidic or basic character of the solution). Acids turn blue litmus red, and cause bromthymol blue to change from blue to yellow.

3. Nonoxidizing acids react with metals above hydrogen in the activity series (see Section 6-8, Part 2) to liberate hydrogen gas, H_2. (Nitric acid, HNO_3, a common oxidizing acid, reacts with metals to produce primarily nitrogen oxides.)

4. Acids react with (neutralize) metal oxides and metal hydroxides to form salts and water (see Section 6-8, Part 1).

5. Acids react with salts of weaker acids to form the weaker acid and the salt of the stronger acid; for example,

$$\underset{\text{stronger acid}}{3HCl(aq)} + Na_3PO_4(aq) \longrightarrow \underset{\text{weaker acid}}{H_3PO_4(aq)} + 3NaCl(aq).$$

6. Aqueous solutions of acids conduct an electric current because they are totally or partially ionized.

Aqueous solutions of most bases also exhibit certain properties, which are due to the hydrated hydroxide ions present in aqueous solutions of bases.

1. Bases have a bitter taste.

2. Bases have a slippery feeling. Soaps are common examples that are mildly basic. A solution of household bleach feels very slippery because it is quite basic.

3. Bases change the colors of many indicators: bases turn litmus from red to blue, and bromthymol blue changes from yellow to blue.

4. Bases react with (neutralize) acids to form salts and, in most cases, water.

5. Their aqueous solutions conduct an electric current because bases are dissociated or ionized to some extent.

▶ Chemists also use "protonic" to describe these acids.

CAUTION!
We should *never* try to identify a substance in the laboratory by taste. You have, however, probably experienced the sour taste of acetic acid in vinegar or citric acid in foods that contain citrus fruits.

The indicator bromthymol blue is yellow in acidic solution and blue in basic solution.

10-2 The Arrhenius Theory

In 1680, Robert Boyle noted that acids (1) dissolve many substances, (2) change the colors of some natural dyes (indicators), and (3) lose their characteristic properties when mixed with alkalis (bases). By 1814, J. Gay-Lussac concluded that acids *neutralize* bases and that the two classes of substances should be defined in terms of their reactions with each other.

In 1884, Svante Arrhenius (1859–1927) presented his theory of electrolytic dissociation, which resulted in the Arrhenius theory of acid–base reactions. In his view,

▶ This is an extremely important concept.

an **acid** is a substance that contains hydrogen and produces H^+ in aqueous solution.
A **base** is a substance that contains the OH (hydroxyl) group and produces hydroxide ions, OH^-, in aqueous solution.

Neutralization is defined as the reaction of H^+ ions with OH^- ions to form H_2O molecules.

$$H^+(aq) + OH^-(aq) \longrightarrow H_2O(\ell) \qquad \text{(neutralization)}$$

The Arrhenius theory of acid–base behavior satisfactorily explained reactions of *protic acids* with metal hydroxides (hydroxy bases). It was a significant contribution to chemical thought and theory in the latter part of the nineteenth century. The Arrhenius model of acids and bases, although limited in scope, led to the development of more general theories of acid–base behavior. They will be considered in later sections.

▶ Review Sections 5-8, 5-9, 6-1, and 6-9 (Part 1).

10-3 The Hydronium Ion (Hydrated Hydrogen Ion)

Although Arrhenius described H^+ ions in water as bare ions (protons), we now know that they are hydrated in aqueous solution and exist as $H^+(H_2O)_n$, in which n is some small integer. This is due to the attraction of the H^+ ions, or protons, for the oxygen end $(\delta-)$ of water molecules. Although we do not know the extent of hydration of H^+ in most solutions, we usually represent the hydrated hydrogen ion as the **hydronium ion**, H_3O^+, or $H^+(H_2O)_n$, in which $n = 1$.

▶ The most common isotope of hydrogen, ^1H, has no neutrons. Thus, $^1H^+$ is a bare proton. In discussions of acids and bases, we use the terms *hydrogen ion*, *proton*, and H^+ interchangeably.

▶ The actual value of *n* may be as large as 17, but $n = 4$ is the most commonly accepted value.

> The hydrated hydrogen ion is the species that gives aqueous solutions of acids their characteristic acidic properties.

Whether we use the designation $H^+(aq)$ or H_3O^+, we always mean the hydrated hydrogen ion.

$$H^+ + \overset{\cdot\cdot}{\underset{\underset{H}{|}}{O}}-H \longrightarrow \left[H-\overset{\cdot\cdot}{\underset{\underset{H}{|}}{O}}-H \right]^+$$

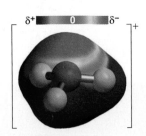

Hydronium ion, H_3O^+

10-4 The Brønsted–Lowry Theory

In 1923, J. N. Brønsted (1879–1947) and T. M. Lowry (1874–1936) independently presented logical extensions of the Arrhenius theory. Brønsted's contribution was more thorough than Lowry's, and the result is known as the **Brønsted theory** or the **Brønsted–Lowry theory**.

▶ The Brønsted–Lowry theory is especially useful for reactions in aqueous solutions. It is widely used in medicine and in the biological sciences.

> An **acid** is defined as a *proton donor* (H^+), and a **base** is defined as a *proton acceptor*.

These definitions are sufficiently broad that any hydrogen-containing molecule or ion capable of releasing a proton, H^+, is an acid, whereas any molecule or ion that can accept a proton is a base. In the Arrhenius theory of acids and bases, only substances that contain the OH^- group would be called bases. The Brønsted-Lowry theory expands the definition of bases to include substances that have one or more lone pairs of electrons that can act as proton acceptors.

> An acid–base reaction is the transfer of a proton from an acid to a base.

Thus, the complete ionization of hydrogen chloride, HCl, a *strong* acid, in water is an acid–base reaction in which water acts as a base or proton acceptor.

Step 1:	$HCl(aq) \longrightarrow H^+(aq) + Cl^-(aq)$	(Arrhenius description)
Step 2:	$H_2O(\ell) + H^+(aq) \longrightarrow H_3O^+$	
Overall:	$H_2O(\ell) + HCl(aq) \longrightarrow H_3O^+ + Cl^-(aq)$	(Brønsted–Lowry description)

▶ Various measurements (electrical conductivity, freezing point depression, etc.) indicate that HF is only *slightly* ionized in water.

The positively charged proton is attracted to one of the two lone pairs on the oxygen atom. The ionization of hydrogen fluoride, a *weak* acid, is similar, but it occurs to only a slight extent, so we use a double arrow to indicate that it is reversible.

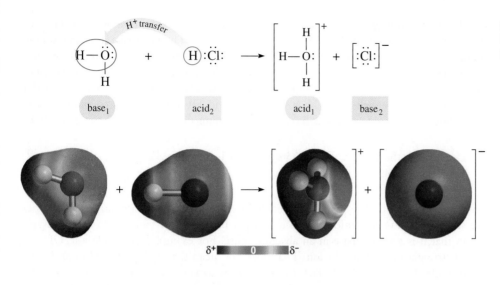

▶ Remember that in this text we use blue to indicate acids and red to indicate bases.

$$H_2O(\ell) + HF(aq) \rightleftharpoons H_3O^+ + F^-(aq)$$

base$_1$ acid$_2$ acid$_1$ base$_2$

▶ The double arrow is used to indicate that the reaction occurs in both the forward and the reverse directions. It does not mean that there are equal amounts of reactants and products present. We use rectangles to indicate one conjugate acid–base pair and ovals to indicate the other pair.

We can describe Brønsted–Lowry acid–base reactions in terms of **conjugate acid–base pairs**. These are two species that differ by a proton. In the preceding equation, HF (acid$_2$) and F$^-$ (base$_2$) are one conjugate acid–base pair, and H$_2$O (base$_1$) and H$_3$O$^+$ (acid$_1$) are the other pair. The members of each conjugate pair are designated by the same numerical subscript. In the forward reaction, HF and H$_2$O act as acid and base, respectively. In the reverse reaction, H$_3$O$^+$ acts as the acid, or proton donor, and F$^-$ acts as the base, or proton acceptor.

▶ It makes no difference which conjugate acid–base pair, HF and F$^-$ or H$_3$O$^+$ and H$_2$O, is assigned the subscripts 1 and 2.

Problem-Solving Tip Conjugate Acid–Base Pairs

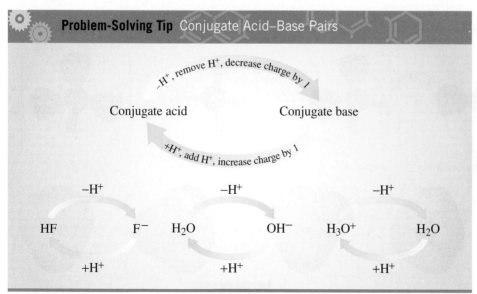

A bottle of hydrochloric acid (HCl, *left*) releases gaseous hydrogen chloride that reacts with gas phase ammonia (NH$_3$, *right*, from an aqueous ammonia solution) in an acid–base reaction. This produces the salt ammonium chloride (NH$_4$Cl) as very small solid particles ("smoke").

▶ Base strength: $F^- > H_2O$ and $H_2O > Cl^-$; therefore $F^- > Cl^-$.

When the *weak* acid, HF, dissolves in water, the HF molecules give up some H^+ ions that can be accepted by either of two bases, F^- or H_2O. The fact that HF is only slightly ionized tells us that F^- is a *stronger* base than H_2O. When the *strong* acid, HCl, dissolves in water, the HCl molecules give up H^+ ions that can be accepted by either of two bases, Cl^- or H_2O. The fact that HCl is completely ionized in dilute aqueous solution tells us that Cl^- is a *weaker* base than H_2O. Thus, the weaker acid, HF, has the stronger conjugate base, F^-, while the stronger acid, HCl, has the weaker conjugate base, Cl^-. We can generalize:

S TOP & THINK
Be sure you fully understand this very important concept in acid–base chemistry.

> The stronger the acid, the weaker is its conjugate base; the weaker the acid, the stronger is its conjugate base.

"Strong" and "weak," like many other adjectives, are used here in a relative sense. When we say that the fluoride anion, F^-, is a stronger base than Cl^- ion we do *not* necessarily mean that it is a strong base in an absolute sense. For example, hydroxide ion, OH^-, is also a stronger base than Cl^- ion. That does not mean that hydroxide and fluoride ions have similar base strengths. In fact, the aqueous hydroxide ion is a far stronger base than the fluoride ion. "Stronger" and "weaker" are therefore just comparative terms that we use to compare the basicity (or acidity) of two ions or molecules. We often compare base strengths either to the hydroxide ion, which is a very strong base, or to the *anions of the strong acids*, which are very weak bases (e.g., Cl^-, Br^-, I^-, NO_3^-).

Ammonia acts as a weak Brønsted–Lowry base, and water acts as an acid in the ionization of aqueous ammonia.

▶ Be careful not to confuse *solubility in water* and *extent of ionization*. They are not necessarily related. Ammonia is very *soluble* in water (≈ 15 mol/L at $25°$ C). In a 0.10 M solution, NH_3 is only 1.3% ionized to form NH_4^+ and 98.7% nonionized.

$$NH_3(aq) \quad + \quad H_2O(\ell) \quad \rightleftharpoons \quad NH_4^+(aq) \quad + \quad OH^-(aq)$$

base$_1$ acid$_2$ acid$_1$ base$_2$

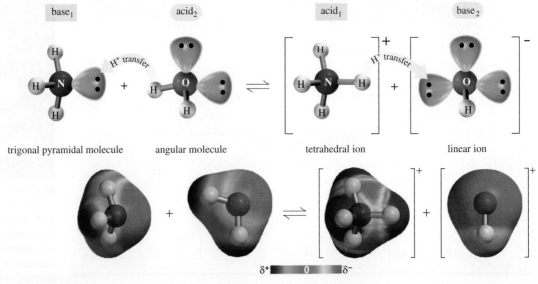

ammonia   water   ammonium ion   hydroxide ion

As we see in the reverse reaction, ammonium ion, NH_4^+, is the conjugate acid of NH_3. The hydroxide ion, OH^-, is the conjugate base of water. The three-dimensional molecular structures are

base$_1$ acid$_2$ acid$_1$ base$_2$

trigonal pyramidal molecule   angular molecule   tetrahedral ion   linear ion

δ^+ ▬▬▬ 0 ▬▬▬ δ^-

Water acts as an acid (H^+ donor) in its reaction with NH_3, whereas it acts as a base (H^+ acceptor) in its reactions with HCl and with HF.

Water can act either as an acid or as a base, depending on the other species present.

▶ The ability of a substance to react as either an acid or a base is known as amphoterism (see Section 10-6).

EXAMPLE 10-1 Identifying Conjugate Acid–Base Pairs

(a) Write the equation for the ionization of HNO_3 in water. (b) Identify the conjugate acid–base pairs in the equation for part (a). (c) What is the conjugate base of H_3PO_4? (d) What is the conjugate acid of SO_4^{2-}?

Plan

When an acid ionizes (loses H^+) the deprotonated product (often anionic) is the conjugate base, while a base that reacts with H^+ forms a protonated product that is the conjugate acid.

(a) HNO_3 is a strong acid and ionizes in water to produce $NO_3^-(aq)$ and $H_3O^+(H^+)$.

(b) HNO_3 is an acid, and its conjugate base is NO_3^-; H_2O is a base, and H_3O^+ is the conjugate acid.

(c) H_3PO_4 is an acid that reacts with water via the following equation:

$$H_3PO_4(aq) + H_2O(\ell) \rightleftharpoons H_2PO_4^-(aq) + H_3O^+(aq)$$

In this reaction the $H_2PO_4^-(aq)$ is the conjugate base to the $H_3PO_4(aq)$ acid.

(d) $SO_4^{2-}(aq)$ can react as a base with H^+ to form the conjugate acid $HSO_4^-(aq)$.

Solution

$$\underset{acid_1}{HNO_3(aq)} + \underset{base_2}{H_2O(\ell)} \longrightarrow \underset{base_1}{NO_3^-(aq)} + \underset{acid_2}{H_3O^+(aq)}$$

(a) $HNO_3(aq) + H_2O(\ell) \longrightarrow NO_3^-(aq) + H_3O^+(aq)$

(b) Conjugate acid/base pairs for the preceding reaction:

HNO_3 (acid) and NO_3^- (conjugate base)

H_2O (base) and H_3O^+ (conjugate acid)

(c) Conjugate base of H_3PO_4: $H_2PO_4^-$

(d) Conjugate acid of SO_4^{2-}: HSO_4^-

STOP & THINK

Study this example carefully. It is very important to be able to write balanced equations for reactions of acids and bases. You *must* be able to identify conjugate acids and conjugate bases.

B—H, C—H, and N—H bonds in neutral molecules are usually too strong to ionize to produce H^+. Most acids have H bonded to an electronegative atom such as O (especially when the O atom is bonded to an electronegative element in a high oxidation state) or to a halogen (F, Cl, Br, I). N—H bonds to cationic nitrogen atoms are also weakly acidic (for example, NH_4^+).

Bases must have at least one lone pair on an atom to be able to form a new bond to H^+. Lone pairs on nitrogen and oxygen are the most common basic sites in molecules (e.g., NH_3 and H_2O). Anions, whether monatomic or polyatomic, typically have lone pairs that are basic; examples are F^-, OH^-, and PO_4^{3-}.

10-5 The Autoionization of Water

Careful measurements show that pure water ionizes ever so slightly to produce equal numbers of hydrated hydrogen ions and hydroxide ions.

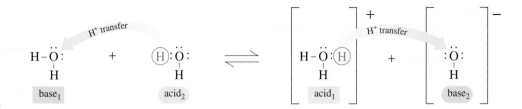

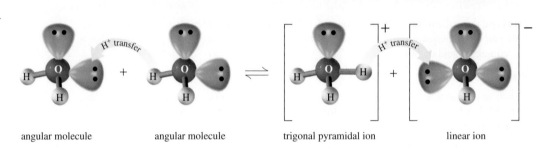

angular molecule   angular molecule   trigonal pyramidal ion   linear ion

▶ Because equal numbers of H⁺ and OH⁻ ions are produced, the solution is neither acidic nor basic. This is referred to in acid–base terms as a *neutral* solution.

We have represented this reaction as $2H_2O(\ell) \rightleftharpoons H_3O^+(aq) + OH^-(aq)$, but we will often show it in the simplified notation

$$H_2O(\ell) \rightleftharpoons H^+(aq) + OH^-(aq)$$

This **autoionization** (self-ionization) of water is an acid–base reaction according to the Brønsted–Lowry theory. One H_2O molecule (the acid) donates a proton to another H_2O molecule (the base). The H_2O molecule that donates a proton becomes an OH^- ion, the conjugate base of water. The H_2O molecule that accepts a proton becomes an H_3O^+ ion. Examination of the reverse reaction (right to left) shows that H_3O^+ (an acid) donates a proton to OH^- (a base) to form two H_2O molecules. One H_2O molecule behaves as an acid and the other acts as a base in the autoionization of water. Water is said to be **amphiprotic**; that is, H_2O molecules can both donate and accept protons.

▶ The prefix "amphi" means *of both kinds*. Amphiprotism refers to the ability to donate or accept a proton in different reactions. In doing so, the compound acts as either an acid or a base. "Amphoterism" is a more general term (see Section 10-6).

As we saw in Section 6-9, Part 1, H^+ (or H_3O^+) ions and OH^- ions combine to form nonionized water molecules when strong acids and strong soluble bases react to form soluble salts and water. The reverse reaction, the autoionization of water, occurs only slightly, as expected.

10-6 Amphoterism

As we have seen, whether a particular substance behaves as an acid or as a base depends on its environment. Earlier we described the amphiprotic nature of water. **Amphoterism** is a more general term that describes the ability of a substance to react either as an acid or as a base. *Amphiprotic behavior* describes the cases in which substances exhibit amphoterism by accepting and by donating a proton, H^+. Several *insoluble* metal hydroxides are amphoteric; that is, they react with acids to form salts and water, but they also dissolve in and react with excess strong bases.

▶ A normal salt (see Section 10-9) contains no ionizable H atoms or OH groups.

Aluminum hydroxide is a typical amphoteric metal hydroxide. Its behavior as a *base* is illustrated by its reaction with nitric acid to form a *normal salt*. The balanced formula unit, total ionic, and net ionic equations for this reaction are, respectively:

formula unit equation: $Al(OH)_3(s) + 3HNO_3(aq) \longrightarrow Al(NO_3)_3(aq) + 3H_2O(\ell)$

total ionic equation: $Al(OH)_3(s) + 3[H^+(aq) + NO_3^-(aq)] \longrightarrow [Al^{3+}(aq) + 3NO_3^-(aq)] + 3H_2O(\ell)$

net ionic equation: $Al(OH)_3(s) + 3H^+(aq) \longrightarrow Al^{3+}(aq) + 3H_2O(\ell)$

Table 10-1 Some Amphoteric Hydroxides

Metal or Metalloid Ions	Insoluble Amphoteric Hydroxide	Complex Ion Formed in an Excess of a Strong Base
Be^{2+}	$Be(OH)_2$	$[Be(OH)_4]^{2-}$
Al^{3+}	$Al(OH)_3$	$[Al(OH)_4]^-$
Cr^{3+}	$Cr(OH)_3$	$[Cr(OH)_4]^-$
Zn^{2+}	$Zn(OH)_2$	$[Zn(OH)_4]^{2-}$
Sn^{2+}	$Sn(OH)_2$	$[Sn(OH)_3]^-$
Sn^{4+}	$Sn(OH)_4$	$[Sn(OH)_6]^{2-}$
Pb^{2+}	$Pb(OH)_2$	$[Pb(OH)_4]^{2-}$
As^{3+}	$As(OH)_3$	$[As(OH)_4]^-$
Sb^{3+}	$Sb(OH)_3$	$[Sb(OH)_4]^-$
Si^{4+}	$Si(OH)_4$	SiO_4^{4-} and SiO_3^{2-}
Co^{2+}	$Co(OH)_2$	$[Co(OH)_4]^{2-}$
Cu^{2+}	$Cu(OH)_2$	$[Cu(OH)_4]^{2-}$

When an excess of a solution of any strong base, such as NaOH, is added to solid aluminum hydroxide, the $Al(OH)_3$ acts as an acid and dissolves. The equation for the reaction is usually written

$$Al(OH)_3(s) + NaOH(aq) \longrightarrow NaAl(OH)_4(aq)$$

$$\text{an acid} \qquad \text{a base} \qquad \substack{\text{sodium aluminate,} \\ \text{a soluble compound}}$$

The total ionic and net ionic equations are

$$Al(OH)_3(s) + [Na^+(aq) + OH^-(aq)] \longrightarrow [Na^+(aq) + Al(OH)_4^-(aq)]$$

$$Al(OH)_3(s) + OH^-(aq) \longrightarrow Al(OH)_4^-(aq)$$

Other amphoteric metal hydroxides undergo similar reactions.

Table 10-1 lists the common amphoteric hydroxides. Three are hydroxides of metalloids, As, Sb, and Si, which are located along the line that divides metals and nonmetals in the periodic table.

▶ All hydroxides containing small, highly charged metal ions are insoluble in water.

▶ Generally, elements of intermediate electronegativity form amphoteric hydroxides. Those of high and low electronegativity form acidic and basic "hydroxides," respectively.

10-7 Strengths of Acids

Binary Acids

The ease of ionization of binary protic acids depends on both (1) the ease of breaking H—X bonds and (2) the stability of the resulting ions in solution. Let us consider the relative strengths of the Group 7A hydrohalic acids. Hydrogen fluoride ionizes only slightly in dilute aqueous solutions.

$$HF(aq) + H_2O(\ell) \rightleftharpoons H_3O^+(aq) + F^-(aq)$$

HCl, HBr, and HI, however, ionize completely or nearly completely in dilute aqueous solutions because the H—X bonds are much weaker.

$$HX(aq) + H_2O(\ell) \longrightarrow H_3O^+(aq) + X^-(aq) \qquad X = Cl, Br, I$$

The order of *bond strengths* for the hydrogen halides is

$$\text{(strongest bonds)} \qquad HF \gg HCl > HBr > HI \qquad \text{(weakest bonds)}$$

S **TOP & THINK**

A *weak* acid may be very reactive. For example, HF dissolves sand and glass. The equation for its reaction with sand is

$$SiO_2(s) + 4HF(g) \longrightarrow$$
$$SiF_4(g) + 2H_2O(\ell)$$

The reaction with glass and other silicates is similar. These reactions are *not* related to acid strength; none of the three *strong* hydrohalic acids (HCl, HBr, or HI) undergoes such a reaction.

To understand why HF is a much weaker acid than the other hydrogen halides, let us consider the following factors.

1. *In HF the electronegativity difference is 1.9*, compared with 0.9 in HCl, 0.7 in HBr, and 0.4 in HI (see Section 7-9). We might expect the very polar H—F bond in HF to ionize easily. The fact that HF is the *weakest* of these acids suggests that this effect must be of minor importance.

2. *The bond strength is considerably greater in HF than in the other three molecules.* This tells us that the H—F bond is harder to break than the H—Cl, H—Br, and H—I bonds.

3. *The small, highly charged F$^-$ ion, formed when HF ionizes, causes increased ordering of the water molecules.* This increase is unfavorable to the process of ionization.

> ▶ Bond strength is shown by the bond energies introduced in Chapter 7 and discussed more fully in Section 15-9. The strength of the H—F bond is due largely to the very small size of the F atom and the strong ionic attraction between the F$^-$ and the H$^+$ ions.

The net result of all factors is that HF is a much weaker acid than the other hydrohalic acids: HCl, HBr, and HI.

In dilute aqueous solutions, hydrochloric, hydrobromic, and hydroiodic acids are completely ionized, and all show the same apparent acid strength. Water is sufficiently basic that it does not distinguish among the acid strengths of HCl, HBr, and HI, and therefore it is referred to as a *leveling solvent* for these acids. It is not possible to determine the order of the strengths of these three acids in water because they are so nearly completely ionized.

When these compounds dissolve in anhydrous acetic acid or other solvents less basic than water, however, they exhibit significant differences in their acid strengths. The observed order of acid strengths is

$$HCl < HBr < HI$$

We observe that

> the hydronium ion is the strongest acid that can exist in aqueous solution. All acids stronger than H_3O^+(aq) react completely with water to produce H_3O^+(aq) and their conjugate bases.

This is called the **leveling effect** of water. For example HClO$_4$ (Table 10-2) reacts completely with H$_2$O to form H$^+$(aq) and ClO$_4^-$(aq).

$$HClO_4(aq) + H_2O(\ell) \longrightarrow H_3O^+(aq) + ClO_4^-(aq)$$

Similar observations have been made for aqueous solutions of strong bases such as NaOH and KOH. Both are completely dissociated in dilute aqueous solutions.

$$NaOH(s) \xrightarrow{H_2O} Na^+(aq) + OH^-(aq)$$

> ▶ The amide ion, NH$_2^-$, is a stronger base than OH$^-$.

> The hydroxide ion is the strongest base that can exist in aqueous solution. Bases stronger than OH$^-$ react completely with H$_2$O to produce OH$^-$ and their conjugate acids.

> **S TOP & THINK**
> The trends in binary acid strengths *across* a period (e.g., CH$_4$ < NH$_3$ < H$_2$O < HF) are not those predicted from trends in bond energies and electronegativity differences. The correlations used for *vertical* trends cannot be used for *horizontal* trends. This is because a "horizontal" series of compounds have different stoichiometries and different numbers of unshared pairs of electrons on the central atoms.

When metal amides such as sodium amide, NaNH$_2$, are placed in H$_2$O, the amide ion, NH$_2^-$, reacts with H$_2$O completely to produce NH$_3$ and OH$^-$.

$$NH_2^-(aq) + H_2O(\ell) \longrightarrow NH_3(aq) + OH^-(aq)$$

Thus, we see that H$_2$O is a leveling solvent for all bases stronger than OH$^-$.

Acid strengths for binary acids of elements in other groups of the periodic table vary in the same way as those of the 7A elements. The order of bond strengths for the 6A hydrides is

(strongest bonds) $\quad H_2O \gg H_2S > H_2Se > H_2Te \quad$ (weakest bonds)

H—O bonds are much stronger than the bonds in the other Group VI hydrides. As we might expect, the order of acid strengths for these hydrides is just the reverse of the order of bond strengths.

(weakest acid) $\quad H_2O \ll H_2S < H_2Se < H_2Te \quad$ (strongest acid)

Table 10-2 Relative Strengths of Conjugate Acid–Base Pairs

Acid		Base
$HClO_4$ HI HBr HCl HNO_3	100% ionized in dilute aq. soln. No molecules of nonionized acid.	ClO_4^- I^- Br^- Cl^- NO_3^-

Negligible base strength in water.

$$\xleftrightarrow{\substack{\text{acid loses } H^+ \\ \text{base gains } H^+}}$$

Acid		Base
H_3O^+ HF CH_3COOH HCN NH_4^+ H_2O NH_3	Equilibrium mixture of nonionized molecules of acid, conjugate base, and $H^+(aq)$.	H_2O F^- CH_3COO^- CN^- NH_3 OH^- NH_2^-

Acid strength increases →

Base strength increases →

NH_2^- reacts completely with H_2O to form OH^-; it cannot exist in aqueous solution.

Table 10-2 displays relative acid and base strengths of a number of conjugate acid–base pairs.

Ternary Acids

Most ternary acids (containing three different elements) are *hydroxyl compounds of non-metals* (oxoacids) that ionize to produce $H^+(aq)$. The formula for nitric acid is commonly written HNO_3 to emphasize the presence of an acidic hydrogen atom. The hydrogen atom is bonded to one of the oxygen atoms so it could also be written as $HONO_2$ (see margin).

In most ternary acids the hydroxyl oxygen is bonded to a fairly electronegative non-metal. In nitric acid the nitrogen draws the electrons of the $N-OH$ bond closer to itself than would a less electronegative element such as sodium. The oxygen pulls the electrons of the $O-H$ bond close enough so that the hydrogen atom easily ionizes as H^+, leaving NO_3^-. The regions of positive charge in HNO_3 are shown in blue in the electrostatic charge potential plot (margin).

$$HNO_3(aq) \longrightarrow H^+(aq) + NO_3^-(aq)$$

Let us consider the hydroxyl compounds of metals. We call these compounds *hydroxides* because they can produce hydroxide ions in water to give basic solutions. Oxygen is much more electronegative than most metals, such as sodium. It draws the electrons of the sodium–oxygen bond in NaOH (a strong base) so close to itself that the bonding is ionic. NaOH therefore exists as Na^+ and OH^- ions, even in the solid state, and dissociates into Na^+ and OH^- ions when it dissolves in H_2O.

$$NaOH(s) \xrightarrow{H_2O} Na^+(aq) + OH^-(aq)$$

Returning to our consideration of ternary acids, we usually write the formula for sulfuric acid as H_2SO_4 to emphasize that it is a polyprotic acid. The formula can also be written as $(HO)_2SO_2$, however, because the structure of sulfuric acid (see margin) shows clearly that H_2SO_4 contains two $O-H$ groups bound to a sulfur atom. Because the $O-H$ bonds are easier to break than the $S-O$ bonds, sulfuric acid ionizes as an acid.

Step 1: $\quad H_2SO_4(aq) \longrightarrow H^+(aq) + HSO_4^-(aq)$

Step 2: $\quad HSO_4^-(aq) \rightleftharpoons H^+(aq) + SO_4^{2-}(aq)$

The first step in the ionization of H_2SO_4 is complete in aqueous solution. The second step is nearly complete in very dilute aqueous solutions. The first step in the ionization of

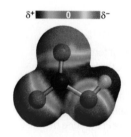

Bond that breaks to form H^+ and NO_3^-

Hydroxyl group

▶ Sulfuric acid is called a **polyprotic acid** because it has more than one ionizable hydrogen atom per molecule. It is the only *common* polyprotic acid that is also a strong acid.

a polyprotic acid always occurs to a greater extent than the second step because it is easier to remove a proton from a neutral acid molecule than from a negatively charged anion.

Sulfurous acid, H_2SO_3, is a polyprotic acid that contains the same elements as H_2SO_4, but with one fewer electronegative, electron-withdrawing oxygen atom. This makes H_2SO_3 a weaker acid, which tells us that the H—O bonds in H_2SO_3 are stronger than those in H_2SO_4.

Similarly, comparison of the acid strengths of nitric acid, HNO_3, and nitrous acid, HNO_2, shows that HNO_3 is a much stronger acid than HNO_2.

Acid strengths of most ternary acids containing the same central element increase with increasing oxidation state of the central element and with increasing numbers of oxygen atoms.

The following orders of increasing acid strength are typical.

$$H_2SO_3 < H_2SO_4$$
$$HNO_2 < HNO_3$$
$$HClO < HClO_2 < HClO_3 < HClO_4$$

(strongest acids are on the right side)

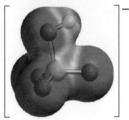

δ⁺ ⬛ 0 ⬛ δ⁻

Electrostatic charge potential plots of H_2SO_4 (top) and HSO_4^- (bottom) showing the decrease in positive charge (blue) on the hydrogen atom in the anionic HSO_4^-. This explains the reduced acidity of HSO_4^- compared to H_2SO_4.

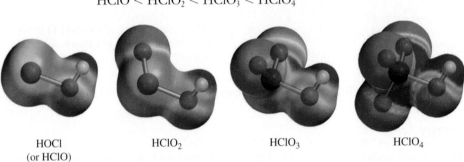

HOCl   HClO₂   HClO₃   HClO₄
(or HClO)

For most ternary acids containing different elements from the same periodic table group, in the same oxidation state, acid strengths increase with increasing electronegativity of the central element.

$$H_2SeO_4 < H_2SO_4 \qquad H_2SeO_3 < H_2SO_3$$
$$H_3PO_4 < HNO_3$$
$$HBrO_4 < HClO_4 \qquad HBrO_3 < HClO_3$$

Contrary to what we might expect, H_3PO_3 is a stronger acid than HNO_2. Care must be exercised to compare acids that have *similar structures*. For example, H_3PO_2, which has two H atoms bonded to the P atom, is a stronger acid than H_3PO_3, which has one H atom bonded to the P atom. H_3PO_3 is a stronger acid than H_3PO_4, which has no H atoms bonded to the P atom.

$$H_3PO_2 \quad > \quad H_3PO_3 \quad > \quad H_3PO_4$$

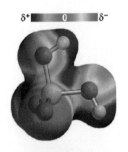

⑤TOP & THINK

In *most* ternary inorganic acids, the H atoms are bonded to the O atoms. But it is very important to be sure of their structures before comparing them. The phosphorus-containing ternary acids are more complicated and can have both P—H and O—H bonding.

10-8 Acid–Base Reactions in Aqueous Solutions

In Section 6-9.1 we introduced classical acid–base reactions. We defined neutralization as the reaction of an acid with a base to form a salt and (in most cases) water. Most *salts* are ionic compounds that contain a cation other than H^+ and an anion other than OH^- or O^{2-}. The common *strong acids* and common *strong bases* are listed in the margin on pages 358-359. All other common acids may be assumed to be weak. The other common metal hydroxides (bases) are insoluble (or only slightly soluble) in water.

Strong Acids	
Binary	*Ternary*
HCl	HClO₄
HBr	HClO₃
HI	HNO₃
	H₂SO₄

Arrhenius and Brønsted–Lowry acid–base neutralization reactions all have one thing in common.

> Neutralization reactions involve the reaction of an acid with a base to form a salt that contains the cation characteristic of the base and the anion characteristic of the acid. Water is also usually formed.

This is indicated in the formula unit equation. The general form of the net ionic equation, however, is different for different acid–base reactions. The net ionic equations depend on the solubility and extent of ionization or dissociation of each reactant and product.

In writing ionic equations, we always write the formulas of the predominant forms of the compounds in, or in contact with, aqueous solution. Writing ionic equations from formula unit equations requires a knowledge of the lists of strong acids and strong bases, as well as of the generalizations on solubilities of inorganic compounds. Please review carefully all of Sections 6-1 and 6-2. Study Tables 6-4 and 6-5 carefully because they summarize much information that you are about to use again.

In Sections 6-1 and 6-9.1, we examined some reactions of strong acids with strong bases to form soluble salts. Let us illustrate one additional example. Perchloric acid, $HClO_4$, reacts with sodium hydroxide to produce sodium perchlorate, $NaClO_4$, a soluble salt.

$$HClO_4(aq) + NaOH(aq) \longrightarrow NaClO_4(aq) + H_2O(\ell)$$

The total ionic equation for this reaction is

$$[H^+(aq) + ClO_4^-(aq)] + [Na^+(aq) + OH^-(aq)] \longrightarrow [Na^+(aq) + ClO_4^-(aq)] + H_2O(\ell)$$

Eliminating the spectator ions, Na^+ and ClO_4^-, gives the net ionic equation

$$H^+(aq) + OH^-(aq) \longrightarrow H_2O(\ell)$$

This is the net ionic equation for the reaction of all strong acids with strong bases to form soluble salts and water.

Many weak acids react with strong bases to form soluble salts and water. For example, acetic acid, CH_3COOH, reacts with sodium hydroxide, NaOH, to produce sodium acetate, $NaCH_3COO$.

$$CH_3COOH(aq) + NaOH(aq) \longrightarrow NaCH_3COO(aq) + H_2O(\ell)$$

The total ionic equation for this reaction is

$$CH_3COOH(aq) + [Na^+(aq) + OH^-(aq)] \longrightarrow [Na^+(aq) + CH_3COO^-(aq)] + H_2O(\ell)$$

Elimination of Na^+ from both sides gives the net ionic equation

$$CH_3COOH(aq) + OH^-(aq) \longrightarrow CH_3COO^-(aq) + H_2O(\ell)$$

In general terms, the reaction of a *weak monoprotic acid* with a *strong base* to form a *soluble salt* may be represented as

$$HA(aq) + OH^-(aq) \longrightarrow A^-(aq) + H_2O(\ell) \qquad \text{(net ionic equation)}$$

The reaction of a strong acid with a strong base to form a soluble salt and the reaction of a weak acid and a strong base to form a soluble salt were displayed earlier. Similar equations can be written for: (1) a strong acid reacting with a strong base to produce an insoluble salt and water, (2) a weak acid reacting with a strong base to produce an insoluble salt and water, (3) a strong acid reacting with a weak base to produce a soluble salt, and (4) a weak acid reacting with a weak base to produce a soluble salt. There are no common examples of a weak base reacting with either a weak or a strong Brønsted–Lowry acid to produce an insoluble salt. Each of the six types of reactions can be represented in general terms by its own unique net ionic equation.

Strong Bases	
LiOH	
NaOH	
KOH	$Ca(OH)_2$
RbOH	$Sr(OH)_2$
CsOH	$Ba(OH)_2$

▶ This is considered to be the same as
$$H_3O^+ + OH^- \longrightarrow 2H_2O$$

▶ The acetate anion has the following structure:

▶ Monoprotic acids contain one, diprotic acids contain two, and triprotic acids contain three acidic (ionizable) hydrogen atoms per formula unit. Polyprotic acids (those that contain more than one ionizable hydrogen atom) are discussed in detail in Chapter 18.

CHEMISTRY IN USE

Everyday Salts of Ternary Acids

You may have encountered some salts of ternary acids without even being aware of them. For example, the iron in many of your breakfast cereals and breads may have been added in the form of iron(II) sulfate, $FeSO_4$, or iron(II) phosphate, $Fe_3(PO_4)_2$; the calcium in these foods often comes from the addition of calcium carbonate, $CaCO_3$. Fruits and vegetables keep fresh longer after an application of sodium sulfite, Na_2SO_3, and sodium hydrogen sulfite, Na_2SO_3. Restaurants also use these two sulfites to keep their salad bars more appetizing. The red color of fresh meat is maintained for much longer by the additives sodium nitrate, $NaNO_3$, and sodium nitrite, $NaNO_2$. Sodium phosphate, Na_3PO_4, is used to prevent metal ion flavors and to control acidity in some canned goods.

Many salts of ternary acids are used in medicine. Lithium carbonate, Li_2CO_3, has been used successfully to combat severe jet lag. Lithium carbonate is also useful in the treatment of mania, depression, alcoholism, and schizophrenia. Magnesium sulfate, $MgSO_4$, sometimes helps to prevent convulsions during pregnancy and to reduce the solubility of toxic barium sulfate in internally administered preparations consumed before gastrointestinal X-ray films are taken.

Other salts of ternary acids that you may find in your home include potassium chlorate, $KClO_3$, in matches as an oxidizing agent and oxygen source; sodium hypochlorite, $NaClO$, in bleaches and mildew removers; and ammonium carbonate, $(NH_4)_2CO_3$, which is the primary ingredient in smelling salts.

The tips of "strike anywhere" matches contain tetraphosphorus trisulfide, red phosphorus, and potassium chlorate. Friction converts kinetic energy into heat, which initiates a spontaneous reaction.

$$P_4S_3(s) + 8O_2 \longrightarrow P_4O_{10}(s) + 3SO_2(g)$$

The thermal decomposition of $KClO_3$ provides additional oxygen for this reaction.

Limestone and marble are calcium carbonate; gypsum and plaster of Paris are primarily calcium sulfate, $CaSO_4$. Fireworks get their brilliant colors from salts such as barium nitrate, $Ba(NO_3)_2$, which imparts a green color; strontium carbonate, $SrCO_3$, which gives a red color; and copper(II) sulfate, $CuSO_4$, which produces a blue color. Should your fireworks get out of hand and accidentally start a fire, the ammonium phosphate, $(NH_4)_3PO_4$, sodium hydrogen carbonate, $NaHCO_3$, and potassium hydrogen carbonate, $KHCO_3$, in your ABC dry fire extinguisher will come in handy.

RONALD DELORENZO

MIDDLE GEORGIA COLLEGE

EXAMPLE 10-2   Equations for Acid–Base Reactions

Write (a) formula unit, (b) total ionic, and (c) net ionic equations for the complete neutralization of phosphoric acid, H_3PO_4, with potassium hydroxide, KOH.

▶ When all the H^+ from the acid *and* all the OH^- of the base have reacted, we say that there has been *complete* neutralization.

Plan

(a) The salt produced in the reaction contains the cation of the base, K^+, and the PO_4^{3-} anion of the acid. The salt is K_3PO_4.

(b) H_3PO_4 is a weak acid—it is not written in ionic form. KOH is a strong base, and so it is written in ionic form. K_3PO_4 is a *soluble salt*, and so it is written in ionic form.

(c) The spectator ions are canceled to give the net ionic equation.

Solution

(a) $H_3PO_4(aq) + 3KOH(aq) \longrightarrow K_3PO_4(aq) + 3H_2O(\ell)$

(b) $H_3PO_4(aq) + 3[K^+(aq) + OH^-(aq)] \longrightarrow [3K^+(aq) + PO_4^{3-}(aq)] + 3H_2O(\ell)$

(c) $H_3PO_4(aq) + 3OH^-(aq) \longrightarrow PO_4^{3-}(aq) + 3H_2O(\ell)$

You should now work Exercise 50.

EXAMPLE 10-3 Equations for Acid–Base Reactions

Write (a) formula unit, (b) total ionic, and (c) net ionic equations for the neutralization of aqueous ammonia with nitric acid.

▶ Neutralization reactions of ammonia, NH_3, form salts but do not form water.

Plan

(a) The salt produced in the reaction contains the cation of the base, NH_4^+, and the anion of the acid, NO_3^-. The salt is NH_4NO_3.

(b) HNO_3 is a strong acid—we write it in ionic form. Ammonia is a weak base. NH_4NO_3 is a soluble salt that is completely dissociated—we write it in ionic form.

(c) We cancel the spectator ions, NO_3^-, and obtain the net ionic equation.

Solution

(a) $HNO_3(aq) + NH_3(aq) \longrightarrow NH_4NO_3(aq)$

(b) $[H^+(aq) + NO_3^-(aq)] + NH_3(aq) \longrightarrow [NH_4^+(aq) + NO_3^-(aq)]$

(c) $H^+(aq) + NH_3(aq) \longrightarrow NH_4^+(aq)$

You should now work Exercise 52.

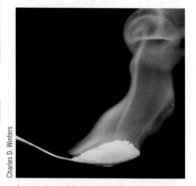

Ammonium chloride (NH_4Cl) is the white salt formed from the reaction of the base ammonia (NH_3) and hydrochloric acid (HCl). Heating NH_4Cl in a spoon produces some gaseous HCl and NH_3 that react again above the spoon to form white NH_4Cl "smoke."

Charles D. Winters

EXAMPLE 10-4 Preparation of Salts

Write the formula unit equation for the reaction of an acid and a base that will produce each of the following salts: (a) Na_3PO_4, (b) $Ca(ClO_3)_2$, (c) $MgSO_4$.

Plan

(a) The salt contains the ions, Na^+ and PO_4^{3-}. Na^+ is the cation in the strong base, NaOH. PO_4^{3-} is the anion in the weak acid, H_3PO_4. The reaction of NaOH with H_3PO_4 should therefore produce the desired salt plus water.

(b) The cation, Ca^{2+}, is from the strong base, $Ca(OH)_2$. The anion, ClO_3^-, is from the strong acid, $HClO_3$. The reaction of $Ca(OH)_2$ with $HClO_3$ will produce water and the desired salt.

(c) $MgSO_4$ is the salt produced in the reaction of $Mg(OH)_2(s)$ and $H_2SO_4(aq)$.

Solution

(a) $H_3PO_4(aq) + 3NaOH(aq) \longrightarrow Na_3PO_4(aq) + 3H_2O(\ell)$

(b) $2HClO_3(aq) + Ca(OH)_2(aq) \longrightarrow Ca(ClO_3)_2(aq) + 2H_2O(\ell)$

(c) $H_2SO_4(aq) + Mg(OH)_2(s) \longrightarrow MgSO_4(aq) + 2H_2O(\ell)$

You should now work Exercise 54.

10-9 Acidic Salts and Basic Salts

To this point we have examined acid–base reactions in which stoichiometric amounts of Arrhenius acids and bases were mixed. Those reactions form *normal salts*. As the name implies, **normal salts** contain no ionizable H atoms or OH groups. The *complete* neutralization of phosphoric acid, H_3PO_4, with sodium hydroxide, NaOH, produces the normal salt, Na_3PO_4. The equation for this complete neutralization is

$$H_3PO_4(aq) + 3NaOH(aq) \longrightarrow Na_3PO_4(aq) + 3H_2O(\ell)$$

1 mole 3 moles sodium phosphate, a normal salt

If less than a stoichiometric amount of a base reacts with a *polyprotic* acid, the resulting salt is classified as an **acidic salt**, because it can neutralize additional base.

Charles D. Winters

Sodium hydrogen carbonate, baking soda, is the most familiar example of an acidic salt. It can neutralize strong bases, but its aqueous solutions are slightly basic, as the blue color of the indicator bromthymol blue shows. $NaHCO_3$ (baking soda) is very handy for neutralizing chemical spills of acids or bases due to its ability to react with and neutralize both strong acids and strong bases. Containers of $NaHCO_3$ are kept in many chemistry labs for this purpose.

S TOP & THINK

Remember that acidic and basic salts do not necessarily form solutions that are acidic or basic, respectively. The acidic and basic names refer to their ability to react with strong acids (basic salts) and bases (acidic salts). They can also often react with both acids and bases (e.g., $NaHCO_3$), but are usually named for their primary acid or base reaction chemistry.

$$H_3PO_4(aq) + NaOH(aq) \longrightarrow \underset{\substack{\text{sodium dihydrogen} \\ \text{phosphate, an acidic salt}}}{NaH_2PO_4(aq)} + H_2O(\ell)$$

1 mole   1 mole

$$H_3PO_4(aq) + 2NaOH(aq) \longrightarrow \underset{\substack{\text{sodium hydrogen phosphate,} \\ \text{an acidic salt}}}{Na_2HPO_4(aq)} + 2H_2O(\ell)$$

1 mole   2 moles

The reaction of phosphoric acid, H_3PO_4, a weak acid, with strong bases can produce the three salts shown in the three preceding equations, depending on the relative amounts of acid and base used. The acidic salts, NaH_2PO_4 and Na_2HPO_4, can react further with strong bases such as NaOH.

$$NaH_2PO_4(aq) + 2NaOH(aq) \longrightarrow Na_3PO_4(aq) + 2H_2O(\ell)$$

$$Na_2HPO_4(aq) + NaOH(aq) \longrightarrow Na_3PO_4(aq) + H_2O(\ell)$$

There are many additional examples of acidic salts. Sodium hydrogen carbonate, $NaHCO_3$, commonly called sodium bicarbonate, is classified as an acidic salt. It is, however, the acidic salt of an extremely weak acid—carbonic acid, H_2CO_3—and solutions of sodium bicarbonate are slightly basic, as are solutions of salts of other extremely weak acids.

Polyhydroxy bases (bases that contain more than one OH per formula unit) react with stoichiometric amounts of acids to form normal salts.

$$Al(OH)_3(s) + 3HCl(aq) \longrightarrow \underset{\substack{\text{aluminum chloride,} \\ \text{a normal salt}}}{AlCl_3(aq)} + 3H_2O(\ell)$$

1 mole   3 moles

The reaction of a *polyhydroxy* base with less than a stoichiometric amount of an acid forms a **basic salt**, that is, a salt that contains unreacted OH groups. For example, the reaction of aluminum hydroxide with hydrochloric acid can produce two different basic salts:

$$Al(OH)_3(s) + HCl(aq) \longrightarrow \underset{\substack{\text{aluminum dihydroxide chloride,} \\ \text{a basic salt}}}{Al(OH)_2Cl(s)} + H_2O(\ell)$$

1 mole   1 mole

$$Al(OH)_3(s) + 2HCl(aq) \longrightarrow \underset{\substack{\text{aluminum hydroxide dichloride,} \\ \text{a basic salt}}}{Al(OH)Cl_2(s)} + 2H_2O(\ell)$$

1 mole   2 moles

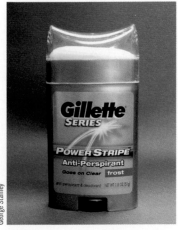

George Stanley

These basic aluminum salts are called "aluminum chlorohydrate." They are components of some antiperspirants.

Aqueous solutions of basic salts are not necessarily basic, but they can neutralize acids, for example,

$$Al(OH)_2Cl + 2HCl \longrightarrow AlCl_3 + 2H_2O$$

Most basic salts are rather insoluble in water.

10-10 The Lewis Theory

In 1923, Professor G. N. Lewis (1875–1946) presented the most comprehensive of the classic acid–base theories. The Lewis definitions follow.

> ► This is the same Lewis who made many contributions to our understanding of chemical bonding.

An **acid** is any species that can accept a share in an electron pair. A **base** is any species that can donate or share one or more lone pairs of electrons.

Lewis acids have low-lying empty valence orbitals that readily interact with lone pair(s) on other atoms (Lewis bases) to move towards a closed shell electronic configuration. These definitions do *not* specify that a lone pair of electrons must be transferred from one atom to another—only that an electron pair, residing originally on one atom (the Lewis base) must be shared with the Lewis acid. *Neutralization* is defined as **coordinate covalent (or dative) bond formation**. This results in a bond in which both electrons are furnished by one atom or ion (the Lewis base).

The reaction of boron trichloride with ammonia is a typical Lewis acid–base reaction. The Lewis theory is sufficiently general that it covers *all* acid–base reactions that the other theories include, plus many additional reactions such as metal complex formation (see Chapter 25).

$$BCl_3(g) \quad + \quad NH_3(g) \quad \longrightarrow \quad Cl_3B : NH_3$$
$$\text{acid} \qquad\qquad \text{base} \qquad\qquad\qquad \text{product}$$

> ► In BCl_3 boron has an empty orbital and only 6 valence electrons. The sharing of the lone pair of electrons from the nitrogen with the boron brings the boron atom up to a filled octet of electrons. Chemists sometimes indicate a coordinate covalent or dative bond with an arrow to emphasize the donation of a lone pair of electrons from the Lewis base to Lewis acid.

The autoionization of water (see Section 10-5) was described in terms of Brønsted–Lowry theory. In Lewis theory terminology, this is also an acid–base reaction. The acceptance of a proton, H^+, by a base involves the formation of a coordinate covalent (dative) bond.

▶ Almost all transition metal complexes (see Chapter 25) form bonds by the donation of available electron pairs from surrounding atoms or molecules to vacant orbitals on the metal atom.

Theoretically, any species that contains a lone pair of electrons could act as a base. In fact, most ions and molecules that contain unshared electron pairs undergo some reactions by sharing their electron pairs with atoms or molecules that have low-energy vacant orbitals. Conversely, many Lewis acids contain only six electrons in the highest occupied energy level of the central element. They react by accepting a share in an additional pair of electrons from a Lewis base. Many compounds of the Group 3A elements are Lewis acids, as illustrated by the reaction of boron trichloride with ammonia, presented earlier.

Anhydrous aluminum chloride, $AlCl_3$, is a common Lewis acid that is used to catalyze many organic reactions. For instance, $AlCl_3$ acts as a Lewis acid when it dissolves in hydrochloric acid to give a solution that contains $AlCl_4^-$ ions.

$$AlCl_3(s) + Cl^-(aq) \longrightarrow AlCl_4^-(aq)$$
$$\text{acid} \qquad \text{base} \qquad \text{product}$$

Other ions and molecules behave as Lewis acids by expansion of the valence shell of the central element, usually through the use of the next higher set of empty d orbitals. Anhydrous tin(IV) chloride is a colorless liquid that also is frequently used as a Lewis acid catalyst. It can accept shares in two additional electron pairs, as its reaction with hydrochloric acid illustrates.

$$SnCl_4(\ell) + 2Cl^-(aq) \longrightarrow SnCl_6^{2-}(aq)$$
$$\text{acid} \qquad \text{base}$$

Many organic and biological reactions are acid–base reactions that do not fit within the Arrhenius or Brønsted–Lowry theories. Experienced chemists find the Lewis theory to be very useful because so many other chemical reactions are covered by it.

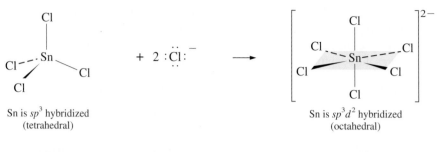

Sn is sp^3 hybridized
(tetrahedral)

Sn is sp^3d^2 hybridized
(octahedral)

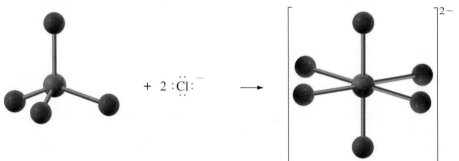

▶ The term *volatile* describes a liquid or solution from which one of its components readily evaporates

Problem-Solving Tip Which Acid–Base Theory Should You Use?

Remember the following:

1. Arrhenius acids and bases are also Brønsted–Lowry acids and bases; the reverse is not true.

2. Brønsted–Lowry acids and bases are also Lewis acids and bases; the reverse is not true.

3. We usually prefer the Arrhenius or the Brønsted–Lowry theory when water or another protic solvent is present.

4. Although the Lewis theory can be used to explain the acidic or basic property of some species in protic solvents, the most important use of the Lewis theory is for acid–base reactions in nonaqueous solvents and with transition metal complexes.

10-11 The Preparation of Acids

Some binary acids may be prepared by combination of the appropriate elements with hydrogen (see Section 5-8).

Small quantities of the hydrogen halides (their solutions are called hydrohalic acids) and other *volatile acids* are usually prepared by adding concentrated nonvolatile acids to the appropriate salts. (Sulfuric and phosphoric acids are classified as *nonvolatile acids* because they have much higher boiling points than other common acids.) The reactions of concentrated sulfuric acid with solid sodium fluoride and sodium chloride produce gaseous hydrogen fluoride and hydrogen chloride, respectively.

The volatile acid HCl can be made by dropping concentrated H_2SO_4 onto solid NaCl. Gaseous HCl is liberated. HCl(g) dissolves in the water on a piece of filter paper. The indicator methyl red on the paper turns red, its color in acidic solution.

$$H_2SO_4(\ell) \; + \; NaF(s) \quad \longrightarrow \quad NaHSO_4(s) \; + \; HF(g)$$

sulfuric acid	sodium fluoride		sodium hydrogen sulfate	hydrogen fluoride
bp = 336°C				bp = 19.6°C

$$H_2SO_4(\ell) \; + \; NaCl(s) \quad \longrightarrow \quad NaHSO_4(s) \; + \; HCl(g)$$

sodium chloride

hydrogen chloride
bp = −84.9°C

Charles D. Winters

Because concentrated sulfuric acid can act as an oxidizing agent, it cannot be used to prepare hydrogen bromide or hydrogen iodide; instead, the free halogens are produced. To produce hydrogen bromide or hydrogen iodide, phosphoric acid, a nonoxidizing acid, is dropped onto solid sodium bromide or sodium iodide, as the following equations show:

$$H_3PO_4(\ell) \quad + \quad NaBr(s) \xrightarrow{\text{heat}} NaH_2PO_4(s) \quad + \quad HBr(g)$$

phosphoric acid   sodium bromide   sodium dihydrogen   hydrogen bromide
bp = 158°C   phosphate   bp = −67.0°C

$$H_3PO_4(\ell) \quad + \quad NaI(s) \xrightarrow{\text{heat}} NaH_2PO_4(s) \quad + \quad HI(g)$$

sodium iodide   hydrogen iodide
                                            bp = −35°C

This kind of reaction may be generalized as

$$\text{nonvolatile acid} \quad + \quad \text{salt of volatile acid} \quad \longrightarrow \quad \text{salt of nonvolatile acid} \quad + \quad \text{volatile acid}$$

Dissolving each of the gaseous hydrogen halides in water gives the corresponding hydrohalic acid.

In Section 5-9, Part 2 we saw that many nonmetal oxides, called acid anhydrides, react with water to form *ternary acids* with no changes in oxidation numbers. For example, dichlorine heptoxide, Cl_2O_7, forms perchloric acid when it dissolves in water.

$$\overset{+7}{Cl_2}O_7(\ell) + H_2O(\ell) \longrightarrow 2[H^+(aq) + \overset{+7}{Cl}O_4^-(aq)]$$

Some *high oxidation state transition metal oxides* are acidic oxides; that is, they dissolve in water to give solutions of ternary acids. Manganese(VII) oxide, Mn_2O_7, and chromium(VI) oxide, CrO_3, are the most common examples.

$$\overset{+7}{Mn_2}O_7(\ell) \quad + H_2O(\ell) \longrightarrow 2[H^+(aq) + \overset{+7}{Mn}O_4^-(aq)]$$

manganese(VII) oxide   permanganic acid

$$2\overset{+6}{Cr}O_3(s) \quad + H_2O(\ell) \longrightarrow [2H^+(aq) + \overset{+6}{Cr_2}O_7^{2-}(aq)]$$

chromium(VI) oxide   dichromic acid

Neither permanganic acid nor dichromic acid has been isolated in pure form. Many stable salts of both are well known.

The halides and oxyhalides of some nonmetals hydrolyze (react with water) to produce two acids: a (binary) hydrohalic acid and a (ternary) oxyacid of the nonmetal. Phosphorus trihalides react with water to produce the corresponding hydrohalic acids and phosphorous acid, a weak diprotic acid, whereas phosphorus pentahalides give phosphoric acid and the corresponding hydrohalic acid. The phosphorus fluorides are an exception to this reactivity trend. The P — F bonds are generally too stable to react with water under mild to moderate conditions.

$$\overset{+3}{P}X_3 + 3H_2O(\ell) \longrightarrow H_3\overset{+3}{P}O_3(aq) + 3HX(aq)$$
$$\overset{+5}{P}X_5 + 4H_2O(\ell) \longrightarrow H_3\overset{+5}{P}O_4(aq) + 5HX(aq)$$

There are no changes in oxidation numbers in these reactions. Examples include the reactions of PCl_3 and PCl_5 with H_2O.

$$\overset{+3}{P}Cl_3(\ell) + 3H_2O(\ell) \longrightarrow H_3\overset{+3}{P}O_3(aq) + 3[H^+(aq) + Cl^-(aq)]$$

phosphorus trichloride   phosphorous acid

$$\overset{+5}{P}Cl_5(s) + 4H_2O(\ell) \longrightarrow H_3\overset{+5}{P}O_4(aq) + 5[H^+(aq) + Cl^-(aq)]$$

phosphorus pentachloride   phosphoric acid

A solution of dichromic acid, $H_2Cr_2O_7$ is deep red.

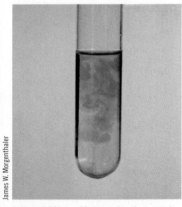

A drop of PCl_3 is added to water that contains the indicator methyl orange. As PCl_3 reacts with water to form HCl and H_3PO_3, the indicator turns red, its color in acidic solution.

James Morgenthaler

James W. Morgenthaler

KEY TERMS

Acid (Arrhenius or Brønsted–Lowry) A substance that produces H^+(aq) ions in aqueous solution. Strong acids ionize completely or almost completely in dilute aqueous solution; weak acids ionize only slightly.

Acid anhydride A nonmetal oxide that reacts with water to form an acid.

Acidic salt A salt that contains an ionizable hydrogen atom; does not necessarily produce acidic solutions.

Amphiprotism The ability of a substance to exhibit amphoterism by accepting or donating protons.

Amphoterism Ability of a substance to act as either an acid or a base.

Anhydrous Without water.

Autoionization An ionization reaction between identical molecules.

Base (Arrhenius) A substance that produces OH^-(aq) ions in aqueous solution. Strong bases are soluble in water and are completely *dissociated*. Weak bases ionize only slightly.

Basic anhydride A metal oxide that reacts with water to form a base.

Basic salt A salt containing a basic OH group.

Brønsted–Lowry acid A proton donor.

Brønsted–Lowry base A proton acceptor.

Brønsted–Lowry theory The description of an acid as a proton donor and a base as a proton acceptor; also known as the *Brønsted theory*.

Conjugate acid–base pair In Brønsted–Lowry terminology, a reactant and product that differ by a proton, H^+.

Coordinate covalent bond A covalent bond in which both shared electrons are furnished by the same species; the bond between a Lewis acid and a Lewis base.

Dative bond See *Coordinate covalent bond*.

Dissociation In aqueous solution, the process in which a *solid ionic compound* separates into its ions.

Electrolyte A substance whose aqueous solutions conduct electricity.

Formula unit equation A chemical equation in which all compounds are represented by complete formulas.

Hydride A binary compound of hydrogen.

Hydronium ion H_3O^+, the usual representation of the hydrated hydrogen ion.

Ionization In aqueous solution, the process in which a *molecular* compound reacts with water to form ions.

Leveling effect The effect by which all acids stronger than the acid that is characteristic of the solvent react with the solvent to produce that acid; a similar statement applies to bases. The strongest acid (base) that can exist in a given solvent is the acid (base) characteristic of that solvent.

Lewis acid Any species that can accept a share in an electron pair to form a coordinate covalent bond.

Lewis base Any species that can make available a share in an electron pair to form a coordinate covalent bond.

Net ionic equation The equation that results from canceling spectator ions and eliminating brackets from a total ionic equation.

Neutralization The reaction of an acid with a base to form a salt and (usually) water; usually, the reaction of hydrogen ions with hydroxide ions to form water molecules.

Nonelectrolyte A substance whose aqueous solutions do not conduct electricity.

Normal salt A salt that contains no ionizable H atoms or OH groups.

Polyprotic acid An acid that contains more than one ionizable hydrogen atom per formula unit.

Protic acid An Arrhenius acid, or a Brønsted–Lowry acid.

Salt A compound that contains a cation other than H^+ and an anion other than OH^- or O^{2-}.

Spectator ions Ions in solution that do not participate in a chemical reaction.

Strong electrolyte A substance that conducts electricity well in dilute aqueous solution.

Ternary acid An acid that contains three elements—usually H, O, and another nonmetal.

Ternary compound A compound that contains three different elements.

Total ionic equation The equation for a chemical reaction written to show the predominant form of all species in aqueous solution or in contact with water.

Weak electrolyte A substance that conducts electricity poorly in dilute aqueous solution.

EXERCISES

 Molecular Reasoning exercises

▲ **More Challenging** exercises

Blue-Numbered exercises are solved in the Student Solutions Manual

---

The Arrhenius Theory

1. Define and illustrate the following terms clearly and concisely. Give an example of each. (a) Strong electrolyte; (b) weak electrolyte; (c) nonelectrolyte; (d) strong acid; (e) strong base; (f) weak acid; (g) weak base; (h) insoluble base. (See Section 6-1.)

2. Outline Arrhenius' ideas about acids and bases. (a) How did he define the following terms: acid, base, neutralization? (b) Give an example that illustrates each term.

3. Classify each of these as an acid or a base. Which are strong and which are weak? What ions are produced when each is dissolved in water? (a) KOH; (b) $Mg(OH)_2$; (c) HClO; (d) HBr; (e) LiOH; (f) H_2SO_3.

 Molecular Reasoning exercises   ▲ **More Challenging** exercises   Blue-Numbered exercises solved in Student Solutions Manual

Unless otherwise noted, all content on this page is © Cengage Learning.

4. Describe an experiment for classifying compounds as strong electrolytes, weak electrolytes, or nonelectrolytes. Tell what would be observed for each of the following compounds and classify each: Na_2SO_4; HCN; CH_3COOH; CH_3OH; HF; $HClO_4$; HCOOH; NH_3. Compare your answer to the experiment described in Figure 6-1.

5. Write formulas and names for (a) the common strong acids; (b) three weak acids; (c) the common strong bases; (d) the most common weak base; (e) four soluble salts; (f) four insoluble salts. (See Section 6-1.)

The Hydrated Hydrogen Ion

6. Write the formula of a hydrated hydrogen ion that contains only one water of hydration. Give another name for the hydrated hydrogen ion.

7. 🔵 Why is the hydrated hydrogen ion important?

8. 🔵 Criticize the following statement: "The hydrated hydrogen ion should always be represented as H_3O^+."

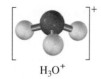

$$H_3O^+$$

Brønsted–Lowry Theory

9. State the basic ideas of the Brønsted–Lowry theory.

10. Use Brønsted–Lowry terminology to define the following terms. Illustrate each with a specific example. (a) acid; (b) conjugate base; (c) base; (d) conjugate acid; (e) conjugate acid–base pair.

11. 🔵 Write balanced equations that describe the ionization of the following acids in dilute aqueous solution. Use a single arrow ($\longrightarrow$) to represent complete, or nearly complete, ionization and a double arrow ($\rightleftharpoons$) to represent a small extent of ionization. (a) HBr; (b) C_2H_5COOH; (c) H_2S; (d) HCN; (e) HF; (f) $HClO_4$.

12. Use words and equations to describe how ammonia can act as a base in (a) aqueous solution and (b) the pure state, that is, as gaseous ammonia molecules, when it reacts with gaseous hydrogen chloride or a similar anhydrous acid.

13. What does autoionization mean? How can the autoionization of water be described as an acid–base reaction? What structural features must a compound have to be able to undergo autoionization?

14. Use equations to illustrate the fact that these species are bases in water: NH_3; HS^-; CH_3COO^-; O^{2-}.

15. In terms of Brønsted–Lowry theory, state the differences between (a) a strong base and a weak base and (b) a strong acid and a weak acid. Write a net ionic equation of an example of each of these two types of reactions.

16. 🔵 Give the products in the following acid–base reactions. Identify the conjugate acid–base pairs. (a) $NH_4^+ + CH_3COO^-$; (b) $S^{2-} + H_2SO_4$; (c) $HClO_4 + [H_2NNH_3]^+$; (d) $NH_2^- + H_2O$.

17. 🔵 Give the conjugate acids of each of the following: H_2O, OH^-, I^-, AsO_4^{3-}, NH_2^-, HPO_4^{2-}, and ClO_2^-.

18. 🔵 Give the conjugate bases of each of the following: H_2O, HS^-, HBr, PH_4^+, and $HOCH_3$.

19. 🔵 Identify the Brønsted–Lowry acids and bases in these reactions and group them into conjugate acid–base pairs.
    (a) $NH_3 + HBr \rightleftharpoons NH_4^+ + Br^-$
    (b) $NH_4^+ + HS^- \rightleftharpoons NH_3 + H_2S$
    (c) $H_3O^+ + PO_4^{3-} \rightleftharpoons HPO_4^{2-} + H_2O$
    (d) $HSO_3^- + CN^- \rightleftharpoons HCN + SO_3^{2-}$
    (e) $O^{2-} + H_2O \rightleftharpoons OH^- + OH^-$

20. 🔵 Identify each species in the following reactions as either an acid or a base, in the Brønsted–Lowry sense.
    (a) $CN^- + H_2O \rightleftharpoons HCN + OH^-$
    (b) $HCO_3^- + H_2SO_4 \rightleftharpoons HSO_4^- + H_2CO_3$
    (c) $CH_3COOH + NO_2^- \rightleftharpoons HNO_2 + CH_3COO^-$
    (d) $NH_2^- + H_2O \rightleftharpoons NH_3 + OH^-$

21. 🔵 Identify each reactant and product in the following chemical reactions as a Brønsted–Lowry acid, a Brønsted–Lowry base, or neither. Arrange the species in each reaction as conjugate acid–base pairs.
    (a) $HNO_2 + H_2O \rightleftharpoons H_3O^+ + NO_2^-$
    (b) $HPO_4^{2-} + H_2O \rightleftharpoons H_3O^+ + PO_4^{3-}$
    (c) $NH_3 + H^- \rightleftharpoons H_2 + NH_2^-$
    (d) $HCl + NH_3 \rightleftharpoons NH_4Cl$
    (e) $NH_4^+ + HSO_3^- \rightleftharpoons NH_3 + H_2SO_3$

22. 🔵 In each of the following acid–base reactions, identify the Brønsted acid and base on the left and their conjugate partners on the right.
    (a) $C_5H_5N(aq) + CH_3CO_2H(aq) \rightleftharpoons$
    $$C_5H_5NH^+(aq) + CH_3CO_2^-(aq)$$
    (b) $N_2H_4(aq) + HSO_4^-(aq) \rightleftharpoons$
    $$N_2H_5^+(aq) + SO_4^{2-}(aq)$$
    (c) $[Al(H_2O)_6]^{3+}(aq) + OH^-(aq) \rightleftharpoons$
    $$[Al(H_2O)_5OH]^{2+}(aq) + H_2O(\ell)$$

23. 🔵 Arrange the species in the reactions of Exercise 20 as Brønsted–Lowry conjugate pairs.

Properties of Aqueous Solutions of Acids and Bases

24. 🔵 Write equations and designate conjugate pairs for the stepwise reactions in water of (a) H_2SO_4 and (b) H_2SO_3.

25. We say that strong acids, weak acids, and weak bases *ionize* in water, but strong bases *dissociate* in water. What is the difference between ionization and dissociation?

26. List five properties of bases in aqueous solution. Does aqueous ammonia exhibit these properties? Why?

27. List six properties of aqueous solutions of protic acids.

Amphoterism

28. Use chemical equations to illustrate the hydroxides of beryllium, zinc, arsenic, and antimony reacting (a) as acids and (b) as bases.

🔵 **Molecular Reasoning** exercises   ▲ **More Challenging** exercises   Blue-Numbered exercises solved in Student Solutions Manual

Unless otherwise noted, all content on this page is © Cengage Learning.

29. 🔵 Draw the Lewis formula of aluminum hydroxide, and explain the features that enable it to possess amphoteric properties.

Strengths of Acids

30. Briefly explain how the following reaction illustrates the leveling effect of water.

$$K_2O(s) + H_2O(\ell) \longrightarrow 2K^+(aq) + 2OH^-(aq)$$

31. 🔵 What property is characteristic of all strong acids and strong bases but not weak acids and weak bases?
32. What does base strength mean? What does acid strength mean?
33. 🔵 Classify each of the following substances as (a) a strong soluble base, (b) an insoluble base, (c) a strong acid, or (d) a weak acid: KOH; HCl; $Ba(OH)_2$; $Cu(OH)_2$; H_2S; H_2CO_3; H_2SO_4; $Zn(OH)_2$.
34. (a) What are binary protic acids? (b) Write names and formulas for four binary protic acids.
35. (a) How can the order of increasing acid strength in a series of similar binary monoprotic acids be explained? (b) Illustrate your answer for the series HF, HCl, HBr, and HI. (c) What is the order of increasing base strength of the conjugate bases of the acids in (b)? Why? (d) Is your explanation applicable to the series H_2O, H_2S, H_2Se, and H_2Te? Why?
36. 🔵 Arrange the members of each group in order of decreasing acidity: (a) H_2O, H_2Se, H_2S; (b) HI, HCl, HF, HBr; (c) H_2S, S^{2-}, HS^-.
37. 🔵 (a) Which is the stronger acid of each pair? (1) NH_4^+, NH_3; (2) H_2O, H_3O^+; (3) HS^-, H_2S; (4) HSO_3^-, H_2SO_3. (b) How are acidity and charge related for each of these pairs?
38. 🔵 Classify each of the compounds NaH, BeH_2, BH_3, CH_4, NH_3, H_2O, and HF as a Brønsted–Lowry base, a Brønsted–Lowry acid, or neither.
39. Illustrate the leveling effect of water by writing equations for the reactions of HCl and HNO_3 with water.

Ternary Acids

40. In what sense can we describe nitric and perchloric acids as hydroxyl compounds of nonmetals?
41. 🔵 What are ternary acids? Write names and formulas for four monoprotic ternary acids.
42. ▲ Among the compounds formed by phosphorus are phosphoric acid (H_3PO_4) and phosphorous acid (H_3PO_3). H_3PO_4 is a triprotic acid, while H_3PO_3 is only diprotic. Draw Lewis formulas of these two compounds that would account for the triprotic nature of H_3PO_4 and the diprotic nature of H_3PO_3, and explain how your structures show this behavior. Suggest an alternative means of writing the formula of phosphorous acid that would better represent its acid–base behavior.
43. 🔵 Explain the order of increasing acid strength for the following groups of acids and the order of increasing base strength for their conjugate bases. (a) H_2SO_3, H_2SO_4; (b) HNO_2, HNO_3; (c) H_3PO_3, H_3PO_4; (d) HClO, $HClO_2$, $HClO_3$, $HClO_4$.
44. 🔵 (a) Write a generalization that describes the order of acid strengths for a series of ternary acids that contain different elements in the same oxidation state from the same group in the periodic table. (b) Indicate the order of acid strengths for the following: (1) HNO_3, H_3PO_4; (2) H_3PO_4, H_3AsO_4; (3) H_2TeO_6, H_2SeO_4; (4) $HClO_3$, $HBrO_3$, HIO_3.
45. 🔵 ▲ List the following acids in order of increasing strength: (a) sulfuric, phosphoric, and perchloric; (b) HIO_3, HIO_2, HIO, and HIO_4; (c) selenous, sulfurous, and tellurous acids; (d) hydrosulfuric, hydroselenic, and hydrotelluric acids; (e) H_2CrO_4, H_2CrO_2, $HCrO_3$, and H_3CrO_3.

Reactions of Acids and Bases

46. Why are acid–base reactions described as neutralization reactions?
47. 🔵 Distinguish among (a) formula unit equations, (b) total ionic equations, and (c) net ionic equations. What are the advantages and limitations of each?
48. 🔵 Classify each substance as either an electrolyte or a nonelectrolyte: NH_4Cl; HI; C_6H_6; RaF_2; $Zn(CH_3COO)_2$; $Cu(NO_3)_2$; CH_3COOH; $C_{12}H_{22}O_{11}$ (table sugar); KOH; $KHCO_3$; $NaClO_4$; $La_2(SO_4)_3$; I_2.
49. 🔵 Classify each substance as either a strong or a weak electrolyte, and then list (a) the strong acids, (b) the strong bases, (c) the weak acids, and (d) the weak bases. NaCl; $MgSO_4$; HCl; CH_3COOH; $Ba(NO_3)_2$; H_3PO_4; $Sr(OH)_2$; HNO_3; HI; $Ba(OH)_2$; LiOH; C_3H_5COOH; NH_3; CH_3NH_2; KOH; HCN; $HClO_4$.

For Exercises 50–52, write balanced (1) formula unit, (2) total ionic, and (3) net ionic equations for reactions between the acid–base pairs. Name all compounds except water. Assume complete neutralization.

50. 🔵 (a) $HNO_2 + LiOH \longrightarrow$
(b) $H_2SO_4 + KOH \longrightarrow$
(c) $HCl + NH_3 \longrightarrow$
(d) $CH_3COOH + NaOH \longrightarrow$
(e) $HI + NaOH \longrightarrow$

51. 🔵 (a) $H_2CO_3 + Ba(OH)_2 \longrightarrow$
(b) $H_2SO_4 + Ba(OH)_2 \longrightarrow$
(c) $H_3PO_4 + Ca(OH)_2 \longrightarrow$
(d) $HBr + NaOH \longrightarrow$
(e) $H_3AsO_4 + NaOH \longrightarrow$

52. 🔵 (a) $HClO_4 + Ba(OH)_2 \longrightarrow$
(b) $HI + Ca(OH)_2 \longrightarrow$
(c) $H_2SO_4 + NH_3 \longrightarrow$
(d) $H_2SO_4 + Fe(OH)_3 \longrightarrow$
(e) $H_2SO_4 + Ba(OH)_2 \longrightarrow$

🔵 **Molecular Reasoning** exercises ▲ **More Challenging** exercises Blue-Numbered exercises solved in Student Solutions Manual

Unless otherwise noted, all content on this page is © Cengage Learning.

53. ♣ Complete these equations by writing the formulas of the omitted compounds.
    (a) $Ba(OH)_2 + ? \longrightarrow Ba(NO_3)_2(aq) + 2H_2O$
    (b) $FeO(s) + ? \longrightarrow FeCl_2(aq) + H_2O$
    (c) $HCl(aq) + ? \longrightarrow AgCl(s) + ?$
    (d) $Na_2O + ? \longrightarrow 2NaOH(aq)$
    (e) $NaOH + ? \longrightarrow Na_2HPO_4(aq) + ?$
    (two possible answers)

54. Although many salts may be formed by a variety of reactions, salts are usually thought of as being derived from the reaction of an acid with a base. For each of the salts listed here, choose the acid and base that would react with each other to form the salt. Write the (i) formula unit, (ii) total ionic, and (iii) net ionic equations for the formation of each salt. (a) $Pb(NO_3)_2$; (b) $SrCl_2$; (c) $(NH_4)_2SO_4$; (d) $Ca(ClO_4)_2$; (e) $Al_2(SO_4)_3$.

55. ♣ (a) Which of the following compounds are salts? $CaCO_3$; Li_2O; $U(NO_3)_5$; $AgNO_3$; $Ca(CH_3COO)_2$. (b) Write an acid–base equation that accounts for the formation of those identified as being salts.

56. ♣ Repeat Exercise 55 for $KMnO_4$, $CaSO_4$, P_4O_{10}, SnF_2, and K_3PO_4.

Acidic and Basic Salts

57. What are polyprotic acids? Write names and formulas for five polyprotic acids.

58. ♣ What are acidic salts? Write balanced equations to show how the following acidic salts can be prepared from the appropriate acid and base: $NaHSO_3$; $NaHCO_3$; KH_2PO_4; Na_2HPO_4; $NaHS$.

59. ♣ Indicate the mole ratio of acid and base required in each case in Exercise 58.

60. The following salts are components of fertilizers. They are made by reacting gaseous NH_3 with concentrated solutions of acids. The heat produced by the reactions evaporates most of the water. Write balanced formula unit equations that show the formation of each. (a) NH_4NO_3; (b) $NH_4H_2PO_4$; (c) $(NH_4)_2HPO_4$; (d) $(NH_4)_3PO_4$; (e) $(NH_4)_2SO_4$.

AGWAY.
GREENLAWN 22-6-8
FERTILIZER

GUARANTEED ANALYSIS
Total Nitrogen (N) 22.00%
  5.5% Water Insoluble Nitrogen
  3.1% Ammoniacal Nitrogen
  13.4% Urea Nitrogen
Available Phosphoric Acid (P_2O_5)... 6.00%
Soluble Potash (K_2O). 8.00%
Iron (Fe) 0.10%
AGWAY Manufactured by
Agway Inc., PO Box 4933, Syracuse, NY 13221

Charles D. Winters

Common lawn fertilizer

61. ♣ What are polyhydroxy bases? Write names and formulas for five polyhydroxy bases.

62. ♣ What are basic salts? (a) Write balanced equations to show how each of the following basic salts can be prepared from the appropriate acid and base: $Ca(OH)Cl$; $Al(OH)_2Cl$; $Al(OH)Cl_2$. (b) Indicate the mole ratio of acid and base required in each case.

63. ♣ What are amphoteric metal hydroxides? (a) Are they bases? (b) Write the names and formulas for four amphoteric metal hydroxides.

64. ♣ Write stepwise equations for protonation or deprotonation of each of these polyprotic acids and bases in water. (a) CO_3^{2-}; (b) H_3AsO_4; (c) $NH_2CH_2COO^-$ (glycinate ion, a diprotic base).

65. ♣ Write the chemical equations for the stepwise ionization of oxalic acid, $(COOH)_2$, a diprotic acid.

66. ♣ Write the chemical equations for the stepwise ionization of citric acid, $C_3H_5O(COOH)_3$, a triprotic acid.

The Lewis Theory

67. Define and illustrate the following terms clearly and concisely. Write an equation to illustrate the meaning of each term. (a) Lewis acid; (b) Lewis base; (c) neutralization according to Lewis theory.

68. ♣ Write a Lewis formula for each species in the following equations. Label the acids and bases using Lewis theory terminology.
    (a) $H_2O + H_2O \rightleftharpoons H_3O^+ + OH^-$
    (b) $HCl(g) + H_2O \longrightarrow H_3O^+ + Cl^-$
    (c) $NH_3(g) + H_2O \rightleftharpoons NH_4^+ + OH^-$
    (d) $NH_3(g) + HBr(g) \longrightarrow NH_4Br(s)$

69. ♣ Explain the differences between the Brønsted–Lowry and the Lewis acid–base theories, using the formation of the ammonium ion from ammonia and water to illustrate your points.

70. Identify the Lewis acid and the Lewis base in each reaction.
    (a) $I_2(s) + I^-(aq) \longrightarrow I_3^-(aq)$
    (b) $SO_2(g) + BF_3(g) \longrightarrow O_2SBF_3(s)$
    (c) $Au^+(aq) + 2CN^-(aq) \longrightarrow [Au(CN)_2]^-(aq)$
    (d) $CO_2(g) + H_2O(\ell) \longrightarrow H_2CO_3(aq)$

71. ♣ Decide whether each of the following substances should be classified as a Lewis acid or a Lewis base.
    (a) BCl_3 (*Hint:* Draw the Lewis dot structure.)
    (b) H_2NNH_2, hydrazine (*Hint:* Draw the Lewis dot structure.)
    (c) the reactants in the reaction
    $Ag^+(aq) + 2NH_3(aq) \rightleftharpoons [Ag(NH_3)_2]^+(aq)$

72. Identify the Lewis acid and base and the donor and acceptor atoms in each of the following reactions.

    (a) $H-\overset{..}{\underset{..}{O}}: + H^+ \rightarrow \left[H-\overset{..}{\underset{..}{O}}-H \right]^+$

♣ **Molecular Reasoning** exercises ▲ **More Challenging** exercises Blue-Numbered exercises solved in Student Solutions Manual

Unless otherwise noted, all content on this page is © Cengage Learning.

(b) $6\left[:\overset{..}{\underset{..}{Cl}}:\right]^{-} + Pt^{4+} \rightarrow \left[\begin{array}{c} :\overset{..}{\underset{..}{Cl}}: \quad :\overset{..}{\underset{..}{Cl}}: \\ :\overset{..}{\underset{..}{Cl}}-Pt-\overset{..}{\underset{..}{Cl}}: \\ :\overset{..}{\underset{..}{Cl}}: \quad :\overset{..}{\underset{..}{Cl}}: \end{array}\right]^{2-}$

73. What is the term for a single covalent bond in which both electrons in the shared pair come from the same atom? Identify the Lewis acid and base and the donor and acceptor atoms in the following reaction.

$$\begin{array}{ccc} H & :\overset{..}{F}: & \\ | & | & \\ H-N: + & B-\overset{..}{F}: \rightarrow \\ | & | & \\ H & :\overset{..}{F}: & \end{array} \begin{array}{cc} H & :\overset{..}{F}: \\ | & | \\ H-N-B-\overset{..}{F}: \\ | & | \\ H & :\overset{..}{F}: \end{array}$$

74. A group of very strong acids are the fluoroacids, H_mXF_n. Two such acids are formed by Lewis acid–base reactions.
(a) Identify the Lewis acid and the Lewis base.

$$HF + SbF_5 \longrightarrow H(SbF_6) \quad \text{(called a "super" acid,}$$
$$\text{hexafluoroantimonic acid)}$$
$$HF + BF_3 \longrightarrow H(BF_4) \quad \text{(tetrafluoroboric acid)}$$

(b) To which atom is the H of the product bonded? How is the H bonded?

Preparation of Acids

75. 🔵 A volatile acid such as nitric acid, HNO_3, can be prepared by adding concentrated H_2SO_4 to a salt of the acid. (a) Write the chemical equation for the reaction of H_2SO_4 with sodium nitrate (called Chile saltpeter). (b) A dilute aqueous solution of H_2SO_4 cannot be used. Why?

76. 🔵 Outline a method of preparing each of the following acids, and write appropriate balanced equations for each preparation: (a) H_2S; (b) HCl; (c) CH_3COOH.

77. 🔵 Repeat Exercise 76 for (a) carbonic acid, (b) chloric acid, (c) permanganic acid, and (d) phosphoric acid (two methods).

Mixed Exercises

78. Give the formula for an example chosen from the representative elements for (a) an acidic oxide, (b) an amphoteric oxide, and (c) a basic oxide.

79. 🔵 Identify each of the following as (i) acidic, (ii) basic, or (iii) amphoteric. Assume all oxides are dissolved in or are in contact with water. Do not be intimidated by the way in which the formula of the compound is written. (a) ORb_2; (b) Cl_2O_5; (c) HCl; (d) $SO_2(OH)_2$; (e) HONO, (f) Al_2O_3; (g) CaO; (h) H_2O; (i) CO_2; (j) OSO.

80. 🔵 Indicate which of the following substances—(a) H_2S; (b) $PO(OH)_3$; (c) H_2CaO_2; (d) $ClO_3(OH)$; (e) $Sb(OH)_3$—can act as (i) an acid, (ii) a base, or (iii) both according to the Arrhenius (classical) theory or the Brønsted–Lowry theory. Do not be confused by the way in which the formulas are written.

81. (a) Write equations for the reactions of HCO_3^- with H_3O^+ and HCO_3^- with OH^-, and indicate the conjugate acid–base pairs in each case. (b) A substance such as HCO_3^- that reacts with both H_3O^+ and OH^- is said to be _____. (Fill in the missing word.)

82. (a) List and name the conjugate bases of H_3PO_4, NH_4^+, and OH^- and the conjugate acids of HSO_4^-, PH_3, and PO_4^{3-}. (b) Given that NO_2^- is a stronger base than NO_3^-, which is the stronger acid—nitric acid, HNO_3, or nitrous acid, HNO_2?

83. 🔵 ▲ A 0.1 M solution of copper(II) chloride, $CuCl_2$, causes the light bulb in the conductivity experiment shown in Figure 6-1 to glow brightly. When hydrogen sulfide, H_2S, a very weak acid, is added to the solution, a black precipitate of copper(II) sulfide, CuS, forms, and the bulb still glows brightly. The experiment is repeated with a 0.1 M solution of copper(II) acetate, $Cu(CH_3COO)_2$, which also causes the bulb to glow brightly. Again, CuS forms, but this time the bulb glows dimly. With the aid of ionic equations, explain the difference in behavior between the $CuCl_2$ and $Cu(CH_3COO)_2$ solutions.

Conductivity experiment

84. 🔵 ▲ Referring again to Figure 6-1, explain the following results of a conductivity experiment (use ionic equations). (a) Individual solutions of NaOH and HCl cause the bulb to glow brightly. When the solutions are mixed, the bulb still glows brightly but not as brightly as before. (b) Individual solutions of NH_3 and CH_3COOH cause the bulb to glow dimly. When the solutions are mixed, the bulb glows brightly.

85. 🔵 ▲ When a 0.1 M aqueous ammonia solution is tested with a conductivity apparatus (see Figure 6-1), the bulb glows dimly. When a 0.1 M hydrochloric acid solution is tested, the bulb glows brightly. Would you expect the bulb to glow more brightly, stop glowing, or stay the same as very pure water is added to each of the solutions? Explain your reasoning.

Conceptual Exercises

86. 🜲 Distinguish between solubility in water and extent of ionization in water. Provide specific examples that illustrate the meanings of both terms.

87. 🜲 Write three general statements that describe the extents to which acids, bases, and salts are ionized in dilute aqueous solutions.

88. The following diagrams are nanoscale representations of different acids in aqueous solution; the water molecules are not shown. The small yellow spheres are hydrogen atoms or ions. The larger spheres represent the anions.

    (a) Which diagram best represents hydrochloric acid?
    (b) Which diagram best represents hydrofluoric acid?

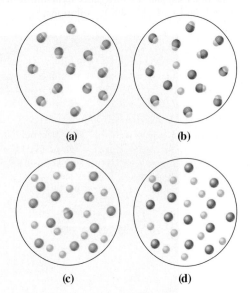

(a)   (b)

(c)   (d)

89. 🜲 One of the chemical products of muscle contraction is lactic acid $(CH_3CH(OH)CO_2H)$, a monoprotic acid whose structure is

Prolonged exercise can temporarily overload the body's capacity for elimination of this substance, and the resulting increase in lactic acid concentration in the muscles causes pain and stiffness. (a) Lactic acid has six H atoms per molecule, yet it acts as a monoprotic acid in an aqueous

environment. Which of the H atoms is ionizable? (b) Draw the structural formula of the conjugate base. (c) Write a net ionic equation that illustrates the ionization of lactic acid in water. (d) Describe the geometry around each of the carbon atoms in lactic acid.

Runners experience lactic acid buildup.

90. ▲ On the planet Baseacidopolous, the major solvent is liquid ammonia, not water. Ammonia autoionizes much like water $(2NH_3 \rightleftharpoons NH_4^+ + NH_2^-)$. If instead of water, ammonia is used as a solvent: (a) What is the formula of the cation that would indicate that a compound is an acid? (b) What is the formula of the anion produced if a compound is a base? (c) Look at the way that NaCl is formed from an acid–base reaction on earth and determine if NaCl can be a salt on Baseacidopolous.

91. Some of the acid formed in tissues is excreted through the kidneys. One of the bases removing the acid is HPO_4^{2-}. Write the equation for the reaction. Could Cl^- serve this function?

92. 🜲 Suppose 1 mole of hydrochloric acid, HCl, is dissolved in 1 liter of water. List the following species in order of decreasing concentration: HCl, H_2O, Cl^-, H_3O^+.

93. 🜲 Suppose 1 mole of acetic acid, CH_3COOH, is dissolved in 1 liter of water. List the following species in order of decreasing concentration: CH_3COOH, H_2O, H^+, CH_3COO^-, H_3O^+.

94. 🜲 (a) Give an example of a substance that is an acid and one that is a base, according to the Arrhenius theory of acids and bases. (b) Give an example of a Brønsted-Lowry acid that is not an Arrhenius acid. (c) Give an example of a Brønsted-Lowry base that is not an Arrhenius base. (d) Can you give an example of an Arrhenius acid or base that is not a Brønsted-Lowry acid or base?

95. 🜲 List the following ions in order of decreasing base strength: HO^-, HS^-, HSe^-, HTe^-.

96. 🜲 Draw a Lewis formula for the base in each of the following Lewis acid–base reactions. What do all of the bases have in common?

$$I_2 + I^- \longrightarrow I_3^-$$
$$Zn^{2+} + 4NH_3 \longrightarrow [Zn(NH_3)_4]^{2+}$$
$$2F^- + SiF_4 \longrightarrow [SiF_6]^{2-}$$
$$BH_3 + CO \longrightarrow H_3BCO$$

🜲 **Molecular Reasoning** exercises   ▲ **More Challenging** exercises   Blue-Numbered exercises solved in Student Solutions Manual

Unless otherwise noted, all content on this page is © Cengage Learning.

97.  Write the formula unit equations, the total ionic equations, and net ionic equations for the reactions of nitric acid, HNO_3, with potassium hydroxide, KOH, and of carbonic acid, H_2CO_3, with potassium hydroxide, KOH. What differences do you observe between the net ionic equation for the reaction of nitric acid, a strong acid, with a strong base and the net ionic equation for the reaction of carbonic acid, a weak acid, with a strong base?

98. Suppose one mole of hydrosulfuric acid, H_2S, reacts with one mole of sodium hydroxide: $H_2S + NaOH \longrightarrow NaHS + H_2O$. Then suppose that one mole of the product of this reaction reacts with one more mole of sodium hydroxide: $NaHS + NaOH \longrightarrow Na_2S + H_2O$. Classify each substance—H_2S, NaOH, NaHS, and Na_2S—as a strong acid, a strong base, a weak acid, a weak base, a normal salt, an acidic salt, or a basic salt.

99. Lead(II) hydroxide, $Pb(OH)_2$, is an insoluble (or "sparingly soluble") base. It cannot produce a strongly basic solution by dissolution in distilled water, but it does react with strong acids. It will also react with an excess of a strong base to produce plumbite, $[Pb(OH)_4]^{2-}$, a complex ion. Explain the solubility of $Pb(OH)_2$ in both strong acids and strong bases by writing the complete, balanced equations for the reactions of $Pb(OH)_2$ with nitric acid, HNO_3(aq), and with potassium hydroxide, KOH(aq).

Building Your Knowledge

100. Autoionization can occur when an ion other than H^+ is transferred, as exemplified by the transfer of a Cl^- ion from one PCl_5 molecule to another. Write the equation for this reaction. What are the shapes of the two ions that are formed?

101. Limestone, $CaCO_3$, is a water-insoluble material, whereas $Ca(HCO_3)_2$ is soluble. Caves are formed when rainwater containing dissolved CO_2 passes over limestone for long periods of time. Write a chemical equation for the acid–base reaction.

© David Muench/Corbis

Cave formation

102. Acids react with metal carbonates and hydrogen carbonates to form carbon dioxide and water. (a) Write the balanced equation for the reaction that occurs when baking soda, $NaHCO_3$, and vinegar, 5% acetic acid, are mixed. What causes the "fizz"? (b) Lactic acid, $CH_3CH(OH)COOH$, is found in sour milk and in buttermilk. Many of its reactions are very similar to those of acetic acid. Write the balanced equation for the reaction of baking soda, $NaHCO_3$, with lactic acid. Explain why bread "rises" during the baking process.

Beyond the Textbook

NOTE: *Whenever the answer to an exercise depends on information obtained from a source other than this textbook, the source must be included as an essential part of the answer.*

103. ▲ Use an internet search engine (such as **http://www .google.com**) to locate information on carbonated beverages known as colas. (a) What acid(s) is (are) present in a cola? (b) What is the molarity of the acids in the best known cola?

104. Go to a suitable site on the web, then search for Lewis acid–base theory and answer the following questions: What was the full name of the person that Lewis acid–base theory is named for? When did he propose the Lewis theory of acids and bases?

105. Go to **www.almaz.com/nobel/chemistry** or another suitable website. How old was Svante Arrhenius when he received the Nobel Prize? Who received the Nobel Prize in Chemistry in 2005? Briefly describe the work for which this prize was awarded (you might need to search elsewhere on the web).

● **Molecular Reasoning** exercises   ▲ **More Challenging** exercises   Blue-Numbered exercises solved in Student Solutions Manual

Unless otherwise noted, all content on this page is © Cengage Learning.

Reactions in Aqueous Solutions II: Calculations

11

Purple potassium permanganate ($KMnO_4$) is added to a solution of Fe^{2+}, oxidizing it to produce light yellow Fe^{3+} and colorless Mn^{2+}.

Charles D. Winters

OBJECTIVES

After you have studied this chapter, you should be able to

▶ Perform molarity calculations

▶ Solve acid–base stoichiometry calculations

▶ Describe titration and standardization

▶ Carry out calculations for acid–base titrations

▶ Balance oxidation–reduction equations

▶ Carry out calculations for redox titrations

Aqueous Acid–Base Reactions

Hydrochloric acid, HCl, is sometimes called "stomach acid" because it is the main acid ($\approx 0.10\ M$) in our digestive juices. When the concentration of HCl is too high in humans, problems result. These problems may range from "heartburn" to ulcers that can eat through the lining of the stomach wall. Snakes have very high concentrations of HCl in their digestive juices so that they can digest whole small animals and birds.

Automobile batteries contain 40% H_2SO_4 by mass. When the battery has "run down," the concentration of H_2SO_4 is significantly lower than 40%. A technician checks an automobile battery by drawing some battery acid into a hydrometer, which indicates the density of the solution. This density is related to the concentration of H_2SO_4, which is more dense than water.

There are many practical applications of acid–base chemistry in which we must know the concentration of a solution of an acid or a base.

11-1 Calculations Involving Molarity

▶ Digestive juice is the acidic fluid secreted by glands in the lining of the stomach.

In Sections 3-6 through 3-8 we introduced methods for expressing concentrations of solutions and discussed some related calculations. Review of those sections will be helpful as we learn more about acid–base reactions in solutions.

The *reaction ratio* (see Section 3-2) is the relative number of moles of reactants and products shown in the balanced equation. In many cases, one mole of an acid reacts with one mole of a base to yield neutralization.

$$HCl + NaOH \longrightarrow NaCl + H_2O$$
$$HNO_3 + KOH \longrightarrow KNO_3 + H_2O$$

These acids have only one acidic hydrogen per formula unit, and these bases have only one hydroxide ion per formula unit, so one formula unit of base reacts with one formula unit of acid. Thus, one mole of each acid reacts with one mole of each base in these cases, so the reaction ratio is

$$\frac{1\ \text{mol acid}}{1\ \text{mol base}} \quad \text{or} \quad \frac{1\ \text{mol base}}{1\ \text{mol acid}}$$

In other cases, however, more than one mole of a base is required to neutralize completely one mole of an acid, or more than one mole of an acid is required to neutralize completely one mole of a base. The balanced equation

$$\underset{1\ \text{mol}}{H_2SO_4} + \underset{2\ \text{mol}}{2NaOH} \longrightarrow \underset{1\ \text{mol}}{Na_2SO_4} + 2H_2O$$

▶ Chemists sometimes use the term *equivalents* instead of moles when referring to reaction ratios. This is because a mole is a specific amount of material, while the term "equivalents" focuses on the relative amounts of materials that react with one another, as shown by the coefficients of the balanced chemical equation.

shows that one mole of H_2SO_4 reacts with two moles of NaOH, so the reaction ratio is written as

$$\frac{1\ \text{mol } H_2SO_4}{2\ \text{mol NaOH}} \quad \text{or} \quad \frac{2\ \text{mol NaOH}}{1\ \text{mol } H_2SO_4}$$

The balanced equation

$$\underset{2\ \text{mol}}{2HCl} + \underset{1\ \text{mol}}{Ca(OH)_2} \longrightarrow \underset{1\ \text{mol}}{CaCl_2} + 2H_2O$$

tells us that two moles of HCl react with one mole of $Ca(OH)_2$, so the reaction ratio is

$$\frac{2 \text{ mol HCl}}{1 \text{ mol Ca(OH)}_2} \quad \text{or} \quad \frac{1 \text{ mol Ca(OH)}_2}{2 \text{ mol HCl}}$$

As with all reaction stoichiometry calculations (see Chapter 3), you must pay close attention to the balanced equation and the resulting reaction ratio in all examples and problems in this chapter. The next several examples illustrate such calculations.

EXAMPLE 11-1 Acid–Base Reactions

If 100. mL of 0.100 M HCl solution and 100. mL of 0.100 M NaOH are mixed, what is the molarity of the salt in the resulting solution? Assume that the volumes are additive.

Plan

We first write the balanced equation for the acid–base reaction and then construct the reaction summary that shows the amounts (moles) of HCl and NaOH. We determine the amount of salt formed from the reaction summary by multiplying the volume times the molarity. Remember that you cannot directly add or subtract molarities, only moles (or mmoles). The final (total) volume is the sum of the volumes mixed. Then we calculate the molarity of the salt.

Solution

The following tabulation, called the *reaction summary*, shows that equal numbers of moles of HCl and NaOH are mixed and, therefore, all of the HCl and NaOH react. The resulting solution contains only NaCl, the salt formed by the reaction, and water (the amount of water produced in this reaction is negligible since the reaction takes place in water).

	HCl	+	NaOH	⟶	NaCl	+ H₂O
Rxn ratio:	1 mol		1 mol		1 mol	1 mol
Start:	$\left[0.100 \text{ L}\left(\frac{0.100 \text{ mol}}{\text{L}}\right)\right]$		$\left[0.100 \text{ L}\left(\frac{0.100 \text{ mol}}{\text{L}}\right)\right]$		0 mol	
	0.0100 mol HCl		0.0100 mol NaOH			
Change:	−0.0100 mol		−0.0100 mol		+ 0.0100 mol	
After rxn:	0 mol		0 mol		0.0100 mol	

The HCl and NaOH neutralize each other exactly, and the resulting solution contains 0.0100 mol of NaCl in 0.200 L of solution. Its molarity is

$$\underset{?}{\frac{\text{mol NaCl}}{\text{L}}} = \frac{0.0100 \text{ mol NaCl}}{0.200 \text{ L}} = 0.0500 \ M \text{ NaCl}$$

We can check the result of this simple example qualitatively by considering that we doubled the total volume of the solution, which represents a dilution of all the species in solution. This reduces the concentration of all the species in solution by a factor of two.

▶ Experiments have shown that volumes of *dilute* aqueous solutions are very nearly additive. No significant error is introduced by making this assumption. 0.100 L of dilute NaOH solution mixed with 0.100 L of dilute HCl solution gives 0.200 L of solution.

Ⓢ TOP & THINK
Remember that the balanced equation shows the relative number of moles of each reactant and product involved in the reaction. Review the definition of molarity and uses of molarity (see Sections 3-6 and 3-8).

Ⓢ TOP & THINK
The most common mistake in working out this type of problem is forgetting to use the combined solution volume when calculating the final concentration.

We often express the volume of a solution in milliliters rather than in liters. Likewise, we may express the amount of solute in millimoles (mmol) rather than in moles. Because one milliliter is 1/1000 of a liter and one **millimole** is 1/1000 of a mole, molarity also may be expressed as the number of millimoles of solute per milliliter of solution:

$$\text{molarity} = \frac{\text{number of millimoles of solute}}{\text{number of milliliters of solution}}$$

1 mol = 1000 mmol
1 L = 1000 mL

$$\text{molarity} = \frac{\text{no. mol}}{\text{L}} = \frac{\text{no. mmol}}{\text{mL}}$$

For volumes and concentrations that are commonly used in laboratory experiments, solving problems in terms of millimoles and milliliters often involves more convenient num-

S TOP & THINK

You cannot mix mmols and mL with moles and L (liters). If you use mmols you must also use volumes in mL.

bers than using moles and liters. We should note also that the reaction ratio that we obtain from any balanced chemical equation is the same whether we express all quantities in moles or in millimoles. We will work many problems in this chapter using millimoles and milliliters. Let us see how we might solve Example 11-1 in these terms.

As in Example 11-1 we first write the balanced equation for the acid–base reaction, and then construct the reaction summary that shows the amounts (millimoles) of NaOH and HCl. We determine the amount of salt formed from the reaction summary. The final (total) volume is the sum of the volumes mixed. Then we can calculate the molarity of the salt.

The tabulation for the solution is

	HCl	+	NaOH	$\longrightarrow$	NaCl + H$_2$O
Rxn ratio:	1 mmol		1 mmol		1 mmol 1 mmol
Start:	$\left[100.\ \text{mL}\left(\dfrac{0.100\ \text{mmol}}{\text{mL}}\right)\right]$		$\left[100.\ \text{mL}\left(\dfrac{0.100\ \text{mmol}}{\text{mL}}\right)\right]$		0 mmol
	= 10.0 mmol HCl		= 10.0 mmol NaOH		
Change:	−10.0 mmol		−10.0 mmol		+ 10.0 mmol
After rxn:	0 mmol		0 mmol		10.0 mmol

$$\underset{?}{\underline{}}\ \frac{\text{mmol NaCl}}{\text{mL}} = \frac{10.0\ \text{mmol NaCl}}{200.\ \text{mL}} = \boxed{0.0500\ M\ \text{NaCl}}$$

EXAMPLE 11-2 Acid–Base Reactions

If 100. mL of 1.00 M HCl and 100. mL of 0.80 M NaOH solutions are mixed, what are the molarities of the solutes in the resulting solution?

Plan

We proceed as we did in Example 11-1. This reaction summary shows that NaOH is the limiting reactant and that we have excess HCl.

Solution

	HCl	+	NaOH	$\longrightarrow$	NaCl	+	H$_2$O
Rxn ratio:	1 mmol		1 mmol		1 mmol		1 mmol
Start:	100. mmol		80. mmol		0 mmol		
Change:	−80. mmol		−80. mmol		+80. mmol		
After rxn:	20. mmol		0 mmol		80. mmol		

Because two solutes are present in the solution after reaction, we must calculate the concentrations of both.

$$\underset{?}{\underline{}}\ \frac{\text{mmol HCl}}{\text{mL}} = \frac{20.\ \text{mmol HCl}}{200.\ \text{mL}} = 0.10\ M\ \text{HCl}$$

$$\underset{?}{\underline{}}\ \frac{\text{mmol NaCl}}{\text{mL}} = \frac{80.\ \text{mmol NaCl}}{200.\ \text{mL}} = 0.40\ M\ \text{HCl}$$

Both HCl and NaCl are strong electrolytes, so the solution is 0.10 M in H$^+$ (aq), (0.10 + 0.40) M = 0.50 M in Cl$^-$, and 0.40 M in Na$^+$ ions.

You should now work Exercise 14.

S TOP & THINK

You should master these initial examples before attempting the following more complex ones.

Problem-Solving Tip Review Limiting Reactant Calculations

To solve many of the problems in this chapter, you will need to apply the limiting reactant concept (see Section 3-3). In Example 11-1, we confirm that the two reactants are initially present in the mole ratio required by the balanced chemical equation; they both react completely, so there is no excess of either one. In Example 11-2, we need to determine which reactant limits the reaction. Before you proceed, be sure you understand how the ideas of Section 3-3 are used in these examples.

EXAMPLE 11-3 Volume of Acid to Neutralize Base

What volume of 0.00300 M HCl solution would just neutralize 30.0 mL of 0.00100 M $Ca(OH)_2$ solution?

Plan

We write the balanced equation for the reaction to determine the reaction ratio. Then we (1) convert milliliters of $Ca(OH)_2$ solution to millimoles of $Ca(OH)_2$ using molarity in the reaction ratio, 0.00100 mmol $Ca(OH)_2$/1.00 mL $Ca(OH)_2$ solution; (2) convert millimoles of $Ca(OH)_2$ to millimoles of HCl using the reaction ratio, 2 mmol HCl/1 mmol $Ca(OH)$ (from the balanced equation); and (3) convert millimoles of HCl to milliliters of HCl solution using the ratio, 1.00 mL HCl/0.00300 mmol HCl, that is, molarity inverted.

> **STOP & THINK**
> Students often mistakenly try to use the relation
> $V_1M_1 = V_2M_2$
> to solve problems about solution stoichiometry. This equation is intended *only* for dilution problems and should never be used for problems involving reactions.

$$
\boxed{\begin{array}{c} \text{mL } Ca(OH)_2 \\ \text{soln} \end{array}} \longrightarrow \boxed{\begin{array}{c} \text{mmol } Ca(OH)_2 \\ \text{present} \end{array}} \longrightarrow \boxed{\begin{array}{c} \text{mmol HCl} \\ \text{needed} \end{array}} \longrightarrow \boxed{\begin{array}{c} \text{mL HCl(aq)} \\ \text{needed} \end{array}}
$$

Solution

The balanced equation for the reaction is

$$2HCl + Ca(OH)_2 \longrightarrow CaCl_2 + 2H_2O$$
$$\text{2 mmol} \quad \text{1 mmol} \qquad \text{1 mmol} \quad \text{2 mmol}$$

$\underline{?}$ mL HCl =

$$30.0 \text{ mL } Ca(OH)_2 \times \frac{0.00100 \text{ mmol } Ca(OH)_2}{1.00 \text{ mL } Ca(OH)_2} \times \frac{2 \text{ mmol HCl}}{1 \text{ mmol } Ca(OH)_2} \times \frac{1.00 \text{ mL HCl}}{0.00300 \text{ mmol HCl}}$$

$$= \boxed{20.0 \text{ mL HCl}}$$

You should now work Exercise 24.

▶ The balanced chemical equation allows us to construct the reaction ratio as either a mole ratio or a millimole ratio.

$$\frac{2 \text{ mol HCl}}{1 \text{ mol } Ca(OH)_2} \quad \text{or}$$

$$\frac{2 \text{ mmol HCl}}{1 \text{ mmol } Ca(OH)_2}$$

We must always write the balanced equation and determine the *reaction ratio*. In Example 11-3, the balanced equation shows that two moles of HCl is required to neutralize one mole of $Ca(OH)_2$. We use the reaction ratio 2 mol HCl/1 mol $Ca(OH)_2$ to convert moles of $Ca(OH)_2$ to moles of HCl.

Problem-Solving Tip There Is More Than One Way to Solve Some Problems

In many problems more than one "plan" can be followed. In Example 11-3 a particular plan was used successfully. Many students can more easily visualize the solution by following a plan such as that in Examples 11-1 and 11-4. We suggest that you use the plan that you find most understandable.

EXAMPLE 11-4 Acid–Base Reactions

If 100. mL of 1.00 M H_2SO_4 solution is mixed with 200. mL of 1.00 M KOH, what salt is produced, and what is its molarity?

Plan

We proceed as we did in Example 11-2. We note that the reaction ratio is 1 mmol of H_2SO_4 to 2 mmol of KOH to 1 mmol of K_2SO_4.

Solution

	H_2SO_4	+	2KOH	$\longrightarrow$	K_2SO_4	$+ 2H_2O$
Rxn ratio:	1 mmol		2 mmol		1 mmol	
Start:	$\left[100.\text{ mL}\left(\dfrac{1.00 \text{ mmol}}{\text{mL}}\right)\right]$		$\left[200.\text{ mL}\left(\dfrac{1.00 \text{ mmol}}{\text{mL}}\right)\right]$			
	= 100. mmol		= 200. mmol		0 mmol	
Change:	−100. mmol		−200. mmol		+100. mmol	
After rxn:	0 mmol		0 mmol		100. mmol	

The reaction produces 100. mmol of potassium sulfate. This is contained in 300. mL of solution, so the concentration is

$$\underset{?}{\frac{\text{mmol } K_2SO_4}{\text{mL}}} = \frac{100.\text{ mmol } K_2SO_4}{300.\text{ mL}} = 0.333 \ M \ K_2SO_4$$

You should now work Exercise 12.

S **TOP & THINK**

Don't forget to add the individual solution volumes to find the volume of the final solution.

▶ Because K_2SO_4 is a soluble salt, this corresponds to 0.666 M K^+ and 0.333 M SO_4^{2-}.

11-2 Titrations

In Examples 3-24 and 11-3, we calculated the volume of one solution that is required to react with a given volume of another solution, with the concentrations of *both* solutions given. In the laboratory we often measure the volume of one solution that is required to react with a given volume of another solution, where only one concentration is known. Then we calculate the concentration of the other solution. This procedure is called *titration* (Figure 11-1).

> **Titration** is the procedure in which a solution of one reactant, the titrant, is carefully added to a solution of another reactant, and the volume of titrant required for complete reaction is measured. The concentration of one solution, usually (but not necessarily) the titrant, is known; this allows one to calculate the concentration or the amount of reactant in the other (unknown) solution, using the known reaction ratio.

How does one know when to stop a titration—that is, when is the chemical reaction just complete? In one method, a few drops of an indicator solution are added to the solution to be titrated. An acid–base **indicator** is a substance that can exist in different forms, with different colors that depend on the concentration of H^+ in the solution. At least one of these forms must be very intensely colored so that even very small amounts of it can be seen.

We can titrate an acid solution of unknown concentration by adding a standardized solution of sodium hydroxide dropwise from a **buret** (see Figure 11-1). A common buret is graduated in large intervals of 1 mL and in smaller intervals of 0.1 mL so that it is possible to estimate the volume of a solution dispensed to within at least ±0.02 mL. (Experienced individuals can often read a buret to ±0.01 mL.) The analyst tries to choose an indicator that changes color clearly at the point at which stoichiometrically equivalent amounts of acid and base have reacted, the **equivalence point**. The point at which the indicator changes color and the titration is stopped is called the **end point**. Ideally, the end point

▶ The choice of indicators will be discussed in Section 19-4.

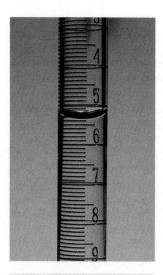

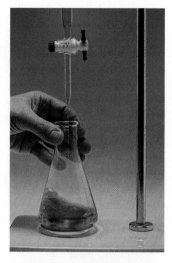

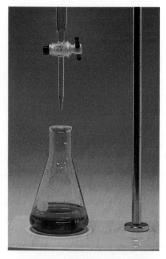

Cengage Learning/Charles D. Winters

Ⓐ A typical setup for titration in a teaching laboratory. The solution to be titrated is placed in an Erlenmeyer flask, and a few drops of indicator are added. The buret is filled with a standard solution (or the solution to be standardized). The volume of solution in the buret is read carefully.

Ⓑ The meniscus describes the surface of the liquid in the buret. Aqueous solutions wet glass, so the meniscus of an aqueous solution is always concave. The position of the *bottom* of the meniscus is read and recorded.

Ⓒ The solution in the buret is added (dropwise near the end point), with stirring, to the Erlenmeyer flask until the end point is reached.

Ⓓ The end point is signaled by the appearance (or change) of color *throughout* the solution being titrated. (A very large excess of indicator was used to make this photograph.) The volume of the liquid is read again—the difference between the final and initial buret readings is the volume of the solution used.

Figure 11-1 The titration procedure.

should coincide with the equivalence point. Phenolphthalein is colorless in acidic solution and reddish violet in basic solution. In a titration in which a base is added to an acid, phenolphthalein is often used as an indicator. The end point is signaled by the first appearance of a faint pink coloration that persists for at least 15 seconds as the solution is swirled.

Solutions with accurately known concentrations are called **standard solutions**. Often we prepare a solution of a substance and then determine its concentration by titration with a standard solution.

Standardization is the process by which one determines the concentration of a solution by measuring accurately the volume of the solution required to react with an accurately known amount of a **primary standard**. The standardized solution is then known as a **secondary standard** and is used in the analysis of unknowns.

The properties of an ideal *primary standard* include the following:

1. It must not react with or absorb the components of the atmosphere, such as water vapor, oxygen, and carbon dioxide.

2. It must react according to one invariable reaction.

3. It must have a high percentage purity.

4. It should have a high formula weight to minimize the effect of error in weighing.

5. It must be soluble in the solvent of interest.

6. It should be nontoxic.

7. It should be readily available (inexpensive).

8. It should be environmentally friendly.

▶ CO_2, H_2O, and O_2 are present in the atmosphere. They react with many substances. In particular, CO_2 gradually reacts with hydroxide bases to neutralize the base. Thus, it is particularly important to use freshly standardized hydroxide solutions in titrations.

The first five of these characteristics are essential to minimize the errors involved in analytical methods. The last three characteristics are just as important as the first five in most analytical laboratories. Because primary standards are often costly and difficult to prepare, secondary standards are often used in day-to-day work.

11-3 Calculations for Acid–Base Titrations

An **acid–base titration** is the quantitative analysis of the amount or concentration of an acid or base in a sample by observing its reaction with a known amount or concentration of a base or acid.

Let us now describe the use of a few primary standards for acids and bases. One primary standard for solutions of acids is sodium carbonate, Na_2CO_3, a solid compound.

$$H_2SO_4 + Na_2CO_3 \longrightarrow Na_2SO_4 + CO_2 + H_2O$$
$$\text{1 mol} \qquad \text{1 mol} \qquad\qquad \text{1 mol} \quad \text{1 mol} \quad \text{1 mol}$$

$$1 \text{ mol } Na_2CO_3 = 106.0 \text{ g} \quad \text{and} \quad 1 \text{ mmol } Na_2CO_3 = 0.1060 \text{ g}$$

► Review the Brønsted–Lowry theory (see Section 10-4).

Sodium carbonate is a salt. Because a base can be broadly defined as a substance that reacts with hydrogen ions, in *this* reaction Na_2CO_3 can be thought of as a base.

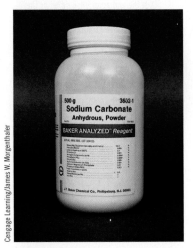

Sodium carbonate is often used as a primary standard for acids.

> **S TOP & THINK**
> We use the definition of the mole, the reaction ratio, and the definition of molarity to write the three unit factors used in this example.

EXAMPLE 11-5 Standardization of an Acid Solution

Calculate the molarity of a solution of H_2SO_4 if 40.0 mL of the solution neutralizes 0.364 g of Na_2CO_3.

Plan

We know from the balanced equation that 1 mol of H_2SO_4 reacts with 1 mol of Na_2CO_3, 106.0 g. This provides the reaction ratio that converts 0.364 g of Na_2CO_3 to the corresponding number of moles of H_2SO_4, from which we can calculate molarity.

$$\boxed{\begin{array}{c}\text{g } Na_2CO_3\\ \text{available}\end{array}} \longrightarrow \boxed{\begin{array}{c}\text{mol } Na_2CO_3\\ \text{present}\end{array}} \longrightarrow \boxed{\begin{array}{c}\text{mol } H_2SO_4\\ \text{used}\end{array}} \longrightarrow \boxed{\begin{array}{c}\text{molarity}\\ \text{of } H_2SO_4\end{array}}$$

Solution

$$\underline{?}\text{ mol } H_2SO_4 = 0.364 \text{ g } Na_2CO_3 \times \frac{1 \text{ mol } Na_2CO_3}{106.0 \text{ g } Na_2CO_3} \times \frac{1 \text{ mol } H_2SO_4}{1 \text{ mol } Na_2CO_3}$$

$$= 0.00343 \text{ mol } H_2SO_4 \qquad (\text{present in } 40.0 \text{ mL of solution})$$

Now we calculate the molarity of the H_2SO_4 solution

$$\frac{\underline{?}\text{ mol } H_2SO_4}{L} = \frac{0.00343 \text{ mol } H_2SO_4}{0.0400 \text{ L}} = 0.0858 \ M \ H_2SO_4$$

You should now work Exercise 26.

► The "ph" in *phthalate* is silent. Phthalate is pronounced "thalate."

Most inorganic bases are metal hydroxides, all of which are solids. Even in the solid state, however, most inorganic bases react rapidly with CO_2 (an acid anhydride) from the atmosphere. Most metal hydroxides also absorb H_2O from the air. These properties make it *very* difficult to weigh out samples of pure metal hydroxides accurately. Chemists obtain solutions of bases of accurately known concentration by standardizing the solutions against an acidic salt, potassium hydrogen phthalate, $KC_6H_4(COO)(COOH)$. This is produced by neutralization of one of the two ionizable hydrogens of an organic acid, phthalic acid.

$C_6H_4(COOH)_2$
phthalic acid

+ KOH $\longrightarrow$ H_2O +

$KC_6H_4(COO)(COOH)$
potassium hydrogen
phthalate (KHP)

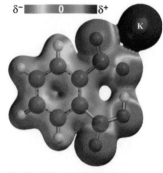

The P in KHP stands for the phthalate ion, $C_6H_4(COO)_2{}^{2-}$, not phosphorus.

This acidic salt, known simply as KHP, has one remaining acidic hydrogen (highlighted) that reacts with bases. KHP is easily obtained in a high state of purity and is soluble in water. It is used as a primary standard for bases.

EXAMPLE 11-6 Standardization of Base Solution

A 20.00-mL sample of a solution of NaOH reacts with 0.3641 g of KHP. Calculate the molarity of the NaOH solution.

Plan

We first write the balanced equation for the reaction between NaOH and KHP. We then calculate the number of moles of NaOH in 20.00 mL of solution from the amount of KHP that reacts with it. Then we can calculate the molarity of the NaOH solution.

$$\boxed{\begin{array}{c}\text{g KHP}\\\text{available}\end{array}} \longrightarrow \boxed{\begin{array}{c}\text{mol KHP}\\\text{available}\end{array}} \longrightarrow \boxed{\begin{array}{c}\text{mol NaOH}\\\text{required}\end{array}} \longrightarrow \boxed{\begin{array}{c}\text{molarity}\\\text{of NaOH}\end{array}}$$

Solution

$$\text{NaOH} + \text{KHP} \longrightarrow \text{NaKP} + \text{H}_2\text{O}$$
$$\quad\; 1 \text{ mol} \quad\; 1 \text{ mol} \qquad\quad 1 \text{ mol} \quad 1 \text{ mol}$$

We see that NaOH and KHP react in a 1:1 reaction ratio. One mole of KHP is 204.2 g.

$$\underline{?}\text{ mol NaOH} = 0.3641 \text{ g KHP} \times \frac{1 \text{ mol KHP}}{204.2 \text{ g KHP}} \times \frac{1 \text{ mol NaOH}}{1 \text{ mol KHP}} = 0.001783 \text{ mol NaOH}$$

Then we calculate the molarity of the NaOH solution.

$$\frac{\underline{?}\text{ mol NaOH}}{\text{L}} = \frac{0.001783 \text{ mol NaOH}}{0.02000 \text{ L}} = 0.08915 \; M \text{ NaOH}$$

You should now work Exercise 28.

Cengage Learning/James W. Morgenthaler

Very pure KHP is readily available.

S TOP & THINK
The use of unit factors helps us set up the solution to this problem.

The concentration of an acid solution can be determined by titration with a standard solution of a base, as illustrated by the following two examples.

EXAMPLE 11-7 Titration

The titration of 36.7 mL of a hydrochloric acid solution requires 43.2 mL of standard 0.236 M sodium hydroxide solution for complete neutralization. What is the molarity of the HCl solution?

$$\text{HCl} + \text{NaOH} \longrightarrow \text{NaCl} + \text{H}_2\text{O}$$

Plan

The balanced equation tells us that the reaction ratio is one millimole of HCl to one millimole of NaOH, which gives the conversion factor, 1 mmol HCl/1 mmol NaOH.

$$HCl + NaOH \longrightarrow NaCl + H_2O$$

1 mmol   1 mmol   1 mmol   1 mmol

First we find the number of millimoles of NaOH. The reaction ratio is one millimole of HCl to one millimole of NaOH, so the HCl solution must contain the same number of millimoles of HCl. Then we can calculate the molarity of the HCl solution because we know its volume.

vol, M of NaOH soln $\longrightarrow$ mmol NaOH $\longrightarrow$ mmol HCl $\longrightarrow$ M HCl soln

Solution

The volume of a solution (in milliliters) multiplied by its molarity gives the number of millimoles of solute.

$$\underline{?}\ \text{mmol NaOH} = 43.2\ \text{mL NaOH soln} \times \frac{0.236\ \text{mmol NaOH}}{1\ \text{mL NaOH soln}} = 10.2\ \text{mmol NaOH}$$

Because the reaction ratio is one millimole of NaOH to one millimole of HCl, the HCl solution must contain 10.2 millimole HCl.

$$\underline{?}\ \text{mmol HCl} = 10.2\ \text{mmol NaOH} \times \frac{1\ \text{mmol HCl}}{1\ \text{mmol NaOH}} = 10.2\ \text{mmol HCl}$$

We know the volume of the HCl solution, so we can calculate its molarity.

$$\frac{\underline{?}\ \text{mmol HCl}}{\text{mL HCl soln}} = \frac{10.2\ \text{mmol HCl}}{36.7\ \text{mL HCl soln}} = \boxed{0.278\ M\ \text{HCl}}$$

STOP & THINK

Remember!

$$\text{molarity} = \frac{\text{mmol of solute}}{\text{mL of solution}}$$

STOP & THINK

Unit factors lead to the appropriate units of the answer (M HCl). The equation shows that equal numbers of moles of HCl and NaOH react, and the volumes of the two solutions are similar. Thus it is reasonable that the answer (0.278 M HCl) is similar to the given molarity of the standard NaOH solution.

A base solution is added from the buret to the acid solution in the beaker. The indicator phenolphthalein changes from colorless, its color in acidic solutions, to pink, its color in basic solutions, when the reaction reaches completion. Note the first appearance of a faint pink coloration in the middle beaker; this signals that the end point is near.

EXAMPLE 11-8 Titration

The titration of 36.7 mL of a sulfuric acid solution requires 43.2 mL of standard 0.236 mL sodium hydroxide solution for complete neutralization. What is the molarity of the H_2SO_4 solution?

$$H_2SO_4 + 2NaOH \longrightarrow Na_2SO_4 + 2H_2O$$

Plan

The balanced equation tells us that the reaction ratio is one millimole of H_2SO_4 to two millimoles of NaOH, which gives the conversion factor, 1 mmol H_2SO_4/2 mmol NaOH.

$$H_2SO_4 + 2NaOH \longrightarrow Na_2SO_4 + 2H_2O$$

1 mmol   2 mmol   1 mmol   2 mmol

First we find the number of millimoles of NaOH. The reaction ratio is one millimole of H_2SO_4 to two millimoles of NaOH, so the number of millimoles of H_2SO_4 must be one half of the number of millimoles of NaOH. Then we can calculate the molarity of the H_2SO_4 solution because we know its volume.

vol, M of NaOH soln $\longrightarrow$ mmol NaOH $\longrightarrow$ mmol H_2SO_4 $\longrightarrow$ M H_2SO_4 soln

Solution

The volume of a solution (in milliliters) multiplied by its molarity gives the number of millimoles of solute.

$$\underline{?} \text{ mmol NaOH} = 43.2 \text{ mL NaOH soln} \times \frac{0.236 \text{ mmol NaOH}}{1 \text{ mL NaOH soln}} = 10.2 \text{ mmol NaOH}$$

Because the reaction ratio is two millimoles of NaOH to one millimole of H_2SO_4, the H_2SO_4 solution must contain 5.10 millimoles of H_2SO_4.

$$\underline{?} \text{ mmol } H_2SO_4 = 10.2 \text{ mmol NaOH} \times \frac{1 \text{ mmol } H_2SO_4}{2 \text{ mmol NaOH}} = 5.10 \text{ mmol } H_2SO_4$$

We know the volume of the H_2SO_4 solution, so we can calculate its molarity.

$$\frac{\underline{?} \text{ mmol } H_2SO_4}{\text{mL } H_2SO_4 \text{ soln}} = \frac{5.10 \text{ mmol } H_2SO_4}{36.7 \text{ mL } H_2SO_4 \text{ soln}} = 0.139 \text{ } M \text{ } H_2SO_4$$

You should now work Exercise 38.

> **STOP & THINK**
>
> Notice the similarity between Examples 11-7 and 11-8 in which the same volumes and molarities are used. In Example 11-7 the reaction ratio is 1 mmol acid/ 1 mmol base, whereas in Example 11-8 the reaction ratio is 1 mmol acid/ 2 mmol base, so the molarity of the HCl solution (0.278 M) is twice the molarity of the H_2SO_4 solution (0.139 M).

Impure samples of acids can be titrated with standard solutions of bases. The results can be used to determine percentage purity of the samples.

EXAMPLE 11-9 Determination of Percent Acid

Oxalic acid, $(COOH)_2$, is used to remove rust stains and some ink stains from fabrics. A 0.1743-g sample of *impure* oxalic acid required 39.82 mL of 0.08915 M NaOH solution for complete neutralization. No acidic impurities were present. Calculate the percentage purity of the $(COOH)_2$.

Plan

We write the balanced equation for the reaction and calculate the number of moles of NaOH in the standard solution. Then we calculate the mass of $(COOH)_2$ in the sample, which gives us the information we need to calculate percentage purity.

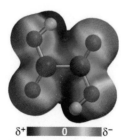

δ^+ ▉▬▬▬ 0 ▬▬▬■ δ^-

Oxalic acid $(COOH)_2$.

Solution

The equation for the complete neutralization of $(COOH)_2$ with NaOH is

$$2NaOH + (COOH)_2 \longrightarrow Na_2(COO)_2 + 2H_2O$$

$$\quad 2 \text{ mol} \qquad 1 \text{ mol} \qquad\qquad 1 \text{ mol} \qquad 2 \text{ mol}$$

▶ Each molecule of $(COOH)_2$ contains two acidic H's.

Two moles of NaOH neutralizes completely one mole of $(COOH)_2$. The number of moles of NaOH that react is the volume times the molarity of the solution.

$$\underline{?} \text{ mol NaOH} = 0.03982 \text{ L} \times \frac{0.08915 \text{ mol NaOH}}{\text{L}} = 0.003550 \text{ mol NaOH}$$

Now we calculate the mass of $(COOH)_2$ that reacts with 0.003550 mol NaOH.

$$\underline{?} \text{ g } (COOH)_2 = 0.003550 \text{ mol NaOH} \times \frac{1 \text{ mol } (COOH)_2}{2 \text{ mol NaOH}} \times \frac{90.04 \text{ g } (COOH)_2}{1 \text{ mol } (COOH)_2}$$

$$= 0.1598 \text{ g } (COOH)_2$$

The 0.1743-g sample contained 0.1598 g of $(COOH)_2$, so its percentage purity was

$$\% \text{ purity} = \frac{0.1598 \text{ g } (COOH)_2}{0.1743 \text{ g sample}} \times 100\% = 91.68\% \text{ pure } (COOH)_2$$

You should now work Exercise 34.

STOP & THINK

Again, we use carefully written unit factors from the stated molarity of $(COOH)_2$, the reaction ratio, the formula weight of $(COOH)_2$, and the definition of percentage to solve this problem. The percentage is reasonable (less than 100%).

Some chemists perform acid–base calculations using equivalent weights. In acid–base reactions, the mass of the acid (expressed in grams) that could furnish 6.022×10^{23} hydrogen ions (1 mol) or that could react with 6.022×10^{23} hydroxide ions (1 mol) is defined as one *equivalent weight* of the acid. Similarly, the mass of the base (expressed in grams) that could furnish 6.022×10^{23} hydroxide ions (1 mol) or that could react with 6.022×10^{23} hydrogen ions (1 mol) is defined as one *equivalent weight* of the base. The results of such calculations are always identical to those of the mole method we have used.

Oxidation–Reduction Reactions

In any balanced redox equation, the total increase in oxidation numbers must equal the total decrease in oxidation numbers. Our procedures for balancing redox equations are constructed to make sure this equivalence results. Many redox equations can be balanced by simple inspection, but you should master the systematic method presented here so that you can use it to balance difficult equations.

All balanced equations must satisfy two criteria.

1. There must be mass balance. That is, the same number of atoms of each kind must appear in reactants and products.

2. There must be charge balance. The sums of actual charges on the left and right sides of the equation must equal each other. In a balanced *formula unit equation*, the total charge on each side will be equal to zero. In a balanced *net ionic equation*, the total charge on each side might not be zero, but it still must be equal on the two sides of the equation.

11-4 Balancing Redox Equations

To balance a redox equation, we separate and completely balance equations describing oxidation and reduction **half-reactions**. Then we equalize the numbers of electrons gained and lost in each. Finally, we add the resulting half-reactions to give the overall balanced equation. The general procedure follows.

1. Write as much of the overall unbalanced equation as possible, omitting spectator ions.
2. Construct unbalanced oxidation and reduction half-reactions (these are usually incomplete as well as unbalanced). Show complete formulas for polyatomic ions and molecules. Tabulating the oxidation states can help you identify the oxidation and reduction half-reactions.
3. Balance by inspection all elements in each half-reaction, except H and O. Then use the chart in Section 11-5 to balance H and O in each half-reaction.
4. Balance the charge in each half-reaction by adding electrons as "products" or "reactants."
5. Balance the electron transfer by multiplying the balanced half-reactions by appropriate integers.
6. Add the resulting half-reactions and eliminate any common terms.
7. Add common species that appear on the same side of the equation, and cancel equal amounts of common species that appear on opposite sides of the equation in equal amounts. The electrons must *always* cancel.
8. Check for mass balance (same number of atoms of each kind as reactants and products); check for charge balance (same total charge on both sides of the equation).

▶ The balancing procedure presented here is called the half-reaction method. Half-reactions are used extensively in electrochemistry (see Chapter 21).

Ⓢ TOP & THINK
If the electrons do not cancel in Step 7, go back and find your error in earlier steps. Students sometimes submit incorrect answers that they could easily avoid if they carefully checked the element balance and charge balance.

EXAMPLE 11-10 Balancing Redox Equations

A useful analytical procedure involves the oxidation of iodide ions to free iodine. The free iodine is then titrated with a standard solution of sodium thiosulfate, $Na_2S_2O_3$. Iodine oxidizes $S_2O_3^{2-}$ ions to tetrathionate ions, $S_4O_6^{2-}$, and is reduced to I^- ions. Write the balanced net ionic equation for this reaction.

Plan

We are given the formulas for two reactants and two products. We use these to write as much of the equations as possible. We construct and balance the appropriate half-reactions using the rules just described. Then we add the half-reactions and eliminate common terms.

Solution

$$I_2 + S_2O_3^{2-} \longrightarrow I^- + S_4O_6^{2-}$$
$$I_2 \longrightarrow I^- \qquad \text{(red. half-reaction)}$$
$$I_2 \longrightarrow 2I^-$$
$$I_2 + 2e^- \longrightarrow 2I^- \qquad \text{(balanced red. half-reaction)}$$
$$\cdots\cdots\cdots\cdots\cdots\cdots\cdots\cdots\cdots\cdots\cdots\cdots\cdots\cdots\cdots\cdots\cdots\cdots\cdots\cdots$$
$$S_2O_3^{2-} \longrightarrow S_4O_6^{2-} \qquad \text{(ox. half-reaction)}$$
$$2S_2O_3^{2-} \longrightarrow S_4O_6^{2-}$$
$$2S_2O_3^{2-} \longrightarrow S_4O_6^{2-} + 2e^- \qquad \text{(balanced ox. half-reaction)}$$

▶ Each I_2 gains $2e^-$. I_2 is reduced; it is the oxidizing agent.

▶ Each $S_2O_3^{2-}$ ion loses an e^-. $S_2O_3^{2-}$ is oxidized; it is the reducing agent.

▶ Oxidizing and reducing agents were defined in Section 6-5.

Each balanced half-reaction involves a transfer of two electrons. Because there are the same numbers of electrons on opposite sides in each half-reaction, we can directly add them together and cancel the electrons on each side.

$$I_2 + 2e^- \longrightarrow 2I^-$$
$$2S_2O_3^{2-} \longrightarrow S_4O_6^{2-} + 2e^-$$
$$\overline{I_2(s) + 2S_2O_3^{2-}(aq) \longrightarrow 2I^-(aq) + S_4O_6^{2-}(aq)}$$

Check for mass balance: All elements appear in equal numbers on both sides.
Check for charge balance: Each side has a total charge of 4−.

11-5 Adding H^+, OH^-, or H_2O to Balance Oxygen or Hydrogen

Frequently we need more oxygen or hydrogen to complete the mass balance for a reaction or half-reaction in aqueous solution. We must be careful, however, not to introduce other changes in oxidation number or to use species that could not actually be present in the solution. We cannot add H_2 or O_2 to equations because these species are not present in aqueous solutions. Acidic solutions do not contain significant concentrations of OH^- ions. Basic solutions do not contain significant concentrations of H^+ ions.

▶ In Section 6-2, we first wrote the *formula unit equation*. We separated any ionized or dissociated species into ions to obtain the *total ionic equation*. Then we eliminated the spectator ions to obtain the *net ionic equation*. In Examples 11-11 and 11-12, we reverse the procedure.

> **S TOP & THINK**
>
> If H^+, H_3O^+, or any other acid appears on either side of the unbalanced equation, the solution is acidic. If OH^- or any other base appears on either side of the unbalanced equation, the solution is basic.

In acidic solution:	We add H^+ or H_2O (*do not add* OH^- in acidic solution).
In basic solution:	We add OH^- or H_2O (*do not add* H^+ in basic solution).

The following chart shows how to balance hydrogen and oxygen.

In *acidic* or *neutral* solution:

To balance O
For *each* O needed, add *one* H_2O

and ↓ then

To balance H
For *each* H needed, add *one* H^+

In *basic* solution:

To balance O
For *each* O needed, add *one* H_2O

and ↓ then

To balance H
For *each* H needed, add *one* H_2O to side needing H *and* add *one* OH^- to *other* side (This adds H without changing O)

When balancing redox equations, we often find it convenient to omit the spectator ions (see Section 6-2) so that we can focus on the oxidation and reduction processes. We use the methods presented in this chapter to balance the net ionic equation. If necessary we then add the spectator ions and combine species to write the balanced formula unit equation. Examples 11-11 and 11-12 illustrate this approach.

EXAMPLE 11-11 Balancing Net Ionic Equations (Acidic Solution)

Permanganate ions oxidize iron(II) to iron(III) in sulfuric acid solution. Permanganate ions are reduced to manganese(II) ions. Write the balanced net ionic equation for this reaction.

Plan

We use the given information to write as much of the equation as possible. Then we follow Steps 2 through 8 in Section 11-4. The reaction occurs in H_2SO_4 solution; we can add H^+ and H_2O as needed to balance H and O in the half-reactions (Step 3).

Solution

$$Fe^{2+} + MnO_4^- \longrightarrow Fe^{3+} + Mn^{2+}$$

$$\overset{+2}{Fe^{2+}} \longrightarrow \overset{+3}{Fe^{3+}} \qquad \text{(ox. half-reaction)}$$

$$Fe^{2+} \longrightarrow Fe^{3+} + \boxed{1e^-} \qquad \text{(balanced ox. half-reaction)}$$

$$\overset{+7}{MnO_4^-} \longrightarrow \overset{+2}{Mn^{2+}} \qquad \text{(red. half-reaction)}$$

$$MnO_4^- + \boxed{8H^+} \longrightarrow Mn^{2+} + \boxed{4H_2O}$$

$$MnO_4^- + 8H^+ + \boxed{5e^-} \longrightarrow Mn^{2+} + 4H_2O \qquad \text{(balanced red. half-reaction)}$$

The oxidation half-reaction involves one electron, and the reduction half-reaction involves five electrons. Now we balance the number of electrons transferred in each half-reaction by multiplying each half-reaction by an integer factor. Then we add the two half-reactions and

Potassium permanganate, $KMnO_4$, is a commonly used oxidizing agent in the laboratory.

cancel out the equal number of electrons on each side. This gives the balanced net ionic equation.

$$5(Fe^{2+} \longrightarrow Fe^{3+} + 1e^-)$$
$$1(MnO_4^- + 8H^+ + 5e^- \longrightarrow Mn^{2+} + 4H_2O)$$
$$\overline{5Fe^{2+}(aq) + MnO_4^-(aq) + 8H^+(aq) \longrightarrow 5Fe^{3+}(aq) + Mn^{2+}(aq) + 4H_2O(\ell)}$$

Check for mass balance: All elements appear in equal numbers on both sides.
Check for charge balance: Each side has a total charge of $17+$.

> **S TOP & THINK**
> In a balanced net ionic equation, the total charge on the left side of the equation must equal the total charge on the right side.

EXAMPLE 11-12 Net Ionic to Total Ionic and Formula Unit Equations

Write the balanced total ionic and the formula unit equations for the reaction in Example 11-11, given that the reactants were $KMnO_4$, $FeSO_4$, and H_2SO_4.

Plan

The cationic spectator ion is K^+, and the anionic spectator ion is SO_4^{2-}. The Fe^{3+} ion will need to occur twice in the product $Fe_2(SO_4)_3$, so there must be an even number of Fe atoms. So the net ionic equation is multiplied by two. It now becomes

$$10Fe^{2+}(aq) + 2MnO_4^-(aq) + 16H^+(aq) \longrightarrow 10Fe^{3+}(aq) + 2Mn^{2+}(aq) + 8H_2O(\ell)$$

Based on the $10Fe^{2+}$ and the $16H^+$, we add $18SO_4^{2-}$ to the reactant side of the equation; we must also add them to the product side to keep the equation balanced. Based on the $2MnO_4^-$, we add $2K^+$ to each side of the equation.

> ▶ The formulas $FeSO_4$ and H_2SO_4 tell us that there is one SO_4^{2-} for every Fe^{2+}, and one SO_4^{2-} for every two H^+.

Solution

Total ionic equation

$$10[Fe^{2+}(aq) + SO_4^{2-}(aq)] + 2[K^+(aq) + MnO_4^-(aq)] + 8[2H^+(aq) + SO_4^{2-}(aq)] \longrightarrow$$
$$5[2Fe^{3+}(aq) + 3SO_4^{2-}(aq)] + 2[Mn^{2+}(aq) + SO_4^{2-}(aq)] + 8H_2O(\ell)$$
$$+ [2K^+(aq) + SO_4^{2-}(aq)]$$

Balanced formula unit equation

$$10FeSO_4(aq) + 2KMnO_4(aq) + 8H_2SO_4(aq) \longrightarrow$$
$$5Fe_2(SO_4)_3(aq) + 2MnSO_4(aq) + K_2SO_4(aq) + 8H_2O(\ell)$$

Check for mass balance: All elements appear in equal numbers on both sides.
Check for charge balance: There is no net charge on either side of a properly balanced
                          total ionic or formula unit equation.

You should now work Exercise 58.

Problem-Solving Tip Converting Ionic to Formula Unit Equations

We learned in Section 6-2 how to convert the formula unit equation to the net ionic equation. To do this, we convert the formulas for all *strong electrolytes* into their ions, and then cancel *spectator ions* from both sides of the equation. When balancing redox equations, we often need to reverse this procedure, as illustrated in Example 11-12. To remove the excess charge that remains in a balanced *net ionic* equation, we must add negatively charged spectator ions to combine with positively charged reactants, and we add positively charged spectator ions to combine with negatively charged reactants. Any spectator ions added to the reactant side of the equation must also be added to the product side. Then we combine species to give complete formula units.

> **S TOP & THINK**
> Spectator ions appear in solution on both sides of the total ionic equation, and undergo no change in the chemical reaction. Review Section 6-2 to be sure you understand how to recognize spectator ions.

CAUTION!

These common household chemicals, ammonia and bleach, should never be mixed because they react to form chloramine (NH_2Cl), a very poisonous volatile compound.

$$NH_3(aq) + ClO^-(aq) \longrightarrow$$
$$NH_2Cl(aq) + OH^-(aq)$$

CAUTION!

These common household chemicals, vinegar and bleach, should never be mixed because they react to form chlorine, a very poisonous gas.

$$2H^+(aq) + ClO^-(aq) + Cl^-(aq) \longrightarrow$$
$$Cl_2(g) + H_2O(\ell)$$

S TOP & THINK

Consider the spectator ions in Exercise 11-13 to be Na^+, and write the total ionic and formula unit equations for the reaction.

Household bleaches sold under trade names such as Clorox and Purex are 5% solutions of sodium hypochlorite. The hypochlorite ion is a very strong oxidizing agent in basic solution. It oxidizes many stains to colorless substances.

EXAMPLE 11-13 Balancing Redox Equations (Basic Solution)

In basic solution, hypochlorite ions, ClO^-, oxidize chromite ions, CrO_2^-, to chromate ions, CrO_4^{2-}, and are reduced to chloride ions. Write the balanced net ionic equation for this reaction.

Plan

We are given the formulas for two reactants and two products; we write as much of the equations as possible. The reaction occurs in basic solution; we can add OH^- and H_2O as needed.

We construct and balance the appropriate half-reactions, equalize the number of electrons in each balanced half-reaction, add the half-reactions, and eliminate common terms. Tracking oxidation states of the key atoms involved in oxidation and reduction can be quite useful as shown below.

Solution

$$CrO_2^- + ClO^- \longrightarrow CrO_4^{2-} + Cl^-$$

$$\overset{+3}{CrO_2^-} \longrightarrow \overset{+6}{CrO_4^{2-}} \qquad \text{(ox. half-rxn)}$$

$$CrO_2^- + 4OH^- \longrightarrow CrO_4^{2-} + 2H_2O$$

$$CrO_2^- + 4OH^- \longrightarrow CrO_4^{2-} + 2H_2O + 3e^- \qquad \text{(balanced ox. half-rxn)}$$

$$\overset{+1}{ClO^-} \longrightarrow \overset{-1}{Cl^-} \qquad \text{(red. half-rxn)}$$

$$ClO^- + H_2O \longrightarrow Cl^- + 2OH^-$$

$$ClO^- + H_2O + 2e^- \longrightarrow Cl^- + 2OH^- \qquad \text{(balanced red. half-rxn)}$$

The oxidation half-reaction involves three electrons, and the reduction half-reaction involves two electrons. We balance the number of electrons transferred in each half-reaction by multiplying each half-reaction by an integer factor. Then we add the two half-reactions together and cancel out the equal number of electrons on each side.

$$2(CrO_2^- + 4OH^- \longrightarrow CrO_4^{2-} + 2H_2O + 3e^-)$$
$$3(ClO^- + H_2O + 2e^- \longrightarrow Cl^- + 2OH^-)$$

$$\overline{2CrO_2^- + 8OH^- + 3ClO^- + 3H_2O \longrightarrow 2CrO_4^{2-} + 4H_2O + 3Cl^- + 6OH^-}$$

We see that $6OH^-$ and $3H_2O$ can be eliminated from both sides to give the balanced net ionic equation.

$$2CrO_2^-(aq) + 2OH^-(aq) + 3ClO^-(aq) \longrightarrow 2CrO_4^{2-}(aq) + H_2O(\ell) + 3Cl^-(aq)$$

Check for mass balance: All elements appear in equal numbers on both sides.
Check for charge balance: Each side has a total charge of $7-$.

You should now work Exercise 54.

11-6 Calculations for Redox Titrations

One method of analyzing samples quantitatively for the presence of *oxidizable* or *reducible* substances is by **redox titration**. In such analyses, the concentration of a solution is determined by allowing it to react with a carefully measured amount of a *standard* solution of an oxidizing or reducing agent. As in other kinds of chemical reactions, we must pay close attention to the mole ratio in which oxidizing agents and reducing agents react. This is even more important for redox titrations where 1:1 reaction ratios, common for acid–base reactions, are rare.

Potassium permanganate, $KMnO_4$, is a strong oxidizing agent. Through the years it has been the "workhorse" of redox titrations. For example, in acidic solution, $KMnO_4$ reacts with iron(II) sulfate, $FeSO_4$, according to the balanced equation in the following example. A strong acid, such as H_2SO_4, is used in such titrations (see Example 11-11).

▶ Because it has an intense purple color, $KMnO_4$ acts as its own indicator. One drop of 0.020 M $KMnO_4$ solution imparts a pink color to a liter of pure water. When $KMnO_4$ solution is added to a solution of a reducing agent, the end point in the titration is taken as the point at which a pale pink color appears in the solution being titrated and persists for at least 30 seconds.

EXAMPLE 11-14 Redox Titration

What volume of 0.0250 M $KMnO_4$ solution is required to oxidize 40.0 mL of 0.100 M $FeSO_4$ in sulfuric acid solution (Figure 11-2)?

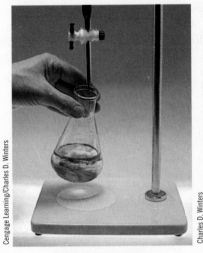
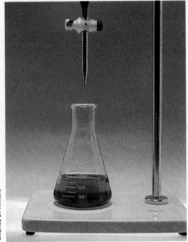

(A) Nearly colorless $FeSO_4$ solution is titrated with deep-purple $KMnO_4$.

(B) The end point is the point at which the solution becomes pink, owing to a *very small* excess of $KMnO_4$. Here a considerable excess of $KMnO_4$ was added so that the pink color could be reproduced photographically.

Figure 11-2

Plan

The balanced equation in Example 11-11 gives the reaction ratio, 1 mol MnO_4^-/5 mol Fe^{2+}. Then we calculate the number of moles of Fe^{2+} to be titrated, which lets us find the number of moles of MnO_4^- required, and then the volume in which this number of moles of $KMnO_4$ is contained.

Solution

The reaction ratio is

$$MnO_4^-(aq) + 8H^+(aq) + 5Fe^{2+}(aq) \longrightarrow 5Fe^{3+}(aq) + Mn^{2+}(aq) + 4H_2O(\ell)$$

rxn ratio: 1 mol   5 mol

The number of moles of Fe^{2+} to be titrated is

$$\underline{?}\ mol\ Fe^{2+} = 40.0\ mL \times \frac{0.100\ mol\ Fe^{2+}}{1000\ mL} = 4.00 \times 10^{-3}\ mol\ Fe^{2+}$$

We use the balanced equation to find the number of moles of MnO_4^- required.

$$\underline{?}\ mol\ MnO_4^- = 4.00 \times 10^{-3}\ mol\ Fe^{2+} \times \frac{1\ mol\ MnO_4^-}{5\ mol\ Fe^{2+}} = 8.00 \times 10^{-4}\ mol\ MnO_4^-$$

Each formula unit of $KMnO_4$ contains one MnO_4^- ion, and so

$$1\ mol\ KMnO_4 = 1\ mol\ MnO_4^-$$

The volume of 0.0250 M $KMnO_4$ solution that contains 8.00×10^{-4} mol of $KMnO_4$ is

$$\underline{?}\ mL\ KMnO_4\ soln = 8.00 \times 10^{-4}\ mol\ KMnO_4 \times \frac{1000\ mL\ KMnO_4\ soln}{0.0250\ mol\ KMnO_4}$$

$$= 32.0\ mL\ KMnO_4\ soln$$

You should now work Exercises 62 and 64.

S TOP & THINK
One mole of $KMnO_4$ contains one mole of MnO_4^- ions. The number of moles of $KMnO_4$ is therefore *always* equal to the number of moles of MnO_4^- ions required in a reaction. Similarly, one mole of $FeSO_4$ contains 1 mole of Fe^{2+} ions.

S TOP & THINK
As before, carefully constructed unit factors, including the reaction ratio, allow us to solve the problem. The concentrations of $FeSO_4$ and $KMnO_4$ solutions are similar, so it is reasonable that the volumes of solutions required are similar.

Dichromate ion, $[Cr_2O_7]^{2-}$

$Cr_2(SO_4)_3$ is green in acidic solution.

$K_2CR_2O_7$ is orange in acidic solution.

A word about terminology. The reaction involves MnO_4^- ions and Fe^{2+} ions in acidic solution. The source of MnO_4^- ions usually is the soluble ionic compound $KMnO_4$. We often refer to "permanganate solutions." Such solutions also contain cations—in this case, K^+. Likewise, we often refer to "iron(II) solutions" without specifying what the anion is.

Potassium dichromate, $K_2Cr_2O_7$, is another frequently used oxidizing agent. However, an indicator must be used when reducing agents are titrated with dichromate solutions. $K_2Cr_2O_7$ is orange, and its reduction product, Cr^{3+}, is green. Neither color is as intense as $KMnO_4$, and the transition from orange to green is not as distinct. This is why an intensely colored indicator must be used with $Cr_2O_7^{2-}$.

Consider the oxidation of sulfite ions, SO_3^{2-}, to sulfate ions, SO_4^{2-}, by $Cr_2O_7^{2-}$ ions in the presence of a strong acid such as sulfuric acid. We shall first balance the equation.

$$\overset{+6}{Cr_2O_7^{2-}} \longrightarrow \overset{+3}{Cr^{3+}} \qquad \text{(red. half-rxn)}$$

$$Cr_2O_7^{2-} \longrightarrow 2Cr^{3+}$$

$$14H^+ + Cr_2O_7^{2-} \longrightarrow 2Cr^{3+} + 7H_2O$$

$$6e^- + 14H^+ + Cr_2O_7^{2-} \longrightarrow 2Cr^{3+} + 7H_2O \qquad \text{(balanced red. half-rxn)}$$

- -

$$\overset{+4}{SO_3^{2-}} \longrightarrow \overset{+6}{SO_4^{2-}} \qquad \text{(ox. half-rxn)}$$

$$SO_3^{2-} + H_2O \longrightarrow SO_4^{2-} + 2H^+$$

$$SO_3^{2-} + H_2O \longrightarrow SO_4^{2-} + 2H^+ + 2e^- \qquad \text{(balanced ox. half-rxn)}$$

We now equalize the electron transfer, add the balanced half-reactions, and eliminate common terms.

$$(6e^- + 14H^+ + Cr_2O_7^{2-} \longrightarrow 2Cr^{3+} + 7H_2O) \qquad \text{(reduction)}$$

$$3(SO_3^{2-} + H_2O \longrightarrow SO_4^{2-} + 2H^+ + 2e^-) \qquad \text{(oxidation)}$$

$$\rule{11cm}{0.4pt}$$

$$8H^+(aq) + Cr_2O_7^{2-}(aq) + 3SO_3^{2-}(aq) \longrightarrow 2Cr^{3+}(aq) + 3SO_4^{2-}(aq) + 4H_2O(\ell)$$

The balanced equation tells us that the reaction ratio is 3 mol SO_3^{2-}/mol $Cr_2O_7^{2-}$ or 1 mol $Cr_2O_7^{2-}$/3 mol SO_3^{2-}. Potassium dichromate is the usual source of $Cr_2O_7^{2-}$ ions, and Na_2SO_3 is the usual source of SO_3^{2-} ions. Thus, the preceding reaction ratio could also be expressed as 1 mol $K_2Cr_2O_7$/3 mol Na_2SO_3.

EXAMPLE 11-15 Redox Titration

A 20.00-mL sample of Na_2SO_3 was titrated with 36.30 mL of 0.05130 M $K_2Cr_2O_7$ solution in the presence of H_2SO_4. Calculate the molarity of the Na_2SO_3 solution.

Plan

We can calculate the number of millimoles of $Cr_2O_7^{2-}$ in the standard solution. Then we refer to the balanced equation in the preceding discussion, which gives us the reaction ratio, 3 mmol SO_3^{2-}/1 mmol $Cr_2O_7^{2-}$. The reaction ratio lets us calculate the number of millimoles of SO_3^{2-} (Na_2SO_3) that reacted and the molarity of the solution.

$$\boxed{\text{mL } Cr_2O_7^{2-} \text{ soln}} \longrightarrow \boxed{\text{mmol } Cr_2O_7^{2-}} \longrightarrow \boxed{\text{mmol } SO_3^{2-}} \longrightarrow \boxed{M \, SO_3^{2-}\text{soln}}$$

Solution

From the preceding discussion we know the balanced equation and the reaction ratio.

$$\underset{\text{3 mmol}}{3SO_3^{2-}} + \underset{\text{1 mmol}}{Cr_2O_7^{2-}} + 8H^+ \longrightarrow 3SO_4^{2+} + 2Cr^{3+} + 4H_2O$$

The number of millimoles of $Cr_2O_7^{2-}$ used is

$$\underline{?} \text{ mmol } Cr_2O_7^{2-} = 36.30 \text{ mL} \times \frac{0.05130 \text{ mmol } Cr_2O_7^{2-}}{\text{mL}} = 1.862 \text{ mmol } Cr_2O_7^{2-}$$

The number of millimoles of SO_3^{2-} that reacts with 1.862 mmol of $Cr_2O_7^{2-}$ is

$$\underset{?}{} \text{ mmol } SO_3^{2-} = 1.862 \text{ mmol } Cr_2O_7^{2-} \times \frac{3 \text{ mmol } SO_3^{2-}}{1 \text{ mmol } Cr_2O_7^{2-}} = 5.586 \text{ mmol } SO_3^{2-}$$

The Na_2SO_3 solution contains 5.586 mmol of SO_3^{2-} (or 5.586 mmol of Na_2SO_3). Its molarity is

$$\underset{?}{} \frac{\text{mmol } Na_2SO_3}{\text{mL}} = \frac{5.586 \text{ mmol } Na_2SO_3}{20.00 \text{ mL}} = 0.2793 \ M \ Na_2SO_3$$

You should now work Exercise 66.

S TOP & THINK
The volumes of the Na_2SO_3 and $K_2Cr_2O_7$ solutions are similar, so it is reasonable that their concentrations are similar. Once again, it is convenient to express molarity as mmol solute/mL solution.

KEY TERMS

Acid–base titration The quantitative analysis of the amount or concentration of an acid or base in a sample by observing its reaction with a known amount or concentration of a base or acid.

Buret A piece of volumetric glassware, usually graduated in 0.1-mL intervals, that is used in titrations to deliver solutions in a quantitative (dropwise) manner.

End point The point at which an indicator changes color and a titration is stopped.

Equivalence point The point at which chemically equivalent amounts of reactants have reacted.

Half-reaction Either the oxidation part or the reduction part of a redox reaction.

Indicator For acid–base titrations, an organic compound that exhibits its different colors in solutions of different acidities; a properly selected indicator is used to determine the point at which the reaction between two solutes is complete.

Millimole 1/1000 mole.

Molarity (M) The number of moles of solute per liter of solution or the number of millimoles of solute per milliliter of solution.

Oxidation An algebraic increase in oxidation number; usually corresponds to a loss of electrons.

Oxidation–reduction reaction A reaction in which oxidation and reduction occur; also known as a *redox reaction*.

Oxidizing agent The substance that oxidizes another substance and is reduced.

Primary standard A substance of a known high degree of purity that undergoes one invariable reaction with the other reactant of interest.

Redox reaction An oxidation-reduction reaction.

Redox titration The quantitative analysis of the amount or concentration of an oxidizing or reducing agent in a sample by observing its reaction with a known amount or concentration of a reducing or oxidizing agent.

Reducing agent The substance that reduces another substance and is oxidized.

Reduction An algebraic decrease in oxidation number; usually corresponds to a gain of electrons.

Secondary standard A solution that has been titrated against a primary standard. A standard solution is a secondary standard.

Standard solution A solution for which the concentration is accurately known.

Standardization The process by which the concentration of a solution is accurately determined by titrating it against an accurately known amount of a primary standard.

Titration A procedure in which a solution of one reactant, the titrant, is carefully added to a solution of another reactant, and the volume of titrant required for complete reaction is measured. The concentration of one solution, usually (but not necessarily) the titrant, is known; this allows one to calculate the concentration or the amount of reactant in the other.

EXERCISES

🔵 **Molecular Reasoning** exercises

▲ **More Challenging** exercises

Blue-Numbered exercises are solved in the Student Solutions Manual

Molarity

1. Why can we describe molarity as a "method of convenience" for expressing concentrations of solutions?

2. Why is the molarity of a solution the same number whether we describe it in mol/L or in mmol/mL?

3. Calculate the molarities of solutions that contain the following masses of solute in the indicated volumes: (a) 35.5 g of H_3AsO_4 in 500. mL of solution; (b) 8.33 g of $(COOH)_2$ in 600. mL of solution; (c) 8.25 g of $(COOH)_2 \cdot 2H_2O$ in 750. mL of solution.

🔵 **Molecular Reasoning** exercises   ▲ **More Challenging** exercises   Blue-Numbered exercises solved in Student Solutions Manual

Unless otherwise noted, all content on this page is © Cengage Learning.

4. What is the molarity of a solution made by dissolving 41.4 g of magnesium sulfate in sufficient water to produce a total of 3.00 L of solution?

5. There are 85.0 g of iron(II) nitrate present in 850. mL of a solution. Calculate the molarity of that solution.

6. Calculate the molarity of a solution that is 39.77% H_2SO_4 by mass. The specific gravity of the solution is 1.305.

7. Calculate the molarity of a solution that is 19.0% HNO_3 by mass. The specific gravity of the solution is 1.11.

8. If 225 mL of 3.35 M HCl solution is added to 426 mL of 1.77 M NaOH solution, the resulting solution will be _____ molar in NaCl. Assume that the volumes are additive.

9. What is the molarity of the salt solution produced when 750. mL of 3.00 M HCl and 750. mL of 3.00 M LiOH are mixed? Assume that the volumes are additive. Give the name and formula of the salt formed.

10. Potassium iodide is sometimes used as a sodium chloride replacement for those people who cannot tolerate table salt. Calculate the molarity of potassium iodide solution produced when 55.5 mL of 8.99 M HI and 35.4 mL of 14.1 M KOH are mixed. Assume that the volumes are additive.

11. If you dilute 25.0 mL of 1.50 M hydrochloric acid to 500. mL, what is the molar concentration of the dilute acid?

12. What is the concentration of barium iodide produced by mixing 7.50 mL of 0.135 M $Ba(OH)_2$ with 19.4 mL of 0.104 M HI?

13. What is the concentration of the ammonium chloride produced when 21.0 mL of 12.0 M HCl and 17.5 mL of 8.00 M NH_3 are mixed? Assume that the volumes are additive.

14. If 250. mL of 5.52 M H_3PO_4 solution is added to 775 mL of 5.52 M NaOH solution, the resulting solution will be _____ molar in Na_3PO_4 and _____ molar in _____.

15. If 100. mL of 0.200 M HCl solution is added to 200. mL of 0.0400 M $Ba(OH)_2$ solution, the resulting solution will be _____ molar in $BaCl_2$ and _____ molar in _____.

16. A vinegar solution is 5.11% acetic acid. Its density is 1.007 g/mL. What is its molarity?

17. A household ammonia solution is 5.03% ammonia. Its density is 0.979 g/mL. What is its molarity?

18. ▲ (a) What volumes of 3.25 M NaOH and 4.50 M H_3PO_4 solutions would be required to form 1.00 mol of Na_3PO_4? (b) What volumes of the solutions would be required to form 1.00 mol of Na_2HPO_4?

Standardization and Acid–Base Titrations

19. Define and illustrate the following terms clearly and concisely: (a) standard solution; (b) titration; (c) primary standard; (d) secondary standard.

20. Describe the preparation of a standard solution of NaOH, a compound that absorbs both CO_2 and H_2O from the air.

21. Distinguish between the *net ionic equation* and the *formula unit equation*.

22. (a) What is potassium hydrogen phthalate, KHP? (b) What is its major use?

23. Why can sodium carbonate be used as a primary standard for solutions of acids?

24. What volume of 0.145 M acetic acid solution would completely neutralize 21.58 mL of 0.105 M $Ba(OH)_2$ solution?

25. What volume of 0.150 M potassium hydroxide solution would completely neutralize 29.1 mL of 0.100 M H_2SO_4 solution?

26. Calculate the molarity of a solution of HNO_3 if 19.55 mL of the solution neutralizes 0.2040 g of Na_2CO_3.

27. If 35.38 mL of a sulfuric acid solution reacts completely with 0.3545 g of Na_2CO_3, what is the molarity of the sulfuric acid solution?

28. A solution of sodium hydroxide is standardized against potassium hydrogen phthalate. From the following data, calculate the molarity of the NaOH solution.

mass of KHP	0.5536 g
buret reading before titration	0.23 mL
buret reading after titration	37.26 mL

29. Calculate the molarity of a KOH solution if 30.68 mL of the KOH solution reacted with 0.4178 g of potassium hydrogen phthalate, KHP.

Antacid tablet reacting with HCl solution

30. Calcium carbonate tablets can be used as an antacid and a source of dietary calcium. A bottle of generic antacid tablets states that each tablet contains 900. mg calcium carbonate. What volume of 1.0 M HCl could be neutralized by the calcium carbonate in one tablet?

31. What volume of 9.00 M H_2SO_4 is required to react with 65.5 mL of 6.00 M NaOH to produce a Na_2SO_4 solution? What volume of water must be added to the resulting solution to obtain a 1.25 M Na_2SO_4 solution?

32. ⬤ (a) What are the properties of an ideal primary standard? (b) What is the importance of each property?

⬤ **Molecular Reasoning** exercises   ▲ **More Challenging** exercises   Blue-Numbered exercises solved in Student Solutions Manual

33. 🔵 The secondary standard solution of NaOH of Exercise 28 was used to titrate a solution of unknown concentration of HCl. A 30.00-mL sample of the HCl solution required 28.21 mL of the NaOH solution for complete neutralization. What is the molarity of the HCl solution?

34. ▲ An impure sample of $(COOH)_2 \cdot 2H_2O$ that had a mass of 1.00 g was dissolved in water and titrated with standard NaOH solution. The titration required 19.16 mL of 0.298 M NaOH solution. Calculate the percent $(COOH)_2 \cdot 2H_2O$ in the sample. Assume that the sample contains no acidic impurities.

35. ▲ A 25.0-mL sample of 0.0500 M $Ca(OH)_2$ is added to 10.0 mL of 0.100 M HNO_3. (a) Is the resulting solution acidic or basic? (b) How many moles of excess acid or base are present? (c) How many additional mL of 0.0500 M $Ca(OH)_2$ or 0.100 M HNO_3 would be required to completely neutralize the solution?

36. ▲ An antacid tablet containing calcium carbonate as an active ingredient required 26.8 mL of 0.112 M HCl for complete neutralization. What mass of $CaCO_3$ did the tablet contain?

37. 🔵 ▲ Butyric acid, whose empirical formula is C_2H_4O, is the acid responsible for the odor of rancid butter. The acid has one ionizable hydrogen per molecule. A 1.000-g sample of butyric acid is neutralized by 36.28 mL of 0.3132 M NaOH solution. What are (a) the molecular weight and (b) the molecular formula of butyric acid?

38. What is the molarity of a solution of sodium hydroxide, NaOH, if 41.4 mL of this solution is required to react with 37.5 mL of 0.0342 M nitric acid solution according to the following reaction?

$$HNO_3 + NaOH \longrightarrow NaNO_3 + H_2O(\ell)$$

39. What is the molarity of a solution of sodium hydroxide, NaOH, if 18.45 mL of this solution is required to react with 17.60 mL of 0.101 M hydrochloric acid solution according to the following reaction?

$$HCl + NaOH \longrightarrow NaCl + H_2O(\ell)$$

40. What is the molarity of a solution that contains 0.978 g of H_3PO_4 in 185 mL of solution? How many milliliters of this solution could be completely neutralized by 11.58 mL of 0.454 M NaOH?

41. What is the molarity of a sulfuric acid solution that is 19.6% H_2SO_4 by mass? The density of the solution is 1.14 g/mL. How many milliliters of this solution could be completely neutralized by 11.58 mL of 0.454 M NaOH?

42. Calculate the molarity of a solution that contains 8.6 g of arsenic acid, H_3AsO_4, in enough water to make 475 mL of solution. How many milliliters of this solution could be completely neutralized by 11.58 mL of 0.454 M NaOH?

43. What volume, in milliliters, of 0.512 M NaOH is required to react completely with 25.0 mL 0.234 M H_2SO_4?

44. Calculate the molarity of an HCl solution if 39.1 mL of the solution reacts with 0.483 g of Na_2CO_3.

$$2HCl + Na_2CO_3 \longrightarrow 2NaCl + CO_2(g) + H_2O(\ell)$$

45. 🔵 To minimize the effect of buret reading errors, titrations performed using a 50-mL buret are most accurate when titrant volumes are in the range of 35 to 45 mL. Suggest a range of sample weights that would yield a 35- to 45-mL titration range for the standardization of solutions of the following approximate concentrations. (a) 0.0533 M NaOH using potassium hydrogen phthalate (KHP), a monoprotic acid. (b) 0.0895 M KOH using primary standard benzoic acid (C_6H_5COOH), a monoprotic acid.

46. ▲ Magnesium hydroxide, $Mg(OH)_2$, is commonly used as the active ingredient in antacid tablets. A student analyzed an antacid tablet for mass percent $Mg(OH)_2$ by dissolving a tablet weighing 1.462 g in 25.00 mL of 0.953 M HCl, and neutralizing the unreacted HCl. That neutralization required 12.29 mL of 0.602 M NaOH. Calculate the mass percent of $Mg(OH)_2$ in the antacid tablet.

47. Vinegar is an aqueous solution of acetic acid, CH_3COOH. Suppose you titrate a 25.00-mL sample of vinegar with 17.62 mL of a standardized 0.1045 N solution of NaOH. (a) What is the molarity of acetic acid in this vinegar? (b) What is the mass of acetic acid contained in 1.000 L of vinegar?

Balancing Redox Equations

In Exercises 48 and 49, write balanced formula unit equations for the reactions described by words.

48. ▲ (a) Iron reacts with hydrochloric acid to form aqueous iron(II) chloride and gaseous hydrogen. (b) Chromium reacts with sulfuric acid to form aqueous chromium(III) sulfate and gaseous hydrogen. (c) Tin reacts with concentrated nitric acid to form tin(IV) oxide, nitrogen dioxide, and water.

49. (a) Carbon reacts with hot concentrated nitric acid to form carbon dioxide, nitrogen dioxide, and water. (b) Sodium reacts with water to form aqueous sodium hydroxide and gaseous hydrogen. (c) Zinc reacts with sodium hydroxide solution to form aqueous sodium tetrahydroxozincate and gaseous hydrogen. (The tetrahydroxozincate ion is $[Zn(OH)_4]^{2-}$.)

50. 🔵 Copper is a widely used metal. Before it is welded (brazed), copper is cleaned by dipping it into nitric acid. HNO_3 oxidizes Cu to Cu^{2+} ions and is reduced to NO. The other product is H_2O. Write the balanced net ionic and formula unit equations for the reaction. Excess HNO_3 is present.

Cengage Learning/Charles Steele

Copper is cleaned by dipping it into nitric acid

51. Balance the following equations. For each equation tell what is oxidized, what is reduced, what the oxidizing agent is, and what the reducing agent is.

   (a) $Cu(NO_3)_2(s) \xrightarrow{heat} CuO(s) + NO_2(g) + O_2(g)$

   (b) $Hg_2Cl_2(s) + NH_3(aq) \longrightarrow$
   $$Hg(\ell) + HgNH_2Cl(s) + NH_4^+(aq) + Cl^-(aq)$$

   (c) $Ba(s) + H_2O(\ell) \longrightarrow Ba(OH)_2(aq) + H_2(g)$

52. Balance the following equations. For each equation tell what is oxidized, what is reduced, what the oxidizing agent is, and what the reducing agent is.

   (a) $MnO_4^-(aq) + H^+(aq) + Br^-(aq) \longrightarrow$
   $$Mn^{2+}(aq) + Br_2(\ell) + H_2O(\ell)$$

   (b) $Cr_2O_7^{2-}(aq) + H^+(aq) + I^-(aq) \longrightarrow$
   $$Cr^{3+}(aq) + I_2(s) + H_2O(\ell)$$

   (c) $MnO_4^-(aq) + SO_3^{2-}(aq) + H^+(aq) \longrightarrow$
   $$Mn^{2+}(aq) + SO_4^{2-}(aq) + H_2O(\ell)$$

   (d) $Cr_2O_7^{2-}(aq) + Fe^{2+}(aq) + H^+(aq) \longrightarrow$
   $$Cr^{3+}(aq) + Fe^{3+}(aq) + H_2O(\ell)$$

53. Balance the following ionic equations. For each equation tell what is oxidized, what is reduced, what the oxidizing agent is, and what the reducing agent is.

   (a) $C_2H_4(g) + MnO_4^-(aq) + H^+(aq) \longrightarrow$
   $$CO_2(g) + Mn^{2+}(aq) + H_2O(\ell)$$

   (b) $H_2S(aq) + H^+(aq) + Cr_2O_7^{2-}(aq) \longrightarrow$
   $$Cr^{3+}(aq) + S(s) + H_2O(\ell)$$

   (c) $ClO_3^-(aq) + H_2O(\ell) + I_2(s) \longrightarrow$
   $$IO_3^-(aq) + Cl^-(aq) + H^+(aq)$$

   (d) $Cu(s) + H^+(aq) + SO_4^{2-}(aq) \longrightarrow$
   $$Cu^{2+}(aq) + H_2O(\ell) + SO_2(g)$$

54. 🌑 Drāno drain cleaner is solid sodium hydroxide that contains some aluminum chips. When Drāno is added to water, the NaOH dissolves rapidly with the evolution of a lot of heat. The Al reduces H_2O in the basic solution to produce $[Al(OH)_4]^-$ ions and H_2 gas, which gives the bubbling action. Write the balanced net ionic and formula unit equations for this reaction.

The Drāno reaction

55. Balance the following ionic equations. For each equation tell what is oxidized, what is reduced, what the oxidizing agent is, and what the reducing agent is.

   (a) $Cr(OH)_4^-(aq) + OH^-(aq) + H_2O_2(aq) \longrightarrow$
   $$CrO_4^{2-}(aq) + H_2O(\ell)$$

   (b) $MnO_2(s) + H^+(aq) + NO_2^-(aq) \longrightarrow$
   $$NO_3^-(aq) + Mn^{2+}(aq) + H_2O(\ell)$$

   (c) $Sn(OH)_3^-(aq) + Bi(OH)_3(s) + OH^-(aq) \longrightarrow$
   $$Sn(OH)_6^{2-}(aq) + Bi(s)$$

   (d) $CrO_4^{2-}(aq) + H_2O(\ell) + HSnO_2^-(aq) \longrightarrow$
   $$CrO_2^-(aq) + OH^-(aq) + HSnO_3^-(aq)$$

56. In the following reactions, decide which reactant is oxidized and which is reduced. Designate the oxidizing agent and the reducing agent.

   (a) $Cr_2O_7^{2-}(aq) + 3Sn^{2+}(aq) + 14H_3O^+(aq) \longrightarrow$
   $$2Cr^{3+}(aq) + 3Sn^{4+}(aq) + 21H_2O(\ell)$$

   (b) $FeS(s) + 3NO_3^-(aq) + 4H_3O^+(aq) \longrightarrow$
   $$3NO(g) + SO_4^{2-}(aq) + Fe^{3+}(aq) + 6H_2O(\ell)$$

57. Balance the following ionic equations for reactions in acidic solution. H^+ or H_2O (but not OH^-) may be added as necessary.

   (a) $P_4(s) + NO_3^-(aq) \longrightarrow H_3PO_4(aq) + NO(g)$

   (b) $H_2O_2(aq) + MnO_4^-(aq) \longrightarrow Mn^{2+}(aq) + O_2(g)$

   (c) $HgS(s) + Cl^-(aq) + NO_3^-(aq) \longrightarrow$
   $$HgCl_4^{2-}(aq) + NO_2(g) + S(s)$$

   (d) $HBrO(aq) \longrightarrow Br^-(aq) + O_2(g)$

58. Write the balanced net ionic equations for the reactions given. Then, using the reactants shown in parentheses, convert each balanced net ionic equation to a balanced formula unit equation.

   (a) $MnO_4^- + C_2O_4^{2-} + H^+ \longrightarrow$
   $$Mn^{2+} + CO_2(g) + H_2O(\ell)$$
   $$(KMnO_4, HCl, and K_2C_2O_4)$$

   (b) $Zn + NO_3^- + H^+ \longrightarrow Zn^{2+} + NH_4^+ + H_2O(\ell)$
   $$(Zn(s) and HNO_3)$$

59. Write balanced equations for the following half-reactions. Specify whether each is an oxidation or reduction.

   (a) $H_2O_2(aq) \longrightarrow O_2(g)$ (in acid)

   (b) $H_2C_2O_4(aq) \longrightarrow CO_2(g)$ (in acid)

   (c) $NO_3^-(aq) \longrightarrow NO(g)$ (in acid)

   (d) $MnO_4^-(aq) \longrightarrow MnO_2(s)$ (in base)

60. Write the balanced net ionic equations for the reactions given. Then, using the reactants shown in parentheses,

🌑 **Molecular Reasoning** exercises   ▲ **More Challenging** exercises   Blue-Numbered exercises solved in Student Solutions Manual

convert each balanced net ionic equation to a balanced formula unit equation.

(a) $Zn(s) + Cu^{2+} \longrightarrow Cu(s) + Zn^{2+}$ (Zn and CuSO$_4$)

(b) $Cr(s) + H^+ \longrightarrow Cr^{3+} + H_2(g)$ (Cr and H$_2$SO$_4$)

61. Balance the following redox equations. All occur in basic solution.

(a) $Al(s) + OH^-(aq) \longrightarrow Al(OH)_4^-(aq) + H_2(g)$

(b) $CrO_4^{2-}(aq) + SO_3^{2-}(aq) \longrightarrow$
$$Cr(OH)_3(s) + SO_4^{2-}(aq)$$

(c) $Zn(s) + Cu(OH)_2(s) \longrightarrow [Zn(OH)_4]^{2-}(aq)$
$+ Cu(s)$

(d) $HS^-(aq) + ClO_3^-(aq) \longrightarrow S(s) + Cl^-(aq)$

Redox Titrations

62. ▲ What volume of 0.233 M KMnO$_4$ would be required to oxidize 25.0 mL of 0.150 M FeSO$_4$ in acidic solution?

63. What volume of 0.142 M K$_2$Cr$_2$O$_7$ would be required to oxidize 70.0 mL of 0.100 M Na$_2$SO$_3$ in acidic solution? The products include Cr^{3+} and SO_4^{2-} ions.

64. What volume of 0.190 M KMnO$_4$ would be required to oxidize 27.0 mL of 0.150 M KI in acidic solution? Products include Mn^{2+} and I$_2$.

65. What volume of 0.190 M K$_2$Cr$_2$O$_7$ would be required to oxidize 27.0 mL of 0.250 M KI in acidic solution? Products include Cr^{3+} and I$_2$.

66. (a) A solution of sodium thiosulfate, Na$_2$S$_2$O$_3$, is 0.1442 M. 37.00 mL of this solution reacts with 28.85 mL of I$_2$ solution. Calculate the molarity of the I$_2$ solution.

$$2Na_2S_2O_3 + I_2 \longrightarrow Na_2S_4O_6 + 2NaI$$

(b) 35.32 mL of the I$_2$ solution is required to titrate a sample containing As$_2$O$_3$. Calculate the mass of As$_2$O$_3$ (197.8 g/mol) in the sample.

$$As_2O_3 + 5H_2O(\ell) + 2I_2 \longrightarrow 2H_3AsO_4 + 4HI$$

67. Copper(II) ions, Cu^{2+}, can be determined by the net reaction

$$2Cu^{2+} + 2I^- + 2S_2O_3^{2-} \longrightarrow 2CuI(s) + S_4O_6^{2-}$$

A 4.115-g sample containing CuSO$_4$ and excess KI is titrated with 32.55 mL of 0.2214 M solution of Na$_2$S$_2$O$_3$. What is the percent CuSO$_4$ (159.6 g/mol) in the sample?

68. What volume of 5.0 M nitrate ion solution would be required to react with 35. mL of 0.75 M sulfide ion solution? (*Hint:* The equation is not balanced.)

$$NO_3^- + S^{2-} \longrightarrow NO + S(s) \quad \text{(acidic solution)}$$

69. ▲ The iron in a 6.675-g sample containing some Fe$_2$O$_3$ is reduced to Fe^{2+}. The Fe^{2+} is titrated with 14.42 mL of 0.1467 M K$_2$Cr$_2$O$_7$ in an acid solution.

$$6Fe^{2+} + Cr_2O_7^{2-} + 14H^+ \longrightarrow$$
$$6Fe^{3+} + 2Cr^{3+} + 7H_2O(\ell)$$

Find (a) the mass of Fe and (b) the percentage of Fe in the sample.

70. Calculate the molarity of a solution that contains 14.6 g of KMnO$_4$ in 750. mL of solution to be used in the reaction that produces MnO_4^{2-} ions as the reduction product.

71. ▲ A 0.855-g sample of an ore of iron is dissolved in acid and converted to Fe(II). The sample is oxidized by 36.50 mL of 0.161 M ceric sulfate, $Ce(SO_4)_2$, solution; the cerium(IV) ion, Ce^{4+}, is reduced to Ce^{3+} ion. (a) Write a balanced equation for the reaction. (b) What is the percent iron in the ore?

Mixed Exercises

72. Calculate the molarity of the solute in a solution containing

(a) 0.0618 g MgNH$_4$PO$_4$ in 250. mL solution

(b) 16.8 g NaCH$_3$COO in 300. mL solution

(c) 0.0250 g CaC$_2$O$_4$ in 750. mL solution

(d) 2.20 g (NH$_4$)$_2$SO$_4$ in 400. mL solution

73. Calculate the molarity of a sulfuric acid solution if 38.75 mL of it reacts completely with 0.3911 g of sodium carbonate.

74. Find the number of mmol of HCl that reacts with 25.5 mL of 0.298 M NaOH. What volume of 0.606 M HCl is needed to furnish this amount of HCl?

75. What is the composition of the final solution when 25.5 mL of 0.298 M NaOH and 24.5 mL of 0.410 M HCl solutions are mixed?

76. What volume of 0.1153 M HCl is needed to completely neutralize 1.98 g of Ca(OH)$_2$?

77. What mass of NaOH is needed to neutralize 34.50 mL of 0.1036 M HCl? If the NaOH is available as a 0.1533 M aqueous solution, what volume will be required?

78. What volume of 0.296 M H$_2$SO$_4$ solution would be required to neutralize completely 34.4 mL of 0.296 M KOH solution?

79. What volume of 0.344 M H$_2$SO$_4$ solution would be required to neutralize completely 34.4 mL of 0.255 M KOH solution?

80. What volume of 0.1945 M sodium hydroxide would be required to neutralize completely 29.41 mL of 0.1023 M H$_2$SO$_4$ solution?

81. Benzoic acid, C$_6$H$_5$COOH, is sometimes used as a primary standard for the standardization of solutions of bases. A 1.862-g sample of this acid is neutralized by 35.00 mL of NaOH solution. What is the molarity of the base solution?

$$C_6H_5COOH(s) + NaOH(aq) \longrightarrow$$
$$C_6H_5COONa(aq) + H_2O(\ell)$$

82. Find the volume of 0.245 M HI solution required to titrate

(a) 25.0 mL of 0.100 M NaOH

(b) 0.503 g of AgNO$_3$ (Ag$^+$ + I$^-$ $\longrightarrow$ AgI(s))

(c) 0.621 g CuSO$_4$ (2Cu^{2+} + 4I$^-$ $\longrightarrow$ 2CuI(s) + I$_2$(s))

🔵 **Molecular Reasoning** exercises   ▲ **More Challenging** exercises   Blue-Numbered exercises solved in Student Solutions Manual

Unless otherwise noted, all content on this page is © Cengage Learning.

Conceptual Exercises

83. Describe how you could prepare 1.00 L of 1.00×10^{-6} M NaCl solution by using a balance that can measure masses only to the nearest 0.01 g.

84. Ascorbic acid (vitamin C), along with having many other reputed properties, acts as an antioxidant. The following equation illustrates its antioxidant properties.

$$H_2C_6H_6O_6 \longrightarrow C_6H_6O_6 + H_2(g)$$

What is an antioxidant? Assign oxidation numbers. Is vitamin C oxidized or reduced in this reaction?

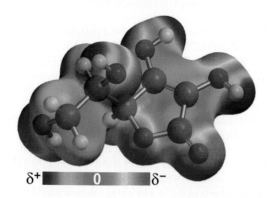

Cengage Learning/Charles D. Winters

δ^+ 0 δ^-

85. 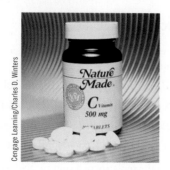 For each of the following substances, give at least one reason why it would be unacceptable as a primary standard for standardizing aqueous solutions of bases: benzoic acid, C_6H_5COOH, technical grade (99.0% purity); calcium chloride, $CaCl_2$, which is hygroscopic; chenodeoxycholic acid, $C_{24}H_{40}O_4$, a monoprotic acid synthesized in the liver from cholesterol; chromic acid, H_2CrO_4; hydrocyanic acid, HCN; hydrofluoric acid, HF; stearic acid, $C_{17}H_{35}COOH$, which is insoluble in water; sulfuric acid, H_2SO_4.

86. When 100. mL of 0.100 M HCl solution and 100. mL of 0.100 M NaOH are mixed,

$$HCl + NaOH \longrightarrow NaCl + H_2O$$

0.0100 mole of HCl reacts completely with 0.0100 mole of NaOH, producing 0.0100 mole of NaCl. Assuming that the amount of water produced by the reaction is negligible, the molarity of the salt in the resulting solution is 0.0500 M NaCl. Is the amount of water produced really negligible? Calculate the volume of water produced by the reaction. Add this volume to the final volume (200. mL).

Is the amount of water produced significant? If the initial volumes had been given as 100.0 mL of 0.1000 M HCl solution and 100.0 mL of 0.1000 M NaOH, would the addition of the volume of water produced by the reaction have been significant?

Building Your Knowledge

87. For the formation of 1.00 mol of water, which reaction uses the most nitric acid?

(a) $3Cu(s) + 8HNO_3(aq) \longrightarrow$
$$3Cu(NO_3)_2(aq) + 2NO(g) + 4H_2O(\ell)$$

(b) $Al_2O_3(s) + 6HNO_3(aq) \longrightarrow$
$$2Al(NO_3)_3(aq) + 3H_2O(\ell)$$

(c) $4Zn(s) + 10HNO_3(aq) \longrightarrow$
$$4Zn(NO_3)_2(aq) + NH_4NO_3(aq) + 3H_2O(\ell)$$

88. Limonite is an ore of iron that contains $2Fe_2O_3 \cdot 3H_2O$. A 0.5166-g sample of limonite is dissolved in acid and treated so that all the iron is converted to ferrous ions, Fe^{2+}. This sample requires 42.96 mL of 0.02130 M sodium dichromate solution, $Na_2Cr_2O_7$, for titration. Fe^{2+} is oxidized to Fe^{3+}, and $Cr_2O_7^{2-}$ is reduced to Cr^{3+}. What is the percent iron in the limonite? If your answer had been over 100% limonite, what conclusion could you make, presuming that the analytical data are correct?

89. One of the troublesome products of a water treatment plant in some areas of the country is $Mg(OH)_2$, a gelatinous precipitate formed during water softening. A suggestion was made that instead of shoveling the precipitate out of the pool during cleaning, the $Mg(OH)_2$ could be neutralized with hydrochloric acid to produce a soluble compound, $MgCl_2$. Then the pool could be flushed out with fresh water. Calculate the volume of 12.0 M HCl necessary to neutralize 3750 L of solution containing 1.50 g of $Mg(OH)_2$ per liter.

90. Silver nitrate and calcium chloride solutions produce a heavy, white precipitate when mixed. Chemical analysis indicates that the precipitate is silver chloride. What mass of silver chloride would be produced if 95 mL of 6.0 M silver nitrate is mixed with 40 mL of 6.0 M calcium chloride?

91. A 0.500-g sample of a crystalline monoprotic acid was dissolved in sufficient water to produce 100. mL of solution. Neutralization of the resulting solution required 75.0 mL of 0.150 M NaOH. How many moles of the acid were present in the initial acid solution?

92. The typical concentration of hydrochloric acid in stomach acid (digestive juice) is about 8.0×10^{-2} M. One experiences "acid stomach" when the stomach contents reach about 1.0×10^{-1} M HCl. One antacid tablet contains 334 mg of active ingredient, $NaAl(OH)_2CO_3$. Assume that you have acid stomach and that your stomach contains 800. mL of 1.0×10^{-1} M HCl. Calculate the number of mmol of HCl in the stomach and the number of mmol of HCl that the tablet *can* neutralize. Which is greater? (The neutralization reaction produces NaCl, $AlCl_3$, CO_2, and H_2O.)

93. An unknown crystalline monoprotic acid was analyzed by titration with a 0.295 M NaOH solution. 1.880 g of the acid required 27.82 mL of the base to be neutralized. What is the molecular weight of the acid?

94. ▲ A few redox reactions have more than one oxidation half-reaction or more than one reduction half-reaction. Balancing the equations for these reactions is more complicated. However, the multiple half-reactions are often stoichiometrically linked. Maintain the correct ratio of the elements and balance the electron transfer by multiplying them both by the same integer. Balance the following net ionic equation for a reaction in basic solution. OH^- or H_2O (but not H^+) may be added as necessary.

$$CrI_3 + H_2O_2 \longrightarrow CrO_4^{2-} + IO_4^-$$

What is oxidized, what is reduced, what is the oxidizing agent, and what is the reducing agent?

95. 🌑 Write a Lewis formula for the anion SiF_6^{2-} that would be produced from the weak acid H_2SiF_6. Use the VSEPR theory to predict the shape of SiF_6^{2-}.

96. 🌑 The etching of glass by hydrofluoric acid may be represented by the simplified reaction of silica with HF.

$$SiO_2(s) + HF(aq) \longrightarrow H_2SiF_6(aq) + H_2O(\ell)$$

This is an acid–base reaction in which a weak acid is used to produce an even weaker acid. Is it also an oxidation–reduction reaction? Balance the equation.

97. Oxalic acid, a poisonous compound, is found in certain vegetables such as spinach and rhubarb, but in concentrations well below toxic limits. The manufacturers of a spinach juice concentrate routinely test their product using an oxalic acid analysis to avoid any problems from an unexpectedly high concentration of this chemical. A titration with potassium permanganate is used for the oxalic acid assay, according to the following net equation.

$$5H_2C_2O_4 + 2MnO_4^- + 6H^+ \longrightarrow 10CO_2 + 2Mn^{2+} + 8H_2O(\ell)$$

Calculate the molarity of an oxalic acid solution requiring 23.2 mL of 0.127 M permanganate for a 25.0 mL portion of the solution.

Spinach and rhubarb

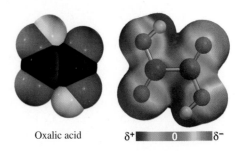

Oxalic acid δ^+ 0 δ^-

98. 🌑 ▲ Consider the two electrostatic charge potential plots for potassium hydrogen phthalate (KHP) shown below. Which is more stable (has a lower energy) and why?

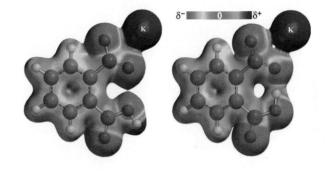

δ^- 0 δ^+

Beyond the Textbook

NOTE: *Whenever the answer to an exercise depends on information obtained from a source other than this textbook, the source must be included as an essential part of the answer.*

99. Use an internet search engine (such as **http://www.google .com**) to locate information on cola soda drinks. (a) What are the acids present in a typical cola? (b) What is the approximate molarity of the principal acid used in a cola?

100. Use an internet search engine (such as **http://www.google .com**) to locate information on each of the following terms. Define three of the four following terms as they relate to titrations: (a) aliquot; (b) analyte; (c) titrant; and (d) scout titration (not associated with Boy Scouts).

101. Use an internet search engine (such as **http://www.google .com**) to locate information on each of the following concepts. Define three of the following four as they relate to titrations: (a) back titration; (b) concave meniscus; (c) Karl Fischer titration; and (d) parallax error.

102. Use an internet search engine (such as **http://www.google .com**) to locate information on "pool chemistry." Define total alkalinity. Why should a pool owner be concerned about total alkalinity?

Gases and the Kinetic–Molecular Theory

12

The lower density of the hot air trapped in these balloons causes them to rise into the more dense atmosphere.

Jim Lozouski/Shutterstock.com

OBJECTIVES

After you have studied this chapter, you should be able to

▶ Understand the properties of gases and compare gases, liquids, and solids

▶ Describe how pressure is measured

▶ Understand and use the absolute (Kelvin) temperature scale

▶ Describe the relationships among pressure, volume, temperature, and amount of gas (Boyle's Law, Charles's Law, Avogadro's Law, and the Combined Gas Law), and the limitations of each

▶ Use Boyle's Law, Charles's Law, Avogadro's Law, and the Combined Gas Law, as appropriate, to calculate changes in pressure, volume, temperature, and amount of gas

▶ Calculate gas densities and the standard molar volume

▶ Use the ideal gas equation to do pressure, volume, temperature, and mole calculations related to gas samples

▶ Determine molecular weights and formulas of gaseous substances from measured properties of gases

▶ Describe how mixtures of gases behave and predict their properties (Dalton's Law of Partial Pressures)

▶ Carry out calculations about the gases involved in chemical reactions

▶ Apply the kinetic–molecular theory of gases and describe how this theory is consistent with the observed gas laws

▶ Describe molecular motion, diffusion, and effusion of gases

▶ Describe the molecular features that are responsible for nonideal behavior of gases; explain when this nonideality is significant

12-1 Comparison of Solids, Liquids, and Gases

Matter exists on earth in three physical states: solids, liquids, and gases. In the solid state H_2O is known as ice, in the liquid state it is called water, and in the gaseous state it is known as steam or water vapor. Most, but not all, substances can exist in all three states. Most solids change to liquids and most liquids turn into gases as they are heated. Liquids and gases are known as **fluids** because they flow freely. Solids and liquids are referred to as **condensed states** because they have much higher densities than gases. Table 12-1 displays the densities of a few common substances in different physical states.

As the data in Table 12-1 indicate, solids and liquids are many times denser than gases. The molecules must be very far apart in gases and much closer together in liquids and solids. For example, the volume of one mole of liquid water is about 18 milliliters, whereas one mole of steam occupies about 30,600 milliliters at 100°C and atmospheric pressure. Gases are easily compressed, and they completely fill any container in which they are present. This tells us that the molecules in a gas are far apart relative to their sizes and that interactions among them are weak. Because they are so far apart, gaseous molecules would not interact with one another were it not for their rapid motion and frequent collisions.

▶ *Volatile* liquids evaporate readily. They have low boiling points, typically between room temperature and about 80°C.

All gases can be liquefied by cooling and compressing them. Volatile liquids easily evaporate to form gases at room temperature or slightly above. The term **vapor** refers to a gas that is formed by evaporation of a liquid or sublimation of a solid. We often use this term when some of the liquid or solid remains in contact with the gas.

Table 12-1 Densities and Molar Volumes of Three Substances at Atmospheric Pressure*

Substance	Solid		Liquid (20°C)		Gas (100°C)	
	Density (g/mL)	*Molar Volume (mL/mol)*	*Density (g/mL)*	*Molar Volume (mL/mol)*	*Density (g/mL)*	*Molar Volume (mL/mol)*
Water (H_2O)	0.917 (0°C)	19.6	0.998	18.0	0.000588	30,600
Benzene (C_6H_6)	0.899 (0°C)	86.9	0.876	89.2	0.00255	30,600
Carbon tetrachloride (CCl_4)	1.70 (−25°C)	90.5	1.59	96.8	0.00503	30,600

*The molar volume of a substance is the volume occupied by one mole of that substance.

12-2 Composition of the Atmosphere and Some Common Properties of Gases

Many important chemical substances are gases at ambient conditions. The earth's atmosphere is a mixture of gases and particles of liquids and solids (Table 12-2). The major gaseous components are N_2 (bp = $-195.79°C$) and O_2 (bp = $-182.98°C$), with smaller concentrations of other gases. All gases are *miscible*; that is, they mix completely *unless* they react with one another.

Several scientists, notably Torricelli (1643), Boyle (1660), Charles (1787), and Graham (1831), laid an experimental foundation on which our present understanding of gases is based. Their investigations showed that

1. Gases can be easily compressed into smaller volumes; that is, their densities can be increased by applying increased pressure.

2. Gases exert pressure on their surroundings; in turn, pressure must be exerted to confine gases.

3. Gases expand without limits, so gas samples completely and uniformly occupy the volume of any container.

4. Gases diffuse into one another, so samples of gas placed in the same container mix completely. Conversely, different gases in a mixture do not separate on standing.

5. The amounts and properties of gases are described in terms of temperature, pressure, the volume occupied, and the number of molecules present. For example, a sample of gas occupies a greater volume when hot than it does when cold at the same pressure, but the number of molecules does not change.

Table 12-2 Composition of Dry Air

Gas	% by Volume
N_2	78.09
O_2	20.94
Ar	0.93
CO_2	0.03*
He, Ne, Kr, Xe	0.002
CH_4	0.00015*
H_2	0.00005
All others combined†	<0.00004

*Variable.
†Atmospheric moisture varies considerably.

▶ Investigating four variables at once is difficult. In Sections 12-4 through 12-8 we shall see how to study these variables two at a time. Section 12-9 will consolidate these descriptions into a single relationship, the ideal gas equation.

12-3 Pressure

Pressure is defined as force per unit area—for example, pounds per square inch (lb/in.^{2}), commonly known as *psi*. Pressure may be expressed in many different units, as we shall see. The mercury **barometer** is a simple device for measuring atmospheric pressures. Figure 12-1a illustrates the "heart" of the mercury barometer. A glass tube (about 800 mm long) is sealed at one end, filled with mercury, and then carefully inverted into a dish of mercury

Br$_2$ (gas)

Br$_2$ (liquid)

Charles D. Winters

Diffusion of bromine vapor in air. Some liquid bromine (*dark reddish brown*) was placed in the small inner bottle. As some of the liquid evaporated, the resulting reddish brown gas diffused to fill the larger container.

without air being allowed to enter. The mercury in the tube falls to the level at which the pressure of the air on the surface of the mercury in the dish equals the gravitational pull downward on the mercury in the tube. The air pressure is measured in terms of the height of the mercury column, that is, the vertical distance between the surface of the mercury in the open dish and that inside the closed tube. The pressure exerted by the atmosphere is equal to the pressure exerted by the column of mercury.

Mercury barometers are simple and well known, so gas pressures are frequently expressed in terms of millimeters of mercury (mm Hg, or just mm). In recent years the unit **torr** has been used to indicate pressure; it is defined as 1 torr = 1 mm Hg.

A mercury **manometer** consists of a glass U–tube partially filled with mercury. One arm is open to the atmosphere, and the other is connected to a container of gas (see Figure 12-1b,c).

Atmospheric pressure varies with atmospheric conditions and distance above sea level. The atmospheric pressure decreases with increasing elevation because there is a smaller mass of air above it. Approximately one-half of the matter in the atmosphere is less than 20,000 feet above sea level. Thus, atmospheric pressure is only about one-half as great at 20,000 feet as it is at sea level. Mountain climbers and pilots use portable barometers to determine their altitudes (Figure 12-2). At sea level, at a latitude of 45°, the average atmospheric pressure supports a column of mercury 760 mm high in a simple mercury barometer when the mercury and air are at 0°C. This average sea-level pressure of 760 mm Hg is called one atmosphere of pressure.

▶ The unit *torr* was named for Evangelista Torricelli (1608–1647), who invented the mercury barometer.

▶ A common pressure unit used in much of the world is the bar, which is nearly equal to an atmosphere of pressure:

1.00 bar = 100. kPa
1.00 atm = 1.01 bar

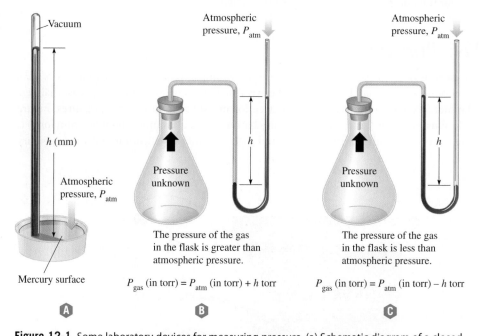

$$P_{gas} \text{ (in torr)} = P_{atm} \text{ (in torr)} + h \text{ torr}$$

$$P_{gas} \text{ (in torr)} = P_{atm} \text{ (in torr)} - h \text{ torr}$$

Figure 12-1 Some laboratory devices for measuring pressure. (a) Schematic diagram of a closed-end barometer. At the level of the lower mercury surface, the pressure both inside and outside the tube must be equal to that of the atmosphere. There is no air inside the tube, so the pressure is exerted only by the mercury column h mm high. Hence, the atmospheric pressure must equal the pressure exerted by h mm Hg, or h torr. (b) The two-arm mercury barometer is called a manometer. In this sample, the pressure of the gas inside the flask is *greater than* the external atmospheric pressure. At the level of the lower mercury surface, the total pressure on the mercury in the left arm must equal the total pressure on the mercury in the right arm. The pressure exerted by the gas is equal to the external pressure *plus* the pressure exerted by the mercury column of height h mm, or P_{gas} (in torr) = P_{atm} (in torr) + h torr. (c) When the gas pressure measured by the manometer is *less than* the external atmospheric pressure, the pressure exerted by the atmosphere is equal to the gas pressure *plus* the pressure exerted by the mercury column, or $P_{atm} = P_{gas} + h$. We can rearrange this to write P_{gas} (in torr) = P_{atm} (in torr) − h torr.

A A commercial mercury barometer

B Portable barometers. This type is called an *aneroid* ("not wet") barometer. Some of the air has been removed from the airtight box, which is made of thin, flexible metal. When the pressure of the atmosphere changes, the remaining air in the box expands or contracts (Boyle's Law), moving the flexible box surface and an attached pointer along a scale.

C A tire gauge. This kind of gauge registers "relative" pressure, that is, the *difference* between internal pressure and the external atmospheric pressure. For instance, when the gauge reads 30 psi (pounds per square inch), the total gas pressure in the tire is 30 psi + 1 atm, or about 45 psi. In engineering terminology, this is termed "psig" (g = gauge). For all calculations involving pressure, the total pressure, not gauge pressure, must be used.

Figure 12-2 Some commercial pressure-measuring devices.

one atmosphere (atm) = 760 mm Hg at 0°C = 760 torr

The SI unit of pressure is the **pascal** (Pa), defined as the pressure exerted by a force of one newton acting on an area of one square meter. By definition, one *newton* (N) is the force required to give a mass of one kilogram an acceleration of one meter per second per second. Symbolically we represent one newton as

▶ Acceleration is the change in velocity (m/s) per unit time (s), m/s².

$$1 \text{ N} = \frac{1 \text{ kg} \cdot \text{m}}{\text{s}^2} \quad \text{so} \quad 1 \text{ Pa} = \frac{1 \text{ N}}{\text{m}^2} = \frac{1 \text{ kg}}{\text{m} \cdot \text{s}^2}$$

One atmosphere of pressure = 1.01325×10^5 Pa, or 101.325 kPa.

12-4 Boyle's Law: The Volume–Pressure Relationship

Early experiments on the behavior of gases were carried out by Robert Boyle (1627–1691). In a typical experiment (Figure 12-3), a sample of a gas was trapped in a U–tube and allowed to come to constant temperature. Then its volume and the difference in the heights of the two mercury columns were recorded. This difference in height plus the pressure of the atmosphere represents the pressure on the gas. Addition of more mercury to the tube increases the pressure by changing the height of the mercury column. As a result, the gas volume decreases. The results of several such experiments are tabulated in Figure 12-4a.

Boyle showed that for a given sample of gas at constant temperature, the product of pressure and volume, $P \times V$, was always the same number.

CHEMISTRY IN USE

The Greenhouse Effect and Climate Change

During the 20th century, the great increase in our use of fossil fuels caused a significant rise in the concentration of carbon dioxide, CO_2, in the atmosphere. Since 1750 (just before the Industrial Revolution), the concentration of atmospheric CO_2 has increased by 37%. Since 2000, acceleration of the annual rate of CO_2 production has increased to more than 3%, from 1.1% per year in the early 1990s. Scientists believe that atmospheric CO_2 concentration could double, compared to 1750, by early in the 21st century. The curve in Figure (a) illustrates the recent steady rise in atmospheric CO_2 concentration.

Energy from the sun reaches the earth in the form of light. Neither CO_2 nor H_2O vapor absorbs the visible light in sunlight, so they do not prevent it from reaching the surface of the earth. The energy given off by the earth in the form of lower-energy infrared (heat) radiation, however, is readily absorbed by CO_2 and H_2O (as it is by the glass or plastic of greenhouses). Thus, some of the heat the earth must lose to maintain its temperature can become trapped in the atmosphere, causing the temperature to rise [Figure (b)]. This phenomenon, called the *greenhouse effect*, has been the subject of much discussion among scientists and the topic of many articles in the popular press.

The Intergovernmental Panel on Climate Change (IPCC) has summarized climate model predictions. The IPCC summary indicates that the average global surface temperature will likely rise an additional 1.1 to 6.4°C (2.0 to 11.5°F) during the 21st century. This may not seem like much. A change of even 4–5°C, however, would be enough to cause a dramatic change in climate, transforming now productive land into desert and altering the habitats of many animals and plants beyond their ability to adapt. Another drastic consequence of even this small temperature rise would be the partial melting of the polar ice caps. The resulting rise in sea level, though only a few feet, would mean that water would inundate coastal cities such as Los Angeles, New York, and Houston, and low-lying coastal areas such as southern Florida and Louisiana. On a global scale, the effects would be devastating.

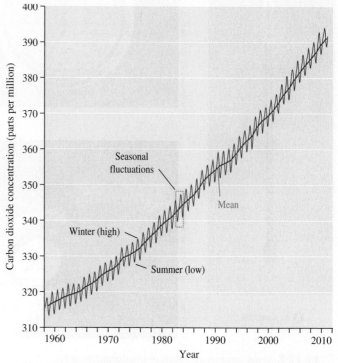

(a) A plot of the monthly average CO_2 concentration in parts per million (ppm), measured at Mauna Loa Observatory, Hawaii, far from significant sources of CO_2 from human activities. Annual fluctuations occur because plants in the Northern Hemisphere absorb CO_2 in the spring and release it as they decay in the fall.

The earth's forests and jungles play a crucial role in maintaining the balance of gases in the atmosphere, removing CO_2 and supplying O_2. The massive destruction, for economic reasons, of heavily forested areas such as the Amazon rain forest in South America is cited as another long-term contributor to global environmental problems. Worldwide, more than 3 million square miles of once-forested land is now barren for some reason; at least 60% of this land is now unused. Environmental scientists estimate that if even one quarter of this

At a given temperature, the product of pressure and volume of a definite mass of gas is constant.

$$PV = k \qquad \text{(constant } n, T\text{)}$$

This relationship is **Boyle's Law**. The value of k depends on the amount (number of moles, n) of gas present and on the temperature, T. Units for k are determined by the units used to express the volume (V) and pressure (P).

When the volume of a gas is plotted against its pressure at constant temperature, the resulting curve is one branch of a hyperbola. Figure 12-4b is a graphic illustration of this inverse relationship. When volume is plotted versus the reciprocal of the pressure, $1/P$,

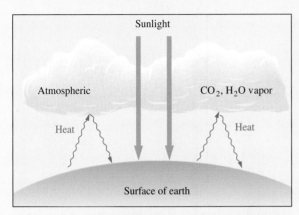

(b) The greenhouse effect. Visible light passes through atmospheric H₂O and CO₂, but heat radiated from the surface of the earth is absorbed by these gases.

land could be reforested, the vegetation would absorb 1.1 billion tons of CO_2 annually.

Some scientists are more skeptical than others about the role of human-produced CO_2 in climate change and, indeed, about whether global warming is a significant phenomenon or simply another of the recognized warm–cold cycles that have occurred throughout the earth's history. All but the most skeptical observers, however, seem to agree that responsible stewardship of the planet urgently requires that we do something in a reasoned fashion to reduce production of greenhouse gases, primarily CO_2, and that this will involve decreasing our dependence on energy from fossil fuels and increasing reliance on renewable energy sources, solar energy, wind power, and geothermal energy. Despite the technical and political problems of waste disposal, increased use of electric energy based on nuclear power is one way of decreasing CO_2 emissions. France, for example, gets 78% of its electricity from nuclear power. Improved ways to recycle the nuclear waste have been developed to minimize the amount needed for long-term storage.

Much CO_2 is eventually absorbed by the vast amount of water in the oceans, where the carbonate–bicarbonate buffer system almost entirely counteracts any adverse effects of ocean water acidity. Ironically, there is also evidence to suggest that other types of air pollution in the form of particulate matter may partially counteract the greenhouse effect. The particles reflect visible (sun) radiation rather than absorbing it, blocking some light from entering the atmosphere. It seems foolish, however, to depend on one form of pollution to help rescue us from the effects of another! Real solutions to current environmental problems such as the greenhouse effect are not subject to quick fixes; they depend on long-term cooperative international efforts that must be based on the firm knowledge resulting from scientific research.

Tropical rain forests are important in maintaining the balance of CO_2 and O_2 in the earth's atmosphere. In recent years a portion of the South American forests (by far the world's largest) larger than France has been destroyed, either by flooding caused by hydroelectric dams or by clearing of forest land for agricultural or ranching use. Such destruction continues at a rate of more than 20,000 square kilometers per year. If current trends continue, many of the world's rain forests will be severely reduced or even obliterated in the next few years. The fundamental question—"What are the long-term consequences of the destruction of tropical rain forests?"—remains unanswered.

a straight line results (see Figure 12-4c). In 1662, Boyle summarized the results of his experiments on various samples of gases in an alternative statement of Boyle's Law:

> At constant temperature the volume, V, occupied by a definite mass of a gas is inversely proportional to the applied pressure, P.
>
> $$V \propto \frac{1}{P} \quad \text{or} \quad V = k\left(\frac{1}{P}\right) \quad \text{(constant } n, T\text{)}$$

▶ The symbol $\propto$ reads "is proportional to." A proportionality is converted into an equality by introducing a proportionality constant, k.

At normal temperatures and pressures, most gases obey Boyle's Law rather well. We call this *ideal behavior*. Deviations from ideality are discussed in Section 12-15.

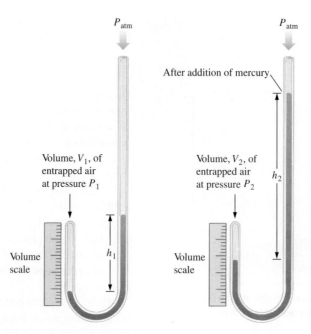

Figure 12-3 A representation of Boyle's experiment. A sample of air is trapped in a tube in such a way that the pressure on the air can be changed and the volume of the air measured. P_{atm} is the atmospheric pressure, measured with a barometer. $P_1 = h_1 + P_{atm}$, $P_2 = h_2 + P_{atm}$.

P	V	$P \times V$	$1/P$
5.0	40.0	200	0.20
10.0	20.0	200	0.10
15.0	13.3	200	0.0667
17.0	11.8	201	0.0588
20.0	10.0	200	0.0500
22.0	9.10	200	0.0455
30.0	6.70	201	0.0333
40.0	5.00	200	0.0250

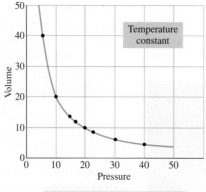

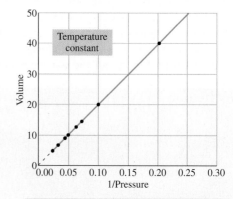

Ⓐ Some typical data from an experiment such as that shown in Figure 12-3. Measured values of P and V are presented in the first two columns, on an arbitrary scale.

Ⓑ Graphical representation of Boyle's Law, using the data of (a); V versus P.

Ⓒ Graphical representation of Boyle's Law, using the data of (a); V versus $1/P$. Although the line would appear to intersect the origin, indicating zero volume when extended to $1/P = 0$ (or infinite pressure), for any real gas the volume levels off at a small but non-zero value at very high pressure.

Figure 12-4 Boyle's Law data and plots of the data.

Let us think about a fixed mass of gas at constant temperature, but at two different conditions of pressure and volume (see Figure 12-3). For the first condition we can write

$$P_1V_1 = k \qquad \text{(constant } n, T\text{)}$$

and for the second condition we can write

$$P_2V_2 = k \qquad \text{(constant } n, T\text{)}$$

Because the constant k on the right-hand sides of these two equations is the same, the left-hand sides must be equal, or

$$P_1V_1 = P_2V_2 \qquad \text{(for a given amount of a gas at constant temperature)}$$

This form of Boyle's Law is useful for calculations involving pressure and volume *changes*, as the following examples demonstrate.

EXAMPLE 12-1 Boyle's Law Calculation

A sample of gas occupies 12 L under a pressure of 1.2 atm. What would its volume be if the pressure were increased to 2.4 atm?

Plan

We know the volume at one pressure and want to find the volume at another pressure (constant temperature). This suggests that we use Boyle's Law. We tabulate what is known and what is asked for, and then solve the Boyle's Law equation for the unknown quantity, V_2.

Solution

We have

$$V_1 = 12 \text{ L} \qquad P_1 = 1.2 \text{ atm}$$
$$V_2 = \underline{?} \qquad P_2 = 2.4 \text{ atm}$$

Solving Boyle's Law, $P_1V_1 = P_2V_2$, for V_2 and substituting gives

$$V_2 = \frac{P_1V_1}{P_2} = \frac{(1.2 \text{ atm})(12 \text{ L})}{2.4 \text{ atm}} = \boxed{6.0 \text{ L}}$$

▶ It is often helpful to tabulate what is given and what is asked for in a problem.

S TOP & THINK
Pressure and volume are inversely proportional. Doubling the pressure halves the volume of a sample of gas at constant temperature.

Problem-Solving Tip Units in Boyle's Law Calculations

"Which units for volume and pressure can be used in Boyle's Law calculations? The units on the two sides of $P_1V_1 = P_2V_2$ must match. Thus you can use *any* volume units—liters, milliliters, cubic feet—and *any* units for pressure—atmospheres, torr, pascals—as long as the *same* units are used on both sides."

EXAMPLE 12-2 Boyle's Law Calculation

A sample of oxygen occupies 10.0 L under a pressure of 790. torr (105 kPa). At what pressure would it occupy 13.4 L if the temperature did not change?

Plan

We know the pressure at one volume and wish to find the pressure at another volume (at constant temperature). We can solve Boyle's Law for the second pressure and substitute.

Solution

We have $P_1 = 790.$ torr; $V_1 = 10.0$ L; $P_2 = \underline{?}$; $V_2 = 13.4$ L. Solving Boyle's Law, $P_1V_1 = P_2V_2$, for P_2 and substituting yields

$$P_2 = \frac{P_1V_1}{V_2} = \frac{(790. \text{ torr})(10.0 \text{ L})}{13.4 \text{ L}} = \boxed{590. \text{ torr}} \quad \left(\times \frac{101.3 \text{ kPa}}{760. \text{ torr}} = 78.6 \text{ kPa} \right)$$

You should now work Exercises 16 and 17.

S TOP & THINK
It is a very good idea to think qualitatively about what the answer should be before doing the numerical calculation. For example, since the volume is *increasing*, we should reason qualitatively from Boyle's Law that the pressure must be *decreasing*. This provides a good check on the final numerical answer you calculate.

Problem-Solving Tip Use What You Can Predict About the Answer

In Example 12-1 the calculated volume decrease is consistent with the increase in pressure. This reasoning suggests another method for solving such problems by setting up a "Boyle's Law factor" to change the volume in the direction required by the pressure change. We reason that the pressure *increase* from 1.2 to 2.4 atm must cause the volume to *decrease* by the factor (1.2 atm/2.4 atm). The solution then becomes

$$\underline{?}\ L = 12\ L\ \times\ (\text{Boyle's Law factor that would decrease the volume})$$

$$= 12\ L\ \times\left(\frac{1.2\ \text{atm}}{2.4\ \text{atm}}\right) = 6.0\ L$$

Now try solving Example 12-2 using a Boyle's Law factor.

An artist's representation of Jacques Charles's first ascent in a hydrogen balloon at the Tuileries, Paris, December 1, 1783.

▶ Lord Kelvin (1824–1907) was born William Thompson. At the age of ten he was admitted to Glasgow University. In 1916, a refrigerator company named its new appliance the Kelvinator, because it was based on Kelvin's theories.

▶ Absolute zero may be thought of as the limit of thermal contraction for an ideal gas.

12-5 Charles's Law: The Volume–Temperature Relationship; The Absolute Temperature Scale

In his pressure–volume studies on gases, Robert Boyle noticed that heating a sample of gas caused some volume change, but he did not follow up on this observation. About 1800, two French scientists—Jacques Charles (1746–1823) and Joseph Gay-Lussac (1778–1850), pioneer balloonists at the time—began studying the expansion of gases with increasing temperature. Their studies showed that the rate of expansion with increased temperature was constant and was the same for all the gases they studied as long as the pressure remained constant. The implications of their discovery were not fully recognized until many years later. Then scientists used this behavior of gases as the basis of a new temperature scale, the absolute temperature scale.

The change of volume with temperature, at constant pressure, is illustrated in Figure 12-5. From the table of typical data in Figure 12-5b, we see that volume (V, mL) increases as temperature (t, °C) increases, but the quantitative relationship is not yet obvious. These data are plotted in Figure 12-5c (line A), together with similar data for the same gas sample at different pressures (lines B and C).

Lord Kelvin, a British physicist, noticed in 1848 that an extension of the different temperature–volume lines back to zero volume (dashed line) yields a common intercept at −273.15°C on the temperature axis. Kelvin named this temperature **absolute zero**. The degrees on this absolute scale and the Celsius scale are the same size, so 0°C becomes 273.15 degrees above absolute zero. In honor of Lord Kelvin's work, this scale is called the Kelvin temperature scale. Temperatures on the Kelvin scale are expressed in kelvins (not degrees Kelvin) and represented by K, not °K. As pointed out in Section 1-12, the relationship between the Celsius and Kelvin temperature scales is K = °C + 273.15°.

If we convert temperatures (°C) to absolute temperatures (K) and plot them using the green scale in Figure 12-5c, the volume–temperature relationship becomes obvious. This relationship is known as **Charles's Law**.

At constant pressure, the volume occupied by a definite mass of a gas is directly proportional to its absolute temperature.

We can express Charles's Law in mathematical terms as

$$V \propto T \qquad \text{or} \qquad V = kT \qquad (\text{constant } n, P)$$

Rearranging the expression gives $V/T = k$, a concise statement of Charles's Law. As the absolute temperature increases, the volume must increase proportionally. If we let

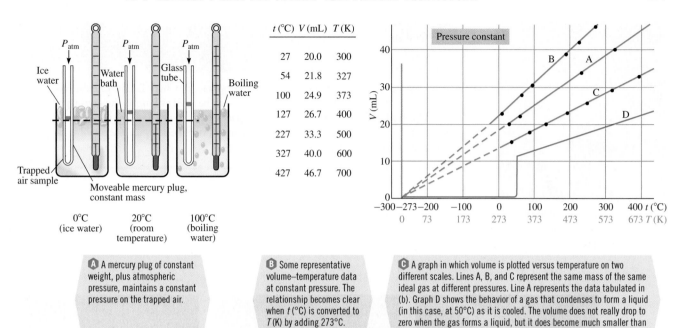

t (°C)	V (mL)	T (K)
27	20.0	300
54	21.8	327
100	24.9	373
127	26.7	400
227	33.3	500
327	40.0	600
427	46.7	700

A A mercury plug of constant weight, plus atmospheric pressure, maintains a constant pressure on the trapped air.

B Some representative volume–temperature data at constant pressure. The relationship becomes clear when t (°C) is converted to T (K) by adding 273°C.

C A graph in which volume is plotted versus temperature on two different scales. Lines A, B, and C represent the same mass of the same ideal gas at different pressures. Line A represents the data tabulated in (b). Graph D shows the behavior of a gas that condenses to form a liquid (in this case, at 50°C) as it is cooled. The volume does not really drop to zero when the gas forms a liquid, but it does become much smaller than the gaseous volume.

Figure 12-5 An experiment showing that the volume of an ideal gas sample increases as the temperature is increased at constant pressure.

subscripts 1 and 2 represent values for the same sample of gas at two different temperatures, we obtain

$$\frac{V_1}{T_1} = \frac{V_2}{T_2} \qquad \text{(for a definite mass of gas at constant pressure)}$$

which is the more useful form of Charles's Law. This relationship is valid *only* when temperature, T, is expressed on the absolute (Kelvin) scale.

EXAMPLE 12-3 Charles's Law Calculation

A sample of nitrogen occupies 117 mL at 100.°C. At what temperature in °C would it occupy 234 mL if the pressure did not change?

Plan

We know the volume of the sample at one temperature and wish to know its temperature corresponding to a second volume (constant pressure). We can solve Charles's Law for the second temperature. We must remember to carry out calculations with all temperatures expressed on the Kelvin scale, converting to or from Celsius as necessary.

Solution

$$V_1 = 117 \text{ mL} \qquad\qquad V_2 = 234 \text{ mL}$$

$$T_1 = 100.°C + 273° = 373 \text{ K} \qquad T_2 = \underline{\ ?\ }$$

$$\frac{V_1}{T_1} = \frac{V_2}{T_2} \quad \text{and} \quad T_2 = \frac{V_2 T_1}{V_1} = \frac{(234 \text{ mL})(373 \text{ K})}{(117 \text{ mL})} = \boxed{746 \text{ K}}$$

$$°C = 746 \text{ K} - 273° = \boxed{473°C}$$

You should now work Exercise 26.

S TOP & THINK
You must remember to convert temperatures into kelvins for all gas law calculations. Don't forget to convert the temperature back to the proper units at the end of the problem!

S TOP & THINK
To double the volume as required (117 mL to 234 mL), we must double the temperature *on the Kelvin scale* (373 K to 746 K). Note that this does *not* correspond to doubling on the Celsius scale (100°C to 473°C).

The lower density of the hot air trapped in these balloons causes them to rise in the more dense atmosphere.

> **Problem-Solving Tip** Be Careful of Units in Charles's Law Calculations
>
> Which units for volume and temperature are appropriate for Charles's Law calculations? *Any* volume units—liters, milliliters, cubic feet—can be used as long as the *same* units are used for both volumes. But the relationship *does not apply at all* unless the temperatures are both expressed on an absolute scale. You must remember to express all temperatures in kelvins for Charles's Law calculations.

When balloons filled with air are cooled in liquid nitrogen (bp = −196°C) each shrinks to a small fraction of its original volume. Because the boiling points of the other components of air, except He and Ne, are higher than −196°C, they condense to form liquids. When the balloons are removed from the liquid nitrogen, the liquids vaporize to form gases again. As the air warms to room temperature, the balloons expand to their original volume (Charles's Law).

12-6 Standard Temperature and Pressure

We have seen that both temperature and pressure affect the volumes (and therefore the densities) of gases. It is often convenient to choose some "standard" temperature and pressure as a reference point for discussing gases. **Standard temperature and pressure (STP)** are, by international agreement, exactly 0°C (273.15 K) and one atmosphere of pressure (760. torr).

12-7 The Combined Gas Law Equation

Boyle's Law relates the pressures and volumes of a sample of gas at constant temperature, $P_1V_1 = P_2V_2$. Charles's Law relates the volumes and temperatures at constant pressure, $V_1/T_1 = V_2/T_2$. Combination of Boyle's Law and Charles's Law into a single expression gives the **Combined Gas Law equation**.

▶ Notice that the Combined Gas Law equation becomes

1. $P_1V_1 = P_2V_2$ (Boyle's Law) when T is constant;

2. $\dfrac{V_1}{T_1} = \dfrac{V_2}{T_2}$ (Charles's Law) when P is constant; and

3. $\dfrac{P_1}{T_1} = \dfrac{P_2}{T_2}$ when V is constant.

$$\frac{P_1V_1}{T_1} = \frac{P_2V_2}{T_2} \qquad \text{(constant amount of gas)}$$

When any five of the variables in the equation are known, the sixth variable can be calculated.

EXAMPLE 12-4 Combined Gas Law Calculation

A sample of neon occupies 105 liters at 27°C under a pressure of 985 torr. What volume would it occupy at standard temperature and pressure (STP)?

Plan

All three quantities P, V, and T are changing for this gas sample. This suggests that we use the Combined Gas Law equation. We tabulate what is known and what is asked for, solve the Combined Gas Law equation for the unknown quantity, V_2, and substitute known values.

Solution

$$V_1 = 105 \text{ L} \qquad P_1 = 985 \text{ torr} \qquad T_1 = 27°C + 273° = 300. \text{ K}$$

$$V_2 = \underline{?} \qquad P_2 = 760. \text{ torr} \qquad T_2 = 273 \text{ K}$$

Solving for V_2,

$$\frac{P_1 V_1}{T_1} = \frac{P_2 V_2}{T_2} \qquad \text{so} \qquad V_2 = \frac{P_1 V_1 T_2}{P_2 T_1} = \frac{(985 \text{ torr})(105 \text{ L})(273 \text{ K})}{(760. \text{ torr})(300. \text{ K})} = 124 \text{ L}$$

Alternatively, we can multiply the original volume by a Boyle's Law factor and a Charles's Law factor. As the pressure decreases from 985 torr to 760. torr, the volume increases, so the Boyle's Law factor is 985 torr/760. torr. As the temperature decreases from 300. K to 273 K, the volume decreases, so the Charles's Law factor is 273 K/300. K. Multiplication of the original volume by these factors gives the same result.

$$\underline{?} \text{ L} = 105 \text{ L} \times \frac{985 \text{ torr}}{760. \text{ torr}} \times \frac{273 \text{ K}}{300. \text{ K}} = \boxed{124 \text{ L}}$$

> **STOP & THINK**
>
> The temperature decrease (from 300. K to 273 K) alone would give only a small *decrease* in the volume of neon, by a factor of 273 K/300. K, or 0.910. The pressure decrease (from 985 torr to 760. torr) alone would result in a greater *increase* in the volume, by a factor of 985 torr/ 760. torr, or 1.30. The combined result of the two changes is that the volume increases from 105 liters to 124 liters.

EXAMPLE 12-5 Combined Gas Law Calculation

A sample of gas occupies 12.0 liters at 240.°C under a pressure of 80.0 kPa. At what temperature would the gas occupy 15.0 liters if the pressure were increased to 107 kPa?

Plan

The approach is the same as for Example 12-4 except that the unknown quantity is now the new temperature, T_2.

Solution

$$V_1 = 12.0 \text{ L} \qquad P_1 = 80.0 \text{ kPa} \qquad T_1 = 240.°C + 273° = 513 \text{ K}$$

$$V_2 = 15.0 \text{ L} \qquad P_2 = 107 \text{ kPa} \qquad T_2 = \underline{?}$$

We solve the Combined Gas Law equation for T_2.

$$\frac{P_1 V_1}{T_1} = \frac{P_2 V_2}{T_2} \qquad \text{so} \qquad T_2 = \frac{P_2 V_2 T_1}{P_1 V_1} = \frac{(107 \text{ kPa})(15.0 \text{ L})(513 \text{ K})}{(80.0 \text{ kPa})(12.0 \text{ L})} = 858 \text{ K}$$

$$K = °C + 273° \qquad \text{so} \qquad °C = 858 \text{ K} - 273° = \boxed{585°C}$$

You should now work Exercises 34 and 35.

> **STOP & THINK**
>
> The pressure is increasing, which would *decrease* the volume; the question asks for a *larger* final volume, so the temperature must increase substantially.

Problem-Solving Tip Units in Combined Gas Law Calculations

The Combined Gas Law equation is derived by combining Boyle's and Charles's Laws, so the comments in earlier Problem-Solving Tips also apply to this equation. Remember to express all temperatures in kelvins. Volumes can be expressed in any units as long as both are in the same units. Similarly, any pressure units can be used, so long as both are in the same units. Example 12-4 uses torr for both pressures; Example 12-5 uses kPa for both pressures.

12-8 Avogadro's Law and the Standard Molar Volume

In 1811, Amedeo Avogadro postulated that

> at the same temperature and pressure, equal volumes of all gases contain the same number of molecules.

▶ Small deviations result from the non-ideal behavior of gases

Many experiments have demonstrated that Avogadro's hypothesis is accurate to within about $\pm 2\%$, and the statement is now known as **Avogadro's Law**.

Avogadro's Law can also be stated as follows.

> At constant temperature and pressure, the volume, V, occupied by a gas sample is directly proportional to the number of moles, n, of gas.

$$V \propto n \quad \text{or} \quad V = kn \quad \text{or} \quad \frac{V}{n} = k \quad \text{(constant } T, P)$$

For two samples of gas at the same temperature and pressure, the relation between volumes and numbers of moles can be represented as

$$\frac{V_1}{n_1} = \frac{V_2}{n_2} \quad \text{(constant } T, P)$$

The volume occupied by a mole of gas at *standard temperature and pressure*, STP, is referred to as the standard molar volume. It is nearly constant for all gases (Table 12-3).

> The **standard molar volume** of an ideal gas is taken to be 22.414 liters per mole at STP.

Table 12-3   Standard Molar Volumes and Densities of Some Gases (0°C)

▶ Deviations in standard molar volume indicate that gases do not behave ideally.

Gas	Formula	(g/mol)	Density at STP (g/L)	Standard Molar Volume (L/mol)
Hydrogen	H_2	2.02	0.090	22.428
Helium	He	4.003	0.178	22.426
Neon	Ne	20.18	0.900	22.425
Nitrogen	N_2	28.01	1.250	22.404
Oxygen	O_2	32.00	1.429	22.394
Argon	Ar	39.95	1.784	22.393
Carbon dioxide	CO_2	44.01	1.977	22.256
Ammonia	NH_3	17.03	0.771	22.094
Chlorine	Cl_2	70.91	3.214	22.063

Gas densities depend on pressure and temperature; however, the number of moles of gas in a given sample does not change with temperature or pressure. Pressure changes affect volumes of gases according to Boyle's Law, and temperature changes affect volumes of gases according to Charles's Law. We can use these laws to convert gas densities at various temperatures and pressures to *standard temperature and pressure*. Table 12-3 gives the experimentally determined densities of several gases at standard temperature and pressure.

EXAMPLE 12-6 **Molecular Weight, Density**

One (1.00) mole of a gas occupies 27.0 liters, and its density is 1.41 g/L at a particular temperature and pressure. What is its molecular weight? What is the density of the gas at STP?

Plan

We can use unit factors to convert the density, 1.41 g/L, to molecular weight, g/mol. To calculate the density at STP, we recall that the volume occupied by one mole would be 22.4 L.

Solution

We multiply the density under the original conditions by the unit factor 27.0 L/1.00 mol to generate the appropriate units, g/mol.

$$\frac{?\ g}{mol} = \frac{1.41\ g}{L} \times \frac{27.0\ L}{mol} = \boxed{38.1\ g/mol}$$

At STP, 1.00 mol of the gas, 38.1 g, would occupy 22.4 L, and its density would be

$$Density = \frac{38.1\ g}{1\ mol} \times \frac{1\ mol}{22.4\ L} = \boxed{1.70\ g/L\ at\ STP}$$

You should now work Exercises 40 and 42.

▶ Density is defined as mass per unit volume. For solids and liquids this is usually expressed in g/mL, but for gases g/L is more convenient.

⑤ TOP & THINK
The appropriate unit factors give the correct units for molecular weight (g/mol) and for density at STP (g/L). The molecular weight is greater than 1, as it must be. The density of a gas is typically much smaller than that of a solid or liquid; these have typical densities on the order of g/mL.

12-9 Summary of Gas Laws: The Ideal Gas Equation

Let us summarize what we have learned about gases. Any sample of gas can be described in terms of its pressure, temperature (in kelvins), volume, and the number of moles, n, present. Any three of these variables determine the fourth. The gas laws we have studied give several relationships among these variables. An **ideal gas** is one that exactly obeys these gas laws. Many gases show slight deviations from ideality, but at normal temperatures and pressures the deviations are usually small enough to be ignored. We will do so for the present and discuss deviations from ideal behavior later.

We can summarize the behavior of ideal gases as follows.

Boyle's Law	$V \propto \dfrac{1}{P}$	(at constant T and n)
Charles's Law	$V \propto T$	(at constant P and n)
Avogadro's Law	$V \propto n$	(at constant T and P)
Summarizing	$V \propto \dfrac{nT}{P}$	(no restrictions)

As before, a proportionality can be written as an equality by introducing a proportionality constant, for which we use the symbol R. This gives

$$V = R\left(\frac{nT}{P}\right) \quad \text{or, rearranging,} \quad \boxed{PV = nRT}$$

This relationship is called the **ideal gas equation** or the *Ideal Gas Law*. The numerical value of R, the **universal gas constant**, depends on the choices of the units for P, V, and T. One mole of an ideal gas occupies 22.414 liters at 1.0000 atmosphere and 273.15 K (STP). Solving the ideal gas equation for R gives

$$R = \frac{PV}{nT} = \frac{(1.0000\ atm)(22.414\ L)}{(1.0000\ mol)(273.15\ K)} = \boxed{0.082057\ \frac{L \cdot atm}{mol \cdot K}}$$

In working problems, we often round R to 0.0821 L·atm/mol·K.

▶ This single equation takes into account the values of n, T, P, and V. Restrictions that apply to the individual gas laws are therefore not needed for the ideal gas equation.

⑤ TOP & THINK
It is important to use the R value whose units match the pressure and volume units in the problem. We will most commonly use atm and liters as units, but remember to pay attention to what is being used in the problem at hand. As mentioned before, one should always use kelvins for the temperature.

EXAMPLE 12-7 Units of R

R can have any *energy* units per mole per kelvin. Calculate R in terms of joules per mole per kelvin and in SI units of $kPa \cdot dm^3/mol \cdot K$.

Plan

We apply dimensional analysis to convert to the required units.

Solution

Appendix C shows that $1 \, L \cdot atm = 101.325$ joules.

$$R = \frac{0.082057 \, L \cdot atm}{mol \cdot K} \times \frac{101.325 \, J}{1 \, L \cdot atm} = \boxed{8.3144 \, J/mol \cdot K}$$

▶ Recall that $1 \, dm^3 = 1 \, L$.

Now evaluate R in SI units. One atmosphere pressure is 101.325 kilopascals, and the molar volume at STP is $22.414 \, dm^3$.

$$R = \frac{PV}{nT} = \frac{101.325 \, kPa \times 22.414 \, dm^3}{1 \, mol \times 273.15 \, K} = \boxed{8.3145 \, \frac{kPa \cdot dm^3}{mol \cdot K}}$$

You should now work Exercise 43.

We can now express R, the universal gas constant, to four digits in three different sets of units.

$$R = 0.08206 \, \frac{L \cdot atm}{mol \cdot K} = 8.314 \, \frac{J}{mol \cdot K} = 8.314 \, \frac{kPa \cdot dm^3}{mol \cdot K}$$

We can express R in other units, as shown inside the back cover of this text. Calorie units, for example, are commonly used in science and engineering.

> The usefulness of the ideal gas equation is that it relates the four variables, P, V, n, and T, that describe a sample of gas at *one set of conditions*. If any three of these variables are known, the fourth can be calculated.

EXAMPLE 12-8 Ideal Gas Equation

What pressure, in atm, is exerted by 54.0 grams of Xe in a 1.00-liter flask at 20.°C?

Plan

We list the variables with the proper units. Then we solve the ideal gas equation for P, substitute values, and evaluate.

Solution

$V = 1.00 \, L$ $n = 54.0 \, g \, Xe \times \dfrac{1 \, mol}{131.3 \, g \, Xe} = 0.411 \, mol$

$T = 20.°C + 273° = 293 \, K$ $P = \underline{\, ? \,}$

Solving $PV = nRT$ for P and substituting gives

STOP & THINK

We are rounding the value of R to three significant figures. The sample is about half a mole of gas, but it is in a much smaller volume than a mole of gas would occupy at or near STP, so it is not surprising that the pressure is much higher than 1 atm.

$$P = \frac{nRT}{V} = \frac{(0.411 \, mol)\left(\dfrac{0.0821 \, L \cdot atm}{mol \cdot K}\right)(293 \, K)}{1.00 \, L} = \boxed{9.89 \, atm}$$

EXAMPLE 12-9 Ideal Gas Equation

What is the volume of a gas balloon filled with 4.00 moles of He when the atmospheric pressure is 748 torr and the temperature is 30.°C?

Plan

We first list the variables with the proper units. Then we solve the ideal gas equation for V, substitute known values, and evaluate.

Solution

$$P = 748 \text{ torr} \times \frac{1 \text{ atm}}{760 \text{ torr}} = 0.984 \text{ atm} \quad n = 4.00 \text{ mol}$$

$$T = 30.°C + 273° = 303 \text{ K} \qquad V = \underline{?}$$

Solving $PV = nRT$ for V and substituting gives

$$V = \frac{nRT}{P} = \frac{(4.00 \text{ mol})\left(0.0821 \dfrac{\text{L} \cdot \text{atm}}{\text{mol} \cdot \text{K}}\right)(303 \text{ K})}{0.984 \text{ atm}} = \boxed{101 \text{ L}}$$

You should now work Exercise 46.

> **S TOP & THINK**
>
> Remember that 1 mole of gas at 0° C and 760 torr (STP) occupies 22.4 L. Because the pressure in this problem is lower and the temperature a little higher, the volume should be somewhat greater than 4×22.4 L.

You may wonder why pressures are given in torr or mm Hg and temperatures in °C. This is because pressures are often measured with mercury barometers, and temperatures are measured with Celsius thermometers.

EXAMPLE 12-10 Ideal Gas Equation

A helium-filled weather balloon has a volume of 7240 cubic feet. How many grams of helium would be required to inflate this balloon to a pressure of 745 torr at 21°C? ($1 \text{ ft}^3 = 28.3$ L)

Plan

We use the ideal gas equation to find n, the number of moles required, and then convert to grams. We must convert each quantity to one of the units stated for R ($R = 0.0821$ L·atm/mol·K).

Solution

$$P = 745 \text{ torr} \times \frac{1 \text{ atm}}{760 \text{ torr}} = 0.980 \text{ atm}; \quad T = 21°C + 273° = 294 \text{ K}$$

$$V = 7240 \text{ ft}^3 \times \frac{28.3 \text{ L}}{1 \text{ ft}^3} = 2.05 \times 10^5 \text{ L}; \quad n = \underline{?}$$

Solving $PV = nRT$ for n and substituting gives

$$n = \frac{PV}{RT} = \frac{(0.980 \text{ atm})(2.05 \times 10^5 \text{ L})}{\left(0.0821 \dfrac{\text{L} \cdot \text{atm}}{\text{mol} \cdot \text{K}}\right)(294 \text{ K})} = 8.32 \times 10^3 \text{ mol He}$$

$$\underline{?} \text{ g He} = (8.32 \times 10^3 \text{ mol He})\left(4.00 \dfrac{\text{g}}{\text{mol}}\right) = \boxed{3.33 \times 10^4 \text{ g He}}$$

You should now work Exercise 47.

A helium-filled weather balloon.

⚙ Problem-Solving Tip Watch Out for Units in Ideal Gas Law Calculations

The units of R that are appropriate for Ideal Gas Law calculations are those that involve units of volume, pressure, moles, and temperature. When you use the value $R = 0.0821$ L·atm/mol·K, remember to express all quantities in a calculation in these units. Pressures should be expressed in atmospheres, volumes in liters, temperature in kelvins, and amount of gas in moles. In Examples 12-9 and 12-10 we converted pressures from torr to atm. In Example 12-10 the volume was converted from ft³ to L.

▶ Each of the individual gas laws can be derived from the ideal gas equation.

Summary of the Ideal Gas Laws

1. The individual gas laws are usually used to calculate the *changes* in conditions for a sample of gas (subscripts can be thought of as "before" and "after").

Boyle's Law	$P_1V_1 = P_2V_2$		(for a given amount of a gas at constant temperature)
Charles's Law	$\dfrac{V_1}{T_1} = \dfrac{V_2}{T_2}$		(for a given amount of a gas at constant pressure)
Combined Gas Law	$\dfrac{P_1V_1}{T_1} = \dfrac{P_2V_2}{T_2}$		(for a given amount of a gas)
Avogadro's Law	$\dfrac{V_1}{n_1} = \dfrac{V_2}{n_2}$		(for gas samples at the same temperature and pressure)

2. The ideal gas equation is used to calculate one of the four variables P, V, n, and T, which describe a sample of gas at *any single set of conditions*.

$$PV = nRT$$

The ideal gas equation can also be used to calculate the densities of gases.

EXAMPLE 12-11 Ideal Gas Equation

Nitric acid, a very important industrial chemical, is made by dissolving the gas nitrogen dioxide, NO_2, in water. Calculate the density of NO_2 gas, in g/L, at 1.24 atm and 50.°C.

Plan

We use the ideal gas equation to find the number of moles, n, in any volume, V, at the specified pressure and temperature. Because we want to express density in g/L, it is convenient to choose a volume of one liter. A different volume could be chosen as long as it is used consistently throughout the solution. Then we convert moles to grams.

Solution

$$V = 1.00 \text{ L} \qquad\qquad n = \underline{\ ?\ }$$

$$T = 50.°C + 273° = 323 \text{ K} \qquad P = 1.24 \text{ atm}$$

Solving $PV = nRT$ for n and substituting gives

$$n = \frac{PV}{RT} = \frac{(1.24 \text{ atm})(1.00 \text{ L})}{\left(0.0821 \dfrac{\text{L} \cdot \text{atm}}{\text{mol} \cdot \text{K}}\right)(323 \text{ K})} = 0.0468 \text{ mol}$$

So there is 0.0468 mol NO_2 in 1.00 L at the specified P and T. Converting this to grams of NO_2 per liter, we obtain

$$\text{Density} = \frac{\underline{\ ?\ } \text{ g}}{\text{L}} = \frac{0.0468 \text{ mol } NO_2}{1.00 \text{ L}} \times \frac{46.0 \text{ g } NO_2}{\text{mol } NO_2} = \boxed{2.15 \text{ g/L}}$$

You should now work Exercise 41.

12-10 Determination of Molecular Weights and Molecular Formulas of Gaseous Substances

In Section 2-9 we distinguished between simplest and molecular formulas of compounds. We showed how simplest formulas can be calculated from percent compositions of compounds. The molecular weight must be known to determine the molecular formula of a compound. For compounds that are gases at convenient temperatures and pressures, the ideal gas law provides a basis for determining molecular weights.

EXAMPLE 12-12 Molecular Weight

A 120.-mL flask contained 0.345 gram of a gaseous compound at 100°C and 760. torr pressure. What is the molecular weight of the compound?

Plan

We use the ideal gas equation, $PV = nRT$, to determine the number of moles of gas that filled the flask. Then, knowing the mass of this number of moles, we can calculate the mass of one mole.

Solution

$$V = 0.120 \text{ L} \qquad P = 760. \text{ torr} = 1.00 \text{ atm} \qquad T = 100.°\text{C} + 273° = 373 \text{ K}$$

The number of moles in this gas sample is

$$n = \frac{PV}{RT} = \frac{(1.00 \text{ atm})(0.120 \text{ L})}{\left(0.0821 \dfrac{\text{L} \cdot \text{atm}}{\text{mol} \cdot \text{K}}\right)(373 \text{ K})} = 0.00392 \text{ mol}$$

The mass of 0.00392 mol of gas is 0.345 g, so the mass of one mole is

$$\frac{? \text{ g}}{\text{mol}} = \frac{0.345 \text{ g}}{0.00392 \text{ mol}} = \boxed{88.0 \text{ g/mol}}$$

You should now work Exercises 55 and 58.

> **S**TOP & THINK
> Remember to convert °C into K and torr into atm. Then rearrange the ideal gas equation to solve for n, the number of moles.

Let's carry the calculation one step further in the next example.

EXAMPLE 12-13 Molecular Formula

Additional analysis of the gaseous compound in Example 12-12 showed that it contained 54.5% carbon, 9.10% hydrogen, and 36.4% oxygen by mass. What is its molecular formula?

Plan

We first find the simplest formula for the compound as we did in Section 2-8 (Examples 2-13 and 2-14). Then we use the molecular weight that we determined in Example 12-12 to find the molecular formula. To find the molecular formula, we reason as in Example 2-17. We use the experimentally known molecular weight to find the ratio

$$n = \frac{\text{molecular weight}}{\text{simplest-formula weight}}$$

The molecular weight is n times the simplest-formula weight, so the molecular formula is n times the simplest formula.

Solution

▶ You may wish to review the calculation of simplest (empirical) formula in Examples 2-13 and 2-14, and the relation between simplest formula and molecular formula in Example 2-17.

Element	Relative Mass of Element	Relative Number of Atoms (divide mass by AW)	Divide by Smallest Number	Smallest Whole-Number Ratio of Atoms
C	54.5	$\dfrac{54.5}{12.0} = 4.54$	$\dfrac{4.54}{2.28} = 1.99$	2
H	9.10	$\dfrac{9.10}{1.01} = 9.01$	$\dfrac{9.01}{2.28} = 3.95$	4 C_2H_4O
O	36.4	$\dfrac{36.4}{16.0} = 2.28$	$\dfrac{2.28}{2.28} = 1.00$	1

The simplest formula is C_2H_4O and the simplest-formula weight is 44.0 amu. Division of the molecular weight by the simplest-formula weight gives

$$\frac{\text{molecular weight}}{\text{simplest-formula weight}} = \frac{88.0 \text{ amu}}{44.0 \text{ amu}} = 2$$

The molecular formula is therefore $2 \times (C_2H_4O) = C_4H_8O_2$.

Ethyl acetate and butyric acid are two compounds with this molecular formula. Both have the formula $C_4H_8O_2$. They have very different odors, however. Ethyl acetate has the odor of nail polish remover. Butyric acid has the foul odor of rancid butter.

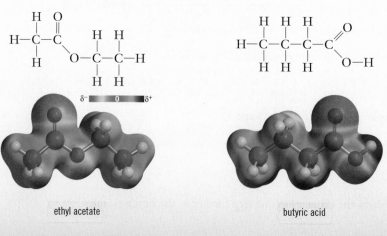

ethyl acetate   butyric acid

You should now work Exercise 56.

12-11 Dalton's Law of Partial Pressures

Many gas samples, including our atmosphere, are mixtures that consist of different kinds of gases. The total number of moles in a mixture of gases is

$$n_{\text{total}} = n_A + n_B + n_C + \cdots$$

where n_A, n_B, and so on represent the number of moles of each kind of gas present. Rearranging the ideal gas equation, $P_{\text{total}}V = n_{\text{total}}RT$, for the total pressure, P_{total}, and then substituting for n_{total} gives

$$P_{\text{total}} = \frac{n_{\text{total}}RT}{V} = \frac{(n_A + n_B + n_C + \cdots)RT}{V}$$

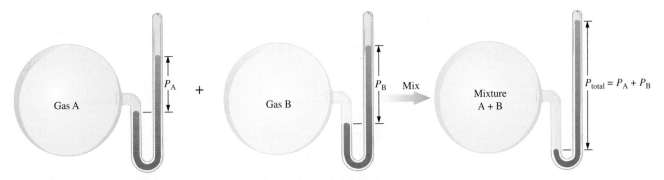

Figure 12-6 An illustration of Dalton's Law. When the two gases A and B are mixed in the same container at the same temperature, they exert a total pressure equal to the sum of their partial pressures.

Multiplying out the right-hand side gives

$$P_{total} = \frac{n_A RT}{V} + \frac{n_B RT}{V} + \frac{n_C RT}{V} + \cdots$$

Now $n_A RT/V$ is the *partial pressure* P_A that the n_A moles of gas A alone would exert in the container at temperature T; similarly, $n_B RT/V = P_B$, and so on. Substituting these into the equation for P_{total}, we obtain **Dalton's Law of Partial Pressures** (Figure 12-6).

$$P_{total} = P_A + P_B + P_C + \cdots \qquad \text{(constant } V, T\text{)}$$

The total pressure exerted by a mixture of ideal gases is the sum of the partial pressures of those gases.

Dalton's Law is useful in describing real gaseous mixtures at moderate pressures because it allows us to relate total measured pressures to the composition of mixtures.

▶ John Dalton was the first to notice this effect. He did so in 1807 while studying the compositions of moist and dry air. The pressure that each gas exerts in a mixture is called its **partial pressure**. No way has been devised to measure the pressure of an individual gas in a mixture; it must be calculated from other quantities.

EXAMPLE 12-14 Mixture of Gases

A 10.0-liter flask contains 0.200 mole of methane, 0.300 mole of hydrogen, and 0.400 mole of nitrogen at 25°C. (a) What is the pressure, in atmospheres, inside the flask? (b) What is the partial pressure of each component of the mixture of gases?

Plan

(a) We are given the number of moles of each component. The ideal gas law can be used to calculate the total pressure from the total number of moles. (b) The partial pressure of each gas in the mixture can be calculated by substituting the number of moles of each gas individually into $PV_A = n_A RT$, $PV_B = n_B RT$, etc.

Solution

(a) $n_{total} = 0.200 \text{ mol CH}_4 + 0.300 \text{ mol H}_2 + 0.400 \text{ mol N}_2 = 0.900 \text{ mol of gas}$

$V = 10.0 \text{ L} \qquad T = 25°C + 273° = 298 \text{ K}$

Rearranging $P_{total}V = n_{total}RT$ gives $P_{total} = n_{total}RT/V$. Substitution gives

$$P_{total} = \frac{(0.900 \text{ mol})\left(0.0821 \dfrac{\text{L} \cdot \text{atm}}{\text{mol} \cdot \text{K}}\right)(298 \text{ K})}{10.0 \text{ L}} = 2.20 \text{ atm}$$

▶ The gas mixture has a single temperature. Each gas expands to fill the entire volume available.

(b) Now we find the partial pressures. For CH_4, $n = 0.200$ mol, and the values for V and T are the same as in part (a).

$$P_{CH_4} = \frac{(n_{CH_4})RT}{V} = \frac{(0.200 \text{ mol})\left(0.0821 \dfrac{\text{L} \cdot \text{atm}}{\text{mol} \cdot \text{K}}\right)(298 \text{ K})}{10.0 \text{ L}} = 0.489 \text{ atm}$$

Similar calculations for the partial pressures of hydrogen and nitrogen give

$$P_{H_2} = 0.734 \text{ atm} \qquad \text{and} \qquad P_{N_2} = 0.979 \text{ atm}$$

As a check, we use Dalton's Law: $P_{total} = P_A + P_B + P_C + \cdots$. Addition of the partial pressures in this mixture gives the total pressure we calculated in part (a).

$$P_{total} = P_{CH_4} + P_{H_2} + P_{N_2} = (0.489 + 0.734 + 0.979) \text{ atm} = 2.20 \text{ atm}$$

You should now work Exercises 62 and 63.

 Problem-Solving Tip Amounts of Gases in Mixtures Can Be Expressed in Various Units

In Example 12-14 we were given the number of moles of each gas. Sometimes the amount of a gas is expressed in other units that can be converted to number of moles. For instance, if we know the formula weight (or the formula), we can convert a given mass of gas to number of moles.

▶ The volume percentages given in Table 12-2 are also equal to mole percentages.

We can describe the composition of any mixture in terms of the mole fraction of each component. The **mole fraction**, X_A, of component A in a mixture is defined as

$$X_A = \frac{\text{no. mol A}}{\text{total no. mol of all components}}$$

Like any other fraction, mole fraction is a dimensionless quantity. For each component in a mixture, the mole fraction is

▶ The sum of all mole fractions in a mixture is equal to 1.

$$X_A + X_B + \cdots = 1 \text{ for any mixture}$$

We can use this relationship to check mole fraction calculations or to find a remaining mole fraction if we know all the others.

$$X_A = \frac{\text{no. mol A}}{\text{no. mol A} + \text{no. mol B} + \cdots},$$

$$X_B = \frac{\text{no. mol B}}{\text{no. mol A} + \text{no. mol B} + \cdots}, \qquad \text{and so on}$$

For a gaseous mixture, we can relate the mole fraction of each component to its partial pressure as follows. From the ideal gas equation, the number of moles of each component can be written as

$$n_A = P_A V/RT, \qquad n_B = P_B V/RT, \qquad \text{and so on}$$

and the total number of moles is

$$n_{total} = P_{total} V/RT$$

Substituting into the definition of X_A,

$$X_A = \frac{n_A}{n_A + n_B + \cdots} = \frac{P_A V/RT}{P_{total} V/RT}$$

The quantities V, R, and T cancel to give

$$X_A = \frac{P_A}{P_{total}}; \quad \text{similarly,} \quad X_B = \frac{P_B}{P_{total}}; \quad \text{and so on}$$

We can rearrange these equations to give another statement of Dalton's Law of Partial Pressures.

$$P_A = X_A \times P_{total}; \quad P_B = X_B \times P_{total}; \quad \text{and so on}$$

The partial pressure of each gas in a gaseous mixture is equal to its mole fraction in the mixture times the total pressure of the mixture.

EXAMPLE 12-15 Mole Fraction, Partial Pressure

Calculate the mole fractions of the three gases in Example 12-14.

Plan

One way to solve this problem is to use the numbers of moles given in the problem. Alternatively we could use the partial pressures and the total pressure from Example 12-14.

▶ Example 12-15 shows that for a gas mixture the relative numbers of moles of components are the same as relative pressures of the components. This is true for all ideal gas mixtures.

Solution

Using the moles given in Example 12-14,

$$X_{CH_4} = \frac{n_{CH_4}}{n_{total}} = \frac{0.200 \text{ mol}}{0.900 \text{ mol}} = 0.222$$

$$X_{H_2} = \frac{n_{H_2}}{n_{total}} = \frac{0.300 \text{ mol}}{0.900 \text{ mol}} = 0.333$$

$$X_{N_2} = \frac{n_{N_2}}{n_{total}} = \frac{0.400 \text{ mol}}{0.900 \text{ mol}} = 0.444$$

Using the partial and total pressures calculated in Example 12-14,

$$X_{CH_4} = \frac{P_{CH_4}}{P_{total}} = \frac{0.489}{2.20 \text{ atm}} = 0.222$$

$$X_{H_2} = \frac{P_{H_2}}{P_{total}} = \frac{0.734 \text{ atm}}{2.20 \text{ atm}} = 0.334$$

$$X_{N_2} = \frac{P_{N_2}}{P_{total}} = \frac{0.979 \text{ atm}}{2.20 \text{ atm}} = 0.445$$

S TOP & THINK
The more moles (n) of a particular gas that are present, the greater its mole fraction (X) in the mixture.

$$n_{N_2} > n_{H_2} > n_{CH_4}$$

so

$$X_{N_2} > X_{H_2} > X_{CH_4}$$

The difference between the two calculated results is due to rounding.

You should now work Exercise 64.

EXAMPLE 12-16 Partial Pressure, Mole Fraction

The mole fraction of oxygen in the atmosphere is 0.2094. Calculate the partial pressure of O_2 in air when the atmospheric pressure is 760. torr.

Plan

The partial pressure of each gas in a mixture is equal to its mole fraction in the mixture times the total pressure of the mixture.

Solution

$$P_{O_2} = X_{O_2} \times P_{total}$$

$$= 0.2094 \times 760. \text{ torr} = \boxed{159 \text{ torr}}$$

S TOP & THINK
The mole fraction tells us that only a small fraction (about 1/5) of the moles present in air are due to O_2. Thus the pressure due to O_2 (its partial pressure) must be only that fraction of the total pressure of air (1 atm or 760 torr).

Dalton's Law can be used in combination with other gas laws, as the following example shows.

EXAMPLE 12-17 Mixture of Gases

Two tanks are connected by a closed valve. Each tank is filled with gas as shown, and both tanks are held at the same temperature. We open the valve and allow the gases to mix.

(a) After the gases mix, what is the partial pressure of each gas, and what is the total pressure?

(b) What is the mole fraction of each gas in the mixture?

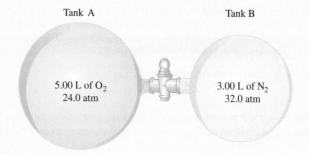

Tank A   Tank B

5.00 L of O_2
24.0 atm

3.00 L of N_2
32.0 atm

Plan

(a) Each gas expands to fill the available volume, 5.00 liters plus 3.00 liters or a total volume of 8.00 liters. We can use Boyle's Law to calculate the partial pressure that each gas would exert after it expands to fill 8.00 L. The total pressure is equal to the sum of the partial pressures of the two gases. (b) The mole fraction of each gas can be calculated from the ratio of the partial pressure of that gas to the total pressure.

Solution

(a) For O_2,

$$P_1V_1 = P_2V_2 \quad \text{or} \quad P_{2,O_2} = \frac{P_1V_1}{V_2} = \frac{24.0 \text{ atm} \times 5.00 \text{ L}}{8.00 \text{ L}} = \boxed{15.0 \text{ atm}}$$

For N_2,

$$P_1V_1 = P_2V_2 \quad \text{or} \quad P_{2,N_2} = \frac{P_1V_1}{V_2} = \frac{32.0 \text{ atm} \times 3.00 \text{ L}}{8.00 \text{ L}} = \boxed{12.0 \text{ atm}}$$

The total pressure is the sum of the partial pressures.

$$P_{\text{total}} = P_{2,O_2} + P_{2,N_2} = 15.0 \text{ atm} + 12.0 \text{ atm} = \boxed{27.0 \text{ atm}}$$

(b) $X_{O_2} = \dfrac{P_{2,O_2}}{P_{\text{total}}} = \dfrac{15.0 \text{ atm}}{27.0 \text{ atm}} = \boxed{0.556}$

$X_{N_2} = \dfrac{P_{2,N_2}}{P_{\text{total}}} = \dfrac{12.0 \text{ atm}}{27.0 \text{ atm}} = \boxed{0.444}$

You should now work Exercise 66.

> **S TOP & THINK**
> Notice that part (b) of this problem has been solved using the mole fraction statement of Dalton's Law, without calculating the number of moles of either gas. As a further check, the sum of the mole fractions is 1.

▶ Gases that are very soluble in water or that react with water cannot be collected by this method. Other liquids can be used.

Some gases can be collected over water. Figure 12-7 illustrates the collection of a sample of hydrogen by displacement of water. A gas produced in a reaction displaces the denser water from the inverted water-filled container. The pressure on the gas inside the collection container could be made equal to atmospheric pressure by collecting gas until the water level inside is the same as that outside.

One complication arises, however. A gas in contact with water soon becomes saturated with water vapor. The pressure inside the container is the sum of the partial pres-

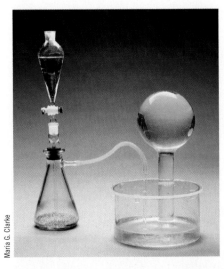 

Figure 12-7 Apparatus for preparing hydrogen from zinc and sulfuric acid.

$$Zn(s) + 2H^+(aq) \rightarrow Zn^{2+}(aq) + H_2(g)$$

The hydrogen is collected by displacement of water.

sure of the gas itself *plus* the partial pressure exerted by the water vapor in the gas mixture (the **vapor pressure** of water). Every liquid shows a characteristic vapor pressure that varies only with temperature, and *not* with the volume of vapor present, so long as both liquid and vapor are present. Table 12-4 displays the vapor pressure of water near room temperature.

The relevant point here is that a gas collected over water is "moist"; that is, it is saturated with water vapor. Measuring the atmospheric pressure at which the gas is collected, we can write

$$P_{atm} = P_{gas} + P_{H_2O} \quad \text{or} \quad P_{gas} = P_{atm} - P_{H_2O}$$

Example 12-18 provides a detailed illustration.

▶ The partial pressure exerted by the vapor above a liquid is called the vapor pressure of that liquid. A more extensive table of the vapor pressure of water appears in Appendix E.

EXAMPLE 12-18 Gas Collected over Water

Hydrogen was collected over water (see Figure 12-7) at 21°C on a day when the atmospheric pressure was 748 torr. The volume of the gas sample collected was 300. mL. (a) How many moles of H_2 were present? (b) How many moles of water vapor were present in the moist gas mixture? (c) What is the mole fraction of hydrogen in the moist gas mixture? (d) What would be the mass of the gas sample if it were dry?

Plan

(a) The vapor pressure of H_2O, $P_{H_2O} = 19$ torr at 21°C, is obtained from Table 12-4. Applying Dalton's Law, $P_{H_2} = P_{atm} - P_{H_2O}$. We then use the partial pressure of H_2 in the ideal gas equation to find the number of moles of H_2 present. (b) The partial pressure of water vapor (the vapor pressure of water at the stated temperature) is used in the ideal gas equation to find the number of moles of water vapor present. (c) The mole fraction of H_2 is the ratio of its partial pressure to the total pressure. (d) The number of moles found in part (a) can be converted to mass of H_2.

Solution

(a) $P_{H_2} = P_{atm} - P_{H_2O} = (748 - 19) \text{ torr} = 729 \text{ torr} \times \dfrac{1 \text{ atm}}{760 \text{ torr}} = 0.959 \text{ atm}$

We also need to convert the volume from mL to L and the temperature to K

$$V = 300. \text{ mL} = 0.300 \text{ L} \quad \text{and} \quad T = 21°C + 273° = 294 \text{ K}$$

Solving the ideal gas equation for n_{H_2} gives

$$n_{H_2} = \frac{P_{H_2}V}{RT} = \frac{(0.959 \text{ atm}) (0.300 \text{ L})}{\left(0.0821 \dfrac{\text{L} \cdot \text{atm}}{\text{mol} \cdot \text{K}}\right) (294 \text{ K})} = \boxed{1.19 \times 10^{-2} \text{ mol } H_2}$$

Table 12-4 Vapor Pressure of Water Near Room Temperature

Temperature (°C)	Vapor Pressure of Water (torr)
19	16.48
20	17.54
21	18.65
22	19.83
23	21.07
24	22.38
25	23.76
26	25.21
27	26.74
28	28.35

▶ Remember that *each* gas occupies the *total* volume of the container.

▶ At STP, this dry hydrogen would occupy 267 mL. Can you calculate this?

(b) $P_{H_2O} = 19 \text{ torr} \times \dfrac{1 \text{ atm}}{760 \text{ torr}} = 0.025 \text{ atm}$

V and T have the same values as in Part (a).

$$n_{H_2O} = \frac{P_{H_2O}V}{RT} = \frac{(0.025 \text{ atm})\,(0.300 \text{ L})}{\left(0.0821 \dfrac{\text{L} \cdot \text{atm}}{\text{mol} \cdot \text{K}}\right)(294 \text{ K})} = \boxed{3.1 \times 10^{-4} \text{ mol } H_2O \text{ vapor}}$$

(c) $X_{H_2} = \dfrac{P_{H_2}}{P_{\text{total}}} = \dfrac{729 \text{ torr}}{748 \text{ torr}} = \boxed{0.975}$

(d) $\underline{?} \text{ g } H_2 = 1.19 \times 10^{-2} \text{ mol} \times \dfrac{2.02 \text{ g}}{1 \text{ mol}} = \boxed{2.40 \times 10^{-2} \text{ g } H_2}$

You should now work Exercise 68.

Caspar Benson/Jupiterimages

The nitrogen gas formed in the rapid reaction

$2NaN_3(s) \longrightarrow 2Na(s) + 3N_2(g)$

fills an automobile air bag during a collision. The air bag fills within 1/20th of a second after a front collision.

12-12 Mass–Volume Relationships in Reactions Involving Gases

Many chemical reactions produce gases. For instance, the combustion of hydrocarbon in excess oxygen at high temperatures produces both carbon dioxide and water as gases, as illustrated for octane.

$$2C_8H_{18}(g) + 25O_2(g) \longrightarrow 16CO_2(g) + 18H_2O(g)$$

The N_2 gas produced by the very rapid decomposition of sodium azide, $NaN_3(s)$, inflates air bags used as safety devices in automobiles.

We know that one mole of gas, measured at STP, occupies 22.4 liters; we can use the ideal gas equation to find the volume of a mole of gas at any other conditions. This information can be utilized in stoichiometry calculations (see Section 3-2).

Small amounts of oxygen can be produced in the laboratory by heating solid potassium chlorate, $KClO_3$, in the presence of a catalyst, manganese(IV) oxide, MnO_2. Solid potassium chloride, KCl, is also produced.

> **CAUTION!**
> Heating $KClO_3$ can be dangerous.

$$2KClO_3(s) \xrightarrow[\text{heat}]{MnO_2} 2KCl(s) + 3O_2(g)$$

$$\begin{array}{ccc} 2 \text{ mol} & 2 \text{ mol} & 3 \text{ mol} \\ 2(122.6 \text{ g}) & 2(74.6 \text{ g}) & 3(22.4 \text{ L}_{STP}) \end{array}$$

The reaction ratio can be constructed as a unit factor using any two of these quantities.

> **EXAMPLE 12-19 Gas Volume in a Chemical Reaction**
>
> What volume of O_2 (STP) could be produced by heating 112 grams of $KClO_3$?
>
> **Plan**
>
> The preceding equation shows that two moles of $KClO_3$ produces three moles of O_2. We construct appropriate unit factors from the balanced equation and the standard molar volume of oxygen to solve the problem.

Solution

$$\underset{?}{\text{L}_{STP}}\,O_2 = 112\text{ g KClO}_3 \times \frac{1\text{ mol KClO}_3}{122.6\text{ g KClO}_3} \times \frac{3\text{ mol O}_2}{2\text{ mol KClO}_3} \times \frac{22.4\text{ L}_{STP}\,O_2}{1\text{ mol O}_2}$$

$$= 30.7\text{ L}_{STP}\,O_2$$

This calculation shows that the thermal decomposition of 112 grams of $KClO_3$ produces 30.7 liters of oxygen measured at standard conditions.

You should now work Exercise 80.

EXAMPLE 12-20 Gas Volume in a Chemical Reaction

A 1.80-gram mixture of potassium chlorate, $KClO_3$, and potassium chloride, KCl, was heated until all of the $KClO_3$ had decomposed. After being dried, the liberated oxygen occupied 405 mL at 25°C when the barometric pressure was 745 torr. (a) How many moles of O_2 were produced? (b) What percentage of the mixture was $KClO_3$?

Plan

(a) The number of moles of O_2 produced can be calculated from the ideal gas equation.
(b) Then we use the balanced chemical equation to relate the known number of moles of O_2 formed and the mass of $KClO_3$ that decomposed to produce it.

Solution

(a) $V = 405$ mL $= 0.405$ L; $P = 745$ torr $\times \dfrac{1\text{ atm}}{760\text{ torr}} = 0.980$ atm

$T = 25°C + 273° = 298$ K

Solving the ideal gas equation for n and evaluating gives

$$n = \frac{PV}{RT} = \frac{(0.980\text{ atm})(0.405\text{ L})}{\left(0.0821\,\dfrac{\text{L}\cdot\text{atm}}{\text{mol}\cdot\text{K}}\right)(298\text{ K})} = 0.0162\text{ mol O}_2$$

(b) $\underset{?}{\text{g KClO}_3} = 0.0162\text{ mol O}_2 \times \dfrac{2\text{ mol KClO}_3}{3\text{ mol O}_2} \times \dfrac{122.6\text{ g KClO}_3}{1\text{ mol KClO}_3} = 1.32\text{ g KClO}_3$

The sample contained 1.32 grams of $KClO_3$. The percent of $KClO_3$ in the sample is

$$\%\text{ KClO}_3 = \frac{\text{g KClO}_3}{\text{g sample}} \times 100\% = \frac{1.32\text{ g}}{1.80\text{ g}} \times 100\% = \boxed{73.3\%\text{ KClO}_3}$$

You should now work Exercise 84.

Our study of stoichiometry has shown that substances react in definite mole and mass proportions. Using previously discussed gas laws, we can show that gases also react in simple, definite proportions by volume. For example, *one* volume of hydrogen always combines (reacts) with *one* volume of chlorine to form *two* volumes of hydrogen chloride, if all volumes are measured at the same temperature and pressure

$$H_2(g) + Cl_2(g) \longrightarrow 2HCl(g)$$
$$\text{1 volume} + \text{1 volume} \longrightarrow \text{2 volumes}$$

Volumes may be expressed in any units as long as the same unit is used for all. Joseph Louis Gay-Lussac (1778–1850) summarized many experimental observations on combining volumes of gases, leading to **Gay-Lussac's Law of Combining Volumes**:

> At constant temperature and pressure, the volumes of gases that react or are formed can be expressed as a ratio of simple whole numbers.

Production of a gas by a reaction.

$$2\text{NaOH}(aq) + 2\text{Al}(s) + 6\text{H}_2\text{O}(\ell) \longrightarrow$$
$$2\text{Na}[\text{Al}(\text{OH})_4](aq) + 3\text{H}_2(g)$$

This reaction is used in some solid drain cleaners.

STOP & THINK
As before, you will find it especially helpful to express units in complete terms—mol O_2, mol $KClO_3$, g $KClO_3$, and g sample.

► Among Gay-Lussac's many contributions to early chemistry were his co-discovery of boron, his thorough report of the properties of the newly discovered iodine, and his development of *volumetric analysis,* in which the volume of a solution of one reactant is used to determine the amount of another reactant.

▶ This applies only to *gaseous* substances at the same temperature and pressure. No generalizations can be made about the volumes of solids and liquids as they undergo chemical reactions.

The ratio corresponds to the coefficients in the balanced equation for the reaction. Hundreds of examples based on experimental observations could be cited. Here are a few.

1. One volume of nitrogen can react with three volumes of hydrogen to form two volumes of ammonia

$$N_2(g) + 3H_2(g) \longrightarrow 2NH_3(g)$$
1 volume + 3 volumes $\longrightarrow$ 2 volumes

2. One volume of methane reacts with (burns in) two volumes of oxygen to give one volume of carbon dioxide and two volumes of steam

$$CH_4(g) + 2O_2(g) \longrightarrow CO_2(g) + 2H_2O(g)$$
1 volume + 2 volumes $\longrightarrow$ 1 volume + 2 volumes

▶ Mole ratios are equal to volume ratios only for gaseous reactants and products. Gay-Lussac's Law does not apply to any solid or liquid reactants or products that might be present.

3. Sulfur (a solid) reacts with one volume of oxygen to form one volume of sulfur dioxide

$$S(s) + O_2(g) \longrightarrow SO_2(g)$$
1 volume $\longrightarrow$ 1 volume

4. Four volumes of ammonia burn in five volumes of oxygen to produce four volumes of nitric oxide and six volumes of steam

$$4NH_3(g) + 5O_2(g) \longrightarrow 4NO(g) + 6H_2O(g)$$
4 volumes   5 volumes $\longrightarrow$ 4 volumes   6 volumes

12-13 The Kinetic–Molecular Theory

As early as 1738, Daniel Bernoulli (1700–1782) envisioned gaseous molecules in ceaseless motion striking the walls of their container and thereby exerting pressure. In 1857, Rudolf Clausius (1822–1888) published a theory that attempted to explain various experimental observations that had been summarized by Boyle's, Dalton's, Charles's, and Avogadro's laws. The basic assumptions of the **kinetic–molecular theory** for an ideal gas follow.

1. Gases consist of discrete molecules. The individual molecules are very small and are very far apart relative to their own sizes.

2. The gas molecules are in continuous, random, straight-line motion with varying velocities.

3. The collisions between gas molecules and with the walls of the container are elastic; the total energy is conserved during a collision; that is, there is no net energy gain or loss.

4. At any given instant, only a small fraction of the molecules are involved in collisions. Between collisions, the molecules exert no attractive or repulsive forces on one another; instead, each molecule travels in a straight line with a constant velocity.

The observation that gases can be easily compressed indicates that the molecules are far apart. At ordinary temperatures and pressures, the gas molecules themselves occupy an insignificant fraction of the total volume of the container. Near temperatures and pressures at which a gas liquefies, the gas does not behave ideally (see Section 12-15) and attractions or repulsions among gas molecules are significant.

Kinetic energy is the energy a body possesses by virtue of its motion. It is $\frac{1}{2}mu^2$, where m, the body's mass, can be expressed in grams and u, its speed, can be expressed in meters per second (m/s). The assumptions of the kinetic–molecular theory can be used to relate temperature and molecular kinetic energy (see the Enrichment section, pages 431–433).

The *average* kinetic energy of gaseous molecules is directly proportional to the absolute temperature of the sample. The *average* kinetic energies of molecules of different gases are equal at a given temperature.

For instance, the average kinetic energies of the molecules are the same in samples of He, H_2O, N_2, and O_2 at the same temperature. But the lightest molecules, He, have much higher average velocities than do the heavier molecules, H_2O, N_2, and O_2, at the same temperature (Figure 12-8).

We can summarize this very important result from the kinetic–molecular theory.

$$\text{average molecular } KE = \overline{KE} \propto T$$

or

$$\text{average molecular speed} = \overline{u} \propto \sqrt{\frac{T}{\text{molecular weight}}}$$

▶ A bar over a quantity denotes an *average* of that quantity.

Molecular kinetic energies of gases increase with increasing temperature and decrease with decreasing temperature. We have referred only to the *average* kinetic energy; in a given sample, some molecules are moving quite rapidly while others are moving more slowly. Figure 12-9 shows the distribution of speeds of gaseous molecules at two temperatures.

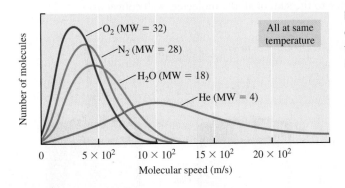

Figure 12-8 The effect of molecular weight on the distribution of molecular speeds at a given temperature. On average, lighter molecules such as He move faster than heavier ones such as O_2.

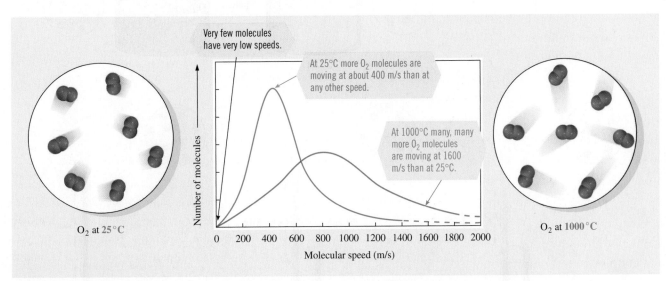

Figure 12-9 The distribution of molecular speeds. This graph shows the relative numbers of O_2 molecules having a given speed at 25°C and at 1000°C. At 25°C, most O_2 molecules have speeds between 200 and 600 m/s (450–1350 miles per hour). Some of the molecules have very high speeds, so the distribution curve approaches the horizontal axis very slowly. The average molecular speed is higher at 1000°C than at 25°C.

▶ The mathematical description of this distribution of molecular speeds is referred to as the *Maxwell-Boltzmann distribution function*.

The kinetic–molecular theory satisfactorily explains most of the observed behavior of gases in terms of molecular behavior. Let's look at the gas laws in terms of the kinetic–molecular theory.

Boyle's Law

The pressure exerted by a gas on the walls of its container is caused by gas molecules striking the walls. Pressure depends on two factors: (1) the number of molecules striking the walls per unit time and (2) how vigorously the molecules strike the walls. If the temperature is held constant, the average speed and the average force of the collisions remain the same. But halving the volume of a sample of gas doubles the pressure because twice as many molecules strike a given area on the walls per unit time. Likewise, doubling the volume of a sample of gas halves the pressure because only half as many gas molecules strike a given area on the walls per unit time (Figure 12-10).

Dalton's Law

In a gas sample the molecules are very far apart and do not attract one another significantly. Each kind of gas molecule acts independently of the presence of the other kind. The molecules of each gas thus collide with the walls with a frequency and vigor that do not change even if other molecules are present (Figure 12-11). As a result, each gas exerts its own partial pressure that is independent of the presence of other gases, and the total pressure is due to the sum of all the molecule–wall collisions.

Figure 12-10 A molecular interpretation of Boyle's Law—the change in pressure of a gas with changes in volume (at constant temperature). The entire apparatus is enclosed in a vacuum. In the smaller volume, more molecules strike the walls per unit time to give a higher pressure.

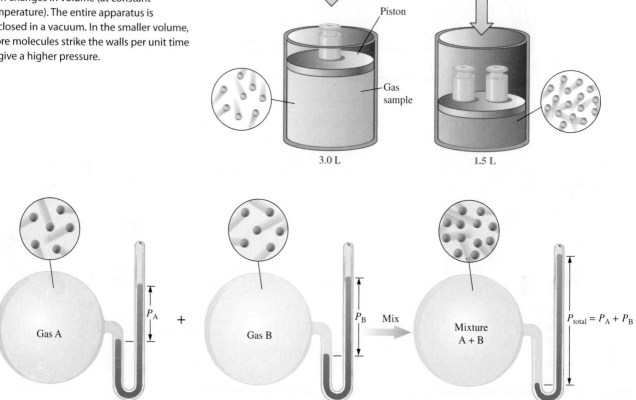

Figure 12-11 A molecular interpretation of Dalton's Law. The molecules act independently in the mixture, so each gas exerts its own partial pressure due to its molecular collisions with the walls. The total gas pressure is the sum of the partial pressures of the component gases.

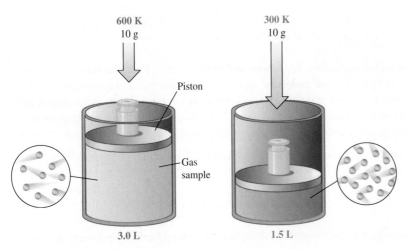

Figure 12-12 A molecular interpretation of Charles's Law—the change in volume of a gas with changes in temperature (at constant pressure). At the lower temperature, molecules strike the walls less often and less vigorously. Thus, the volume must be less to maintain the same pressure.

Charles's Law

Recall that average kinetic energy is directly proportional to the absolute temperature. Doubling the *absolute* temperature of a sample of gas doubles the average kinetic energy of the gaseous molecules, and the increased force of the collisions of molecules with the walls doubles the volume at constant pressure. Similarly, halving the absolute temperature decreases kinetic energy to half its original value; at constant pressure, the volume decreases by half because of the reduced vigor of the collision of gaseous molecules with the container walls (Figure 12-12).

ENRICHMENT

Kinetic–Molecular Theory, the Ideal Gas Equation, and Molecular Speeds

In 1738, Daniel Bernoulli derived Boyle's Law from Newton's laws of motion applied to gas molecules. This derivation was the basis for an extensive mathematical development of the kinetic–molecular theory more than a century later by Clausius, Maxwell, Boltzmann, and others. Although we do not need to study the detailed mathematical presentation of this theory, we can gain some insight into its concepts from the reasoning behind Bernoulli's derivation. Here we present that reasoning based on proportionality arguments.

In the kinetic–molecular theory pressure is viewed as the result of collisions of gas molecules with the walls of the container. As each molecule strikes a wall, it exerts a small impulse. The pressure is the total force thus exerted on the walls divided by the area of the walls. The total force on the walls (and thus the pressure) is proportional to two factors: (1) the impulse exerted by each collision and (2) the rate of collisions (number of collisions in a given time interval).

$$P \propto (\text{impulse per collision}) \times (\text{rate of collisions})$$

Let us represent the mass of an individual molecule by m and its speed by u. The heavier the molecule is (greater m) and the faster it is moving (greater u), the harder it pushes on the wall when it collides. The impulse due to each molecule is proportional to its *momentum, mu*.

▶ Recall that momentum is mass × speed.

$$\text{impulse per collision} \propto mu$$

(continued)

(Enrichment, continued)

The rate of collisions, in turn, is proportional to two factors. First, the rate of collision must be proportional to the molecular speed; the faster the molecules move, the more often they reach the wall to collide. Second, this collision rate must be proportional to the number of molecules per unit volume, N/V. The greater the number of molecules, N, in a given volume, the more molecules collide in a given time interval.

$$\text{rate of collisions} \propto (\text{molecular speed}) \times (\text{molecules per unit volume})$$

or

$$\text{rate of collisions} \propto (u) \times \left(\frac{N}{V}\right)$$

We can introduce these proportionalities into the one describing pressure, to conclude that

$$P \propto (mu) \times u \times \frac{N}{V} \quad \text{or} \quad P \propto \frac{Nmu^2}{V} \quad \text{or} \quad PV \propto Nmu^2$$

At any instant not all molecules are moving at the same speed, u. We should reason in terms of the *average* behavior of the molecules, and express the quantity u^2 in average terms as $\overline{u^2}$, the *mean-square speed*.

$$PV \propto Nm\overline{u^2}$$

▶ $\overline{u^2}$ is the average of the squares of the molecular speeds. It is proportional to the square of the average speed, but the two quantities are not equal.

Not all molecules collide with the walls at right angles, so we must average (using calculus) over all the trajectories. This gives a proportionality constant of $\frac{1}{3}$, and

$$PV = \tfrac{1}{3} Nm\overline{u^2}$$

This describes the quantity PV (pressure × volume) in terms of *molecular quantities*—number of molecules, molecular masses, and molecular speeds. The number of molecules, N, is given by the number of moles, n, times Avogadro's number, N_{Av}, or $N = nN_{Av}$. Making this substitution, we obtain

$$PV = \tfrac{1}{3} nN_{Av}\, m\overline{u^2}$$

The ideal gas equation describes (pressure × volume) in terms of *measurable quantities*—number of moles and absolute temperature.

$$PV = nRT$$

So we see that the ideas of the kinetic–molecular theory lead to an equation of the same form as the macroscopic ideal gas equation. Thus, the molecular picture of the theory is consistent with the ideal gas equation and gives support to the theory. Equating the right-hand sides of these last two equations and canceling n gives

$$\tfrac{1}{3} N_{Av}\, m\overline{u^2} = RT$$

This equation can also be written as

$$\tfrac{1}{3} N_{Av} \times (2 \times \tfrac{1}{2}\, m\overline{u^2}) = RT$$

From physics we know that the *kinetic energy* of a particle of mass m moving at speed u is $\frac{1}{2} mu^2$. So we can write

$$\tfrac{2}{3} N_{Av} \times (\text{avg } KE \text{ per molecule}) = RT$$

or

$$N_{Av} \times (\text{avg } KE \text{ per molecule}) = \tfrac{3}{2} RT$$

This equation shows that the absolute temperature is directly proportional to the average molecular kinetic energy, as postulated by the kinetic–molecular theory. Because there are N_{Av} molecules in a mole, the left-hand side of this equation is equal to the total kinetic energy of a mole of molecules.

$$\text{total kinetic energy per mole of gas} = \tfrac{3}{2}RT$$

With this interpretation, the total molecular–kinetic energy of a mole of gas depends only on the temperature, and not on the mass of the molecules or the gas density.

We can also obtain some useful equations for molecular speeds from the previous reasoning. Solving the equation

$$\tfrac{1}{3} N_{Av}\, m\overline{u^2} = RT$$

for **root-mean-square speed**, $u_{rms} = \sqrt{\overline{u^2}}$, we obtain

$$u_{rms} = \sqrt{\frac{3RT}{N_{Av}\, m}}$$

We recall that m is the mass of a single molecule. So $N_{Av}\, m$ is the mass of Avogadro's number of molecules, or one mole of substance; this is equal to the *molecular weight*, M, of the gas.

$$u_{rms} = \sqrt{\frac{3RT}{M}}$$

EXAMPLE 12-21 Molecular Speed

Calculate the root-mean-square speed of H_2 molecules in meters per second at 20°C. Recall that

$$1\,J = 1\frac{kg \cdot m^2}{s^2}$$

Plan

We substitute the appropriate values into the equation relating u_{rms} to temperature and molecular weight. Remember that R must be expressed in the appropriate units.

$$R = 8.314\,\frac{J}{mol \cdot K} = 8.314\,\frac{kg \cdot m^2}{mol \cdot K \cdot s^2}$$

Solution

$$u_{rms} = \sqrt{\frac{3RT}{M}} = \sqrt{\frac{3 \times 8.314\,\dfrac{kg \cdot m^2}{mol \cdot K \cdot s} \times 293\ K}{2.016\,\dfrac{g}{mol} \times \dfrac{1\ kg}{1000\ g}}}$$

$$u_{rms} = \sqrt{3.62 \times 10^6\,m^2/s^2} = 1.90 \times 10^3\ m/s \quad (\text{about 4250 mph})$$

You should now work Exercise 92.

> **S TOP & THINK**
> As this example illustrates, gas molecules are traveling at very high speeds at most temperatures—the higher the temperature and the lighter the molecules, the faster they travel.

12-14 Diffusion and Effusion of Gases

Because gas molecules are in constant, rapid, random motion, they diffuse quickly throughout any container (Figure 12-13). For example, if hydrogen sulfide (the smell of rotten eggs) is released in a large room, the odor can eventually be detected throughout the room.

▶ **Effusion** is the escape of a gas through a tiny hole. **Diffusion** of a gas is the movement, due to random molecular motion, of a gas into a space or the mixing of one gas with another.

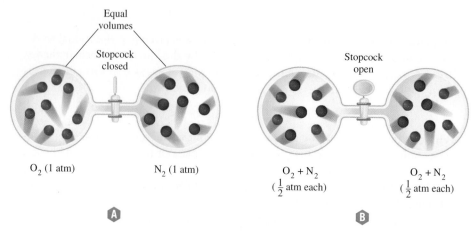

Equal
volumes

Stopcock
closed

Stopcock
open

O_2 (1 atm) N_2 (1 atm)

$O_2 + N_2$
($\frac{1}{2}$ atm each)

$O_2 + N_2$
($\frac{1}{2}$ atm each)

A   **B**

Figure 12-13 A representation of diffusion of gases. The space between the molecules allows for ease of mixing one gas with another. Collisions of molecules with the walls of the container are responsible for the pressure of the gas.

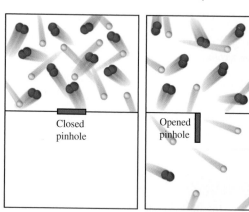

Closed
pinhole

Opened
pinhole

Charles Steele

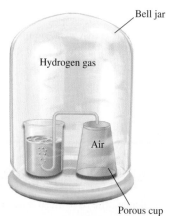

Bell jar

Hydrogen gas

Air

Porous cup

A A molecular view of effusion. Gas molecules are in rapid motion. When a small pinhole is opened, they occasionally strike the pinhole and escape into the previously evacuated bottom chamber. Because He molecules (*yellow*) are lighter than N_2 (*blue*), they move more rapidly. This causes He molecules to strike the pinhole more often, so He escapes into the other chamber more rapidly than N_2.

B Latex balloons were filled with the same volume of He (*yellow*), N_2 (*blue*), and O_2 (*red*). The lighter He molecules effuse through the tiny pores of the latex balloons more rapidly than does N_2 or O_2. The silver party balloon is made of a metal-coated polymer with pores that are too small to allow rapid He effusion.

C If a bell jar full of hydrogen is brought down over a porous cup full of air, rapidly moving hydrogen effuses into the cup faster than the oxygen and nitrogen in the air can effuse out of the cup. This causes an increase in pressure in the cup sufficient to produce bubbles in the water in the beaker.

Figure 12-14 Effusion of gases.

Charles Steele

NH_3 gas (*left*) and HCl gas (*right*) escape from concentrated aqueous solutions. The gases mix and react to form solid ammonium chloride, which appears as a white smoke.

$$NH_3(g) + HCl(g) \longrightarrow NH_4Cl(s)$$

Suggest why the smoke is more prominent nearer the HCl solution.

If a mixture of gases is placed in a container with thin porous walls, the molecules effuse through the walls. Because they move faster, lighter gas molecules effuse through the tiny openings of porous materials faster than heavier molecules (Figure 12-14).

Although they are the most abundant elements in the universe, the gases hydrogen and helium occur only in trace amounts in our atmosphere. This is due to the high average molecular speeds resulting from their low molecular weights. At temperatures in our atmosphere, these molecules reach speeds exceeding the escape velocity required for them to break out of the earth's gravitational pull and diffuse into interplanetary space. Thus, most of the gaseous hydrogen and helium that were probably present in large concentrations in the earth's early atmosphere have long since diffused away. The same is true for the abundance of these gases on other small planets in our solar system, especially those with higher average temperatures than ours (Mercury and Venus). Massive bodies such as stars (including our own sun) are mainly composed of H and He.

12-15 Deviations from Ideal Gas Behavior

Until now our discussions have dealt with *ideal* behavior of gases. By this we mean that the identity of a gas does not affect how it behaves, and the same equations should work equally well for all gases. Under ordinary conditions most gases do behave ideally; their P and V are well described by the ideal gas laws, so they do obey the postulates of the kinetic–molecular theory. According to the kinetic–molecular model, (1) all but a negligible volume of a gas sample is empty space, and (2) the molecules of *ideal* gases do not attract one another because they are so far apart and are considered point masses without any volume.

Under some conditions, however, most gases can have pressures and/or volumes that are *not* accurately predicted by the ideal gas laws. Figure 12-15 illustrates the nonideal behavior of several gases. The ratio of PV/nRT versus pressure should equal 1.0 for an ideal gas. Most gases, however, show marked deviations from ideal behavior at high pressures. This tells us that they are not behaving entirely as postulated by the kinetic–molecular theory.

> Nonideal gas behavior (deviation from the predictions of the ideal gas laws) is most significant at *high pressures* and/or *low temperatures*, that is, near the conditions under which the gas liquefies.

Johannes van der Waals (1837–1923) studied deviations of gases from ideal behavior. In 1867, he empirically adjusted the ideal gas equation

$$P_{ideal}V_{ideal} = nRT$$

to take into account two complicating factors.

1. According to the kinetic–molecular theory, the molecules are so small, relative to the total volume of the gas, that each molecule can move through virtually the entire measured volume of the container, $V_{measured}$ (Figure 12-16a). But under high pressures, a gas is compressed so that the volume of the molecules themselves becomes a significant fraction of the total volume occupied by the gas. As a result, the *available volume*, $V_{available}$, for any molecule to move in is less than the *measured volume* by an amount that depends on the volume excluded by the presence of the other molecules (see Figure 12-16b). To account for this, we subtract a correction factor, nb.

$$V_{available} = V_{measured} - nb$$

▶ The larger the molecular volume, the larger the value of van der Waals' constant b for the gas.

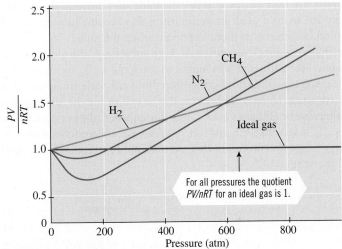

Figure 12-15 Comparison of ideal and nonideal behavior of gases. For a gas that behaves ideally, $PV = nRT$ at all pressures, so $PV/nRT = 1$ at all pressures (*horizontal line*). We can test a gas for ideal behavior by measuring P, V, n, and T for a sample of the gas at various pressures and then calculating PV/nRT. At pressures up to a few atmospheres, all of these plots show PV/nRT near 1, or nearly ideal behavior. Different gases deviate differently from ideal behavior, and these deviations from ideality become more pronounced at higher pressures.

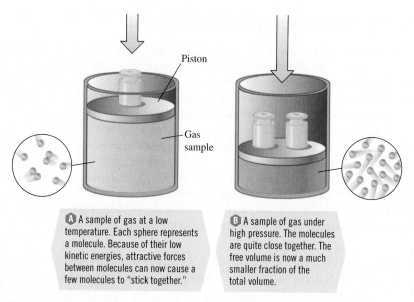

Figure 12-16 A molecular interpretation of deviations from ideal behavior.

The factor nb corrects for the volume occupied by the molecules themselves. Larger molecules have greater values of b, and the greater the number of molecules in a sample (higher n), the larger is the volume correction. The correction term becomes negligibly small, however, when the volume is large (or the pressure is low).

2. The kinetic–molecular theory describes pressure as resulting from molecular collisions with the walls of the container; this theory assumes that attractive forces between molecules are insignificant. For any real gas, the molecules can attract one another. But at higher temperatures, the potential energy due to intermolecular attractions is negligibly small compared with the high kinetic energy due to the rapid motion of the molecules and to the great distances between them. When the temperature is quite low (low kinetic energy), the molecules move so slowly that the potential energy due to even small attractive forces *does* become important. This perturbation becomes even more important when the molecules are very close together (at high pressure). As a result of these attractions, the molecules deviate from their straight-line paths and take longer to reach the walls, so fewer collisions take place in a given time interval. Furthermore for a molecule about to collide with the wall, the attraction by its neighbors causes the collision to be less energetic than it would otherwise be (Figure 12-17). As a consequence, the pressure that the gas exerts, P_{measured}, is less than the pressure it would exert if attractions were truly negligible, $P_{\text{ideally exerted}}$. To correct for this, we subtract a correction factor, n^2a/V^2, from the ideal pressure.

$$P_{\text{measured}} = P_{\text{ideally exerted}} - \frac{n^2a}{V^2_{\text{measured}}}$$

or

$$P_{\text{ideally exerted}} = P_{\text{measured}} + \frac{n^2a}{V^2_{\text{measured}}}$$

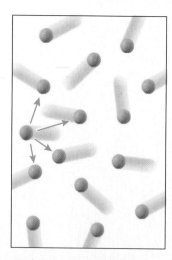

Figure 12-17 A gas molecule strikes the walls of a container with diminished force. The attractive forces between a molecule and its neighbors are significant.

In this correction term, large values of a indicate strong attractive forces. When more molecules are present (greater n) and when the molecules are close together (smaller V^2 in the denominator), the correction term becomes larger. The correction term becomes negligibly small, however, when the volume is large.

When we substitute these two expressions for corrections into the ideal gas equation, we obtain the equation

$$\left(P_{\text{measured}} + \frac{n^2 a}{V^2_{\text{measured}}}\right)(V_{\text{measured}} - nb) = nRT$$

or

$$\left(P + \frac{n^2 a}{V^2}\right)(V - nb) = nRT$$

This is the **van der Waals equation**. In this equation, P, V, T, and n represent the *measured* values of pressure, volume, temperature (expressed on the absolute scale), and number of moles, respectively, just as in the ideal gas equation. The quantities a and b are experimentally derived constants that differ for different gases (Table 12-5). When a and b are both zero, the van der Waals equation reduces to the ideal gas equation.

We can understand the relative values of a and b in Table 12-5 in terms of molecular properties. Note that a for helium is very small. This is the case for all noble gases and many other nonpolar molecules, because only very weak attractive forces, called dispersion forces, exist between them. **Dispersion forces** result from short-lived electrical dipoles produced by the attraction of one atom's nucleus for an adjacent atom's electrons. These forces exist for all molecules but are especially important for nonpolar molecules such as N_2, which lack stronger attractive forces and would never liquefy if dispersion forces did not exist. Polar molecules such as ammonia, NH_3, have permanent charge separations (dipoles), so they exhibit greater forces of attraction for one another. This explains the high value of a for ammonia. Dispersion forces and permanent dipole forces of attraction are discussed in more detail in Chapter 13.

Larger molecules have greater values of b. For instance, H_2, a first-row diatomic molecule, has a greater b value than the first-row monatomic He. The b value for CO_2, which contains three second-row atoms, is greater than that for N_2, which contains only two second-row atoms.

The following example illustrates the deviation of methane, CH_4, from ideal gas behavior under high pressure.

▶ The van der Waals equation, like the ideal gas equation, is known as an *equation of state*, that is, an equation that describes a state of matter.

Table 12-5 van der Waals Constants

Gas	a $(L^2 \cdot atm/mol^2)$	b (L/mol)
H_2	0.244	0.0266
He	0.034	0.0237
N_2	1.39	0.0391
NH_3	4.17	0.0371
CO_2	3.59	0.0427
CH_4	2.25	0.0428

▶ The larger the intermolecular attraction, the larger the value of van der Waals' constant a for the gas.

EXAMPLE 12-22 van der Waals Equation

Calculate the pressure exerted by 1.00 mole of methane, CH_4, in a 500.-mL vessel at 25.0°C assuming (a) ideal behavior and (b) nonideal behavior.

Plan

(a) Ideal gases obey the ideal gas equation. We can solve this equation for P. (b) To describe methane as a nonideal gas, we use the van der Waals equation and solve for P.

Solution

(a) Using the ideal gas equation to describe ideal gas behavior,

$$PV = nRT$$

$$P = \frac{nRT}{V} = \frac{(1.00 \text{ mol})\left(\dfrac{0.0821 \text{ L} \cdot \text{atm}}{\text{mol} \cdot \text{K}}\right)(298 \text{ K})}{0.500 \text{ L}} = 48.9 \text{ atm}$$

(b) Using the van der Waals equation to describe nonideal gas behavior,

$$\left(P + \frac{n^2 a}{V^2}\right)(V - nb) = nRT$$

For CH_4, $a = 2.25$ L^2 atm/mol^2 and $b = 0.0428$ L/mol (see Table 12-5).

$$\left[P + \frac{(1.00 \text{ mol})^2(2.25 \text{ L}^2 \cdot \text{atm/mol}^2)}{(0.500 \text{ L})^2}\right]\left[0.500 \text{ L} - (1.00 \text{ mol})\left(0.0428 \frac{\text{L}}{\text{mol}}\right)\right]$$

$$= (1.00 \text{ mol})\left(\frac{0.0821 \text{ L} \cdot \text{atm}}{\text{mol} \cdot \text{K}}\right)(298 \text{ K})$$

Combining terms and canceling units, we get

$$P + 9.00 \text{ atm} = \frac{24.5 \text{ L} \cdot \text{atm}}{0.457 \text{ L}} = 53.6 \text{ atm}$$

$$P = \boxed{44.6 \text{ atm}}$$

You should now work Exercise 98.

S TOP & THINK
The pressure is less than that calculated from the ideal gas law by 4.3 atm (8.8%). A significant error would be introduced by assuming ideal behavior at this high pressure.

Repeating the calculations of Example 12-22 with the volume twenty times higher ($V = 10.0$ L) gives ideal and nonideal pressures, respectively, of 2.45 and 2.44 atm, a difference of only 0.4%.

Many other equations have been developed to describe the nonideal behavior of gases. Each of these equations contains quantities that must be empirically derived for each gas.

KEY TERMS

Absolute zero   The zero point on the absolute temperature scale; $-273.15°C$ or 0 K; theoretically, the temperature at which molecular motion is a minimum.

Atmosphere (atm)   A unit of pressure; the pressure that will support a column of mercury 760 mm high at 0°C; 760 torr.

Avogadro's Law   At the same temperature and pressure, equal volumes of all gases contain the same number of molecules.

Bar   A unit of pressure; 1.00 bar is equal to 100. kPa (or 0.987 atm).

Barometer   A device for measuring atmospheric pressure (see Figures 12-1 and 12-2). The liquid is usually mercury.

Boyle's Law   At constant temperature, the volume occupied by a given mass of a gas is inversely proportional to the applied pressure.

Charles's Law   At constant pressure, the volume occupied by a definite mass of a gas is directly proportional to its absolute temperature.

Condensed states   The solid and liquid states.

Dalton's Law of Partial Pressures   The total pressure exerted by a mixture of gases is the sum of the partial pressures of the individual gases.

Diffusion   The movement of a substance (e.g., a gas) into a space or the mixing of one substance (e.g., a gas) with another.

Dispersion forces   Weak, short-range attractive forces between short-lived temporary dipoles.

Effusion   The escape of a gas through a tiny hole or a thin porous wall.

Fluids   Substances that flow freely; gases and liquids.

Gay-Lussac's Law of Combining Volumes   At constant temperature and pressure, the volumes of gases that react or are formed can be expressed as ratios of small whole numbers.

Ideal gas   A hypothetical gas that obeys exactly all postulates of the kinetic-molecular theory.

Ideal gas equation   The product of the pressure and volume of an ideal gas is directly proportional to the number of moles of the gas and the absolute temperature.

Kinetic-molecular theory   A theory that attempts to explain macroscopic observations of gases in microscopic or molecular terms.

Manometer   A two-armed barometer (see Figure 12-1).

Mole fraction   The number of moles of a component of a mixture divided by the total number of moles in the mixture.

Partial pressure   The pressure exerted by one gas in a mixture of gases.

Pascal (Pa)   The SI unit of pressure; it is defined as the pressure exerted by a force of one newton acting on an area of one square meter.

Pressure   Force per unit area.

Root-mean-square speed, u_{rms}   The square root of the mean-square speed, $\sqrt{\overline{u^2}}$. This is equal to $\sqrt{\dfrac{3RT}{M}}$ for an ideal gas.

The root-mean-square speed is slightly different from the average speed, but the two quantities are proportional.

Standard molar volume   The volume occupied by one mole of an ideal gas under standard conditions, 22.414 liters.

Standard temperature and pressure (STP)   Standard temperature 0°C (273.15 K), and standard pressure, one atmosphere, are standard conditions for gases.

Torr   A unit of pressure; the pressure that will support a column of mercury 1 mm high at 0°C.

Universal gas constant R, the proportionality constant in the ideal gas equation, $PV = nRT$.

van der Waals equation   An equation of state that extends the ideal gas law to real gases by inclusion of two empirically determined parameters, which are different for different gases.

Vapor   A gas formed by boiling or evaporation of a liquid or sublimation of a solid; a term commonly used when some of the liquid or solid remains in contact with the gas.

Vapor pressure   The pressure exerted by a vapor in equilibrium with its liquid or solid.

EXERCISES

Basic Ideas

1. 🔵 Define pressure. Give a precise scientific definition—one that can be understood by someone without any scientific training.
2. State whether each property is characteristic of all gases, some gases, or no gas: (a) transparent to light; (b) colorless; (c) unable to pass through filter paper; (d) more difficult to compress than liquid water; (e) odorless; (f) settles on standing.
3. Describe the mercury barometer. How does it work?

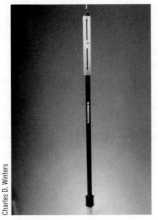

Barometer

4. What is a manometer? How does it work?
5. Express a pressure of 675 torr in the following units: (a) mm Hg; (b) atm; (c) Pa; (d) kPa.
6. A typical laboratory atmospheric pressure reading is 742 torr. Convert this value to (a) psi, (b) cm Hg, (c) inches Hg, (d) kPa, (e) atm, and (f) ft H_2O.
7. Complete the following table.

	atm	torr	Pa	kPa
Standard atmosphere	1			
Partial pressure of nitrogen in the atmosphere		593		
A tank of compressed hydrogen			1.61×10^5	
Atmospheric pressure at the summit of Mt. Everest				33.7

8. State whether each of the following samples of matter is a gas. If the information is insufficient for you to decide, write "insufficient information." (a) A material is in a steel tank at 100. atm pressure. The density of the content is uniform throughout. When the tank is opened to the atmosphere, the material immediately expands, increasing its volume many-fold. (b) A material, on being emitted from an industrial smokestack, rises about 10 m into the air. Viewed against a clear sky, it has a white appearance. (c) 1.0 mL of material weighs 8.2 g. (d) When a material is released from a point 30 ft below the level of a lake at sea level (equivalent in pressure to about 76 cm of mercury), it rises rapidly to the surface, at the same time increasing its volume. (e) A material is transparent and pale green in color. (f) One cubic meter of a material contains as many molecules as 1 m^3 of air at the same temperature and pressure.

9. ▲ The densities of mercury and corn oil are 13.5 g/mL and 0.92 g/mL, respectively. If corn oil were used in a barometer, what would be the height of the column, in meters, at standard atmospheric pressure? (The vapor pressure of the oil is negligible.)
10. Steel tanks for storage of gases are capable of withstanding pressures greater than 150. atm. Express this pressure in psi.
11. Automobile tires are normally inflated to a pressure of 33 psi as measured by a tire gauge. (a) Express this pressure in atmospheres. (b) Assuming standard atmospheric pressure, calculate the internal pressure of the tire.

Tire gauge

Boyle's Law: The Pressure–Volume Relationship

12. (a) On what kinds of observations (measurements) is Boyle's Law based? State the law. (b) Use the statement of Boyle's Law to derive a simple mathematical expression for Boyle's Law.
13. 🔵 Could the words "a fixed number of moles" be substituted for "a definite mass" in the statement of Boyle's Law? Explain.
14. A gas sample contained in a cylinder equipped with a moveable piston occupied 300. mL at a pressure of 2.00 atm. What would be the final pressure if the volume were increased to 567 mL at constant temperature?
15. A balloon that contains 1.50 liters of air at 1.00 atm is taken under water to a depth at which the pressure is 2.50 atm. Calculate the new volume of the balloon. Assume that the temperature remains constant.

🔵 **Molecular Reasoning** exercises   ▲ **More Challenging** exercises   Blue-Numbered exercises solved in Student Solutions Manual

Unless otherwise noted, all content on this page is © Cengage Learning.

16. A 35.0-L sample of gas collected in the upper atmosphere at a pressure of 59.4 torr is compressed into a 150.-mL container at the same temperature. (a) What is the new pressure, in atmospheres? (b) To what volume would the original sample have had to be compressed to exert a pressure of 10.0 atm?

17. A sample of krypton gas occupies 95.0 mL at 0.500 atm. If the temperature remained constant, what volume would the krypton occupy at (a) 5.00 atm, (b) 0.0500 atm, (c) 555 torr, (d) 5.00 torr, and (e) 5.5×10^{-2} torr?

18. ▲ A cylinder containing 10.0 L of helium gas at a pressure of 165 atm is to be used to fill toy balloons to a pressure of 1.1 atm. Each inflated balloon has a volume of 2.5 L. What is the maximum number of balloons that can be inflated? (Remember that 10.0 L of helium at 1.1 atm will remain in the "exhausted" cylinder.)

Charles's Law: The Volume–Temperature Relationship

19. (a) Can an absolute temperature scale based on Fahrenheit rather than Celsius degrees be developed? Why? (b) Can an absolute temperature scale that is based on a "degree" twice as large as a Celsius degree be developed? Why?

20. (a) What does "absolute temperature scale" mean? (b) Describe the experiments that led to the evolution of the absolute temperature scale. What is the relationship between the Celsius and Kelvin temperature scales? (c) What does "absolute zero" mean?

21. Complete the table by making the required temperature conversions. Pay attention to significant figures.

	Temperature		
	K	**°C**	**°F**
Normal boiling point of water		100	
Reference for thermodynamic data	298.15		
Dry ice becomes a gas at atmospheric pressure		−78.5	
The center of the sun (estimated)	1.53×10^7		

Exercises 22 and 24 refer to the plot at the top of the next column. In this figure line A is the plot of volume of a gas versus temperature at a constant pressure for an ideal gas and line B is a plot of the actual behavior of a gas.

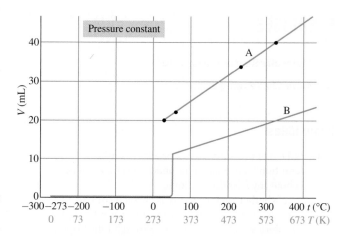

22. (a) Why is a plot of volume versus temperature at constant pressure, such as the preceding plot, a straight line? (b) On what kind of observations (measurements) is Charles's Law based? State the law.

23. A sample of air is originally at 32°C. If P and n are kept constant, to what temperature must the air be cooled to (a) decrease its volume by 25%? (b) decrease its volume to 25% of its original volume?

24. Why does the volume drop to nearly zero at about 50°C on line B? Does this gas show ideal behavior at temperatures above 50°C? Would all gases show similar behavior?

25. A gas occupies a volume of 31.0 L at 19.0°C. If the gas temperature rises to 38.0°C at constant pressure, (a) would you expect the volume to double to 62.0 L? Explain. Calculate the new volume (b) at 38.0°C, (c) at 400. K, and (d) at 0°C.

26. Several balloons are inflated with helium to a volume of 0.82 L at 26°C. One of the balloons was found several hours later; the temperature had dropped to 21°C. What would be the volume of the balloon when found, if no helium has escaped?

Balloons at different temperatures

27. Which of the following statements are true? Which are false? Why is each true or false? *Assume constant pressure* in each case. (a) If a sample of gas is heated from 100°C to 200°C, the volume will double. (b) If a sample of gas is heated from 0.°C to 273°C, the volume will double. (c) If a sample of gas is cooled from 1273°C to 500.°C, the volume will decrease by a factor of 2. (d) If a sample of gas is cooled

🔵 **Molecular Reasoning** exercises   ▲ **More Challenging** exercises   Blue-Numbered exercises solved in Student Solutions Manual

Unless otherwise noted, all content on this page is © Cengage Learning.

from 100.°C to 200.°C, the volume will decrease by a factor of 5. (e) If a sample of gas is heated from 473°C to 1219°C, the volume will increase by a factor of 2.

28. ▲ The device shown here is a gas thermometer. (a) At the ice point, the gas volume is 1.400 L. What would be the new volume if the gas temperature were raised from the ice point to 8.0°C? (b) Assume the cross-sectional area of the graduated arm is 1.0 cm². What would be the difference in height if the gas temperature changed from 0°C to 8.0°C? (c) What modifications could be made to increase the sensitivity of the thermometer?

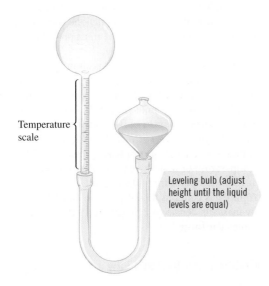

Temperature scale

Leveling bulb (adjust height until the liquid levels are equal)

29. A weather balloon is filled to the volume of 135. L on a day when the temperature is 21°C. If no gases escaped, what would be the volume of the weather balloon after it rises to an altitude where the temperature is −4°C?

30. Calculate the volume of an ideal gas at the temperatures of dry ice (−78.5°C), liquid N_2 (−195.8°C), and liquid He (−268.9°C) if it occupies 5.00 L at 25.0°C. Assume constant pressure. Plot your results, and extrapolate to zero volume. At what temperature would zero volume be theoretically reached?

The Combined Gas Law

31. Classify the relationship between the variables (a) P and V, (b) V and T, and (c) P and T as either (i) directly proportional or (ii) inversely proportional.

32. Prepare sketches of plots of (a) P versus V, (b) P versus $1/V$, (c) V versus T, and (d) P versus T for an ideal gas.

33. A sample of gas occupies 363. mL at STP. Under what pressure would this sample occupy 236. mL if the temperature were increased to 819°C?

34. A 385-mL sample of neon exerts a pressure of 670. torr at 26°C. At what temperature in °C would it exert a pressure of 940. torr in a volume of 560. mL?

35. A 256-mL sample of a gas exerts a pressure of 2.75 atm at 16.0°C. What volume would it occupy at 1.00 atm and 100.°C?

36. Show how Boyle's and Charles's gas laws can be obtained from the combined gas law equation.

STP, Standard Molar Volume, and Gas Densities

37. ☁ How many molecules of an ideal gas are contained in a 2.50-L flask at STP?

38. ☁ (a) What is Avogadro's Law? What does it mean? (b) What does "standard molar volume" mean? (c) Does "standard molar volume" refer to liquids and solids as well as gases? (d) Are there conditions other than STP at which 1 mole of an ideal gas would occupy 22.4 L? Explain.

39. ☁ Using a ground-based telescope and a spectrometer, it has been found that sodium vapor is a significant component of the thin atmosphere of Mercury. Its concentration is estimated to be about 1.0×10^5 atoms per cm³. (a) Express this in moles per liter. (b) The maximum temperature of the atmosphere was measured by Mariner 10 to be about 970.°C. What is the approximate partial pressure of sodium vapor at that temperature?

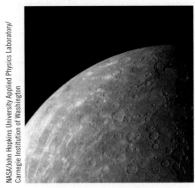

NASA/John Hopkins University Applied Physics Laboratory/ Carnegie Institution of Washington

The surface of the planet Mercury

40. ☁ Ethylene dibromide (EDB) was formerly used as a fumigant for fruits and grains, but now it is banned because it is a potential health hazard. EDB is a liquid that boils at 109°C. Its molecular weight is 188 g/mol. Calculate its density as a gas at 165°C and 1.00 atm.

41. ☁ Nitrogen is slightly less dense than is a sample of air at the same temperature and pressure. Calculate the density of N_2, in g/L, at 1.25 atm and 35°C. If the average molecular weight of the air is 29.2, what is the density of air at the same conditions?

42. ☁ A laboratory technician forgot what the color coding on some commercial cylinders of gas meant but remembered that each of two specific tanks contained one of the following gases: He, Ne, Ar, or Kr. Measurements at STP made on samples of the gases from the two cylinders showed the gas densities to be 3.74 g/L and 0.900 g/L. (a) Determine by calculation which of these gases was present in each tank. (b) Could this determination be made if the densities had been at a temperature and pressure different from STP?

☁ **Molecular Reasoning** exercises ▲ **More Challenging** exercises Blue-Numbered exercises solved in Student Solutions Manual

Unless otherwise noted, all content on this page is © Cengage Learning.

The Ideal Gas Equation

43. Calculate R in $L \cdot atm/mol \cdot K$, in $kPa \cdot dm^3/mol \cdot K$, in $J/mol \cdot K$, and in $kJ/mol \cdot K$.

44. (a) What is an ideal gas? (b) What is the ideal gas equation? (c) Outline the logic used to obtain the ideal gas equation. (d) What is R? How can it be derived?

45. (a) A chemist is preparing to carry out a reaction at high pressure that requires 36.0 mol of hydrogen gas. The chemist pumps the hydrogen into a 12.3-L rigid steel container at 25°C. To what pressure (in atmospheres) must the hydrogen be compressed? (b) What would be the density of the high-pressure hydrogen?

46. Calculate the pressure needed to contain 2.54 mol of an ideal gas at 45°C in a volume of 12.75 L.

47. ☁ (a) How many molecules are in a 500.-mL container of gaseous oxygen if the pressure is 2.50×10^{-7} torr and the temperature is 1225 K? (b) How many grams of oxygen are in the container?

48. ☁ ▲ A barge containing 565 tons of liquid chlorine was involved in an accident. (a) What volume would this amount of chlorine occupy if it were all converted to a gas at 750. torr and 18°C? (b) Assume that the chlorine is confined to a width of 0.500 mile and an average depth of 60. ft. What would be the length, in feet, of this chlorine "cloud"?

49. A piece of dry ice ($CO_2(s)$) has a mass of 22.50 g. It is dropped into an evacuated 2.50-L flask. What is the pressure in the flask at -4°C?

50. What mass of helium, in grams, is required to fill a 5.0-L balloon to a pressure of 1.1 atm at 25°C?

51. What is the pressure exerted by 1.55 g Xe gas at 20.°C in a 560-mL flask?

52. The standard molar volume of an ideal gas is 22.414 liters per mole at STP. However, the standard molar volume of a gas that has a high molecular weight or strong intermolecular attractive forces can deviate significantly from this value. Calculate the standard molar volume of sulfur hexafluoride (SF_6), density = 6.65 g/L at STP, and hydrogen fluoride (HF), density = 0.922 g/L at STP.

Molecular Weights and Formulas for Gaseous Compounds

53. Analysis of a volatile liquid shows that it contains 37.23% carbon, 7.81% hydrogen, and 54.96% chlorine by mass. At 150.°C and 1.00 atm, 500. mL of the vapor has a mass of 0.922 g. (a) What is the molecular weight (mass) of the compound? (b) What is its molecular formula?

54. ▲ A student was given a container of ethane, C_2H_6, that had been closed at STP. By making appropriate measurements, the student found that the mass of the sample of ethane was 0.244 g and the volume of the container was 185 mL. Use the student's data to calculate the molecular weight (mass) of ethane. What percent error is obtained? Suggest some possible sources of the error.

55. Calculate the molecular weight (mass) of a gaseous element if 0.480 g of the gas occupies 367 mL at 365 torr and 45°C. Suggest the identity of the element.

56. A cylinder was found in a storeroom of a manufacturing plant. The label on the cylinder was gone, and no one remembered what the cylinder held. A 0.00500-gram sample was found to occupy 4.13 mL at 23°C and 745 torr. The sample was also found to be composed of only carbon and hydrogen. Identify the gas.

57. ☁ A sample of porous rock was brought back from the planet Farout on the other side of the galaxy. Trapped in the rock was a carbon–oxygen gas. The unknown gas was extracted and evaluated. A volume of 3.70 mL of the gas was collected under the conditions of STP. The mass of the gas sample was determined to be 0.00726 grams. Additional analysis proved that there was only one compound present in the gas sample. What was the most probable identity of the gas based on these analyses?

58. ☁ ▲ A highly volatile liquid was allowed to vaporize completely into a 250.-mL flask immersed in boiling water. From the following data, calculate the molecular weight (in amu per molecule) of the liquid. Mass of empty flask = 65.347 g; mass of flask filled with water at room temperature = 327.4 g; mass of flask and condensed liquid = 65.739 g; atmospheric pressure = 743.3 torr; temperature of boiling water = 99.8°C; density of water at room temperature = 0.997 g/mL.

59. A pure gas contains 85.63% carbon and 14.37% hydrogen by mass. Its density is 2.50 g/L at STP. What is its molecular formula?

Gas Mixtures and Dalton's Law

60. (a) What are partial pressures of gases? (b) State Dalton's Law. Express it symbolically.

61. A sample of oxygen of mass 25.0 g is confined in a vessel at 0°C and 1000. torr. Then 6.00 g of hydrogen is pumped into the vessel at constant temperature. What will be the final pressure in the vessel (assuming only mixing with no reaction)?

62. A gaseous mixture contains 3.23 g of chloroform, $CHCl_3$, and 1.22 g of methane, CH_4. Assuming that both compounds remain as gases, what pressure is exerted by the mixture inside a 50.0-mL metal container at 275°C? What pressure is contributed by the $CHCl_3$?

63. A cyclopropane–oxygen mixture can be used as an anesthetic. If the partial pressures of cyclopropane and oxygen are 140. torr and 560. torr, respectively, what is the ratio of the number of moles of cyclopropane to the number of moles of oxygen in this mixture? What is the corresponding ratio of molecules?

64. What is the mole fraction of each gas in a mixture having the partial pressures of 0.467 atm of He, 0.317 atm of Ar, and 0.277 atm of Xe?

65. ☁ ▲ Assume that unpolluted air has the composition shown in Table 12-2. (a) Calculate the number of molecules of N_2, of O_2, and of Ar in 1.00 L of air at 21°C and 1.00 atm. (b) Calculate the mole fractions of N_2, O_2, and Ar in the air.

66. Individual samples of O_2, N_2, and He are present in three 2.50-L vessels. Each exerts a pressure of 1.50 atm. (a) If

☁ **Molecular Reasoning** exercises　　▲ **More Challenging** exercises　　Blue-Numbered exercises solved in Student Solutions Manual

Unless otherwise noted, all content on this page is © Cengage Learning.

all three gases are forced into the same 1.00-L container with no change in temperature, what will be the resulting pressure? (b) What is the partial pressure of O_2 in the mixture? (c) What are the partial pressures of N_2 and He?

67. Hydrogen was collected over water at 20°C and 757 torr. The volume of this gas sample was 35.3 mL. What volume would the dry hydrogen occupy at STP?

H_2 collected over water

68. A nitrogen sample occupies 249 mL at STP. If the same sample were collected over water at 25°C and 750. torr, what would be the volume of the gas sample?

69. ▲ A study of climbers who reached the summit of Mt. Everest without supplemental oxygen revealed that the partial pressures of O_2 and CO_2 in their lungs were 35 torr and 7.5 torr, respectively. The barometric pressure at the summit was 253 torr. Assume that the lung gases are saturated with moisture at a body temperature of 37°C. Calculate the partial pressure of inert gas (mostly nitrogen) in the climbers' lungs.

70. A 4.00-L flask containing He at 6.00 atm is connected to a 2.00-L flask containing N_2 at 3.00 atm and the gases are allowed to mix. (a) Find the partial pressures of each gas after they are allowed to mix. (b) Find the total pressure of the mixture. (c) What is the mole fraction of helium?

71. A 3.46-liter sample of a gas was collected over water on a day when the temperature was 21°C and the barometric pressure was 718 torr. The dry sample of gas had a mass of 4.20 g. What is the molecular weight of the gas?

Stoichiometry in Reactions Involving Gases

72. ● During a collision, automobile air bags are inflated by the N_2 gas formed by the explosive decomposition of sodium azide, NaN_3.

$$2NaN_3 \longrightarrow 2Na + 3N_2$$

What mass of sodium azide would be needed to inflate a 25.0-L bag to a pressure of 1.40 atm at 25°C?

73. Assuming the volumes of all gases in the reaction are measured at the same temperature and pressure, calculate the volume of water vapor obtainable by the explosive reaction of a mixture of 725 mL of hydrogen gas and 325 mL of oxygen gas.

74. ▲ One liter of sulfur vapor, $S_8(g)$, at 600°C and 1.00 atm is burned in excess pure oxygen to give sulfur dioxide gas, SO_2, measured at the same temperature and pressure. What mass of SO_2 gas is obtained?

75. ● Calculate the volume of methane, CH_4, measured at 300. K and 825 torr, that can be produced by the bacterial breakdown of 1.10 kg of a simple sugar.

$$C_6H_{12}O_6 \longrightarrow 3CH_4 + 3CO_2$$

76. ▲ A common laboratory preparation of oxygen is

$$2KClO_3(s) \xrightarrow{\text{heat/MnO}_2} 2KCl(s) + 3O_2(g)$$

If you were designing an experiment to generate four bottles (each containing 250. mL) of O_2 at 25°C and 762 torr and allowing for 25% waste, what mass of potassium chlorate would be required?

77. Many campers use small propane stoves to cook meals. What volume of air (see Table 12-2) will be required to burn 8.50 L of propane, C_3H_8? Assume all gas volumes are measured at the same temperature and pressure.

$$C_3H_8(g) + 5O_2(g) \longrightarrow 3CO_2(g) + 4H_2O(g)$$

Propane stove

78. If 3.00 L of nitrogen and 7.00 L of hydrogen were allowed to react, how many liters of $NH_3(g)$ could form? Assume all gases are at the same temperature and pressure, and that the limiting reactant is used up.

$$N_2(g) + 3H_2(g) \longrightarrow 2NH_3(g)$$

79. We burn 12.50 L of ammonia in 20.00 L of oxygen at 500.°C. What volume of nitric oxide, NO, gas can form? What volume of steam, $H_2O(g)$, is formed? Assume that all gases are at the same temperature and pressure, and that the limiting reactant is used up.

$$4NH_3(g) + 5O_2(g) \longrightarrow 4NO(g) + 6H_2O(g)$$

80. What mass of KNO_3 would have to be decomposed to produce 21.1 L of oxygen measured at STP?

$$2KNO_3(s) \xrightarrow{\text{heat}} 2KNO_2(s) + O_2(g)$$

81. ● Refer to Exercise 80. An impure sample of KNO_3 that had a mass of 55.8 g was heated until all of the KNO_3 had decomposed. The liberated oxygen occupied 4.22 L at STP. What percentage of the sample was KNO_3? Assume that no impurities decompose to produce oxygen.

● **Molecular Reasoning** exercises ▲ **More Challenging** exercises Blue-Numbered exercises solved in Student Solutions Manual

Unless otherwise noted, all content on this page is © Cengage Learning.

82. 🔵 ▲ Heating a 5.913-g sample of an ore containing a metal sulfide, in the presence of excess oxygen, produces 1.177 L of dry SO_2, measured at 35.0°C and 755 torr. Calculate the percentage by mass of sulfur in the ore.

83. 🔵 ▲ The following reactions occur in a gas mask (a self-contained breathing apparatus) sometimes used by underground miners. The H_2O and CO_2 come from exhaled air, and O_2 is inhaled as it is produced. KO_2 is potassium superoxide. The CO_2 is converted to the solid salt potassium hydrogen carbonate, $KHCO_3$, so that CO_2 is not inhaled in significant amounts.

$$4KO_2(s) + 2H_2O(\ell) \longrightarrow 4KOH(s) + 3O_2(g)$$
$$CO_2(g) + KOH(s) \longrightarrow KHCO_3(s)$$

(a) What volume of O_2, measured at STP, is produced by the complete reaction of 1.25 g of KO_2? (b) What is this volume at body temperature, 37°C, and 1.00 atm? (c) What mass of KOH is produced in part (a)? (d) What volume of CO_2, measured at STP, will react with the mass of KOH of part (c)? (e) What is the volume of CO_2 in part (d) measured at 37°C and 1.00 atm?

84. ▲ Let us represent gasoline as octane, C_8H_{18}. When hydrocarbon fuels burn in the presence of sufficient oxygen, CO_2 is formed.

Reaction A: $2C_8H_{18} + 25O_2 \longrightarrow 16CO_2 + 18H_2O$

But when the supply of oxygen is limited, the poisonous gas carbon monoxide, CO, is formed.

Reaction B: $2C_8H_{18} + 17O_2 \longrightarrow 16CO + 18H_2O$

Any automobile engine, no matter how well tuned, burns its fuel by some combination of these two reactions. Suppose an automobile engine is running at idle speed in a closed garage with air volume 97.5 m³. This engine burns 95.0% of its fuel by reaction A, and the remainder by reaction B. (a) How many liters of octane, density 0.702 g/mL, must be burned for the CO to reach a concentration of 2.00 g/m³? (b) If the engine running at idle speed burns fuel at the rate of 1.00 gal/h (0.0631 L/min), how long does it take to reach the CO concentration in (a)?

The Kinetic–Molecular Theory and Molecular Speeds

85. 🔵 Outline the kinetic–molecular theory.
86. 🔵 Place these gases in order of increasing average molecular speed at 25°C: Kr, CH_4, N_2, CH_2Cl_2.
87. 🔵 How does the kinetic–molecular theory explain (a) Boyle's Law? (b) Dalton's Law? (c) Charles's Law?
88. 🔵 SiH_4 molecules are heavier than CH_4 molecules; yet, according to kinetic–molecular theory, the average kinetic energies of the two gases at the same temperature are equal. How can this be?
89. 🔵 ▲ At 22°C, Cl_2 molecules have some rms speed (which we need not calculate). At what temperature would the rms speed of F_2 molecules be the same?
90. 🔵 ▲(a) How do average speeds of gaseous molecules vary with temperature? (b) Calculate the ratio of the rms speed

of N_2 molecules at 100.°C to the rms speed of the same molecules at 0.0°C.

91. 🔵 How do the average kinetic energies and average speeds of each gas in a mixture compare?
92. 🔵 (a) If you heat a gaseous sample in a fixed volume container, the pressure increases. Use the kinetic–molecular theory to explain the increased pressure. (b) If the volume of a gaseous sample is reduced at constant temperature, the pressure increases. Use the kinetic–molecular theory to explain the increase in pressure.

Deviations from Ideal Gas Behavior

93. 🔵 What is the van der Waals equation? How does it differ from the ideal gas equation?
94. 🔵 Which of the following gases would be expected to behave most nearly ideally under the same conditions: H_2, F_2, HF? Which one would be expected to deviate from ideal behavior the most? Explain both answers.
95. 🔵 Does the effect of intermolecular attraction on the properties of a gas become more significant or less significant if (a) the gas is compressed to a smaller volume at constant temperature? (b) more gas is forced into the same volume at the same temperature? (c) the temperature of the gas is raised at constant pressure?
96. 🔵 Does the effect of molecular volume on the properties of a gas become more significant or less significant if (a) the gas is compressed to a smaller volume at constant temperature? (b) more gas is forced into the same volume at the same temperature? (c) the temperature of the gas is raised at constant pressure?
97. 🔵 In each pair of gases below, tell which will effuse faster: (a) CO_2 or F_2; (b) O_2 or N_2; (c) C_2H_4 or C_2H_6; (d) two chlorofluorocarbons: $CFCl_3$ or $C_2Cl_2F_4$.
98. Find the pressure of a sample of carbon tetrachloride, CCl_4, if 1.00 mol occupies 35.0 L at 77.0°C (slightly above its normal boiling point). Assume that CCl_4 obeys (a) the Ideal Gas Law; (b) the van der Waals equation. The van der Waals constants for CCl_4 are $a = 20.39$ L² · atm/mol² and $b = 0.1383$ L/mol. (c) Repeat the calculations in parts (a) and (b) using a 3.10-mol gas sample confined to 5.75 L at 135°C.
99. A sample of gas has a molar volume of 10.1 L at a pressure of 745 torr and a temperature of −138°C. Is the gas behaving ideally?
100. You want to store 165 g of CO_2 gas in a 12.5-L tank at room temperature (25°C). Calculate the pressure the gas would have using (a) the Ideal Gas Law and (b) the van der Waals equation. For CO_2, $a = 3.59$ atm · L²/mol² and $b = 0.0427$ L/mol.
101. 🔵 At higher temperatures and very low pressures, gases behave ideally, but as the pressure is increased the product PV becomes less than the product nRT. Give a molecular level explanation of this fact.

Mixed Exercises

102. Liquid iron at 1600.°C has a density of 6.88 g/cm³, and at 20.°C solid iron has a density of 7.86 g/cm³. Using these data, calculate the molar volume of iron at each temperature. Compare your calculated value with those in Table 12-1 for different compounds.

103. Given that the molar volume of liquid carbon dioxide at −37°C is 39.9 mL/mol and the molar volume of solid carbon dioxide at −79°C is 28.2 mL/mol, calculate the density of carbon dioxide at each set of conditions. If carbon dioxide were to act as an ideal gas, what would be its density at 50°C? When one compares each value for density to the state of the carbon dioxide, which phase change results in the greater change in density?

104. A student is to perform a laboratory experiment that requires the evolution and collection of 85 mL of dry oxygen gas at one atmosphere and 25°C. What is the minimum mass of water required to generate the oxygen by electrolysis of water?

105. A tilting McLeod gauge is used to measure very low pressures of gases in glass vacuum lines in the laboratory. It operates by compressing a large volume of gas at low pressure to a much smaller volume so that the pressure is more easily measured. What is the pressure of a gas in a vacuum line if a 53.3-mL volume of the gas, when compressed to 0.235 mL, supports a 16.9-mm column of mercury?

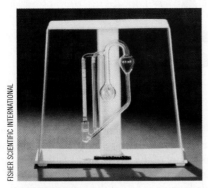

A McLeod gauge

FISHER SCIENTIFIC INTERNATIONAL

106. Imagine that you live in a cabin with an interior volume of 175 m³. On a cold morning your indoor air temperature is 10.°C, but by the afternoon the sun has warmed the cabin air to 18.°C. The cabin is not sealed; therefore, the pressure inside is the same as it is outdoors. Assume that the pressure remains constant during the day. How many cubic meters of air would have been forced out of the cabin by the sun's warming? How many liters?

107. A particular tank can safely hold gas up to a pressure of 44.3 atm. When the tank contains 38.1 g of N_2 at 25°C, the gas exerts a pressure of 10.1 atm. What is the highest temperature to which the gas sample can be heated safely?

108. 🔹 Find the molecular weight (mass) of Freon-12 (a chlorofluorocarbon) if 8.29 L of vapor at 200.°C and 790. torr has a mass of 26.8 g.

109. Write an equation in which density is set equal to the terms R, P, T, and other terms, if needed.

110. Write an equation in which the relationship between P and T is expressed at constant n and V. Give a nonlaboratory example in which this relationship can be applied.

111. A flask of unknown volume was filled with air to a pressure of 3.25 atm. This flask was then attached to an evacuated flask with a known volume of 5.00 L, and the air was allowed to expand into the flask. The final pressure of the air (in both flasks) was 2.40 atm. Calculate the volume of the first flask.

112. ▲ Relative humidity is the ratio of the pressure of water vapor in the air to the pressure of water vapor in air that is saturated with water vapor at the same temperature.

$$\text{relative humidity} = \frac{\text{actual partial pressure of } H_2O}{\text{partial pressure of } H_2O \text{ vapor if sat'd}}$$

Often this quantity is multiplied by 100 to give the percent relative humidity. Suppose the percent relative humidity is 80.0% at 91.4°F (33.0°C) in a house with volume 245 m³. Then an air conditioner is turned on. Due to the condensation of water vapor on the cold coils of the air conditioner, water vapor is also removed from the air as it cools. After the air temperature has reached 77.0°F (25.0°C), the percent relative humidity is measured to be 15.0%. (a) What mass of water has been removed from the air in the house? (*Reminder*: Take into account the difference in saturated water vapor pressure at the two temperatures.) (b) What volume would this liquid water occupy at 25°C? (Density of liquid water at 25.0°C = 0.997 g/cm³.)

113. A 450.-mL flask contains 0.500 g of nitrogen gas at a pressure of 744 torr. Are these data sufficient to allow you to calculate the temperature of the gas? If not, what is missing? If so, what is the temperature in °C?

114. Use both the Ideal Gas Law and the van der Waals equation to calculate the pressure exerted by a 4.00-mol sample of ammonia in a 25.0-L container at 100.°C. By what percentage of the ideal pressure do the two results differ?

115. What volume of hydrogen fluoride at 743 torr and 24°C will be formed by the reaction of 38.3 g of xenon difluoride with a stoichiometric amount of water? The *unbalanced* equation is

$$XeF_2(s) + H_2O(\ell) \longrightarrow Xe(g) + O_2(g) + HF(g)$$

What volumes of oxygen and xenon will be formed under these conditions?

116. Cyanogen is 46.2% carbon and 53.8% nitrogen by mass. At a temperature of 25°C and a pressure of 750. torr, 1.00 g of cyanogen gas occupies 0.476 L. Determine the empirical formula and the molecular formula of cyanogen.

117. 🔹 Incandescent light bulbs contain noble gases, such as argon, so that the filament will last longer. The approximate volume of a 100-watt bulb is 130. cm³, and the bulb contains 0.125 g of argon. How many grams of argon would be contained in a 150-watt bulb under the same pressure and temperature conditions if the volume of the larger wattage bulb were 180. cm³?

🔹 **Molecular Reasoning** exercises ▲ **More Challenging** exercises Blue-Numbered exercises solved in Student Solutions Manual

Unless otherwise noted, all content on this page is © Cengage Learning.

Conceptual Exercises

118. In the United Kingdom the Celsius scale has been used almost exclusively for expressing temperatures since the 1970s, except that some broadcasters and publications still quote Fahrenheit temperatures in weather forecasts for the benefit of those born before 1950. In London the average minimum temperature in December is 38. Is that more likely to be 38°F, 38°C, or 38 K? In July the average maximum temperature is 22. Is that more likely to be 22°F, 22°C, or 22 K? By contrast, in the permanently shaded south polar basin of the moon the surface temperature may be 40. Is that more likely to be 40°F, 40°C, or 40 K?

119. The effectiveness of a steam engine depends, in part, on the large change in volume that occurs when liquid water is converted to steam. The density of liquid water at 100°C is 0.958 g/mL and the density of steam at 100°C is 0.598 g/L. Calculate the molar volume of liquid water and steam at 100°C and the ratio of the molar volume of steam to that of liquid water.

120. ▲ An attempt was made to collect carbon dioxide, isolated from the decomposition of a carbonate-containing mineral, by first bubbling the gas through pure liquid acetic acid. The experiment yielded 500. mL of a gaseous mixture of acetic acid and carbon dioxide at 1.00 atm and 16.0°C. The vapor pressure of pure acetic acid at 16.0°C is 400. torr. What should be the total mass of the collected sample?

121. Acetylene (C_2H_2), the gas used in welders' torches, is produced by the reaction of calcium carbide (CaC_2) with water. The other reaction product is calcium hydroxide. (a) Write the chemical equation for the production of C_2H_2. (b) What volume of C_2H_2, measured at 22°C and 965 torr, would be produced from the complete reaction of 10.2 g of CaC_2 with 5.23 g of H_2O?

Acetylene torch

122. Redraw Figure 12-12 so that it not only depicts the decrease in space between molecules as the system is cooled from 600. K to 300. K but also emphasizes the change in kinetic energy.

123. Suppose you were asked to supply a particular mass of a specified gas in a container of fixed volume at a specified pressure and temperature. Is it likely that you could fulfill the request? Explain.

124. 🞈 The gas molecules in the box undergo a reaction at constant temperature and pressure.

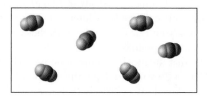

(a) If the initial volume is 2.5 L and the final volume is 1.25 L, which of the following boxes (i–v) could be the products of the reaction? Explain your reasoning.
(b) Represent the pink atoms as "A" and the yellow atoms as "B," and write the equation for the chemical reaction that occurs.

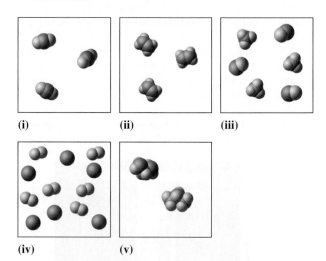

(i)   (ii)   (iii)

(iv)   (v)

125. A 503-mL flask contains 0.0243 mol of an ideal gas at a given temperature and pressure. Another flask contains 0.0388 mol of the gas at the same temperature and pressure. What is the volume of the second flask?

126. Mole fraction is one of the few quantities that is expressed as a fraction. Frequently, percent is used instead. Cite an example earlier in this textbook where percent was used instead of a fraction. Write an equation that relates mole fraction and mole percent.

127. 🞈 Explain why gases at high pressure or low temperature are less likely to behave ideally.

128. Nitrogen, oxygen, argon, and carbon dioxide make up 99.997% (by volume) of air. However, a small amount of each of the other noble gases is present in air:

Gas	Partial Pressure, atm
Neon	0.00001818
Helium	0.00000524
Krypton	0.00000114
Xenon	0.000000087

How many atoms of xenon are there in each liter of air?

🞈 **Molecular Reasoning** exercises   ▲ **More Challenging** exercises   Blue-Numbered exercises solved in Student Solutions Manual

Unless otherwise noted, all content on this page is © Cengage Learning.

129. The octane rating of a gasoline is a measure of its autoignition (knock) resistance. It is a number that gives the percentage of isooctane (C_8H_{18}) in a mixture of isooctane and n-heptane (C_7H_{16}) that would have the same anti-knocking capacity. For example, "regular" gasoline, with an octane rating of 87, has the same tendency to knock as a mixture with 87% isooctane and 13% n-heptane. When isooctane combusts, it reacts with oxygen to produce carbon dioxide and water. Write the complete, balanced equation for the combustion of isooctane. One gallon of isooctane will produce 509 L of vapor at STP. When this gas burns, what volume of carbon dioxide, at STP, would be produced?

130. Because the average kinetic energies of molecules of different gases are equal at a given temperature, and the kinetic energy of a molecule is directly proportional to its mass and the square of its velocity, molecules of gases that have lower molecular weights have higher average velocities than molecules of gases that have higher molecular weights. At 25°C, does every molecule of hydrogen (H_2) have a higher velocity than every molecule of oxygen (O_2)? Would any molecules of hydrogen have velocities near 0 m/s? Would any molecules of oxygen have velocities greater than the average velocity of all the hydrogen molecules?

131. A gas that is "lighter than air" has a molecular weight less than the weighted average of the molecular weights of the gases in air, 28.966. So, how does a molecule like Freon-12 (CCl_2F_2), with a molecular weight of 120.9, get into the stratosphere?

Building Your Knowledge

132. A 5.00-L reaction vessel contains hydrogen at a partial pressure of 0.588 atm and oxygen gas at a partial pressure of 0.302 atm. Which element is the limiting reactant in the following reaction?

$$2H_2(g) + O_2(g) \longrightarrow 2H_2O(g)$$

133. Suppose the gas mixture in Exercise 132 is ignited and the reaction produces the theoretical yield of the product. What would be the partial pressure of each substance present in the final mixture?

134. A sample of carbon was burned in pure oxygen, forming carbon dioxide. The CO_2 was then bubbled into 3.50 L of 0.437 M NaOH, forming sodium carbonate, as shown by the following reaction.

$$CO_2 + 2NaOH \longrightarrow Na_2CO_3 + H_2O$$

Following the reaction, the excess NaOH was exactly neutralized with 1.71 L of 0.350 M HCl. What volume of O_2, measured at 8.6 atm and 20°C, was consumed in the process?

135. When magnesium carbonate, $MgCO_3$, is heated to a high temperature, it decomposes.

$$MgCO_3(s) \xrightarrow{\text{heat}} MgO(s) + CO_2(g)$$

A 20.29-gram sample of impure magnesium carbonate is completely decomposed at 1000.°C in a previously evacuated 2.00-L reaction vessel. After the reaction was complete, the solid residue (consisting only of MgO and the original impurities) had a mass of 15.90 grams. Assume that no other constituent of the sample produced a gas and that the volume of any solid was negligible compared with the gas volume. (a) How many grams of CO_2 were produced? (b) What was the pressure of the CO_2 produced? (c) What percent of the original sample was magnesium carbonate?

136. One natural source of atmospheric carbon dioxide is precipitation reactions such as the precipitation of silicates in the oceans.

$$Mg^{2+}(aq) + SiO_2(\text{dispersed}) + 2HCO_3^-(aq) \longrightarrow$$
$$MgSiO_3(s) + 2CO_2(g) + H_2O(\ell)$$

How many grams of magnesium silicate would be precipitated during the formation of 100. L of carbon dioxide at 30.°C and 775 torr?

137. Table 12-2 states that dry air is 20.94% (by volume) oxygen. What is the partial pressure of oxygen under the conditions of STP? *Hint:* For gaseous samples the mole ratios are equal to the volume ratios.

138. Sulfur dioxide is a common air pollutant. It is known to cause health problems, coughing, even death at concentrations of 1.4 mg/L of air. (a) What is the molarity of sulfur dioxide when its concentration is 0.135 mg/L? (b) What is the mole fraction of sulfur dioxide at a concentration of 1.4 mg/L? Assume that the density of dry air is 1.29 g/L.

139. ⬢ Which graph represents the distribution of molecular speeds for the gases acetylene (C_2H_2) and N_2? Both gases are in the same container.

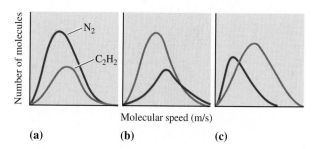

(a)   (b)   (c)

Beyond the Textbook

NOTE: *Whenever the answer to an exercise depends on information obtained from a source other than this textbook, the source must be included as an essential part of the answer.*

140. Go to **www.liv.ac.uk/chemistry/links/refbiog.html** and subsequent pages as needed or another website and locate information on gas laws as they relate to Boyle, Charles, and Dalton. (a) Did the careers of Boyle, Charles, and Dalton overlap? Which one's work is the most recent? (b) What physical impairment is also known as Daltonism? How is Daltonism related to John Dalton's death?

⬢ **Molecular Reasoning** exercises   ▲ **More Challenging** exercises   Blue-Numbered exercises solved in Student Solutions Manual

Unless otherwise noted, all content on this page is © Cengage Learning.

141. Go to **www.aquaholic.com/gasses/charles.htm** and locate information on Charles's Law. (a) The relationship that "at constant volume, pressure divided by temperature is equal to a constant" was not given a name in this book by Whitten, Davis, Peck, and Stanley. In this website what is the name given to this relationship? What is wrong with this law as stated on this web page? (b) In the calculation of pressure, why was 14.7 subtracted from the calculated value of 3412.8?

142. Go to **www.liv.ac.uk/chemistry/links/refbiog.html** or another website and locate information on the lives of Amedeo Avogadro, Stanislao Cannizzaro, and Jean Baptiste Dumas. (a) How were the careers of Amedeo Avogadro and Stanislao Cannizzaro intertwined? (b) How was Jean Baptiste Dumas associated with early studies of gases?

Chemical Thermodynamics

15

Thousands of windmills such as these in west Texas are becoming an increasingly important source of electricity. The kinetic energy of wind turns large windmill-powered turbines, which in turn convert their kinetic energy to electrical (potential) energy.

Raymond E. Davis

OBJECTIVES

After you have studied this chapter, you should be able to

▶ Understand the terminology of thermodynamics, and the meaning of the signs of changes

▶ Use the concept of state functions

▶ Carry out calculations of calorimetry to determine changes in energy and enthalpy

▶ Use Hess's Law to find the enthalpy change, ΔH, for a reaction from other thermochemical equations with known ΔH values

▶ Use Hess's Law to find the standard enthalpy change, ΔH^0, for a reaction by using tabulated values of standard molar enthalpies of formation

▶ Use Hess's Law to find the molar enthalpy of formation, ΔH_f^0, given ΔH^0 for a reaction and the known molar enthalpies of formation of the other substances in the reaction

▶ Use the First Law of Thermodynamics to relate heat, work, and energy changes

▶ Relate the work done on or by a system to changes in its volume

▶ Use bond energies to estimate heats of reaction for gas phase reactions; use ΔH values for gas phase reactions to find bond energies

▶ Understand what is meant by a product-favored (spontaneous) process and by a reactant-favored (nonspontaneous) process

▶ Understand the relationship of entropy to the dispersal of energy and dispersal of matter (disorder) in a system

▶ Use tabulated values of absolute entropies to calculate the entropy change, ΔS^0

▶ Understand how the spontaneity of a process is related to entropy changes—the Second Law of Thermodynamics

▶ Calculate changes in Gibbs free energy, ΔG, by two methods: (a) from values of ΔH and ΔS and (b) from tabulated values of standard molar free energies of formation; know when to use each type of calculation

▶ Use ΔG^0 to predict whether a process is product-favored (spontaneous) at constant T and P

▶ Understand how changes in temperature can affect the spontaneity of a process

▶ Predict the temperature range of spontaneity of a chemical or physical process

▶ Some forms of energy are potential, kinetic, electrical, nuclear, heat, and light.

Energy is very important in every aspect of our daily lives. The food we eat supplies the energy to sustain life with all of its activities and concerns. The availability of relatively inexpensive energy is an important factor in our technological society. This is seen in the costs of fuel, heating and cooling of our homes and workplaces, and electricity to power our lights, appliances, and computers. It is also seen in the costs of goods and services we purchase because a substantial part of the cost of production and delivery is for energy in one form or another. We must understand the scientific basis of the storage and use of energy to learn how to decrease our dependence on consumable oil and natural gas as our main energy sources. Such understanding will have profound ramifications, ranging from our daily lifestyles to international relations.

The concept of energy is at the very heart of science. All physical and chemical processes, including those in all living systems, are accompanied by the transfer of energy. Because energy cannot be created or destroyed, we must understand how to do the "accounting" of energy transfers from one body or one substance to another, or from one form of energy to another.

In **thermodynamics** we study the energy changes that accompany physical and chemical processes. These energy changes usually involve *heat*—hence the "thermo-" part of the term. In this chapter we will study the two main aspects of thermodynamics. The first is **thermochemistry**. This is how we *observe*, *measure*, and *predict* energy changes for both physical changes and chemical reactions. The second part of the chapter will address a more fundamental aspect of thermodynamics. There we will learn to use energy changes to tell whether or not a given process can occur under specified conditions to give predominantly products (or reactants) and how to make a process more (or less) favorable.

Heat Changes and Thermochemistry

15-1 The First Law of Thermodynamics

We can define energy as follows.

> Energy is the capacity to do work or to transfer heat.

We classify energy into two general types: kinetic and potential. **Kinetic energy** is the energy of motion. The kinetic energy of an object is equal to one half its mass, m, times the square of its velocity, v.

$$E_{\text{kinetic}} = \tfrac{1}{2}\, mv^2$$

The heavier a hammer is and the more rapidly it moves, the greater its kinetic energy and the more work it can accomplish.

Potential energy is the energy that a system possesses by virtue of its position or composition. The work that we do to lift an object in a gravitational field is stored in the object as potential energy. If we drop a hammer, its potential energy is converted into kinetic energy as it falls, and it could do work on something it hits—for example, drive a nail or break a piece of glass. Similarly, an electron in an atom has potential energy because of the electrostatic force on it that is due to the positively charged nucleus and the other electrons in that atom and surrounding atoms. Energy can take many other forms: electrical energy, radiant energy (light), nuclear energy, and chemical energy. At the atomic or molecular level, we can think of these as either kinetic or potential energy.

The chemical energy in a fuel or food comes from potential energy stored in atoms due to their arrangements in the molecules. This stored chemical energy can be released when compounds undergo chemical changes, such as those that occur in combustion and metabolism.

Reactions that release energy in the form of heat are called **exothermic** reactions. Combustion reactions of fossil fuels are familiar examples of exothermic reactions. Hydrocarbons—including methane (CH_4), the main component of natural gas, and octane (C_8H_{18}), a minor component of gasoline—undergo combustion with an excess of O_2 to yield CO_2 and H_2O. These reactions release heat energy. The amounts of heat energy released at constant pressure are shown for the reactions of one mole of methane and of two moles of octane.

$$CH_4(g) + 2O_2(g) \longrightarrow CO_2(g) + 2H_2O(\ell) + 890 \text{ kJ}$$
$$2C_8H_{18}(\ell) + 25O_2(g) \longrightarrow 16CO_2(g) + 18H_2O(\ell) + 1.090 \times 10^4 \text{ kJ}$$

In such reactions, the total energy of the products is lower than that of the reactants by the amount of energy released, most of which is heat. Some initial activation (e.g., by heat) is needed to get these reactions started. This is shown for CH_4 in Figure 15-1. This activation energy *plus* 890 kJ is released as one mole of $CO_2(g)$ and two moles of $H_2O(\ell)$ are formed.

A process that absorbs energy from its surroundings is called **endothermic**. One such process is shown in Figure 15-2.

Energy changes accompany physical changes, too (see Chapter 13). For example, the melting of one mole of ice at 0°C at constant pressure must be accompanied by the absorption of 6.02 kJ of energy.

$$H_2O(s) + 6.02 \text{ kJ} \longrightarrow H_2O(\ell)$$

This tells us that the total energy of the water is raised by 6.02 kJ in the form of heat during the phase change, even though the temperature remains constant.

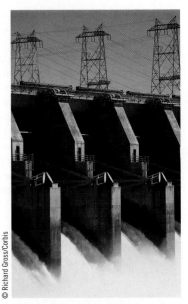

As matter falls from a higher to a lower level, its gravitational potential energy is converted into kinetic energy. A hydroelectric power plant converts the kinetic energy of falling water into electrical (potential) energy.

▶ A hydrocarbon is a binary compound of only hydrogen and carbon. Hydrocarbons may be gaseous, liquid, or solid. All burn.

The amount of heat shown in such an equation always refers to the reaction for the number of moles of reactants and products specified by the coefficients. We call this *one mole of reaction* (even though more than one mole of reactants or products may be shown).

S TOP & THINK
It is important to specify the physical states of all substances because different physical states have different energy contents.

Figure 15-1 The difference between the potential energy of the reactants—one mole of $CH_4(g)$ and two moles of $O_2(g)$—and that of the products—one mole of $CO_2(g)$ and two moles of $H_2O(\ell)$—is the amount of heat evolved in this *exothermic* reaction at constant pressure. For this reaction, it is 890 kJ/mol of reaction. In this chapter, we see how to measure the heat absorbed or released and how to calculate it from other known heat changes. Some initial activation, by heat, for example, is needed to get this reaction started (see Section 16-6). In the absence of such activation energy, a mixture of CH_4 and O_2 can be kept at room temperature for a long time without reacting. For an *endothermic* reaction, the final level is higher than the initial level.

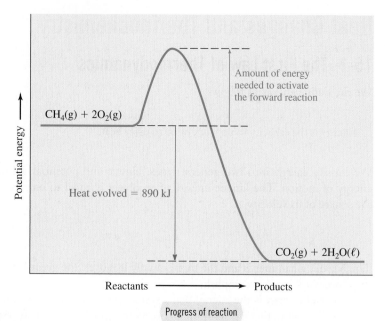

A When solid hydrated barium hydroxide, $Ba(OH)_2 \cdot 8H_2O$, and *excess* solid ammonium nitrate, NH_4NO_3, are mixed, an endothermic reaction occurs.

$$Ba(OH)_2 \cdot 8H_2O(s) + 2NH_4NO_3(s) \longrightarrow Ba(NO_3)_2(s) + 2NH_3(g) + 10H_2O(\ell)$$

The excess ammonium nitrate dissolves in the water produced in the reaction.

B The dissolution process is also very endothermic. If the flask is placed on a wet wooden block, the water freezes and attaches the block to the flask.

Figure 15-2 An endothermic process.

Some important ideas about energy are summarized in the **First Law of Thermodynamics**.

> The combined amount of matter and energy in the universe is constant.

The **Law of Conservation of Energy** is just another statement of the First Law of Thermodynamics.

> Energy can never be created nor destroyed in any process. Energy can be transformed into other forms of energy or converted into matter under special circumstances such as nuclear reactions.

15-2 Some Thermodynamic Terms

The substances involved in the chemical and physical changes that we are studying are called the **system**. Everything in the system's environment constitutes its **surroundings**. The **universe** is the system plus its surroundings. The system may be thought of as the part of the universe under investigation. The First Law of Thermodynamics tells us that energy is neither created nor destroyed; it is only transferred between the system and its surroundings.

The **thermodynamic state of a system** is defined by a set of conditions that completely specifies all the properties of the system. This set commonly includes the temperature, pressure, composition (identity and number of moles of each component), and physical state (gas, liquid, or solid) of each part of the system. Once the state has been specified, all other properties—both physical and chemical—are fixed.

The properties of a system—such as P, V, T—are called **state functions**. The *value* of a state function depends only on the state of the system and not on the way in which the system came to be in that state. A *change* in a state function describes a *difference* between the two states. It is independent of the process or pathway by which the change occurs.

For instance, consider a sample of one mole of pure liquid water at 30°C and 1 atm pressure. If at some later time the temperature of the sample is 22°C at the same pressure, then it is in a different thermodynamic state. We can tell that the *net* temperature change is −8°C. It does not matter whether (1) the cooling took place directly (either slowly or rapidly) from 30°C to 22°C, or (2) the sample was first heated to 36°C, then cooled to 10°C, and finally warmed to 22°C, or (3) any other conceivable path was followed from the initial state to the final state. The change in other properties (e.g., the pressure) of the sample is likewise independent of path.

The most important use of state functions in thermodynamics is to describe *changes*. We describe the difference in any quantity, X, as

$$\Delta X = X_{final} - X_{initial}$$

When X increases, the final value is greater than the initial value, so ΔX is *positive*; a decrease in X makes ΔX a *negative* value.

You can consider a state function as analogous to a bank account. With a bank account, at any time you can measure the amount of money in your account (your balance) in convenient terms—dollars and cents. Changes in this balance can occur for several reasons, such as deposit of your paycheck, writing of checks, or service charges assessed by the bank. In our analogy these transactions are *not* state functions, but they do cause *changes in* the state function (the balance in the account). You can think of the bank balance on a vertical scale; a deposit of $150 changes the balance by +$150, no matter what it was at the start, just as a withdrawal of $150 would change the balance by −$150. Similarly, we shall see that the energy of a system is a state function that can be changed—for instance, by an energy "deposit" of heat absorbed or work done on the system, or by an energy "withdrawal" of heat given off or work done by the system.

We can describe *differences* between levels of a state function, regardless of where the zero level is located. In the case of a bank balance, the "natural" zero level is obviously the point at which we open the account, before any deposits or withdrawals. In contrast, the zero levels on most temperature scales are set arbitrarily. When we say that the temperature of an ice–water mixture is "zero degrees Celsius," we are not saying that the mixture contains no temperature! We have simply chosen to describe this point on the temperature scale by the number *zero*; conditions of higher temperature are described by positive temperature values, and those of lower temperature have negative values, "below zero." The phrase "15 degrees cooler" has the same meaning anywhere on the scale. Many of the scales that we use in thermodynamics are arbitrarily defined in this way. Arbitrary scales are useful when we are interested only in *changes* in the quantity being described.

Any property of a system that depends only on the values of its state functions is also a state function. For instance, the volume of a given sample of water depends only on tem-

▶ State functions are represented by capital letters. Here P refers to pressure, V to volume, and T to absolute temperature.

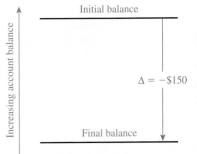

Here is a graphical representation of a $150 decrease in your bank balance. We express the change in your bank balance as $\Delta\$ = \$_{final} - \$_{initial}$. Your final balance is *less* than your initial balance, so the result is *negative*, indicating a *decrease*. There are many ways to get this same net change— one large withdrawal or some combination of deposits, withdrawals, interest earned, and service charges. All of the Δ values we will see in this chapter can be thought of in this way.

perature, pressure, and physical state; therefore, volume is a state function. We shall encounter other thermodynamic state functions.

15-3 Enthalpy Changes

Most chemical reactions and physical changes occur at constant (usually atmospheric) pressure.

▶ The symbol q represents the amount of heat absorbed by the system. The subscript p indicates a constant-pressure process.

> The quantity of heat transferred into or out of a system as it undergoes a chemical or physical change at constant pressure, q_p, is defined as the **enthalpy change, ΔH,** of the process.

An enthalpy change is sometimes loosely referred to as a *heat change* or a *heat of reaction*. The enthalpy change is equal to the enthalpy or "heat content," H, of the substances produced minus the enthalpy of the substances consumed.

$$\Delta H = H_{\text{final}} - H_{\text{initial}} \qquad \text{or} \qquad \Delta H = H_{\text{substances produced}} - H_{\text{substances consumed}}$$

It is impossible to know the absolute enthalpy (heat content) of a system. *Enthalpy is a state function,* however, and it is the *change in enthalpy* in which we are interested; this can be measured for many processes. In the next several sections, we focus on chemical reactions and the enthalpy changes that occur in these processes. We first discuss the experimental determination of enthalpy changes.

15-4 Calorimetry: Measurement of Heat Transfer

We can determine the energy change associated with a chemical or physical process by using an experimental technique called *calorimetry*. This technique is based on observing the temperature change when a system absorbs or releases energy in the form of heat. The experiment is carried out in a device called a **calorimeter**, in which the temperature change of a known amount of substance (often water) of known specific heat is measured. The temperature change is caused by the absorption or release of heat by the chemical or physical process under study.

▶ A review of calculations involved with heat transfer (see Sections 1-14, 13-9, and 13-11) will help you understand this section.

▶ The polystyrene insulation of the simple coffee-cup calorimeter ensures that little heat escapes from or enters the container.

A "coffee-cup" calorimeter (Figure 15-3) is often used in laboratory classes to measure "heats of reaction" at constant pressure, q_p, in aqueous solutions. Reactions are chosen so that there are no gaseous reactants or products. Thus, all reactants and products remain in the vessel throughout the experiment. Such a calorimeter could be used to measure the amount of heat absorbed or released when a reaction takes place in aqueous solution. We can consider the reactants and products as the system and the calorimeter plus the solution (mostly water) as the surroundings. For an exothermic reaction, the amount of heat evolved by the reaction can be calculated from the amount by which it causes the temperature of the calorimeter and the solution to rise. The heat can be visualized as divided into two parts.

$$\begin{pmatrix} \text{amount of heat} \\ \text{released by reaction} \end{pmatrix} = \begin{pmatrix} \text{amount of heat absorbed} \\ \text{by calorimeter} \end{pmatrix} + \begin{pmatrix} \text{amount of heat} \\ \text{absorbed by solution} \end{pmatrix}$$

The amount of heat absorbed by a calorimeter is sometimes expressed as the *heat capacity* of the calorimeter, in joules per degree. The heat capacity of a calorimeter is determined by adding a known amount of heat and measuring the rise in temperature of the calorimeter and of the solution it contains. This heat capacity of a calorimeter is sometimes called its *calorimeter constant.*

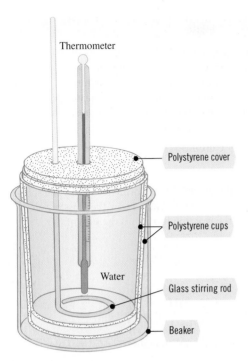

Thermometer

Polystyrene cover

Polystyrene cups

Water

Glass stirring rod

Beaker

Figure 15-3 A coffee-cup calorimeter. The stirring rod is moved up and down to ensure thorough mixing and uniform heating of the solution during reaction. The polystyrene walls and top provide insulation so that very little heat escapes. This kind of calorimeter measures q_p, the heat transfer due to a reaction occurring at constant *pressure*.

EXAMPLE 15-1 Heat Capacity of a Calorimeter

We add 3.358 kJ of heat to a calorimeter that contains 50.00 g of water. The temperature of the water and the calorimeter, originally at 22.34°C, increases to 36.74°C. Calculate the heat capacity of the calorimeter in J/°C. The specific heat of water is 4.184 J/g · °C.

▶ One way to add a measurable amount of heat is to use an electric heater.

Plan

We first calculate the amount of heat gained by the water in the calorimeter. The rest of the heat must have been gained by the calorimeter, so we can determine the heat capacity of the calorimeter.

Solution

$$50.00 \text{ g H}_2\text{O}(\ell) \text{ at } 22.34°C \longrightarrow 50.00 \text{ g H}_2\text{O}(\ell) \text{ at } 36.74°C$$

The temperature change is $(36.74 - 22.34)°C = 14.40°C$.

$$\underline{?} \text{ J} = 50.00 \text{ g} \times \frac{4.184 \text{ J}}{\text{g} \cdot °C} \times 14.40°C = 3.012 \times 10^3 \text{ J}$$

The total amount of heat added was 3.358 kJ or 3.358×10^3 J. The difference between these heat values is the amount of heat absorbed by the calorimeter.

$$\underline{?} \text{ J} = 3.358 \times 10^3 \text{ J} - 3.012 \times 10^3 \text{ J} = 0.346 \times 10^3 \text{ J, or } 346 \text{ J absorbed by the calorimeter}$$

To obtain the heat capacity of the calorimeter, we divide the amount of heat absorbed by the calorimeter, 346 J, by its temperature change.

$$\underline{?} \frac{\text{J}}{°C} = \frac{346 \text{ J}}{14.40°C} = 24.0 \text{ J/°C}$$

The calorimeter absorbs 24.0 J of heat for each degree Celsius increase in its temperature.

You should now work Exercise 60.

🛑 **TOP & THINK**
Note that, because we are using the *change* in temperature (ΔT) in this example, temperatures can be expressed as °C or K. That is because the magnitude of a change of 1°C is equal to 1 K. In this problem $\Delta T = 14.40°C = 14.40$ K. But, when working with mathematical equations that use absolute temperatures T (not ΔT!), it is important to express temperatures in kelvins. In this chapter, we will see mathematical formulas that use T and ΔT, so it is important to keep track of which is being used.

EXAMPLE 15-2 Heat Measurements Using a Calorimeter

A 50.0-mL sample of 0.400 M copper(II) sulfate solution at 23.35°C is mixed with 50.0 mL of 0.600 M sodium hydroxide solution, also at 23.35°C, in the coffee-cup calorimeter of Example 15-1. After the reaction occurs, the temperature of the resulting mixture is measured to be 25.23°C. The density of the final solution is 1.02 g/mL. Calculate the amount of heat evolved. Assume that the specific heat of the solution is the same as that of pure water, 4.184 J/g · °C.

$$CuSO_4(aq) + 2NaOH(aq) \longrightarrow Cu(OH)_2(s) + Na_2SO_4(aq)$$

Plan

The amount of heat released by the reaction is absorbed by the calorimeter *and* by the solution. To find the amount of heat absorbed by the solution, we must know the mass of solution; to find that, we assume that the volume of the reaction mixture is the sum of the volumes of the original solutions.

Solution

The mass of solution is

$$\underline{?}\ g\ soln = (50.0 + 50.0)\ mL \times \frac{1.02g\ soln}{mL} = 102\ g\ soln$$

The amount of heat absorbed by the calorimeter *plus* the amount absorbed by the solution is

$$\underline{?}\ J = \overbrace{\frac{24.0\ J}{°C} \times (25.23 - 23.35)°C}^{\substack{\text{amount of heat} \\ \text{absorbed by calorimeter}}} + \overbrace{102\ g \times \frac{4.18\ J}{g \cdot °C} \times (25.23 - 23.35)°C}^{\substack{\text{amount of heat} \\ \text{absorbed by solution}}}$$

$$= 45\ J + 801\ J = 846\ J\ \text{absorbed by solution plus calorimeter}$$

Thus, the reaction must have liberated 846 J, or 0.846 kJ, of heat.

You should now work Exercise 64(a).

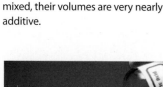

▶ When *dilute aqueous solutions* are mixed, their volumes are very nearly additive.

The heat released by the reaction of HCl(aq) with NaOH(aq) causes the temperature of the solution to rise.

Increasing enthalpy

$C_2H_5OH(\ell) + 3O_2(g)$

$\Delta H = -1367$ kJ

$2CO_2(g) + 3H_2O(\ell)$

15-5 Thermochemical Equations

A balanced chemical equation, written together with a description of the corresponding heat change, is called a **thermochemical equation**. For example,

$$\underset{\text{1 mol}}{C_2H_5OH(\ell)} + \underset{\text{3 mol}}{3O_2(g)} \longrightarrow \underset{\text{2 mol}}{2CO_2(g)} + \underset{\text{3 mol}}{3H_2O(\ell)} + 1367\ kJ$$

is a thermochemical equation that describes the combustion (burning) of one mole of liquid ethanol at a particular temperature and pressure. The coefficients in a balanced thermochemical equation *must* be interpreted as *numbers of moles* of each reactant and product. Thus, 1367 kJ of heat is released when *one* mole of $C_2H_5OH(\ell)$ reacts with *three* moles of $O_2(g)$ to give *two* moles of $CO_2(g)$ and *three* moles of $H_2O(\ell)$. We refer to this amount of reaction as one **mole of reaction**, which we abbreviate "mol rxn." This interpretation allows us to write various unit factors as desired.

$$\frac{1\ mol\ C_2H_5OH(\ell)}{1\ mol\ rxn}, \quad \frac{2\ mol\ CO_2(g)}{1\ mol\ rxn}, \quad \frac{1367\ kJ\ of\ heat\ released}{1\ mol\ rxn}, \text{ and so on}$$

The thermochemical equation is more commonly written as

$$C_2H_5OH(\ell) + 3O_2(g) \longrightarrow 2CO_2(g) + 3H_2O(\ell) \qquad \Delta H = -1367\ kJ/mol\ rxn$$

The negative sign indicates that this is an *exothermic* reaction (i.e., it gives *off* heat).

Charles D. Winters

We always interpret ΔH as the enthalpy change for the reaction as written; that is, as (enthalpy change)/(mole of reaction), where "mole of reaction" means "for the number of moles of each substance shown by the coefficients in the balanced equation."

We can then use several unit factors to interpret this thermochemical equation.

$$\frac{1367 \text{ kJ given off}}{\text{mol of reaction}} = \frac{1367 \text{ kJ given off}}{\text{mol } C_2H_5OH(\ell) \text{ consumed}} = \frac{1367 \text{ kJ given off}}{3 \text{ mol } O_2(g) \text{ consumed}}$$

$$= \frac{1367 \text{ kJ given off}}{2 \text{ mol } CO_2(g) \text{ formed}} = \frac{1367 \text{ kJ given off}}{3 \text{ mol } H_2O(\ell) \text{ formed}}$$

▶ To interpret what a value of ΔH means, we must know the balanced chemical equation to which it refers.

The reverse reaction would require the absorption of 1367 kJ under the same conditions.

$$1367 \text{ kJ} + 2CO_2(g) + 3H_2O(\ell) \longrightarrow C_2H_5OH(\ell) + 3O_2(g)$$

That is, it is *endothermic*, with $\Delta H = +1367$ kJ.

$$2CO_2(g) + 3H_2O(\ell) \longrightarrow C_2H_5OH(\ell) + 3O_2(g) \qquad \Delta H = +1367 \text{ kJ/mol rxn}$$

It is important to remember the following conventions regarding thermochemical equations:

1. The coefficients in a balanced thermochemical equation refer to the numbers of *moles* of reactants and products involved. In the thermodynamic interpretation of equations, we *never* interpret the coefficients as *numbers of molecules*. Thus, it is acceptable to write coefficients as fractions rather than as integers, when convenient. But most chemists prefer to use the smallest integer values for the coefficients.

2. The numerical value of ΔH (or any other thermodynamic change) is specific to the *number of moles* of substances specified by the balanced equation. This amount of change is called *one mole of reaction*, so we can express ΔH in units of energy/mol rxn. For brevity, the units of ΔH are sometimes written kJ/mol or even just kJ. No matter what units are used, be sure that you interpret the thermodynamic change *per mole of reaction for the balanced chemical equation to which it refers*. If a different amount of material is involved in the reaction, then the ΔH (or other change) must be scaled accordingly.

3. The physical states of all species are important and must be specified. Heat is given off or absorbed when phase changes occur, so different amounts of heat could be involved in a reaction depending on the phases of reactants and products.

4. The value of ΔH usually does not change significantly with moderate changes in temperature.

The launch of the space shuttle requires about 2×10^{10} kilojoules of energy. About one-sixth of this comes from the reaction of hydrogen, H_2, and oxygen, O_2. The rest comes from the explosive decomposition of ammonium perchlorate, NH_4ClO_4, in solid-fuel rockets. The final launch was on July 8, 2011, by the shuttle Atlantis.

EXAMPLE 15-3 Thermochemical Equations

When 2.61 grams of dimethyl ether, CH_3OCH_3, is burned at constant pressure, 82.5 kJ of heat is given off. Find ΔH for the reaction

$$CH_3OCH_3(\ell) + 3O_2(g) \longrightarrow 2CO_2(g) + 3H_2O(\ell)$$

Plan

We scale the amount of heat given off in the experiment to correspond to the amount of CH_3OCH_3 shown in the balanced equation.

Solution

$$\frac{?\ \text{kJ given off}}{\text{mol rxn}} = \frac{82.5\ \text{kJ given off}}{2.61\ \text{g CH}_3\text{OCH}_3} \times \frac{46.0\ \text{g CH}_3\text{OCH}_3}{\text{mol CH}_3\text{OCH}_3} \times \frac{1\ \text{mol CH}_3\text{OCH}_3}{\text{mol rxn}}$$

$$= 1450\ \text{kJ/mol rxn}$$

Because heat is given off, we know that the reaction is exothermic so the value of ΔH should be negative.

$$\Delta H = -1450\ \text{kJ/mol rxn}$$

You should now work Exercise 21.

EXAMPLE 15-4 Thermochemical Equations

Write the thermochemical equation for the reaction in Example 15-2.

Plan

We must determine *how much* reaction occurred—that is, how many moles of reactants were consumed. We first multiply the volume, in liters, of each solution by its concentration in mol/L (molarity) to determine the number of moles of each reactant mixed. Then we identify the limiting reactant. We scale the amount of heat released in the experiment to correspond to the number of moles of that reactant shown in the balanced equation.

Solution

Using the data from Example 15-2,

$$?\ \text{mol CuSO}_4 = 0.0500\ \text{L} \times \frac{0.400\ \text{mol CuSO}_4}{1.00\ \text{L}} = 0.0200\ \text{mol CuSO}_4$$

$$?\ \text{mol NaOH} = 0.0500\ \text{L} \times \frac{0.600\ \text{mol NaOH}}{1.00\ \text{L}} = 0.0300\ \text{mol NaOH}$$

We determine which is the limiting reactant (review Section 3-3).

Required Ratio	**Available Ratio**
$\dfrac{1\ \text{mol CuSO}_4}{2\ \text{mol NaOH}} = \dfrac{0.500\ \text{mol CuSO}_4}{1.00\ \text{mol NaOH}}$	$\dfrac{0.0200\ \text{mol CuSO}_4}{0.0300\ \text{mol NaOH}} = \dfrac{0.667\ \text{mol CuSO}_4}{1.00\ \text{mol NaOH}}$

▶ NaOH is the limiting reactant.

More $CuSO_4$ is available than is required to react with the NaOH. Thus, 0.846 kJ of heat was given off during the consumption of 0.0300 mol of NaOH. The amount of heat given off per "mole of reaction" is

$$\frac{?\ \text{kJ released}}{\text{mol rxn}} = \frac{0.846\ \text{kJ given off}}{0.0300\ \text{mol NaOH}} \times \frac{2\ \text{mol NaOH}}{\text{mol rxn}} = \frac{56.4\ \text{kJ given off}}{\text{mol rxn}}$$

Thus, when the reaction occurs *to the extent indicated by the balanced chemical equation*, 56.4 kJ is released. Remembering that exothermic reactions have negative values of ΔH_{rxn}, we write

$$\text{CuSO}_4(\text{aq}) + 2\text{NaOH}(\text{aq}) \longrightarrow \text{Cu(OH)}_2(\text{s}) + \text{Na}_2\text{SO}_4(\text{aq}) \quad \Delta H_{rxn} = -56.4\ \text{kJ/mol rxn}$$

You should now work Exercise 64(b).

EXAMPLE 15-5 Amount of Heat Produced

When aluminum metal is exposed to atmospheric oxygen (as in aluminum doors and windows), it is oxidized to form aluminum oxide. How much heat is released by the complete oxidation of 24.2 grams of aluminum at 25°C and 1 atm? The thermochemical equation is

$$4\text{Al}(\text{s}) + 3\text{O}_2(\text{g}) \longrightarrow 2\text{Al}_2\text{O}_3(\text{s}) \quad \Delta H = -3352\ \text{kJ/mol rxn}$$

Plan

The thermochemical equation tells us that 3352 kJ of heat is released for every mole of re-action, that is, for every 4 moles of Al that reacts. We convert 24.2 g of Al to moles and then calculate the number of kilojoules corresponding to that number of moles of Al, using the unit factors

$$\frac{-3352 \text{ kJ}}{\text{mol rxn}} \quad \text{and} \quad \frac{1 \text{ mol rxn}}{4 \text{ mol Al}}$$

Solution

For 24.2 g Al,

$$\underline{?} \text{ kJ} = 24.2 \text{ g Al} \times \frac{1 \text{ mol Al}}{27.0 \text{ g Al}} \times \frac{1 \text{ mol rxn}}{4 \text{ mol Al}} \times \frac{-3352 \text{ kJ}}{\text{mol rxn}} = -751 \text{ kJ}$$

This tells us that 751 kJ of heat is released to the surroundings during the oxidation of 24.2 grams of aluminum.

You should now work Exercises 16 and 17.

Problem-Solving Tip Mole of Reaction

Remember that a thermochemical equation can have *different* coefficients (numbers of moles) of *different* reactants or products, which need not equal one. In Example 15-5 one mole of reaction corresponds to 4 moles of Al(s), 3 moles of $O_2(g)$, and 2 moles of $Al_2O_3(s)$.

15-6 Standard States and Standard Enthalpy Changes

The **thermodynamic standard state** of a substance is its most stable pure form under standard pressure (one atmosphere)* and at some specific temperature (25°C or 298 K unless otherwise specified). Examples of elements in their standard states at 25°C are hydrogen, gaseous diatomic molecules, $H_2(g)$; mercury, a silver-colored liquid metal, $Hg(\ell)$; sodium, a silvery-white solid metal, Na(s); and carbon, a grayish-black solid called graphite, C(graphite). We use C(graphite) instead of C(s) to distinguish it from other solid forms of carbon, such as C(diamond). The reaction C(diamond) $\longrightarrow$ C(graphite) would be *exothermic* by 1.897 kJ/mol rxn; C(graphite) is thus more stable than C(diamond). Examples of standard states of compounds include ethanol (ethyl alcohol or grain alcohol), a liquid, $C_2H_5OH(\ell)$; water, a liquid, $H_2O(\ell)$; calcium carbonate, a solid, $CaCO_3(s)$; and carbon dioxide, a gas, $CO_2(g)$. Keep in mind the following conventions for thermochemical standard states.

1. For a *pure* substance in the liquid or solid phase, the standard state is the pure liquid or solid.
2. For a gas, the standard state is the gas at a pressure of *one atmosphere*; in a mixture of gases, its partial pressure must be one atmosphere.
3. For a substance in solution, the standard state refers to *one-molar* concentration.

For ease of comparison and tabulation, we often refer to thermochemical or thermodynamic changes "at standard states" or, more simply, to a *standard change*. To indicate a change at standard pressure, we add a superscript zero, which is read as "naught." If some temperature other than the standard temperature of 25°C (298 K) is specified, we indicate it with a subscript; if no subscript appears, a temperature of 25°C (298 K) is implied.

*IUPAC has changed the standard pressure from 1 atm to 1 bar. Because 1 bar is equal to 0.987 atm, the differences in thermodynamic calculations are negligible except in work of very high precision. Many tables of thermodynamic data are still based on a standard pressure of 1 atm, so we use that pressure in this text.

▶ A temperature of 25°C is 77°F. This is slightly above typical room temperature. Notice that these thermodynamic "standard conditions" are not the same as the "standard temperature and pressure (STP)" that we used in gas calculations (see Chapter 12).

▶ If the substance exists in several different forms, the form that is most stable at 25°C and 1 atm is the standard state.

▶ For gas laws (see Chapter 12), standard temperature is taken as 0°C. For thermodynamics, it is taken as 25°C.

▶ This is sometimes referred to as the *standard heat of reaction.* We verbally refer to this as "delta H naught reaction."

The **standard enthalpy change**, ΔH^0_{rxn}, for a reaction

$$\text{reactants} \longrightarrow \text{products}$$

refers to the ΔH when the specified number of moles of reactants, all at standard states, are converted *completely* to the specified number of moles of products, all at standard states.

We allow a reaction to take place, with changes in temperature or pressure if necessary; when the reaction is complete, we return the products to the same conditions of temperature and pressure that we started with, *keeping track of energy or enthalpy changes* as we do so. When we describe a process as taking place "at constant T and P," we mean that the initial and final conditions are the same. Because we are dealing with changes in state functions, the net change is the same as the change we would have obtained hypothetically with T and P actually held constant.

15-7 Standard Molar Enthalpies of Formation, ΔH^0_f

It is not possible to determine the total enthalpy content of a substance on an absolute scale. Because we need to describe only *changes* in this state function, we can define an *arbitrary scale* as follows.

▶ We can think of ΔH^0_f as the enthalpy content of each substance, in its standard state, relative to the enthalpy content of the elements, in their standard states. This is why ΔH^0_f for an element in its standard state is zero.

The **standard molar enthalpy of formation**, ΔH^0_f, of a substance is the enthalpy change for the reaction in which *one mole* of the substance in a specified state is formed from its elements in their standard states. By convention, the ΔH^0_f value for any *element in its standard state* is defined as zero.

Standard molar enthalpy of formation is often called **standard molar heat of formation** or, more simply, **heat of formation**. The superscript zero in ΔH^0_f signifies standard pressure, 1 atmosphere. Negative values for ΔH^0_f describe exothermic formation reactions, whereas positive values for ΔH^0_f describe endothermic formation reactions.

The enthalpy change for a balanced equation that gives a compound from its elements does not necessarily give a molar enthalpy of formation for the compound. Consider the following exothermic reaction at standard conditions.

$$H_2(g) + Br_2(\ell) \longrightarrow 2HBr(g) \qquad \Delta H^0_{rxn} = -72.8 \text{ kJ/mol rxn}$$

We see that *two* moles of HBr(g) are formed in the reaction as written. Half as much energy, 36.4 kJ, is liberated when *one mole* of HBr(g) is produced from its constituent elements in their standard states. For HBr(g), $\Delta H^0_f = -36.4$ kJ/mol. This can be shown by dividing all coefficients in the balanced equation by 2.

▶ The coefficients $\frac{1}{2}$ preceding $H_2(g)$ and $Br_2(\ell)$ do *not* imply half a molecule of each. In thermochemical equations, the coefficients always refer to the number of *moles* under consideration.

$$\frac{1}{2}H_2(g) + \frac{1}{2}Br_2(\ell) \longrightarrow HBr(g) \qquad \Delta H^0_{rxn} = -36.4 \text{ kJ/mol rxn}$$
$$\Delta H^0_{f\ HBr(g)} = -36.4 \text{ kJ/mol HBr(g)}$$

Standard heats of formation of some common substances are tabulated in Table 15-1. Appendix K contains a more extensive listing.

When referring to a thermodynamic quantity for a *substance*, we often omit the description of the substance from the units. Units for tabulated ΔH^0_f values are given as "kJ/mol"; we must interpret this as "per mole of the substance in the specified state." For instance, for HBr(g) the tabulated ΔH^0_f value of -36.4 kJ/mol should be interpreted as $\dfrac{-36.4 \text{ kJ}}{\text{mol HBr}(g)}$.

Table 15-1 Selected Standard Molar Enthalpies of Formation at 298 K

Substance	ΔH_f^0 (kJ/mol)	Substance	ΔH_f^0 (kJ/mol)
$Br_2(\ell)$	0	HgS(s) red	−58.2
$Br_2(g)$	30.91	$H_2(g)$	0
C(diamond)	1.897	HBr(g)	−36.4
C(graphite)	0	$H_2O(\ell)$	−285.8
$CH_4(g)$	−74.81	$H_2O(g)$	−241.8
$C_2H_4(g)$	52.26	NO(g)	90.25
$C_6H_6(\ell)$	49.03	Na(s)	0
$C_2H_5OH(\ell)$	−277.7	NaCl(s)	−411.0
CO(g)	−110.5	$O_2(g)$	0
$CO_2(g)$	−393.5	$SO_2(g)$	−296.8
CaO(s)	−635.5	$SiH_4(g)$	34.0
$CaCO_3(s)$	−1207.0	$SiCl_4(g)$	−657.0
$Cl_2(g)$	0	$SiO_2(s)$	−910.9

S **TOP & THINK**
The ΔH_f^0 values of $Br_2(g)$ and C(diamond) are *not equal to 0* at 298 K. This is because the standard states of these elements are $Br_2(\ell)$ and C(graphite), respectively.

EXAMPLE 15-6 Interpretation of ΔH_f^0

The standard molar enthalpy of formation of ethanol, $C_2H_5OH(\ell)$, is −277.7 kJ/mol. Write the thermochemical equation for the reaction for which $\Delta H_{rxn}^0 = $ −277.7 kJ/mol rxn.

Plan

The definition of ΔH_f^0 of a substance refers to a reaction in which *one mole* of the substance in a specified state is formed from the elements *in their standard states*. We put one mole of $C_2H_5OH(\ell)$ on the right side of the chemical equation and put the appropriate elements in their standard states on the left. We balance the equation *without changing the coefficient of the product*, even if we must use fractional coefficients on the left.

Solution

$$2C(\text{graphite}) + 3H_2(g) + \tfrac{1}{2}O_2(g) \longrightarrow C_2H_5OH(\ell) \qquad \Delta H = -277.7 \text{ kJ/mol rxn}$$

You should now work Exercise 28.

Problem-Solving Tip How Do We Interpret Fractional Coefficients?

Remember that we *always* interpret the coefficients in thermochemical equations as numbers of *moles* of reactants or products. The $\tfrac{1}{2}O_2(g)$ in the answer to Example 15-6 refers to $\tfrac{1}{2}$ *mole* of O_2 molecules, or

$$\tfrac{1}{2} \text{ mol } O_2 \times \frac{32.0 \text{ g } O_2}{\text{mol } O_2} = 16.0 \text{ g } O_2$$

It is important to realize that this is *not* the same as one mole of O atoms (though that would also weigh 16.0 g).

Similarly, the fractional coefficients in

$$\tfrac{1}{2}H_2(g) + \tfrac{1}{2}Br_2(\ell) \longrightarrow HBr(g)$$

refer to

$$\tfrac{1}{2} \text{ mol } H_2 \times \frac{2.0 \text{ g } H_2}{\text{mol } H_2} = 1.0 \text{ g } H_2$$

and

$$\tfrac{1}{2} \text{ mol } Br_2 \times \frac{159.8 \text{ g } Br_2}{\text{mol } Br_2} = 79.9 \text{ g } Br_2$$

respectively.

15-8 Hess's Law

In 1840, G. H. Hess (1802–1850) published his **law of heat summation,** which he derived on the basis of numerous thermochemical observations.

> The enthalpy change for a reaction is the same whether it occurs by one step or by any series of steps.

▶ As an analogy, consider traveling from Kansas City (elevation 884 ft above sea level) to Denver (elevation 5280 ft). The change in elevation is (5280 − 884) ft = 4396 ft, regardless of the route taken.

Enthalpy is a state function. Its *change* is therefore independent of the pathway by which a reaction occurs. We do not need to know whether the reaction *does*, or even *can*, occur by the series of steps used in the calculation. The steps must (if only "on paper") result in the overall reaction. Hess's Law lets us calculate enthalpy changes for reactions for which the changes could be measured only with difficulty, if at all. In general terms, Hess's Law of heat summation may be represented as

$$\Delta H^0_{rxn} = \Delta H^0_a + \Delta H^0_b + \Delta H^0_c + \cdots$$

Here a, b, c, . . . refer to balanced thermochemical equations that can be summed to give the equation for the desired reaction.

Consider the following reaction.

$$C(graphite) + \tfrac{1}{2}O_2(g) \longrightarrow CO(g) \qquad \Delta H^0_{rxn} = \underline{?}$$

The enthalpy change for this reaction cannot be measured directly. Even though CO(g) is the predominant product of the reaction of graphite with a *limited* amount of $O_2(g)$, some $CO_2(g)$ is always produced as well. The following reactions do go to completion with excess $O_2(g)$; therefore, ΔH^0 values have been measured experimentally for them. [Pure CO(g) is readily available.]

$$C(graphite) + O_2(g) \longrightarrow CO_2(g) \qquad \Delta H^0_{rxn} = -393.5 \text{ kJ/mol rxn} \qquad (1)$$
$$CO(g) + \tfrac{1}{2}O_2(g) \longrightarrow CO_2(g) \qquad \Delta H^0_{rxn} = -283.0 \text{ kJ/mol rxn} \qquad (2)$$

▶ You are familiar with the addition and subtraction of algebraic equations. This method of combining thermochemical equations is analogous.

We can "work backward" to find out how to combine these two known equations to obtain the desired equation. We want one mole of CO on the right, so we reverse equation (2) [designated below as (−2)]; heat is then absorbed instead of released, so we must change the sign of its ΔH^0 value. Then we add it to equation (1), canceling equal numbers of moles of the same species on each side. This gives the equation for the reaction we want. Adding the corresponding enthalpy changes gives the enthalpy change we seek.

Above is a schematic representation of the enthalpy changes for the reaction

$$C(graphite) + \tfrac{1}{2}O_2(g) \longrightarrow CO(g).$$

The ΔH value for each step is based on the number of moles of each substance indicated.

$$\Delta H^0$$

	ΔH^0	
$C(graphite) + O_2(g) \longrightarrow \cancel{CO_2(g)}$	$-393.5 \text{ kJ/mol rxn)}$	(1)
$\cancel{CO_2(g)} \longrightarrow CO(g) + \tfrac{1}{2}O_2(g)$	$-(-283.0 \text{ kJ/mol rxn)}$	(−2)
$C(graphite) + \tfrac{1}{2}O_2(g) \longrightarrow CO(g)$	$\Delta H^0_{rxn} = -110.5 \text{ kJ/mol rxn}$	

This equation shows the formation of one mole of CO(g) in its standard state from the elements in their standard states. In this way, we determine that ΔH^0_f for CO(g) is −110.5 kJ/mol.

EXAMPLE 15-7 Combining Thermochemical Equations: Hess's Law

Use the thermochemical equations shown here to determine ΔH^0_{rxn} at 25°C for the following reaction.

$$C(graphite) + 2H_2(g) \longrightarrow CH_4(g)$$

$$\Delta H^0$$

$C(graphite) + O_2(g) \longrightarrow CO_2(g)$	-393.5 kJ/mol rxn	(1)
$H_2(g) + \frac{1}{2}O_2(g) \longrightarrow H_2O(\ell)$	-285.8 kJ/mol rxn	(2)
$CH_4(g) + 2O_2(g) \longrightarrow CO_2(g) + 2H_2O(\ell)$	-890.3 kJ/mol rxn	(3)

▶ These are combustion reactions, for which ΔH^0_{rxn} values can be readily determined from calorimetry experiments.

Plan

(i) We want one mole of C(graphite) as overall reactant, so we write down thermochemical equation (1).

(ii) We want two moles of $H_2(g)$ as overall reactants, so we multiply thermochemical equation (2) by 2 [designated below as $2 \times (2)$].

(iii) We want one mole of $CH_4(g)$ as overall product, so we reverse thermochemical equation (3) to give (-3).

(iv) Then we add these thermochemical equations term by term. The result is the desired thermochemical equation, with all unwanted substances canceling. The sum of the ΔH^0 values is the ΔH^0 for the desired reaction.

S TOP & THINK
Remember that multiplying a thermochemical equation also multiplies its ΔH^0 by the same factor. Reversing a thermochemical equation changes the sign of its ΔH^0.

Solution

$$\Delta H^0$$

$C(graphite) + \cancel{O_2(g)} \longrightarrow \cancel{CO_2(g)}$	-393.5 kJ/mol rxn)	(1)
$2H_2(g) + \cancel{O_2(g)} \longrightarrow \cancel{2H_2O(\ell)}$	$2(-285.8$ kJ/mol rxn) $2 \times (2)$	
$\cancel{CO_2(g)} + \cancel{2H_2O(\ell)} \longrightarrow CH_4(g) + \cancel{2O_2(g)}$	$+890.3$ kJ/mol rxn)	(-3)
$C(graphite) + 2H_2(g) \longrightarrow CH_4(g)$	$\Delta H^0_{rxn} = -74.8$ kJ/mol rxn)	

S TOP & THINK
We have used a series of reactions for which ΔH^0 values can be easily measured to calculate ΔH^0 for a reaction that cannot be carried out.

$CH_4(g)$ cannot be formed directly from C(graphite) and $H_2(g)$, so its ΔH^0_f value cannot be measured directly. The result of this example tells us that this value is -74.8 kJ/mol.

EXAMPLE 15-8 Combining Thermochemical Equations: Hess's Law

Given the following thermochemical equations, calculate the heat of reaction at 298 K for the reaction of ethylene with water to form ethanol.

$$C_2H_4(g) + H_2O(\ell) \longrightarrow C_2H_5OH(\ell)$$

$$\Delta H^0$$

$C_2H_5OH(\ell) + 3O_2(g) \longrightarrow 2CO_2(g) + 3H_2O(\ell)$	-1367 kJ/mol rxn	(1)
$C_2H_4(g) + 3O_2(g) \longrightarrow 2CO_2(g) + 2H_2O(\ell)$	-1411 kJ/mol rxn	(2)

Plan

We reverse equation (1) to give (-1); when the equation is reversed, the sign of ΔH^0 is changed because the reverse of an exothermic reaction is endothermic. Then we add the thermochemical equations.

Solution

$$\Delta H^0$$

$\cancel{2CO_2(g)} + 3H_2O(\ell) \longrightarrow C_2H_5OH(\ell) + \cancel{3O_2(g)}$	$+1367$ kJ/mol rxn	(-1)
$C_2H_4(g) + \cancel{3O_2(g)} \longrightarrow \cancel{2CO_2(g)} + 2H_2O(\ell)$	-1411 kJ/mol rxn	(2)
$C_2H_4(g) + H_2O(\ell) \longrightarrow C_2H_5OH(\ell)$	$\Delta H^0_{rxn} = -44$ kJ/mol rxn	

S TOP & THINK
If you reverse a chemical equation, remember to switch the sign of its ΔH^0_{rxn}.

You should now work Exercises 32 and 34.

Problem Solving Tip ΔH_f^0 Refers to a Specific Reaction

The ΔH^0 for the reaction in Example 15-8 is -44 kJ for each mole of $C_2H_5OH(\ell)$ formed. This reaction, however, does *not* involve formation of $C_2H_5OH(\ell)$ *from its constituent elements* because C_2H_4 and H_2O are not elements; therefore, ΔH_{rxn}^0 is *not* ΔH_f^0 for $C_2H_5OH(\ell)$. We have seen the reaction for ΔH_f^0 of $C_2H_5OH(\ell)$ in Example 15-6.

     Similarly, the ΔH_{rxn}^0 for

$$CO(g) + \tfrac{1}{2} O_2(g) \longrightarrow CO_2(g)$$

is *not* ΔH_f^0 for $CO_2(g)$.

Another interpretation of Hess's Law lets us use tables of ΔH_f^0 values to calculate the enthalpy change for a reaction. Let us consider again the reaction of Example 15-8.

$$C_2H_4(g) + H_2O(\ell) \longrightarrow C_2H_5OH(\ell)$$

A table of ΔH_f^0 values (see Appendix K) gives $\Delta H_{f\,C_2H_5OH(\ell)}^0 = -277.7$ kJ/mol, $\Delta H_{f\,C_2H_4(g)}^0 = 52.3$ kJ/mol, and $\Delta H_{f\,H_2O(\ell)}^0 = -285.8$ kJ/mol. We may express this information in the form of the following thermochemical equations.

$$\Delta H^0$$

$$2C(\text{graphite}) + 3H_2(g) + \tfrac{1}{2}O_2(g) \longrightarrow C_2H_5OH(\ell) \qquad -277.7 \text{ kJ/mol rxn} \qquad (1)$$
$$2C(\text{graphite}) + 2H_2(g) \longrightarrow C_2H_4(g) \qquad 52.3 \text{ kJ/mol rxn} \qquad (2)$$
$$H_2(g) + \tfrac{1}{2}O_2(g) \longrightarrow H_2O(\ell) \qquad -285.8 \text{ kJ/mol rxn} \qquad (3)$$

We may generate the equation for the desired net reaction by adding equation (1) to the reverse of equations (2) and (3). The value of ΔH^0 for the desired reaction is then the sum of the corresponding ΔH^0 values.

$$\Delta H^0$$

$$2\cancel{C(\text{graphite})} + 3\cancel{H_2(g)} + \cancel{\tfrac{1}{2}O_2(g)} \longrightarrow C_2H_5OH(\ell) \qquad -277.7 \text{ kJ/mol rxn} \qquad (1)$$
$$C_2H_4(g) \longrightarrow 2\cancel{C(\text{graphite})} + 2\cancel{H_2(g)} \quad -52.3 \text{ kJ/mol rxn} \quad (-2)$$
$$H_2O(\ell) \longrightarrow \cancel{H_2(g)} + \cancel{\tfrac{1}{2}O_2(g)} \qquad +285.8 \text{ kJ/mol rxn} \quad (-3)$$

net rxn: $C_2H_4(g) + H_2O(\ell) \longrightarrow C_2H_5OH(\ell)$ $\Delta H_{rxn}^0 = -44.2$ kJ/mol rxn

We see that ΔH^0 for this reaction is given by

$$\Delta H_{rxn}^0 = \Delta H_{(1)}^0 + \Delta H_{(-2)}^0 + \Delta H_{(-3)}^0$$

or by

$$\Delta H_{rxn}^0 = \overset{\text{product}}{\Delta H_{f\,C_2H_5OH(\ell)}^0} - [\overset{\text{reactants}}{\Delta H_{f\,C_2H_4(g)}^0 + \Delta H_{f\,H_2O(\ell)}^0}]$$

In general terms this is a very useful form of Hess's Law.

▶ The capital Greek letter sigma (Σ) is read "the sum of." The Σn means that the ΔH_f^0 value of each product and reactant must be multiplied by its coefficient, n, in the balanced equation. The resulting values are then added.

$$\Delta H_{rxn}^0 = \Sigma \, n \, \Delta H_{f\,\text{products}}^0 - \Sigma \, n \, \Delta H_{f\,\text{reactants}}^0$$

The standard enthalpy change of a reaction is equal to the sum of the standard molar enthalpies of formation of the products, each multiplied by its coefficient, n, in the *balanced equation*, minus the corresponding sum of the standard molar enthalpies of formation of the reactants.

In effect this form of Hess's Law supposes that the reaction occurs by converting reactants to the elements in their standard states, then converting these to products (Figure 15-4). Few, if any, reactions actually occur by such a pathway. Nevertheless, because H is a state function the ΔH^0 for this *hypothetical* pathway for *reactants ⟶ products* would be the same as that for any other pathway—including the one by which the reaction actually occurs.

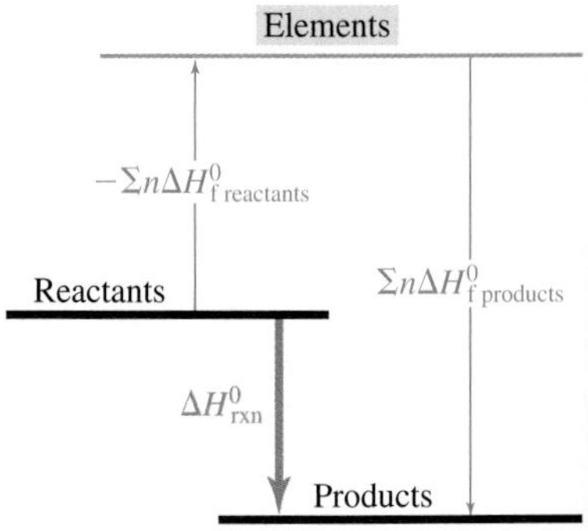

Figure 15-4 A schematic representation of Hess's Law. The red arrow represents the *direct* path from reactants to products. The series of blue arrows is a path (hypothetical) in which reactants are converted to elements, and they in turn are converted to products—all in their standard states.

EXAMPLE 15-9   Using ΔH_f^0 Values: Hess's Law

Calculate ΔH_{rxn}^0 for the following reaction at 298 K.

$$SiH_4(g) + 2O_2(g) \longrightarrow SiO_2(s) + 2H_2O(\ell)$$

Plan

We apply Hess's Law in the form $\Delta H_{rxn}^0 = \Sigma\, n\, \Delta H_f^0$ products $- \Sigma\, n\, \Delta H_f^0$ reactants, so we use the ΔH_f^0 values tabulated in Appendix K.

Solution

We can first list the ΔH_f^0 values we obtain from Appendix K:

	$SiH_4(g)$	$O_2(g)$	$SiO_2(s)$	$H_2O(\ell)$
ΔH_f^0, kJ/mol:	34.3	0	−910.9	−285.8

$\Delta H_{rxn}^0 = \Sigma\, n\, \Delta H_f^0$ products $- \Sigma\, n\, \Delta H_f^0$ reactants

$\Delta H_{rxn}^0 = [\Delta H_{f\,SiO_2(s)}^0 + 2\,\Delta H_{f\,H_2O(\ell)}^0] - [\Delta H_{f\,SiH_4(g)}^0 + 2\,\Delta H_{f\,O_2(g)}^0]$

$\Delta H_{rxn}^0 = \left[\dfrac{1\ \text{mol}\ SiO_2(s)}{\text{mol rxn}} \times \dfrac{-910.9\ \text{kJ}}{\text{mol}\ SiO_2(s)} + \dfrac{2\ \text{mol}\ H_2O(\ell)}{\text{mol rxn}} \times \dfrac{-285.8\ \text{kJ}}{\text{mol}\ H_2O(\ell)}\right]$

$\qquad\quad - \left[\dfrac{1\ \text{mol}\ SiH_4(g)}{\text{mol rxn}} \times \dfrac{+34.3\ \text{kJ}}{\text{mol}\ SiH_4(g)} + \dfrac{2\ \text{mol}\ O_2(g)}{\text{mol rxn}} \times \dfrac{0\ \text{kJ}}{\text{mol}\ O_2(g)}\right]$

$\boxed{\Delta H_{rxn}^0 = -1516.8\ \text{kJ/mol rxn}}$

You should now work Exercise 38.

▶ $O_2(g)$ is an element in its standard state, so its ΔH_f^0 is zero.

Each term in the sums on the right-hand side of the solution in Example 15-9 has the units

$$\dfrac{\text{mol substance}}{\text{mol rxn}} \times \dfrac{\text{kJ}}{\text{mol substance}} \qquad \text{or} \qquad \dfrac{\text{kJ}}{\text{mol rxn}}$$

For brevity, we shall omit units in the intermediate steps of calculations of this type, and just assign the proper units to the answer. Be sure that you understand how these units arise.

Suppose we measure ΔH_{rxn}^0 at 298 K and know all but one of the ΔH_f^0 values for reactants and products. We can then calculate the unknown ΔH_f^0 value.

EXAMPLE 15-10   Using ΔH_f^0 Values: Hess's Law

Use the following information to determine ΔH_f^0 for PbO(s, yellow).

$$PbO(s, \text{yellow}) + CO(g) \longrightarrow Pb(s) + CO_2(g) \qquad \Delta H_{rxn}^0 = -65.69\ \text{kJ}$$

$$\Delta H_f^0 = \text{for}\ CO_2(g) = -393.5\ \text{kJ/mol} \qquad \text{and} \qquad \Delta H_f^0\ \text{for}\ CO(g) = -110.5\ \text{kJ/mol}$$

▶ We will consult Appendix K to check the answer only after working the problem.

Plan

We again use Hess's Law in the form $\Delta H^0_{rxn} = \Sigma\, n\, \Delta H^0_{f\,products} - \Sigma\, n\, \Delta H^0_{f\,reactants}$. The standard state of lead is Pb(s), so $\Delta H^0_{f\,Pb(s)} = 0$ kJ/mol. Now we are given ΔH^0_{rxn} and the ΔH^0_f values for all substances *except* PbO(s, yellow). We can solve for this unknown.

Solution

We list the known ΔH^0_f values:

	PbO(s, yellow)	CO(g)	Pb(s)	CO$_2$(g)
ΔH^0_f, kJ/mol:	$\Delta H^0_{f\,PbO_2(s,\,yellow)}$	-110.5	0	-393.5

$$\Delta H^0_{rxn} = \Sigma\, n\, \Delta H^0_{f\,products} \qquad -\Sigma\, n\, \Delta H^0_{f\,reactants}$$

$$\Delta H^0_{rxn} = \Delta H^0_{f\,Pb(s)} + \Delta H^0_{f\,CO_2(g)} - [\Delta H^0_{f\,PbO(s,\,yellow)} + \Delta H^0_{f\,CO(g)}]$$

Substituting values stated in the problem gives

$$-65.69 = 0 \qquad + (-393.5) \quad -[\Delta H^0_{f\,PbO(s,\,yellow)} + (-110.5)]$$

Rearranging to solve for, $\Delta H^0_{f\,PbO(s,\,yellow)}$, we have

$$\Delta H^0_{f\,PbO(s,\,yellow)} = 65.69 - 393.5 + 110.5 = \boxed{-217.3 \text{ kJ/mol of PbO}}$$

You should now work Exercise 44.

Problem-Solving Tip Remember the Values of ΔH^0_f for Elements

In Example 15-10, we were not given the value of ΔH^0_f for Pb(s). We should know without reference to tables that ΔH^0_f for an *element* in its most stable form is exactly 0 kJ/mol, so ΔH^0_f for Pb(s) = 0 kJ/mol. But the element *must* be in its most stable form. Thus, ΔH^0_f for O$_2$(g) is zero, because ordinary oxygen is gaseous and diatomic. We would *not* assume that ΔH^0_f would be zero for oxygen atoms, O(g), or for ozone, O$_3$(g). Similarly, ΔH^0_f is zero for Cl$_2$(g) and for Br$_2$(ℓ), but not for Br$_2$(g). Recall that bromine is one of the few elements that is liquid at room temperature and 1 atm pressure.

15-9 Bond Energies

Chemical reactions involve the breaking and making of chemical bonds. Energy is always required to break a chemical bond (see Section 7-4). Often this energy is supplied in the form of heat.

▶ For all practical purposes, the bond energy is the same as bond enthalpy. Tabulated values of average bond energies are actually average bond enthalpies. We use the term "bond *energy*" rather than "bond *enthalpy*" because it is common practice to do so.

> The **bond energy (B.E.)** is the amount of energy necessary to break *one mole* of bonds in a gaseous covalent substance to form products in the gaseous state at constant temperature and pressure.

The greater the bond energy, the more stable (stronger) the bond is, and the harder it is to break. Thus bond energy is a measure of bond strengths.

Consider the following reaction.

$$H_2(g) \longrightarrow 2H(g) \qquad \Delta H^0_{rxn} = \Delta H_{H-H} = +436 \text{ kJ/mol H—H bonds}$$

▶ We have discussed these changes in terms of absorption or release of heat. Another way of breaking bonds is by absorption of light energy (see Chapter 4). Bond energies can be determined from the energies of the photons that cause bond dissociation.

The bond energy of the hydrogen–hydrogen bond is 436 kJ/mol of bonds. In other words, 436 kJ of energy must be absorbed for every mole of H—H bonds that are broken. This endothermic reaction (ΔH^0_{rxn} is positive) can be written

$$H_2(g) + 436 \text{ kJ} \longrightarrow 2H(g)$$

Table 15-2 Some Average Single Bond Energies (kJ/mol of bonds)

H	C	N	O	F	Si	P	S	Cl	Br	I	
436	413	391	463	565	318	322	347	432	366	299	**H**
	346	305	358	485			272	339	285	213	**C**
		163	201	283				192			**N**
			146	190	452	335		218	201	201	**O**
				155	565	490	284	253	249	278	**F**
					222		293	381	310	234	**Si**
						201		326		184	**P**
							226	255			**S**
								242	216	208	**Cl**
									193	175	**Br**
										151	**I**

Table 15-3 Comparison of Some Average Single and Multiple Bond Energies
(kJ/mol of bonds)

Single Bonds		Double Bonds		Triple Bonds	
C—C	346	C=C	602	C≡C	835
N—N	163	N=N	418	N≡N	945
O—O	146	O=O	498		
C—N	305	C=N	615	C≡N	887
C—O	358	C=O	732*	C≡O	1072

*Except in CO_2, where it is 799 kJ/mol.

Some average bond energies are listed in Tables 15-2 and 15-3. We see from Table 15-3 that for any combination of elements, a triple bond is stronger than a double bond, which in turn is stronger than a single bond. Bond energies for double and triple bonds are *not* simply two or three times those for the corresponding single bonds. A single bond is a σ bond, whereas double and triple bonds involve a combination of σ and π bonding. The bond energy measures the effectiveness of orbital overlap, and we should not expect the strength of a π bond to be the same as that of a σ bond between the same two atoms because π bonds have poorer orbital overlap than σ bonds.

We should keep in mind that each of the values listed is the average bond energy from a variety of compounds. The *average C—H bond energy* is 413 kJ/mol of bonds. Average C—H bond energies differ slightly from compound to compound, as in CH_4, CH_3Cl, CH_3NO_2, and so on. Nevertheless, they are sufficiently constant to be useful in estimating thermodynamic data that are not readily available by another approach. Values of ΔH^0_{rxn} estimated in this way are not as reliable as those obtained from ΔH^0_f values for the substances involved in the reaction.

A special case of Hess's Law involves the use of bond energies to *estimate* heats of reaction. Consider the enthalpy diagrams in Figure 15-5. In general terms, ΔH^0_{rxn} is related to the bond energies of the reactants and products in *gas phase reactions* by the following version of Hess's Law.

$$\Delta H^0_{rxn} = \Sigma \text{ B.E.}_{reactants} - \Sigma \text{ B.E.}_{products} \qquad \text{for gas phase reactions only}$$

The net enthalpy change of a reaction is the amount of energy required to break all the bonds in reactant molecules *minus* the amount of energy required to break all the bonds in product molecules. Stated in another way, the amount of energy released when a bond is

S TOP & THINK
Remember that this equation involves bond energies of *reactants* minus bond energies of *products*. This is opposite Hess's Law, where it is the sum of the products minus the sum of the reactants.

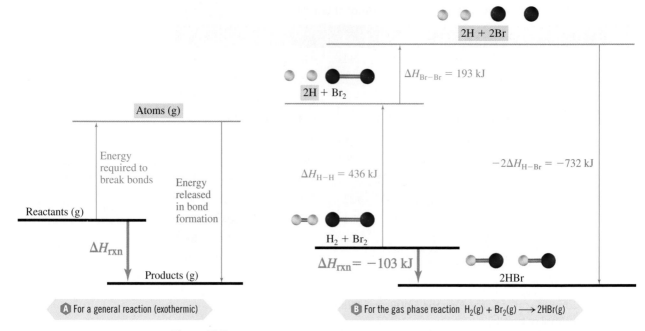

Figure 15-5 A schematic representation of the relationship between bond energies and ΔH_{rxn} for gas phase reactions. As usual for such diagrams, the value shown for each change refers to the number of moles of substances or bonds indicated in the diagram.

▶ Very few real reactions occur by breaking and forming *all* bonds. But because bond energy is a state function, we can assume *any* pathway between reactants and products and get the same result.

formed is equal to the amount absorbed when the same bond is broken. The heat of reaction for a gas phase reaction can be described as the amount of energy released in forming all the bonds in the products minus the amount of energy released in forming all the bonds in the reactants (see Figure 15-5). This heat of reaction can be estimated using the average bond energies in Tables 15-2 and 15-3.

The definition of bond energies is limited to the bond-breaking process *only* and does not include any provision for changes of state. Thus, it is valid only for substances in the gaseous state. The calculations of this section therefore apply *only* when all substances in the reaction are gases. If liquids or solids were involved, then additional information such as heats of vaporization and fusion would be needed to account for phase changes.

EXAMPLE 15-11 Bond Energies

MOLECULAR REASONING

Use the bond energies listed in Table 15-2 to estimate the heat of reaction at 298 K for the following reaction.

$$N_2(g) + 3H_2(g) \longrightarrow 2NH_3(g)$$

Plan

Each NH_3 molecule contains three $N-H$ bonds, so two moles of NH_3 contain six moles of $N-H$ bonds. Three moles of H_2 contain a total of three moles of $H-H$ bonds, and one mole of N_2 contains one mole of $N{\equiv}N$ bonds. From this we can estimate the heat of reaction.

$$H-\overset{\displaystyle ..}{N}-H$$
$$\underset{\textstyle H}{|}$$

▶ For each term in the sum, the units are $\dfrac{\text{mol bonds}}{\text{mol rxn}} \times \dfrac{\text{kJ}}{\text{mol bonds}}$

Solution

Using the bond energy form of Hess's Law,

$$\Delta H^0_{rxn} = [\Delta H_{N{\equiv}N} + 3\,\Delta H_{H-H}] - [6\,\Delta H_{N-H}]$$

$$= 945 + 3(436) - 6(391) = \boxed{-93 \text{ kJ/mol rxn}}$$

You should now work Exercise 48.

EXAMPLE 15-12 Bond Energies

Use the bond energies listed in Table 15-2 to estimate the heat of reaction at 298 K for the following reaction.

$$C_3H_8(g) \quad + Cl_2(g) \quad \longrightarrow \quad C_3H_7Cl(g) \quad + HCl(g)$$

$$
\begin{array}{ccc}
\text{H} \; \text{H} \; \text{H} & & \text{H} \; \text{H} \; \text{H} \\
| \;\; | \;\; | & & | \;\; | \;\; | \\
\text{H}-\text{C}-\text{C}-\text{C}-\text{H} + \text{Cl}-\text{Cl} & \longrightarrow & \text{H}-\text{C}-\text{C}-\text{C}-\text{Cl} + \text{H}-\text{Cl} \\
| \;\; | \;\; | & & | \;\; | \;\; | \\
\text{H} \; \text{H} \; \text{H} & & \text{H} \; \text{H} \; \text{H}
\end{array}
$$

Plan

Two moles of C — C bonds and seven moles of C — H bonds are the same before and after reaction, so we do not need to include them in the bond energy calculation. The only reactant bonds that are broken are one mole of C — H bonds and one mole of Cl — Cl bonds. On the product side, the only new bonds formed are one mole of C — Cl bonds and one mole of H — Cl bonds. We need to take into account only the bonds that are different on the two sides of the equation. As before, we add and subtract the appropriate bond energies, using values from Table 15-2.

Solution

$$\Delta H^0_{rxn} = [\Delta H_{C-H} + \Delta H_{Cl-Cl}] - [\Delta H_{C-Cl} + \Delta H_{H-Cl}]$$

$$= [413 + 242] - [339 + 432] = \boxed{-116 \text{ kJ/mol rxn}}$$

You should now work Exercises 50 and 52.

> **⬡ TOP & THINK**
> We would get the same value for ΔH^0_{rxn} if we used the full bond energy form of Hess's Law and assumed that *all* bonds in reactants were broken and then *all* bonds in products were formed. In such a calculation the bond energies for the unchanged bonds would cancel. Why? Try it!

15-10 Changes in Internal Energy, ΔE

The **internal energy, E,** of a specific amount of a substance represents all the energy contained within the substance. It includes such forms as kinetic energies of the molecules; energies of attraction and repulsion among subatomic particles, atoms, ions, or molecules; and other forms of energy. The internal energy of a collection of molecules is a state function. The difference between the internal energy of the products and the internal energy of the reactants of a chemical reaction or physical change, ΔE, is given by the equation

▶ Internal energy is a state function, so it is represented by a capital letter.

$$\Delta E = E_{final} - E_{initial} = E_{products} - E_{reactants} = q + w$$

The terms q and w represent heat and work, respectively. These are two ways in which energy can flow into or out of a system. **Work** involves a change of energy in which a body is moved through a distance, d, against some force, f; that is, $w = fd$.

$$\Delta E = (\text{amount of heat absorbed by system}) + (\text{amount of work done on system})$$

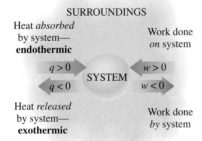

Sign conventions for q and w.

A Some powdered dry ice (solid CO_2) is placed into a flexible bag, which is then sealed.

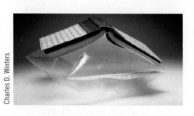

B As the dry ice absorbs heat from the surroundings, some solid CO_2 sublimes to form gaseous CO_2. The larger volume of the gas causes the bag to expand. The expanding gas does the work of raising a book that has been placed on the bag. Work would be done by the expansion, even if the book were not present, as the bag pushes against the surrounding atmosphere. The heat absorbed by such a process at constant pressure, q_p, is equal to ΔH for the process.

Figure 15-6 A system that absorbs heat and does work.

$$\frac{F}{d^2} \times d^3 = Fd = w$$

$$\uparrow \qquad \uparrow$$
$$P \qquad V$$

▶ At 25° the change in internal energy for the combustion of methane is -887 kJ/ mol CH_4. The change in heat content is -890 kJ/ mol CH_4 (see Section 15-1). The small difference is due to work done on the system as it is compressed by the atmosphere.

The following conventions apply to the signs of q and w.

q is positive:	Heat is *absorbed* by the system from the surroundings (endothermic).
q is negative:	Heat is *released* by the system to the surroundings (exothermic).
w is positive:	Work is done *on* the system by the surroundings.
w is negative:	Work is done *by* the system on the surroundings.

Whenever a given amount of energy is added to or removed from a system, either as heat or as work, the energy of the system changes by that same amount. The equation $\Delta E = q + w$ is another way of expressing the First Law of Thermodynamics (see Section 15-1).

The only type of work involved in most chemical and physical changes is pressure–volume work. From dimensional analysis we can see that the product of pressure and volume is work. Pressure is the force exerted per unit area, where area is distance squared, d^2; volume is distance cubed, d^3. Thus, the product of pressure and volume is force times distance, which is work. An example of a physical change (a phase change) in which the system expands and thus does work as it absorbs heat is shown in Figure 15-6. Even if the book had not been present, the expanding system pushing against the atmosphere would have done work for the expansion.

When energy is released by a reacting system, ΔE is negative; energy can be written as a product in the equation for the reaction. When the system absorbs energy from the surroundings, ΔE is positive; energy can be written as a reactant in the equation.

For example, the complete combustion of CH_4 at constant volume at 25°C *releases* energy.

$$CH_4(g) + 2O_2(g) \longrightarrow CO_2(g) + 2H_2O(\ell) + 887 \text{ kJ}$$

indicates release of energy

We can write the *change in energy* that accompanies this reaction as

$$CH_4(g) + 2O_2(g) \longrightarrow CO_2(g) + 2H_2O(\ell) \qquad \Delta E = -887 \text{ kJ/mol rxn}$$

As discussed in Section 15-2, the negative sign indicates a *decrease* in energy of the system, or a *release* of energy by the system.

The reverse of this reaction *absorbs* energy. It can be written as

$$CO_2(g) + 2H_2O(\ell) + 887 \text{ kJ} \longrightarrow CH_4(g) + 2O_2(g)$$

or

indicates absorption of energy

$$CO_2(g) + 2H_2O(\ell) \longrightarrow CH_4(g) + 2O_2(g) \qquad \Delta E = +887 \text{ kJ/mol rxn}$$

If the latter reaction could be forced to occur, the system would have to absorb 887 kJ of energy per mole of reaction from its surroundings.

When a gas is produced against constant external pressure, such as in an open vessel at atmospheric pressure, the gas does work as it expands against the pressure of the atmosphere. If no heat is absorbed during the expansion, the result is a decrease in the internal energy of the system. On the other hand, when a gas is consumed in a process, the atmosphere does work on the reacting system.

Let us illustrate the latter case. Consider the complete reaction of a 2:1 mole ratio of H_2 and O_2 to produce steam at some constant temperature above 100°C and at one atmosphere pressure (Figure 15-7).

$$2H_2(g) + O_2(g) \longrightarrow 2H_2O(g) + \text{heat}$$

Assume that the constant-temperature bath surrounding the reaction vessel completely absorbs all the evolved heat so that the temperature of the gases does not change. The volume of the system decreases by one third (3 mol gaseous reactants → 2 mol gaseous products). The surroundings exert a constant pressure of one atmosphere and do work on the system by compressing it. The internal energy of the system increases by an amount equal to the amount of work done on it.

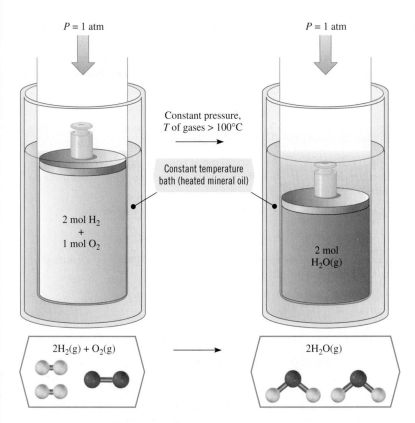

Figure 15-7 An illustration of the one-third decrease in volume that accompanies the reaction of H_2 with O_2 at constant temperature. The temperature is above 100°C.

The work done on or by a system depends on the *external* pressure and the volume. When the external pressure is constant during a change, the amount of work done is equal to this pressure times the change in volume. The work done *on* a system equals $-P\,\Delta V$ or $-P(V_2 - V_1)$.

▶ V_2 is the final volume, and V_1 is the initial volume.

Compression (volume decreases)	Expansion (volume increases)
Work is done *by* the surroundings *on* the system, so the sign of w is positive	Work is done *by* the system *on* the surroundings, so the sign of w is negative
V_2 is less than V_1, so $\Delta V = (V_2 - V_1)$ is negative	V_2 is greater than V_1, so $\Delta V = (V_2 - V_1)$ is positive
$w = -P\,\Delta V$ is positive $(-) \times (+) \times (-) = +$	$w = -P\,\Delta V$ is negative $(-) \times (+) \times (+) = -$
Can be due to a *decrease* in number of moles of gas (Δn negative)	Can be due to an *increase* in number of moles of gas (Δn positive)

We substitute $-P\,\Delta V$ for w in the equation $\Delta E = q + w$ to obtain

$$\Delta E = q - P\,\Delta V$$

In constant-volume reactions, no $P\,\Delta V$ work is done. Volume does not change, so nothing "moves through a distance," and $d = 0$ and $fd = 0$. The change in internal energy of the system is just the amount of heat absorbed or released at constant volume, q_v.

$$\Delta E = q_v$$

Figure 15-8 shows the same phase change process as in Figure 15-6, but at constant volume condition, so no work is done.

Solids and liquids do not expand or contract significantly when the pressure changes ($\Delta V \approx 0$). In reactions in which equal numbers of moles of gases are produced and con-

▶ Do not make the error of setting work equal to $V\,\Delta P$.

▶ A subscript v indicates a constant-volume process; a subscript p indicates a constant-pressure process.

Charles D. Winters

Figure 15-8 A system that absorbs heat at constant volume. Some dry ice [$CO_2(s)$] is placed into a rigid flask, which is then sealed. As the dry ice absorbs heat from the surroundings, some $CO_2(s)$ sublimes to form $CO_2(g)$. In contrast to the case in Figure 15-6, this system cannot expand ($\Delta V = 0$), so no work is done, and the pressure in the flask increases. Thus, the heat absorbed at constant volume, q_v, is equal to ΔE for the process.

sumed at constant temperature and pressure, essentially no work is done. By the ideal gas equation, $P \Delta V = (\Delta n)RT$ and $\Delta n = 0$, where Δn equals the number of moles of gaseous products minus the number of moles of gaseous reactants. Thus, the work term w has a significant value at constant pressure only when there are different numbers of moles of gaseous products and reactants so that the volume of the system changes.

EXAMPLE 15-13 Predicting the Sign of Work

For each of the following chemical reactions carried out at constant temperature and constant pressure, predict the sign of w and tell whether work is done *on* or *by* the system. Consider the reaction mixture to be the system.

(a) Ammonium nitrate, commonly used as a fertilizer, decomposes explosively.

$$2NH_4NO_3(s) \longrightarrow 2N_2(g) + 4H_2O(g) + O_2(g)$$

This reaction was responsible for an explosion in 1947 that destroyed nearly the entire port of Texas City, Texas, and killed 576 people.

(b) Hydrogen and chlorine combine to form hydrogen chloride gas.

$$H_2(g) + Cl_2(g) \longrightarrow 2HCl(g)$$

(c) Sulfur dioxide is oxidized to sulfur trioxide, one step in the production of sulfuric acid.

$$2SO_2(g) + O_2(g) \longrightarrow 2SO_3(g)$$

Plan

▶ Δn refers to the balanced equation.

For a process at constant pressure, $w = -P \Delta V = -(\Delta n)RT$. For each reaction, we evaluate Δn, the change in the number of moles of *gaseous* substances in the reaction.

$$\Delta n = \text{(no. of moles of gaseous products)} - \text{(no. of moles of gaseous reactants)}$$

Because both R and T (on the Kelvin scale) are positive quantities, the sign of w is opposite from that of Δn; it tells us whether the work is done *on* ($w = +$) or *by* ($w = -$) the system.

© AFP/Getty Images

The decomposition of NH_4NO_3 produces large amounts of gas, which expands rapidly as the very fast reaction occurs. This explosive reaction was the main cause of the destruction of the Federal Building in Oklahoma City in 1995.

Solution

▶ Here there are no gaseous reactants.

(a) $\Delta n = [2 \text{ mol } N_2(g) + 4 \text{ mol } H_2O(g) + 1 \text{ mol } O_2(g)] - 0 \text{ mol}$

$\qquad = 7 \text{ mol} - 0 \text{ mol} = +7 \text{ mol}$

Δn is positive, so w is negative. This tells us that work is done *by* the system. The large amount of gas formed by the reaction pushes against the surroundings (as happened with devastating effect in the Texas City disaster).

(b) $\Delta n = [2 \text{ mol } HCl(g)] - [1 \text{ mol } H_2(g) + 1 \text{ mol } Cl_2(g)]$

$\qquad = 2 \text{ mol} - 2 \text{ mol} = 0 \text{ mol}$

Thus, $w = 0$, and no work is done as the reaction proceeds. We can see from the balanced equation that for every two moles (total) of gas that react, two moles of gas are formed, so the volume neither expands nor contracts as the reaction occurs.

(c) $\Delta n = [2 \text{ mol } SO_3(g)] - [2 \text{ mol } SO_2(g) + 1 \text{ mol } O_2(g)]$

$= 2 \text{ mol} - 3 \text{ mol} = -1 \text{ mol}$

Δn is negative, so w is positive. This tells us that work is done *on* the system as the reaction proceeds. The surroundings push against the diminishing volume of gas.

You should now work Exercises 77 and 78.

> **S TOP & THINK**
> When the number of moles of gas *increases*, work is done *by* the system, so w is *negative*. When the number of moles of gas *decreases*, work is done *on* the system, so w is *positive*.

A **bomb calorimeter** is a device that measures the amount of heat evolved or absorbed by a reaction occurring at constant volume (Figure 15-9). A strong steel vessel (the bomb) is immersed in a large volume of water. As heat is produced or absorbed by a reaction inside the steel vessel, the heat is transferred to or from the large volume of water. Thus, only rather small temperature changes occur. For all practical purposes, the energy changes associated with the reactions are measured at constant volume and constant temperature. No work is done when a reaction is carried out in a bomb calorimeter, even if gases are involved, because $\Delta V = 0$. Therefore,

$$\Delta E = q_v \qquad \text{(constant volume)}$$

▶ The "calorie content" of a food can be determined by burning it in excess oxygen inside a bomb calorimeter and determining the heat released. 1 "nutritional Calorie" = 1 kcal = 4.184 kJ.

EXAMPLE 15-14 Bomb Calorimeter

A 1.000-gram sample of ethanol, C_2H_5OH, was burned in a bomb calorimeter whose heat capacity had been determined to be 2.71 kJ/°C. The temperature of 3000 grams of water rose from 24.284°C to 26.225°C. Determine ΔE for the reaction in joules per gram of ethanol, and then in kilojoules per mole of ethanol. The specific heat of water is $4.184 \text{ J/g} \cdot °C$. The combustion reaction is

$$C_2H_5OH(\ell) + 3O_2(g) \longrightarrow 2CO_2(g) + 3H_2O(\ell)$$

Plan

The amount of heat given off by the system (in the sealed compartment) raises the temperature of the calorimeter and its water. The amount of heat absorbed by the water can be calculated using the specific heat of water; similarly, we use the heat capacity of the calorimeter to find the amount of heat absorbed by the calorimeter. The sum of these two amounts of heat is the total amount of heat released by the combustion of 1.000 gram of ethanol. We must then scale that result to correspond to one mole of ethanol.

Solution

The increase in temperature is

$$\underline{?} \ °C = 26.225°C - 24.284°C = 1.941°C \text{ rise}$$

The amount of heat responsible for this increase in temperature of 3000 grams of water is

$$\text{heat to warm water} = 1.941°C \times \frac{4.184 \text{ J}}{\text{g} \cdot °C} \times 3000 \text{ g} = 2.436 \times 10^4 \text{ J} = 24.36 \text{ kJ}$$

The amount of heat responsible for the warming of the calorimeter is

$$\text{heat to warm calorimeter} = 1.941°C \times \frac{2.71 \text{ kJ}}{°C} = 5.26 \text{ kJ}$$

The total amount of heat absorbed by the calorimeter *and* by the water is

$$\text{total amount of heat} = 24.36 \text{ kJ} + 5.26 \text{ kJ} = 29.62 \text{ kJ}$$

Combustion of one gram of C_2H_5OH liberates 29.62 kJ of energy in the form of heat, that is

$$\Delta E = q_v = -29.62 \text{ kJ/g ethanol}$$

▶ Benzoic acid, C_6H_5COOH, is often used to determine the heat capacity of a calorimeter. It is a solid that can be compressed into pellets. Its heat of combustion is accurately known: 3227 kJ/mol benzoic acid, or 26.46 kJ/g benzoic acid. Another way to measure the heat capacity of a calorimeter is to add a known amount of heat electrically.

A disassembled bomb calorimeter

Charles D. Winters

The negative sign indicates that energy is released by the system to the surroundings. Now we may evaluate ΔE in kJ/mol of ethanol by converting grams of C_2H_5OH to moles.

$$\frac{?\ kJ}{mol\ ethanol} = \frac{-29.62\ kJ}{g} \times \frac{46.07g\ C_2H_5OH}{1\ mol\ C_2H_2OH} = -1365\ kJ/mol\ ethanol$$

$$\Delta E = -1365\ kJ/mol\ ethanol$$

This calculation shows that for the combustion of ethanol at constant temperature and constant volume, the change in internal energy is -1365 kJ/mol ethanol.

You should now work Exercises 66 and 67.

The balanced chemical equation involves one mole of ethanol, so we can write the unit factor $\dfrac{1\ mol\ ethanol}{1\ mol\ rxn}$. Then we express the result of Example 15-14 as

$$\Delta E = \frac{-1365\ kJ}{mol\ ethanol} \times \frac{1\ mol\ ethanol}{1\ mol\ rxn} = -1365\ kJ/mol\ rxn$$

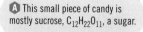

Ⓐ This small piece of candy is mostly sucrose, $C_{12}H_{22}O_{11}$, a sugar.

Charles D. Winters

Ⓑ When the piece of candy is heated together with potassium chlorate, $KClO_3$ (a good oxidizing agent), a highly product-favored reaction occurs.

$$C_{12}H_{22}O_{11}(s) + 12O_2(g) \longrightarrow 12CO_2(g) + 11H_2O(g)$$

If that amount of sucrose is completely metabolized to carbon dioxide and water vapor in your body, the same amount of energy is released, though more slowly.

Oxidation of sugar.

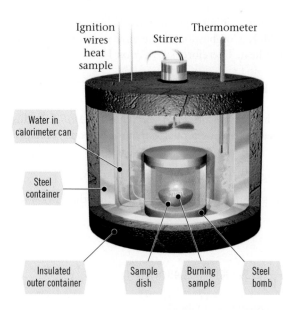

Figure 15-9 A bomb calorimeter measures q_v, the amount of heat given off or absorbed by a reaction occurring at constant *volume*. The amount of energy introduced via the ignition wires is measured and taken into account.

Labels in figure:
- Ignition wires heat sample
- Stirrer
- Thermometer
- Water in calorimeter can
- Steel container
- Insulated outer container
- Sample dish
- Burning sample
- Steel bomb

15-11 Relationship Between ΔH and ΔE

The fundamental definition of enthalpy, H, is

$$H = E + PV$$

For a process at constant temperature and pressure,

$$\Delta H = \Delta E + P\,\Delta V \qquad \text{(constant } T \text{ and } P\text{)}$$

From Section 15-10, we know that $\Delta E = q + w$, so

$$\Delta H = q + w + P\,\Delta V \qquad \text{(constant } T \text{ and } P\text{)}$$

At constant pressure, $w = -P\,\Delta V$, so

$$\Delta H = q + (-P\,\Delta V) + P\,\Delta V$$

$$\Delta H = q_p \qquad \text{(constant } T \text{ and } P\text{)}$$

The difference between ΔE and ΔH is the amount of expansion work ($P\,\Delta V$ work) that the system can do. Unless there is a change in the number of moles of gas present, this difference is extremely small and can usually be neglected. For an ideal gas, $PV = nRT$. At constant temperature and constant pressure, $P\,\Delta V = (\Delta n)RT$, a work term. Substituting gives

$$\Delta H = \Delta E + (\Delta n)RT \qquad \text{or} \qquad \Delta E = \Delta H - (\Delta n)RT \qquad \text{(constant } T \text{ and } P\text{)}$$

> **STOP & THINK**
>
> As usual, Δn refers to the number of moles of *gaseous products* minus the number of moles of *gaseous reactants* in the *balanced chemical equation.*

Problem-Solving Tip Two Equations Relate ΔH and ΔE—Which One Should Be Used?

The relationship $\Delta H = \Delta E + P\,\Delta V$ is valid for *any* process that takes place at constant temperature and pressure. It is very useful for physical changes that involve volume changes, such as expansion or compression of a gas.

When a chemical reaction occurring at constant T and P results in a change in the number of moles of gas, it is more convenient to use the relationship in the form $\Delta H = \Delta E + (\Delta n)RT$. You should always remember that Δn refers to the change in the number of moles of *gas in the balanced chemical equation.*

In Example 15-14 we found that the change in internal energy, ΔE, for the combustion of ethanol is -1365 kJ/mol ethanol at 298 K. Combustion of one mole of ethanol at 298 K and constant pressure releases 1367 kJ of heat. Therefore (see Section 15-5)

$$\Delta H = -1367 \ \frac{\text{kJ}}{\text{mol ethanol}}$$

The difference between ΔH and ΔE is due to the work term, $-P\,\Delta V$ or $-(\Delta n)RT$. In this balanced equation there are fewer moles of gaseous products than of gaseous reactants: $\Delta n = 2 - 3 = -1$.

$$C_2H_5OH(\ell) + 3O_2(g) \longrightarrow 2CO_2(g) + 3H_2O(\ell)$$

Thus, the atmosphere does work on the system (compresses it). Let us find the work done on the system per mole of reaction.

$$w = -P\,\Delta V = -(\Delta n)RT$$

$$= -(-1 \ \text{mol}) \left(\frac{8.314\,\text{J}}{\text{mol} \cdot \text{K}} \right) (298 \ \text{K}) = +2.48 \times 10^3 \ \text{J}$$

$$w = +2.48 \ \text{kJ} \quad \text{or} \quad (\Delta n)RT = -2.48 \ \text{kJ}$$

S TOP & THINK

The positive sign for w is consistent with the fact that work is done on the system. The balanced equation involves one mole of ethanol, so this is the amount of work done when one mole of ethanol undergoes combustion.

We can now calculate ΔE for the reaction from ΔH and $(\Delta n)RT$ values.

$$\Delta E = \Delta H - (\Delta n)RT = [-1367 - (-2.48)] = -1365 \ \text{kJ/mol rxn}$$

This value agrees with the result that we obtained in Example 15-14. The size of the work term ($+2.48$ kJ) is very small compared with ΔH (-1367 kJ/mol rxn). This is true for many reactions. Of course, if $\Delta n = 0$, then $\Delta H = \Delta E$, and the same amount of heat would be absorbed or given off by the reaction whether it is carried out at constant pressure or at constant volume.

Spontaneity of Physical and Chemical Changes

Another major concern of thermodynamics is predicting *whether* a particular process can occur under specified conditions to give predominantly products. We may summarize this concern in the question "Which would be more stable at the given conditions—the reactants or the products?" A change for which the collection of products is thermodynamically *more stable* than the collection of reactants under the given conditions is said to be **product-favored**, or **spontaneous**, under those conditions. A change for which the products are thermodynamically *less stable* than the reactants under the given conditions is described as **reactant-favored**, or **nonspontaneous**, under those conditions. Some changes are spontaneous under all conditions; others are nonspontaneous under all conditions. The great majority of changes, however, are spontaneous under some conditions but not under others. We use thermodynamics to predict conditions for which the latter type of reactions can occur to give predominantly products.

The concept of spontaneity has a specific interpretation in thermodynamics. A spontaneous chemical reaction or physical change is one that can happen without any continuing outside influence. Examples are the loss of heat by a hot metal to its cooler surroundings, the rusting of a piece of iron, the expansion of a gas into a larger volume, or the melting of ice at room temperature. Such changes have a tendency to occur without being driven by an external influence. We can think of a spontaneous process as one for which products are favored over reactants *at the specified conditions*. The reverse of each of the spontaneous changes just listed is nonspontaneous at the same conditions, that is, it does not occur naturally. We can, however, cause some *nonspontaneous* changes to occur. For example, forcing an electric current through a block of metal can heat it to a temperature higher than that of its surroundings. We can compress a gas into a smaller volume by pressing on it with a piston. But to cause a process to occur in its *nonspontaneous* direction, we must influence it from outside the system; that is, energy must be added to the system.

A hot piece of metal (a) is placed into cooler water. Heat is transferred *spontaneously* from the hotter metal to the cooler water (b), until the two are at the same temperature (the condition of *thermal equilibrium*).

Figure 15-10 The diffusion of two gases into one another is spontaneous. (a) A sample of gas in which all molecules of one gas are in one bulb and all molecules of the other gas are in the other bulb. (b) A sample of gas that contains the same number of each kind of molecule as in (a), but with the two kinds randomly mixed in the two bulbs. Sample (b) has greater dispersal of both matter and energy, and is thus more probable.

Although a spontaneous reaction *might* occur rapidly, thermodynamic spontaneity is not related to speed. The fact that a process is spontaneous does not mean that it will occur at an observable rate. It may occur rapidly, at a moderate rate, or very slowly. The rate at which a spontaneous reaction occurs is addressed by kinetics (see Chapter 16).

We now study the factors that influence spontaneity of a physical or chemical change.

15-12 The Two Aspects of Spontaneity

Many product-favored reactions are exothermic. For instance, the combustion (burning) reactions of hydrocarbons such as methane and octane are all exothermic and highly product-favored (spontaneous). The total enthalpy content of the products is lower than that of the reactants. Not all exothermic changes are spontaneous, however, nor are all spontaneous changes exothermic. As an example, consider the freezing of water, which is an exothermic process (heat is released). This process is spontaneous at temperatures below 0°C, but we know it is not spontaneous at temperatures above 0°C. Likewise, we know there are conditions at which the melting of ice, an endothermic process, is spontaneous. Spontaneity is *favored* but not required when heat is released during a chemical reaction or a physical change.

There is another factor that also plays a fundamental role in determining spontaneity. Let's think about two spontaneous processes. Figure 15-10 shows what happens when two gas samples at the same pressure are allowed to mix. The molecules move randomly throughout the two containers to mix the gases (a spontaneous process). We don't expect the more homogeneous sample in Figure 15-10b to spontaneously "unmix" to give the arrangement in Figure 15-10a (a nonspontaneous process).

As a hot metal cools, some of the energy of its vibrating atoms is transferred to the surroundings (a spontaneous process). This warms the surroundings until the two temperatures are equal. We do not expect to observe the reverse process in which energy is transferred from the surroundings to a block of metal, originally at the same temperature, to raise the temperature of the metal (a nonspontaneous process).

▶ Recall that the temperature of a sample is a measure of the average kinetic energy of its particles.

In these examples, we see that *energy and matter tend to become dispersed (spread out)*. We shall see that this dispersal is a fundamental driving force that affects the spontaneity of any process.

Two factors affect the spontaneity of any physical or chemical change:

1. Spontaneity is *favored* when *heat is released* during the change (exothermic).

2. Spontaneity is *favored* when the change causes an *increase in the dispersal of energy and matter.*

The balance of these two effects is considered in Section 15-16.

15-13 Dispersal of Energy and Matter

Dispersal of Energy

The **dispersal of energy** in a system results in the energy being spread over many particles rather than being concentrated in just a few.

To understand this concept, think about a system consisting of just two molecules, A and B, with a total of two units of energy. Denoting one unit of energy with a*, we can list the three ways to distribute these two energy units over the two molecules as

A**   (Molecule A has two units of energy, B has none.)

A*B* (Each molecule has one unit of energy.)

B**   (Molecule B has two units of energy, A has none.)

Suppose these two molecules are mixed with two other molecules, C and D, that initially have no energy. When collisions occur, energy can be transferred from one molecule to another. Now the energy can be dispersed among the four molecules in ten different ways:

A**   B**   C**   D**   A*B*   A*C*   A*D*   B*C*   B*D*   C*D*

Now there are obviously more ways (ten) the energy can be dispersed than before. In only three of these ways would all of the energy be distributed as before—A**, A*B*, and B**. Put another way, there is only a 3/10 probability that the energy will be restricted to the original molecules, A and B. There are seven ways out of ten, or a probability of 7/10, that at least some of the energy has been transferred to C or D.

What would happen if large numbers of molecules were present, as in any real sample? The probability that the energy is dispersed would be huge, and there would be only an infinitesimally small chance that all of the energy would be concentrated in one or a few molecules. This reasoning leads us to an important conclusion.

If energy can be dispersed over a larger number of particles, it will be.

To see what happens if there is more energy to distribute (as at a higher temperature), let's consider another system with four molecules, but with two of the molecules (A and B) initially having three units of energy and the other two (C and D) initially with no energy, as shown in Figure 15-11a. When these molecules are brought together and allowed to exchange energy by colliding, the energy can be distributed in a total of 84 different ways, as shown in Figure 15-11b. For example, one molecule can have all six units of energy and the other three have no energy, as shown in the leftmost drawing of Figure 15-11b; the six-unit molecule could be any one of the four, so there are four ways to achieve this arrangement. Thus, the probability is only 4/84 (or 1/21) that all of the energy of the system is concentrated in one molecule. There are six ways to distribute the energy to arrive at the rightmost drawing (see Figure 15-11c). Some of the other energy distributions can be achieved in many more ways, leading to a much higher probability for their occurrence. This leads to a broader statement of our earlier conclusion.

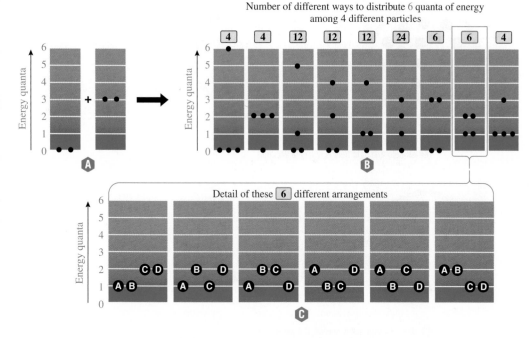

Number of different ways to distribute 6 quanta of energy among 4 different particles

Detail of these 6 different arrangements

Figure 15-11 Possible ways of distributing six quanta of energy among four molecules. (a) Initially four molecules are separated from each other. Two molecules each have three quanta of energy, and the other two have none. A total of six quanta of energy will be distributed once the molecules interact. (b) Once the molecules begin to interact, there are nine ways to distribute the six available quanta. Each of these arrangements will have multiple ways of distributing the energy among the four molecules. (c) The six different ways to arrange four molecules (A, B, C, and D) such that two molecules have two quanta of energy and the other two have one quanta of energy.

The greater the number of molecules and the higher the total energy of the system, the less likely the energy will be concentrated in a few molecules. Therefore, the energy will be more dispersed.

This generalization provides the molecular explanation behind the Maxwell-Boltzmann distribution of molecular speeds (kinetic energies) that was discussed in Section 12-13 (see Figure 12-9) and in relation to evaporation and vapor pressures of liquids in Sections 13-6 and 13-7.

Dispersal of Matter

Let us apply the idea of dispersal to the arrangements of matter and its molecules. Our experience tells us that a gas originally confined in a bulb (Figure 15-12a) will expand freely into a vacuum (see Figure 15-12b). We don't expect the gas then to concentrate spontaneously into only one bulb. We can consider this expansion from the molecular point of view.

Suppose there are four molecules of gas in the two-part container of Figure 15-13. The probability that a particular molecule is on the left at any given time is $\frac{1}{2}$. A second specific molecule has its own probability of $\frac{1}{2}$ of being on the left, so the probability that *both* of these are on the left at the same time is $\frac{1}{2} \times \frac{1}{2} = \frac{1}{4}$. There are 16 ways that the molecules can be arranged in this container. But in only one of these arrangements are all four molecules in the left-hand portion of the container. The probability of that "concentrated" arrangement is

$$\frac{1}{2} \times \frac{1}{2} \times \frac{1}{2} \times \frac{1}{2} = \left(\frac{1}{2}\right)^4 = \frac{1}{16}$$

We see that there is only a small likelihood that this gas would spontaneously concentrate into the left side of the container.

Similar reasoning shows that the probability of one mole, or 6.0×10^{23} molecules, spontaneously concentrating into the left-hand bulb of Figure 15-12 would be

$$\frac{1}{2} \times \frac{1}{2} \times \ldots \times \frac{1}{2} = \left(\frac{1}{2}\right)^{6.0 \times 10^{23}} = \frac{1}{2^{6.0 \times 10^{23}}}$$

Without writing the number in the denominator explicitly, we can mention that it is larger than the number of molecules in the entire universe! Thus there is virtually no chance that

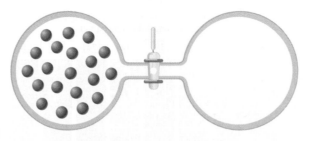

Ⓐ The stopcock is closed, keeping all of the gas in the left bulb; the right bulb is empty (a vacuum).

Ⓑ When the stopcock is opened, the gas expands to fill the entire available volume, with half of the gas in each bulb.

Figure 15-12 The expansion of a gas into a vacuum.

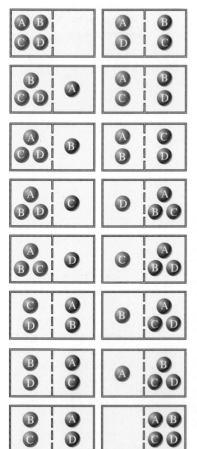

Figure 15-13 The 16 possible ways of arranging four molecules in a two-part container. Only one of these arrangements has all four molecules on the left side, so the probability of that arrangement is 1/16.

all 6.0×10^{23} molecules in a mole of gas would spontaneously concentrate into half the available volume, leaving no molecules in the other half.

The dispersal of matter, as in the expansion of a gas, also often contributes to energy dispersal. Consider the expansion of a gas into a vacuum, as shown in Figure 15-14. When the gas is allowed to occupy the larger volume in Figure 15-14b, its energy levels become closer together than in the smaller volume of Figure 15-14a. This means that there are even more ways for the expanded gas to disperse its energy to arrive at the same total energy. The concept of dispersal of energy thus also predicts that the gas is far more likely to exist in the expanded state of Figure 15-14b, and we would not expect it to concentrate spontaneously to occupy only one chamber as in Figure 15-14a. Similar reasoning helps us to describe the spontaneous mixing of two gases in Figure 15-10. Each gas can have its energy more dispersed in its own more closely spaced energy levels when expanded into both containers. But in addition, the molecules of one gas can transfer energy to the molecules of the other gas by collision. This results in an even larger number of ways for the total energy of the mixture to be dispersed, leading to a much higher probability that the gases will be mixed (see Figure 15-10b) than unmixed (see Figure 15-10a). Thus the spatial dispersal of matter also results in a greater dispersal of energy.

When a soluble substance dissolves in a liquid, the solute particles become dispersed in the solvent (see Sections 14-1 through 14-4). This allows the particles to transfer energy to one another, giving a larger number of ways of distributing the same total energy than if the substances remained in separate phases. In this case, too, dispersal of the two kinds of matter in one another allows more dispersal of energy. In more general terms, we often describe the dispersal of matter as an increase in **disorder**.

To summarize the conclusions of this section:

The final state of a system can be more probable than its initial state (spontaneous, product-favored) in either or both of two ways:

1. Energy can be dispersed over a greater number and variety of molecules.

2. The particles of the system can be more dispersed (more disordered).

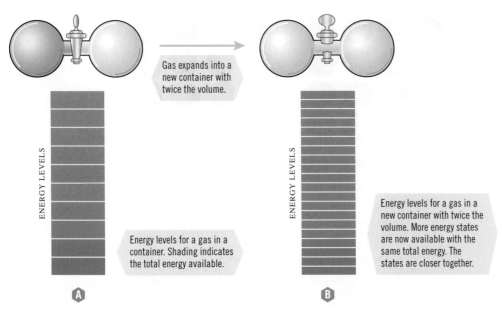

Figure 15-14 Larger gas volumes give more energy levels.

15-14 Entropy, *S*, and Entropy Change, Δ*S*

The dispersal of energy and matter is described by the thermodynamic state function **entropy, *S*.** In the most fundamental description, the greater the energy dispersal in a system, the higher is its entropy. We have said that greater disorder (dispersal of matter, both in space and in variety) can lead to greater dispersal of energy, and hence to higher entropy. This connection allows us to discuss many entropy changes in terms of increases or decreases in the disorder and the energy dispersal of the system. Let us first see how entropy is tabulated and how entropy changes are calculated.

The **Third Law of Thermodynamics** establishes the zero of the entropy scale.

> The entropy of a pure, perfect crystalline substance (perfectly ordered) is zero at absolute zero (0 K).

As the temperature of a substance increases, the particles vibrate more vigorously, so the entropy increases (Figure 15-15). Further heat input causes either increased temperature (still higher entropy) or phase transitions (melting, sublimation, or boiling) that also result in higher entropy. The entropy of a substance at any condition is its **absolute entropy,** also called **standard molar entropy.** Consider the absolute entropies at 298 K listed in Table 15-4. At 298 K, *any* substance is more disordered than if it were in a perfect crystalline state at absolute zero, so tabulated S^0_{298} values for compounds and elements are *always positive.* Notice especially that S^0_{298} of an element, unlike its ΔH^0_f, is *not* equal to zero. The reference state for absolute entropy is specified by the Third Law of Thermodynamics. It is different from the reference state for ΔH^0_f (see Section 15-7). The absolute entropies, S^0_{298}, of various substances under standard conditions are tabulated in Appendix K.

Just as for other thermodynamic quantities, the entropy change for a system, ΔS_{system}, is the difference between final and initial states:

$$\Delta S_{system} = S_{system,\,final} - S_{system,\,initial}$$

The **standard entropy change,** ΔS^0, of a reaction can be determined from the absolute entropies of reactants and products. The relationship is analogous to Hess's Law.

$$\Delta S^0_{rxn} = \Sigma\, n\, S^0_{products} - \Sigma\, n\, S^0_{reactants}$$

▶ Enthalpies are measured only as *differences* with respect to an arbitrary standard state. Entropies, in contrast, are defined relative to an absolute zero level. In either case, the *per mole* designation means *per mole of substance in the specified state.*

▶ The Σ*n* means that each S^0 value must be multiplied by the appropriate coefficient, *n*, from the balanced equation. These values are then added.

Table 15-4 Absolute Entropies at 298 K for a Few Common Substances

Substance	S^0 (J/mol · K)
C(diamond)	2.38
C(g)	158.0
$H_2O(\ell)$	69.91
$H_2O(g)$	188.7
$I_2(s)$	116.1
$I_2(g)$	260.6

Ⓐ A simplified representation of a side view of a "perfect" crystal of a polar substance at 0 K. Note the perfect alignment of the dipoles in all molecules in a perfect crystal. This causes its entropy to be zero at 0 K. There are no perfect crystals, however, because even the purest substances that scientists have prepared are contaminated by traces of impurities that occupy a few of the positions in the crystal structure. Additionally, there are some vacancies in the crystal structures of even very highly purified substances such as those used in semiconductors (Section 13-17).

Ⓑ A simplified representation of the same "perfect" crystal at a temperature above 0 K. Vibrations of the individual molecules within the crystal cause some dipoles to be oriented in directions other than those in a perfect arrangement. The entropy of such a crystalline solid is greater than zero because there is disorder in the crystal. Many different arrangements are possible for such a disordered array, so there is a greater dispersal of energy than in the perfectly ordered crystal.

Figure 15-15

S^0 values are tabulated in units of *J/mol · K* rather than the larger units involving kilojoules that are used for enthalpy changes. The "mol" term in the units for a *substance* refers to a mole of the substance, whereas for a *reaction* it refers to a mole of reaction. Each term in the sums on the right-hand side of the equation has the units

$$\frac{\text{mol substance}}{\text{mol rxn}} \times \frac{\text{J}}{(\text{mol substance}) \cdot \text{K}} = \frac{\text{J}}{(\text{mol rxn}) \cdot \text{K}}$$

The result is usually abbreviated as J/mol · K, or sometimes even as J/K. As before, we will usually omit units in intermediate steps and then apply appropriate units to the result.

We now illustrate this calculation for a phase change and for a chemical reaction.

EXAMPLE 15-15   **Calculation of ΔS^0 for a Phase Change**

Use the values of standard molar entropies in Appendix K to calculate the entropy change for the vaporization of one mole of bromine at 25°C.

$$Br_2(\ell) \longrightarrow Br_2(g)$$

Plan

We use the equation for standard entropy change to calculate ΔS^0 from the tabulated values of standard molar entropies, S^0, for the final and initial states shown in the process.

Solution

We list the ΔS^0_{298} values from Appendix K:

	$Br_2(\ell)$	$Br_2(g)$
S^0, J/mol · K:	152.2	245.4

$$\Delta S^0 = \Sigma \, n \, S^0_{\text{products}} - \Sigma \, n \, S^0_{\text{reactants}}$$

$$= 1(245.4) - 1(152.2) = 93.2 \text{ J/mol} \cdot \text{K}$$

The "mol" designation for J/mol · K refers to a mole of reaction. The reaction as written shows one mole of Br_2, so this is the entropy change for the vaporization of one mole of Br_2. It can be called the *molar entropy of vaporization* of Br_2 at 25°C.

Ⓢ TOP & THINK

The matter in a gaseous sample is far more greatly dispersed than in a liquid. Thus vaporization is always accompanied by an increase in entropy ($\Delta S > 0$).

EXAMPLE 15-16 Calculation of ΔS^0_{rxn} for a Chemical Reaction

Use the values of standard molar entropies in Appendix K to calculate the entropy change at 25°C and one atmosphere pressure for the reaction of hydrazine with hydrogen peroxide. This explosive reaction has been used for rocket propulsion. Do you think the reaction is spontaneous? The balanced equation for the reaction is

$$N_2H_4(\ell) + 2H_2O_2(\ell) \longrightarrow N_2(g) + 4H_2O(g) \qquad \Delta H^0_{rxn} = -642.2 \text{ kJ/mol reaction}$$

Plan

We use the equation for standard entropy change to calculate ΔS^0_{rxn} from the tabulated values of standard molar entropies, S^0_{298}, for the substances in the reaction.

Solution

We can list the S^0_{298} values that we obtain from Appendix K for each substance:

	$N_2H_4(\ell)$	$H_2O_2(\ell)$	$N_2(g)$	$H_2O(g)$
S^0, J/mol · K:	121.2	109.6	191.5	188.7

$$\Delta S^0_{rxn} = \Sigma\, n\, S^0_{products} - \Sigma\, n\, S^0_{reactants}$$

$$= [S^0_{N_2(g)} + 4S^0_{H_2O(g)}] - [S^0_{N_2H_4(\ell)} + 2S^0_{H_2O_2(\ell)}]$$

$$= [1(191.5) + 4(188.7)] - [1(121.2) + 2(109.6)]$$

$$\Delta S^0_{rxn} = +605.9 \text{ J/mol} \cdot \text{K}$$

The "mol" designation for ΔS^0_{rxn} refers to a mole of reaction, that is, one mole of $N_2H_4(\ell)$, two moles of $H_2O_2(\ell)$, and so on. Although it may not appear to be, +605.9 J/mol · K is a relatively large value of ΔS^0_{sys}. The positive entropy change favors spontaneity. This reaction is also exothermic (ΔH^0 is negative). As we shall see, this reaction *must* be spontaneous, because both factors are favorable: the reaction is exothermic (ΔH^0_{rxn} is negative) and the disorder of the system increases (ΔS^0_{rxn} is positive).

You should now work Exercise 104.

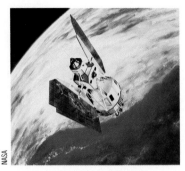

NASA

Small booster rockets adjust the course of a satellite in orbit. Some of these small rockets are powered by the N_2H_4–H_2O_2 reaction.

S TOP & THINK

In this reaction, liquid reactants are converted into a larger number of moles of gaseous products. Thus it is reasonable that entropy increases ($\Delta S^0 > 0$).

Because changes in the thermodynamic quantity *entropy* may be understood in terms of changes in *energy dispersal* and *molecular disorder*, we can often predict the sign of ΔS_{sys}. The following illustrations emphasize several common types of processes that result in predictable entropy changes for the system.

Phase changes. In a solid, the molecules are in an ordered arrangement, where they can vibrate only around their relatively fixed positions. In a liquid, the molecules are more disordered, so they exchange energy much more freely, and the entropy is higher than in the solid. Similarly, gas molecules are in a much larger volume, and they are far less restrained than in the liquid. In the gas, they move even more randomly, both in direction and in speed; this gives any substance a much higher entropy as a gas than as a liquid or a solid (Figure 15-16). Thus the processes of melting, vaporization, and sublimation are always accompanied by an increase in entropy (Figure 15-17). The reverse processes of freezing, condensation, and deposition always correspond to a decrease in entropy.

For any substance, entropy increases in the order solid < liquid < gas.

Melting, vaporization, and sublimation always have $\Delta S_{system} > 0$.

Freezing, condensation, and deposition always have $\Delta S_{system} < 0$.

Temperature changes. As the temperature of any sample increases, its molecules have increased total kinetic energy; this higher energy can be dispersed among these molecules in more ways, increasing the entropy of the sample. Furthermore, the greater motion of the molecules (translational for gases and liquids, vibrational for solids) corresponds to a state

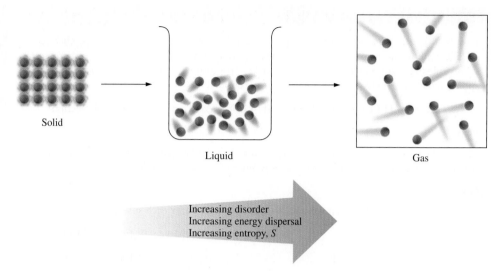

Figure 15-16 As a sample changes from solid to liquid to gas, its particles become increasingly more disordered, allowing greater dispersal of energy, so its entropy increases.

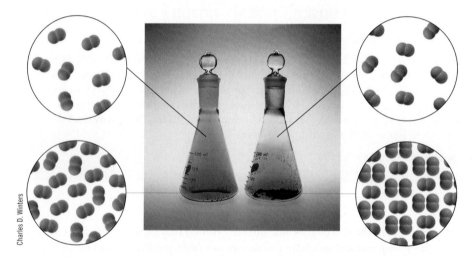

Charles D. Winters

Figure 15-17 The vaporization of bromine, $Br_2(\ell) \rightarrow Br_2(g)$ (*left*) and the sublimation of iodine, $I_2(s) \rightarrow I_2(g)$ (*right*) both lead to an increase in disorder, so $\Delta S_{sys} > 0$ for each process. Which do you think results in the more positive ΔS? Carry out the calculation using values from Appendix K to check whether your prediction was correct.

of greater matter dispersal. The increased dispersal of matter and energy leads to the following result.

> The entropy of any sample increases as its temperature increases.

Volume changes. When the volume of a sample of gas increases, the molecules can occupy more positions, and hence are more randomly arranged (greater dispersal of matter). As pointed out in Section 15-13, the energy levels available to the molecules are closer together in the larger volume, leading to more ways to distribute the same total energy (greater dispersal of energy). Thus a gas has higher entropy at higher volume.

> The entropy of a gas increases as its volume increases.
> For an increase in gas volume, $\Delta S_{system} > 0$.

Mixing of substances, even without chemical reaction. Situations in which particles of more than one kind are "mixed up" are more disordered (greater dispersal of matter) and can exchange energy among both like and unlike particles (greater dispersal of energy). The entropy of the mixture is thus greater than that of the individual substances. This increase in entropy favors processes such as the mixing of gases (see Figure 15-10) and the dissolving of solid and liquid solutes in liquid solvents (Figures 15-18 and 15-19; see also Section 14-2). For example, when one mole of solid NaCl dissolves in water, NaCl(s) $\longrightarrow$ NaCl(aq), the entropy (Appendix K) increases from 72.4 J/mol · K to 115.5 J/mol · K, or $\Delta S^0 = +43.1$ J/mol · K. The term "mixing" can be interpreted rather liberally. For example, the reaction $H_2(g) + Cl_2(g) \longrightarrow 2HCl(g)$ has $\Delta S^0 > 0$; in the reactants, each atom is bonded to an identical atom, a less "mixed-up" situation than in the products, where unlike atoms are bonded together.

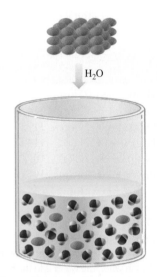

Figure 15-18 As particles leave a crystal to go into solution, they become more disordered and energy dispersal increases. This favors dissolution of the solid.

> Mixing of substances or dissolving a solid in a liquid causes an increase in entropy, $\Delta S_{\text{system}} > 0$.

Changes in the number of particles, as in the dissociation of a diatomic gas such as $F_2(g) \longrightarrow 2F(g)$. Any process in which the number of particles increases results in an increase in entropy, $\Delta S_{\text{sys}} > 0$. Values of ΔS^0 calculated for several reactions of this type are given in Table 15-5. As you can see, the ΔS^0 values for the dissociation process $X_2 \longrightarrow 2X$ are all similar for X = H, F, Cl, and N. Why is the value given in Table 15-5 so much larger for X = Br? This process starts with *liquid* Br_2. The total process $Br_2(\ell) \longrightarrow 2Br(g)$, for which $\Delta S^0 = 197.6$ J/mol · K, can be treated as the result of *two* processes. The first of these is *vaporization*, $Br_2(\ell) \longrightarrow Br_2(g)$, for which $\Delta S^0 = 93.2$ J/mol · K. The second step is the dissociation of gaseous bromine, $Br_2(g) \longrightarrow 2Br(g)$, for

Figure 15-19 When water, H_2O, and propyl alcohol, $CH_3CH_2CH_2OH$ (*left*) are mixed to form a solution (*right*), disorder increases. $\Delta S > 0$ for the mixing of any two molecular substances.

Charles D. Winters

Table 15-5 Entropy Changes for Some Processes $X_2 \longrightarrow 2X$

Reaction	ΔS^0 (J/mol · K)
$H_2(g) \longrightarrow 2H(g)$	98.0
$N_2(g) \longrightarrow 2N(g)$	114.9
$O_2(g) \longrightarrow 2O(g)$	117.0
$F_2(g) \longrightarrow 2F(g)$	114.5
$Cl_2(g) \longrightarrow 2Cl(g)$	107.2
$Br_2(\ell) \longrightarrow 2Br(g)$	197.6
$I_2(s) \longrightarrow 2I(g)$	245.3

▶ Do you think that the reaction
$2H_2(g) + O_2(g) \longrightarrow 2H_2O(\ell)$
would have a higher or lower value of ΔS^0 than when the water is in the gas phase? Confirm by calculation.

which $\Delta S^0 = 104.4$ J/mol · K; this entropy increase is about the same as for the other processes that involve *only* dissociation of a gaseous diatomic species. Can you rationalize the even higher value given in the table for the process $I_2(s) \longrightarrow 2I(g)$?

> Increasing the number of particles causes an increase in entropy, $\Delta S_{system} > 0$.

Changes in the number of moles of gaseous substances. Processes that result in an increase in the number of moles of gaseous substances have $\Delta S_{sys} > 0$. Example 15-16 illustrates this. There are no gaseous reactants, but the products include five moles of gas. Conversely, we would predict that the process $2H_2(g) + O_2(g) \longrightarrow 2H_2O(g)$ has a negative ΔS^0 value; here, three moles of gas is consumed while only two moles is produced, for a net decrease in the number of moles in the gas phase. You should be able to calculate the value of ΔS^0 for this reaction from the values in Appendix K.

> An increase in the number of moles of gaseous substances causes an increase in entropy, $\Delta S_{system} > 0$.

The following guidelines for absolute entropy (standard molar entropy) for individual substances can also be helpful in predicting entropy changes.

Molecular size and complexity. For molecules with similar formulas, absolute entropies usually increase with increasing molecular weight. For instance, the entropies of the gaseous hydrogen halide increase in the order HF (173.7 J/mol · K) < HCl (186.8 J/mol · K) < HBr (198.59 J/mol · K) < HI (206.5 J/mol · K). In more complicated molecular structures, there are more ways for the atoms to move about in three-dimensional space, so there is greater entropy. This trend is especially strong for a series of related compounds. For instance, the absolute entropy of liquid hydrogen peroxide, H_2O_2 (109.6 J/mol · K), is greater than that of liquid water, H_2O (69.91 J/mol · K). Gaseous PCl_5 has a greater absolute entropy (353 J/mol · K) than gaseous PCl_3 (311.7 J/mol · K). Note that molecular complexity and molecular weight play an increasingly important role in the entropy when comparing molecules. For example, gases usually have the highest entropy values when comparing molecules of similar molecular weight. But a solid with a high molecular weight and complexity can have a higher entropy than a lighter gas. Solid sucrose ($C_{12}H_{22}O_{11}$; MW = 342 g/mol) has S^0 = 392 J/mol, whereas $PCl_5(g)$ (MW = 208 g/mol) has a lower entropy of 353 J/mol.

Ionic compounds with similar formulas but different charges. Stronger ionic attractions (due to higher charges or closer approach) hold the ions more tightly in their crystal positions, so they vibrate less, leading to lower entropy. For instance, CaS and KCl have similar formula weights; but CaS (2+ and 2− ionic charges) has stronger ionic attractive forces than KCl (1+, 1− charges), consistent with their relative entropies CaS (56.5 J/mol · K) < KCl (82.6 J/mol · K).

Problem-Solving Tip

Of the factors just listed, *changes in number of particles* and *changes in number of moles of gas* are usually the most important factors in predicting the sign of an entropy change for a reaction.

EXAMPLE 15-17 Predicting the Sign of ΔS^0 for a Chemical Reaction

Without doing a calculation, predict whether the entropy change will be positive or negative when each reaction occurs in the direction it is written.

    (a) $C_2H_6(g) + \frac{7}{2}O_2(g) \longrightarrow 3H_2O(g) + 2CO_2(g)$

    (b) $3C_2H_2(g) \longrightarrow C_6H_6(\ell)$

    (c) $C_6H_{12}O_6(s) + 6O_2(g) \longrightarrow 6CO_2(g) + 6H_2O(\ell)$

Plan

We use the qualitative guidelines described above to predict whether entropy increases or decreases.

Solution

(a) In this reaction, 9/2 moles (4.5 moles) of gaseous reactants produce 5 moles of gaseous products. This increase in number of moles of gas leads to an increase in entropy, $\Delta S^0 > 0$.

(b) Here 3 moles of gaseous reactants produce only liquid product. This decrease in number of moles of gas leads to a decrease in entropy, $\Delta S^0 < 0$.

(c) In this reaction, there are 6 moles of gaseous reactants and the same number of moles of gaseous products, so the prediction cannot be made on this basis. One of the reactants, $C_6H_{12}O_6$, is a solid. The total entropy of one mole of solid and six moles of gas (reactants) is less than the total entropy of six moles of gas and six moles of liquid (products), so we predict an increase in entropy, $\Delta S^0 > 0$.

You should now work Exercise 100.

> **S TOP & THINK**
> You can apply this kind of reasoning to help you judge whether a calculated entropy change has the correct sign.

EXAMPLE 15-18 Predicting the Order of Absolute Entropies

Rank each group of substances in order of increasing absolute entropy at 25°C. Give reasons for your ranking.

(a) Hg(ℓ), Hg(s), Hg(g)

(b) C_2H_6(g), CH_4(g), C_3H_8(g)

(c) CaS(s), CaO(s)

Plan

We use the qualitative comparisons of this section to rank the absolute entropies within each group.

Solution

(a) For any substance, entropy increases in the order solid < liquid < gas, so we predict the absolute entropies to increase as Hg(s) < Hg(ℓ) < Hg(g).

(b) Entropy increases with molecular complexity, so we predict the absolute entropies to increase in the order CH_4(g) < C_2H_6(g) < C_3H_8(g).

(c) Both of these ionic compounds contain 2+ and 2− ions, so charge differences alone will not allow us to rank them. But O^{2-} ions are smaller than S^{2-} ions, so they are held closer to the Ca^{2+} ions, giving a stronger attraction in CaO and hence lower entropy. We expect the absolute entropies to increase in the order CaO(s) < CaS(s).

> ▶ You can check the rankings in Example 15-18 by comparing the S^0 values listed in Appendix K.

You should now work Exercise 98.

15-15 The Second Law of Thermodynamics

We now know that two factors determine whether a reaction is spontaneous under a given set of conditions. The effect of the first factor, the enthalpy change, is that spontaneity is favored (but not required) by exothermicity, and nonspontaneity is favored (but not required) by endothermicity. The effect of the other factor is summarized by the **Second Law of Thermodynamics**.

In any spontaneous change, entropy of the universe increases, $\Delta S_{universe} > 0$.

The Second Law of Thermodynamics is based on our experiences, as seen by the following examples. Gases mix spontaneously. When a drop of food coloring is added to a glass of water, it diffuses until a homogeneously colored solution results. When a truck is driven down the street, it consumes fuel and oxygen, producing carbon dioxide, water vapor, and other emitted substances.

Time

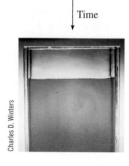

Charles D. Winters

The reverse of any spontaneous change is nonspontaneous, because if it did occur, the universe would tend toward a state of lower entropy (greater order, more concentration of energy). This is contrary to our experience. A gas mixture does not spontaneously separate into its components. A colored solution does not spontaneously concentrate all of its color in a small volume. A truck cannot be driven along the street, even in reverse gear, so that it sucks up CO_2, water vapor, and other substances to produce fuel and oxygen.

If the entropy of a system increases during a process, the spontaneity of the process is favored but not required. The Second Law of Thermodynamics says that the entropy of the *universe* (but not necessarily the system) increases during a spontaneous process, that is,

$$\Delta S_{universe} = \Delta S_{system} + \Delta S_{surroundings} > 0 \qquad \text{(spontaneous process)}$$

Of the two ideal gas samples in Figure 15-10, the more ordered arrangement (Figure 15-10a) has lower entropy than the randomly mixed arrangement with the same volume (Figure 15-10b). Because these ideal gas samples mix without absorbing or releasing heat and without a change in total volume, they do not interact with the surroundings, so the entropy of the surroundings does not change. In this case

$$\Delta S_{universe} = \Delta S_{system}$$

If we open the stopcock between the two bulbs in Figure 15-10a, we expect the gases to mix spontaneously, with an increase in the disorder of the system, that is, ΔS_{system} is positive.

unmixed gases $\longrightarrow$ mixed gases $\Delta S_{universe} = \Delta S_{system} > 0$

We do not expect the more homogeneous sample in Figure 15-10b to spontaneously "unmix" to give the arrangement in Figure 15-10a (which would correspond to a decrease in ΔS_{system}).

mixed gases $\longrightarrow$ unmixed gases $\Delta S_{universe} = \Delta S_{system} < 0$

► We abbreviate these subscripts as follows: system = sys, surroundings = surr, and universe = univ.

The entropy of a system can decrease during a spontaneous process or increase during a nonspontaneous process, depending on the accompanying ΔS_{surr}. If ΔS_{sys} is negative (decrease in disorder), then ΔS_{univ} may still be positive (overall increase in disorder) *if* ΔS_{surr} is more positive than ΔS_{sys} is negative. A refrigerator provides an illustration. It removes heat from inside the box (the system) and ejects that heat, *plus* the heat generated by the compressor, into the room (the surroundings). The entropy of the system decreases because the air molecules inside the box move more slowly. But the increase in the entropy of the surroundings more than makes up for that, so the entropy of the universe (refrigerator + room) increases.

Similarly, if ΔS_{sys} is positive but ΔS_{surr} is even more negative, then ΔS_{univ} is still negative. Such a process will be nonspontaneous.

Let's consider the entropy changes that occur when a liquid solidifies at a temperature *below* its freezing (melting) point (Figure 15-20a). ΔS_{sys} is negative because a solid forms from its liquid, yet we know that this is a spontaneous process. A liquid releases heat to its surroundings (atmosphere) as it crystallizes. The released heat increases the motion (more disorder, greater dispersal of matter) of the molecules of the surroundings, so ΔS_{surr} is positive. As the temperature decreases, the ΔS_{surr} contribution becomes more important. When the temperature is low enough (below the freezing point), the positive ΔS_{surr} outweighs the negative ΔS_{sys}. Then ΔS_{univ} becomes positive, and the freezing process becomes spontaneous.

The situation is reversed when a liquid is boiled or a solid is melted (see Figure 15-20b). For example, at temperatures above its melting point, a solid spontaneously melts, the system becomes more disordered (greater dispersal of matter), and ΔS_{sys} is positive. The heat absorbed when the solid (system) melts comes from its surroundings. This decreases the motion of the molecules of the surroundings. Thus, ΔS_{surr} is negative (the surroundings become less disordered). The positive ΔS_{sys} is greater in magnitude than the negative ΔS_{surr}, however, so ΔS_{univ} is positive and the process is spontaneous.

Above the melting point, ΔS_{univ} is positive for melting. Below the melting point, ΔS_{univ} is positive for freezing. At the melting point, ΔS_{surr} is equal in magnitude and opposite in

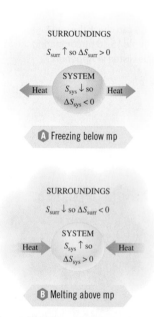

SURROUNDINGS

$S_{surr} \uparrow$ so $\Delta S_{surr} > 0$

SYSTEM
$S_{sys} \downarrow$ so
$\Delta S_{sys} < 0$

Heat → | → Heat

Ⓐ Freezing below mp

SURROUNDINGS

$S_{surr} \downarrow$ so $\Delta S_{surr} < 0$

SYSTEM
$S_{sys} \uparrow$ so
$\Delta S_{sys} > 0$

Heat → | ← Heat

Ⓑ Melting above mp

Figure 15-20 A schematic representation of heat flow and entropy changes for (a) freezing and (b) melting of a pure substance.

Table 15-6 Entropy Effects Associated with Melting and Freezing

Change	Temperature	Sign of ΔS_{sys}	Sign of ΔS_{surr}	(Magnitude of ΔS_{sys}) Compared with (Magnitude of ΔS_{surr})	$\Delta S_{univ} = \Delta S_{sys} + \Delta S_{surr}$	Spontaneity
1. Melting (solid → liquid)	> mp	+	−	>	> 0	Spontaneous
	= mp	+	−	=	= 0	Equilibrium
	< mp	+	−	<	< 0	Nonspontaneous
2. Freezing (liquid → solid)	> mp	−	+	>	< 0	Nonspontaneous
	= mp	−	+	=	= 0	Equilibrium
	< mp	−	+	<	> 0	Spontaneous

sign to ΔS_{sys}. Then ΔS_{univ} is zero for both melting and freezing; the system is at *equilibrium*. Table 15-6 lists the entropy effects for these changes of physical state.

We have said that ΔS_{univ} is positive for all spontaneous (product-favored) processes. Unfortunately, it is not possible to make direct measurements of ΔS_{univ}. Consequently, entropy changes accompanying physical and chemical changes are reported in terms of ΔS_{sys}. The subscript "sys" for system can be replaced with rxn if we wish to indicate a chemical reaction. The symbol ΔS_{rxn} refers to the change in entropy of a reacting system, just as ΔH_{rxn} refers to the change in enthalpy of the reacting system.

▶ Can you develop a comparable table for boiling (liquid → gas) and condensation (gas → liquid)? (Study Table 15-6 carefully.)

15-16 Free Energy Change, ΔG, and Spontaneity

Energy is the capacity to do work. If heat is released in a chemical reaction (ΔH is negative), *some* of the heat energy may be converted into useful work. If ΔS is negative, some of the energy must be expended to increase the order of the system. If the system becomes more disordered ($\Delta S > 0$), however, more useful energy becomes available than indicated by ΔH alone. J. Willard Gibbs (1839–1903), a prominent 19th-century American professor

Ⓐ The entropy of an organism decreases (unfavorable) when new cells are formed. The energy to sustain animal life is provided by the metabolism of food. This energy is released when the chemical bonds in the food are broken. Exhalation of gases and excretion of waste materials increase the entropy of the surroundings enough so that the entropy of the universe increases and the overall process can occur.

Ⓑ Stored chemical energy can later be transformed by the organism to the mechanical energy for muscle contraction, to the electrical energy for brain function, or to another needed form.

▶ Entropy plays an important role in the energy transfer in cell growth and maintenance in all living organisms.

of mathematics and physics, formulated the relationship between enthalpy and entropy in terms of another state function that we now call the **Gibbs free energy, G.** It is defined as

$$G = H - TS$$

The **Gibbs free energy change, ΔG,** at constant temperature and pressure, is

▶ This is often called simply the *Gibbs energy change* or the *free energy change*.

$$\Delta G = \Delta H - T \Delta S \qquad \text{(constant T and P)}$$

The amount by which the Gibbs free energy decreases is the *maximum useful energy* obtainable in the form of work from a given process at constant temperature and pressure. It is also the *indicator of spontaneity of a reaction or physical change* at constant T and P. If there is a net decrease of free energy, ΔG is negative and the process is spontaneous (product-favored). We see from the equation that ΔG becomes more negative as (1) ΔH becomes more negative (the process gives off more heat) and (2) ΔS becomes more positive (the process results in greater disorder); *both* factors are favorable so the process *must be* spontaneous (product-favored). If there is a net increase in free energy of the system during a process, ΔG is positive and the process is nonspontaneous (reactant-favored). This means that the reverse process is spontaneous under the given conditions. When $\Delta G = 0$, there is no net transfer of free energy; both the forward and reverse processes are equally favorable. Thus, $\Delta G = 0$ describes a system at *equilibrium*.

The relationship between ΔG and spontaneity may be summarized as follows.

ΔG	**Spontaneity of Reaction (constant T and P)**
ΔG is positive	Reaction is nonspontaneous (reactant-favored)
ΔG is zero	System is at equilibrium
ΔG is negative	Reaction is spontaneous (product-favored)

−	0	+
$\Delta G < 0$		$\Delta G > 0$
Reaction is spontaneous		Reaction is not spontaneous
Product-favored reaction		Reactant-favored reaction
Forward reaction is favored		Reverse reaction is favored

The free energy content of a system depends on temperature and pressure (and, for mixtures, on concentrations). The value of ΔG for a process depends on the states and the concentrations of the various substances involved. It also depends strongly on temperature, because the equation $\Delta G = \Delta H - T \Delta S$ includes temperature. Just as for other thermodynamic variables, we choose some set of conditions as a standard state reference. The standard state for ΔG^0 is the same as for ΔH^0; 1 atm and the specified temperature, usually 25°C (298 K). Values of standard molar free energy of formation, ΔG_f^0, for many substances are tabulated in Appendix K. For *elements* in their standard states, $\Delta G_f^0 = 0$. The values of ΔG_f^0 may be used to calculate the standard free energy change of a reaction *at 298 K* by using the following relationship.

$$\Delta G_{rxn}^0 = \Sigma \, n \, \Delta G_{f\,products}^0 - \Sigma \, n \, \Delta G_{f\,reactants}^0 \qquad \text{(1 atm and 298 K \textit{only})}$$

▶ We want to know which are more stable *at standard conditions*—the *reactants* or the *products*.

The value of ΔG_{rxn}^0 allows us to predict the spontaneity of a hypothetical reaction in which the numbers of moles of reactants shown in the balanced equation, all at standard conditions, are *completely* converted to the numbers of moles of products shown in the balanced equation, all at standard conditions.

We must remember that it is ΔG, and not ΔG^0, that is the general criterion for spontaneity. ΔG depends on concentrations of reactants and products in the mixture. For most reactions, there is an *equilibrium mixture* of reactant and product concentrations that is more stable than either all reactants or all products. In Chapter 17 we will study the concept of equilibrium and see how to find ΔG for mixtures.

EXAMPLE 15-19 Spontaneity of Reaction

Diatomic nitrogen and oxygen molecules make up about 99% of all the molecules in reasonably "unpolluted" dry air. Evaluate ΔG^0 for the following reaction at 298 K, using ΔG^0_f values from Appendix K. Is the reaction spontaneous?

$$N_2(g) + O_2(g) \longrightarrow 2NO(g) \qquad \text{(nitrogen oxide)}$$

Plan

The reaction conditions are 1 atm and 298 K, so we can use the tabulated values of ΔG^0_f for each substance in Appendix K to evaluate ΔG^0_{rxn} in the preceding equation. The treatment of units for calculation of ΔG^0 is the same as that for ΔH^0 in Example 15-9.

Solution

We obtain the following values of ΔG^0_f from Appendix K:

$$\begin{array}{cccc} & N_2(g) & O_2(g) & NO(g) \end{array}$$

$$\Delta G^0_f, \text{kJ/mol:} \qquad 0 \qquad\quad 0 \qquad\qquad 86.57$$

$$\Delta G^0_{rxn} = \Sigma\, n\, \Delta G^0_{f\ \text{products}} - \Sigma\, n\, \Delta G^0_{f\ \text{reactants}}$$

$$= 2\ \Delta G^0_{f\ NO(g)} \quad - [\,\Delta G^0_{f\ N_2(g)} + \Delta G^0_{f\ O_2(g)}\,]$$

$$= 2(86.57) \qquad - [0 + 0]$$

$$\Delta G^0_{rxn} = +173.1 \text{ kJ/mol rxn} \qquad \text{for the reaction as written}$$

Because ΔG^0 is positive, the reaction is nonspontaneous at 298 K under standard state conditions.

You should now work Exercise 111.

▶ For the reverse reaction at 298 K, $\Delta G^0_{rxn} = -173.1$ kJ/mol rxn. So the reverse reaction is product-favored, although it is very slow at room temperature. The NO formed in automobile engines is oxidized to even more harmful NO_2 much more rapidly than it decomposes to N_2 and O_2. Thermodynamic spontaneity does not guarantee that a process occurs at an observable rate. The oxides of nitrogen in the atmosphere represent a major environmental problem.

The value of ΔG^0 can also be calculated by the equation

$$\Delta G^0 = \Delta H^0 - T\,\Delta S^0 \qquad \text{(constant } T \text{ and } P\text{)}$$

Strictly, this last equation applies to standard conditions; however, ΔH^0 and ΔS^0 often do not vary much with temperature, so the equation can often be used to *estimate* free energy changes at other temperatures.

Problem-Solving Tip Some Common Pitfalls in Calculating ΔG^0_{rxn}

Be careful of these points when you carry out calculations that involve ΔG^0:

1. The calculation of ΔG^0_{rxn} from tabulated values of ΔG^0_f is valid *only* for the reaction at 25°C (298 K) and one atmosphere.

2. Calculations with the equation $\Delta G^0 = \Delta H^0 - T\,\Delta S^0$ must be carried out with the temperature in kelvins.

3. The energy term in ΔS^0 is usually in joules, whereas that in ΔH^0 is usually in kilojoules; remember to convert one of these so that units are consistent before you combine them.

EXAMPLE 15-20 Spontaneity of Reaction

Make the same determination as in Example 15-19, using heats of formation and absolute entropies rather than free energies of formation.

Plan

First we calculate ΔH^0_{rxn} and ΔS^0_{rxn}. We use the relationship $\Delta G^0 = \Delta H^0 - T\,\Delta S^0$ to evaluate the free energy change under standard state conditions at 298 K.

Solution

The values we obtain from Appendix K are

	$N_2(g)$	$O_2(g)$	$NO(g)$
ΔH^0_f, kJ/mol:	0	0	90.25
S^0, J/mol · K:	191.5	205.0	210.7

$$\Delta H^0_{rxn} = \Sigma\, n\, \Delta H^0_{f\,products} \quad - \Sigma\, n\, \Delta H^0_{f\,reactants}$$

$$= 2\, \Delta H^0_{f\,NO(g)} \quad - [\Delta H^0_{f\,N_2(g)} + \Delta H^0_{f\,O_2(g)}]$$

$$= [2(90.25) \quad - (0 + 0)] = 180.5 \text{ kJ/mol}$$

$$\Delta S^0_{rxn} = \Sigma\, n\, S^0_{products} \quad - \Sigma\, n\, S^0_{reactants}$$

$$= 2S^0_{NO(g)} \quad - [S^0_{N_2(g)} + S^0_{O_2(g)}]$$

$$= [2(210.7) \quad - (191.5 + 205.0)] = 24.9 \text{ J/mol} \cdot \text{K} = 0.0249 \text{ kJ/mol} \cdot \text{K}$$

STOP & THINK
As with all calculations of ΔG, you should be careful to make the energy units in ΔH and ΔS consistent—either both in J or both in kJ.

Now we use the relationship $\Delta G^0 = \Delta H^0 - T\,\Delta S^0$, with $T = 298$ K, to evaluate the free energy change under standard state conditions at 298 K.

$$\Delta G^0_{rxn} = \Delta H^0_{rxn} \quad - T\,\Delta S^0_{rxn}$$

$$= 180.5 \text{ kJ/mol} - (298 \text{ K})(0.0249 \text{ kJ/mol} \cdot \text{K})$$

$$= 180.5 \text{ kJ/mol} - 7.42 \text{ kJ/mol}$$

$$\Delta G^0_{rxn} = +173.1 \text{ kJ/mol rxn, } \text{ the same value obtained in Example 15-19.}$$

You should now work Exercise 113.

15-17 The Temperature Dependence of Spontaneity

The methods developed in Section 15-16 can also be used to estimate the temperature at which a process is in equilibrium. When a system is at equilibrium, $\Delta G = 0$. Thus,

$$\Delta G_{rxn} = \Delta H_{rxn} - T\,\Delta S_{rxn} \quad \text{or} \quad 0 = \Delta H_{rxn} - T\,\Delta S_{rxn}$$

so

$$\Delta H_{rxn} = T\,\Delta S_{rxn} \quad \text{or} \quad T = \frac{\Delta H_{rxn}}{\Delta S_{rxn}} \quad \text{(at equilibrium)}$$

EXAMPLE 15-21 Estimation of Boiling Point

Use the thermodynamic data in Appendix K to estimate the normal boiling point of bromine, Br_2. Assume that ΔH and ΔS do not change with temperature.

Plan

The process we must consider is

$$Br_2(\ell) \longrightarrow Br_2(g)$$

▶ Actually, both ΔH^0_{rxn} and ΔS^0_{rxn} vary with temperature, but usually not enough to introduce significant errors for modest temperature changes. The value of ΔG^0_{rxn}, on the other hand, is strongly dependent on the temperature.

By definition, the normal boiling point of a liquid is the temperature at which pure liquid and pure gas coexist in equilibrium at 1 atm. Therefore, $\Delta G = 0$ for the process as written. We assume that $\Delta H_{rxn} = \Delta H^0_{rxn}$ and $\Delta S_{rxn} = \Delta S^0_{rxn}$. We can evaluate these two quantities, substitute them in the relationship $\Delta G = \Delta H - T\Delta S$, and then solve for the value of T that makes $\Delta G = 0$.

Solution

The required values (see Appendix K) are as follows:

	$Br_2(\ell)$	$Br_2(g)$
ΔH^0_f, kJ/mol:	0	30.91
S^0, J/mol · K:	152.2	245.4

$$\Delta H_{rxn} = \Delta H^0_{f\,Br_2(g)} \quad - \Delta H^0_{f\,Br_2(\ell)}$$

$$= 30.91 \quad - 0 = 30.91 \text{ kJ/mol}$$

$$\Delta S_{rxn} = S^0_{Br_2(g)} \quad - S^0_{Br_2(\ell)}$$

$$= (245.4 \quad - 152.2) = 93.2 \text{ J/mol} \cdot \text{K} = 0.0932 \text{ kJ/mol} \cdot \text{K}$$

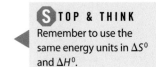

STOP & THINK

Remember to use the same energy units in ΔS^0 and ΔH^0.

We can now solve for the temperature at which the system is in equilibrium, that is, the boiling point of Br_2.

$$\Delta G_{rxn} = \Delta H_{rxn} - T\Delta S_{rxn} = 0 \quad \text{so} \quad \Delta H_{rxn} = T\Delta S_{rxn}$$

$$T = \frac{\Delta H_{rxn}}{\Delta S_{rxn}} = \frac{30.91 \text{ kJ/mol}}{0.0932 \text{ kJ/mol} \cdot \text{K}} = 332 \text{ K } (59°C)$$

This is the temperature at which the reactant (liquid) is in equilibrium with the product (gas), that is, the boiling point of Br_2. The experimentally measured value is 58.78°C.

You should now work Exercise 122.

The free energy change and spontaneity of a reaction depend on both enthalpy and entropy changes. Both ΔH and ΔS may be either positive or negative, so we can group reactions in four classes with respect to spontaneity (Figure 15-21).

$$\Delta G = \Delta H - T\Delta S \qquad \text{(constant temperature and pressure)}$$

1. $\Delta H = -$ (favorable)	$\Delta S = +$ (favorable)	Reactions are spontaneous (product-favored) at all temperatures
2. $\Delta H = -$ (favorable)	$\Delta S = -$ (unfavorable)	Reactions become spontaneous (product-favored) below a definite temperature
3. $\Delta H = +$ (unfavorable)	$\Delta S = +$ (favorable)	Reactions become spontaneous (product-favored) above a definite temperature
4. $\Delta H = +$ (unfavorable)	$\Delta S = -$ (unfavorable)	Reactions are nonspontaneous (reactant-favored) at all temperatures

When ΔH and ΔS have opposite signs (classes 1 and 4), they act in the same direction, so the direction of spontaneous change does not depend on temperature. When ΔH and ΔS have the same signs (classes 2 and 3), their effects oppose one another, so changes in temperature can cause one factor or the other to dominate, and spontaneity depends on temperature. For class 2, decreasing the temperature decreases the importance of the *unfavorable* $T\Delta S$ term, so the reaction becomes spontaneous at lower temperatures. For class 3, increasing the temperature increases the importance of the *favorable* $T\Delta S$ term, so the reaction becomes spontaneous at higher temperatures.

The temperature at which $\Delta G_{rxn}^0 = 0$ is the temperature limit of spontaneity. The sign of ΔS_{rxn}^0 tells us whether the reaction is spontaneous *below* or *above* this limit (Table 15-7). We can estimate the temperature range over which a chemical reaction in class 2 or 3 is spontaneous by evaluating ΔH_{rxn}^0 and ΔS_{rxn}^0 from tabulated data.

Figure 15-21 A graphical representation of the dependence of ΔG and spontaneity on temperature for each of the four classes of reactions listed in the text and in Table 15-7.

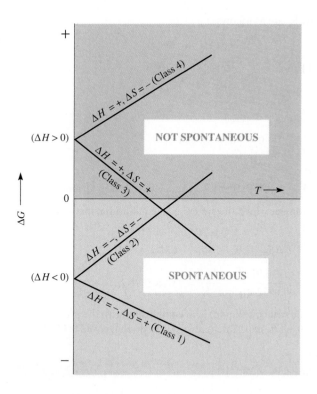

Table 15-7 Thermodynamic Classes of Reactions

Class	Examples	ΔH (kJ/mol)	ΔS (J/mol · K)	Temperature Range of Spontaneity
1	$2H_2O_2(\ell) \longrightarrow 2H_2O(\ell) + O_2(g)$	-196	$+126$	All temperatures
	$H_2(g) + Br_2(\ell) \longrightarrow 2HBr(g)$	-72.8	$+114$	All temperatures
2	$NH_3(g) + HCl(g) \longrightarrow NH_4Cl(s)$	-176	-285	Lower temperatures (< 619 K)
	$2H_2S(g) + SO_2(g) \longrightarrow 3S(s) + 2H_2O(\ell)$	-233	-424	Lower temperatures (< 550 K)
3	$NH_4Cl(s) \longrightarrow NH_3(g) + HCl(g)$	$+176$	$+285$	Higher temperatures (> 619 K)
	$CCl_4(\ell) \longrightarrow C(graphite) + 2Cl_2(g)$	$+135$	$+235$	Higher temperatures (> 574 K)
4	$2H_2O(\ell) + O_2(g) \longrightarrow 2H_2O_2(\ell)$	$+196$	-126	Nonspontaneous, all temperatures
	$3O_2(g) \longrightarrow 2O_3(g)$	$+285$	-137	Nonspontaneous, all temperatures

---

EXAMPLE 15-22 Temperature Range of Spontaneity

Mercury(II) sulfide is a dark red mineral called cinnabar. Metallic mercury is obtained by roasting the sulfide in a limited amount of air. Estimate the temperature range in which the reaction is product-favored.

$$HgS(s) + O_2(g) \longrightarrow Hg(\ell) + SO_2(g)$$

Plan

We evaluate ΔH_{rxn}^0 and ΔS_{rxn}^0 and assume that these values are independent of temperature. Each of these values allows us to assess its contribution to spontaneity.

Solution

From Appendix K:

	HgS(s)	O_2	Hg(ℓ)	SO_2(g)
ΔH_f^0, kJ/mol:	−58.2	0	0	−296.8
S^0, J/mol · K:	82.4	205.0	76.0	248.1

$$\Delta H_{rxn}^0 = \Delta H_{f\,Hg(\ell)}^0 + \Delta H_{f\,SO_2(g)}^0 - [\Delta H_{f\,HgS(s)}^0 + \Delta H_{f\,O_2(g)}^0]$$
$$= 0 - 296.8 \qquad - [-58.2 + 0] = -238.6 \text{ kJ/mol}$$

$$\Delta S_{rxn}^0 = S_{Hg(\ell)}^0 + S_{SO_2(g)}^0 - [S_{HgS(s)}^0 + S_{O_2(g)}^0]$$
$$= 76.02 + 248.1 - [82.4 + 205.0] = +36.7 \text{ J/mol} \cdot \text{K}$$

Heating red HgS in air produces liquid Hg. Gaseous SO_2 escapes. Cinnabar, an important ore of mercury, contains HgS.

When ΔH_{rxn}^0 is negative (favorable to spontaneity) and ΔS_{rxn}^0 is positive (favorable to spontaneity), the reaction must be spontaneous (product-favored) at all temperatures; no further calculation is necessary. The reverse reaction is, therefore, nonspontaneous at all temperatures.

The fact that a reaction is spontaneous at all temperatures does not mean that the reaction occurs rapidly enough to be useful at all temperatures. As a matter of fact, Hg(ℓ) can be obtained from HgS(s) by this reaction at a reasonable rate only at high temperatures.

> **S TOP & THINK**
>
> When ΔH^0 and ΔS^0 are both *favorable*, we know without further calculation that ΔG^0 must be *negative* and the reaction must be *spontaneous (product-favored)* at all temperatures. When ΔH^0 and ΔS^0 are both *unfavorable*, we know without further calculation that ΔG^0 must be *positive* and the reaction must be *nonspontaneous (reactant-favored)* at all temperatures.

EXAMPLE 15-23 Temperature Range of Spontaneity

Estimate the temperature range for which the following reaction is product-favored.

$$SiO_2(s) + 2C(graphite) + 2Cl_2(g) \longrightarrow SiCl_4(g) + 2CO(g)$$

Plan

When we proceed as in Example 15-22, we find that ΔS_{rxn}^0 is favorable to spontaneity, whereas ΔH_{rxn}^0 is unfavorable. Thus, we know that the reaction becomes product-favored *above* some temperature. We can set ΔG^0 equal to zero in the equation $\Delta G^0 = \Delta H^0 - T \Delta S^0$ and solve for the temperature at which the system is *at equilibrium*. This will represent the temperature above which the reaction would be product-favored.

Solution

From Appendix K:

	SiO_2(s)	C(graphite)	Cl_2(g)	$SiCl_4$(g)	CO(g)
ΔH_f^0, kJ/mol:	−910.9	0	0	−657.0	−110.5
S^0, J/mol · K:	41.84	5.740	223.0	330.6	197.6

$$\Delta H_{rxn}^0 = [\Delta H_{f\,SiCl_4(g)}^0 + 2\,\Delta H_{f\,CO(g)}^0] - [\Delta H_{f\,SiO_2(s)}^0 + 2\Delta H_{f\,C(graphite)}^0 + 2\Delta H_{f\,Cl_2(g)}^0]$$
$$= [(-657.0) + 2(-110.5)] - [(-910.9) + 2(0) \qquad + 2(0)]$$
$$= +32.9 \text{ kJ/mol (unfavorable to spontaneity)}$$

$$\Delta S_{rxn}^0 = \Delta S_{SiCl_4(g)}^0 + 2S_{CO(g)}^0 - [\Delta S_{SiO_s(s)}^0 + 2S_{C(graphite)}^0 + 2S_{Cl_2(g)}^0]$$
$$= [330.6 + 2(197.6)] - [41.84 + 2(5.740) + 2(223.0)]$$
$$= 226.5 \text{ J/mol} \cdot \text{K} = 0.2265 \text{ kJ/mol} \cdot \text{K (favorable to spontaneity)}$$

At the temperature at which $\Delta G^0 = 0$, neither the forward nor the reverse reaction is favored and the system is at equilibrium. Let's find this temperature.

$$0 = \Delta G^0 = \Delta H^0 - T\Delta S^0$$

$$\Delta H^0 = T\,\Delta S^0$$

$$T = \frac{\Delta H^0}{\Delta S^0} = \frac{+32.9 \text{ kJ/mol}}{+0.2265 \text{ kJ/mol}\cdot\text{K}} = 145 \text{ K}$$

At temperatures above 145 K, the $T\,\Delta S^0$ term would be greater ($-T\,\Delta S^0$ would be more negative) than the ΔH^0 term, which would make ΔG^0 negative; so the reaction would be spontaneous (produced–favored) above 145 K. At temperatures below 145 K, the $T\,\Delta S^0$ term would be smaller than the ΔH^0 term, which would make ΔG^0 positive; so the reaction would be nonspontaneous below 145 K.

However, 145 K ($-128°C$) is a very low temperature. For all practical purposes, the reaction is product-favored at all but very low temperatures. In practice, it is carried out at 800°C to 1000°C because of the greater reaction rate at these higher temperatures. This gives a useful and economical rate of production of $SiCl_4$, an important industrial chemical.

You should now work Exercises 116 and 120.

KEY TERMS

Absolute entropy (of a substance)   The entropy of a substance relative to its entropy in a perfectly ordered crystalline form at 0 K (where its entropy is zero).

Bomb calorimeter   A device used to measure the heat transfer between system and surroundings at constant volume.

Bond energy   The amount of energy necessary to break one mole of bonds in a gaseous substance to form gaseous products at the same temperature and pressure.

Calorimeter   A device used to measure the heat transfer that accompanies a physical or chemical change.

Dispersal of energy   The degree to which the total energy of a system can be distributed among its particles.

Dispersal of matter   The degree to which the particles of a sample can be distributed in space; also known as *disorder*.

Endothermic process   A process that absorbs heat.

Enthalpy change, ΔH   The quantity of heat transferred into or out of a system as it undergoes a chemical or physical change at constant temperature and pressure.

Entropy (S)   A thermodynamic state function that measures the dispersal of energy and the dispersal of matter (disorder) of a system.

Equilibrium   A state of dynamic balance in which the rates of forward and reverse processes (reactions) are equal; the state of a system when neither the forward nor the reverse process is thermodynamically favored.

Exothermic process   A process that gives off (releases) heat.

First Law of Thermodynamics   The total amount of energy in the universe is constant (also known as the Law of Conservation of Energy); energy is neither created nor destroyed in ordinary chemical reactions and physical changes.

Gibbs free energy (G)   The thermodynamic state function of a system that indicates the amount of energy available for the system to do useful work at constant T and P. It is defined as $G = H - TS$; also known as *free energy*.

Heat of formation   See *Standard molar enthalpy of formation*.

Hess's Law of Heat Summation   The enthalpy change for a reaction is the same whether it occurs in one step or a series of steps.

Internal energy (E)   All forms of energy associated with a specific amount of a substance.

Kinetic energy   The energy of motion. The kinetic energy of an object is equal to one half its mass times the square of its velocity.

Law of Conservation of Energy   Energy cannot be created or destroyed in a chemical reaction or in a physical change; it may be changed from one form to another; see *First Law of Thermodynamics*.

Mole of reaction (mol rxn)   The amount of reaction that corresponds to the number of moles of each substance shown in the balanced equation.

Nonspontaneous change   A change for which the collection of reactants is more stable than the collection of products under the given conditions; also known as *reactant-favored change*.

Potential energy   The energy that a system or object possesses by virtue of its position or composition.

Pressure–volume work   Work done by a gas when it expands against an external pressure, or work done on a system as gases are compressed or consumed in the presence of an external pressure.

Product-favored change   See *Spontaneous change*.

Reactant-favored change   See *Nonspontaneous change*.

Second Law of Thermodynamics   The universe tends toward a state of greater disorder in spontaneous processes.

Spontaneous change   A change for which the collection of products is more stable than the collection of reactants under the given conditions; also known as *product-favored change*.

Standard enthalpy change (ΔH^0)   The enthalpy change in which the number of moles of reactants specified in the balanced chemical equation, all at standard states, is converted completely to the specified number of moles of products, all at standard states.

Standard entropy change (ΔS^0)   The entropy change in which the number of moles of reactants specified in the balanced chemical equation, all at standard states, is converted completely to the specified number of moles of products, all at standard states.

Standard Gibbs free energy change (ΔG^0)   The indicator of spontaneity of a process at constant T and P. If ΔG^0 is negative, the process is product-favored (spontaneous); if ΔG^0 is positive, the reverse process is reactant-favored (nonspontaneous).

Standard molar enthalpy of formation (ΔH_f^0) (of a substance)   The enthalpy change for the formation of one mole of a substance in a specified state from its elements in their standard states; also known as *standard molar heat of formation* or just *heat of formation*.

Standard molar heat of formation   See *Standard molar enthalpy of formation*.

Standard molar entropy (S^0) (of a substance)   The absolute entropy of a substance in its standard state at 298 K.

Standard state (of a substance)   See *Thermodynamic standard state of a substance*.

State function   A variable that defines the state of a system; a function that is independent of the pathway by which a process occurs.

Surroundings   Everything in the environment of the system.

System   The substances of interest in a process; the part of the universe under investigation.

Thermochemical equation   A balanced chemical equation together with a designation of the corresponding value of ΔH_{rxn}. Sometimes used with changes in other thermodynamic quantities.

Thermochemistry   The observation, measurement, and prediction of energy changes for both physical changes and chemical reactions.

Thermodynamics   The study of the energy transfers accompanying physical and chemical processes.

Thermodynamic state of a system   A set of conditions that completely specifies all of the properties of the system.

Thermodynamic standard state of a substance   The most stable state of the substance at one atmosphere pressure and at some specific temperature (25°C unless otherwise specified); also known as *standard state (of a substance)*.

Third Law of Thermodynamics   The entropy of a hypothetical pure, perfect, crystalline substance at absolute zero temperature is zero.

Universe   The system plus the surroundings.

Work   The application of a force through a distance; for physical changes or chemical reactions at constant external pressure, the work done on the system is $-P\Delta V$; for chemical reactions that involve gases, the work done on the system can be expressed as $-(\Delta n)RT$.

EXERCISES

- 🔵 **Molecular Reasoning** exercises
- ▲ **More Challenging** exercises

Blue-Numbered exercises are solved in the Student Solutions Manual

General Concepts

1. State precisely the meaning of each of the following terms. You may need to review Chapter 1 to refresh your memory concerning terms introduced there. (a) energy; (b) kinetic energy; (c) potential energy; (d) joule.

2. State precisely the meaning of each of the following terms. You may need to review Chapter 1 to refresh your memory about terms introduced there. (a) heat; (b) temperature; (c) system; (d) surroundings; (e) thermodynamic state of system; (f) work.

3. (a) Give an example of the conversion of heat into work. (b) Give an example of the conversion of work into heat.

4. (a) Give an example of heat being given off by the system. (b) Give an example of work being done on the system.

5. (a) Give an example of heat being added to the system. (b) Give an example of work being done by the system.

6. Distinguish between endothermic and exothermic processes. If we know that a reaction is endothermic in one direction, what can be said about the reaction in the reverse direction?

7. According to the First Law of Thermodynamics, the total amount of energy in the universe is constant. Why, then, do we say that we are experiencing a declining supply of energy?

8. 🔵 Use the First Law of Thermodynamics to describe what occurs when an incandescent light is turned on.

9. 🔵 Define enthalpy and give an example of a reaction that has a negative enthalpy change.

10. 🔵 Which of the following are examples of state functions? (a) your bank balance; (b) the mass of a candy bar; (c) your weight; (d) the heat lost by perspiration during a climb up a mountain along a fixed path.

11. 🔵 What is a state function? Would Hess's Law be a law if enthalpy were not a state function?

Enthalpy and Changes in Enthalpy

12. (a) Distinguish between ΔH and ΔH^0 for a reaction. (b) Distinguish between ΔH_{rxn}^0 and ΔH_f^0.

13. A reaction is characterized by $\Delta H_{rxn} = +450$ kJ/mol. Does the reaction mixture absorb heat from the surroundings or release heat to them?

14. For each of the following reactions, (a) does the enthalpy increase or decrease; (b) is $H_{reactants} > H_{products}$ or is $H_{products} > H_{reactants}$; (c) is ΔH positive or negative?
    (i) $Al_2O_3(s) \longrightarrow 2Al(s) + \frac{3}{2} O_2(g)$ (endothermic)
    (ii) $Sn(s) + Cl_2(g) \longrightarrow SnCl_2(s)$ (exothermic)

15. (a) The combustion of 0.0222 g of isooctane vapor, $C_8H_{18}(g)$, at constant pressure raises the temperature of a calorimeter 0.400°C. The heat capacity of the calorimeter and water combined is 2.48 kJ/°C. Find the molar heat of combustion of gaseous isooctane.

$$C_8H_{18}(g) + 12\tfrac{1}{2} O_2(g) \longrightarrow 8CO_2(g) + 9H_2O(\ell)$$

(b) How many grams of $C_8H_{18}(g)$ must be burned to obtain 495 kJ of heat energy?

16. Methanol, CH_3OH, is an efficient fuel with a high octane rating.

$$CH_3OH(g) + \tfrac{3}{2} O_2(g) \longrightarrow CO_2(g) + 2H_2O(\ell)$$
$$\Delta H = -764 \text{ kJ/mol rxn}$$

(a) Find the heat evolved when 115.0 g $CH_3OH(g)$ burns in excess oxygen. (b) What mass of O_2 is consumed when 925 kJ of heat is given off?

17. How much heat is liberated when 0.113 mole of sodium reacts with excess water according to the following equation?

$$2Na(s) + 2H_2O(\ell) \longrightarrow H_2(g) + 2NaOH(aq)$$
$$\Delta H = -368 \text{ kJ/mol rxn}$$

18. What is ΔH for the reaction

$$PbO(s) + C(s) \longrightarrow Pb(s) + CO(g)$$

if 5.95 kJ must be supplied to convert 13.43 g lead(II) oxide to lead?

19. From the data in Appendix K, determine the form that represents the standard state for each of the following elements: iodine, oxygen, sulfur.

20. Why is the standard molar enthalpy of formation, ΔH_f^0 for liquid water different than ΔH_f^0 for water vapor, both at 25°C? Which formation reaction is more exothermic? Does your answer indicate that $H_2O(\ell)$ is at a higher or lower enthalpy than $H_2O(g)$?

21. Methylhydrazine is burned with dinitrogen tetroxide in the attitude-control engines of the space shuttles.

$$CH_6N_2(\ell) + \tfrac{5}{4} N_2O_4(\ell) \longrightarrow$$
$$CO_2(g) + 3H_2O(\ell) + \tfrac{9}{4} N_2(g)$$

The two substances ignite instantly on contact, producing a flame temperature of 3000. K. The energy liberated per 0.100 g of CH_6N_2 at constant atmospheric pressure after the products are cooled back to 25°C is 750. J. (a) Find ΔH for the reaction as written. (b) How many kilojoules are liberated when 87.5 g of N_2 is produced?

A space shuttle

22. 🐾Which is more exothermic, the combustion of one mole of methane to form $CO_2(g)$ and liquid water or the combustion of one mole of methane to form $CO_2(g)$ and steam? Why? (No calculations are necessary.)

23. 🐾Which is more exothermic, the combustion of one mole of gaseous benzene, C_6H_6, or the combustion of one mole of liquid benzene? Why? (No calculations are necessary.)

Thermochemical Equations, ΔH_f^0, and Hess's Law

24. 🐾 Explain the meaning of the phrase "thermodynamic standard state of a substance."

25. 🐾 Explain the meaning of the phrase "standard molar enthalpy of formation." Give an example.

26. 🐾 From the data in Appendix K, determine the form that represents the standard state for each of the following elements: (a) chlorine; (b) chromium; (c) bromine; (d) iodine; (e) sulfur; (f) nitrogen.

27. 🐾 From the data in Appendix K, determine the form that represents the standard state for each of the following elements: (a) oxygen; (b) carbon; (c) phosphorus; (d) rubidium; (e) mercury; (f) tin.

28. 🐾 Write the balanced chemical equation whose ΔH_{rxn}^0 value is equal to ΔH_f^0 for each of the following substances: (a) calcium hydroxide, $Ca(OH)_2(s)$; (b) benzene, $C_6H_6(\ell)$; (c) sodium bicarbonate, $NaHCO_3(s)$; (d) calcium fluoride, $CaF_2(s)$; (e) phosphine, $PH_3(g)$; (f) propane, $C_3H_8(g)$; (g) atomic sulfur, $S(g)$; (h) water, $H_2O(\ell)$.

29. 🐾 Write the balanced chemical equation for the formation of one mole of each of the following substances from its elements in the standard state (the equation whose ΔH_{rxn}^0 value is equal to ΔH_f^0 for the substance): hydrogen peroxide [$H_2O_2(\ell)$], calcium fluoride [$CaF_2(s)$], ruthenium(III) hydroxide [$Ru(OH)_3(s)$].

30. ▲ We burn 3.47 g of lithium in excess oxygen at constant atmospheric pressure to form Li_2O. Then we bring the reaction mixture back to 25°C. In this process 146 kJ of heat is given off. What is the standard molar enthalpy of formation of Li_2O?

31. ▲ We burn 7.20 g of magnesium in excess nitrogen at constant atmospheric pressure to form Mg_3N_2. Then we bring the reaction mixture back to 25°C. In this process 68.35 kJ of heat is given off. What is the standard molar enthalpy of formation of Mg_3N_2?

32. From the following enthalpies of reaction,

$$4HCl(g) + O_2(g) \longrightarrow 2H_2O(\ell) + 2Cl_2(g)$$
$$\Delta H = -202.4 \text{ kJ/mol rxn}$$

$$\tfrac{1}{2} H_2(g) + \tfrac{1}{2} F_2(g) \longrightarrow HF(\ell)$$
$$\Delta H = -600.0 \text{ kJ/mol rxn}$$

$$H_2(g) + \tfrac{1}{2} O_2(g) \longrightarrow H_2O(\ell)$$
$$\Delta H = -285.8 \text{ kJ/mol rxn}$$

find ΔH_{rxn} for $2HCl(g) + F_2(g) \longrightarrow 2HF(\ell) + Cl_2(g)$.

🐾 **Molecular Reasoning** exercises   ▲ **More Challenging** exercises   Blue-Numbered exercises solved in Student Solutions Manual

Unless otherwise noted, all content on this page is © Cengage Learning.

33. From the following enthalpies of reaction,

$$CaCO_3(s) \longrightarrow CaO(s) + CO_2(g)$$
$$\Delta H = -178.1 \text{ kJ/mol rxn}$$

$$CaO(s) + H_2O(\ell) \longrightarrow Ca(OH)_2(s)$$
$$\Delta H = -65.3 \text{ kJ/mol rxn}$$

$$Ca(OH)_2(s) \longrightarrow Ca^{2+}(aq) + 2OH^-(aq)$$
$$\Delta H = -16.2 \text{ kJ/mol rxn}$$

calculate ΔH_{rxn} for

$$Ca^{2+}(aq) + 2OH^-(aq) + CO_2(g) \longrightarrow$$
$$CaCO_3(s) + H_2O(\ell)$$

34. Given that

$$S(s) + O_2(g) \longrightarrow SO_2(g) \quad \Delta H = -296.8 \text{ kJ/mol}$$
$$S(s) + \tfrac{3}{2}O_2(g) \longrightarrow SO_3(g) \quad \Delta H = -395.6 \text{ kJ/mol}$$

determine the enthalpy change for the decomposition reaction

$$2SO_3(g) \longrightarrow 2SO_2(g) + O_2(g)$$

35. Evaluate ΔH_{rxn}^0 for the reaction below at 25°C, using the heats of formation.

$$Fe_3O_4(s) + CO(g) \longrightarrow 3FeO(s) + CO_2(g)$$
$$\Delta H_f^0, \text{ kJ/mol: } -1118 \quad -110.5 \quad\quad -272 \quad -393.5$$

36. Given that

$$2H_2(g) + O_2(g) \longrightarrow 2H_2O(\ell)$$
$$\Delta H = -571.6 \text{ kJ/mol}$$

$$C_3H_4(g) + 4O_2(g) \longrightarrow 3CO_2(g) + 2H_2O(\ell)$$
$$\Delta H = -1937 \text{ kJ/mol}$$

$$C_3H_8(g) + 5O_2(g) \longrightarrow 3CO_2(g) + 4H_2O(\ell)$$
$$\Delta H = -2220. \text{ kJ/mol}$$

determine the heat of the hydrogenation reaction

$$C_3H_4(g) + 2H_2(g) \longrightarrow C_3H_8(g)$$

37. Determine the heat of formation of liquid hydrogen peroxide at 25°C from the following thermochemical equations.

$$H_2(g) + \tfrac{1}{2}O_2(g) \longrightarrow H_2O(g)$$
$$\Delta H^0 = -241.82 \text{ kJ/mol}$$

$$2H(g) + O(g) \longrightarrow H_2O(g)$$
$$\Delta H^0 = -926.92 \text{ kJ/mol}$$

$$2H(g) + 2O(g) \longrightarrow H_2O_2(g)$$
$$\Delta H^0 = -1070.60 \text{ kJ/mol}$$

$$2O(g) \longrightarrow O_2(g)$$
$$\Delta H^0 = -498.34 \text{ kJ/mol}$$

$$H_2O_2(\ell) \longrightarrow H_2O_2(g)$$
$$\Delta H^0 = 51.46 \text{ kJ/mol}$$

38. Use data in Appendix K to find the enthalpy of reaction for
(a) $NH_4NO_3(s) \longrightarrow N_2O(g) + 2H_2O(\ell)$
(b) $2FeS_2(s) + \tfrac{11}{2}O_2(g) \longrightarrow Fe_2O_3(s) + 4SO_2(g)$
(c) $SiO_2(s) + 3C(\text{graphite}) \longrightarrow SiC(s) + 2CO(g)$

39. Repeat Exercise 38 for
(a) $CaCO_3(s) \longrightarrow CaO(s) + CO_2(g)$
(b) $2HI(g) + F_2(g) \longrightarrow 2HF(g) + I_2(s)$
(c) $SF_6(g) + 3H_2O(\ell) \longrightarrow 6HF(g) + SO_3(g)$

40. The internal combustion engine uses heat produced during the burning of a fuel. Propane, $C_3H_8(g)$, is sometimes used as the fuel. Gasoline is the most commonly used fuel. Assume that the gasoline is pure octane, $C_8H_{18}(\ell)$, and the fuel and oxygen are completely converted into $CO_2(g)$ and $H_2O(g)$. For each of these fuels, determine the heat released per gram of fuel burned.

41. Write the balanced equation for the complete combustion (in excess O_2) of kerosene. Assume that kerosene is $C_{10}H_{22}(\ell)$ and that the products are $CO_2(g)$ and $H_2O(\ell)$. Calculate ΔH_{rxn}^0 at 25°C for this reaction.
$\Delta H_f^0 \, C_{10}H_{22}(\ell) = -249.6 \text{ kJ/mol}$
$\Delta H_f^0 \, CO_2(g) = -393.5 \text{ kJ/mol}$
$\Delta H_f^0 \, H_2O(\ell) = -285.8 \text{ kJ/mol}$

42. The thermite reaction, used for welding iron, is the reaction of Fe_3O_4 with Al.

$$8Al(s) + 3Fe_3O_4(s) \longrightarrow 4Al_2O_3(s) + 9Fe(s)$$
$$\Delta H^0 = -3350. \text{ kJ/mol rxn}$$

Because this large amount of heat cannot be rapidly dissipated to the surroundings, the reacting mass may reach temperatures near 3000.°C. How much heat is released by the reaction of 27.6 g of Al with 69.12 g of Fe_3O_4?

The thermite reaction

43. When a welder uses an acetylene torch, the combustion of acetylene liberates the intense heat needed for welding metals together. The equation for this combustion reaction is

$$2C_2H_2(g) + 5O_2(g) \longrightarrow 4CO_2(g) + 2H_2O(g)$$

The heat of combustion of acetylene is -1255.5 kJ/mol of C_2H_2. How much heat is liberated when 1.731 kg of C_2H_2 is burned?

🔴 **Molecular Reasoning** exercises ▲ **More Challenging** exercises   Blue-Numbered exercises solved in Student Solutions Manual

44. ▲ Write balanced equations for the oxidation of sucrose (a carbohydrate) and tristearin (a fat). Assume that each reacts with $O_2(g)$, producing $CO_2(g)$ and $H_2O(g)$.

Sucrose, $C_{12}H_{22}O_{11}$ Tristearin, $C_{57}H_{110}O_6$

Use tabulated bond energies to estimate ΔH^0_{rxn} for each reaction in kJ/mol (ignoring phase changes). Convert to kJ/g and kcal/g. Which has the greater energy density?

45. Natural gas is mainly methane, $CH_4(g)$. Assume that gasoline is octane, $C_8H_{18}(\ell)$, and that kerosene is $C_{10}H_{22}(\ell)$. (a) Write the balanced equations for the combustion of each of these three hydrocarbons in excess O_2. The products are $CO_2(g)$ and $H_2O(\ell)$. (b) Calculate at 25°C for each combustion reaction. ΔH^0_f for $C_{10}H_{22}$ is -300.9 kJ/mol. (c) When burned at standard conditions, which of these three fuels would produce the most heat per mole? (d) When burned at standard conditions, which of the three would produce the most heat per gram?

Bond Energies

46. (a) How is the heat released or absorbed in a *gas phase reaction* related to bond energies of products and reactants? (b) Hess's Law states that

$$\Delta H^0_{rxn} = \Sigma\, n\, \Delta H^0_{f\,products} - \Sigma\, n\, \Delta H^0_{f\,reactants}$$

The relationship between ΔH^0_{rxn} and bond energies for a *gas phase reaction* is

$$\Delta H^0_{rxn} = \Sigma\, \text{bond energies}_{reactants} - \Sigma\, \text{bond energies}_{products}$$

It is *not* true, in general, that ΔH^0_f for a substance is equal to the negative of the sum of the bond energies of the substance. Why?

47. (a) Suggest a reason for the fact that different amounts of energy are required for the successive removal of the three hydrogen atoms of an ammonia molecule, even though all $N-H$ bonds in ammonia are equivalent. (b) Suggest why the $N-H$ bonds in different compounds such as ammonia, NH_3; methylamine, CH_3NH_2; and ethylamine, $C_2H_5NH_2$, have slightly different bond energies.

48. Use tabulated bond energies to estimate the enthalpy of reaction for each of the following gas phase reactions.
(a) $H_2C=CH_2 + Br_2 \longrightarrow BrH_2C-CH_2Br$
(b) $H_2O_2 \longrightarrow H_2O + \frac{1}{2}O_2$

49. Use tabulated bond energies to estimate the enthalpy of reaction for each of the following gas phase reactions.
(a) $N_2 + 3H_2 \longrightarrow 2NH_3$
(b) $CH_4 + Cl_2 \longrightarrow CH_3Cl + HCl$
(c) $CO + H_2O \longrightarrow CO_2 + H_2$

50. Use the bond energies listed in Table 15-2 to estimate the heat of reaction for

51. Estimate ΔH for the burning of one mole of butane, using the bond energies listed in Tables 15-2 and 15-3.

$$4\,O=C=O(g) + 5\,H-O-H(g)$$

52. (a) Use the bond energies listed in Table 15-2 to estimate the heats of formation of $HCl(g)$ and $HF(g)$. (b) Compare your answers to the standard heats of formation in Appendix K.

53. (a) Use the bond energies listed in Table 15-2 to estimate the heats of formation of $H_2O(g)$ and $O_3(g)$. (b) Compare your answers to the standard heats of formation in Appendix K.

54. Using data in Appendix K, calculate the average $P-Cl$ bond energy in $PCl_3(g)$.

55. Using data in Appendix K, calculate the average $P-H$ bond energy in $PH_3(g)$.

56. Using data in Appendix K, calculate the average $P-Cl$ bond energy in $PCl_5(g)$. Compare your answer with the value calculated in Exercise 54.

57. 🔵 ▲ Methane undergoes several different exothermic reactions with gaseous chlorine. One of these forms chloroform, $CHCl_3(g)$.

$$CH_4(g) + 3Cl_2(g) \longrightarrow CHCl_3(g) + 3HCl(g)$$
$$\Delta H^0_{rxn} = -305.2 \text{ kJ/mol rxn}$$

Average bond energies per mole of bonds are: $C-H = 413$ kJ; $Cl-Cl = 242$ kJ; $H-Cl = 432$ kJ. Use these to calculate the average $C-Cl$ bond energy in chloroform. Compare this with the value in Table 15-2.

58. ▲ Ethylamine undergoes an endothermic gas phase dissociation to produce ethylene (or ethene) and ammonia.

$$\Delta H^0_{rxn} = +53.6 \text{ kJ/mol rxn}$$

The following average bond energies per mole of bonds are given: $C-H = 413$ kJ; $C-C = 346$ kJ; $C=C = 602$ kJ; $N-H = 391$ kJ. Calculate the $C-N$ bond energy in ethylamine. Compare this with the value in Table 15-2.

Calorimetry

59. 🔵 What is a coffee-cup calorimeter? How do coffee-cup calorimeters give us useful information?

🔵 **Molecular Reasoning** exercises   ▲ **More Challenging** exercises   Blue-Numbered exercises solved in Student Solutions Manual

Unless otherwise noted, all content on this page is © Cengage Learning.

60. A calorimeter contained 75.0 g of water at 16.95°C. A 93.3-g sample of iron at 65.58°C was placed in it, giving a final temperature of 19.68°C for the system. Calculate the heat capacity of the calorimeter. Specific heats are 4.184 J/g · °C for H_2O and 0.444 J/g · °C for Fe.

61. ▲ A student wishes to determine the heat capacity of a coffee-cup calorimeter. After she mixes 100.0 g of water at 58.5°C with 100.0 g of water, already in the calorimeter, at 22.8°C, the final temperature of the water is 39.7°C. (a) Calculate the heat capacity of the calorimeter in J/°C. Use 4.184 J/g · °C as the specific heat of water. (b) Why is it more useful to express the value in J/°C rather than units of J/(g calorimeter · °C)?

62. A coffee-cup calorimeter is used to determine the specific heat of a metallic sample. The calorimeter is filled with 50.0 mL of water at 25.0°C (density = 0.997 g/mL). A 36.5-gram sample of the metallic material is taken from water boiling at 100.0°C and placed in the calorimeter. The equilibrium temperature of the water and sample is 32.5°C. The calorimeter constant is known to be 1.87 J/°C. Calculate the specific heat of the metallic material.

63. A 5.1-gram piece of gold jewelry is removed from water at 100.0°C and placed in a coffee-cup calorimeter containing 16.9 g of water at 22.5°C. The equilibrium temperature of the water and jewelry is 23.2°C. The calorimeter constant is known from calibration experiments to be 1.54 J/°C. What is the specific heat of this piece of jewelry? The specific heat of pure gold is 0.129 J/g · °C. Is the jewelry pure gold?

64. A coffee-cup calorimeter having a heat capacity of 472 J/°C is used to measure the heat evolved when the following aqueous solutions, both initially at 22.6°C, are mixed: 100. g of solution containing 6.62 g of lead(II) nitrate, $Pb(NO_3)_2$, and 100. g of solution containing 6.00 g of sodium iodide, NaI. The final temperature is 24.2°C. Assume that the specific heat of the mixture is the same as that for water, 4.184 J/g · °C. The reaction is

$$Pb(NO_3)_2(aq) + 2NaI(aq) \longrightarrow PbI_2(s) + 2NaNO_3(aq)$$

(a) Calculate the heat evolved in the reaction. (b) Calculate the ΔH for the reaction under the conditions of the experiment.

65. A coffee-cup calorimeter is used to determine the heat of reaction for the acid–base neutralization

$$CH_3COOH(aq) + NaOH(aq) \longrightarrow$$
$$NaCH_3COO(aq) + H_2O(\ell)$$

When we add 20.00 mL of 0.625 M NaOH at 21.400°C to 30.00 mL of 0.500 M CH_3COOH already in the calorimeter at the same temperature, the resulting temperature is observed to be 24.347°C. The heat capacity of the calorimeter has previously been determined to be 27.8 J/°C. Assume that the specific heat of the mixture is the same as that of water, 4.184 J/g · °C, and that the density of the mixture is 1.02 g/mL. (a) Calculate the amount of heat given off in the reaction. (b) Determine ΔH for the reaction under the conditions of the experiment.

66. In a bomb calorimeter compartment surrounded by 945 g of water, the combustion of 1.048 g of benzene, $C_6H_6(\ell)$, raised the temperature of the water from 23.640°C to 32.692°C. The heat capacity of the calorimeter is 891 J/°C. (a) Write the balanced equation for the combustion reaction, assuming that $CO_2(g)$ and $H_2O(\ell)$ are the only products. (b) Use the calorimetric data to calculate ΔE for the combustion of benzene in kJ/g and in kJ/mol.

67. A 2.00-g sample of hydrazine, N_2H_4, is burned in a bomb calorimeter that contains 6.40×10^3 g of H_2O, and the temperature increases from 25.00°C to 26.17°C. The heat capacity of the calorimeter is 3.76 kJ/°C. Calculate ΔE for the combustion of N_2H_4 in kJ/g and in kJ/mol.

68. ▲ A strip of magnesium metal having a mass of 1.22 g dissolves in 100. mL of 6.02 M HCl, which has a specific gravity of 1.10. The hydrochloric acid is initially at 23.0°C, and the resulting solution reaches a final temperature of 45.5°C. The heat capacity of the calorimeter in which the reaction occurs is 562 J/°C. Calculate ΔH for the reaction under the conditions of the experiment, assuming the specific heat of the final solution is the same as that for water, 4.184 J/g · °C.

$$Mg(s) + 2HCl(aq) \longrightarrow MgCl_2(aq) + H_2(g)$$

69. When 3.16 g of salicylic acid, $C_7H_6O_3$, is burned in a bomb calorimeter containing 5.00 kg of water originally at 23.00°C, 69.3 kJ of heat is evolved. The calorimeter constant is 3255 J/°C. Calculate the final temperature.

70. A 6.620-g sample of decane, $C_{10}H_{22}(\ell)$, was burned in a bomb calorimeter whose heat capacity had been determined to be 2.45 kJ/°C. The temperature of 1250.0 g of water rose from 24.6°C to 26.4°C. Calculate ΔE for the reaction in joules per gram of decane and in kilojoules per mole of decane. The specific heat of water is 4.184 J/g · °C.

71. A nutritionist determines the caloric value of a 10.00-g sample of beef fat by burning it in a bomb calorimeter. The calorimeter held 2.500 kg of water, the heat capacity of the bomb is 1.360 kJ/°C, and the temperature of the calorimeter increased from 25.0°C to 56.9°C. (a) Calculate the number of joules released per gram of beef fat. (b) One nutritional Calorie is 1 kcal or 4184 joules. What is the dietary, caloric value of beef fat, in nutritional Calories per gram?

Internal Energy and Changes in Internal Energy

72. (a) What are the sign conventions for q, the amount of heat added to or removed from a system? (b) What are the sign conventions for w, the amount of work done on or by a system?

73. What happens to ΔE for a system during a process in which (a) $q < 0$ and $w < 0$, (b) $q = 0$ and $w > 0$, and (c) $q > 0$ and $w < 0$.

74. Ammonium nitrate, commonly used as a fertilizer, decomposes explosively:

$$2NH_4NO_3(s) \longrightarrow 2N_2(g) + 4H_2O(g) + O_2(g)$$

(This reaction has been responsible for several major explosions.) For this reaction:
(a) Is work (w) positive, negative, or 0?
(b) If $w < 0$, is work done on the system or by the system?

🔵 **Molecular Reasoning** exercises   ▲ **More Challenging** exercises   Blue-Numbered exercises solved in Student Solutions Manual

Unless otherwise noted, all content on this page is © Cengage Learning.

75. A system performs 720. L · atm of pressure–volume work (1 L · atm = 101.325 J) on its surroundings and absorbs 5750. J of heat from its surroundings. What is the change in internal energy of the system?

76. A system receives 96 J of electrical work, performs 257 J of pressure–volume work, and releases 175 J of heat. What is the change in internal energy of the system?

77. For each of the following chemical and physical changes carried out at constant pressure, state whether work is done by the system on the surroundings or by the surroundings on the system, or whether the amount of work is negligible.
    (a) $C_6H_6(\ell) \longrightarrow C_6H_6(g)$
    (b) $\frac{1}{2}N_2(g) + \frac{3}{2}H_2(g) \longrightarrow NH_3(g)$
    (c) $SiO_2(s) + 3C(s) \longrightarrow SiC(s) + 2CO(g)$

78. Repeat Exercise 77 for
    (a) $2SO_2(g) + O_2(g) \longrightarrow 2SO_3(g)$
    (b) $CaCO_3(s) \longrightarrow CaO(s) + CO_2(g)$
    (c) $CO_2(g) + H_2O(\ell) + CaCO_3(s) \longrightarrow$
    $$Ca^{2+}(aq) + 2HCO_3{}^-(aq)$$

79. Assuming that the gases are ideal, calculate the amount of work done (in joules) in each of the following reactions. In each case, is the work done *on* or *by* the system? (a) A reaction in the Mond process for purifying nickel that involves formation of the gas nickel(0) tetracarbonyl at $50-100°C$. Assume one mole of nickel is used and a constant temperature of 75°C is maintained.

    $$Ni(s) + 4CO(g) \longrightarrow Ni(CO)_4(g)$$

    (b) The conversion of one mole of brown nitrogen dioxide into colorless dinitrogen tetroxide at 8.0°C.

    $$2NO_2(g) \longrightarrow N_2O_4(g)$$

80. Assuming that the gases are ideal, calculate the amount of work done (in joules) in each of the following reactions. In each case, is the work done *on* or *by* the system? (a) The oxidation of one mole of HCl(g) at 200°C.

    $$4HCl(g) + O_2(g) \longrightarrow 2Cl_2(g) + 2H_2O(g)$$

    (b) The decomposition of one mole of nitric oxide (an air pollutant) at 300.°C.

    $$2NO(g) \longrightarrow N_2(g) + O_2(g)$$

81. ▲ When an ideal gas expands at *constant temperature*, there is no change in molecular kinetic energy (kinetic energy is proportional to temperature), and there is no change in potential energy due to intermolecular attractions (these are zero for an ideal gas). Thus for the isothermal (constant temperature) expansion of an ideal gas, $\Delta E = 0$. Suppose we allow an ideal gas to expand isothermally from 2.50 L to 5.50 L in two steps: (a) against a constant external pressure of 3.50 atm until equilibrium is reached, then (b) against a constant external pressure of 2.50 atm until equilibrium is reached. Calculate q and w for this two-step expansion.

Entropy and Entropy Changes

82. 🔬 A car uses gasoline as a fuel. Describe the burning of the fuel in terms of chemical and physical changes. Relate your answer to the Second Law of Thermodynamics.

83. State the Second Law of Thermodynamics. Why can't we use ΔS_{univ} directly as a measure of the spontaneity of a reaction?

84. State the Third Law of Thermodynamics. What does it mean?

85. Explain why ΔS may be referred to as a contributor to spontaneity.

86. Suppose you flip a coin. (a) What is the probability that it will come up heads? (b) What is the probability that it will come up heads two times in a row? (c) What is the probability that it will come up heads ten times in a row?

87. 🔬 Consider two equal-sized flasks connected as shown in the figure.

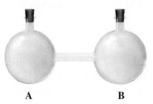

    A   **B**

    (a) Suppose you put one molecule inside. What is the probability that the molecule will be in flask A? What is the probability that it will be in flask B?
    (b) If you put 100 molecules into the two-flask system, what is the most likely distribution of molecules? Which distribution corresponds to the highest entropy?
    (c) Write a mathematical expression for the probability that all 100 molecules in part (b) will be in flask A. (You do not need to evaluate this expression.)

88. 🔬 Suppose you have two identical red molecules labeled A and B, and two identical blue molecules labeled C and D. Draw a simple two-flask diagram as in the figure for Exercise 87, and then draw all possible arrangements of the four molecules in the two flasks.
    (a) How many different arrangements are possible?
    (b) How many of the arrangements have a mixture of unlike molecules in at least one of the flasks?
    (c) What is the probability that at least one of the flasks contains a mixture of unlike molecules?
    (d) What is the probability that the gases are not mixed (each flask contains only like molecules)?

89. 🔬 For each process, tell whether the entropy change of the system is positive or negative. (a) Water vapor (the system) condenses as droplets on a cold windowpane. (b) Water boils. (c) A can of carbonated beverage loses its fizz. (Consider the beverage, but not the can, as the system. What happens to the entropy of the dissolved gas?)

90. 🔬 For each process, tell whether the entropy change of the system is positive or negative. (a) A glassblower heats glass (the system) to its softening temperature.

🔬 **Molecular Reasoning** exercises   ▲ **More Challenging** exercises   Blue-Numbered exercises solved in Student Solutions Manual

(b) A teaspoon of sugar dissolves in a cup of coffee. (The system consists of both sugar and coffee.) (c) Calcium carbonate precipitates out of water in a cave to form stalactites and stalagmites. (Consider only the calcium carbonate to be the system.)

91. ♣ For each of the following processes, tell whether the entropy of the *universe* increases, decreases, or remains constant: (a) melting one mole of ice to water at 0.°C; (b) freezing one mole of water to ice at 0.°C; (c) freezing one mole of water to ice at −15°C; (d) freezing one mole of water to ice at 0.°C and then cooling it to −15°C.

92. ▲ In which of the following changes is there an increase in entropy?
(a) the freezing of water
(b) the condensation of steam
(c) the sublimation of dry ice, solid CO_2
(d) the separation of salts and pure water from seawater

93. ♣ When solid sodium chloride is cooled from 25°C to 0.°C, the entropy change is −4.4 J/mol · K. Is this an increase or decrease in randomness? Explain this entropy change in terms of what happens in the solid at the molecular level.

94. ♣ When a one-mole sample of argon gas at 0.°C is compressed to one half its original volume, the entropy change is −5.76 J/mol · K. Is this an increase or a decrease in dispersal of energy? Explain this entropy change in terms of what happens in the gas at the molecular level.

95. ♣ Which of the following processes are accompanied by an increase in entropy of the system? (No calculation is necessary.) (a) Dry ice, $CO_2(s)$, sublimes at −78°C and then the resulting $CO_2(g)$ is warmed to 0°C. (b) Water vapor forms snowflakes, $H_2O(s)$. (c) Iodine sublimes, $I_2(s) \longrightarrow I_2(g)$. (d) White silver sulfate, Ag_2SO_4, precipitates from a solution containing silver ions and sulfate ions. (e) A partition is removed to allow two gases to mix.

96. ♣ ▲ Which of the following processes are accompanied by an increase in entropy of the system? (No calculation is necessary.) (a) Solid NaCl is dissolved in water at room temperature. (b) A saturated solution of NaCl is cooled, causing some solid NaCl to precipitate. (c) Water freezes. (d) Carbon tetrachloride, CCl_4, evaporates. (e) The reaction $PCl_5(g) \longrightarrow PCl_3(g) + Cl_2(g)$ occurs. (f) The reaction $PCl_3(g) + Cl_2(g) \longrightarrow PCl_5(g)$ occurs.

97. ♣ For each pair, tell which would have the greater absolute entropy per mole (standard molar entropy) at the same temperature. Give the reasons for your choice.
(a) NaCl(s) or CaO(s)
(b) $Cl_2(g)$ or $P_4(g)$
(c) $AsH_3(g)$ or Kr(g)
(d) $NH_4NO_3(s)$ or $NH_4NO_3(aq)$
(e) Ga(s) or Ga(ℓ)

98. ♣ For each pair, tell which would have the greater absolute entropy per mole (standard molar entropy) at the same temperature. Give the reasons for your choice.
(a) NaF(s) or MgO(s)
(b) Au(s) or Hg(ℓ)
(c) $H_2O(g)$ or $H_2S(g)$
(d) $CH_3OH(\ell)$ or $C_2H_5OH(\ell)$
(e) NaOH(s) or NaOH(aq)

99. ♣ (a) For which change would the entropy change by the greatest amount: (i) condensation of one mole of water vapor to make one mole of liquid water, or (ii) deposition of one mole of water vapor to make one mole of ice? (b) Would the entropy changes for the changes in (a) be positive or negative? Give reasons for your answer.

100. ♣ Without doing a calculation predict whether the entropy change will be positive or negative when each reaction occurs in the direction it is written.
(a) $C_3H_6(g) + H_2(g) \longrightarrow C_3H_8(g)$
(b) $N_2(g) + 3H_2(g) \longrightarrow 2NH_3(g)$
(c) $CaCO_3(s) \longrightarrow CaO(s) + CO_2(g)$
(d) $Mg(s) + \frac{1}{2}O_2(g) \longrightarrow MgO(s)$
(e) $Ag^+(aq) + Cl^-(aq) \longrightarrow AgCl(s)$

101. ♣ Without doing a calculation predict whether the entropy change will be positive or negative when each reaction occurs in the direction it is written.
(a) $CH_3OH(\ell) + \frac{3}{2}O_2(g) \longrightarrow CO_2(g) + 2H_2O(g)$
(b) $Br_2(\ell) + H_2(g) \longrightarrow 2HBr(g)$
(c) $Na(s) + \frac{1}{2}F_2(g) \longrightarrow NaF(s)$
(d) $CO_2(g) + 2H_2(g) \longrightarrow CH_3OH(\ell)$
(e) $NH_3(g) \longrightarrow N_2(g) + 3H_2(g)$

102. ♣ ▲ Consider the boiling of a pure liquid at constant pressure. Is each of the following greater than, less than, or equal to zero? (a) ΔS_{sys}; (b) ΔH_{sys}; (c) ΔT_{sys}.

103. Use S^0 data from Appendix K to calculate the value of ΔS^0_{298} for each of the following reactions. Compare the signs and magnitudes for these ΔS^0_{298} values and explain your observations.
(a) $2NO(g) + H_2(g) \longrightarrow N_2O(g) + H_2O(g)$
(b) $2N_2O_5(g) \longrightarrow 4NO_2(g) + O_2(g)$
(c) $NH_4NO_3(s) \longrightarrow N_2O(g) + 2H_2O(g)$

104. Use S^0 data from Appendix K to calculate the value of ΔS^0_{298} for each of the following reactions. Compare the signs and magnitudes for these ΔS^0_{298} values and explain your observations.
(a) $4HCl(g) + O_2(g) \longrightarrow 2Cl_2(g) + 2H_2O(g)$
(b) $PCl_3(g) + Cl_2(g) \longrightarrow PCl_5(g)$
(c) $2N_2O(g) \longrightarrow 2N_2(g) + O_2(g)$

Gibbs Free Energy Changes and Spontaneity

105. ♣ (a) What are the two factors that favor spontaneity of a process? (b) What is Gibbs free energy? What is change in Gibbs free energy? (c) Most spontaneous reactions are exothermic, but some are not. Explain. (d) Explain how the signs and magnitudes of ΔH and ΔS are related to the spontaneity of a process.

106. Which of the following conditions would predict a process that is (a) always spontaneous, (b) always nonspontaneous, or (c) spontaneous or nonspontaneous depending on the temperature and magnitudes of ΔH and ΔS? (i) $\Delta H > 0$, $\Delta S > 0$; (ii) $\Delta H > 0$, $\Delta S < 0$; (iii) $\Delta H < 0$, $\Delta S > 0$; (iv) $\Delta H < 0$, $\Delta S < 0$

107. Calculate ΔG^0 at 45°C for reactions for which
(a) $\Delta H^0 = 293$ kJ; $\Delta S^0 = -695$ J/K.
(b) $\Delta H^0 = -1137$ kJ; $\Delta S^0 = 0.496$ kJ/K.
(c) $\Delta H^0 = -86.6$ kJ; $\Delta S^0 = -382$ J/K.

♣ **Molecular Reasoning** exercises   ▲ **More Challenging** exercises   Blue-Numbered exercises solved in Student Solutions Manual

108. Evaluate ΔS^0 at 25°C and 1 atm for the reaction:

$$SiH_4(g) + 2O_2(g) \longrightarrow SiO_2(s) + 2H_2O(\ell)$$
$S^0, J/mol \cdot K$: 204.5   205.0   41.84   69.91

109. The standard Gibbs free energy of formation is −286.06 kJ/mol for NaI(s), −261.90 kJ/mol for Na⁺(aq), and −51.57 kJ/mol for I⁻(aq) at 25°C. Calculate ΔG^0 for the reaction

$$NaI(s) \xrightarrow{H_2O} Na^+(aq) + I^-(aq)$$

110. ▲ Use the following equations to find ΔG_f^0 for HBr(g) at 25°C.

$Br_2(\ell) \longrightarrow Br_2(g)$	$\Delta G^0 = 3.14$ kJ/mol
$HBr(g) \longrightarrow H(g) + Br(g)$	$\Delta G^0 = 339.09$ kJ/mol
$Br_2(g) \longrightarrow 2Br(g)$	$\Delta G^0 = 161.7$ kJ/mol
$H_2(g) \longrightarrow 2H(g)$	$\Delta G^0 = 406.494$ kJ/mol

111. Use values of standard free energy of formation, ΔG_f^0, from Appendix K to calculate the standard free energy change for each of the following reactions at 25°C and 1 atm.
(a) $3NO_2(g) + H_2O(\ell) \longrightarrow 2HNO_3(\ell) + NO(g)$
(b) $SnO_2(s) + 2CO(g) \longrightarrow 2CO_2(g) + Sn(s)$
(c) $2Na(s) + 2H_2O(\ell) \longrightarrow 2NaOH(aq) + H_2(g)$

112. Make the same calculations as in Exercise 111, using values of standard enthalpy of formation and absolute entropy instead of values of ΔG_f^0.

113. Calculate ΔG^0 at 298 K for the reaction:

$$P_4O_{10}(s) + 6H_2O(\ell) \longrightarrow 4H_3PO_4(s)$$
$\Delta H_f^0, kJ/mol$:   −2984   −285.8   −1281
$S^0, J/mol \cdot K$:   228.9   69.91   110.5

Temperature Range of Spontaneity

114. Are the following statements true or false? Justify your answers. (a) An exothermic reaction is always spontaneous. (b) If ΔH and ΔS are both positive, then ΔG will decrease when the temperature increases. (c) A reaction for which ΔS_{sys} is positive is spontaneous.

115. For the reaction

$$C(s) + O_2(g) \longrightarrow CO_2(g)$$

$\Delta H^0 = -393.51$ kJ/mol and $\Delta S^0 = 2.86$ J/mol · K at 25°C. (a) Does this reaction become more or less favorable as the temperature increases? (b) For the reaction

$$C(s) + \tfrac{1}{2}O_2(g) \longrightarrow CO(g)$$

$\Delta H^0 = -110.52$ kJ/mol and $\Delta S^0 = 89.36$ J/mol · K at 25°C. Does this reaction become more or less favorable as the temperature increases? (c) Compare the temperature dependencies of these reactions.

116. (a) Calculate ΔH^0, ΔG^0, and ΔS^0 for the reaction

$$2H_2O_2(\ell) \longrightarrow 2H_2O(\ell) + O_2(g) \text{ at 25°C.}$$

(b) Is there any temperature at which $H_2O_2(\ell)$ is stable at 1 atm?

117. When is it true that $\Delta S = \dfrac{\Delta H}{T}$?

118. ⬤ Dissociation reactions are those in which molecules break apart. Why do high temperatures favor the spontaneity of most dissociation reactions?

119. Estimate the temperature range over which each of the following standard reactions is spontaneous.
(a) $2Al(s) + 3Cl_2(g) \longrightarrow 2AlCl_3(s)$
(b) $2NOCl(g) \longrightarrow 2NO(g) + Cl_2(g)$
(c) $4NO(g) + 6H_2O(g) \longrightarrow 4NH_3(g) + 5O_2(g)$
(d) $2PH_3(g) \longrightarrow 3H_2(g) + 2P(g)$

120. Estimate the temperature range over which each of the following standard reactions is spontaneous. (a) The reaction by which sulfuric acid droplets from polluted air convert water-insoluble limestone or marble (calcium carbonate) to slightly soluble calcium sulfate, which is slowly washed away by rain:

$$CaCO_3(s) + H_2SO_4(\ell) \longrightarrow CaSO_4(s) + H_2O(\ell) + CO_2(g)$$

(b) The reaction by which Antoine Lavoisier achieved the first laboratory preparation of oxygen in the late eighteenth century: the thermal decomposition of the red-orange powder, mercury(II) oxide, to oxygen and the silvery liquid metal, mercury:

$$2HgO(s) \longrightarrow 2Hg(\ell) + O_2(g)$$

(c) The reaction of coke (carbon) with carbon dioxide to form the reducing agent, carbon monoxide, which is used to reduce some metal ores to metals:

$$CO_2(g) + C(s) \longrightarrow 2CO(g)$$

(d) The reverse of the reaction by which iron rusts:

$$2Fe_2O_3(s) \longrightarrow 4Fe(s) + 3O_2(g)$$

121. Estimate the normal boiling point of pentacarbonyliron(0), $Fe(CO)_5$, at 1 atm pressure, using Appendix K.

122. (a) Estimate the normal boiling point of water, at 1 atm pressure, using Appendix K. (b) Compare the temperature obtained with the known boiling point of water. Can you explain the discrepancy?

123. Sublimation and subsequent deposition onto a cold surface are a common method of purification of I_2 and other solids that sublime readily. Estimate the sublimation temperature (solid to vapor) of the dark violet solid iodine, I_2, at 1 atm pressure, using the data of Appendix K.

Sublimation and deposition of I_2

124. Some metal oxides can be decomposed to the metal and oxygen under reasonable conditions. Is the decomposition of nickel(II) oxide product-favored at 25°C?

$$2NiO(s) \longrightarrow 2Ni(s) + O_2(g)$$

If not, can it become so if the temperature is raised? At what temperature does the reaction become product-favored?

⬤ **Molecular Reasoning** exercises   ▲ **More Challenging** exercises   Blue-Numbered exercises solved in Student Solutions Manual

Unless otherwise noted, all content on this page is © Cengage Learning.

125. Calculate ΔH^0 and ΔS^0 for the reaction of tin(IV) oxide with carbon.

$$SnO_2(s) + C(s) \longrightarrow Sn(s) + CO_2(g)$$

(a) Is the reaction spontaneous under standard conditions at 298 K?
(b) Is the reaction predicted to be spontaneous at higher temperatures?

126. Calculate ΔS^0 system at 25°C for the reaction

$$C_2H_4(g) + H_2O(g) \longrightarrow C_2H_5OH(\ell)$$

Can you tell from the result of this calculation whether this reaction is product-favored? If you cannot tell, what additional information do you need? Obtain that information and determine whether the reaction is product-favored.

Mixed Exercises

127. ▲ An ice calorimeter, shown below, can be used to measure the amount of heat released or absorbed by a reaction that is carried out at a constant temperature of 0.°C. If heat is transferred from the system to the bath, some of the ice melts. A given mass of liquid water has a smaller volume than the same mass of ice, so the total volume of the ice and water mixture decreases. Measuring the volume decrease using the scale at the left indicates the amount of heat released by the reacting system. As long as some ice remains in the bath, the temperature remains at 0.°C. In Example 15-2 we saw that the reaction

$$CuSO_4(aq) + 2NaOH(aq) \longrightarrow Cu(OH)_2(s) + Na_2SO_4(aq)$$

releases 846 J of heat at constant temperature and pressure when 50.0 mL of 0.400 M CuSO$_4$ solution and 50.0 mL of 0.600 M NaOH solution are allowed to react. (Because no gases are involved in the reaction, the volume change of the reaction mixture is negligible.) Calculate the change in volume of the ice and water mixture that would be observed if we carried out the same experiment in an ice calorimeter. The density of $H_2O(\ell)$ at 0.°C is 0.99987 g/mL and that of ice is 0.917 g/mL. The heat of fusion of ice at 0°C is 334 J/g.

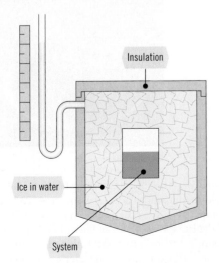

Insulation

Ice in water

System

128. It is difficult to prepare many compounds directly from their elements, so ΔH_f^0 values for these compounds cannot be measured directly. For many organic compounds, it is easier to measure the standard enthalpy of combustion by reaction of the compound with excess $O_2(g)$ to form $CO_2(g)$ and $H_2O(\ell)$. From the following standard enthalpies of combustion at 25°C, determine ΔH_f^0 for the compound. (a) cyclohexane, $C_6H_{12}(\ell)$, a useful organic solvent: $\Delta H_{combustion}^0 = -3920.$ kJ/mol; (b) phenol, $C_6H_5OH(s)$, used as a disinfectant and in the production of thermo-setting plastics: $\Delta H_{combustion}^0 = -3053$ kJ/mol.

129. ▲ Standard entropy changes cannot be measured directly in the laboratory. They are calculated from experimentally obtained values of ΔG^0 and ΔH^0. From the data given here, calculate ΔS^0 at 298 K for each of the following reactions.

(a) $OF_2(g) + H_2O(g) \longrightarrow O_2(g) + 2HF(g)$
$\Delta H^0 = -323.2$ kJ/mol $\Delta G^0 = -358.4$ kJ/mol

(b) $CaC_2(s) + 2H_2O(\ell) \longrightarrow Ca(OH)_2(s) + C_2H_2(g)$
$\Delta H^0 = -125.4$ kJ/mol $\Delta G^0 = -145.4$ kJ/mol

(c) $CaO(s) + H_2O(\ell) \longrightarrow Ca(OH)_2(aq)$
$\Delta H^0 = 81.5$ kJ/mol $\Delta G^0 = -26.20$ kJ/mol

130. ▲ Calculate q, w, and ΔE for the vaporization of 12.5 g of liquid ethanol (C_2H_5OH) at 1.00 atm at 78.0°C, to form gaseous ethanol at 1.00 atm at 78.0°C. Make the following simplifying assumptions: (a) the density of liquid ethanol at 78.0°C is 0.789 g/mL, and (b) gaseous ethanol is adequately described by the ideal gas equation. The heat of vaporization of ethanol is 855 J/g.

131. We add 0.100 g of CaO(s) to 125 g H_2O at 23.6°C in a coffee-cup calorimeter. The following reaction occurs.
$CaO(s) + H_2O(\ell) \longrightarrow Ca(OH)_2(aq)$
$\Delta H^0 = 81.5$ kJ/mol rxn

What will be the final temperature of the solution?

132. (a) The accurately known molar heat of combustion of naphthalene, $C_{10}H_8(s)$, $\Delta H = -5156.8$ kJ/mol $C_{10}H_8$, is used to calibrate calorimeters. The complete combustion of 0.01520 g of $C_{10}H_8$ at constant pressure raises the temperature of a calorimeter by 0.212°C. Find the heat capacity of the calorimeter. (b) The initial temperature of the calorimeter (part a) is 22.102°C; 0.1040 g of $C_8H_{18}(\ell)$, octane (molar heat of combustion $\Delta H = -5451.4$ kJ/mol C_8H_{18},) is completely burned in the calorimeter. Find the final temperature of the calorimeter.

Conceptual Exercises

133. When a gas expands suddenly, it may not have time to absorb a significant amount of heat: $q = 0$. Assume that 1.00 mol N_2 expands suddenly, doing 3000. J of work. (a) What is ΔE for the process? (b) The heat capacity of N_2 is 20.9 J/mol ? °C. How much does its temperature fall during this expansion? (This is the principle of most snow-making machines, which use compressed air mixed with water vapor.)

🞉 **Molecular Reasoning** exercises   ▲ **More Challenging** exercises   Blue-Numbered exercises solved in Student Solutions Manual

Unless otherwise noted, all content on this page is © Cengage Learning.

134. As a rubber band is stretched, it gets warmer; when released, it gets cooler. To obtain the more nearly linear arrangement of the rubber band's polymeric material from the more random relaxed rubber band requires that there be rotation about carbon–carbon single bonds. Based on these data, give the sign of ΔG, ΔH, and ΔS for the stretching of a rubber band and for the relaxing of a stretched rubber band. What drives the spontaneous process?

135. 🔵 (a) The decomposition of mercury(II) oxide has been used as a method for producing oxygen, but this is not a recommended method. Why? (b) Write the balanced equation for the decomposition of mercury(II) oxide. (c) Calculate the ΔH^0, ΔS^0, and ΔG^0 for the reaction. (d) Is the reaction spontaneous at room temperature?

136. ▲ (a) A student heated a sample of a metal weighing 32.6 g to 99.83°C and put it into 100.0 g of water at 23.62°C in a calorimeter. The final temperature was 24.41°C. The student calculated the specific heat of the metal, but neglected to use the heat capacity of the calorimeter. The specific heat of water is 4.184 J/g · °C. What was his answer? The metal was known to be chromium, molybdenum, or tungsten. By comparing the value of the specific heat to those of the metals (Cr, 0.460; Mo, 0.250; W, 0.135 J/g · °C), the student identified the metal. What was the metal? (b) A student at the next laboratory bench did the same experiment, obtained the same data, and used the heat capacity of the calorimeter in his calculations. The heat capacity of the calorimeter was 410. J/°C. Was his identification of the metal different?

137. 🔵 According to the Second Law of Thermodynamics what would be the ultimate state or condition of the universe?

138. For each of the following changes, estimate the signs (positive, negative, or 0) of ΔS and ΔG.
(a) The growth of a crystal from a supersaturated solution
(b) Sugar cube + cup of hot tea $\longrightarrow$
 cup of hot, sweetened tea
(c) $H_2O(s) \longrightarrow H_2O(\ell)$

139. Estimate the boiling point of tin(IV) chloride, $SnCl_4$, at one atmosphere pressure:

$$SnCl_4(\ell) \rightleftharpoons SnCl_4(g)$$

$$SnCl_4(\ell): \Delta H_f^0 = -511.3 \text{ kJ/mol}, S^0 = 258.6 \text{ J/mol} \cdot K$$

$$SnCl_4(g): \Delta H_f^0 = -471.5 \text{ kJ/mol}, S^0 = 366 \text{ J/mol} \cdot K$$

Building Your Knowledge

140. ▲ Energy to power muscular work is produced from stored carbohydrates (glycogen) or fat (triglycerides). Metabolic consumption and production of energy are described with the nutritional "Calorie," which is equal to 1 kilocalorie. Average energy output per minute for various activities follows: sitting, 1.7 kcal; walking, level, 3.5 mph, 5.5 kcal; cycling, level, 13 mph, 10. kcal; swimming, 8.4 kcal; running, 10. mph, 19 kcal. Approximate energy values of some common foods are also given: large apple, 100. kcal;

8-oz cola drink, 105 kcal; malted milkshake, 500. kcal; $\frac{3}{4}$ cup pasta with tomato sauce and cheese, 195 kcal; hamburger on bun with sauce, 350. kcal; 10.-oz sirloin steak, including fat, 1000. kcal. To maintain body weight, fuel intake should balance energy output. Prepare a table showing (a) each given food, (b) its fuel value, and (c) the minutes of each activity that would balance the kcal of each food.

141. From its heat of fusion, calculate the entropy change associated with the melting of one mole of ice at its melting point. From its heat of vaporization, calculate the entropy change associated with the boiling of one mole of water at its boiling point. Are your calculated values consistent with the simple model that we use to describe order in solids, liquids, and gases?

142. The energy content of dietary fat is 39 kJ/g, and for protein and carbohydrates it is 17 and 16 kJ/g, respectively. A 70.0-kg (155-lb) person utilizes 335 kJ/h while resting and 1250. kJ/h while walking 6 km/h. How many hours would the person need to walk per day instead of resting if he or she consumed 100. g (about $\frac{1}{4}$ lb) of fat instead of 100. g of protein in order to not gain weight?

143. The enthalpy change for melting one mole of water at 273 K is $\Delta H_{273}^0 = 6010.$ J/mol, whereas that for vaporizing a mole of water at 373 K is $\Delta H_{273}^0 = 40,660$ J/mol. Why is the second value so much larger?

144. A 43.6-g chunk of lead was removed from a beaker of boiling water, quickly dried, and dropped into a polystyrene cup containing 50.0 g of water at 25.0°C. As the system reached equilibrium, the water temperature rose to 26.8°C. The heat capacity of the polystyrene cup had previously been determined to be 18.6 J/°C. Calculate the molar heat capacity and the specific heat of lead.

145. Methane, $CH_4(g)$, is the main constituent of natural gas. In excess oxygen, methane burns to form $CO_2(g)$ and $H_2O(\ell)$, whereas in limited oxygen, the products are $CO(g)$ and $H_2O(\ell)$. Which would result in a higher temperature: a gas–air flame or a gas–oxygen flame? How can you tell?

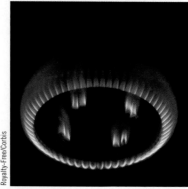

A methane flame

146. A 0.483-g sample of butter was burned in a bomb calorimeter whose heat capacity was 4572 J/°C, and the temperature was observed to rise from 24.76 to 27.93°C. Calculate the fuel value of butter in (a) kJ/g; (b) nutritional Calories/g (one nutritional Calorie is equal to one kilocalorie); (c) nutritional Calories/5-gram pat.

🔵 **Molecular Reasoning** exercises   ▲ **More Challenging** exercises   Blue-Numbered exercises solved in Student Solutions Manual

Unless otherwise noted, all content on this page is © Cengage Learning.

Beyond the Textbook

NOTE: *Whenever the answer to an exercise depends on information obtained from a source other than this textbook, the source must be included, as an essential part of the answer.*

Go to a suitable site and find the answers to the next two questions about Germain Henri Hess.

147. Hess's Law is also known as the Law of _____ _____
_____.

148. Before he became a professor of chemistry at 28 years of age, what career did Germain Hess pursue?

149. Go to a website that describes the events in the life of Josiah Willard Gibbs.
(a) In what way was the doctorate degree granted to Gibbs, from whom Gibbs free energy gets its name, a first? (b) At what university did he spend nearly all his academic career?

150. Use the *Handbook of Chemistry and Physics* or another suitable reference to find the heats of formation of the following hydrocarbons: methane, ethane, propane, and *n*-butane. (a) What are the units of the values you have found? (b) Is there a trend when you compare the formula weight of each hydrocarbon with its heat of formation?

151. ♣ Why does $Al_2O_3(s)$ have a lower entropy than $Fe_2O_3(s)$? There are two primary qualitative reasons for this. You may have to use the chemistry library or some other source to get more information on the properties of these two common compounds to answer the question.

152. Steel is made by the high-temperature reaction of iron oxide (Fe_2O_3) with coke (a form of carbon) to produce metallic iron and CO_2. This same reaction can NOT be done with alumina (Al_2O_3) and carbon to make metallic Al and CO_2. Why not? Explain fully and give thermodynamic reasons for your answer. You may need to obtain further information from outside sources on the properties of the substances involved.

♣ **Molecular Reasoning** exercises   ▲ **More Challenging** exercises   Blue-Numbered exercises solved in Student Solutions Manual

Unless otherwise noted, all content on this page is © Cengage Learning.

Some Mathematical Operations

In chemistry we frequently use very large or very small numbers. Such numbers are conveniently expressed in *scientific*, or *exponential*, *notation*.

A-1 Scientific Notation

In scientific notation, a number is expressed as the *product of two numbers*. By convention, the first number, called the *digit term*, is between 1 and 10. The second number, called the *exponential term*, is an integer power of 10. Some examples follow.

$$10000 = 1 \times 10^4 \qquad\qquad 24327 = 2.4327 \times 10^4$$
$$1000 = 1 \times 10^3 \qquad\qquad 7958 = 7.958 \ \times 10^3$$
$$100 = 1 \times 10^2 \qquad\qquad 594 = 5.94 \ \ \times 10^2$$
$$10 = 1 \times 10^1 \qquad\qquad 98 = 9.8 \ \ \ \times 10^1$$
$$1 = 1 \times 10^0$$
$$1/10 = 0.1 = 1 \times 10^{-1} \qquad 0.32 = 3.2 \ \ \ \times 10^{-1}$$
$$1/100 = 0.01 = 1 \times 10^{-2} \qquad 0.067 = 6.7 \ \ \times 10^{-2}$$
$$1/1000 = 0.001 = 1 \times 10^{-3} \qquad 0.0049 = 4.9 \ \ \times 10^{-3}$$
$$1/10000 = 0.0001 = 1 \times 10^{-4} \qquad 0.00017 = 1.7 \ \ \times 10^{-4}$$

▶ Recall that, by definition, $(\text{any base})^0 = 1$.

The exponent of 10 is the number of places the decimal point must be shifted to give the number in long form. A *positive exponent* indicates that the decimal point is *shifted right* that number of places. A *negative exponent* indicates that the decimal point is *shifted left*. When numbers are written in *standard scientific notation*, there is one nonzero digit to the left of the decimal point.

$$7.3 \times 10^3 = 73 \times 10^2 \qquad = 730 \times 10^1 \qquad = 7300$$
$$4.36 \times 10^{-2} = 0.436 \times 10^{-1} \ = 0.0436$$
$$0.00862 = 0.0862 \times 10^{-1} = 0.862 \times 10^{-2} = 8.62 \times 10^{-3}$$

In scientific notation the digit term indicates the number of significant figures in the number. The exponential term merely locates the decimal point and does not represent significant figures.

Problem-Solving Tip Know How to Use Your Calculator

Students sometimes make mistakes when they try to enter numbers into their calculators in scientific notation. Suppose you want to enter the number 4.36×10^{-2}. On most calculators, you would

1. Press 4.36

2. Press E, EE, or EXP, which stands for "times ten to the"

3. Press 2 (the magnitude of the exponent) and then $\pm$ or CHS (to change its sign)

▶ To be sure you know how to use your calculator, you should use it to check the answers to all calculations in this appendix.

The calculator display might show the value as $\boxed{4.36 \quad -02}$ or as $\boxed{0.0436}$. Different calculators show different numbers of digits, which can sometimes be adjusted.

If you wished to enter -4.36×10^2, you would

1. Press 4.36, then press $\pm$ or CHS to change its sign,

2. Press E, EE, or EXP, and then press 2

The calculator would then show $\boxed{-4.36 \quad 02}$ or $\boxed{-436.0}$.

Caution: Be sure you remember that the E, EE, or EXP button *includes* the "times 10" operation. An error that beginners often make is to enter "$\times 10$" explicitly when trying to enter a number in scientific notation. Suppose you mistakenly enter 3.7×10^2 as follows:

1. Enter 3.7

2. Press $\times$ and then enter 10

3. Press E, EE, or EXP and then enter 2

The calculator then shows the result as 3.7×10^3 or 3700—why? This sequence is processed by the calculator as follows: Step 1 enters the number 3.7; step 2 multiplies by 10, to give 37; step 3 multiplies this by 10^2, to give 37×10^2 or 3.7×10^3.

Other common errors include changing the sign of the exponent when the intent was to change the sign of the entire number (e.g., -3.48×10^4 entered as 3.48×10^{-4}).

When in doubt, carry out a trial calculation for which you already know the answer. For instance, multiply 300 by 2 by entering the first value as 3.00×10^2 and then multiplying by 2; you know the answer should be 600, and if you get any other answer, you know you have done something wrong. If you cannot find (or understand) the printed instructions for *your calculator*, your instructor or a classmate might be able to help.

Addition and Subtraction

In addition and subtraction all numbers are converted to the same power of 10, and then the digit terms are added or subtracted.

$$(4.21 \times 10^{-3}) + (1.4 \times 10^{-4}) = (4.21 \times 10^{-3}) + (0.14 \times 10^{-3}) = \boxed{4.35 \times 10^{-3}}$$

$$(8.97 \times 10^4) - (2.31 \times 10^3) = (8.97 \times 10^4) - (0.231 \times 10^4) = \boxed{8.74 \times 10^4}$$

Multiplication

The digit terms are multiplied in the usual way, the exponents are added algebraically, and the product is written with one nonzero digit to the left of the decimal.

▶ Two significant figures in answer. $$(4.7 \times 10^7)(1.6 \times 10^2) = (4.7)(1.6) \times 10^{7+2} = 7.52 \times 10^9 = \boxed{7.5 \times 10^9}$$

▶ Two significant figures in answer. $$(8.3 \times 10^4)(9.3 \times 10^{-9}) = (8.3)(9.3) \times 10^{4-9} = 77.19 \times 10^{-5} = \boxed{7.7 \times 10^{-4}}$$

Division

The digit term of the numerator is divided by the digit term of the denominator, the exponents are subtracted algebraically, and the quotient is written with one nonzero digit to the left of the decimal.

$$\frac{8.4 \times 10^7}{2.0 \times 10^3} = \frac{8.4}{2.0} \times 10^{7-3} = \boxed{4.2 \times 10^4}$$

▶ Three significant figures in answer. $$\frac{3.81 \times 10^9}{8.412 \times 10^{-3}} = \frac{3.81}{8.412} \times 10^{[9-(-3)]} = 0.45292 \times 10^{12} = \boxed{4.53 \times 10^{11}}$$

Powers of Exponentials

The digit term is raised to the indicated power, and the exponent is multiplied by the number that indicates the power.

$$(1.2 \times 10^3)^2 = (1.2)^2 \times 10^{3 \times 2} = 1.44 \times 10^6 = \boxed{1.4 \times 10^6}$$

$$(3.0 \times 10^{-3})^4 = (3.0)^4 \times 10^{-3 \times 4} = 81 \times 10^{-12} = \boxed{8.1 \times 10^{-11}}$$

Electronic Calculators. *To square a number*: (1) enter the number and (2) touch the (x^2) button.

$$(7.3)^2 = 53.29 = 53 \qquad \text{(two sig. figs.)}$$

To raise a number y to power x: (1) enter the number; (2) touch the (y^x) button; (3) enter the power; and (4) touch the $(=)$ button.

$$(7.3)^4 = 2839.8241 = 2.8 \times 10^3 \qquad \text{(two sig. figs.)}$$
$$(7.30 \times 10^2)^5 = 2.0730716 \times 10^{14} = 2.07 \times 10^{14} \qquad \text{(three sig. figs.)}$$

Roots of Exponentials

If a calculator is not used, the exponent must be divisible by the desired root. The root of the digit term is extracted in the usual way, and the exponent is divided by the desired root.

$$\sqrt{2.5 \times 10^5} = \sqrt{2.5 \times 10^4} = \sqrt{25} \times \sqrt{10^4} = 5.0 \times 10^2$$
$$\sqrt[3]{2.7 \times 10^{-8}} = \sqrt[3]{27 \times 10^{-9}} = \sqrt[3]{27} = \sqrt[3]{10^{-9}} = 3.0 \times 10^{-3}$$

Electronic Calculators. *To extract the square root of a number*: (1) enter the number and (2) touch the $(\sqrt{x})$ button.

$$\sqrt{23} = 4.7958315 = 4.8 \qquad \text{(two sig. figs.)}$$

To extract some other root: (1) enter the number y; (2) touch the (INV) and then the (y^x) button; (3) enter the root to be extracted, x; and (4) touch the $(=)$ button.

▶ These instructions are applicable to most calculators. If your calculator has other notation, consult the instructions for your calculator.

▶ On some calculator models, this function is performed by the $\sqrt[x]{y}$ button.

A-2 Logarithms

The logarithm of a number is the power to which a base must be raised to obtain the number. Two types of logarithms are frequently used in chemistry: (1) common logarithms (abbreviated log), whose base is 10, and (2) natural logarithms (abbreviated ln), whose base is $e = 2.71828$. The general properties of logarithms are the same no matter what base is used. Many equations in science were derived by the use of calculus, and these often involve natural (base e) logarithms. The relationship between $\log x$ and $\ln x$ is as follows.

$$\ln x = 2.303 \log x$$

▶ $\ln 10 = 2.303$

Finding Logarithms. The common logarithm of a number is the power to which 10 must be raised to obtain the number. The number 10 must be raised to the third power to equal 1000. Therefore, the logarithm of 1000 is 3, written $\log 1000 = 3$. Some examples follow.

Number	Exponential Expression	Logarithm
1000	10^3	3
100	10^2	2
10	10^1	1
1	10^0	0
$1/10 = 0.1$	10^{-1}	-1
$1/100 = 0.01$	10^{-2}	-2
$1/1000 = 0.001$	10^{-3}	-3

To obtain the logarithm of a number other than an integral power of 10, you must use either an electronic calculator or a logarithm table. On most calculators, you do this by (1) entering the number and then (2) pressing the (log) button.

$$\log 7.39 = 0.8686444 = 0.869$$
$$\log 7.39 \times 10^3 = 3.8686 \qquad = 3.869$$
$$\log 7.39 \times 10^{-3} = -2.1314 \qquad = -2.131$$

The number to the left of the decimal point in a logarithm is called the *characteristic*, and the number to the right of the decimal point is called the *mantissa*. The characteristic only locates the decimal point of the number, so it is usually not included when counting significant figures. The mantissa has as many significant figures as the number whose log was found.

To obtain the natural logarithm of a number on an electronic calculator, (1) enter the number and (2) press the (ln) or (ln x) button.

$$\ln 4.45 = 1.4929041 = 1.493$$
$$\ln 1.27 \times 10^3 = 7.1468 \quad = 7.147$$

▶ On some calculators, the inverse log is found as follows:
1. enter the value of the log
2. press the (2ndF) (second function) button
3. press (10^x)

On some calculators, the inverse natural logarithm is found as follows:
1. enter the value of the ln
2. press the (2ndF) (second function) button
3. press (e^x)

Finding Antilogarithms. Sometimes we know the logarithm of a number and must find the number. This is called finding the *antilogarithm* (or *inverse logarithm*). To do this on a calculator, (1) enter the value of the log; (2) press the (INV) button; and (3) press the (log) button.

$$\log x = 6.131; \quad \text{so } x = \text{inverse log of } 6.131 = 1.352 \times 10^6$$
$$\log x = -1.562; \quad \text{so } x = \text{inverse log of } -1.562 = 2.74 \times 10^{-2}$$

To find the inverse natural logarithm, (1) enter the value of the ln; (2) press the (INV) button; and (3) press the (ln) or (ln x) button.

$$\ln x = 3.552; \quad \text{so } x = \text{inverse ln of } 3.552 = 3.49 \times 10^1$$
$$\ln x = -1.248; \quad \text{so } x = \text{inverse ln of } -1.248 = 2.87 \times 10^{-1}$$

Calculations Involving Logarithms

Because logarithms are exponents, operations involving them follow the same rules as the use of exponents. The following relationships are useful.

$$\log xy = \log x + \log y \qquad \text{or} \qquad \ln xy = \ln x + \ln y$$
$$\log \frac{x}{y} = \log x - \log y \qquad \text{or} \qquad \ln \frac{x}{y} = \ln x - \ln y$$
$$\log x^y = y \log x \qquad \text{or} \qquad \ln x^y = y \ln x$$
$$\log \sqrt[y]{x} = \log x^{1/y} = \frac{1}{y} \log x \qquad \text{or} \qquad \ln \sqrt[y]{x} = \ln x^{1/y} = \frac{1}{y} \ln x$$

A-3 Quadratic Equations

Algebraic expressions of the form

$$ax^2 + bx + c = 0$$

are called **quadratic equations**. Each of the constant terms (a, b, and c) may be either positive or negative. All quadratic equations may be solved by the **quadratic formula**.

$$x = \frac{-b \pm \sqrt{b^2 - 4ac}}{2a}$$

To solve the quadratic equation $3x^2 - 4x - 8 = 0$, we use $a = 3$, $b = -4$, and $c = -8$. Substitution of these values into the quadratic formula gives

$$x = \frac{-(-4) \pm \sqrt{(-4)^2 - 4(3)(-8)}}{2(3)} = \frac{4 \pm \sqrt{16 + 96}}{6}$$

$$= \frac{4 \pm \sqrt{112}}{6} = \frac{4 \pm 10.6}{6}$$

The two roots of this quadratic equation are

$$x = 2.4 \qquad \text{and} \qquad x = -1.1$$

As you construct and solve quadratic equations based on the observed behavior of matter, you must decide which root has physical significance. Examination of the *equation that defines x* always gives clues about possible values for *x*. In this way you can tell which is extraneous (has no physical significance). Negative roots are often extraneous.

When you have solved a quadratic equation, you should always check the values you obtained by substituting them into the original equation. In the preceding example we obtained $x = 2.4$ and $x = -1.1$. Substitution of these values into the original quadratic equation, $3x^2 - 4x - 8 = 0$, shows that both roots are correct. Such substitutions often do not give a perfect check because some round-off error has been introduced.

A-4 Significant Figures

There are two kinds of numbers. *Numbers obtained by counting or from definitions are* **exact numbers**. They are known to be absolutely accurate. For example, the exact number of people in a closed room can be counted, and there is no doubt about the number of people. A dozen eggs is defined as exactly 12 eggs, no more, no fewer (Figure A-1).

Numbers obtained from measurements are not exact. Every measurement involves an estimate. For example, suppose you are asked to measure the length of this page to the nearest 0.1 mm. How do you do it? The smallest divisions (calibration lines) on a meter stick are 1 mm apart (see Figure 1-17). An attempt to measure to 0.1 mm requires estimation. If three different people measure the length of the page to 0.1 mm, will they get the same answer? Probably not. We deal with this problem by using significant figures.

Significant figures are digits believed to be correct by the person who makes a measurement. We assume that the person is competent to use the measuring device. Suppose one measures a distance with a meter stick and reports the distance as 343.5 mm. What does this number mean? In this person's judgment, the distance is greater than 343.4 mm but less than 343.6 mm, and the best estimate is 343.5 mm. The number 343.5 mm contains four significant figures. The last digit, 5, is a *best estimate* and is therefore doubtful, but it is considered to be a significant figure. In reporting numbers obtained from measurements, *we report one estimated digit, and no more.* Because the person making the measurement is not certain that the 5 is correct, it would be meaningless to report the distance as 343.53 mm.

To see more clearly the part significant figures play in reporting the results of measurements, consider Figure A-2a. Graduated cylinders are used to measure volumes of liquids when a high degree of accuracy is not necessary. The calibration lines on a 50-mL graduated cylinder represent 1-mL increments. Estimation of the volume of liquid in a 50-mL cylinder to within 0.2 mL ($\frac{1}{5}$ of one calibration increment) with reasonable certainty is possible. We might measure a volume of liquid in such a cylinder and report the volume as 38.6 mL, that is, to three significant figures.

Burets are used to measure volumes of liquids when higher accuracy is required. The calibration lines on a 50-mL buret represent 0.1-mL increments, allowing us to make estimates to within 0.02 mL ($\frac{1}{5}$ of one calibration increment) with reasonable certainty (Figure A-2b). Experienced individuals estimate volumes in 50-mL burets to 0.01 mL with considerable reproducibility. For example, using a 50-mL buret, we can measure out 38.56 mL (four significant figures) of liquid with reasonable accuracy.

Accuracy refers to how closely a measured value agrees with the correct value. **Precision** refers to how closely individual measurements agree with one another. Ideally, all measurements should be both accurate and precise. Measurements may be quite precise yet quite inaccurate because of some *systematic error*, which is an error repeated in each measurement. (A faulty balance, for example, might produce a systematic error.) Very accurate measurements are seldom imprecise.

Measurements are usually repeated to improve accuracy and precision. Average values obtained from several measurements are usually more reliable than individual measurements. Significant figures indicate how precisely measurements have been made (assuming the person who made the measurements was competent).

Some simple rules govern the use of significant figures.

1. Nonzero digits are always significant.

▶ An *exact* number may be thought of as containing an *infinite* number of significant figures.

▶ There is some uncertainty in all measurements.

▶ Significant figures indicate the *uncertainty* in measurements.

A A dozen eggs is exactly 12 eggs.

B A specific swarm of honeybees contains an *exact* number of live bees (though it would be difficult to count them, and any two *swarms* would be unlikely to contain the same exact number of bees).

Figure A-1

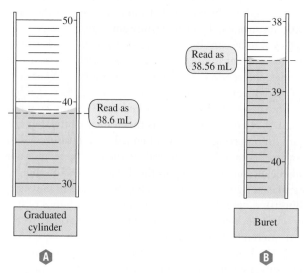

Read as 38.6 mL

Read as 38.56 mL

Graduated cylinder

Buret

A

B

Figure A-2 Measurement of the volume of water using two types of volumetric glassware. For consistency, we always read the bottom of the meniscus (the curved surface of the water). (a) A graduated cylinder is used to measure the amount of liquid *contained* in the glassware, so the scale increases from bottom to top. The level in a 50-mL graduated cylinder can usually be estimated to within 0.2 mL. The level here is 38.6 mL (three significant figures). (b) We use a buret to measure the amount of liquid *delivered* from the glassware, by taking the difference between an initial and a final volume reading. The level in a 50-mL buret can be read to within 0.02 mL. The level here is 38.56 mL (four significant figures).

For example, 38.56 mL has four significant figures; 288 g has three significant figures.

2. Zeroes are sometimes significant, and sometimes they are not.
   a. Zeroes at the *beginning* of a number (used just to position the decimal point) are never significant.

For example, 0.052 g has two significant figures; 0.00364 m has three significant figures. These could also be reported in scientific notation as 5.2×10^{-2} g and 3.64×10^{-3} m, respectively.

   b. Zeroes *between* nonzero digits are always significant.

For example, 2007 g has four significant figures; 6.08 km has three significant figures.

    c. Zeroes at the *end* of a number that contains a decimal point are always significant.

For example, 38.0 cm has three significant figures; 440.0 m has four significant figures. These could also be reported as 3.80×10^1 cm and 4.400×10^2 m, respectively.

    d. Zeroes at the *end* of a number that does not contain a decimal point may or may not be significant.

For example, does the quantity 24,300 km represent three, four, or five significant figures? Writing the number in this format gives insufficient information to answer the question. If both of the zeroes are used just to place the decimal point, the number should appear as 2.43×10^4 km (three significant figures). If only one of the zeroes is used to place the decimal point (i.e., the number was measured ± 10), the number is 2.430 ± 10^4 km (four significant figures). If the number is actually known to be $24,300 \pm 1$, it should be written as 2.4300×10^4 km (five significant figures).

▶ When we wish to specify that all of the zeroes in such a number *are* significant, we may indicate this by placing a decimal point after the number. For instance, 130. grams represents a mass known to *three* significant figures, that is, 130 ± 1 gram.

    3. Exact numbers can be considered as having an unlimited number of significant figures. This applies to defined quantities.

    For example, in the equivalence 1 yard = 3 feet, the numbers 1 and 3 are exact, and we do not apply the rules of significant figures to them. The equivalence 1 inch = 2.54 centimeters is an exact one.

    A calculated number can never be more precise than the numbers used to calculate it. The following rules show how to get the number of significant figures in a calculated number.

    4. In addition and subtraction, the last digit retained in the sum or difference is determined by the position of the first doubtful digit.

Example A-1 Significant Figures (Addition and Subtraction)

(a) Add 37.24 mL and 10.3 mL. **(b)** Subtract 21.2342 g from 27.87 g.

Plan

We first check to see that the quantities to be added or subtracted are expressed in the same units. We carry out the addition or subtraction. Then we follow Rule 4 for significant figures to express the answer to the correct number of significant figures.

Solution

$$
\begin{array}{ll}
& 37.24 \text{ mL} \\
\textbf{(a)} & +10.3 \text{ mL} \quad \text{is reported as } 47.5 \text{ mL (calculator gives 47.54)} \\
\hline
& 47.54 \text{ mL}
\end{array}
$$

$$
\begin{array}{ll}
& 27.87 \quad \text{g} \\
\textbf{(b)} & -21.2342 \text{ g} \quad \text{is reported as } 6.64 \text{ g (calculator gives 6.6358)} \\
\hline
& 6.6358 \text{ g}
\end{array}
$$

S TOP & THINK
The doubtful digits are underlined in Example A-1. In addition or subtraction, the last significant digit in the answer is determined by the position of the least doubtful digit. In (a), this is the first digit after the decimal point. In (b), this is the second digit after the decimal point.

5. In multiplication and division, an answer contains no more significant figures than the least number of significant figures used in the operation.

Example A-2 Significant Figures (Multiplication)

What is the area of a rectangle 1.23 cm wide and 12.34 cm long?

Plan

The area of a rectangle is its length times its width. We must first check to see that the width and length are expressed in the same units. (They are, but if they were not, we should first convert one to the units of the other.) Then we multiply the width by the length. We then follow Rule 5 for significant figures to find the correct number of significant figures. The units for the result are equal to the product of the units for the individual terms in the multiplication.

Solution

$$A = \ell \times w = (12.34 \text{ cm})(1.23 \text{ cm}) = 15.2 \text{ cm}^2$$

$$(\text{calculator result} = 15.1782)$$

Because three is the smallest number of significant figures used, the answer should contain only three significant figures. The number generated by an electronic calculator (15.1782) implies more accuracy than is justified; the result cannot be more accurate than the information that led to it. Calculators have no judgment, so you must exercise yours.

$$
\begin{array}{r}
12.34 \text{ cm} \\
\times \quad 1.23 \text{ cm} \\
\hline
3702 \\
2468 \\
1234 \\
\hline
15.17 \quad 82 \text{ cm}^2 = 15.2 \text{ cm}^2
\end{array}
$$

The step-by-step calculation in the margin demonstrates why the area is reported as 15.2 cm^2 rather than 15.1782 cm^2. The length, 12.34 cm, contains four significant figures, whereas the width, 1.23 cm, contains only three. If we underline each uncertain figure, as well as each figure obtained from an uncertain figure, the step-by-step multiplication gives the result reported in Example A-2. We see that there are only two certain figures (15) in the result. We report the first doubtful figure (.2), but no more. Division is just the reverse of multiplication, and the same rules apply.

In the three simple arithmetic operations we have performed, the number combination generated by an electronic calculator is not the "answer" in a single case! The correct result of each calculation, however, can be obtained by "rounding." The rules of significant figures tell us where to round.

▶ Rounding to an even number is intended to reduce the accumulation of errors in chains of calculations.

In rounding off, certain conventions have been adopted. When the number to be dropped is less than 5, the preceding number is left unchanged (e.g., 7.34 rounds to 7.3). When it is more than 5, the preceding number is increased by 1 (e.g., 7.37 rounds to 7.4). When the number to be dropped is 5, the preceding number is set to the nearest even number (e.g., 7.45 rounds to 7.4, and 7.35 rounds to 7.4).

Problem-Solving Tip When Do We Round?

When a calculation involves several steps, we often show the answer to each step to the correct number of significant figures. *But we carry all digits in the calculator to the end of the calculation; then we round the final answer to the appropriate number of significant figures.* When carrying out such a calculation, it is safest to carry extra figures through all steps and then to round the final answer appropriately.

Electronic Configurations of the Atoms of the Elements

Group	1A	2A	3B													4B	5B	6B	7B		8B		1B	2B	3A	4A	5A	6A	7A	8A
	(1)	(2)	(3)													(4)	(5)	(6)	(7)	(8)	(9)	(10)	(11)	(12)	(13)	(14)	(15)	(16)	(17)	(18)

Period

Period																														
1	1 H **1s**																												2 He **1s**
2	3 Li **2s**	4 Be																						5 B **2p**	6 C	7 N	8 O	9 F	10 Ne
3	11 Na **3s**	12 Mg																						13 Al **3p**	14 Si	15 P	16 S	17 Cl	18 Ar
4	19 K **4s**	20 Ca	21 Sc													22 Ti **3d**	23 V	24 Cr	25 Mn	26 Fe	27 Co	28 Ni	29 Cu	30 Zn	31 Ga **4p**	32 Ge	33 As	34 Se	35 Br	36 Kr
5	37 Rb **5s**	38 Sr	39 Y													40 Zr **4d**	41 Nb	42 Mo	43 Tc	44 Ru	45 Rh	46 Pd	47 Ag	48 Cd	49 In **5p**	50 Sn	51 Sb	52 Te	53 I	54 Xe
6	55 Cs **6s**	56 Ba	57 La													72 Hf **5d**	73 Ta	74 W	75 Re	76 Os	77 Ir	78 Pt	79 Au	80 Hg	81 Tl **6p**	82 Pb	83 Bi	84 Po	85 At	86 Rn
7	87 Fr **7s**	88 Ra	89 Ac													104 Rf **6d**	105 Db	106 Sg	107 Bh	108 Hs	109 Mt	110 Ds	111 Rg	112						

58 Ce **4f**	59 Pr	60 Nd	61 Pm	62 Sm	63 Eu	64 Gd	65 Tb	66 Dy	67 Ho	68 Er	69 Tm	70 Yb	71 Lu
90 Th **5f**	91 Pa	92 U	93 Np	94 Pu	95 Am	96 Cm	97 Bk	98 Cf	99 Es	100 Fm	101 Md	102 No	103 Lr

A periodic table colored to show the kinds of atomic orbitals (subshells) that are being filled in different parts of the periodic table. The atomic orbitals are given below the symbols of blocks of elements. The electronic structures of the A group elements are quite regular and can be predicted from their positions in the periodic table, but there are many exceptions in the *d* and *f* blocks. The populations of subshells are given in the table on pages A-6 and A-7.

Electron Configurations of the Atoms of the Elements

Element	Atomic Number	Populations of Subshells											
		1s	2s	2p	3s	3p	3d	4s	4p	4d	4f	5s
H	1	1										
He	2	2										
Li	3	2	1									
Be	4	2	2									
B	5	2	2	1								
C	6	2	2	2								
N	7	2	2	3								
O	8	2	2	4								
F	9	2	2	5								
Ne	10	2	2	6								
Na	11				1							
Mg	12				2							
Al	13				2	1						
Si	14	Neon core			2	2						
P	15				2	3						
S	16				2	4						
Cl	17				2	5						
Ar	18	2	2	6	2	6						
K	19							1				
Ca	20							2				
Sc	21						1	2				
Ti	22						2	2				
V	23						3	2				
Cr	24						5	1				
Mn	25						5	2				
Fe	26						6	2				
Co	27		Argon core				7	2				
Ni	28						8	2				
Cu	29						10	1				
Zn	30						10	2				
Ga	31						10	2	1			
Ge	32						10	2	2			
As	33						10	2	3			
Se	34						10	2	4			
Br	35						10	2	5			
Kr	36	2	2	6	2	6	10	2	6			
Rb	37											1
Sr	38											2
Y	39									1		2
Zr	40									2		2
Nb	41									4		1
Mo	42									5		1
Tc	43			Krypton core						5		2
Ru	44									7		1
Rh	45									8		1
Pd	46									10		
Ag	47									10		1
Cd	48									10		2

Electron Configurations of the Atoms of the Elements (continued)

Element	Atomic Number		4d	4f	5s	5p	5d	5f	6s	6p	6d	7s
							Populations of Subshells					
In	49		10		2	1						
Sn	50		10		2	2						
Sb	51		10		2	3						
Te	52		10		2	4						
I	53		10		2	5						
Xe	54		10		2	6						
Cs	55		10		2	6			1			
Ba	56		10		2	6			2			
La	57		10		2	6	1		2			
Ce	58		10	1	2	6	1		2			
Pr	59		10	3	2	6			2			
Nd	60		10	4	2	6			2			
Pm	61		10	5	2	6			2			
Sm	62		10	6	2	6			2			
Eu	63		10	7	2	6			2			
Gd	64		10	7	2	6	1		2			
Tb	65		10	9	2	6			2			
Dy	66		10	10	2	6			2			
Ho	67		10	11	2	6			2			
Er	68		10	12	2	6			2			
Tm	69		10	13	2	6			2			
Yb	70		10	14	2	6			2			
Lu	71		10	14	2	6	1		2			
Hf	72		10	14	2	6	2		2			
Ta	73		10	14	2	6	3		2			
W	74		10	14	2	6	4		2			
Re	75	Krypton core	10	14	2	6	5		2			
Os	76		10	14	2	6	6		2			
Ir	77		10	14	2	6	7		2			
Pt	78		10	14	2	6	9		1			
Au	79		10	14	2	6	10		1			
Hg	80		10	14	2	6	10		2			
Tl	81		10	14	2	6	10		2	1		
Pb	82		10	14	2	6	10		2	2		
Bi	83		10	14	2	6	10		2	3		
Po	84		10	14	2	6	10		2	4		
At	85		10	14	2	6	10		2	5		
Rn	86		10	14	2	6	10		2	6		
Fr	87		10	14	2	6	10		2	6		1
Ra	88		10	14	2	6	10		2	6		2
Ac	89		10	14	2	6	10		2	6	1	2
Th	90		10	14	2	6	10		2	6	2	2
Pa	91		10	14	2	6	10	2	2	6	1	2
U	92		10	14	2	6	10	3	2	6	1	2
Np	93		10	14	2	6	10	4	2	6	1	2
Pu	94		10	14	2	6	10	6	2	6		2
Am	95		10	14	2	6	10	7	2	6		2
Cm	96		10	14	2	6	10	7	2	6	1	2
Bk	97		10	14	2	6	10	9	2	6		2
Cf	98		10	14	2	6	10	10	2	6		2
Es	99		10	14	2	6	10	11	2	6		2
Fm	100		10	14	2	6	10	12	2	6		2
Md	101		10	14	2	6	10	13	2	6		2
No	102		10	14	2	6	10	14	2	6		2
Lr	103		10	14	2	6	10	14	2	6	1	2
Rf	104		10	14	2	6	10	14	2	6	2	2
Db	105		10	14	2	6	10	14	2	6	3	2
Sg	106		10	14	2	6	10	14	2	6	4	2
Bh	107		10	14	2	6	10	14	2	6	5	2
Hs	108		10	14	2	6	10	14	2	6	6	2
Mt	109		10	14	2	6	10	14	2	6	7	2
Ds	110		10	14	2	6	10	14	2	6	9	1
Rg	111		10	14	2	6	10	14	2	6	10	1

Common Units, Equivalences, and Conversion Factors

C-1 Fundamental Units of the SI System

The metric system was implemented by the French National Assembly in 1790 and has been modified many times. The International System of Units, or *le Système International* (SI), represents an extension of the metric system. It was adopted by the eleventh General Conference of Weights and Measures in 1960 and has also been modified since. It is constructed from seven base units, each of which represents a particular physical quantity (Table I).

The first five units listed in Table I are particularly useful in general chemistry. They are defined as follows.

▶ Alternatives for the standard mass have been proposed.

1. The *meter* is defined as the distance light travels in a vacuum in 1/299,792,458 second.

2. The *kilogram* represents the mass of a platinum–iridium block kept at the International Bureau of Weights and Measures at Sèvres, France.

3. The *second* was redefined in 1967 as the duration of 9,192,631,770 periods of a certain line in the microwave spectrum of cesium-133.

4. The *kelvin* is 1/273.16 of the temperature interval between absolute zero and the triple point of water.

5. The *mole* is the amount of substance that contains as many entities as there are atoms in exactly 0.012 kg of carbon-12 (12 g of ^{12}C atoms).

Table I SI Fundamental Units

Physical Quantity	Name of Unit	Symbol
length	meter	m
mass	kilogram	kg
time	second	s
temperature	kelvin	K
amount of substance	mole	mol
electric current	ampere	A
luminous intensity	candela	cd

Prefixes Used with Metric Units and SI Units

Decimal fractions and multiples of metric and SI units are designated by the prefixes listed in Table II. Those most commonly used in general chemistry are underlined.

Table II Traditional Metric and SI Prefixes

Factor	Prefix	Symbol	Factor	Prefix	Symbol
10^{12}	tera	T	10^{-1}	deci	d
10^{9}	giga	G	10^{-2}	centi	c
10^{6}	mega	M	10^{-3}	milli	m
10^{3}	kilo	k	10^{-6}	micro	μ
10^{2}	hecto	h	10^{-9}	nano	n
10^{1}	deka	da	10^{-12}	pico	p
			10^{-15}	femto	f
			10^{-18}	atto	a

C-2 Derived SI Units

In the International System of Units all physical quantities are represented by appropriate combinations of the base units listed in Table I. A list of the derived units frequently used in general chemistry is given in Table III.

Table III Derived SI Units

Physical Quantity	Name of Unit	Symbol	Definition
area	square meter	m^2	
volume	cubic meter	m^3	
density	kilogram per cubic meter	kg/m^3	
force	newton	N	$kg \cdot m/s^2$
pressure	pascal	Pa	N/m^2
energy	joule	J	$kg \cdot m^2/s^2$
electric charge	coulomb	C	$A \cdot s$
electric potential difference	volt	V	$J/(A \cdot s)$

Common Units of Mass and Weight

1 pound = 453.59 grams
1 pound = 453.59 grams = 0.45359 kilogram
1 kilogram = 1000 grams = 2.205 pounds
1 gram = 10 decigrams = 100 centigrams = 1000 milligrams
1 gram = 6.022×10^{23} atomic mass units
1 atomic mass unit = 1.6605×10^{-24} gram
1 short ton = 2000 pounds = 907.2 kilograms
1 long ton = 2240 pounds
1 metric tonne = 1000 kilograms = 2205 pounds

Common Units of Length

1 inch = 2.54 centimeters (exactly)
1 mile = 5280 feet = 1.609 kilometers
1 yard = 36 inches = 0.9144 meter
1 meter = 100 centimeters = 39.37 inches = 3.281 feet = 1.094 yards
1 kilometer = 1000 meters = 1094 yards = 0.6215 mile
1 Ångstrom = 1.0×10^{-8} centimeter = 0.10 nanometer = 1.0×10^{-10} meter = 3.937×10^{-9} inch

Common Units of Volume

1 quart = 0.9463 liter 1 liter = 1.056 quarts
1 liter = 1 cubic decimeter = 1000 cubic centimeters = 0.001 cubic meter
1 milliliter = 1 cubic centimeter = 0.001 liter = 1.056×10^{-3} quart
1 cubic foot = 28.316 liters = 29.902 quarts = 7.475 gallons

Common Units of Force* and Pressure

1 atmosphere = 760 millimeters of mercury = 1.01325×10^5 pascals = 1.01325 bar = 14.70 pounds per square inch
1 bar = 10^5 pascals = 0.98692 atm
1 torr = 1 millimeter of mercury
1 pascal = 1 kg/m · s^2 = 1 N/m^2

*Force: 1 newton (N) = 1 kg · m/s^2, i.e., the force that, when applied for 1 second, gives a 1-kilogram mass a velocity of 1 meter per second.

Common Units of Energy

1 joule = 1×10^7 ergs
1 thermochemical calorie* = 4.184 joules = 4.184×10^7 ergs = 4.129×10^{-2} liter-atmospheres = 2.612×10^{19} electron volts
1 erg = 1×10^{-7} joule = 2.3901×10^{-8} calorie
1 electron volt = 1.6022×10^{-19} joule = 1.6022×10^{-12} erg = 96.487 kJ/mol[†]
1 liter-atmosphere = 24.217 calories = 101.325 joules = 1.01325×10^9 ergs
1 British thermal unit = 1055.06 joules = 1.05506×10^{10} ergs = 252.2 calories

*The amount of heat required to raise the temperature of one gram of water from 14.5°C to 15.5°C.

[†]Note that the other units are per particle and must be multiplied by 6.022×10^{23} to be strictly comparable.

Physical Constants

Quantity	Symbol	Traditional Units	SI Units
Acceleration of gravity	g	980.665 cm/s	9.80665 m/s
Atomic mass unit ($\frac{1}{12}$ the mass of ^{12}C atom)	amu or u	1.660539×10^{-24} g	1.660539×10^{-27} kg
Avogadro's number	N	$6.02214129 \times 10^{23}$ particles/mol	$6.02214129 \times 10^{23}$ particles/mol
Bohr radius	a_0	0.52918 Å 5.2918×10^{-9} cm	5.2918×10^{-11} m
Boltzmann constant	k	1.3807×10^{-16} erg/K	1.3807×10^{-23} J/K
Charge-to-mass ratio of electron	e/m	1.75882×10^{8} coulomb/g	1.75882×10^{11} C/kg
Electronic charge	e	$1.60217656 \times 10^{-19}$ coulomb 4.8033×10^{-10} esu	$1.60217648 \times 10^{-19}$ C
Electron rest mass	m_e	9.1094×10^{-28} g 0.00054858 amu	9.1094×10^{-31} kg
Faraday constant	F	96,485 coulombs/eq 23.06 kcal/volt · eq	96,485 C/mol e^- 96,485 J/V · mol e^-
Gas constant	R	$0.08206 \dfrac{L \cdot atm}{mol \cdot K}$ $1.987 \dfrac{cal}{mol \cdot K}$	$8.3145 \dfrac{kPa \cdot dm^3}{mol \cdot K}$ 8.3145 J/mol · K
Molar volume (STP)	V_m	22.414 L/mol	22.414×10^{-3} m^3/mol 22.414 dm^3/mol
Neutron rest mass	m_n	1.67493×10^{-24} g 1.008665 amu	1.67493×10^{-27} kg
Planck constant	h	$6.62606957 \times 10^{-27}$ erg · s	$6.62606896 \times 10^{-34}$ J · s
Proton rest mass	m_p	1.6726×10^{-24} g 1.007277 amu	1.6726×10^{-27} kg
Rydberg constant	R_∞	3.2898×10^{15} cycles/s 2.17987×10^{-11} erg	1.09737×10^{7} m^{-1} 2.17987×10^{-18} J
Speed of light (in a vacuum)	c	$2.99792458 \times 10^{10}$ cm/s (186,281 miles/second)	2.99792458×10^{8} m/s

$\pi = 3.1416$ $2.303\,R = 4.576$ cal/mol · K = 19.15 J/mol · K

$e = 2.71828$ $2.303\,RT$ (at 25°C) = 1364 cal/mol = 5709 J/mol

$\ln X = 2.303 \log X$

Some Physical Constants for a Few Common Substances

Specific Heats and Heat Capacities for Some Common Substances

Substance	Specific Heat (J/g · °C)	Molar Heat Capacity (J/mol · °C)
Al(s)	0.900	24.3
Ca(s)	0.653	26.2
Cu(s)	0.385	24.5
Fe(s)	0.444	24.8
Hg(ℓ)	0.138	27.7
H_2O(s), ice	2.09	37.7
H_2O(ℓ), water	4.18	75.3
H_2O(g), steam	2.03	36.4
C_6H_6(ℓ), benzene	1.74	136
C_6H_6(g), benzene	1.04	81.6
C_2H_5OH(ℓ), ethanol	2.46	113
C_2H_5OH(g), ethanol	0.954	420
$(C_2H_5)_2O$(ℓ), diethyl ether	3.74	172
$(C_2H_5)_2O$(g), diethyl ether	2.35	108

Heats of Transformation and Transformation Temperatures of Several Substances

Substance	mp (°C)	Heat of Fusion (J/g)	ΔH_{fus} (kJ/mol)	bp (°C)	Heat of Vaporization (J/g)	ΔH_{vap} (kJ/mol)
Al	658	395	10.6	2467	10520	284
Ca	851	233	9.33	1487	4030	162
Cu	1083	205	13.0	2595	4790	305
H_2O	0.0	334	6.02	100	2260	40.7
Fe	1530	267	14.9	2735	6340	354
Hg	−39	11	23.3	357	292	58.6
CH_4	−182	58.6	0.92	−164	—	—
C_2H_5OH	−117	109	5.02	78.3	855	39.3
C_6H_6	5.48	127	9.92	80.1	395	30.8
$(C_2H_5)_2O$	−116	97.9	7.66	35	351	26.0

Vapor Pressure of Water at Various Temperatures

Temperature (°C)	Vapor Pressure (torr)	Temperature (°C)	Vapor Pressure (torr)	Temperature (°C)	Vapor Pressure (torr)	Temperature (°C)	Vapor Pressure (torr)
−10	2.1	21	18.7	51	97.2	81	369.7
−9	2.3	22	19.8	52	102.1	82	384.9
−8	2.5	23	21.1	53	107.2	83	400.6
−7	2.7	24	22.4	54	112.5	84	416.8
−6	2.9	25	23.8	55	118.0	85	433.6
−5	3.2	26	25.2	56	123.8	86	450.9
−4	3.4	27	26.7	57	129.8	87	468.7
−3	3.7	28	28.3	58	136.1	88	487.1
−2	4.0	29	30.0	59	142.6	89	506.1
−1	4.3	30	31.8	60	149.4	90	525.8
0	4.6	31	33.7	61	156.4	91	546.1
1	4.9	32	35.7	62	163.8	92	567.0
2	5.3	33	37.7	63	171.4	93	588.6
3	5.7	34	39.9	64	179.3	94	610.9
4	6.1	35	42.2	65	187.5	95	633.9
5	6.5	36	44.6	66	196.1	96	657.6
6	7.0	37	47.1	67	205.0	97	682.1
7	7.5	38	49.7	68	214.2	98	707.3
8	8.0	39	52.4	69	223.7	99	733.2
9	8.6	40	55.3	70	233.7	100	760.0
10	9.2	41	58.3	71	243.9	101	787.6
11	9.8	42	61.5	72	254.6	102	815.9
12	10.5	43	64.8	73	265.7	103	845.1
13	11.2	44	68.3	74	277.2	104	875.1
14	12.0	45	71.9	75	289.1	105	906.1
15	12.8	46	75.7	76	301.4	106	937.9
16	13.6	47	79.6	77	314.1	107	970.6
17	14.5	48	83.7	78	327.3	108	1004.4
18	15.5	49	88.0	79	341.0	109	1038.9
19	16.5	50	92.5	80	355.1	110	1074.6
20	17.5						

Ionization Constants for Weak Acids at 25°C

Acid	Formula and Ionization Equation		K_a	pK_a
Acetic	CH_3COOH	$\rightleftharpoons H^+ + CH_3COO^-$	1.8×10^{-5}	4.74
Arsenic	H_3AsO_4	$\rightleftharpoons H^+ + H_2AsO_4^-$	$2.5 \times 10^{-4} = K_{a1}$	3.60
	$H_2AsO_4^-$	$\rightleftharpoons H^+ + HAsO_4^{2-}$	$5.6 \times 10^{-8} = K_{a2}$	7.25
	$HAsO_4^{2-}$	$\rightleftharpoons H^+ + AsO_4^{3-}$	$3.0 \times 10^{-13} = K_{a3}$	12.52
Arsenous	H_3AsO_3	$\rightleftharpoons H^+ + H_2AsO_3^-$	$6.0 \times 10^{-10} = K_{a1}$	9.22
	$H_2AsO_3^-$	$\rightleftharpoons H^+ + HAsO_3^{2-}$	$3.0 \times 10^{-14} = K_{a2}$	13.52
Benzoic	C_6H_5COOH	$\rightleftharpoons H^+ + C_6H_5COO^-$	6.3×10^{-5}	4.20
Boric*	$B(OH)_3$	$\rightleftharpoons H^+ + BO(OH)_2^-$	$7.3 \times 10^{-10} = K_{a1}$	9.14
	$BO(OH)_2^-$	$\rightleftharpoons H^+ + BO_2(OH)^{2-}$	$1.8 \times 10^{-13} = K_{a2}$	12.74
	$BO_2(OH)^{2-}$	$\rightleftharpoons H^+ + BO_3^{3-}$	$1.6 \times 10^{-14} = K_{a3}$	13.80
Carbonic	H_2CO_3	$\rightleftharpoons H^+ + HCO_3^-$	$4.2 \times 10^{-7} = K_{a1}$	6.38
	HCO_3^-	$\rightleftharpoons H^+ + CO_3^{2-}$	$4.8 \times 10^{-11} = K_{a2}$	10.32
Citric	$C_3H_5O(COOH)_3$	$\rightleftharpoons H^+ + C_4H_5O_3(COOH)_2^-$	$7.4 \times 10^{-3} = K_{a1}$	2.13
	$C_4H_5O_3(COOH)_2^-$	$\rightleftharpoons H^+ + C_5H_5O_5COOH^{2-}$	$1.7 \times 10^{-5} = K_{a2}$	4.77
	$C_5H_5O_5COOH^{2-}$	$\rightleftharpoons H^+ + C_6H_5O_7^{3-}$	$7.4 \times 10^{-7} = K_{a3}$	6.13
Cyanic	$HOCN$	$\rightleftharpoons H^+ + OCN^-$	3.5×10^{-4}	3.46
Formic	$HCOOH$	$\rightleftharpoons H^+ + HCOO^-$	1.8×10^{-4}	3.74
Hydrazoic	HN_3	$\rightleftharpoons H^+ + N_3^-$	1.9×10^{-5}	4.72
Hydrocyanic	HCN	$\rightleftharpoons H^+ + CN^-$	4.0×10^{-10}	9.40
Hydrofluoric	HF	$\rightleftharpoons H^+ + F^-$	7.2×10^{-4}	3.14
Hydrogen peroxide	H_2O_2	$\rightleftharpoons H^+ + HO_2^-$	2.4×10^{-12}	11.62
Hydrosulfuric	H_2S	$\rightleftharpoons H^+ + HS^2$	$1.0 \times 10^{-7} = K_{a1}$	7.00
	HS^-	$\rightleftharpoons H^+ + S^{2-}$	$1.0 \times 10^{-19} = K_{a2}$	19.00
Hypobromous	$HOBr$	$\rightleftharpoons H^+ + OBr^-$	2.5×10^{-9}	8.60

Acid	Formula and Ionization Equation		K_a	pK_a
Hypochlorous	$HOCl$	$\rightleftharpoons H^+ + OCl^-$	3.5×10^{-8}	7.46
Hypoiodous	HOI	$\rightleftharpoons H^+ + OI^-$	2.3×10^{-11}	10.64
Nitrous	HNO_2	$\rightleftharpoons H^+ + NO_2^-$	4.5×10^{-4}	3.35
Oxalic	$(COOH)_2$	$\rightleftharpoons H^+ + COOCOOH^-$	$5.9 \times 10^{-2} = K_{a1}$	1.23
	$COOCOOH^-$	$\rightleftharpoons H^+ + (COO)_2^{2-}$	$6.4 \times 10^{-5} = K_{a2}$	4.19
Phenol	HC_6H_5O	$\rightleftharpoons H^+ + C_6H_5O^-$	1.3×10^{-10}	9.89
Phosphoric	H_3PO_4	$\rightleftharpoons H^+ + H_2PO_4^-$	$7.5 \times 10^{-3} = K_{a1}$	2.12
	$H_2PO_4^-$	$\rightleftharpoons H^+ + HPO_4^{2-}$	$6.2 \times 10^{-8} = K_{a2}$	7.21
	HPO_4^{2-}	$\rightleftharpoons H^+ + PO_4^{3-}$	$3.6 \times 10^{-13} = K_{a3}$	12.44
Phosphorous	H_3PO_3	$\rightleftharpoons H^+ + H_2PO_3^-$	$1.6 \times 10^{-2} = K_{a1}$	1.80
	$H_2PO_3^-$	$\rightleftharpoons H^+ + HPO_3^{2-}$	$7.0 \times 10^{-7} = K_{a2}$	6.15
Selenic	H_2SeO_4	$\rightleftharpoons H^+ + HSeO_4^-$	Very large $= K_{a1}$	
	$HSeO_4^-$	$\rightleftharpoons H^+ + SeO_4^{2-}$	$1.2 \times 10^{-2} = K_{a2}$	1.92
Selenous	H_2SeO_3	$\rightleftharpoons H^+ + HSeO_3^-$	$2.7 \times 10^{-3} = K_{a1}$	2.57
	$HSeO_3^-$	$\rightleftharpoons H^+ + SeO_3^{2-}$	$2.5 \times 10^{-7} = K_{a2}$	6.60
Sulfuric	H_2SO_4	$\rightleftharpoons H^+ + HSO_4^-$	Very large $= K_{a1}$	
	HSO_4^-	$\rightleftharpoons H^+ + SO_4^{2-}$	$1.2 \times 10^{-2} = K_{a2}$	1.92
Sulfurous	H_2SO_3	$\rightleftharpoons H^+ + HSO_3^-$	$1.2 \times 10^{-2} = K_{a1}$	1.92
	HSO_3^-	$\rightleftharpoons H^+ + SO_3^{2-}$	$6.2 \times 10^{-8} = K_{a2}$	7.21
Tellurous	H_2TeO_3	$\rightleftharpoons H^+ + HTeO_3^-$	$2 \times 10^{-3} = K_{a1}$	2.70
	$HTeO_3^-$	$\rightleftharpoons H^+ + TeO_3^{2-}$	$1 \times 10^{-8} = K_{a2}$	8.00

*Boric acid acts as a Lewis acid in aqueous solution.

Base	Formula and Ionization Equation			K_b	pK_b
Ammonia	NH_3	$+ H_2O \rightleftharpoons NH_4^+$	$+ OH^-$	1.8×10^{-5}	7.74
Aniline	$C_6H_5NH_2$	$+ H_2O \rightleftharpoons C_6H_5NH_3^+$	$+ OH^-$	4.2×10^{-10}	9.38
Dimethylamine	$(CH_3)_2NH$	$+ H_2O \rightleftharpoons (CH_3)_2NH_2^+$	$+ OH^-$	7.4×10^{-4}	3.13
Ethylenediamine	$(CH_2)_2(NH_2)_2$	$+ H_2O \rightleftharpoons (CH_2)_2(NH_2)_2H^+$	$+ OH^-$	$8.5 \times 10^{-5} = K_{b1}$	4.07
	$(CH_2)_2(NH_2)_2H^+$	$+ H_2O \rightleftharpoons (CH_2)_2(NH_2)_2H_2^{2+}$	$+ OH^-$	$2.7 \times 10^{-8} = K_{b2}$	7.57
Hydrazine	N_2H_4	$+ H_2O \rightleftharpoons N_2H_5^+$	$+ OH^-$	$8.5 \times 10^{-7} = K_{b1}$	6.07
	$N_2H_5^+$	$+ H_2O \rightleftharpoons N_2H_6^{2+}$	$+ OH^-$	$8.9 \times 10^{-16} = K_{b2}$	15.05
Hydroxylamine	NH_2OH	$+ H_2O \rightleftharpoons NH_3OH^+$	$+ OH^-$	6.6×10^{-9}	8.18
Methylamine	CH_3NH_2	$+ H_2O \rightleftharpoons CH_3NH_3^+$	$+ OH^-$	5.0×10^{-4}	3.30
Pyridine	C_5H_5N	$+ H_2O \rightleftharpoons C_5H_5NH^+$	$+ OH^-$	1.5×10^{-9}	8.82
Trimethylamine	$(CH_3)_3N$	$+ H_2O \rightleftharpoons (CH_3)_3NH^+$	$+ OH^-$	7.4×10^{-5}	4.13

Solubility Product Constants for Some Inorganic Compounds at 25°C

Substance	K_{sp}	Substance	K_{sp}
Aluminum compounds		**Chromium compounds**	
$AlAsO_4$	1.6×10^{-16}	$CrAsO_4$	7.8×10^{-21}
$Al(OH)_3$	1.9×10^{-33}	$Cr(OH)_3$	6.7×10^{-31}
$AlPO_4$	1.3×10^{-20}	$CrPO_4$	2.4×10^{-23}
Antimony compounds		**Cobalt compounds**	
Sb_2S_3	1.6×10^{-93}	$Co_3(AsO_4)_2$	7.6×10^{-29}
Barium compounds		$CoCO_3$	8.0×10^{-13}
$Ba_3(AsO_4)_2$	1.1×10^{-13}	$Co(OH)_2$	2.5×10^{-16}
$BaCO_3$	8.1×10^{-9}	$CoS (\alpha)$	5.9×10^{-21}
$BaC_2O_4 \cdot 2H_2O*$	1.1×10^{-7}	$CoS (\beta)$	8.7×10^{-23}
$BaCrO_4$	2.0×10^{-10}	$Co(OH)_3$	4.0×10^{-45}
BaF_2	1.7×10^{-6}	Co_2S_3	2.6×10^{-124}
$Ba(OH)_2 \cdot 8H_2O*$	5.0×10^{-3}	**Copper compounds**	
$Ba_3(PO_4)_2$	1.3×10^{-29}	$CuBr$	5.3×10^{-9}
$BaSeO_4$	2.8×10^{-11}	$CuCl$	1.9×10^{-7}
$BaSO_3$	8.0×10^{-7}	$CuCN$	3.2×10^{-20}
$BaSO_4$	1.1×10^{-10}	$Cu_2O (Cu^+ + OH^-)^\dagger$	1.0×10^{-14}
Bismuth compounds		CuI	5.1×10^{-12}
$BiOCl$	7.0×10^{-9}	Cu_2S	1.6×10^{-48}
$BiO(OH)$	1.0×10^{-12}	$CuSCN$	1.6×10^{-11}
$Bi(OH)_3$	3.2×10^{-40}	$Cu_3(AsO_4)_2$	7.6×10^{-36}
BiI_3	8.1×10^{-19}	$CuCO_3$	2.5×10^{-10}
$BiPO_4$	1.3×10^{-23}	$Cu_2[Fe(CN)_6]$	1.3×10^{-16}
Bi_2S_3	1.6×10^{-72}	$Cu(OH)_2$	1.6×10^{-19}
Cadmium compounds		CuS	8.7×10^{-36}
$Cd_3(AsO_4)_2$	2.2×10^{-32}	**Gold compounds**	
$CdCO_3$	2.5×10^{-14}	$AuBr$	5.0×10^{-17}
$Cd(CN)_2$	1.0×10^{-8}	$AuCl$	2.0×10^{-13}
$Cd_2[Fe(CN)_6]$	3.2×10^{-17}	AuI	1.6×10^{-23}
$Cd(OH)_2$	1.2×10^{-14}	$AuBr_3$	4.0×10^{-36}
CdS	3.6×10^{-29}	$AuCl_3$	3.2×10^{-25}
Calcium compounds		$Au(OH)_3$	1.0×10^{-53}
$Ca_3(AsO_4)_2$	6.8×10^{-19}	AuI_3	1.0×10^{-46}
$CaCO_3$	4.8×10^{-9}	**Iron compounds**	
$CaCrO_4$	7.1×10^{-4}	$FeCO_3$	3.5×10^{-11}
$CaC_2O_4 \cdot H_2O*$	2.3×10^{-9}	$Fe(OH)_2$	7.9×10^{-15}
CaF_2	3.9×10^{-11}	FeS	4.9×10^{-18}
$Ca(OH)_2$	7.9×10^{-6}	$Fe_4[Fe(CN)_6]_3$	3.0×10^{-41}
$CaHPO_4$	2.7×10^{-7}	$Fe(OH)_3$	6.3×10^{-38}
$Ca(H_2PO_4)_2$	1.0×10^{-3}	Fe_2S_3	1.4×10^{-88}
$Ca_3(PO_4)_2$	1.0×10^{-25}	**Lead compounds**	
$CaSO_3 \cdot 2H_2O*$	1.3×10^{-8}	$Pb_3(AsO_4)_2$	4.1×10^{-36}
$CaSO_4 \cdot 2H_2O*$	2.4×10^{-5}	$PbBr_2$	6.3×10^{-6}

Substance	K_{sp}	Substance	K_{sp}
Lead compounds (cont.)		*Nickel compounds (cont.)*	
$PbCO_3$	1.5×10^{-13}	$NiS\ (\alpha)$	3.0×10^{-21}
$PbCl_2$	1.7×10^{-5}	$NiS\ (\beta)$	1.0×10^{-26}
$PbCrO_4$	1.8×10^{-14}	$NiS\ (\gamma)$	2.0×10^{-28}
PbF_2	3.7×10^{-8}	*Silver compounds*	
$Pb(OH)_2$	2.8×10^{-16}	Ag_3AsO_4	1.1×10^{-20}
PbI_2	8.7×10^{-9}	$AgBr$	3.3×10^{-13}
$Pb_3(PO_4)_2$	3.0×10^{-44}	Ag_2CO_3	8.1×10^{-12}
$PbSeO_4$	1.5×10^{-7}	$AgCl$	1.8×10^{-10}
$PbSO_4$	1.8×10^{-8}	Ag_2CrO_4	9.0×10^{-12}
PbS	8.4×10^{-28}	$AgCN$	1.2×10^{-16}
Magnesium compounds		$Ag_4[Fe(CN)_6]$	1.6×10^{-41}
$Mg_3(AsO_4)_2$	2.1×10^{-20}	$Ag_2O\ (Ag^+ + OH^-)^\dagger$	2.0×10^{-8}
$MgCO_3 \cdot 3H_2O^*$	4.0×10^{-5}	AgI	1.5×10^{-16}
MgC_2O_4	8.6×10^{-5}	Ag_3PO_4	1.3×10^{-20}
MgF_2	6.4×10^{-9}	Ag_2SO_3	1.5×10^{-14}
$Mg(OH)_2$	1.5×10^{-11}	Ag_2SO_4	1.7×10^{-5}
$MgNH_4PO_4$	2.5×10^{-12}	Ag_2S	1.0×10^{-49}
Manganese compounds		$AgSCN$	1.0×10^{-12}
$Mn_3(AsO_4)_2$	1.9×10^{-11}	*Strontium compounds*	
$MnCO_3$	1.8×10^{-11}	$Sr_3(AsO_4)_2$	1.3×10^{-18}
$Mn(OH)_2$	4.6×10^{-14}	$SrCO_3$	9.4×10^{-10}
MnS	5.1×10^{-15}	$SrC_2O_4 \cdot 2H_2O^*$	5.6×10^{-8}
$Mn(OH)_3$	$\approx 1.0 \times 10^{-36}$	$SrCrO_4$	3.6×10^{-5}
Mercury compounds		$Sr(OH)_2 \cdot 8H_2O^*$	3.2×10^{-4}
Hg_2Br_2	1.3×10^{-22}	$Sr_3(PO_4)_2$	1.0×10^{-31}
Hg_2CO_3	8.9×10^{-17}	$SrSO_3$	4.0×10^{-8}
Hg_2Cl_2	1.1×10^{-18}	$SrSO_4$	2.8×10^{-7}
Hg_2CrO_4	5.0×10^{-9}	*Tin compounds*	
Hg_2I_2	4.5×10^{-29}	$Sn(OH)_2$	2.0×10^{-26}
$Hg_2O \cdot H_2O^*$		SnI_2	1.0×10^{-4}
$(Hg_2^{2+} + 2OH^-)^\dagger$	1.6×10^{-23}	SnS	1.0×10^{-28}
Hg_2SO_4	6.8×10^{-7}	$Sn(OH)_4$	1.0×10^{-57}
Hg_2S	5.8×10^{-44}	SnS_2	1.0×10^{-70}
$Hg(CN)_2$	3.0×10^{-23}	*Zinc compounds*	
$Hg(OH)_2$	2.5×10^{-26}	$Zn_3(AsO_4)_2$	1.1×10^{-27}
HgI_2	4.0×10^{-29}	$ZnCO_3$	1.5×10^{-11}
HgS	3.0×10^{-53}	$Zn(CN)_2$	8.0×10^{-12}
Nickel compounds		$Zn_2[Fe(CN)_6]$	4.1×10^{-16}
$Ni_3(AsO_4)_2$	1.9×10^{-26}	$Zn(OH)_2$	4.5×10^{-17}
$NiCO_3$	6.6×10^{-9}	$Zn_3(PO_4)_2$	9.1×10^{-33}
$Ni(CN)_2$	3.0×10^{-23}	ZnS	1.1×10^{-21}
$Ni(OH)_2$	2.8×10^{-16}		

*[H₂O] does not appear in equilibrium constants for equilibria in aqueous solution in general, so it does *not* appear in the K_{sp} expressions for hydrated solids.

†Very small amounts of oxides dissolve in water to give the ions indicated in parentheses. These solid hydroxides are unstable and decompose to oxides as rapidly as they are formed.

Dissociation Constants for Some Complex Ions

Dissociation Equilibrium			K_d
$[AgBr_2]^-$	$\rightleftharpoons$	$Ag^+ + 2Br^-$	7.8×10^{-8}
$[AgCl_2]^-$	$\rightleftharpoons$	$Ag^+ + 2Cl^-$	4.0×10^{-6}
$[Ag(CN)_2]^-$	$\rightleftharpoons$	$Ag^+ + 2CN^-$	1.8×10^{-19}
$[Ag(S_2O_3)_2]^{3-}$	$\rightleftharpoons$	$Ag^+ + 2S_2O_3^{2-}$	5.0×10^{-14}
$[Ag(NH_3)_2]^+$	$\rightleftharpoons$	$Ag^+ + 2NH_3$	6.3×10^{-8}
$[Ag(en)]^+$	$\rightleftharpoons$	$Ag^+ + en^*$	1.0×10^{-5}
$[AlF_6]^{3-}$	$\rightleftharpoons$	$Al^{3+} + 6F^-$	2.0×10^{-24}
$[Al(OH)_4]^-$	$\rightleftharpoons$	$Al^{3+} + 4OH^-$	1.3×10^{-34}
$[Au(CN)_2]^-$	$\rightleftharpoons$	$Au^+ + 2CN^-$	5.0×10^{-39}
$[Cd(CN)_4]^{2-}$	$\rightleftharpoons$	$Cd^{2+} + 4CN^-$	7.8×10^{-18}
$[CdCl_4]^{2-}$	$\rightleftharpoons$	$Cd^{2+} + 4Cl^-$	1.0×10^{-4}
$[Cd(NH_3)_4]^{2+}$	$\rightleftharpoons$	$Cd^{2+} + 4NH_3$	1.0×10^{-7}
$[Co(NH_3)_6]^{2+}$	$\rightleftharpoons$	$Co^{2+} + 6NH_3$	1.3×10^{-5}
$[Co(NH_3)_6]^{3+}$	$\rightleftharpoons$	$Co^{3+} + 6NH_3$	2.2×10^{-34}
$[Co(en)_3]^{2+}$	$\rightleftharpoons$	$Co^{2+} + 3en^*$	1.5×10^{-14}
$[Co(en)_3]^{3+}$	$\rightleftharpoons$	$Co^{3+} + 3en^*$	2.0×10^{-49}
$[Cu(CN)_2]^-$	$\rightleftharpoons$	$Cu^+ + 2CN^-$	1.0×10^{-16}
$[CuCl_2]^-$	$\rightleftharpoons$	$Cu^+ + 2Cl^-$	1.0×10^{-5}
$[Cu(NH_3)_2]^+$	$\rightleftharpoons$	$Cu^+ + 2NH_3$	1.4×10^{-11}
$[Cu(NH_3)_4]^{2+}$	$\rightleftharpoons$	$Cu^{2+} + 4NH_3$	8.5×10^{-13}
$[Fe(CN)_6]^{4-}$	$\rightleftharpoons$	$Fe^{2+} + 6CN^-$	1.3×10^{-37}
$[Fe(CN)_6]^{3-}$	$\rightleftharpoons$	$Fe^{3+} + 6CN^-$	1.3×10^{-44}
$[HgCl_4]^{2-}$	$\rightleftharpoons$	$Hg^{2+} + 4Cl^-$	8.3×10^{-16}
$[Ni(CN)_4]^{2-}$	$\rightleftharpoons$	$Ni^{2+} + 4CN^-$	1.0×10^{-31}
$[Ni(NH_3)_6]^{2+}$	$\rightleftharpoons$	$Ni^{2+} + 6NH_3$	1.8×10^{-9}
$[Zn(OH)_4]^{2-}$	$\rightleftharpoons$	$Zn^{2+} + 4OH^-$	3.5×10^{-16}
$[Zn(NH_3)_4]^{2+}$	$\rightleftharpoons$	$Zn^{2+} + 4NH_3$	3.4×10^{-10}

*The abbreviation "en" represents ethylenediamine, $H_2NCH_2CH_2NH_2$.

APPENDIX J

Standard Reduction Potentials in Aqueous Solution at 25°C

Acidic Solution	Standard Reduction Potential, E^0 (volts)
$Li^+(aq) + e^- \longrightarrow Li(s)$	-3.045
$K^+(aq) + e^- \longrightarrow K(s)$	-2.925
$Rb^+(aq) + e^- \longrightarrow Rb(s)$	-2.925
$Ba^{2+}(aq) + 2e^- \longrightarrow Ba(s)$	-2.90
$Sr^{2+}(aq) + 2e^- \longrightarrow Sr(s)$	-2.89
$Ca^{2+}(aq) + 2e^- \longrightarrow Ca(s)$	-2.87
$Na^+(aq) + e^- \longrightarrow Na(s)$	-2.714
$Mg^{2+}(aq) + 2e^- \longrightarrow Mg(s)$	-2.37
$H_2(g) + 2e^- \longrightarrow 2H^-(aq)$	-2.25
$Al^{3+}(aq) + 3e^- \longrightarrow Al(s)$	-1.66
$Zr^{4+}(aq) + 4e^- \longrightarrow Zr(s)$	-1.53
$ZnS(s) + 2e^- \longrightarrow Zn(s) + S^{2-}(aq)$	-1.44
$CdS(s) + 2e^- \longrightarrow Cd(s) + S^{2-}(aq)$	-1.21
$V^{2+}(aq) + 2e^- \longrightarrow V(s)$	-1.18
$Mn^{2+}(aq) + 2e^- \longrightarrow Mn(s)$	-1.18
$FeS(s) + 2e^- \longrightarrow Fe(s) + S^{2-}(aq)$	-1.01
$Cr^{2+}(aq) + 2e^- \longrightarrow Cr(s)$	-0.91
$Zn^{2+}(aq) + 2e^- \longrightarrow Zn(s)$	-0.763
$Cr^{3+}(aq) + 3e^- \longrightarrow Cr(s)$	-0.74
$HgS(s) + 2H^+(aq) + 2e^- \longrightarrow Hg(\ell) + H_2S(g)$	-0.72
$Ga^{3+}(aq) + 3e^- \longrightarrow Ga(s)$	-0.53
$2CO_2(g) + 2H^+(aq) + 2e^- \longrightarrow (COOH)_2(aq)$	-0.49
$Fe^{2+}(aq) + 2e^- \longrightarrow Fe(s)$	-0.44
$Cr^{3+}(aq) + e^- \longrightarrow Cr^{2+}(aq)$	-0.41
$Cd^{2+}(aq) + 2e^- \longrightarrow Cd(s)$	-0.403
$Se(s) + 2H^+(aq) + 2e^- \longrightarrow H_2Se(aq)$	-0.40
$PbSO_4(s) + 2e^- \longrightarrow Pb(s) + SO_4^{2-}(aq)$	-0.356
$Tl^+(aq) + e^- \longrightarrow Tl(s)$	-0.34
$Co^{2+}(aq) + 2e^- \longrightarrow Co(s)$	-0.28
$Ni^{2+}(aq) + 2e^- \longrightarrow Ni(s)$	-0.25
$[SnF_6]^{2-}(aq) + 4e^- \longrightarrow Sn(s) + 6F^-(aq)$	-0.25

Acidic Solution	Standard Reduction Potential, E^0 (volts)
$AgI(s) + e^- \longrightarrow Ag(s) + I^-(aq)$	-0.15
$Sn^{2+}(aq) + 2e^- \longrightarrow Sn(s)$	-0.14
$Pb^{2+}(aq) + 2e^- \longrightarrow Pb(s)$	-0.126
$N_2O(g) + 6H^+(aq) + H_2O + 4e^- \longrightarrow 2NH_3OH^+(aq)$	-0.05
$2H^+(aq) + 2e^- \longrightarrow H_2(g)$ (reference electrode)	0.000
$AgBr(s) + e^- \longrightarrow Ag(s) + Br^-(aq)$	0.10
$S(s) + 2H^+(aq) + 2e^- \longrightarrow H_2S(aq)$	0.14
$Sn^{4+}(aq) + 2e^- \longrightarrow Sn^{2+}(aq)$	0.15
$Cu^{2+}(aq) + e^- \longrightarrow Cu^+(aq)$	0.153
$SO_4^{2-}(aq) + 4H^+(aq) + 2e^- \longrightarrow H_2SO_3(aq) + H_2O$	0.17
$SO_4^{2-}(aq) + 4H^+(aq) + 2e^- \longrightarrow SO_2(g) + 2H_2O$	0.20
$AgCl(s) + e^- \longrightarrow Ag(s) + Cl^-(aq)$	0.222
$Hg_2Cl_2(s) + 2e^- \longrightarrow 2Hg(\ell) + 2Cl^-(aq)$	0.27
$Cu^{2+}(aq) + 2e^- \longrightarrow Cu(s)$	0.337
$[RhCl_6]^{3-}(aq) + 3e^- \longrightarrow Rh(s) + 6Cl^-(aq)$	0.44
$Cu^+(aq) + e^- \longrightarrow Cu(s)$	0.521
$TeO_2(s) + 4H^+(aq) + 4e^- \longrightarrow Te(s) + 2H_2O$	0.529
$I_2(s) + 2e^- \longrightarrow 2I^-(aq)$	0.535
$H_3AsO_4(aq) + 2H^+(aq) + 2e^- \longrightarrow H_3AsO_3(aq) + H_2O$	0.58
$[PtCl_6]^{2-}(aq) + 2e^- \longrightarrow [PtCl_4]^{2-}(aq) + 2Cl^-(aq)$	0.68
$O_2(g) + 2H^+(aq) + 2e^- \longrightarrow H_2O_2(aq)$	0.682
$[PtCl_4]^{2-}(aq) + 2e^- \longrightarrow Pt(s) + 4Cl^-(aq)$	0.73
$SbCl_6^-(aq) + 2e^- \longrightarrow SbCl_4^-(aq) + 2Cl^-(aq)$	0.75
$Fe^{3+}(aq) + e^- \longrightarrow Fe^{2+}(aq)$	0.771
$Hg_2^{2+}(aq) + 2e^- \longrightarrow 2Hg(\ell)$	0.789
$Ag^+(aq) + e^- \longrightarrow Ag(s)$	0.7994
$Hg^{2+}(aq) + 2e^- \longrightarrow Hg(\ell)$	0.855
$2Hg^{2+}(aq) + 2e^- \longrightarrow Hg_2^{2+}(aq)$	0.920
$NO_3^-(aq) + 3H^+(aq) + 2e^- \longrightarrow HNO_2(aq) + H_2O$	0.94
$NO_3^-(aq) + 4H^+(aq) + 3e^- \longrightarrow NO(g) + 2H_2O$	0.96
$Pd^{2+}(aq) + 2e^- \longrightarrow Pd(s)$	0.987
$AuCl_4^-(aq) + 3e^- \longrightarrow Au(s) + 4Cl^-(aq)$	1.00
$Br_2(\ell) + 2e^- \longrightarrow 2Br^-(aq)$	1.08
$ClO_4^-(aq) + 2H^+(aq) + 2e^- \longrightarrow ClO_3^-(aq) + H_2O$	1.19
$IO_3^-(aq) + 6H^+(aq) + 5e^- \longrightarrow \frac{1}{2}I_2(aq) + 3H_2O$	1.195
$Pt^{2+}(aq) + 2e^- \longrightarrow Pt(s)$	1.2
$O_2(g) + 4H^+(aq) + 4e^- \longrightarrow 2H_2O$	1.229
$MnO_2(s) + 4H^+(aq) + 2e^- \longrightarrow Mn^{2+}(aq) + 2H_2O$	1.23
$N_2H_5^+(aq) + 3H^+(aq) + 2e^- \longrightarrow 2NH_4^+(aq)$	1.24
$Cr_2O_7^{2-}(aq) + 14H^+(aq) + 6e^- \longrightarrow 2Cr^{3+}(aq) + 7H_2O$	1.33
$Cl_2(g) + 2e^- \longrightarrow 2Cl^-(aq)$	1.360
$BrO_3^-(aq) + 6H^+(aq) + 6e^- \longrightarrow Br^-(aq) + 3H_2O$	1.44
$ClO_3^-(aq) + 6H^+(aq) + 5e^- \longrightarrow \frac{1}{2}Cl_2(g) + 3H_2O$	1.47
$Au^{3+}(aq) + 3e^- \longrightarrow Au(s)$	1.50

Basic Solution	Standard Reduction Potential, E^0 (volts)
$MnO_4^-(aq) + 8H^+(aq) + 5e^- \longrightarrow Mn^{2+}(aq) + 4H_2O$	1.507
$NaBiO_3(s) + 6H^+(aq) + 2e^- \longrightarrow Bi^{3+}(aq) + Na^+(aq) + 3H_2O$	1.6
$Ce^{4+}(aq) + e^- \longrightarrow Ce^{3+}(aq)$	1.61
$2HOCl(aq) + 2H^+(aq) + 2e^- \longrightarrow Cl_2(g) + 2H_2O$	1.63
$Au^+(aq) + e^- \longrightarrow Au(s)$	1.68
$PbO_2(s) + SO_4^{2-}(aq) + 4H^+(aq) + 2e^- \longrightarrow PbSO_4(s) + 2H_2O$	1.685
$NiO_2(s) + 4H^+(aq) + 2e^- \longrightarrow Ni^{2+}(aq) + 2H_2O$	1.7
$H_2O_2(aq) + 2H^+(aq) + 2e^- \longrightarrow 2H_2O$	1.77
$Pb^{4+}(aq) + 2e^- \longrightarrow Pb^{2+}(aq)$	1.8
$Co^{3+}(aq) + e^- \longrightarrow Co^{2+}(aq)$	1.82
$F_2(g) + 2e^- \longrightarrow 2F^-(aq)$	2.87
$SiO_3^{2-}(aq) + 3H_2O + 4e^- \longrightarrow Si(s) + 6OH^-(aq)$	−1.70
$Cr(OH)_3(s) + 3e^- \longrightarrow Cr(s) + 3OH^-(aq)$	−1.30
$[Zn(CN)_4]^{2-}(aq) + 2e^- \longrightarrow Zn(s) + 4CN^-(aq)$	−1.26
$Zn(OH)_2(s) + 2e^- \longrightarrow Zn(s) + 2OH^-(aq)$	−1.245
$[Zn(OH)_4]^{2-}(aq) + 2e^- \longrightarrow Zn(s) + 4OH^-(aq)$	−1.22
$N_2(g) + 4H_2O + 4e^- \longrightarrow N_2H_4(aq) + 4OH^-(aq)$	−1.15
$SO_4^{2-}(aq) + H_2O + 2e^- \longrightarrow SO_3^{2-}(aq) + 2OH^-(aq)$	−0.93
$Fe(OH)_2(s) + 2e^- \longrightarrow Fe(s) + 2OH^-(aq)$	−0.877
$2NO_3^-(aq) + 2H_2O + 2e^- \longrightarrow N_2O_4(g) + 4OH^-(aq)$	−0.85
$2H_2O + 2e^- \longrightarrow H_2(g) + 2OH^-(aq)$	−0.828
$Fe(OH)_3(s) + e^- \longrightarrow Fe(OH)_2(s) + OH^-(aq)$	−0.56
$S(s) + 2e^- \longrightarrow S^{2-}(aq)$	−0.48
$Cu(OH)_2(s) + 2e^- \longrightarrow Cu(s) + 2OH^-(aq)$	−0.36
$CrO_4^{2-}(aq) + 4H_2O + 3e^- \longrightarrow Cr(OH)_3(s) + 5OH^-(aq)$	−0.12
$MnO_2(s) + 2H_2O + 2e^- \longrightarrow Mn(OH)_2(s) + 2OH^-(aq)$	−0.05
$NO_3^-(aq) + H_2O + 2e^- \longrightarrow NO_2^-(aq) + 2OH^-(aq)$	0.01
$O_2(g) + H_2O + 2e^- \longrightarrow OOH^-(aq) + OH^-(aq)$	0.076
$HgO(s) + H_2O + 2e^- \longrightarrow Hg(\ell) + 2OH^-(aq)$	0.0984
$[Co(NH_3)_6]^{3+}(aq) + e^- \longrightarrow [Co(NH_3)_6]^{2+}(aq)$	0.10
$N_2H_4(aq) + 2H_2O + 2e^- \longrightarrow 2NH_3(aq) + 2OH^-(aq)$	0.10
$2NO_2^-(aq) + 3H_2O + 4e^- \longrightarrow N_2O(g) + 6OH^-(aq)$	0.15
$Ag_2O(s) + H_2O + 2e^- \longrightarrow 2Ag(s) + 2OH^-(aq)$	0.34
$ClO_4^-(aq) + H_2O + 2e^- \longrightarrow ClO_3^-(aq) + 2OH^-(aq)$	0.36
$O_2(g) + 2H_2O + 4e^- \longrightarrow 4OH^-(aq)$	0.40
$Ag_2CrO_4(s) + 2e^- \longrightarrow 2Ag(s) + CrO_4^{2-}(aq)$	0.446
$NiO_2(s) + 2H_2O + 2e^- \longrightarrow Ni(OH)_2(s) + 2OH^-(aq)$	0.49
$MnO_4^-(aq) + e^- \longrightarrow MnO_4^{2-}(aq)$	0.564
$MnO_4^-(aq) + 2H_2O + 3e^- \longrightarrow MnO_2(s) + 4OH^-(aq)$	0.588
$ClO_3^-(aq) + 3H_2O + 6e^- \longrightarrow Cl^-(aq) + 6OH^-(aq)$	0.62
$2NH_2OH(aq) + 2e^- \longrightarrow N_2H_4(aq) + 2OH^-(aq)$	0.74
$OOH^-(aq) + H_2O + 2e^- \longrightarrow 3OH^-(aq)$	0.88
$ClO^-(aq) + H_2O + 2e^- \longrightarrow Cl^-(aq) + 2OH^-(aq)$	0.89

Selected Thermodynamic Values at 298.15 K

Species	ΔH_f^0 (kJ/mol)	S^0 (J/mol · K)	ΔG_f^0 (kJ/mol)
Aluminum			
Al(s)	0	28.3	0
AlCl$_3$(s)	−704.2	110.7	−628.9
Al$_2$O$_3$(s)	−1676	50.92	−1582
Barium			
BaCl$_2$(s)	−860.1	126	−810.9
BaSO$_4$(s)	−1465	132	−1353
Beryllium			
Be(s)	0	9.54	0
Be(OH)$_2$(s)	−907.1	—	—
Bromine			
Br(g)	111.8	174.9	82.4
Br$_2$(ℓ)	0	152.23	0
Br$_2$(g)	30.91	245.4	3.14
BrF$_3$(g)	−255.6	292.4	−229.5
HBr(g)	−36.4	198.59	−53.43
Calcium			
Ca(s)	0	41.6	0
Ca(g)	192.6	154.8	158.9
Ca^{2+}(g)	1920	—	—
CaC$_2$(s)	−62.8	70.3	−67.8
CaCO$_3$(s)	−1207	92.9	−1129
CaCl$_2$(s)	−795.0	114	−750.2
CaF$_2$(s)	−1215	68.87	−1162
CaH$_2$(s)	−189	42	−150
CaO(s)	−635.5	40	−604.2
CaS(s)	−482.4	56.5	−477.4
Ca(OH)$_2$(s)	−986.6	76.1	−896.8
Ca(OH)$_2$(aq)	−1002.8	76.15	−867.6
CaSO$_4$(s)	−1433	107	−1320
Carbon			
C(s, graphite)	0	5.740	0
C(s, diamond)	1.897	2.38	2.900
C(g)	716.7	158.0	671.3
CCl$_4$(ℓ)	−135.4	216.4	−65.27
CCl$_4$(g)	−103	309.7	−60.63
CHCl$_3$(ℓ)	−134.5	202	−73.72

Species	ΔH_f^0 (kJ/mol)	S^0 (J/mol · K)	ΔG_f^0 (kJ/mol)
CHCl$_3$(g)	−103.1	295.6	−70.37
CH$_4$(g)	−74.81	186.2	−50.75
C$_2$H$_2$(g)	226.7	200.8	209.2
C$_2$H$_4$(g)	52.26	219.5	68.12
C$_2$H$_6$(g)	−84.86	229.5	−32.9
C$_3$H$_8$(g)	−103.8	269.9	−23.49
C$_6$H$_6$(ℓ)	49.03	172.8	124.5
C$_8$H$_{18}$(ℓ)	−268.8	—	—
C$_2$H$_5$OH(ℓ)	−277.7	161	−174.9
C$_2$H$_5$OH(g)	−235.1	282.6	−168.6
CO(g)	−110.5	197.6	−137.2
CO$_2$(g)	−393.5	213.6	−394.4
CS$_2$(g)	117.4	237.7	67.15
COCl$_2$(g)	−223.0	289.2	−210.5
Cesium			
Cs$^+$(aq)	−248	133	−282.0
CsF(aq)	−568.6	123	−558.5
Chlorine			
Cl(g)	121.7	165.1	105.7
Cl$^-$(g)	−226	—	—
Cl$_2$(g)	0	223.0	0
HCl(g)	−92.31	186.8	−95.30
HCl(aq)	−167.4	55.10	−131.2
Chromium			
Cr(s)	0	23.8	0
(NH$_4$)$_2$Cr$_2$O$_7$(s)	−1807	—	—
Copper			
Cu(s)	0	33.15	0
CuO(s)	−157	42.63	−130
Fluorine			
F$^-$(g)	−322	—	—
F$^-$(aq)	−332.6	—	−278.8
F(g)	78.99	158.6	61.92
F$_2$(g)	0	202.7	0
HF(g)	−271	173.7	−273
HF(aq)	−320.8	—	−296.8

Species	ΔH_f^0 (kJ/mol)	S^0 (J/mol·K)	ΔG_f^0 (kJ/mol)	Species	ΔH_f^0 (kJ/mol)	S^0 (J/mol·K)	ΔG_f^0 (kJ/mol)
Hydrogen				$NH_4Cl(s)$	−314.4	94.6	−201.5
$H(g)$	218.0	114.6	203.3	$NH_4Cl(aq)$	−300.2	—	—
$H_2(g)$	0	130.6	0	$NH_4I(s)$	−201.4	117	−113
$H_2O(\ell)$	−285.8	69.91	−237.2	$NH_4NO_3(s)$	−365.6	151.1	−184.0
$H_2O(g)$	−241.8	188.7	−228.6	$NO(g)$	90.25	210.7	86.57
$H_2O_2(\ell)$	−187.8	109.6	−120.4	$NO_2(g)$	33.2	240.0	51.30
Iodine				$N_2O(g)$	82.05	219.7	104.2
$I(g)$	106.6	180.66	70.16	$N_2O_4(g)$	9.16	304.2	97.82
$I_2(s)$	0	116.1	0	$N_2O_5(g)$	11	356	115
$I_2(g)$	62.44	260.6	19.36	$N_2O_5(s)$	−43.1	178	114
$ICl(g)$	17.78	247.4	−5.52	$NOCl(g)$	52.59	264	66.36
$HI(g)$	26.5	206.5	1.72	$HNO_3(\ell)$	−174.1	155.6	−80.79
Iron				$HNO_3(g)$	−135.1	266.2	−74.77
$Fe(s)$	0	27.3	0	$HNO_3(aq)$	−206.6	146	−110.5
$FeO(s)$	−272	—	—	**Oxygen**			
$Fe_2O_3(s, hematite)$	−824.2	87.40	−742.2	$O(g)$	249.2	161.0	231.8
$Fe_3O_4(s, magnetite)$	−1118	146	−1015	$O_2(g)$	0	205.0	0
$FeS_2(s)$	−177.5	122.2	−166.7	$O_3(g)$	143	238.8	163
$Fe(CO)_5(\ell)$	−774.0	338	−705.4	$OF_2(g)$	23	246.6	41
$Fe(CO)_5(g)$	−733.8	445.2	−697.3	**Phosphorus**			
Lead				$P(g)$	314.6	163.1	278.3
$Pb(s)$	0	64.81	0	$P_4(s, white)$	0	177	0
$PbCl_2(s)$	−359.4	136	−314.1	$P_4(s, red)$	−73.6	91.2	−48.5
$PbO(s, yellow)$	−217.3	68.70	−187.9	$PCl_3(g)$	−306.4	311.7	−286.3
$Pb(OH)_2(s)$	−515.9	88	−420.9	$PCl_5(g)$	−398.9	353	−324.6
$PbS(s)$	−100.4	91.2	−98.7	$PH_3(g)$	5.4	210.1	13
Lithium				$P_4O_{10}(s)$	−2984	228.9	−2698
$Li(s)$	0	28.0	0	$H_3PO_4(s)$	−1281	110.5	−1119
$LiOH(s)$	−487.23	50	−443.9	**Potassium**			
$LiOH(aq)$	−508.4	4	−451.1	$K(s)$	0	63.6	0
Magnesium				$KCl(s)$	−436.5	82.6	−408.8
$Mg(s)$	0	32.5	0	$KClO_3(s)$	−391.2	143.1	−289.9
$MgCl_2(s)$	−641.8	89.5	−592.3	$KI(s)$	−327.9	106.4	−323.0
$MgO(s)$	−601.8	27	−569.6	$KOH(s)$	−424.7	78.91	−378.9
$Mg(OH)_2(s)$	−924.7	63.14	−833.7	$KOH(aq)$	−481.2	92.0	−439.6
$MgS(s)$	−347	—	—	**Rubidium**			
Mercury				$Rb(s)$	0	76.78	0
$Hg(\ell)$	0	76.02	0	$RbOH(aq)$	−481.16	110.75	−441.24
$HgCl_2(s)$	−224	146	−179	**Silicon**			
$HgO(s, red)$	−90.83	70.29	−58.56	$Si(s)$	0	18.8	0
$HgS(s, red)$	−58.2	82.4	−50.6	$SiBr_4(\ell)$	−457.3	277.8	−443.9
Nickel				$SiC(s)$	−65.3	16.6	−62.8
$Ni(s)$	0	30.1	0	$SiCl_4(g)$	−657.0	330.6	−617.0
$Ni(CO)_4(g)$	−602.9	410.4	−587.3	$SiH_4(g)$	34.3	204.5	56.9
$NiO(s)$	−244	38.6	−216	$SiF_4(g)$	−1615	282.4	−1573
Nitrogen				$SiI_4(g)$	−132	—	—
$N_2(g)$	0	191.5	0	$SiO_2(s)$	−910.9	41.84	−856.7
$N(g)$	472.704	153.19	455.579	$H_2SiO_3(s)$	−1189	134	−1092
$NH_3(g)$	−46.11	192.3	−16.5	$Na_2SiO_3(s)$	−1079	—	—
$N_2H_4(\ell)$	50.63	121.2	149.2	$H_2SiF_6(aq)$	−2331	—	—
$(NH_4)_3AsO_4(aq)$	−1268	—	—	**Silver**			
				$Ag(s)$	0	42.55	0

Species	ΔH_f^0 (kJ/mol)	S^0 (J/mol · K)	ΔG_f^0 (kJ/mol)	Species	ΔH_f^0 (kJ/mol)	S^0 (J/mol · K)	ΔG_f^0 (kJ/mol)
Sodium				$H_2SO_4(\ell)$	−814.0	156.9	−690.1
Na(s)	0	51.0	0	$H_2SO_4(aq)$	−907.5	17	−742.0
Na(g)	108.7	153.6	78.11	**Tin**			
$Na^+(g)$	601	—	—	Sn(s, white)	0	51.55	0
NaBr(s)	−359.9	—	—	Sn(s, grey)	−2.09	44.1	0.13
NaCl(s)	−411.0	72.38	−384	$SnCl_2(s)$	−350	—	—
NaCl(aq)	−407.1	115.5	−393.0	$SnCl_4(\ell)$	−511.3	258.6	−440.2
$Na_2CO_3(s)$	−1131	136	−1048	$SnCl_4(g)$	−471.5	366	−432.2
NaOH(s)	−426.7	—	—	$SnO_2(s)$	−580.7	52.3	−519.7
NaOH(aq)	−469.6	49.8	−419.2	**Titanium**			
Sulfur				$TiCl_4(\ell)$	−804.2	252.3	−737.2
S(s, rhombic)	0	31.8	0	$TiCl_4(g)$	−763.2	354.8	−726.8
S(g)	278.8	167.8	238.3	**Tungsten**			
$S_2Cl_2(g)$	−18	331	−31.8	W(s)	0	32.6	0
$SF_6(g)$	−1209	291.7	−1105	$WO_3(s)$	−842.9	75.90	−764.1
$H_2S(g)$	−20.6	205.7	−33.6	**Zinc**			
$SO_2(g)$	−296.8	248.1	−300.2	ZnO(s)	−348.3	43.64	−318.3
$SO_3(g)$	−395.6	256.6	−371.1	ZnS(s)	−205.6	57.7	−201.3
$SOCl_2(\ell)$	−206	—	—				
$SO_2Cl_2(\ell)$	−389	—	—				

Chapter 1

30. **(a)** 423.<u>006</u> mL = 4.23006×10^2 mL (6 sig. fig.)
    (b) 0.001<u>073040</u> g = 1.073040×10^{-3} g (7 sig. fig.)
    (c) 1 <u>081.02</u> pounds = 1.08102×10^3 pounds (6 sig. fig.)

32. **(a)** 50600 **(b)** 0.0004060 **(c)** 0.1610 **(d)** 0.000206 **(e)** 90000. **(f)** 0.0009000

34. 3.0×10^4 cm^3

36. **(a)** 0.4534 km **(b)** 3.63×10^4 m **(c)** 4.87×10^5 g **(d)** 1.32×10^3 mL **(e)** 5.59 L **(f)** 6.251×10^6 cm^3

38. 82.42 cents/L

40. **(a)** 21.2 L **(b)** 2.11 pt **(c)** 0.4252 km/L

42. 57.3%

44. **(a)** 9.0 qt **(b)** 88.5 km/hr **(c)** 73 s

46. 1.65 g/cm^3

48. **(a)** 42.2 cm^3 **(b)** 3.48 cm **(c)** 1.37 in

50. 504 m

52. 3.2×10^2 g

54. **(a)** $-9.4°C$ **(b)** 273.8 K **(c)** 130°F **(d)** 52.3°F

56. **(c)** 285.3°R

58. For Al, 660.4°C and 1221°F; for Ag, 961.9°C and 1763°F

60. 39.8°C, 312.1 K

62. 1440 J

64. **(a)** 9.12×10^5 J **(b)** 11.8°C

66. 0.49 J/g°C

68. **(a)** 62.7 tons of ore **(b)** 69.3 kg of ore

70. 7.16 m

72. 110 mg drug (2 sig. fig.)

74. 500 mL (1 sig. fig.)

84. 4.79×10^7 atoms

Chapter 2

24. 1.070

28. **(a)** 159.808 amu **(b)** 34.014 amu **(c)** 183.18 amu **(d)** 194.189 amu

30. **(a)** 34.08 amu **(b)** 137.3 amu **(c)** 52.46 amu **(d)** 127.91 amu

32. 364.7 g CCl$_4$, 0.3647 kg CCl$_4$

34. 1.82×10^{25} H atoms

36. **(a)** 0.7340 mol NH$_3$

38. **(a)** 4.32×10^{23} molecules CO$_2$ **(b)** 6.79×10^{23} molecules N$_2$ **(c)** 1.53×10^{23} molecules P$_4$ **(d)** 3.07×10^{23} molecules P$_2$

44. 1.59×10^{-16} g CH$_4$

48. 78.25% Ag

50. **(a)** C$_9$H$_9$N **(b)** 131.2 g/mol

52. **(a)** C$_{13}$H$_{24}$N$_4$O$_3$S (FW = 316 g/mol) **(b)** same

54. C$_8$H$_{11}$O$_3$N

56. NaHCO$_3$

58. C$_6$H$_{14}$N$_2$O$_2$

60. C$_2$O$_2$

62. **(a)** 54.82% C, 5.624% H, 7.104% N, 32.45% O **(b)** 80.87% C, 11.70% H, 7.430% O **(c)** 63.15% C, 5.300% H, 31.55% O

64. Cu$_3$(CO$_3$)$_2$(OH)$_2$ is 55.31% Cu, Cu$_2$S is 79.84% Cu, CuFeS$_2$ is 34.63% Cu, CuS is 66.47% Cu, Cu$_2$O is 88.82% Cu, Cu$_2$CO$_3$(OH)$_2$ is 57.49% Cu

66. 0.1088 g C and 0.00647 g H giving 94.36% C and 5.61% H

68. 0.720 g CO$_2$

70. C$_2$H$_6$O

72. **(a)** 3.43 g O **(b)** 6.86 g O

74. **(a)** 9.02 g O **(b)** 13.5 g O

76. 498 g Hg

78. 209 g KMnO$_4$

80. 181 lb Cu$_2$S

82. **(a)** 352 g CuSO$_4$·H$_2$O **(b)** 296 g CuSO$_4$

84. 49.2 g Cr in ore, 75.7 g Cr recovered

86. **(a)** 73.4 lb MgCO$_3$ **(b)** 202 lb impurity **(c)** 21.2 lb Mg

88. **(a)** 63.92% **(b)** 47.6%

90. **(a)** 2.00 mol O$_3$ **(b)** 6.00 mol O **(c)** 96.0 g O$_2$ **(d)** 64.0 g O$_2$

92. C$_{14}$H$_{24}$O

96. **(a)** C$_3$H$_5$O$_2$ **(b)** C$_6$H$_{10}$O$_4$

102. ReO$_2$ (85.3358% Re^{+4}), ReO$_3$ (79.5063% Re^{+6}), Re$_2$O$_3$ (88.5833% Re^{+3}), Re$_2$O$_7$ (76.8804% Re^{+7})

104. CH$_3$CH$_2$OH and CH$_3$OCH$_3$ will produce the most water

106. 261 g NaCl

108. ZnSO$_4$ is 35.95% more economical

110. **(a)** 844 g **(b)** 4.12×10^3 g **(c)** 3.84×10^3 g

112. C$_3$H$_6$O$_2$, C$_3$H$_6$O$_2$

114. 1230 mL ethanol

116. **(a)** 2.16 g/mL **(b)** 4.930 g/mL **(c)** 13.59 g/mL **(d)** 2.165 g/mL

Chapter 3

12. **(b)** 450. molecules H_2 **(c)** 300. molecules NH_3
14. **(b)** 5.2 mol HCl **(c)** 2.6 mol H_2O
16. 882 g $NaHCO_3$ (to 3 sig. fig.)
18. **(a)** 9.6 mol O_2 **(b)** 3.2 mol O_2 **(c)** 3.2 mol O_2
    (d) 3.2 mol O_2 **(e)** 13 mol O_2
20. **(a)** 8.00 mol O_2 **(b)** 6.40 mol NO **(c)** 9.60 mol H_2O
22. 178 g O_2
24. 87.22 g Fe_3O_4
26. **(b)** 55.80 g NaI
28. 79.9 g C_3H_8
30. **(c)** 211.59 g CO_2
32. 326.5 g superphosphate
34. **(a)** S_8 **(b)** 67.4 g S_2Cl_2 **(c)** 35.6 g Cl_2
36. 18.0 g $Ca_3(PO_4)_2$
38. **(a)** $AgNO_3$ **(b)** 14.9 g $BaCl_2$ **(c)** 52.7 g AgCl
40. 107 g PCl_5
42. **(a)** 2.27 g O_2 **(b)** 46.3%
44. 95.3%
46. 74.5%
48. **(a)** 349.7 g Fe **(b)** 47.61%
50. 82.6 g H_2TeO_3
52. 803.9 g $KClO_3$
54. **(b)** 2 mol N atoms **(c)** 106.4 g NH_3
56. 252 kg Zn
58. 149 g $(NH_4)_2SO_4$
60. 631 mL $(NH_4)_2SO_4$ soln
62. 0.866 M Na_3PO_4
64. 5.08×10^3 mL
66. **(a)** 20.0% $CaCl_2$ **(b)** 2.13 M $CaCl_2$
68. 0.00940 M $BaCl_2$ soln
70. 28.7 M HF soln
72. 0.250 L conc. HCl soln
76. 231 mL NaOH soln
78. 0.0408 L KOH soln
80. 8.41 mL HNO_3 soln
82. 0.00453 M $AlCl_3$ soln
84. 3.89% Fe_3O_4 in ore
86. 1.42 g Br_2
92. 3 mol Be, 0.966 g Be
94. 1.0% $SnCl_2$ < 1.0% $AlCl_3$ < 1.0% NaCl in molarity
96. 68.0 mL HNO_3
100. **(a)** 62.7% yield
104. **(a)** CH_3CH_2OH **(b)** 81.6% yield
106. 0.522 M NaCl
108. 623 g H_3PO_4
110. 0.0867 g AgCl
112. for Zn: \$65.4/mol H_2; for Al: \$36.0/mol H_2

Chapter 4

6. The charge on each droplet is a multiple of 1.22×10^{-19} coulombs
10. 2.3×10^{-14}
14. **(a)** mass % for e^- = 0.026265% **(b)** mass % for p = 48.228% **(c)** mass % for n = 51.745%
26. ^{69}Ga: 60.13%; ^{71}Ga: 39.87%

28. 87.61 amu
30. 55.85 amu
32. 69.17% ^{63}Cu
34. O, 15.999 amu; Cl, 35.453 amu
36. 73.3 amu
38. 52.0 amu
54. **(a)** 3.34×10^{14} s^{-1} **(b)** 6.79×10^{14} s^{-1}
    (c) 6.10×10^9 s^{-1} **(d)** 6.59×10^{18} s^{-1}
56. **(a)** 4.47×10^{14} s^{-1} **(b)** 2.96×10^{-19} J/photon **(c)** red
58. 5.85×10^{-19} J/photon, 352 kJ/mol
60. 2.5×10^{13} miles
64. 320 nm (violet/near ultraviolet)
68. 218 kJ/mol
70. 3.20×10^{15} s^{-1}
74. 2.53×10^{18} photons
76. **(a)** 1.59×10^{-14} m **(b)** 3.97×10^{-34} m
78. 1.88×10^3 m/s
122. **(a)** $n=3, \ell=1, m=-1,0,+1$ **(b)** $n=6, \ell=2, m=-2, -1,0,+1,+2$ **(c)** $n=3, \ell=1, m=-1,0,+1$ **(d)** $n=4, \ell=3, m=-3,-2,-1,0,+1,+2,+3$
132. 14.8 miles
136. 6 electrons
144. 3.76×10^{-36} kg
146. 216 kJ/mol
148. 3.35 m
150. **(a)** 8.43×10^{24} electrons **(b)** 1.00×10^{25} electrons

Chapter 5

46. **(a)** oxidation no. of P: in PCl_3, +3; in P_2O_5, +5; in P_4O_{10}, +5; in HPO_3, +5; in H_3PO_3, +3; in $POCl_3$, +5; in $H_4P_2O_7$, +5; in $Mg_3(PO_4)_2$, +5 **(b)** oxidation no. of Br: in Br^-, −1; in BrO^-, +1; in BrO_2^-, +3; in BrO_3^-, +5; in BrO_4^-, +7 **(c)** oxidation no. of Mn: in MnO, +2; in MnO_2, +4; in $Mn(OH)_2$, +2; in K_2MnO_4, +6; in $KMnO_4$, +7; in Mn_2O_7, +7 **(d)** oxidation no. of O: in OF_2, +2; in Na_2O, −2; in Na_2O_2, −1; in KO_2, −1/2
48. **(a)** oxidation no. of N: in N^{3-}, −3; in NO_2^-, +3; in NO_3^-, +5; in N_3^-, −1/3; in NH_4^+, −3 **(b)** oxidation no. of Cl: in Cl_2, 0; in HCl, −1; in HClO, +1; in $HClO_2$, +3; in $KClO_3$, +5; in Cl_2O_7, +7; in $Ca(ClO_4)_2$, +7, in PCl_5, −1
80. 122 pm
90. 1.05×10^{15} s^{-1}
92. 158 kJ

Chapter 6

128. **(a)** 0.294 mol **(b)** 0.353 mol, 0.0554 mol

Chapters 7 and 8

No numerical exercises in these chapters.

Chapter 9

20. **(a)** Ne_2^+, bo = 0.5 **(b)** Ne_2, bo = 0 **(c)** Ne_2^{2+}, bo = 1
22. **(a)** Li_2, bo = 1 **(b)** Li_2^+, bo = 0.5 **(c)** O_2^{2-}, bo = 1
24. **(a)** X_2, bo = 3 **(b)** X_2, bo = 0 **(c)** X_2^-, bo = 2.5
28. **(b)** N_2, bo = 3, N_2^-, bo = 2.5, N_2^+, bo = 2.5
30. NO^+, bo = 3

32. CN, bo = 2.5; CN$^+$, bo = 2.0; CN^{2+}, bo = 1.5; CN$^-$, bo = 3; CN^{2-}, bo = 2.5

46. NO, bo = 2.5; NO$^+$, bo = 3; NO$^-$, bo = 2. Bond lengths are inversely related to bond order.

Chapter 10

No numerical problems in this chapter.

Chapter 11

4. 0.115 M MgSO$_4$

6. 5.292 M H$_2$SO$_4$

8. 1.16 M NaCl

10. 5.49 M KI

12. 0.0375 M BaI$_2$

14. 1.35 M Na$_3$PO$_4$, 0.137 M NaOH

16. 0.857 M CH$_3$COOH

18. **(a)** 0.923 L NaOH soln, 0.222 L H$_3$PO$_4$ soln
  (b) 0.615 L NaOH soln, 0.222 L H$_3$PO$_4$ soln

24. 31.3 mL of CH$_3$COOH soln

26. 0.1969 M HNO$_3$

28. 0.07321 M NaOH

30. 18.0 mL HCl soln

34. 36.0% (COOH)$_2$·2H$_2$O

36. 0.150 g CaCO$_3$

38. 0.0310 M NaOH

40. 0.0539 M H$_3$PO$_4$, 32.5 mL H$_3$PO$_4$

42. 0.13 M H$_3$AsO$_4$, 14 mL H$_3$AsO$_4$

44. 0.233 M HCl

46. 32.7% Mg(OH)$_2$

52. oxidizing agents: **(a)** MnO$_4^-$ **(b)** Cr$_2$O$_7^{2-}$ **(c)** MnO$_4^-$
  (d) Cr$_2$O$_7^{2-}$

62. 3.22 mL KMnO$_4$ soln

64. 4.26 mL KMnO$_4$ soln

66. **(a)** 0.09247 M I$_2$ **(b)** 0.3230 g As$_2$O$_3$

68. 3.5 mL NO$_3^-$ soln

70. 0.123 M KMnO$_4$

72. **(a)** 1.80 × 10^{-3} M MgNH$_4$PO$_4$ **(b)** 0.683 M
  NaCH$_3$COO **(c)** 2.60 × 10^{-4} M CaC$_2$O$_4$
  (d) 0.0416 M (NH$_4$)$_2$SO$_4$

74. 7.60 mmol HCl, 12.5 mL HCl

76. 463 mL HCl soln

78. 17.2 mL H$_2$SO$_4$ soln

80. 30.94 mL NaOH soln

82. **(a)** 10.2 mL HI soln **(b)** 12.1 mL HI soln
  (c) 31.8 mL HI soln

88. 59.36% Fe

90. 69 g AgCl

92. 80. mmol HCl in stomach; 9.28 mmol HCl

Chapter 12

6. **(a)** 14.4 psi **(b)** 74.2 cm Hg **(c)** 29.2 in Hg **(d)** 98.9 kPa
  (e) 0.976 atm **(f)** 33.1 ft H$_2$O

10. 2.20 × 10^3 psi

14. 1.06 atm

16. **(a)** 18.2 atm **(b)** 0.274 L

18. 6.0 × 10^2 balloons

26. 0.81 L

28. **(a)** 1.441 L **(b)** increase by 41 cm

30. −78.5°C, 3.26 L; −195.8°C, 1.30 L; −268.9°C, 0.0713 L

34. 610. K or 337°C

40. 5.23 g/L

42. **(a)** #1 – Kr, #2 – Ne

46. 5.20 atm

48. **(a)** 1.75 × 10^8 L Cl$_2$, 6.18 × 10^6 ft^3 Cl$_2$ **(b)** 39.0 ft

50. 0.88 g He

52. 22.0 L/mol for SF$_6$, 21.7 L/mol for HF

54. 29.6 g/mol, 2% error

56. 30.0 g/mol, C$_2$H$_6$(g)

58. 46.7 amu/molecule

62. P_{total} = 92.8 atm, P_{CHCl_3} = 24.4 atm

64. X_{He} = 0.440, X_{Ar} = 0.299, X_{Xe} = 0.261

66. **(a)** 11.25 atm **(b)** 3.75 atm **(c)** 3.75 atm

68. 285 mL

70. **(a)** He, 4.00 atm; N$_2$, 1.00 atm **(b)** 5.00 atm
  (c) X_{He}, 0.800

72. 62.0 g NaN$_3$

74. 7.15 g SO$_2$

76. 4.45 g KClO$_3$

78. 4.67 L NH$_3$

80. 190. g KNO$_3$

82. 25.1% S by mass

84. **(a)** 2.83 L C$_8$H$_{18}$ **(b)** 44.8 min

90. **(b)** 1.17

98. **(a)** 0.821 atm **(b)** 0.805 atm **(c)** 18.1 atm, 13.6 atm

100. **(a)** 7.34 atm **(b)** 7.14 atm

102. liquid Fe: 8.12 cm^3/mol, solid Fe: 7.11 cm^3/mol

104. 0.13 g H$_2$O

106. 5000 L air (1 sig. fig.)

108. 121 g/mol

112. **(a)** 6130 g H$_2$O **(b)** 6150 mL H$_2$O

114. 4.90 atm, 4.78 atm, 2.4%

116. C$_2$N$_2$ (MW = 52.1 g/mol)

118. 38°F, 22°C, 40K

120. 1.106 g

128. 2.1 × 10^{15} atoms Xe

132. H$_2$ is the limiting reactant

134. 1.3 L O$_2$

136. 206 g MgSiO$_3$

138. **(a)** 2.11 × 10^{-6} M SO$_2$ **(b)** 4.74 × 10^{-5}

Chapter 13

36. bp = ~34°C.

40. **(a)** 43.4 kJ/mol

42. bp = ~ −1°C

44. 2.7 × 10^4 J

48. boiling Br$_2$ (9660 J)

50. 2.48 × 10^5 J

52. 52.6°C

54. 58.7°C

56. **(a)** 6.14 × 10^3 J **(b)** 19.2 g H$_2$O

58. for H$_2$O, 361.8 torr; for D$_2$O, 338.0 torr

60. **(c)** ΔH$_{vap}$ = 3.72 × 10^4 J/mol **(d)** 3.48 × 10^2 K or 75°C

62. 4.34 × 10^4 J or 43.4 kJ

64. 2.93 × 10^{-3} torr

88. **(a)** a/2 **(b)** 6 Cl^- ions **(c)** a($2^{1/2}$)/2 **(d)** 6 Na^+ ions
90. 1.00 g/cm^3
92. 22.4 g/cm^3
94. **(a)** 8 **(b)** tetrahedron with 4 nearest neighbors
    (c) $\sqrt{3}$(a/4) **(d)** 1.545 Å **(e)** 3.515 g/cm^3
96. AW = (1.37 × 10^{-21} g)/(6.64 × 10^{-24} mol) =
    206 g/mol, Pb (207.2 g/mol)
100. 1.542 Å
112. **(a)** true **(b)** false **(c)** false
114. CS$_2$ < acetone < ethanol
130. 63 g/mol, Cu
136. deviation at 0°C = 0.9%, deviation at 100°C = 0.8%

Chapter 14

18. X_{CH_4} (at 25°C) = 2.4 × 10^{-4}; X_{CH_4} (at 50°C) =
    1.7 × 10^{-4}; decreases
26. 0.886 m C$_{10}$H$_{16}$O; $X_{C_{10}H_{16}O}$ = 0.0393; 11.9%
28. 1.7 m C$_6$H$_5$COOH in C$_2$H$_5$OH
30. $X_{C_2H_5OH}$ = 0.322; X_{H_2O} = 0.678
32. 0.7767 M K$_2$SO$_4$, 0.8197 m K$_2$SO$_4$, 12.50% K$_2$SO$_4$,
    X_{H_2O} = 0.9854
34. **(a)** 1.48 m C$_6$H$_{12}$O$_6$
38. **(a)** 14.12 torr **(b)** 16.72 torr **(c)** 19.00 torr
40. $P_{acetone}$ = 172 torr, $P_{chloroform}$ = 148 torr
42. P_{total} = 320. torr, $X_{acetone}$ = 0.538, $X_{chloroform}$ = 0.462
44. **(a)** $P_{chloroform}$ = 65 torr **(b)** $P_{acetone}$ = 215 torr
    (c) P_{total} = 280 torr
46. 101.52°C
48. −5.52°C
50. **(a)** camphor **(b)** water **(c)** camphor **(d)** nitrobenzene
52. −18.6°C
54. 78.54°C
56. 1035°C
58. 170 g/mol
60. C$_2$H$_8$O$_2$ (64.08 g/mol)
62. **(a)** 70.% C$_{10}$H$_8$, 30.% C$_{14}$H$_{10}$ **(b)** 80.4°C
66. **(a)** 3 **(b)** 2 **(c)** 5 **(d)** 2
68. CaCl$_2$ < KClO$_3$ < CH$_3$COOH < CH$_3$OH (based on i)
70. 752 torr
72. 0.100 m Na$_2$SO$_4$ has lower fp
76. 100.247°C
78. 1%
80. i = 1.79, 79%
84. 0.571 atm
86. ΔT_f = 0.100°C, ΔT_b = 0.0276°C
88. 58.0 atm
90. **(a)** −1.02 × 10^{-4} °C **(b)** 1.35 × 10^{-3} atm or 1.02 torr
    (c) 1000% error **(d)** 10% error
98. bp = 100.44°C; π = 20.5 atm
100. **(a)** 60.5 g/mol **(b)** 117 g/mol
104. 37% lactose by mass
108. For water: 215 mL, 215 g, 11.9 mol; for ethanol:
    285 mL, 225 g, 4.88 mol; for glycerol: 630. g, 6.84 mol;
    X_{water} = 0.504, $X_{ethanol}$ = 0.207, $X_{glycerol}$ = 0.290
118. 1.0 m, 80% ionization; 2.0 m, 65% ionization; 4.0 m,
    17% ionization
126. 1.3 atm, 0.055 M

Chapter 15

16. **(a)** 2750 kJ **(b)** 58.1 g O$_2$
18. +98.9 kJ/mol rxn
30. −584 kJ/mol
32. −1015.4 kJ/mol rxn
34. +197.6 kJ/mol rxn
36. −289 kJ/mol rxn
38. **(a)** −124.0 kJ/mol rxn **(b)** −1656 kJ/mol rxn
    (c) +624.6 kJ/mol rxn
40. +46.36 kJ/g C$_3$H$_8$; +44.27 kJ/g C$_8$H$_{18}$
42. +333 kJ heat released
44. sucrose: −5430 kJ/mol, −15.9 kJ/g, −3.79 kcal/g;
    tristearin: −2900 kJ/mol, −3.3 kJ/g, −0.78 kcal/g
48. **(a)** −121 kJ/mol rxn **(b)** −103 kJ/mol rxn
50. −379 kJ/mol rxn
52. −93 kJ/mol HCl; −270 kJ/mol HF
54. 329 kJ/mol
56. 264 kJ/mol
58. 288 kJ/mol
60. 381 J/°C
62. 0.66 J/g·°C
64. **(a)** +2.1 × 10^3 J **(b)** −1.0 × 10^2 kJ/mol rxn
66. −41.9 kJ/g C$_6$H$_6$(l); −3270 kJ/mol C$_6$H$_6$(l)
68. −23.1 kJ; −460. kJ/mol rxn
70. −2.08 × 10^3 J/g C$_{10}$H$_{22}$(l); −297 kJ/mol C$_{10}$H$_{22}$(l)
76. −336 J
78. **(a)** by surroundings **(b)** by system **(c)** by surroundings
80. **(a)** +983 J **(b)** 0 J
86. **(a)** ½ **(b)** ¼ **(c)** 1/1024
88. **(a)** 16 **(b)** 14 of 16 **(c)** 7/8 **(d)** 1/8
104. **(a)** −128.8 J/(mol rxn)·K **(b)** −182 J/(mol rxn)·K
    (c) +148.6 J/(mol rxn)·K
108. −432.8 J/(mol rxn)·K
110. −53.42 kJ/mol rxn
112. **(a)** ΔH^0 = −71.75 kJ/mol rxn, ΔS^0 = −268.0 J/
    (mol rxn)·K, ΔG^0 = +8.15 kJ/mol rxn
    (b) ΔH^0 = +14.7 kJ/mol rxn, ΔS^0 = +31.2 J/
    (mol rxn)·K, ΔG^0 = +5.4 kJ/mol rxn
    (c) ΔH^0 = −367.6 kJ/mol rxn, ΔS^0 = −11.62 J/
    (mol rxn)·K, ΔG^0 = −364.1 kJ/mol rxn
116. **(a)** ΔH^0 = −196.0 kJ/mol rxn, ΔG^0 = −233.6 kJ/
    mol rxn, ΔS^0 = +125.6 J/(mol rxn)·K
120. **(a)** spontaneous at all temperatures **(b)** spontaneous at
    T > 839.3 K **(c)** spontaneous at T > 980.7 K
    (d) spontaneous at T > 3000. K
122. **(a)** 97°C
126. ΔS^0 = −247 J/(mol rxn)·K, ΔH^0 = −88.2 kJ/mol rxn,
    product favored at T < 357 K
128. **(a)** −156 kJ/mol C$_6$H$_{12}$(l) **(b)** −165 kJ/mol C$_6$H$_5$OH(s)
130. q = +10700 J; w = −788 J; ΔE = 9900 J
132. **(a)** 2.88 kJ/°C **(b)** 23.82°C
136. **(a)** sp. ht. = 0.13 J/g°C, tungsten, W (0.135 J/g°C)
    (b) yes, sp. ht = 0.26 J/g°C, molybdenum, Mo
142. 2.4 hr walking
144. for Pb: sp. ht = 0.13 J/g°C; molar heat capacity,
    27 J/mol°C
146. **(a)** 30.0 kJ/g **(b)** 7.17 kcal/g **(c)** 35.9 kcal

Chapter 16

10. O_2: 1.50 M/min, NO: 1.20 M/min, H_2O: 1.80 M/min
14. 1/2
18. Rate = $(2.5 \times 10^{-2}\ M^{-1}\cdot min^{-1})[B][C]$
22. Rate = $(1.2 \times 10^2\ M^{-2}\cdot s^{-1})[ClO_2]^2[OH^-]$
24. Rate = $(2.5 \times 10^{-3}\ M^{-2}\cdot s^{-1})[A]^2[B]$
26. Rate = $(20.\ M^{-4}\cdot s^{-1})[A]^3[B]^2$
28. 0.300 M/s, 1.20 M/s
32. 5.29 s
34. (a) 2.5×10^6 s (b) 41 days (c) 0.724 g Cs (d) 0.67 g
36. (a) 2.4×10^9 s or 76 yrs (b) 0.59 M NO_2, 54 g NO_2 (c) 0.91 M NO reacted, 0.91 M NO produced
38. 1680 s or 28.0 min
40. $k_2/k_1 = 1.6$ for 90°C to 100°C, $k_2/k_1 = 2.2$ for 0°C to 10°C
42. (a) zero order rxn, rate = k = 0.00273 $mM \cdot s^{-1}$, [HI] = [HI]$_o$ - akt = 5.46 mM - (2)(0.00273 $mM \cdot s^{-1}$)t (b) 2.18 mmol/L
44. 8.4 s
46. 462 d
48. (a) $4.52 \times 10^{-29}\ s^{-1}$ (b) $4.04 \times 10^{-10}\ s^{-1}$
54. 340 kJ/mol rxn
56. 84 kJ/mol rxn
58. 103 kJ/mol rxn
60. (a) 270. kJ/mol (b) $7.7 \times 10^{-14}\ s^{-1}$ (c) 730. K
62. 2600 g CO_2/L·min
64. (a) 0.24 s^{-1} (b) 9°C
66. (a) yes (b) no (c) no
68. (a) Rate = $k[A]^2[B]^2$ (b) Rate = $k[A][B][D]$
70. Rate = $k[O_3]^2/[O_2]$
72. (a) N_2Cl (b) yes
74. (b) yes
78. (a) 8.7×10^{-13} mol N_2O_5 (b) 19 s
80. (a) Rate = $k[Hb][CO]$ (b) 0.280 L/μmol·s (c) 0.252 μmol/L·s
94. (1) 21 min, 42 min, 63 min (2) 21 min, 63 min, 150 min (3) same as (2)
96. 64 kJ/mol
100. −200. kJ/mol rxn

Chapter 17

24. $K_c = 1.1 \times 10^{-5}$
26. $K_c = 0.13$
28. $K_c = 0.12$
30. (a) $K_c' = 8.9 \times 10^5$ (b) $K_c'' = 1.3 \times 10^{-12}$ (c) $K_c''' = 1.6 \times 10^{-24}$
32. $K_c = 75$
34. (a) $K_c = 4.49 \times 10^{-2}$ (b) $[SbCl_5] = 3.7 \times 10^{-3}\ M$, $[SbCl_3] = [Cl_2] = 1.30 \times 10^{-2}\ M$
36. $K_c' = 6.502 \times 10^{-4}$
42. (a) false (b) false (c) true (d) false
44. 0.044 M
46. 5.3 M
48. 0.079 M
50. 1 g (1 sig. fig.)
52. [HI] = 0.140 M, [H_2] = [I_2] = 0.127 M
64. (a) $K_c = 16$ (b) 0.35 M

66. (a) $K_c = 0.21$ (b) [A] = 0.12 M, [B] = [C] = 0.15 M (c) [A] = 0.71 M, [B] = [C] = 0.39 M
68. (a) [N_2O_4] = 0.0167 M, [NO_2] = $9.90 \times 10^{-3}\ M$ (b) [N_2O_4] = $1.05 \times 10^{-2}\ M$, [NO_2] = $7.82 \times 10^{-3}\ M$ (c) [N_2O_4] = 0.0360 M, [NO_2] = 0.0145 M
72. $K_p = 1.6 \times 10^{-9}$
74. $P_{N_2O_4}$ = 16 atm, P_{NO_2} = 3.3 atm
76. $K_p = 0.771$
78. $K_c = 7.76$
80. (a) 33.2%
84. (a) $K_p = 1.1 \times 10^5$ (b) $K_p = 2.3 \times 10^2$ (c) $K_p = 1.0 \times 10^5$
86. $K_p = 7.0 \times 10^{24}$
88. (a) −37.9 kJ/mol rxn at 25°C (b) $K_{p\ 1073\ K} = 4.9 \times 10^{-4}$ (c) ΔG^o = +68.0 kJ/mol rxn at 800°C
92. P_{CO} = 0.685 atm, P_{CO_2} = 0.315 atm
96. At 400°C: $K_p = 8.3 \times 10^{-3}$, $K_c = 1.5 \times 10^{-4}$; at 800°C: $K_p = 16$, $K_c = 0.18$
98. $K_p = 0.00432$
112. $P_{H_2O} = 0.39$

Chapter 18

4. (a) 1.76 M NaCl (b) 0.770 M H_2SO_4 (c) 1.34×10^{-3} M C_6H_5OH
6. (a) [H^+] = [Br^-] = 0.45 M (b) [K^+] = [OH^-] = 0.045 M (c) [Ca^{2+}] = 0.0112 M, [Cl^-] = 0.0224 M
8. (a) [K^+] = [OH^-] = 0.0149 M (b) [Ba^{2+}] = 0.00585 M, [OH^-] = 0.0117 M (c) [Ca^{2+}] = 0.0768 M, [NO_3^-] = 0.154 M
14. $2.2 \times 10^{-13}\ M$; $4.76 \times 10^{-13}\ M$; $8.55 \times 10^{-13}\ M$; $1.00 \times 10^{-7}\ M$
16. 55.6 M H_2O; 3.0×10^{-23} H_3O^+ ions
18. (a) 0.00, 14.00, acidic (b) 3.77, 10.23, acidic (c) 7.17, 6.83, basic (d) 10.03, 3.97, basic
20. $3.5 \times 10^{-8}\ M$, $2.9 \times 10^{-7}\ M$ at 25°C, $6.9 \times 10^{-7}\ M$ at 37°C
22. (a) 0.70 (b) 1.30 (c) 2.19 (d) 10.99
24. $3.0 \times 10^{-4}\ M$
26. (a) pH = 12.93 (b) pH = 1.12 (c) pH = 13.18
32. triethylamine: [OH^-] = $2.8 \times 10^{-3}\ M$; trimethylamine: [OH^-] = $1.1 \times 10^{-3}\ M$
34. (a) pH = 6.82 (b) neutral
38. pH = 3.096, $K_a = 8.67 \times 10^{-6}$
40. $K_a = 1.4 \times 10^{-3}$
42. [C_6H_5COOH] = 0.51 M, [H_3O^+] = [$C_6H_5COO^-$] = $5.7 \times 10^{-3}\ M$, [OH^-] = $1.8 \times 10^{-12}\ M$
44. pH = 1.78
46. pH = 11.79
48. 4.9% ionized
50. For weak acid #1: pK_a = 4.14; for weak acid #2: pK_a = 9.38
52. pK_b = 8.82
54. $K_b = 5.0 \times 10^{-4}$
56. (a) [OH^-] = $2.1 \times 10^{-3}\ M$, 0.85% ionized, pH = 11.32 (b) [OH^-] = 0.011 M, 4.4% ionized, pH = 12.04

58.

0.100 M H$_3$AsO$_4$ Solution		0.100 M H$_3$PO$_4$ Solution	
Species	Concentration (m)	Species	Concentration (m)
H$_3$AsO$_4$	0.095	H$_3$PO$_4$	0.076
H$_3$O$^+$	0.0050	H$_3$O$^+$	0.024
H$_2$AsO$_4^-$	0.0050	H$_2$PO$_4^-$	0.024
HAsO$_4^{2-}$	5.6×10^{-8}	HPO$_4^{2-}$	6.2×10^{-8}
OH$^-$	2.0×10^{-12}	OH$^-$	4.2×10^{-13}
AsO$_4^{3-}$	3.4×10^{-18}	PO$_4^{3-}$	9.3×10^{-19}

60. [H$_3$O$^+$] = 0.16 M, [OH$^-$] = 6.2×10^{-14} M, [HSeO$_4^-$] = 0.14 M, [SeO$_4^{2-}$] = 0.01 M

62. pH = 1.52

74. $K = 5.3 \times 10^{-10}$

76. (a) $K_b = 2.2 \times 10^{-11}$ (b) $K_b = 4.0 \times 10^{-6}$ (c) $K_b = 5.6 \times 10^{-11}$

78. (a) pH = 9.46 (b) pH = 11.39 (c) pH = 11.79

80. (a) pH = 11.94 (b) pH = 8.20

84. (a) $K_a = 1.4 \times 10^{-11}$ (b) $K_a = 6.7 \times 10^{-6}$ (c) $K_a = 1.4 \times 10^{-10}$

86. (a) pH = 4.92 (b) pH = 5.64 (c) pH = 2.60

92. (a) pH = 2.89, 0.87% hydrolysis (b) pH = 5.21, 8.2×10^{-3}% hydrolysis (c) pH = 6.17, 4.5×10^{-4}% hydrolysis

94. [A$^-$] = 6.7×10^{-4} M

114. [H$_3$O$^+$] = 2.9×10^{-3} M, pH = 2.54

116. pH = 2.04

118. +57 kJ/mol

Chapter 19

10. (a) pH = 3.27 (b) pH = 4.84

12. (a) [OH$^-$] = 3.0×10^{-5} M, pH = 9.48 (b) [OH$^-$] = 6.8×10^{-6} M, pH = 8.83

18. (a) [OH$^-$] = 2.3×10^{-3} M, [H$_3$O$^+$] = 4.3×10^{-12} M (b) [OH$^-$] = 1.4×10^{-5} M, [H$_3$O$^+$] = 7.4×10^{-10} M

22. pH = 0.70

24. pH decreases by 0.40 units (9.48 → 9.08)

26. (a) pH = 9.31 (b) pH = 9.20 (c) pH = 1.00

28. [BrCH$_2$COOH] = 4.1×10^{-2} M, [NaBrCH$_2$COO] = 0.26 M

30. [C$_2$H$_5$NH$_3^+$] = 0.0010 M

32. [CH$_3$CH$_2$COOH] = 0.36 M

34. 0.40 L NaOH, 0.60 L CH$_3$COOH

36. (a) 0.625 M CH$_3$COOH (b) 0.150 M Ca^{2+} (c) 0.300 M CH$_3$COO$^-$ (d) 3.8×10^{-5} M H$^+$ (d) pH = 4.42

38. 0.024 M ClCH$_2$COOH

42. $K_a = 6 \times 10^{-9}$, pK_a = 8.2

44. pH between 7.6 and 8

46. pH = 8.40, phenolphthalein

50. (a) pH = 0.8239 (b) pH = 0.9931 (c) pH = 1.250 (d) pH = 1.87 (e) pH = 4.0 (f) pH = 12.03

52. (a) pH = 0.839 (b) pH = 1.217 (c) pH = 1.85 (d) pH = 12.265 (e) pH = 12.529 (f) pH = 12.618

54. (a) pH = 3.22 (b) pH = 4.14 (c) pH = 4.57 (d) pH = 4.74 (halfway to the equivalence pt.) (e) pH = 5.11 (f) pH = 5.70 (g) pH = 6.02 (h) pH = 8.52 (at the equivalence pt.) (i) pH = 11.00 (j) pH = 11.60 (k) pH = 12.00

56. (a) pH = 2.74 (b) pH = 4.72 (c) pH = 4.97 (d) pH = 5.23 (e) pH = 5.51 (f) pH = 8.86 (g) pH = 11.54

58. (a) pH = 8.90 (b) pH = 8.79 (c) pH = 8.69

60. (b) 8.09 mL HCl (c) [(CH$_3$CH$_2$)$_3$N] = [H$_3$O$^+$] = 1.7×10^{-6} M, [(CH$_3$CH$_2$)$_3$NH$^+$] = [Cl$^-$] = 0.157 M

66. (a) pH = 2.00 (b) pH = 2.05 (c) pH = 2.22 (d) pH = 2.30 (e) pH = 3.00 (f) pH = 3.3 (g) pH = 5.62 (h) pH = 8.0 (i) pH = 8.73

68. pH (NaCl) = 7.00, pH (NH$_4$Cl) = 4.76

70. pH = 12.2

74. (a) K_a for NH$_4^+$ = 5.6×10^{-10} (b) K_b for ClO$^-$ = 2.9×10^{-7} (c) basic

80. 78.1% KHSO$_4$ by mass

82. pH = 4.00

84. 0.22 L HCl

Chapter 20

8. (a) $K_{sp} = 3.5 \times 10^{-5}$ (b) $K_{sp} = 7.7 \times 10^{-19}$ (c) $K_{sp} = 6.9 \times 10^{-15}$ (d) $K_{sp} = 1.01 \times 10^{-4}$

12. $K_{sp} = 3.65 \times 10^{-11}$

14. 6.9×10^{-3} g CaCO$_3$/L

16. (a) 4.4×10^{-4} mol CuCl/L; 4.4×10^{-4} M Cu$^+$; 4.4×10^{-4} M Cl$^-$; 0.043 g CuCl/L
(b) 6.5×10^{-7} mol Ba$_3$(PO$_4$)$_2$/L; 2.0×10^{-6} M Ba^{2+}; 1.3×10^{-6} M PO$_4^{3-}$; 3.9×10^{-4} g Ba$_3$(PO$_4$)$_2$/L
(c) 2.1×10^{-3} mol PbF$_2$/L; 2.1×10^{-3} M Pb^{2+}; 4.2×10^{-3} M F$^-$; 0.51 g PbF$_2$/L
(d) 2.5×10^{-7} mol Sr$_3$(PO$_4$)$_2$/L; 7.4×10^{-7} M Sr^{2+}; 4.9×10^{-7} M PO$_4^{3-}$; 1.1×10^{-4} g Sr$_3$(PO$_4$)$_2$/L

18. 0.012 g BaSO$_4$

20. 6.0×10^{-3} mol Ag$_2$SO$_4$/L of 0.12 M K$_2$SO$_4$

28. precipitation does not occur

30. precipitation does occur

32. 0.013% Pb^{2+} in soln

36. (a) AuBr (b) 1.5×10^{-6} M Au$^+$; 99.985% Au$^+$ precipitated (c) 9.4×10^{-11} M Au$^+$; 6.2×10^{-7} M Ag$^+$

38. (a) PbCrO$_4$ (b) 3.6×10^{-13} M Pb^{2+} (c) 3.6×10^{-7} M Pb^{2+} (d) 0.050 M SO$_4^{2-}$, 5.0×10^{-8} M CrO$_4^{2-}$

40. (a) (i) 2.0×10^{-11} M Zn^{2+} (ii) 1.0×10^{-8} M Zn^{2+} (iii) 3.6×10^{-6} M Zn^{2+}
(b) (i) 1.7×10^{-7} M OH$^-$ (ii) 1.0×10^{-8} M CO$_3^{2-}$ (iii) 7.3×10^{-5} M CN$^-$

42. pH = 7.59

44. 2.5×10^{-7} mol CaF$_2$/L

46. a precipitate will form but not be seen

48. (a) 6.7×10^{-8} mol Mg(OH)$_2$/L of 0.015 M NaOH (b) 1.6×10^{-5} mol Mg(OH)$_2$/L of 0.015 M MgCl$_2$

50. precipitation will not occur

52. (a) pH = 9.40 (b) 1.1×10^{-4} g Fe(OH)$_2$/100 mL

54. 4.5×10^{-9} M Zn^{2+}

56. a precipitate will form but not be seen

64. precipitation will not occur

66. 99.955% I$^-$ removed

74. 6.0×10^{-6} M Cl$^-$

78. (a) 1.1×10^{-9} M (b) 0.017 M

80. 0.6 g Ca^{2+}/L

82. 29% loss of MgCO$_3$

Chapter 21

18. (i) (a) 3 (b) 2 (c) 1
   (ii) (a) 5.18×10^3 C (b) 1.63×10^3 C (c) 481 C
20. (a) 0.142 A (b) 1.12 g Cu
22. 0.242 g Rh
24. 0.873 C
26. 8.39 g Ag
28. (a) 0.0830 faradays (b) 8.01×10^3 C (c) 0.930 L_{STP} H_2
   (d) pH = 13.220
30. 3.2 L Cl_2
32. 5.2 hr, 4.6 g Cu
34. (a) 0.0214 faradays (b) 2.31 g Ag (c) 5.18 g $Fe(NO_3)_3$
54. (a) +3.17 V (b) +0.62 V
56. 0.71 V
58. (a) yes (b) no
60. (a) yes (b) no
62. +1.78 V
64. (a) +1.08 V (b) −1.202 V
66. (a) no (b) yes (c) yes (d) no
68. (a) H_2 (b) Sn (c) Hg (d) Cl^- in base (e) H_2S (f) Ag
70. −1.207 V
72. (a) yes (b) +0.57 V
74. +5.80 V (K^+/K with F_2/F^-)
78. 0.0257
82. (a) 1.202 V (b) +1.16 V (c) 2.0 M
84. (a) +2.123 V (b) +2.143 V
86. $P_{F_2} = 2.2 \times 10^{-7}$ atm
88. +0.95 V
90. (a) +0.870 V (b) +0.148 V (c) +0.0527 V
92. +0.38 V
94. (a) $[Zn^{2+}]/[Ni^{2+}] = 2 \times 10^{17}$ (b) 1×10^{-17} M Ni^{2+};
   2.00 M Zn^{2+}
96. pH = 6.15
100. (a) $E^0_{cell} = +0.736$ V; $\Delta G^0 = -355$ kJ/mol rxn;
   $K = 1 \times 10^{62}$
   (b) $E^0_{cell} = +0.368$ V; $\Delta G^0 = -35.5$ kJ/mol rxn;
   $K = 1.6 \times 10^6$
   (c) $E^0_{cell} = +1.833$ V; $\Delta G^0 = -1061$ kJ/mol rxn;
   $K = 8.6 \times 10^{185}$
102. (a) −0.25 V (b) −0.13 V (c) −0.065 B
104. $K = 2$ (1 sig. fig.)
116. (b) +2.33 V (c) +2.44 V (d) 0.0227 g Mg
118. 955 C
120. $[Mn^{2+}]/[Fe^{2+}] = 10^{-24}$
122. (a) +4 (b) +4 (c) 0 (d) Mg(s) (e) UF_4(s) (f) 10.2 A
   (g) 0.0206 L HF(g) (h) yes, 2.45 g U
134. (a) $K_{sp} = 10^{-12}$ (b) $\Delta G^\circ = +68$ kJ/mol rxn

Chapter 22

14. (a) 0.587 g/mol (b) 5.28×10^{10} kJ/mol of ^{62}Ni atoms
16. (a) 0.602 amu/atom (b) 0.602 g/mol (c) 9.00×10^{-11}
   J/atom (d) 5.42×10^{10} kJ/mol (e) 8.79 MeV/nucleon
18. (a) 1.04×10^{11} kJ/mol of ^{127}I atoms (b) 6.83×10^{10}
   kJ/mol of ^{81}Br atoms (c) 2.89×10^{10} kJ/mol of
   ^{35}Cl atoms
54. 67.5 min (90.0%), 88.0 min (95.0%)
56. 7×10^{-16} s
58. 0.17 μg
60. 0.00236

62. 1.98×10^4 yr
66. (b) $\Delta E = -1.68 \times 10^9$ kJ/mol rxn
74. (b) $\Delta E = +1.15 \times 10^8$ kJ/mol rxn
76. 2.52×10^9 yr
78. fission = -1.40×10^{-13} J/amu ^{235}U; fusion =
   -1.53×10^{-13} J/amu ^{2}H

Chapter 23

34. 2 isomers

Chapter 24

20. $[C_6H_5NH_2] = 0.12$ M; $[C_6H_5NH_3^+] = [OH^-] =$
   7.1×10^{-6} M; $[H_3O^+] = 1.4 \times 10^{-9}$ M
28. pH = 10.78
48. 24 isomers
52. 9; A-A, A-B, A-C, B-A, B-B, B-C, C-A, C-B, C-C
72. pH (sodium benzoate) = 8.64; more acidic

Chapter 25

4. (a) 4 (b) 4
6. (a) ox. no. +3 (b) +3 (c) +2 (d) +2
20. (a) ox. no. +2 (b) +3 (c) +1 (d) +2 (e) +2 (f) +3
32. (a) 2 isomers (b) 2 isomers
36. (a) 2 isomers (b) 2 isomers (c) 2 optical isomers
   (d) 3 isomers (e) 6 isomers
52. 8
58. $\Delta S^0_{rxn} = -153.5$ J/(mol rxn)·K
60. pH = 10.43
64. (a) 2.2×10^{-6} mol $Zn(OH)_2$/L (b) 0.010 mol
   $Zn(OH)_2$/L (c) $[Zn(OH)_4^{2-}] = 0.010$ M

Chapter 26

16. 39.997 g NaOH, 1.008 g H_2, 35.45 g Cl_2
40. 1.7×10^7 tons bauxite
46. (a) −15 kJ/mol rxn (b) +5 kJ/mol rxn (c) −25 J/
   (mol rxn)·K
50. 21.0 g Cu
52. bornite (63.33% Cu)
54. 104 tons SO_2
56. 33.4 tons C (coke)

Chapter 27

32. (a) −201.4 kJ/mol rxn (b) −138.9 kJ/mol rxn
   (c) −415.0 kJ/mol rxn
46. $Be(OH)_2$: $[OH^-] = 1.6 \times 10^{-7}$ M, pOH = 6.80,
   $Mg(OH)_2$: $[OH^-] = 3.1 \times 10^{-4}$ M, pOH = 3.51,
   $Ca(OH)_2$: $[OH^-] = 0.025$ M, pOH = 1.60, $Sr(OH)_2$:
   $[OH^-] = 0.086$ M, pOH = 1.06, $Ba(OH)_2$: $[OH^-] =$
   0.22 M; pOH = 0.67
48. 22.61% Cr
56. 384 g Co_3O_4
58. $\Delta H^0_{rxn} = -195.4$ kJ/mol Rb(s), $\Delta S^0_{rxn} = 29.4$ J/K per
   1 mol Rb(s), $\Delta G^0_{rxn} = -204.0$ kJ/mol Rb(s)
60. 0.200 mol CO_2, Q = Li in Li_2CO_3

Chapter 28

8. 2.19 g XeF_6
42. 2.04 tons H_2SO_4
44. $K_c = 2.7$
52. (a) 0 (b) +1 (c) +4 (d) +5 (e) +3
82. −140 kJ/mol rxn
86. 2.2×10^{25} g Si
88. 1.92 Å

Index of Equations

Bold entries in parentheses are chapter and section numbers, followed by the page number.

Molarity, M

$$\text{molarity} = \frac{\text{number of moles of solute}}{\text{number of liters of solution}} \qquad \textbf{(3-6)}, 99$$

$$\text{molarity} = \frac{\text{number of millimoles of solute}}{\text{number of milliliters of solution}} \qquad \textbf{(11-1)}, 377$$

Molarity, dilution

$$V_1M_1 = V_2M_2 \qquad \text{(for dilution only)} \qquad \textbf{(3-7)}, 102$$

Molality, m

$$\text{molality} = \frac{\text{number of moles solute}}{\text{number of kilograms solvent}} \qquad \textbf{(14-8)}, 516$$

Mole fraction, X

$$X_A = \frac{\text{no. mol A}}{\text{total no. mol of all components}} \qquad \textbf{(12-11)}, 422$$

Coulomb's law (electrostatic attraction)

$$F \propto \frac{q^+ q^-}{d^2} \qquad \textbf{(5-3)}, 180$$

$$\textbf{(13-2)}, 453$$

Dalton's Law of partial pressures

$$P_{\text{total}} = P_A + P_B + P_C + \cdots \qquad \text{(constant } V, T)$$

$$\textbf{(12-11)}, 421$$

de Broglie equation

$$\lambda = \frac{h}{mv} \qquad \textbf{(4-14)}, 144$$

Density, D

$$\text{density} = \frac{\text{mass}}{\text{volume}} \quad \text{or} \quad D = \frac{m}{V} \qquad \textbf{(1-11)}, 26$$

Dilution

$$V_1M_1 = V_2M_2 \qquad \text{(for dilution only)} \qquad \textbf{(3-7)}, 102$$

Electrochemical potential vs. equilibrium constant

$$nFE^0_{\text{cell}} = RT \ln K \qquad \textbf{(21-21)}, 835$$

Electrochemical potential vs. standard free energy change

$$\Delta G^0 = -nFE^0_{\text{cell}} \qquad \textbf{(21-21)}, 835$$

Energy:

Matter–energy conversion
$$E = mc^2 \qquad \textbf{(1-1)}, 5$$

Photon energy

$$E = h\nu \quad \text{or} \quad E = \frac{hc}{\lambda} \qquad \textbf{(4-11)}, 137$$

Kinetic energy
$$E_{\text{kinetic}} = \tfrac{1}{2}mv^2 \qquad \textbf{(15-1)}, 553$$

Enthalpy change, ΔH

$$\Delta H = H_{\text{final}} - H_{\text{initial}} \qquad \text{or}$$
$$\Delta H = H_{\text{substances produced}} - H_{\text{substances consumed}} \qquad \textbf{(15-3)}, 556$$
$$\Delta H = \Delta E + P\,\Delta V \qquad \text{(constant } T \text{ and } P) \qquad \textbf{(15-11)}, 577$$
$$\Delta H = q_p \qquad \text{(constant } T \text{ and } P) \qquad \textbf{(15-11)}, 577$$

Enthalpy of reaction, ΔH^0_{rxn} (gas-phase reaction, estimation from bond energies)

$$\Delta H^0_{\text{rxn}} = \sum \text{B.E.}_{\text{reactants}} - \sum \text{B.E.}_{\text{products}} \qquad \textbf{(15-9)}, 569$$

Enthalpy of reaction, ΔH^0_{rxn} (Hess's Law), from enthalpies of formation

$$\Delta H^0_{\text{rxn}} = \sum n\,\Delta H^0_{\text{f products}} - \sum n\,\Delta H^0_{\text{f reactants}} \qquad \textbf{(15-8)}, 566$$

Enthalpy of reaction, ΔH^0_{rxn} (Hess's Law), from enthalpies of related reactions

$$\Delta H^0_{\text{rxn}} = \Delta H^0_a + \Delta H^0_b + \Delta H^0_c + \cdots \qquad \textbf{(15-8)}, 564$$

Enthalpy of solution, $\Delta H_{\text{solution}}$

$$\Delta H_{\text{solution}} = (\text{heat of solvation}) - (\text{crystal lattice energy}) \qquad \textbf{(14-2)}, 509$$

Entropy of reaction, ΔS^0_{rxn}

$$\Delta S^0_{\text{rxn}} = \sum n\,S^0_{\text{products}} - \sum n\,S^0_{\text{reactants}} \qquad \textbf{(15-14)}, 583$$

Equilibrium constant—Gibbs free energy relationship

$$\Delta G^0_{\text{rxn}} = -RT \ln K \qquad \textbf{(17-12)}, 696$$

Equilibrium constant in terms of concentrations, K_c

$$\textbf{(17-2)}, 670$$

$$K_c = \frac{\overbrace{[C]^c_{\text{eq}} [D]^d_{\text{eq}}}^{\text{product concentrations}}}{\underbrace{[A]^a_{\text{eq}} [B]^b_{\text{eq}}}_{\text{reactant concentrations}}}$$

Equilibrium constant in terms of pressures, K_P

$$K_P = \frac{(P_C)^c (P_D)^d}{(P_A)^a (P_B)^b} \qquad \textbf{(17-9)}, 691$$

Equilibrium constant, K_a, for weak acid HA

$$K_a = \frac{[H_3O^+][A^-]}{[HA]} \qquad \textbf{(18-4)}, 718$$

Equilibrium constant, K_b, for weak base B

$$K_b = \frac{[BH^+][OH^-]}{[B]} \qquad \textbf{(18-4)}, 727$$

Equilibrium constant, K_{sp}, for slightly soluble salt M_yX_z

For $M_y^{x+} X_z^{y-} (s) \rightleftharpoons yM^{x+}(aq) + zX^{y-}(aq)$,
$$K_{\text{sp}} = [M^{x+}]^y [X^{y-}]^z \qquad \textbf{(20-1)}, 781$$

Equilibrium constant, relationship between K_c and K_P

$$K_P = K_c(RT)^{\Delta n} \qquad \text{or} \qquad K_c = K_P(RT)^{-\Delta n}$$
$$\Delta n = (n_{\text{gas prod}}) - (n_{\text{gas react}}) \qquad \textbf{(17-10)}, 692$$

Equilibrium constant, thermodynamic

$$K = \frac{(a_C)^c(a_D)^d}{(a_A)^a(a_B)^b}$$

(17-12), 696

Equilibrium constants for conjugate acid–base pair

$$K_a K_b = K_w$$

(18-8), 734

First Law of Thermodynamics

$$\Delta E = q + w$$

(15-10), 571

Formal charge (for Group A elements)

$$FC = (\text{group number}) - [(\text{number of bonds}) + (\text{number of unshared } e^-)]$$

(7-7), 268

Formula weight (FW)

$$FW = \frac{\text{mass in grams}}{\text{no. of mol}}$$

(2-6), 58

Free energy change, ΔG

$$\Delta G = \Delta H - T \Delta S \qquad (\text{constant } T \text{ and } P)$$

(15-16), 592

Free energy–equilibrium constant relationship

$$\Delta G^0_{rxn} = -RT \ln K$$

(17-12), 696

Free energy of reaction, ΔG^0_{rxn}

$$\Delta G^0_{rxn} = \Sigma\, n\, \Delta G^0_{f\,products} - \Sigma\, n\, \Delta G^0_{f\,reactants}$$
(1 atm and 298 K *only*)

(15-16), 592

Freezing point depression

$$\Delta T_f = K_f m$$

(14-12), 525

Frequency vs. wavelength

$$\lambda \nu = c$$

(4-11), 134

Half-life (first order, radioactive decay)

$$t_{1/2} = \frac{\ln 2}{k} = \frac{0.693}{k}$$

(16-4), 627
(22-10), 863

Henderson–Hasselbalch equations

$$pH = pK_a + \log\frac{[\text{conjugate base}]}{[\text{acid}]}$$

(for acid/salt buffer)

(19-1), 753

and

$$pOH = pK_b + \log\frac{[\text{conjugate acid}]}{[\text{base}]}$$

(for base/salt buffer)

(19-1), 756

Henry's Law (gas solubility)

$$C_{gas} = kP_{gas}$$

(14-7), 515

Hess's Law, enthalpy of reaction, ΔH^0_{rxn}, from enthalpies of formation

$$\Delta H^0_{rxn} = \Sigma\, n\, \Delta H^0_{f\,products} - \Sigma\, n\, \Delta H^0_{f\,reactants}$$

(15-8), 566

Hess's Law, enthalpy of reaction, ΔH^0_{rxn}, from enthalpies of related reactions

$$\Delta H^0_{rxn} = \Delta H^0_a + \Delta H^0_b + \Delta H^0_c + \cdots$$

(15-8), 564

Ideal gas equation

$$PV = nRT$$

(12-9), 415

Integrated rate equation, first order

$$\ln\left(\frac{[A]_0}{[A]}\right) = akt$$

(16-4), 627

Integrated rate equation, second order

$$\frac{1}{[A]} - \frac{1}{[A]_0} = akt$$

(16-4), 629

Integrated rate equation, zero order

$$[A] = [A]_0 - akt$$

(16-4), 631

Internal energy

$$\Delta E = E_{final} - E_{initial} = E_{products} - E_{reactants} = q + w \quad \textbf{(15-10)}, 571$$
$$\Delta E = q_v \qquad \textbf{(15-10)}, 573$$

Ion product for water, K_w

$$K_w = [H_3O^+][OH^-] = 1 \times 10^{-14} \qquad (\text{at } 25°C)$$

(18-2), 711

K_a, ionization constant for weak acid HA

$$K_a = \frac{[H_3O^+][A^-]}{[HA]}$$

(18-4), 718

K_b, ionization constant for weak base B

$$K_b = \frac{[BH^+][OH^-]}{[B]}$$

(18-4), 727

K_{sp}, solubility product constant for slightly soluble salt M_yX_z

For $M_y^{x+} X_z^{y-}(s) \rightleftharpoons yM^{x+}(aq) + zX^{y-}(aq)$,

$$K_{sp} = [M^{x+}]^y[X^{y-}]^z$$

(20-1), 781

K_w, ion product for water

$$K_w = [H_3O^+][OH^-] = 1 \times 10^{\times 14} \qquad (\text{at } 25°C)$$

(18-2), 711

Kinetic energy, average molecular, $\overline{KE}$

$$\overline{KE} \propto T$$

(12-13), 429

Light, wavelength vs. frequency

$$\lambda \nu = c$$

(4-11), 134

Mass number (*A*)

$$\text{Mass number} = \text{number of protons} + \text{number of neutrons}$$
$$= \text{atomic number} + \text{neutron number} \quad \textbf{(4-7)}, 123$$

Molality, *m*

$$\text{molality} = \frac{\text{number of moles solute}}{\text{number of kilograms solvent}} \qquad \textbf{(14-8)}, 516$$

Molarity, *M*

$$\text{molarity} = \frac{\text{number of moles of solute}}{\text{number of liters of solution}} \qquad \textbf{(3-6)}, 99$$

$$\text{molarity} = \frac{\text{number of millimoles of solute}}{\text{number of milliliters of solution}} \qquad \textbf{(11-1)}, 377$$

Mole fraction, *X*

$$X_A = \frac{\text{no. mol A}}{\text{total no. mol of all components}} \qquad \textbf{(12-11)}, 422$$

Mole fraction, *X*, in gas mixture

$$X_A = \frac{P_A}{P_{\text{total}}} \qquad \textbf{(12-11)}, 423$$

Moles, from mass

$$\text{mol} = \frac{\text{mass in grams}}{\text{formula weight}} \qquad \textbf{(2-6)}, 56$$

Moles, solute in solution

$$\text{moles solute} = \text{molarity} \times \text{L solution} \qquad \textbf{(3-6)}, 99$$
$$\text{millimoles solute} = \text{molarity} \times \text{mL solution} \qquad \textbf{(11-1)}, 377$$

Nernst equation

$$E = E^0 - \frac{2.303\,RT}{nF} \log Q \qquad \textbf{(21-19)}, 828$$

or

$$E = E^0 - \frac{0.0592}{n} \log Q$$

Nuclear binding energy

$$BE = (\Delta m)c^2 \qquad \textbf{(22-3)}, 855$$

Nuclear mass deficiency

$$\Delta m = (\text{sum of masses of all } e^-, p^+, \text{ and } n^0)$$
$$- (\text{actual mass of atom}) \qquad \textbf{(22-3)}, 854$$

Osmotic pressure

$$\pi = MRT \qquad \textbf{(14-15)}, 531$$

Percent solute

$$\text{percent solute} = \frac{\text{mass of solute}}{\text{mass of solution}} \times 100\% \qquad \textbf{(3-6)}, 98$$

Percent yield

$$\text{percent yield} = \frac{\text{actual yield of product}}{\text{theoretical yield of product}} \times 100\% \qquad \textbf{(3-4)}, 95$$

pH

$$\text{pH} = -\log\,[H_3O^+] \quad \text{or} \quad [H_3O^+] = 10^{-\text{pH}} \quad \textbf{(18-3)}, 713$$
$$\text{pH} + \text{pOH} = 14.00 \quad (\text{at } 25°C) \qquad \textbf{(18-3)}, 714$$

p*K*$_w$

$$pK_w = -\log K_w \quad (= 14.0 \text{ at } 25°C) \qquad \textbf{(18-3)}, 713$$

pOH

$$\text{pOH} = -\log\,[OH^-] \quad \text{or} \quad [OH^-] = 10^{-\text{pOH}} \quad \textbf{(18-3)}, 713$$

Quadratic formula

$$x = \frac{-b \pm \sqrt{b^2 - 4ac}}{2a} \qquad \textbf{(17-5)}, 679$$

Radioactive decay

$$\ln\left(\frac{A_0}{A}\right) = kt \ \text{ or } \ \ln\left(\frac{N_0}{N}\right) = kt \qquad \textbf{(22-10)}, 863$$

Raoult's Law

$$P_{\text{solvent}} = X_{\text{solvent}} P^0_{\text{solvent}} \qquad \textbf{(14-9)}, 518$$

Raoult's Law, two volatile components

$$P_{\text{total}} = X_A P^0_A + X_B P^0_B \qquad \textbf{(14-9)}, 519$$

Rate equation, integrated, first order

$$\ln\left(\frac{[A]_0}{[A]}\right) = akt \qquad \textbf{(16-4)}, 627$$

Rate equation, integrated, second order

$$\frac{1}{[A]} - \frac{1}{[A]_0} = akt \qquad \textbf{(16-4)}, 629$$

Rate equation, integrated, zero order

$$[A] = [A]_0 - akt \qquad \textbf{(16-4)}, 631$$

Rate law expression

$$\text{rate} = k[A]^x[B]^y \ldots \qquad \textbf{(16-3)}, 620$$

Rate of reaction

$$\text{rate of reaction} = -\frac{1}{a}\left(\frac{\Delta[A]}{\Delta t}\right) = -\frac{1}{b}\left(\frac{\Delta[B]}{\Delta t}\right)$$
$$= \frac{1}{c}\left(\frac{\Delta[C]}{\Delta t}\right) = \frac{1}{d}\left(\frac{\Delta[D]}{\Delta t}\right) \qquad \textbf{(16-1)}, 615$$

Reaction quotient, Q

For $a\text{A} + b\text{B} \rightleftharpoons c\text{C} + d\text{D}$ **(17-4)**, 674

$$Q = \frac{[\text{C}]^c[\text{D}]^d}{[\text{A}]^a[\text{B}]^b} \longleftarrow \begin{array}{l}\text{not necessarily}\\ \text{equilibrium}\\ \text{concentrations}\end{array}$$

Second Law of Thermodynamics

$\Delta S_{\text{universe}} = \Delta S_{\text{system}} + \Delta S_{\text{surroundings}} > 0$ **(15-15)**, 590

Solubility product constant, K_{sp}, for slightly soluble salt M_yX_z

For $\text{M}_y^{x+}\text{X}_z^{y-}\,(s) \rightleftharpoons y\text{M}^{x+}(aq) + z\text{X}^{y-}(aq)$,

$K_{\text{sp}} = [\text{M}^{x+}]^y[\text{X}^{y-}]^z$ **(20-1)**, 781

Specific gravity

$\text{Sp. Gr} = \dfrac{D_{\text{substance}}}{D_{\text{water}}}$ **(1-11)**, 28

Specific heat

$\text{specific heat} = \dfrac{(\text{amount of heat in J})}{(\text{mass of substance in g})(\text{temperature change in °C})}$

(1-13), 32

Speed, average molecular, $\bar{u}$

$\bar{u} \propto \sqrt{\dfrac{T}{\text{molecular weight}}}$ **(12-13)**, 429

Speed, gas molecule (root mean square)

$u_{\text{rms}} = \sqrt{\dfrac{3RT}{M}}$ **(12-13)**, 433

Temperature conversions:

°C to K	$°\text{C} = \text{K} - 273.15°$	**(1-12)**, 30
K to °C	$\text{K} = °\text{C} + 273.15°$	**(1-12)**, 30
°C to °F	$°\text{F} = \left(x°\text{C} \times \dfrac{1.8°\text{F}}{1.0°\text{C}}\right) + 32°\text{F}$	**(1-12)**, 31
°F to °C	$°\text{C} = \dfrac{1.0°\text{C}}{1.8°\text{F}}(x°\text{F} - 32°\text{F})$	**(1-12)**, 31

van der Waals equation

$\left(P + \dfrac{n^2 a}{V^2}\right)(V - nb) = nRT$ **(12-15)**, 437

van't Hoff equation

$\ln\left(\dfrac{K_{T_2}}{K_{T_1}}\right) = \dfrac{\Delta H^0}{R}\left(\dfrac{1}{T_1} - \dfrac{1}{T_2}\right)$ **(17-13)**, 699

van't Hoff factor, i

$i = \dfrac{\Delta T_{f(\text{actual})}}{\Delta T_{f(\text{if nonelectrolyte})}} = \dfrac{K_f m_{\text{effective}}}{K_f m_{\text{stated}}} = \dfrac{m_{\text{effective}}}{m_{\text{stated}}}$ **(14-14)**, 529

or more generally, as

$i = \dfrac{\text{colligative property}_{\text{actual}}}{\text{colligative property}_{\text{if nonelectrolyte}}}$

Vapor pressure lowering

$\Delta P_{\text{solvent}} = P^0_{\text{solvent}} - P_{\text{solvent}}$

$\Delta P_{\text{solvent}} = X_{\text{solute}} P^0_{\text{solvent}}$ **(14-9)**, 518

Wavelength vs. frequency

$\lambda \nu = c$ **(4-11)**, 134

Work

$w = fd$ **(15-10)**, 571

Work, due to change in number of moles of gas (e.g., phase change or chemical reaction)

$w = -(\Delta n)RT$ **(15-10)**, 574

Work, due to expansion

$w = -P\,\Delta V$ **(15-10)**, 573

Glossary/Index

Glossary terms, printed in **boldface**, are defined here as well as in the text (location indicated by boldface page numbers) and in Key Terms. Page numbers followed by i indicate illustrations or their captions; page numbers followed by t indicate tables.

2-Deoxyribose The carbohydrate found in DNA, 978–981, 980–981f, **982**

***α*-Amino acid** A compound containing both an amino group and a carboxylic acid group connected to a carbon atom (the a-carbon) that can have a variety of other organic groups attached. There are 22 common amino acids that are the building blocks for proteins and other biological molecules, 925–926, **943**, 975, 976t

Absolute entropy (of a substance) The entropy of a substance relative to its entropy in a perfectly ordered crystalline form at 0 K (where its entropy if zero), **583, 598**

Absolute zero The zero point on the absolute temperature scale, −273.15°C or 0 K; theoretically, the temperature at which molecular motion is a minimum, **410, 438**

Absorption spectrum The spectrum associated with absorption of electromagnetic radiation by atoms (or other species) resulting from transitions from lower to higher electronic energy states, **139**, 140f, **162**

Accuracy How closely a measured value agrees with the correct value, **35**

Acetic acid, 12t, 733, 756–757, 961, 961t

Acetylene, 267, 319, 889f, 905f, 968

Achiral Describes an object that *can* be superimposed with its mirror image, **956, 982**

Acid A substance that produces H⁺ (aq) ions in aqueous solution. Strong acids ionize completely or almost completely in dilute aqueous solution. Weak acids ionize only slightly, **208, 240, 349, 363**. *see also* **Strong acid; Weak acid**
  amphoterism, 354–355, 355f
  Arrhenius theory of, 349–350
  binary, 355–356
  Brønsted-Lowry theory, 350–353
  Lewis, 363–365, 363–365f
  organic, 961–962, 961–962t, 968–969

pH and pOH scales, 713–716, 717f
polyprotic, 729–732, 731t
preparation of, 365–366, 365–366f
properties of protic, 349
strength of, 355–358, 357t
strong and weak, 209–211, 211f, 211t, 212f
ternary, 197, 202, 219–221, 220t, 240, 357–358, 366, 367

Acid (Arrhenius or Brønsted-Lowry) A substance that produces H⁺ (aq) ions in aqueous solution. Strong acids ionize completely or almost completely in dilute aqueous solution; weak acids ionize only slightly, **367**

Acid anhydride A nonmetal oxide that reacts with water to form an acid, 195f, **197, 201, 367**

Acid-base reaction. *see also* **Buffer solution; Coordination compound or complex; Neutralization reaction**
  calculations summary, 771t
  indicators, 763–765, 764f, 766t
  molarity and, 376–380

Acid-base titration The quantitative analysis of the amount or concentration of an acid or base in a sample by observing its reaction with a known amount or concentration of a base or acid, **382, 393**

Acid halide. *see* **Acyl halide**

Acidic oxide. *see* **Acid anhydride**

Acidic salt A salt that contains an ionizable hydrogen atom; does not necessarily produce acidic solutions, **361–362, 362f, 367**

Actinides Elements 90 through 103 (after actinium), **201**

Activation energy, 639, 645–647

Active metal A metal that readily loses electrons to form cations, **240**

Activity (of a component of an ideal mixture) A dimensionless quantity whose magnitude is equal to molar concentration in an ideal solution, equal to partial pressure (in atmospheres) in an ideal gas

mixture, and defined as 1 for pure solids or liquids, **700**

Activity series A listing of metals (and hydrogen) in order of decreasing activity, 229, **240**

Actual yield The amount of a specified pure product actually obtained from a given reaction. Compare with Theoretical yield, **95, 106**

Acyl group The group of atoms remaining after removal of an —OH group of a carboxylic acid, 926, **943**

Acyl halide A compound derived from a carboxylic acid by replacing the —OH group with a halogen (X), usually —Cl;

general formula is $R-\overset{\overset{\textstyle O}{\|}}{C}-X$;; also known as an *Acid halide*, **926–927, 943,** 968–969

Addition polymer A polymer formed by an addition reaction, **938, 943**

Addition reaction A reaction in which two atoms or groups of atoms are added to a molecule, one on each side of a double or triple bond. The number of groups attached to carbon *increases*, and the molecule becomes more nearly saturated, **935–937, 943**

Adhesive force Force of attraction between a liquid and another surface, 460, **494**

Adsorption Adhesion of species onto surfaces of particles, 535–537, 538f, 538t, **542**

Air
  composition of, 403, 403t
  pollution and fossil fuels, 199–200, 199f, 200f, 200t

Alchymist in the Search of the Philosopher's Stone Discovers Phosphorus, The, 175, 175f

Alcohol A hydrocarbon derivative in which an H attached to a carbon atom not part of an aromatic ring has been replaced by an —OH group, **913–918**, 913f, 917f, 917t, **943**

Henry's Law The concentration or solubility of a gas in a liquid at any given temperature is directly proportional to the partial pressure of the gas over the solution, **515**, 515f, **543**

Heptane, 519, 520

Hertz, Heinrich, 134

Hess, G. H., 564

Hess's Law of Heat Summation The enthalpy change for a reaction is the same whether it occurs in one step or a series of steps, **564**–568, 569, 583, **598**

Heteroatom An atom other than C or H in an organic molecule; the most common heteroatoms are O, N, S, P, and the halogens, **943**

Heterocyclic amine An amine in which nitrogen is part of a ring, **943**

Heterogeneous catalyst A catalyst that exists in a different phase (solid, liquid, or gas) from the reactants; the vast majority of heterogeneous catalysts are solids, **649**–653, 650–652f, **656**

Heterogeneous equilibria Equilibria involving species in more than one phase, **694**–695, **700**

Heterogenous mixture A mixture that does not have uniform composition and properties throughout, **13**, 13f, 14f, **35**

Heteronuclear Consisting of different elements, 276, **280**, **343**
diatomic molecules, 339–340, 339f, 340f, 341f

High spin complex A complex in which the crystal field splitting energy is smaller than the pairing energy so that all d orbitals are singly occupied before pairing occurs; there are the same number of unpaired d electrons on the metal atom as when the metal is uncomplexed. In an octahedral high spin complex, all t_{2g} and e_g orbitals are singly occupied before any pairing occurs, **1007**, **1010**

Homogeneous catalyst A catalyst that exists in the same phase (liquid or gas) as the reactants, **648**–649, **656**

Homogeneous mixture A mixture that has uniform composition and properties throughout, **13**, 13f, **35**, 506

Homologous series A series of compound in which each member differs from the next by a specific number and kind of atoms, **892**, **943**

Homonuclear Consisting of only one element, **280**, 333, **343**
diatomic molecules, 335–339, 336f, 337t

Hund's Rule Each orbital of a given subshell is occupied by a single electron before pairing begins. See Aufbau Principle, **155**, 158, **163**, 296, 333

Hybridization The mixing of a set of atomic orbitals on an atom to form a new set of hybrid orbitals with the same total electron capacity and with properties and energies intermediate between those of the original unhybridized orbitals, **294**, 294t, 297, **322**
of carbon in covalent bond formation, 889, 889t

Hybrid orbitals Orbitals formed on an atom by the process of hybridization, **294**, 296, 314, **322**

Hydrate A crystalline sample that contains water, H_2O, and another compound in a fixed mole ratio. Examples include $CuSO_4 \cdot 5H_2O$ and $(COOH)_2 \cdot 2H_2O$, **69**, **72**
isomers, 999–1000

Hydrate isomers Isomers of crystalline complexes that differ in terms of the presence of water inside or outside the coordination sphere, **1010**

Hydration The interaction (surrounding) of solute particles with water molecules, **508**–510, **543**

Hydration energy (molar) of an ion The energy change accompanying the hydration of a mole of gaseous ions, **508**, **543**

Hydration reaction A reaction in which the elements of water, H and OH, add across a double or triple bond, **943**

Hydride A binary compound of hydrogen, **367**
boiling point, 455, 455f
of group 6A elements, 1067
periodicity, 190–193

Hydrocarbon A compound that contains only carbon and hydrogen, **890**, 910–911f, **943**. *see also* **Aliphatic hydrogens; Aromatic hydrocarbons; Saturated hydrocarbons; Unsaturated hydrocarbons**

Hydrochloric acid, 348, 361f, 376

Hydrofluoric acid, 210, 724, 1064, 1079

Hydrogen, 7f
balancing redox reactions and, 388–390
chemical reactions and periodicity, 190–193
compounds of nitrogen, 1072–1073, 1073f
covalent bonds, 258, 258f
isotopes, 123f
molecule, 336, 336f
oxidation state, 188

Hydrogenation The reaction in which hydrogen adds across a double or triple bond, **936**, **943**

Hydrogen bond A fairly strong dipole-dipole interaction (but still considerably weaker than covalent or ionic bonds) between molecules containing hydrogen directly bonded to a small, highly electronegative atom, such as N, O, or F, **495**
dipole-dipole interaction, 454–455, 455f

Hydrogen chloride, 85–86

Hydrogen fluoride, 340, 340f, 341f

Hydrogen halides, 365, 1063–1064, 1064f
dissolution, 512

Hydrogen-oxygen fuel cell A fuel cell in which hydrogen is the fuel (reducing agent) and oxygen is the oxidizing agent, **840**–841, 841f, **842**

Hydrohalic acids, 355–356, 365–366, 512, 1063–1064, 1064f

Hydrolysis The reaction of a substance with water, **732**, 733–736, **742**, 962
effect on solubility, 787
of esters, 969–970, 970f

Hydrolysis constant An equilibrium constant for a hydrolysis reaction, **742**

Hydronium ion H_3O^+, the usual representation of the hydrated hydrogen ion, **350**, **367**

Hydrophilic colloids Colloidal particles that repel water molecules, **539**, **543**

Hydroxides, 1050–1051, 1051t
metal, 993, 994t

Hypervalent. *see* **Expanded valence shell**

Ideal gas A hypothetical gas that obeys exactly all postulates of the kinetic-molecular theory, **415**, **438**
deviations, 435–436f, 435–437, 437t

Ideal gas equation The product of the pressure and volume of an ideal gas is directly proportional to the number of moles of the gas and the absolute temperature, **415**–418, 431–433, **438**

Ideal solution A solution that obeys Raoult's Law exactly, **519**, **543**

Indicator (for acid-base reaction) An organic compound that exhibits different colors in solutions of different acidities; used to indicate the point at which reaction between an acid and a base is complete, 380, 384f, 393, 716, 763–765, 766t, **772**

Indium, 1045t, 1047

Inert electrode An electrode that does not take part in the electrochemical reaction, **842**

Inert s-pair effect The tendency of the two outermost s electrons to remain nonionized or unshared in compounds; characteristic of the post-transition metals, **1053**

Inner transition elements. *see* f-**Transition elements (metals)**

Inorganic chemistry
defined, **3**

Inorganic compounds, 44
naming, 217–218, 219t

Insoluble bases, 212

Insulator A poor conductor of electricity and heat, **491**, 491f, **495**

Integrated rate equation An equation that relates the concentration of a reactant remaining to the time elapsed; has different mathematical forms for different orders of reaction, **627**–637, 630f, 632t, 633–637, **656**

Intensive property A property that is independent of the amount of material in a sample, **11**, **35**

Intermolecular forces Forces between individual particles (atoms, molecules, ions) of a substance, **452**, **495**
boiling points *versus*, 469
dissolution and, 507–508
phase changes and, 451–458, 452f, 453t, 454–456f, 457t
physical properties of liquids and, 468t

Internal energy (E) All forms of energy associated with a specific amount of a substance, **571**–576, 572–574f, 576–577f, **598**

Reactions in Aqueous Solutions II: Calculations

Automatic titrators are used in modern analytical laboratories. Such titrators rely on electrical properties of the solutions. Methyl red indicator changes from yellow to red at the end point of the titration.

OBJECTIVES

After you have studied this chapter, you should be able to

- Perform molarity calculations
- Solve acid–base stoichiometry calculations
- Describe titration and standardization
- Use the mole method and molarity in acid–base titration reactions
- Perform calculations involving equivalent weights and normality of acid and base solutions
- Balance oxidation–reduction equations
- Perform calculations associated with redox reactions

AQUEOUS ACID–BASE REACTIONS

Digestive juice is the acidic fluid secreted by glands in the lining of the stomach.

Hydrochloric acid, HCl, is called "stomach acid" because it is the main acid ($\approx 0.10\ M$) in our digestive juices. When the concentration of HCl is too high in humans, problems result. These problems may range from "heartburn" to ulcers that can eat through the lining of the stomach wall. Snakes have very high concentrations of HCl in their digestive juices so that they can digest whole small animals and birds.

Automobile batteries contain 40% H_2SO_4 by mass. When the battery has "run down," the concentration of H_2SO_4 is significantly lower than 40%. A technician checks an automobile battery by drawing some battery acid into a hydrometer, which indicates the density of the solution. This density is related to the concentration of H_2SO_4.

There are many practical applications of acid–base chemistry in which we must know the concentration of a solution of an acid or a base.

11-1 CALCULATIONS INVOLVING MOLARITY

In Sections 3-6 through 3-8 we introduced methods for expressing concentrations of solutions and discussed some related calculations. Review of those sections will be helpful as we learn more about acid–base reactions in solutions.

In *some cases*, one mole of an acid reacts with one mole of a base to yield neutralization.

$$HCl + NaOH \longrightarrow NaCl + H_2O$$

$$HNO_3 + KOH \longrightarrow KNO_3 + H_2O$$

Because one mole of each acid reacts with one mole of each base in these cases, *one liter of a one-molar solution of either of these acids* reacts with *one liter of a one-molar solution of either of these bases*. These acids have only one acidic hydrogen per formula unit, and these bases have one hydroxide ion per formula unit, so one formula unit of base reacts with one formula unit of acid.

The *reaction ratio* is the relative numbers of moles of reactants and products shown in the balanced equation.

EXAMPLE 11-1   *Acid–Base Reactions*

If 100. mL of 0.100 M HCl solution and 100. mL of 0.100 M NaOH are mixed, what is the molarity of the salt in the resulting solution? Assume that the volumes are additive.

Plan

We first write the balanced equation for the acid–base reaction and then construct the reaction summary that shows the amounts (moles) of HCl and NaOH. We determine the amount of salt formed from the reaction summary. The final (total) volume is the sum of the volumes mixed. Then we calculate the molarity of the salt.

Solution

The following tabulation shows that equal numbers of moles of HCl and NaOH are mixed and, therefore, all of the HCl and NaOH react. The resulting solution contains only NaCl, the salt formed by the reaction, and water.

	HCl	+	NaOH	⟶	NaCl	+	H₂O
Rxn ratio:	1 mol		1 mol		1 mol		1 mol
Start:	$\left[0.100 \text{ L}\left(\dfrac{0.100 \text{ mol}}{\text{L}}\right)\right]$		$\left[0.100 \text{ L}\left(\dfrac{0.100 \text{ mol}}{\text{L}}\right)\right]$		0 mol		
	0.0100 mol HCl		0.0100 mol NaOH				
Change:	−0.0100 mol		−0.0100 mol		+0.0100 mol		
After rxn:	0 mol		0 mol		0.0100 mol		

The HCl and NaOH neutralize each other exactly, and the resulting solution contains 0.0100 mol of NaCl in 0.200 L of solution. Its molarity is

$$? \frac{\text{mol NaCl}}{\text{L}} = \frac{0.0100 \text{ mol NaCl}}{0.200 \text{ L}} = \boxed{0.0500 \, M \text{ NaCl}}$$

Experiments have shown that volumes of dilute aqueous solutions are very nearly additive. No significant error is introduced by making this assumption. 0.100 L of dilute NaOH solution mixed with 0.100 L of dilute HCl solution gives 0.200 L of solution.

The amount of water produced by the reaction is negligible.

We often express the volume of a solution in milliliters rather than in liters. Likewise, we may express the amount of solute in millimoles (mmol) rather than in moles. Because one milliliter is 1/1000 of a liter and one **millimole** is 1/1000 of a mole, molarity also may be expressed as the number of millimoles of solute per milliliter of solution:

1 mol = 1000 mmol

1 L = 1000 mL

$$\text{molarity} = \frac{\text{no. mol}}{\text{L}} = \frac{\text{no. mmol}}{\text{mL}}$$

$$\text{molarity} = \frac{\text{number of millimoles of solute}}{\text{number of milliliters of solution}}$$

For volumes and concentrations that are commonly used in laboratory experiments, solving problems in terms of millimoles and milliliters often involves more convenient numbers than using moles and liters. We should note also that the reaction ratio that we obtain from any balanced chemical equation is exactly the same whether we express all quantities in moles or in millimoles. We will work many problems in this chapter using millimoles and milliliters. Let us see how we might solve Example 11-1 in these terms.

As in Example 11-1 we first write the balanced equation for the acid–base reaction, and then construct the reaction summary that shows the amounts (millimoles) of NaOH and HCl. We determine the amount of salt formed from the reaction summary. The final (total) volume is the sum of the volumes mixed. Then we can calculate the molarity of the salt.

The tabulation for the solution is

	HCl	+	NaOH	⟶	NaCl	+	H₂O
Rxn ratio:	1 mmol		1 mmol		1 mmol		1 mmol
Start:	$\left[100.\ \text{mL}\left(\dfrac{0.100\ \text{mmol}}{\text{mL}}\right)\right]$		$\left[100.\ \text{mL}\left(\dfrac{0.100\ \text{mmol}}{\text{mL}}\right)\right]$		0 mmol		
	= 10.0 mmol HCl		= 10.0 mmol NaOH				
Change:	−10.0 mmol		−10.0 mmol		+10.0 mmol		
After rxn:	0 mmol		0 mmol		10.0 mmol		

$$? \frac{\text{mmol NaCl}}{\text{mL}} = \frac{10.0\ \text{mmol NaCl}}{200.\ \text{mL}} = \boxed{0.0500\ M\ \text{NaCl}}$$

EXAMPLE 11-2   Acid–Base Reactions

If 100. mL of 1.00 M HCl and 100. mL of 0.80 M NaOH solutions are mixed, what are the molarities of the solutes in the resulting solution?

Plan

We proceed as we did in Example 11-1. This reaction summary shows that NaOH is the limiting reactant and that we have excess HCl.

Solution

CD-ROM   Screen 5.15, Solution Concentration—Molarity.

	HCl	+	NaOH	⟶	NaCl	+	H₂O
Rxn ratio:	1 mmol		1 mmol		1 mmol		1 mmol
Start:	100. mmol		80. mmol		0 mmol		
Change:	−80. mmol		−80. mmol		+80. mmol		
After rxn:	20. mmol		0 mmol		80. mmol		

Because two solutes are present in the solution after reaction, we must calculate the concentrations of both.

$$? \frac{\text{mmol HCl}}{\text{mL}} = \frac{20.\ \text{mmol HCl}}{200.\ \text{mL}} = \boxed{0.10\ M\ \text{HCl}}$$

$$? \frac{\text{mmol NaCl}}{\text{mL}} = \frac{80.\ \text{mmol NaCl}}{200.\ \text{mL}} = \boxed{0.40\ M\ \text{NaCl}}$$

Both HCl and NaCl are strong electrolytes, so the solution is 0.10 M in H$^+$(aq), (0.10 + 0.40) M = 0.50 M in Cl$^-$, and 0.40 M in Na$^+$ ions.

You should now work Exercise 14.

You should master these initial examples before attempting the following more complex ones.

✓ Problem-Solving Tip: *Review Limiting Reactant Calculations*

To solve many of the problems in this chapter, you will need to apply the limiting reactant concept (Section 3-3). In Example 11-1, we confirm that the two reactants are initially present in the mole ratio required by the balanced chemical equation; they both react completely, so there is no excess of either one. In Example 11-2, we need to determine which reactant limits the reaction. Before you proceed, be sure you understand how the ideas of Section 3-3 are used in these examples.

In many cases more than one mole of a base will be required to neutralize completely one mole of an acid, or more than one mole of an acid will be required to neutralize completely one mole of a base.

$$\underset{1\ \text{mol}}{H_2SO_4} + \underset{2\ \text{mol}}{2NaOH} \longrightarrow \underset{1\ \text{mol}}{Na_2SO_4} + 2H_2O$$

$$\underset{2\ \text{mol}}{2HCl} + \underset{1\ \text{mol}}{Ca(OH)_2} \longrightarrow \underset{1\ \text{mol}}{CaCl_2} + 2H_2O$$

The first equation shows that one mole of H$_2$SO$_4$ reacts with two moles of NaOH. Thus, *two* liters of 1 M NaOH solution are required to neutralize one liter of 1 M H$_2$SO$_4$ solution. The second equation shows that two moles of HCl react with one mole of Ca(OH)$_2$. Thus, *two* liters of HCl solution are required to neutralize one liter of Ca(OH)$_2$ solution of equal molarity.

Students often mistakenly try to use the relation

$$V_1 M_1 = V_2 M_2$$

to solve problems about solution stoichiometry. This equation is intended *only* for dilution problems, and not for problems involving reactions.

EXAMPLE 11-3 *Volume of Acid to Neutralize Base*

What volume of 0.00300 M HCl solution would just neutralize 30.0 mL of 0.00100 M Ca(OH)$_2$ solution?

Plan

We write the balanced equation for the reaction to determine the reaction ratio. Then we (1) convert milliliters of Ca(OH)$_2$ solution to millimoles of Ca(OH)$_2$ using molarity in the reaction ratio, 0.00100 mmol Ca$_2$(OH)/1.00 mL Ca(OH)$_2$ solution; (2) convert millimoles of Ca(OH)$_2$ to millimoles of HCl using the reaction ratio, 2 mmol HCl/1 mmol Ca(OH) (from the balanced equation); and (3) convert millimoles of HCl to milliliters of HCl solution using the reaction ratio, 1.00 mL HCl/0.00300 mmol HCl, that is, molarity inverted.

CD-ROM Screen 5.18, Stoichiometry of Reactions in Solution.

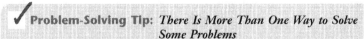

Solution

The balanced equation for the reaction is

$$2HCl + Ca(OH)_2 \longrightarrow CaCl_2 + 2H_2O$$

$$\begin{array}{cccc} 2 \text{ mmol} & 1 \text{ mmol} & 1 \text{ mmol} & 2 \text{ mmol} \end{array}$$

$$\underline{?}\text{ mL HCl} =$$

$$30.0 \text{ mL Ca(OH)}_2 \times \frac{0.00100 \text{ mmol Ca(OH)}_2}{1.00 \text{ mL Ca(OH)}_2} \times \frac{2 \text{ mmol HCl}}{1 \text{ mmol Ca(OH)}_2} \times \frac{1.00 \text{ mL HCl}}{0.00300 \text{ mmol HCl}}$$

$$= 20.0 \text{ mL HCl}$$

You should now work Exercise 16.

> The balanced chemical equation allows us to construct the reaction ratio as either a mole ratio or a milli-mole ratio.
>
> $$\frac{2 \text{ mol HCl}}{1 \text{ mol Ca(OH)}_2} \quad \text{or} \quad \frac{2 \text{ mmol HCl}}{1 \text{ mmol Ca(OH)}_2}$$

In the preceding example we used the unit factor, 2 mol HCl/1 mol Ca(OH)$_2$, to convert moles of Ca(OH)$_2$ to moles of HCl because the balanced equation shows that two moles of HCl are required to neutralize one mole of Ca(OH)$_2$. We must always write the balanced equation and determine the *reaction ratio*.

✔ **Problem-Solving Tip:** *There Is More Than One Way to Solve Some Problems*

In many problems more than one "plan" can be followed. In Example 11-3 a particular plan was used successfully. Many students can more easily visualize the solution by following a plan like that in Examples 11-1 and 11-4. We suggest that you use the plan that you find most understandable.

EXAMPLE 11-4 *Acid–Base Reactions*

If 100. mL of 1.00 M H$_2$SO$_4$ solution is mixed with 200. mL of 1.00 M KOH, what salt is produced, and what is its molarity?

Plan

We proceed as we did in Example 11-2. We note that the reaction ratio is 1 mmol of H$_2$SO$_4$ to 2 mmol of KOH to 1 mmol of K$_2$SO$_4$.

Solution

> Don't forget to add the solution volumes to find the volume of the final solution.

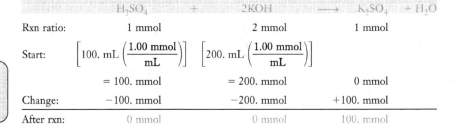

	H$_2$SO$_4$	+	2KOH	$\longrightarrow$	K$_2$SO$_4$	+ H$_2$O
Rxn ratio:	1 mmol		2 mmol		1 mmol	
Start:	$\left[100.\text{ mL}\left(\dfrac{1.00 \text{ mmol}}{\text{mL}}\right)\right]$		$\left[200.\text{ mL}\left(\dfrac{1.00 \text{ mmol}}{\text{mL}}\right)\right]$			
	= 100. mmol		= 200. mmol		0 mmol	
Change:	−100. mmol		−200. mmol		+100. mmol	
After rxn:	0 mmol		0 mmol		100. mmol	

The reaction produces 100. mmol of potassium sulfate. This is contained in 300. mL of solution, and so the concentration is

$$\underline{?}\ \frac{\text{mmol } K_2SO_4}{\text{mL}} = \frac{100. \text{ mmol } K_2SO_4}{300. \text{ mL}} = \boxed{0.333\ M\ K_2SO_4}$$

You should now work Exercise 12.

Because K_2SO_4 is a soluble salt, this corresponds to 0.666 M K^+ and 0.333 M SO_4^{2-}.

11-2 TITRATIONS

In Examples 3-24 and 11-3, we calculated the volume of one solution that is required to react with a given volume of another solution, with the concentrations of *both* solutions given. In the laboratory we often measure the volume of one solution that is required to react with a given volume of another solution of known concentration. Then we calculate the concentration of the first solution. The process is called **titration** (Figure 11-1).

$SC_{LINKS.}^{i}$

TOPIC: Titration
GO TO: www.scilinks.org
*sci*LINKS CODE: WCH1110

(a)

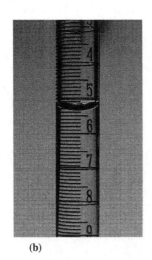
(b)

(c)

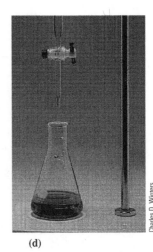
(d)

Charles D. Winters

Figure 11-1 The titration process. (a) A typical setup for titration in a teaching laboratory. The solution to be titrated is placed in an Erlenmeyer flask, and a few drops of indicator are added. The buret is filled with a standard solution (or the solution to be standardized). The volume of solution in the buret is read carefully. (b) The meniscus describes the surface of the liquid in the buret. Aqueous solutions wet glass, so the meniscus of an aqueous solution is always concave. The position of the *bottom* of the meniscus is read and recorded. (c) The solution in the buret is added (dropwise near the end point), with stirring, to the Erlenmeyer flask until the end point is reached. (d) The end point is signaled by the appearance (or change) of color *throughout* the solution being titrated. (A very large excess of indicator was used to make this photograph.) The volume of the liquid is read again — the difference between the final and initial buret readings is the volume of the solution used.

> Titration is the process in which a solution of one reactant, the titrant, is carefully added to a solution of another reactant, and the volume of titrant required for complete reaction is measured.

How does one know when to stop a titration—that is, when is the chemical reaction just complete? In one method, a few drops of an indicator solution are added to the solution to be titrated. An acid–base **indicator** is a substance that can exist in different forms, with different colors that depend on the concentration of H^+ in the solution. At least one of these forms must be very intensely colored so that even very small amounts of it can be seen.

We can titrate an acid solution of unknown concentration by adding a standardized solution of sodium hydroxide dropwise from a **buret** (see Figure 11-1). A common buret is graduated in large intervals of 1 mL and in smaller intervals of 0.1 mL so that it is possible to estimate the volume of a solution dispensed to within at least ±0.02 mL. (Experienced individuals can often read a buret to ±0.01 mL.) The analyst tries to choose an indicator that changes color clearly at the point at which stoichiometrically equivalent amounts of acid and base have reacted, the **equivalence point.** The point at which the indicator changes color and the titration is stopped is called the **end point.** Ideally, the end point should coincide with the equivalence point. Phenolphthalein is colorless in acidic solution and reddish violet in basic solution. In a titration in which a base is added to an acid, phenolphthalein is often used as an indicator. The end point is signaled by the first appearance of a faint pink coloration that persists for at least 15 seconds as the solution is swirled.

The choice of indicators will be discussed in Section 19.4.

EXAMPLE 11-5 *Titration*

What is the molarity of a hydrochloric acid solution if 36.7 mL of the HCl solution is required to react with 43.2 mL of 0.236 M sodium hydroxide solution?

$$HCl + NaOH \longrightarrow NaCl + H_2O$$

Plan

The balanced equation tells us that the reaction ratio is one millimole of HCl to one millimole of NaOH, which gives the conversion factor, 1 mmol HCl/1 mmol NaOH.

$$HCl \ + \ NaOH \longrightarrow \ NaCl \ + \ H_2O$$
$$\text{1 mmol} \quad \text{1 mmol} \qquad \text{1 mmol} \quad \text{1 mmol}$$

First we find the number of millimoles of NaOH. The reaction ratio is one millimole of HCl to one millimole of NaOH, so the HCl solution must contain the same number of millimoles of HCl. Then we can calculate the molarity of the HCl solution because we know its volume.

Solution

The volume of a solution (in milliliters) multiplied by its molarity gives the number of millimoles of solute.

$$\underline{?}\text{ mmol NaOH} = 43.2 \text{ mL NaOH soln} \times \frac{0.236 \text{ mmol NaOH}}{1 \text{ mL NaOH soln}} = 10.2 \text{ mmol NaOH}$$

Because the reaction ratio is one millimole of NaOH to one millimole of HCl, the HCl solution must contain 10.2 millimole HCl.

$$\underline{?}\text{ mol HCl} = 10.2 \text{ mmol NaOH} \times \frac{1 \text{ mmol HCl}}{1 \text{ mmol NaOH}} = 10.2 \text{ mmol HCl}$$

CD-ROM Screen 5.15, Titrations; view the simulation in that screen.

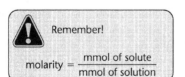

Remember!

$$\text{molarity} = \frac{\text{mmol of solute}}{\text{mmol of solution}}$$

The indicator phenolphthalein changes from colorless, its color in acidic solutions, to pink, its color in basic solutions, when the reaction in Example 11-5 reaches completion. Note the first appearance of a faint pink coloration in the middle beaker; this signals that the end point is near.

We know the volume of the HCl solution, so we can calculate its molarity.

$$\frac{?\ \text{mmol HCl}}{\text{mL HCl soln}} = \frac{10.2\ \text{mmol HCl}}{36.7\ \text{mL HCl soln}} = \boxed{0.278\ M\ \text{HCl}}$$

EXAMPLE 11-6 *Titration*

A 43.2-mL sample of 0.236 *M* sodium hydroxide solution reacts completely with 36.7 mL of a sulfuric acid solution. What is the molarity of the H_2SO_4 solution?

$$H_2SO_4 + 2NaOH \longrightarrow Na_2SO_4 + 2H_2O$$

Plan

The balanced equation tells us that the reaction ratio is one millimole of H_2SO_4 to two millimoles of NaOH, which gives the conversion factor, 1 mmol H_2SO_4/2 mmol NaOH.

$$H_2SO_4 + 2NaOH \longrightarrow Na_2SO_4 + 2H_2O$$
$$\text{1 mmol} \quad \text{2 mmol} \qquad \text{1 mmol} \quad \text{2 mmol}$$

First we find the number of millimoles of NaOH. The reaction ratio is one millimole of H_2SO_4 to two millimoles of NaOH, so the number of millimoles of H_2SO_4 must be one half of the number of millimoles of NaOH. Then we can calculate the molarity of the H_2SO_4 solution because we know its volume.

Solution

The volume of a solution (in milliliters) multiplied by its molarity gives the number of millimoles of solute.

$$?\ \text{mmol NaOH} = 43.2\ \text{mL NaOH soln} \times \frac{0.236\ \text{mmol NaOH}}{1\ \text{mL NaOH soln}} = 10.2\ \text{mmol NaOH}$$

Because the reaction ratio is two millimoles of NaOH to one millimole of H_2SO_4, the H_2SO_4 solution must contain 5.10 millimoles of H_2SO_4.

$$\underline{?}\ \text{mmol}\ H_2SO_4 = 10.2\ \text{mmol NaOH} \times \frac{1\ \text{mmol}\ H_2SO_4}{2\ \text{mmol NaOH}} = 5.10\ \text{mmol}\ H_2SO_4$$

We know the volume of the H_2SO_4 solution, so we can calculate its molarity.

$$\frac{\underline{?}\ \text{mmol}\ H_2SO_4}{\text{mL}\ H_2SO_4\ \text{soln}} = \frac{5.10\ \text{mmol}\ H_2SO_4}{36.7\ \text{mL}\ H_2SO_4\ \text{soln}} = \boxed{0.139\ M\ H_2SO_4}$$

You should now work Exercise 38.

Notice the similarity between Examples 11-5 and 11-6 in which 43.2 mL of 0.236 M NaOH solution is used. In Example 11-5 the reaction ratio is 1 mmol acid/1 mmol base, whereas in Example 11-6 the reaction ratio is 1 mmol acid/2 mmol base, and so the molarity of the HCl solution (0.278 M) is twice the molarity of the H_2SO_4 solution (0.139 M).

Solutions with accurately known concentrations are called **standard solutions.** Often we prepare a solution of a substance and then determine its concentration by titration with a standard solution.

Standardization is the process by which one determines the concentration of a solution by measuring accurately the volume of the solution required to react with an accurately known amount of a **primary standard.** The standardized solution is then known as a **secondary standard** and is used in the analysis of unknowns.

The properties of an ideal *primary standard* include the following:

CO_2, H_2O, and O_2 are present in the atmosphere. They react with many substances.

1. It must not react with or absorb the components of the atmosphere, such as water vapor, oxygen, and carbon dioxide.
2. It must react according to one invariable reaction.
3. It must have a high percentage purity.
4. It should have a high formula weight to minimize the effect of error in weighing.
5. It must be soluble in the solvent of interest.
6. It should be nontoxic.
7. It should be readily available (inexpensive).
8. It should be environmentally friendly.

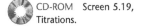 CD-ROM   Screen 5.19, Titrations.

The first five of these characteristics are essential to minimize the errors involved in analytical methods. The last three characteristics are just as important as the first five in most analytical laboratories. Because primary standards are often costly and difficult to prepare, secondary standards are often used in day-to-day work.

11-3 THE MOLE METHOD AND MOLARITY

Let us now describe the use of a few primary standards for acids and bases. One primary standard for solutions of acids is sodium carbonate, Na_2CO_3, a solid compound.

$$\underset{\text{1 mol}}{H_2SO_4} + \underset{\text{1 mol}}{Na_2CO_3} \longrightarrow \underset{\text{1 mol}}{Na_2SO_4} + \underset{\text{1 mol}}{CO_2} + \underset{\text{1 mol}}{H_2O}$$

$$1\ \text{mol}\ Na_2CO_3 = 106.0\ \text{g} \qquad \text{and} \qquad 1\ \text{mmol}\ Na_2CO_3 = 0.1060\ \text{g}$$

Refer to the Brønsted–Lowry theory. (Section 10-4).

Sodium carbonate is a salt. Because a base can be broadly defined as a substance that reacts with hydrogen ions, in *this* reaction Na_2CO_3 can be thought of as a base.

EXAMPLE 11-7 *Standardization of an Acid Solution*

Calculate the molarity of a solution of H_2SO_4 if 40.0 mL of the solution neutralizes 0.364 g of Na_2CO_3.

Plan

We know from the balanced equation that 1 mol of H_2SO_4 reacts with 1 mol of Na_2CO_3, 106.0 g. This provides the reaction ratio that converts 0.364 g of Na_2CO_3 to the corresponding number of moles of H_2SO_4, from which we can calculate molarity.

$$\boxed{\begin{array}{c} g\ Na_2CO_3 \\ available \end{array}} \longrightarrow \boxed{\begin{array}{c} mol\ Na_2CO_3 \\ present \end{array}} \longrightarrow \boxed{\begin{array}{c} mol\ H_2SO_4 \\ used \end{array}} \longrightarrow \boxed{\begin{array}{c} molarity \\ of\ H_2SO_4 \end{array}}$$

Solution

$$\underline{?}\ mol\ H_2SO_4 = 0.364\ g\ Na_2CO_3 \times \frac{1\ mol\ Na_2CO_3}{106.0\ g\ Na_2CO_3} \times \frac{1\ mol\ H_2SO_4}{1\ mol\ Na_2CO_3}$$

$$= 0.00343\ mol\ H_2SO_4 \quad \text{(present in 40.0 mL of solution)}$$

Now we calculate the molarity of the H_2SO_4 solution

$$\frac{\underline{?}\ mol\ H_2SO_4}{L} = \frac{0.00343\ mol\ H_2SO_4}{0.0400\ L} = \boxed{0.0858\ M\ H_2SO_4}$$

You should now work Exercise 26.

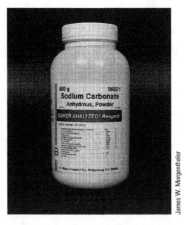

Sodium carbonate is often used as a primary standard for acids.

Most inorganic bases are metal hydroxides, all of which are solids. Even in the solid state, however, most inorganic bases react rapidly with CO_2 (an acid anhydride) from the atmosphere. Most metal hydroxides also absorb H_2O from the air. These properties make it *very* difficult to weigh out samples of pure metal hydroxides accurately. Chemists obtain solutions of bases of accurately known concentration by standardizing the solutions against an acidic salt, potassium hydrogen phthalate, $KC_6H_4(COO)(COOH)$. This is produced by neutralization of one of the two ionizable hydrogens of an organic acid, phthalic acid.

The "ph" in *phthalate* is silent. Phthalate is pronounced "thalate."

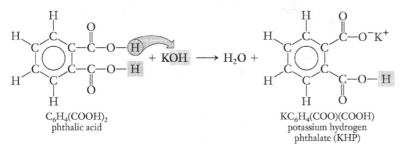

$C_6H_4(COOH)_2$
phthalic acid

$KC_6H_4(COO)(COOH)$
potassium hydrogen
phthalate (KHP)

This acidic salt, known simply as KHP, has one acidic hydrogen (highlighted) that reacts with bases. KHP is easily obtained in a high state of purity and is soluble in water. It is used as a primary standard for bases.

The P in KHP stands for the phthalate ion, $C_6H_4(COO)_2^{2-}$, *not* phosphorus.

EXAMPLE 11-8 *Standardization of Base Solution*

A 20.00-mL sample of a solution of NaOH reacts with 0.3641 g of KHP. Calculate the molarity of the NaOH solution.

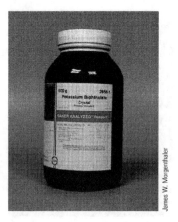

Very pure KHP is readily available.

James W. Morgenthaler

Plan

We first write the balanced equation for the reaction between NaOH and KHP. We then calculate the number of moles of NaOH in 20.00 mL of solution from the amount of KHP that reacts with it. Then we can calculate the molarity of the NaOH solution.

$$\boxed{\begin{array}{c}\text{g KHP}\\\text{available}\end{array}} \longrightarrow \boxed{\begin{array}{c}\text{mol KHP}\\\text{available}\end{array}} \longrightarrow \boxed{\begin{array}{c}\text{mol NaOH}\\\text{required}\end{array}} \longrightarrow \boxed{\begin{array}{c}\text{molarity}\\\text{of NaOH}\end{array}}$$

Solution

$$\text{NaOH} + \text{KHP} \longrightarrow \text{NaKP} + \text{H}_2\text{O}$$
$$\text{1 mol} \quad\; \text{1 mol} \qquad\quad \text{1 mol} \quad\; \text{1 mol}$$

We see that NaOH and KHP react in a 1:1 reaction ratio. One mole of KHP is 204.2 g.

$$\underline{?}\text{ mol NaOH} = 0.3641\text{ g KHP} \times \frac{1\text{ mol KHP}}{204.2\text{ g KHP}} \times \frac{1\text{ mol NaOH}}{1\text{ mol KHP}} = 0.001783\text{ mol NaOH}$$

Then we calculate the molarity of the NaOH solution.

$$\frac{\underline{?}\text{ mol NaOH}}{\text{L}} = \frac{0.001783\text{ mol NaOH}}{0.02000\text{ L}} = \boxed{0.08915\ M\text{ NaOH}}$$

You should now work Exercise 28.

Impure samples of acids can be titrated with standard solutions of bases. The results can be used to determine percentage purity of the samples.

EXAMPLE 11-9   *Determination of Percent Acid*

Oxalic acid, $(\text{COOH})_2$, is used to remove rust stains and some ink stains from fabrics. A 0.1743-g sample of *impure* oxalic acid required 39.82 mL of 0.08915 M NaOH solution for complete neutralization. No acidic impurities were present. Calculate the percentage purity of the $(\text{COOH})_2$.

Plan

We write the balanced equation for the reaction and calculate the number of moles of NaOH in the standard solution. Then we calculate the mass of $(\text{COOH})_2$ in the sample, which gives us the information we need to calculate percentage purity.

Solution

The equation for the complete neutralization of $(\text{COOH})_2$ with NaOH is

$$2\text{NaOH} + (\text{COOH})_2 \longrightarrow \text{Na}_2(\text{COO})_2 + 2\text{H}_2\text{O}$$
$$\text{2 mol} \qquad \text{1 mol} \qquad\qquad \text{1 mol} \qquad \text{2 mol}$$

Each molecule of $(\text{COOH})_2$ contains two acidic H's.

$$\begin{array}{ccc} & \text{O} & \text{O} \\ & \| & \| \\ \text{H}-\text{O}-&\text{C}-\text{C}&-\text{O}-\text{H} \end{array}$$
1 mol = 90.04 g

Two moles of NaOH neutralizes completely one mole of $(\text{COOH})_2$. The number of moles of NaOH that react is the volume times the molarity of the solution.

$$\underline{?}\text{ mol NaOH} = 0.03982\text{ L} \times \frac{0.08915\text{ mol NaOH}}{\text{L}} = 0.003550\text{ mol NaOH}$$

Now we calculate the mass of $(\text{COOH})_2$ that reacts with 0.003550 mol NaOH.

$$? \text{ g (COOH)}_2 = 0.003550 \text{ mol NaOH} \times \frac{1 \text{ mol (COOH)}_2}{2 \text{ mol NaOH}} \times \frac{90.04 \text{ g (COOH)}_2}{1 \text{ mol (COOH)}_2}$$

$$= 0.1598 \text{ g (COOH)}_2$$

The 0.1743-g sample contained 0.1598 g of $(COOH)_2$, so its percentage purity was

$$\% \text{ purity} = \frac{0.1598 \text{ g (COOH)}_2}{0.1743 \text{ g sample}} \times 100\% = \boxed{91.68\% \text{ pure (COOH)}_2}$$

You should now work Exercise 34.

11-4 EQUIVALENT WEIGHTS AND NORMALITY

In acid–base reactions, the mass of the acid (expressed in grams) that could furnish 6.022×10^{23} hydrogen ions (1 mol) or that could react with 6.022×10^{23} hydroxide ions (1 mol) is defined as one **equivalent weight,** or **equivalent (eq), of acid.** One mole of an acid contains 6.022×10^{23} formula units of the acid. Consider hydrochloric acid as a typical monoprotic acid.

$$HCl \xrightarrow{\text{H}_2\text{O}} H^+(aq) + Cl^-(aq)$$

1 mol	1 mol	1 mol
36.46 g	1.008 g	35.45 g
6.022×10^{23} formula units	6.022×10^{23} formula units	6.022×10^{23} formula units

We see that one mole of HCl can produce 6.022×10^{23} H$^+$ ions, and so *one mole of HCl is one equivalent.* The same is true for all monoprotic acids.

Sulfuric acid is a diprotic acid. One molecule of H_2SO_4 can furnish $2H^+$ ions.

$$H_2SO_4 \xrightarrow{\text{H}_2\text{O}} 2H^+(aq) + SO_4{}^{2-}(aq)$$

1 mol	2 mol	1 mol
98.08 g	2(1.008 g)	96.06 g
6.022×10^{23} formula units	$2(6.022 \times 10^{23})$ formula units	6.022×10^{23} formula units

This equation shows that one mole of H_2SO_4 can produce $2(6.022 \times 10^{23})$ H$^+$; therefore, one mole of H_2SO_4 is *two* equivalent weights in all reactions in which *both* acidic hydrogen atoms react.

One **equivalent weight of a base** is defined as the mass of the base (expressed in grams) that will furnish 6.022×10^{23} hydroxide ions or the mass of the base that will react with 6.022×10^{23} hydrogen ions.

The equivalent weight of an *acid* is obtained by dividing its formula weight in grams either by the number of acidic hydrogens that could be furnished by one formula unit of the acid *or* by the number of hydroxide ions with which one formula unit of the acid reacts. The equivalent weight of a *base* is obtained by dividing its formula weight in grams either by the number of hydroxide ions furnished by one formula unit *or* by the number of hydrogen ions with which one formula unit of the base reacts. Equivalent weights of some common acids and bases are given in Table 11-1.

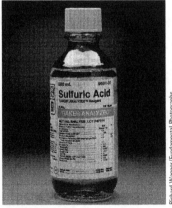

One mole of H_2SO_4 is two equivalent weights of H_2SO_4.

TABLE 11-1	Equivalent Weights* of Some Acids and Bases		
Acids		**Bases**	
Symbolic representation	*One equivalent*	*Symbolic representation*	*One equivalent*
$\dfrac{HNO_3}{1}$ $= \dfrac{63.02\ g}{1} = 63.02\ g\ HNO_3$		$\dfrac{NaOH}{1}$ $= \dfrac{40.00\ g}{1} = 40.00\ g\ NaOH$	
$\dfrac{CH_3COOH}{1}$ $= \dfrac{60.03\ g}{1} = 60.03\ g\ CH_3COOH$		$\dfrac{NH_3}{1}$ $= \dfrac{17.04\ g}{1} = 17.04\ g\ NH_3$	
$\dfrac{KHP}{1}$ $= \dfrac{204.2\ g}{1} = 204.2\ g\ KHP$		$\dfrac{Ca(OH)_2}{2}$ $= \dfrac{74.10\ g}{2} = 37.05\ g\ Ca(OH)_2$	
$\dfrac{H_2SO_4}{2}$ $= \dfrac{98.08\ g}{2} = 49.04\ g\ H_2SO_4$		$\dfrac{Ba(OH)_2}{2}$ $= \dfrac{171.36\ g}{2} = 85.68\ g\ Ba(OH)_2$	

*Complete neutralization is assumed.

Any calculation that can be carried out with equivalent weights and normality can also be done by the mole method using molarity. The methods of this section are widely used, however, in health-related fields and in many industrial laboratories.

An **equivalent weight** is often referred to simply as an **equivalent** (eq).

A **milliequivalent weight** is often referred to simply as a **milliequivalent** (meq).

Because one mole of an acid does not necessarily neutralize one mole of a base, some chemists prefer a method of expressing concentration other than molarity to retain a one-to-one relationship. Concentrations of solutions of acids and bases are frequently expressed as *normality* (N). The **normality** of a solution is defined as the number of equivalent weights, or simply equivalents (eq), of solute per liter of solution. Normality may be represented symbolically as

$$\text{normality} = \frac{\text{number of equivalent weights of solute}}{\text{liter of solution}} = \frac{\text{no. eq}}{L}$$

By definition there are 1000 milliequivalent weights (meq) in one equivalent weight of an acid or base. Normality may also be represented as

$$\text{normality} = \frac{\text{number of milliequivalent weights of solute}}{\text{milliliter of solution}} = \frac{\text{no. meq}}{mL}$$

EXAMPLE 11-10 *Concentration of a Solution*

Calculate the normality of a solution of 4.202 grams of HNO_3 in 600. mL of solution.

Plan

We convert grams of HNO_3 to moles of HNO_3 and then to equivalents of HNO_3, which lets us calculate the normality.

$$\frac{g\ HNO_3}{L} \longrightarrow \frac{mol\ HNO_3}{L} \longrightarrow \frac{eq\ HNO_3}{L} = N\ HNO_3$$

Solution

$$N = \frac{\text{no. eq } HNO_3}{L}$$

$$\underset{?}{\underbrace{\frac{\text{eq } HNO_3}{L}}} = \underbrace{\frac{4.202 \text{ g } HNO_3}{0.600 \text{ L}}}_{M_{HNO_3}} \times \frac{1 \text{ mol } HNO_3}{63.02 \text{ g } HNO_3} \times \frac{1 \text{ eq } HNO_3}{\text{mol } HNO_3} = \boxed{0.111 \; N \; HNO_3}$$

Because normality is equal to molarity times the number of equivalents per mole of solute, a solution's normality is always equal to or greater than its molarity.

$$\text{normality} = \text{molarity} \times \frac{\text{no. eq}}{\text{mol}} \quad \text{or} \quad N = M \times \frac{\text{no. eq}}{\text{mol}}$$

EXAMPLE 11-11

Calculate (a) the molarity and (b) the normality of a solution that contains 9.50 grams of barium hydroxide in 2000. mL of solution.

Plan

(a) We use the same kind of logic we used in Example 11-10.

(b) Because each mole of $Ba(OH)_2$ produces 2 moles of OH^- ions, 1 mole of $Ba(OH)_2$ is 2 equivalents. Thus,

$$N = M \times \frac{2 \text{ eq}}{\text{mol}} \quad \text{or} \quad M = \frac{N}{2 \text{ eq/mol}}$$

Solution

(a) $\underset{?}{\underbrace{}}\dfrac{\text{mol } Ba(OH)_2}{L} = \dfrac{9.50 \text{ g } Ba(OH)_2}{2.00 \text{ L}} \times \dfrac{1 \text{ mol } Ba (OH)_2}{171.36 \text{ g } Ba(OH)_2} = \boxed{0.0277 \; M \; Ba(OH)_2}$

(b) $\underset{?}{\underbrace{}}\dfrac{\text{eq } Ba(OH)_2}{L} = \dfrac{0.0277 \text{ mol } Ba(OH)_2}{L} \times \dfrac{2 \text{ eq } Ba(OH)_2}{1 \text{ mol } Ba(OH)_2} = \boxed{0.0554 \; N \; Ba(OH)_2}$

You should now work Exercises 40 through 42.

Because each formula unit of $Ba(OH)_2$ contains two OH^- ions,

$$1 \text{ mol } Ba(OH)_2 = 2 \text{ eq } Ba(OH)_2$$

Thus, molarity is one half of normality for $Ba(OH)_2$ solutions.

From the definitions of one equivalent of an acid and of a base, we see that *one equivalent of an acid reacts with one equivalent of any base.* It is *not* true that one mole of any acid reacts with one mole of any base in any specific chemical reaction that goes to completion. As a consequence of the definition of equivalents, 1 eq acid $\cong$ 1 eq base. We may write the following for *all* acid–base reactions that go to completion.

The notation $\cong$ is read "is equivalent to."

number of equivalents of acid = number of equivalents of base

The product of the volume of a solution, in liters, and its normality is equal to the number of equivalents of solute contained in the solution. For a solution of an acid,

$$L_{acid} \times N_{acid} = L_{acid} \times \frac{\text{eq acid}}{L_{acid}} = \text{eq acid}$$

Remember that the product of volume and concentration equals the amount of solute.

Similar relationships can be written for a solution of a base. Because 1 eq of acid *always* reacts with 1 eq of base, we may write

$$\text{number of equivalents of acid} = \text{number of equivalents of base}$$

so

The conversion factors needed to convert liters to milliliters on each side of this equation will cancel.

$$L_{acid} \times N_{acid} = L_{base} \times N_{base} \qquad \text{or} \qquad mL_{acid} \times N_{acid} = mL_{base} \times N_{base}$$

EXAMPLE 11-12 *Volume Required for Neutralization*

What volume of 0.100 N HNO$_3$ solution is required to neutralize completely 50.0 mL of a 0.150 N solution of Ba(OH)$_2$?

Plan

We know three of the four variables in the relationship

$$mL_{acid} \times N_{acid} = mL_{base} \times N_{base}$$

and so we solve for mL acid.

Solution

$$\underline{?}\ mL_{acid} = \frac{mL_{base} \times N_{base}}{N_{acid}} = \frac{50.0\ mL \times 0.150\ N}{0.100\ N} = \boxed{75.0\ mL\ of\ HNO_3\ solution}$$

You should now work Exercise 49.

In Example 11-13 let's again solve Example 11-7, this time using normality rather than molarity. The balanced equation for the reaction of H$_2$SO$_4$ with Na$_2$CO$_3$, interpreted in terms of equivalent weights, is

By definition, there must be equal numbers of equivalents of reactants in a balanced chemical equation.

$$\begin{array}{ccccccccc}
H_2SO_4 & + & Na_2CO_3 & \longrightarrow & Na_2SO_4 & + & CO_2 & + & H_2O \\
1\ mol & & 1\ mol & & 1\ mol & & 1\ mol & & 1\ mol \\
2\ eq & & 2\ eq & & & & & & \\
98.08\ g & & 106.0\ g & & & & & &
\end{array}$$

So, 1 eq Na$_2$CO$_3$ = 53.0 g

EXAMPLE 11-13

Calculate the normality of a solution of H$_2$SO$_4$ if 40.0 mL of the solution reacts completely with 0.364 gram of Na$_2$CO$_3$.

Plan

We refer to the balanced equation. We are given the mass of Na$_2$CO$_3$, so we convert grams of Na$_2$CO$_3$ to equivalents of Na$_2$CO$_3$, then to equivalents of H$_2$SO$_4$, which lets us calculate the normality of the H$_2$SO$_4$ solution.

$$\boxed{\begin{array}{c}g\ Na_2CO_3 \\ present\end{array}} \longrightarrow \boxed{\begin{array}{c}eq\ Na_2CO_3 \\ present\end{array}} \longrightarrow \boxed{\begin{array}{c}eq\ H_2SO_4 \\ needed\end{array}} \longrightarrow \boxed{\begin{array}{c}eq\ H_2SO_4 \\ \hline L\end{array}}$$

Solution

First we calculate the number of equivalents of Na_2CO_3 in the sample.

$$\text{no. eq } Na_2CO_3 = 0.364 \text{ g } Na_2CO_3 \times \frac{1 \text{ eq } Na_2CO_3}{53.0 \text{ g } Na_2CO_3} = 6.87 \times 10^{-3} \text{ eq } Na_2CO_3$$

Because no. eq H_2SO_4 = no. eq Na_2CO_3, we can write

$$L_{H_2SO_4} \times N_{H_2SO_4} = 6.87 \times 10^{-3} \text{ eq } H_2SO_4$$

$$N_{H_2SO_4} = \frac{6.87 \times 10^{-3} \text{ eq } H_2SO_4}{L_{H_2SO_4}} = \frac{6.87 \times 10^{-3} \text{ eq } H_2SO_4}{0.040 \text{ L}} = \boxed{0.172 \text{ } N \text{ } H_2SO_4}$$

You should now work Exercise 46.

The starting values in this example are the same as those in Example 11-7. The normality of this H_2SO_4 solution is twice the molarity obtained in Example 11-7 because 1 mol of H_2SO_4 is 2 eq.

OXIDATION–REDUCTION REACTIONS

Our rules for assigning oxidation numbers are constructed so that in all redox reactions

the total increase in oxidation numbers must equal the total decrease in oxidation numbers.

This equivalence provides the basis for balancing redox equations. Although there is no single "best method" for balancing all redox equations, the half-reaction method is the most widely used. Many redox equations can be balanced by simple inspection, but you should master the half-reaction method so it can be used to balance difficult equations.

This method is used extensively in electrochemistry (Chapter 21).

SC*i*LINKS.
TOPIC: Redox Reactions
GO TO: www.scilinks.org
*sci*LINKS CODE: WCH0460

All balanced equations must satisfy two criteria.

1. There must be mass balance. That is, the same number of atoms of each kind must appear in reactants and products.
2. There must be charge balance. The sums of actual charges on the left and right sides of the equation must equal each other. In a balanced *formula unit equation,* the total charge on each side will be equal to zero. In a balanced *net ionic equation,* the total charge on each side might not be zero, but it still must be equal on the two sides of the equation.

11-5 THE HALF-REACTION METHOD

In the half-reaction method we separate and completely balance equations describing oxidation and reduction **half-reactions.** Then we equalize the numbers of electrons gained and lost in each. Finally, we add the resulting half-reactions to give the overall balanced equation. The general procedure follows.

1. Write as much of the overall unbalanced equation as possible, omitting spectator ions.

2. Construct unbalanced oxidation and reduction half-reactions (these are usually incomplete as well as unbalanced). Show complete formulas for polyatomic ions and molecules.

3. Balance by inspection all elements in each half-reaction, except H and O. Then use the chart in Section 11-6 to balance H and O in each half-reaction.

4. Balance the charge in each half-reaction by adding electrons as "products" or "reactants."

5. Balance the electron transfer by multiplying the balanced half-reactions by appropriate integers.

6. Add the resulting half-reactions and eliminate any common terms.

CD-ROM   Screen 20.3, Balancing Equations for Redox Reactions.

EXAMPLE 11-14   *Balancing Redox Equations*

A useful analytical procedure involves the oxidation of iodide ions to free iodine. The free iodine is then titrated with a standard solution of sodium thiosulfate, $Na_2S_2O_3$. Iodine oxidizes $S_2O_3^{2-}$ ions to tetrathionate ions, $S_4O_6^{2-}$, and is reduced to I^- ions. Write the balanced net ionic equation for this reaction.

Plan

We are given the formulas for two reactants and two products. We use these to write as much of the equations as possible. We construct and balance the appropriate half-reactions using the rules just described. Then we add the half-reactions and eliminate common terms.

Solution

$$I_2 + S_2O_3^{2-} \longrightarrow I^- + S_4O_6^{2-}$$

$$I_2 \longrightarrow I^- \qquad \text{(red. half-reaction)}$$

$$I_2 \longrightarrow 2I^-$$

Each I_2 gains $2e^-$. I_2 is reduced; it is the oxidizing agent.

$$I_2 + 2e^- \longrightarrow 2I^- \qquad \text{(balanced red. half-reaction)}$$

$$- -$$

$$S_2O_3^{2-} \longrightarrow S_4O_6^{2-} \qquad \text{(ox. half-reaction)}$$

$$2S_2O_3^{2-} \longrightarrow S_4O_6^{2-}$$

Each $S_2O_3^{2-}$ ion loses an e^-. $S_2O_3^{2-}$ is oxidized; it is the reducing agent.

$$2S_2O_3^{2-} \longrightarrow S_4O_6^{2-} + 2e^- \qquad \text{(balanced ox. half-reaction)}$$

Each balanced half-reaction involves a transfer of two electrons. We add these half-reactions and cancel the electrons.

Oxidizing and reducing agents were defined in Section 4-7.

$$I_2 + 2e^- \longrightarrow 2I^-$$

$$2S_2O_3^{2-} \longrightarrow S_4O_6^{2-} + 2e^-$$

$$\overline{I_2(s) + 2S_2O_3^{2-}(aq) \longrightarrow 2I^-(aq) + S_4O_6^{2-}(aq)}$$

11-6 ADDING H⁺, OH⁻, OR H₂O TO BALANCE OXYGEN OR HYDROGEN

Frequently we need more oxygen or hydrogen to complete the mass balance for a reaction or half-reaction in aqueous solution. We must be careful, however, not to introduce other changes in oxidation number or to use species that could not actually be present in the solution. We cannot add H_2 or O_2 to equations because these species are not present in aqueous solutions. Acidic solutions do not contain significant concentrations of OH^- ions. Basic solutions do not contain significant concentrations of H^+ ions.

| In acidic solution: | We add only H^+ or H_2O (*not* OH^- in acidic solution). |
| In basic solution: | We add only OH^- or H_2O (*not* H^+ in basic solution). |

The following chart shows how to balance hydrogen and oxygen.

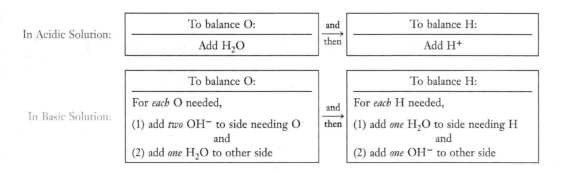

When balancing redox equations, we often find it convenient to omit the spectator ions (Section 4-3) so that we can focus on the oxidation and reduction processes. We use the methods presented in this chapter to balance the net ionic equation. If necessary we add the spectator ions and combine species to write the balanced formula unit equation. Examples 11-15 and 11-16 illustrate this approach.

In Section 4-3, we first wrote the formula unit equation. We separated any ionized or dissociated species into ions to obtain the total ionic equation. Then we eliminated the spectator ions to obtain the net ionic equation. In Examples 11-15 and 11-16, we reverse the procedure.

EXAMPLE 11-15 *Net Ionic Equations*

Permanganate ions oxidize iron(II) to iron(III) in sulfuric acid solution. Permanganate ions are reduced to manganese(II) ions. Write the balanced net ionic equation for this reaction.

Plan

We use the given information to write as much of the equation as possible. Then we follow Steps 2 through 6 in Section 11-5. The reaction occurs in H_2SO_4 solution; we can add H^+ and H_2O as needed to balance H and O in the half-reactions (Step 3).

Potassium permanganate, $KMnO_4$, is a commonly used oxidizing agent in the laboratory

Solution

$$Fe^{2+} + MnO_4^- \longrightarrow Fe^{3+} + Mn^{2+}$$

$$Fe^{2+} \longrightarrow Fe^{3+} \qquad \text{(ox. half-reaction)}$$

$$Fe^{2+} \longrightarrow Fe^{3+} + \boxed{1e^-} \qquad \text{(balanced ox. half-reaction)}$$

$$MnO_4^- \longrightarrow Mn^{2+} \qquad \text{(red. half-reaction)}$$

$$MnO_4^- + \boxed{8H^+} \longrightarrow Mn^{2+} + \boxed{4H_2O}$$

$$MnO_4^- + 8H^+ + \boxed{5e^-} \longrightarrow Mn^{2+} + 4H_2O \qquad \text{(balanced red. half-reaction)}$$

The oxidation half-reaction involves one electron, and the reduction half-reaction involves five electrons. Now we balance the electron transfer and then add the two equations term by term. This gives the balanced net ionic equation.

$$5(Fe^{2+} \longrightarrow Fe^{3+} + 1e^-)$$
$$1(MnO_4^- + 8H^+ + 5e^- \longrightarrow Mn^{2+} + 4H_2O)$$
$$\overline{5Fe^{2+}(aq) + MnO_4^-(aq) + 8H^+(aq) \longrightarrow 5Fe^{3+}(aq) + Mn^{2+}(aq) + 4H_2O(\ell)}$$

EXAMPLE 11-16

Write the balanced total ionic and the formula unit equations for the reaction in Example 11-15, given that the reactants were $KMnO_4$, $FeSO_4$, and H_2SO_4.

Plan

The K^+ is the cationic spectator ion, and the anionic spectator ion is SO_4^{2-}. The Fe^{3+} ion will need to occur twice in the product $Fe_2(SO_4)_3$, so there must be an even number of Fe atoms. So the net ionic equation is multiplied by two. It now becomes

$$10Fe^{2+}(aq) + 2MnO_4^-(aq) + 16H^+(aq) \longrightarrow 10Fe^{3+}(aq) + 2Mn^{2+}(aq) + 8H_2O(\ell)$$

Based on the $10Fe^{2+}$ and the $16H^+$, we add $18SO_4^{2-}$ to the reactant side of the equation; we must also add them to the product side to keep the equation balanced. Based on the $2MnO_4^-$, we add $2K^+$ to each side of the equation.

Solution

Total ionic equation

$$10[Fe^{2+}(aq) + SO_4^{2-}(aq)] + 2[K^+(aq) + MnO_4^-(aq)] + 8[2H^+(aq) + SO_4^{2-}(aq)] \longrightarrow$$
$$5[2Fe^{3+}(aq) + 3SO_4^{2-}(aq)] + 2[Mn^{2+}(aq) + SO_4^{2-}(aq)] + 8H_2O(\ell)$$
$$+ [2K^+(aq) + SO_4^{2-}(aq)]$$

Balanced formula unit equation

$$10FeSO_4(aq) + 2KMnO_4(aq) + 8H_2SO_4(aq) \longrightarrow$$
$$5Fe_2(SO_4)_3(aq) + 2MnSO_4(aq) + K_2SO_4(aq) + 8H_2O(\ell)$$

You should now work Exercise 60.

Caution: These common household chemicals, ammonia and bleach, should never be mixed because they react to form chloramine (NH_2Cl), a very poisonous volatile compound.

$$NH_3(aq) + ClO^-(aq) \longrightarrow NH_2Cl(aq) + OH^-(aq)$$

Bleaches sold under trade names such as Clorox and Purex are 5% solutions of sodium hypochlorite. The hypochlorite ion is a very strong oxidizing agent in basic solution. It oxidizes many stains to colorless substances.

James W. Morgenthaler

EXAMPLE 11-17

In basic solution, hypochlorite ions, ClO^-, oxidize chromite ions, CrO_2^-, to chromate ions, CrO_4^{2-}, and are reduced to chloride ions. Write the balanced net ionic equation for this reaction.

Plan

We are given the formulas for two reactants and two products; we write as much of the equations as possible. The reaction occurs in basic solution; we can add OH^- and H_2O as needed. We construct and balance the appropriate half-reactions, equalize the electron transfer, add the half-reactions, and eliminate common terms.

Solution

$$CrO_2^- + ClO^- \longrightarrow CrO_4^{2-} + Cl^-$$

$$CrO_2^- \longrightarrow CrO_4^{2-} \qquad \text{(ox. half-rxn)}$$

$$CrO_2^- + 4OH^- \longrightarrow CrO_4^{2-} + 2H_2O$$

$$CrO_2^- + 4OH^- \longrightarrow CrO_4^{2-} + 2H_2O + 3e^- \qquad \text{(balanced ox. half-rxn)}$$

- -

$$ClO^- \longrightarrow Cl^- \qquad \text{(red. half-rxn)}$$

$$ClO^- + H_2O \longrightarrow Cl^- + 2OH^-$$

$$ClO^- + H_2O + 2e^- \longrightarrow Cl^- + 2OH^- \qquad \text{(balanced red. half-rxn)}$$

The oxidation half-reaction involves three electrons, and the reduction half-reaction involves two electrons. We balance the electron transfer and add the half-reactions term by term.

$$2(CrO_2^- + 4OH^- \longrightarrow CrO_4^{2-} + 2H_2O + 3e^-)$$
$$3(ClO^- + H_2O + 2e^- \longrightarrow Cl^- + 2OH^-)$$
$$\overline{2CrO_2^- + 8OH^- + 3ClO^- + 3H_2O \longrightarrow 2CrO_4^{2-} + 4H_2O + 3Cl^- + 6OH^-}$$

We see that 6 OH^- and 3 H_2O can be eliminated from both sides to give the balanced net ionic equation.

$$2CrO_2^-(aq) + 2OH^-(aq) + 3ClO^-(aq) \longrightarrow 2CrO_4^{2-}(aq) + H_2O(\ell) + 3Cl^-(aq)$$

You should now work Exercise 56.

James W. Morgenthaler

Caution: These common household chemicals, vinegar and bleach, should never be mixed because they react to form chlorine, a very poisonous gas.

$$2H^+(aq) + ClO^-(aq) + Cl^-(aq) \longrightarrow Cl_2(g) + H_2O(\ell)$$

✓ **Problem-Solving Tip:** *Converting Ionic to Formula Unit Equations*

We learned in Section 4-3 how to convert the formula unit equation to the net ionic equation. To do this, we convert the formulas for all *strong electrolytes* into their ions, and then cancel *spectator ions* from both sides of the equation. In Example 11-16 we reverse this procedure. To balance this excess charge, we must add negatively charged spectator ions to combine with the positively charged reactants, and we add positively charged spectator ions to combine with the negatively charged reactants. Any spectator ions added to the reactant side of the equation must also be added to the product side. Then we combine species to give complete formula units. Now we can write total ionic and formula unit equations for Exercise 11-17 if we know what spectator ions are present. Just for practice, consider the spectator ions to be Na^+.

⚠ In a balanced ionic equation, the total charge on the left side of the equation must equal the total charge on the right side.

Every balanced equation must have both mass balance and charge balance. Once the redox part of an equation has been balanced, we must next count *either* atoms or charges. Suppose we had balanced a redox equation in ionic form to give

$$H^+ + 3C_2H_5OH + Cr_2O_7^{2-} \longrightarrow 2Cr^{3+} + 3C_2H_4O + H_2O$$

The net charge on the left side is $(1 + 2-) = 1-$. On the right, it is $2(3+) = 6+$. Because H^+ is the *only charged species whose coefficient isn't known*, we add 7 *more* H^+ to give a net charge of $6+$ on both sides.

$$8H^+ + 3C_2H_5OH + Cr_2O_7^{2-} \longrightarrow 2Cr^{3+} + 3C_2H_4O + H_2O$$

Now we have 10 O on the left and only 4 O on the right. We add six *more* H_2O molecules to give the balanced net ionic equation.

$$8H^+(aq) + 3C_2H_5OH(\ell) + Cr_2O_7^{2-}(aq) \longrightarrow 2Cr^{3+}(aq) + 3C_2H_4O(\ell) + 7H_2O(\ell)$$

How can you tell whether to balance atoms or charges first? Look at the equation *after you have balanced the redox part.* Decide which is simpler, and do that. In the preceding equation, it is easier to balance charges than to balance atoms.

11-7 STOICHIOMETRY OF REDOX REACTIONS

One method of analyzing samples quantitatively for the presence of *oxidizable* or *reducible* substances is by **redox titration.** In such analyses, the concentration of a solution is determined by allowing it to react with a carefully measured amount of a *standard* solution of an oxidizing or reducing agent.

As in other kinds of chemical reactions, we must pay particular attention to the mole ratio in which oxidizing agents and reducing agents react.

Potassium permanganate, $KMnO_4$, is a strong oxidizing agent. Through the years it has been the "workhorse" of redox titrations. For example, in acidic solution, $KMnO_4$ reacts with iron(II) sulfate, $FeSO_4$, according to the balanced equation in the following example. A strong acid, such as H_2SO_4, is used in such titrations (Example 11-15).

A word about terminology. The reaction involves MnO_4^- ions and Fe^{2+} ions in acidic solution. The source of MnO_4^- ions usually is the soluble ionic compound $KMnO_4$. We often refer to "permanganate solutions." Such solutions also contain cations—in this case, K^+. Likewise, we often refer to "iron(II) solutions" without specifying what the anion is.

Because it has an intense purple color, $KMnO_4$ acts as its own indicator. One drop of 0.020 M $KMnO_4$ solution imparts a pink color to a liter of pure water. When $KMnO_4$ solution is added to a solution of a reducing agent, the end point in the titration is taken as the point at which a pale pink color appears in the solution being titrated and persists for at least 30 seconds.

(a)   (b)

Charles D. Winters

Figure 11-2 (a) Nearly colorless FeSO$_4$ solution is titrated with deep-purple KMnO$_4$. (b) The end point is the point at which the solution becomes pink, owing to a *very small* excess of KMnO$_4$. Here a considerable excess of KMnO$_4$ was added so that the pink color could be reproduced photographically.

EXAMPLE 11-18   *Redox Titration*

What volume of 0.0200 M KMnO$_4$ solution is required to oxidize 40.0 mL of 0.100 M FeSO$_4$ in sulfuric acid solution (Figure 11-2)?

Plan

The balanced equation in Example 11-15 gives the reaction ratio, 1 mol MnO$_4$$^-$/5 mol Fe^{2+}. Then we calculate the number of moles of Fe^{2+} to be titrated, which lets us find the number of moles of MnO$_4$$^-$ required *and* the volume in which this number of moles of KMnO$_4$ is contained.

One mole of KMnO$_4$ contains one mole of MnO$_4$$^-$ ions. The number of moles of KMnO$_4$ is therefore *always* equal to the number of moles of MnO$_4$$^-$ ions required in a reaction. Similarly, one mole of FeSO$_4$ contains 1 mole of Fe^{2+} ions.

Solution

The reaction ratio is

$$MnO_4^-(aq) + 8H^+(aq) + 5Fe^{2+}(aq) \longrightarrow 5Fe^{3+}(aq) + Mn^{2+}(aq) + 4H_2O(\ell)$$
rxn ratio: 1 mol   5 mol

The number of moles of Fe^{2+} to be titrated is

$$\underline{?}\,mol\,Fe^{2+} = 40.0\;mL \times \frac{0.100\;mol\;Fe^{2+}}{1000\;mL} = 4.00 \times 10^{-3}\;mol\;Fe^{2+}$$

We use the balanced equation to find the number of moles of MnO$_4$$^-$ required.

$$\underline{?}\,mol\,MnO_4^- = 4.00 \times 10^{-3}\;mol\;Fe^{2+} \times \frac{1\;mol\;MnO_4^-}{5\;mol\;Fe^{2+}} = 8.00 \times 10^{-4}\;mol\;MnO_4^-$$

Each formula unit of KMnO$_4$ contains one MnO$_4$$^-$ ion, and so

$$1\;mol\;KMnO_4 \cong 1\;mol\;MnO_4^-$$

The volume of 0.0200 M KMnO$_4$ solution that contains 8.00 × 10^{-4} mol of KMnO$_4$ is

$$\underline{?}\,mL\,KMnO_4\;soln = 8.00 \times 10^{-4}\;mol\;KMnO_4 \times \frac{1000\;mL\;KMnO_4\;soln}{0.0200\;mol\;KMnO_4}$$
$$= 40.0\;mL\;KMnO_4\;soln$$

You should now work Exercises 64 and 66.

Potassium dichromate, $K_2Cr_2O_7$, is another frequently used oxidizing agent. However, an indicator must be used when reducing agents are titrated with dichromate solutions. $K_2Cr_2O_7$ is orange, and its reduction product, Cr^{3+}, is green.

Consider the oxidation of sulfite ions, SO_3^{2-}, to sulfate ions, SO_4^{2-}, by $Cr_2O_7^{2-}$ ions in the presence of a strong acid such as sulfuric acid. We shall balance the equation by the half-reaction method.

$$Cr_2O_7^{2-} \longrightarrow Cr^{3+} \qquad \text{(red. half-rxn)}$$

$$Cr_2O_7^{2-} \longrightarrow 2Cr^{3+}$$

$$14H^+ + Cr_2O_7^{2-} \longrightarrow 2Cr^{3+} + 7H_2O$$

$$6e^- + 14H^+ + Cr_2O_7^{2-} \longrightarrow 2Cr^{3+} + 7H_2O \qquad \text{(balanced red. half-rxn)}$$

- -

$$SO_3^{2-} \longrightarrow SO_4^{2-} \qquad \text{(ox. half-rxn)}$$

$$SO_3^{2-} + H_2O \longrightarrow SO_4^{2-} + 2H^+$$

$$SO_3^{2-} + H_2O \longrightarrow SO_4^{2-} + 2H^+ + 2e^- \qquad \text{(balanced ox. half-rxn)}$$

We now equalize the electron transfer, add the balanced half-reactions, and eliminate common terms.

$$(6e^- + 14H^+ + Cr_2O_7^{2-} \longrightarrow 2Cr^{3+} + 7H_2O) \qquad \text{(reduction)}$$

$$3(SO_3^{2-} + H_2O \longrightarrow SO_4^{2-} + 2H^+ + 2e^-) \qquad \text{(oxidation)}$$

$$\overline{8H^+(aq) + Cr_2O_7^{2-}(aq) + 3SO_3^{2-}(aq) \longrightarrow 2Cr^{3+}(aq) + 3SO_4^{2-}(aq) + 4H_2O(\ell)}$$

The balanced equation tells us that the reaction ratio is 3 mol SO_3^{2-}/mol $Cr_2O_7^{2-}$ or 1 mol $Cr_2O_7^{2-}$/3 mol SO_3^{2-}. Potassium dichromate is the usual source of $Cr_2O_7^{2-}$ ions, and Na_2SO_3 is the usual source of SO_3^{2-} ions. Thus, the preceding reaction ratio could also be expressed as 1 mol $K_2Cr_2O_7$/3 mol Na_2SO_3.

EXAMPLE 11-19

A 20.00-mL sample of Na_2SO_3 was titrated with 36.30 mL of 0.05130 M $K_2Cr_2O_7$ solution in the presence of H_2SO_4. Calculate the molarity of the Na_2SO_3 solution.

Plan

We can calculate the number of millimoles of $Cr_2O_7^{2-}$ in the standard solution. Then we refer to the balanced equation in the preceding discussion, which gives us the reaction ratio, 3 mmol SO_3^{2-}/1 mmol $Cr_2O_7^{2-}$. The reaction ratio lets us calculate the number of millimoles of SO_3^{2-} (Na_2SO_3) that reacted and the molarity of the solution.

$$\text{mL } Cr_2O_7^{2-} \text{ soln} \longrightarrow \text{mmol } Cr_2O_7^{2-} \longrightarrow \text{mmol } SO_3^{2-} \longrightarrow M \text{ } SO_3^{2-} \text{ soln}$$

Solution

From the preceding discussion we know the balanced equation and the reaction ratio.

$$3SO_3^{2-} + Cr_2O_7^{2-} + 8H^+ \longrightarrow 3SO_4^{2-} + 2Cr^{3+} + 4H_2O$$
$$\;\;\;\text{3 mmol} \quad\;\; \text{1 mmol}$$

The number of millimoles of $Cr_2O_7^{2-}$ used is

$$\underline{?} \text{ mmol } Cr_2O_7^{2-} = 36.30 \text{ mL} \times \frac{0.05130 \text{ mmol } Cr_2O_7^{2-}}{\text{mL}} = 1.862 \text{ mmol } Cr_2O_7^{2-}$$

$Cr_2(SO_4)_3$ is green in acidic solution.
$K_2Cr_2O_7$ is orange in acidic solution.

Charles Steele

The number of millimoles of SO_3^{2-} that reacted with 1.862 mmol of $Cr_2O_7^{2-}$ is

$$\text{? mmol } SO_3^{2-} = 1.862 \text{ mmol } Cr_2O_7^{2-} \times \frac{3 \text{ mmol } SO_3^{2-}}{1 \text{ mmol } Cr_2O_7^{2-}} = 5.586 \text{ mmol } SO_3^{2-}$$

The Na_2SO_3 solution contained 5.586 mmol of SO_3^{2-} (or 5.586 mmol of Na_2SO_3). Its molarity is

$$\text{? } \frac{\text{mmol } Na_2SO_3}{\text{mL}} = \frac{5.586 \text{ mmol } Na_2SO_3}{20.00 \text{ mL}} = 0.2793 \ M \ Na_2SO_3$$

You should now work Exercise 68.

Key Terms

Buret A piece of volumetric glassware, usually graduated in 0.1-mL intervals, that is used in titrations to deliver solutions in a quantitative (dropwise) manner.

End point The point at which an indicator changes color and a titration is stopped.

Equivalence point The point at which chemically equivalent amounts of reactants have reacted.

Equivalent weight in acid–base reactions The mass of an acid or base that furnishes or reacts with 6.022×10^{23} H_3O^+ or OH^- ions.

Half-reaction Either the oxidation part or the reduction part of a redox reaction.

Indicator For acid–base titrations, an organic compound that exhibits its different colors in solutions of different acidities; used to determine the point at which the reaction between two solutes is complete.

Milliequivalent 1/1000 equivalent.

Millimole 1/1000 mole.

Molarity (*M*) The number of moles of solute per liter of solution or the number of millimoles of solute per milliliter of solution.

Normality (*N*) The number of equivalent weights (equivalents) of solute per liter of solution.

Oxidation An algebraic increase in oxidation number; may correspond to a loss of electrons.

Oxidation–reduction reaction A reaction in which oxidation and reduction occur; also called redox reaction.

Oxidizing agent The substance that oxidizes another substance and is reduced.

Primary standard A substance of a known high degree of purity that undergoes one invariable reaction with the other reactant of interest.

Redox reaction An oxidation-reduction reaction.

Redox titration The quantitative analysis of the amount or concentration of an oxidizing or reducing agent in a sample by observing its reaction with a known amount or concentration of a reducing or oxidizing agent.

Reducing agent The substance that reduces another substance and is oxidized.

Reduction An algebraic decrease in oxidation number; may correspond to a gain of electrons.

Secondary standard A solution that has been titrated against a primary standard. A standard solution in a secondary standard.

Standard solution A solution of accurately known concentration.

Standardization The process by which the concentration of a solution is accurately determined by titrating it against an accurately known amount of a primary standard.

Titration The process by which the volume of a standard solution required to react with a specific amount of a substance is determined.

Exercises

You may assume that all species shown in chemical equations are *in aqueous solutions* unless otherwise indicated.

Molarity

1. Why can we describe molarity as a "method of convenience" for expressing concentrations of solutions?

2. Why is the molarity of a solution the same number whether we describe it in mol/L or in mmol/mL?

3. Calculate the molarities of solutions that contain the following masses of solute in the indicated volumes: (a) 35.5 g of H_3AsO_4 in 500. mL of solution; (b) 8.33 g of $(COOH)_2$ in 600. mL of solution; (c) 8.25 g of $(COOH)_2 \cdot 2H_2O$ in 750. mL of solution.

4. What is the molarity of a solution made by dissolving 66.3 g of magnesium sulfate in sufficient water to produce a total of 3.50 L?

5. There are 85.0 g of iron(II) nitrate present in 850. mL of a solution. Calculate the molarity of that solution.

6. Calculate the molarity of a solution that is 39.77% H_2SO_4 by mass. The specific gravity of the solution is 1.305.

7. Calculate the molarity of a solution that is 19.0% HNO_3 by mass. The specific gravity of the solution is 1.11.

8. If 225. mL of 4.32 M HCl solution is added to 450. mL of 2.16 M NaOH solution, the resulting solution will be _____ molar in NaCl.

9. What is the molarity of the salt solution produced when 750. mL of 3.00 M HCl and 750. mL of 3.00 M LiOH are mixed? (Assume that the volumes are additive.) Give the name and formula of the salt formed.

10. Potassium iodide is sometimes used as a sodium chloride replacement for those people who cannot tolerate table salt. Calculate the molarity of potassium iodide solution produced when 35.5 mL of 9.00 M HI and 35.5 mL of 9.00 M KOH are mixed.

11. What is the salt concentration produced if we mix 8.00 mL of 4.50 M HCl with 4.50 mL of 4.00 M Ba(OH)$_2$? Give the name and formula of the salt formed.

12. What is the concentration of barium iodide produced by mixing 7.50 mL of 0.125 M Ba(OH)$_2$ with 18.0 mL of 0.0650 M HI?

13. What is the concentration of the ammonium chloride produced when 22.0 mL of 12.0 M HCl and 18.5 mL of 8.00 M NH$_3$ are mixed?

14. If 225 mL of 5.52 M H$_3$PO$_4$ solution is added to 775 mL of 5.52 M NaOH solution, the resulting solution will be _____ molar in Na$_3$PO$_4$ and _____ molar in _____.

15. If 100. mL of 0.200 M HCl solution is added to 200. mL of 0.0400 M Ba(OH)$_2$ solution, the resulting solution will be _____ molar in BaCl$_2$ and _____ molar in _____.

16. What volume of 0.0125 M acetic acid solution would completely neutralize 15.58 mL of 0.0105 M Ba(OH)$_2$ solution?

17. What volume of 0.150 M potassium hydroxide solution would completely neutralize 17.5 mL of 0.100 M H$_2$SO$_4$ solution?

18. A vinegar solution is 5.11% acetic acid. Its density is 1.007 g/mL. What is its molarity?

19. A household ammonia solution is 5.03% ammonia. Its density is 0.979 g/mL. What is its molarity?

20. (a) What volumes of 2.25 M NaOH and 4.50 M H$_3$PO$_4$ solutions would be required to form 1.00 mol of Na$_3$PO$_4$? (b) What volumes of the solutions would be required to form 1.00 mol of Na$_2$HPO$_4$?

Standardization and Acid–Base Titrations: Mole Method

21. Define and illustrate the following terms clearly and concisely: (a) standard solution; (b) titration; (c) primary standard; (d) secondary standard.

22. Describe the preparation of a standard solution of NaOH, a compound that absorbs both CO_2 and H_2O from the air.

23. Distinguish between the *net ionic equation* and the *formula unit equation*.

24. (a) What is potassium hydrogen phthalate, KHP? (b) For what is it used?

25. Why can sodium carbonate be used as a primary standard for solutions of acids?

26. Calculate the molarity of a solution of HNO_3 if 35.72 mL of the solution neutralizes 0.4040 g of Na$_2$CO$_3$.

27. If 35.38 mL of a sulfuric acid solution reacts completely with 0.3545 g of Na$_2$CO$_3$, what is the molarity of the sulfuric acid solution?

28. A solution of sodium hydroxide is standardized against potassium hydrogen phthalate. From the following data, calculate the molarity of the NaOH solution.

mass of KHP used	0.4536 g
buret reading before titration	0.23 mL
buret reading after titration	31.26 mL

29. Calculate the molarity of a KOH solution if 30.68 mL of the KOH solution reacted with 0.4084 g of potassium hydrogen phthalate, KHP.

30. Calcium carbonate tablets can be used as an antacid and a source of dietary calcium. A bottle of generic antacid tablets states that each tablet contains 600. mg calcium carbonate. What volume of 6.0 M HNO_3 could be neutralized by the calcium carbonate in one tablet?

31. What volume of 18.0 M H$_2$SO$_4$ is required to react with 65.5 mL of 6.00 M NaOH to produce a Na$_2$SO$_4$ solution? What volume of water must be added to the resulting solution to obtain a 1.25 M Na$_2$SO$_4$ solution?

32. (a) What are the properties of an ideal primary standard? (b) What is the importance of each property?

33. The secondary standard solution of NaOH of Exercise 28 was used to titrate a solution of unknown concentration of HCl. A 30.00-mL sample of the HCl solution required 34.21 mL of the NaOH solution for complete neutralization. What is the molarity of the HCl solution?

*34. An impure sample of (COOH)$_2$ · 2H$_2$O that had a mass of 1.00 g was dissolved in water and titrated with standard NaOH solution. The titration required 19.16 mL of 0.198 M NaOH solution. Calculate the percent (COOH)$_2$ · 2H$_2$O in the sample. Assume that the sample contains no acidic impurities.

*35. A 25.0-mL sample of 0.0500 M Ca(OH)$_2$ is added to 10.0 mL of 0.100 M HNO$_3$. (a) Is the resulting solution acidic or basic? (b) How many moles of excess acid or base are present? (c) How many additional mL of 0.0500 M Ca(OH)$_2$ or 0.100 M HNO$_3$ would be required to completely neutralize the solution?

*36. An antacid tablet containing calcium carbonate as an active ingredient required 22.3 mL of 0.0932 M HCl for complete neutralization. What mass of CaCO$_3$ did the tablet contain?

*37. Butyric acid, whose empirical formula is C$_2$H$_4$O, is the acid responsible for the odor of rancid butter. The acid has one ionizable hydrogen per molecule. A 1.000-g sample of butyric acid is neutralized by 36.28 mL of 0.3132 M NaOH solution. What are (a) the molecular weight and (b) the molecular formula of butyric acid?

38. What is the molarity of a solution of sodium hydroxide, NaOH, if 36.2 mL of this solution is required to react with 37.5 mL of 0.0342 M nitric acid solution according to the following reaction?

$$HNO_3 + NaOH \longrightarrow NaNO_3 + H_2O(\ell)$$

39. What is the molarity of a solution of sodium hydroxide, NaOH, if 18.45 mL of this solution is required to react with 17.60 mL of 0.101 M hydrochloric acid solution according to the following reaction?

$$HCl + NaOH \longrightarrow NaCl + H_2O(\ell)$$

Standardization and Acid–Base Titrations: Equivalent Weight Method

In answering Exercises 40–49, assume that the acids and bases will be completely neutralized.

40. What is the normality of each of the following acid or base solutions? (a) 0.55 M HCl; (b) 0.55 M H_2SO_4; (c) 0.55 M H_3PO_4; (d) 0.55 M NaOH.

41. What is the normality of each of the following acid or base solutions? (a) 0.215 M $Ca(OH)_2$; (b) 0.215 M $Al(OH)_3$; (c) 0.215 M HNO_3; (d) 0.105 M H_2Se.

42. What is the normality of a solution that contains 9.78 g of H_3PO_4 in 185 mL of solution?

43. What are the molarity and normality of a sulfuric acid solution that is 19.6% H_2SO_4 by mass? The density of the solution is 1.14 g/mL.

44. Calculate the molarity and the normality of a solution that contains 16.6 g of arsenic acid, H_3AsO_4, in enough water to make 470. mL of solution.

45. Calculate the normality and molarity of an H_2SO_4 solution if 44.3 mL of the solution reacts with 0.484 g of Na_2CO_3.

$$H_2SO_4 + Na_2CO_3 \longrightarrow Na_2SO_4 + CO_2(g) + H_2O(\ell)$$

46. Calculate the normality and molarity of an HCl solution if 38.1 mL of the solution reacts with 0.438 g of Na_2CO_3.

$$2HCl + Na_2CO_3 \longrightarrow 2NaCl + CO_2(g) + H_2O(\ell)$$

47. To minimize the effect of buret reading errors, titrations performed using a 50-mL buret are most accurate when titrant volumes are in the range of 35–45 mL. Suggest a range of sample weights that would yield a 35–45 mL titration range for the standardization of solutions of the following approximate concentrations. (a) 0.0325 M NaOH using potassium hydrogen phthalate ($C_8H_5KO_4$), a monoprotic acid. (b) 0.060 M KOH using primary standard benzoic acid (C_6H_5COOH) a monoprotic acid.

48. Magnesium hydroxide, $Mg(OH)_2$, is commonly used as the active ingredient in antacid tablets. A student analyzed an antacid tablet for mass percent $Mg(OH)_2$ by dissolving a tablet weighing 1.462 g in 25.00 mL of 0.953 M HCl, and neutralizing the unreacted HCl. That neutral-

ization required 12.29 mL of 0.602 M NaOH. Calculate the mass percent of $Mg(OH)_2$ in the antacid tablet.

49. Vinegar is an aqueous solution of acetic acid, CH_3COOH. Suppose you titrate a 25.00-mL sample of vinegar with 17.62 mL of a standardized 0.1045 N solution of NaOH. (a) What is the normality of acetic acid in this vinegar? (b) What is the mass of acetic acid contained in 1.000 L of vinegar?

Balancing Redox Equations

In Exercises 50 and 51, write balanced formula unit equations for the reactions described by words.

50. (a) Iron reacts with hydrochloric acid to form aqueous iron(II) chloride and gaseous hydrogen. (b) Chromium reacts with sulfuric acid to form aqueous chromium(III) sulfate and gaseous hydrogen. (c) Tin reacts with concentrated nitric acid to form tin(IV) oxide, nitrogen dioxide, and water.

51. (a) Carbon reacts with hot concentrated nitric acid to form carbon dioxide, nitrogen dioxide, and water. (b) Sodium reacts with water to form aqueous sodium hydroxide and gaseous hydrogen. (c) Zinc reacts with sodium hydroxide solution to form aqueous sodium tetrahydroxozincate and gaseous hydrogen. (The tetrahydroxozincate ion is $[Zn(OH)_4]^{2-}$.)

52. Copper is a widely used metal. Before it is welded (brazed), copper is cleaned by dipping it into nitric acid. HNO_3 oxidizes Cu to Cu^{2+} ions and is reduced to NO. The other product is H_2O. Write the balanced net ionic and formula unit equations for the reaction. Excess HNO_3 is present.

Copper is cleaned by dipping it into nitric acid.

53. Balance the following equations. For each equation tell what is oxidized, what is reduced, what is the oxidizing agent, and what is the reducing agent.
(a) $Cu(NO_3)_2(s) \xrightarrow{\text{heat}} CuO(s) + NO_2(g) + O_2(g)$
(b) $Hg_2Cl_2(s) + NH_3(aq) \longrightarrow$
$$Hg(\ell) + HgNH_2Cl(s) + NH_4^+(aq) + Cl^-(aq)$$
(c) $Ba(s) + H_2O(\ell) \longrightarrow Ba(OH)_2(aq) + H_2(g)$

54. Balance the following equations. For each equation tell what is oxidized, what is reduced, what is the oxidizing agent, and what is the reducing agent.
   (a) $MnO_4^-(aq) + H^+(aq) + Br^-(aq) \longrightarrow$
$$Mn^{2+}(aq) + Br_2(\ell) + H_2O(\ell)$$
   (b) $Cr_2O_7^{2-}(aq) + H^+(aq) + I^-(aq) \longrightarrow$
$$Cr^{3+}(aq) + I_2(s) + H_2O(\ell)$$
   (c) $MnO_4^-(aq) + SO_3^{2-}(aq) + H^+(aq) \longrightarrow$
$$Mn^{2+}(aq) + SO_4^{2-}(aq) + H_2O(\ell)$$
   (d) $Cr_2O_7^{2-}(aq) + Fe^{2+}(aq) + H^+(aq) \longrightarrow$
$$Cr^{3+}(aq) + Fe^{3+}(aq) + H_2O(\ell)$$

55. Balance the following ionic equations. For each equation tell what is oxidized, what is reduced, what is the oxidizing agent, and what is the reducing agent.
   (a) $C_2H_4(g) + MnO_4^-(aq) + H^+(aq) \longrightarrow$
$$CO_2(g) + Mn^{2+}(aq) + H_2O(\ell)$$
   (b) $H_2S(aq) + H^+(aq) + Cr_2O_7^{2-}(aq) \longrightarrow$
$$Cr^{3+}(aq) + S(s) + H_2O(\ell)$$
   (c) $ClO_3^-(aq) + H_2O(\ell) + I_2(s) \longrightarrow$
$$IO_3^-(aq) + Cl^-(aq) + H^+(aq)$$
   (d) $Cu(s) + H^+(aq) + SO_4^{2-}(aq) \longrightarrow$
$$Cu^{2+}(aq) + H_2O(\ell) + SO_2(g)$$

56. Drāno drain cleaner is solid sodium hydroxide that contains some aluminum chips. When Drāno is added to water, the NaOH dissolves rapidly with the evolution of a lot of heat. The Al reduces H_2O in the basic solution to produce $[Al(OH)_4]^-$ ions and H_2 gas, which gives the bubbling action. Write the balanced net ionic and formula unit equations for this reaction.

The Drāno reaction.

57. Balance the following ionic equations. For each equation tell what is oxidized, what is reduced, what is the oxidizing agent, and what is the reducing agent.
   (a) $Cr(OH)_4^-(aq) + OH^-(aq) + H_2O_2(aq) \longrightarrow$
$$CrO_4^{2-}(aq) + H_2O(\ell)$$
   (b) $MnO_2(s) + H^+(aq) + NO_2^-(aq) \longrightarrow$
$$NO_3^-(aq) + Mn^{2+}(aq) + H_2O(\ell)$$
   (c) $Sn(OH)_3^-(aq) + Bi(OH)_3(s) + OH^-(aq) \longrightarrow$
$$Sn(OH)_6^{2-}(aq) + Bi(s)$$

(d) $CrO_4^{2-}(aq) + H_2O(\ell) + HSnO_2^-(aq) \longrightarrow$
$$CrO_2^-(aq) + OH^-(aq) + HSnO_3^-(aq)$$

58. Balance the following ionic equations for reactions in acidic solution. H^+ or H_2O (but not OH^-) may be added as necessary.
   (a) $Fe^{2+}(aq) + MnO_4^-(aq) \longrightarrow Fe^{3+}(aq) + Mn^{2+}(aq)$
   (b) $Br_2(\ell) + SO_2(g) \longrightarrow Br^-(aq) + SO_4^{2-}(aq)$
   (c) $Cu(s) + NO_3^-(aq) \longrightarrow Cu^{2+}(aq) + NO_2(g)$
   (d) $PbO_2(s) + Cl^-(aq) \longrightarrow PbCl_2(s) + Cl_2(g)$
   (e) $Zn(s) + NO_3^-(aq) \longrightarrow Zn^{2+}(aq) + N_2(g)$

59. Balance the following ionic equations for reactions in acidic solution. H^+ or H_2O (but not OH^-) may be added as necessary.
   (a) $P_4(s) + NO_3^-(aq) \longrightarrow H_3PO_4(aq) + NO(g)$
   (b) $H_2O_2(aq) + MnO_4^-(aq) \longrightarrow Mn^{2+}(aq) + O_2(g)$
   (c) $HgS(s) + Cl^-(aq) + NO_3^-(aq) \longrightarrow$
$$HgCl_4^{2-}(aq) + NO_2(g) + S(s)$$
   (d) $HBrO(aq) \longrightarrow Br^-(aq) + O_2(g)$

60. Write the balanced net ionic equations for the reactions given. Then, using the reactants shown in parentheses convert each balanced net ionic equation to a balanced formula unit equation.
   (a) $MnO_4^- + C_2O_4^{2-} + H^+ \longrightarrow$
$$Mn^{2+} + CO_2(g) + H_2O(\ell)$$
$$(KMnO_4, HCl, \text{ and } K_2C_2O_4)$$
   (b) $Zn + NO_3^- + H^+ \longrightarrow Zn^{2+} + NH_4^+ + H_2O(\ell)$
$$(Zn(s) \text{ and } HNO_3)$$

61. Write the balanced net ionic equations for the reactions given. Then, using the reactants shown in parentheses convert each balanced net ionic equation to a balanced formula unit equation.
   (a) $I_2 + S_2O_3^{2-} \longrightarrow I^- + S_4O_6^{2-}$ (I_2 and $Na_2S_2O_3$)
   (b) $IO_3^- + N_2H_4 + Cl^- + H^+ \longrightarrow$
$$N_2(g) + ICl_2^- + H_2O(\ell)$$
$$(NaIO_3 + N_2H_4, \text{ and } HCl)$$

62. Write the balanced net ionic equations for the reactions given. Then, using the reactants shown in parentheses convert each balanced net ionic equation to a balanced formula unit equation.
   (a) $Zn(s) + Cu^{2+} \longrightarrow Cu(s) + Zn^{2+}$ (Zn and $CuSO_4$)
   (b) $Cr(s) + H^+ \longrightarrow Cr^{3+} + H_2(g)$ (Cr and H_2SO_4)

63. Write the balanced net ionic equations for the reactions given. Then, using the reactants shown in parentheses convert each balanced net ionic equation to a balanced formula unit equation.
   (a) $Cl_2 + OH^- \longrightarrow ClO_3^- + Cl^- + H_2O(\ell)$
$$(Cl_2 \text{ and hot NaOH})$$
   (b) $Pb(s) + H^+ + Br^- \longrightarrow PbBr_2(s) + H_2(g)$
$$(Pb(s) \text{ and HBr})$$

Redox Titrations: Mole Method and Molarity

64. What volume of 0.142 M $KMnO_4$ would be required to oxidize 25.0 mL of 0.100 M $FeSO_4$ in acidic solution? Refer to Example 11-18.

65. What volume of 0.142 M $K_2Cr_2O_7$ would be required

to oxidize 70.0 mL of 0.100 M Na_2SO_3 in acidic solution? The products include Cr^{3+} and SO_4^{2-} ions. Refer to Example 11-19.

66. What volume of 0.190 M $KMnO_4$ would be required to oxidize 40.0 mL of 0.100 M KI in acidic solution? Products include Mn^{2+} and I_2.

67. What volume of 0.190 M $K_2Cr_2O_7$ would be required to oxidize 50.0 mL of 0.150 M KI in acidic solution? Products include Cr^{3+} and I_2.

68. (a) A solution of sodium thiosulfate, $Na_2S_2O_3$, is 0.1442 M. 44.00 mL of this solution reacts with 26.85 mL of I_2 solution. Calculate the molarity of the I_2 solution.

$$2Na_2S_2O_3 + I_2 \longrightarrow Na_2S_4O_6 + 2NaI$$

(b) 25.32 mL of the I_2 solution is required to titrate a sample containing As_2O_3. Calculate the mass of As_2O_3 (197.8 g/mol) in the sample.

$$As_2O_3 + 5H_2O(\ell) + 2I_2 \longrightarrow 2H_3AsO_4 + 4HI$$

69. Copper(II) ions, Cu^{2+}, can be determined by the net reaction

$$2Cu^{2+} + 2I^- + 2S_2O_3^{2-} \longrightarrow 2CuI(s) + S_4O_6^{2-}$$

A 2.115-g sample containing $CuSO_4$ and excess KI is titrated with 32.55 mL of 0.1214 M solution of $Na_2S_2O_3$. What is the percent $CuSO_4$ (159.6 g/mol) in the sample?

70. What volume of 3.0 M nitrate ion solution would be required to react with 25. mL of 0.75 M sulfide ion solution? (*Hint:* The equation is not balanced.)

$$NO_3^- + S^{2-} \longrightarrow NO + S(s) \quad \text{(acidic solution)}$$

*71. The iron in a 5.675-g sample containing some Fe_2O_3 is reduced to Fe^{2+}. The Fe^{2+} is titrated with 12.42 mL of 0.1467 M $K_2Cr_2O_7$ in an acid solution.

$$6Fe^{2+} + Cr_2O_7^{2-} + 14H^+ \longrightarrow$$
$$6Fe^{3+} + 2Cr^{3+} + 7H_2O(\ell)$$

Find (a) the mass of Fe and (b) the percentage of Fe in the sample.

72. Calculate the molarity of a solution that contains 12.6 g of $KMnO_4$ in 500. mL of solution to be used in the reaction that produces MnO_4^{2-} ions as the reduction product.

*73. A 0.823-g sample of an ore of iron is dissolved in acid and converted to Fe(II). The sample is oxidized by 38.50 mL of 0.161 M ceric sulfate, $Ce(SO_4)_2$, solution; the cerium(IV) ion, Ce^{4+}, is reduced to Ce^{3+} ion. (a) Write a balanced equation for the reaction. (b) What is the percent iron in the ore?

Mixed Exercises

74. Calculate the molarity of a hydrochloric acid solution if 32.75 mL of it reacts with 0.3811 g of sodium carbonate.

75. Calculate the molarity and the normality of a sulfuric acid solution if 32.75 mL of it reacts with 0.3811 g of sodium carbonate.

76. Find the number of mmol of HCl that reacts with 25.5 mL of 0.220 M NaOH. What volume of 0.606 M HCl is needed to furnish this amount of HCl?

77. What is the composition of the final solution when 25.5 mL of 0.220 M NaOH and 25.5 mL of 0.410 M HCl solutions are mixed?

78. What volume of 0.1123 M HCl is needed to completely neutralize 1.79 g of $Ca(OH)_2$?

79. What mass of NaOH is needed to neutralize 33.50 mL of 0.1036 M HCl? If the NaOH is available as a 0.1533 M aqueous solution, what volume will be required?

80. What volume of 0.246 M H_2SO_4 solution would be required to completely neutralize 34.4 mL of 0.302 M KOH solution?

81. What volume of 0.388 N H_2SO_4 solution would be required to completely neutralize 34.4 mL of 0.302 N KOH solution?

82. What volume of 0.1945 normal sodium hydroxide would be required to neutralize completely 34.38 mL of 0.1023 normal H_2SO_4 solution?

83. Benzoic acid, C_6H_5COOH, is sometimes used as a primary standard for the standardization of solutions of bases. A 1.862-g sample of this acid is neutralized by 29.00 mL of NaOH solution. What is the molarity of the base solution?

$$C_6H_5COOH(s) + NaOH(aq) \longrightarrow$$
$$C_6H_5COONa(aq) + H_2O(\ell)$$

84. Find the volume of 0.225 M HI solution required to titrate
  (a) 25.0 mL of 0.100 M NaOH
  (b) 5.03 g of $AgNO_3$ ($Ag^+ + I^- \longrightarrow AgI(s)$)
  (c) 0.621 g $CuSO_4$ ($2Cu^{2+} + 4I^- \longrightarrow 2CuI(s) + I_2(s)$)

CONCEPTUAL EXERCISES

85. Describe how you could prepare 1.00 L of $1.00 \times 10^{-6} M$ NaCl solution by using a balance that can measure masses to only 0.01 g.

86. Ascorbic acid (vitamin C), along with many other reputed properties, acts as an antioxidant. The following equation illustrates its antioxidant properties.

$$H_2C_6H_6O_6 \longrightarrow C_6H_6O_6 + H_2(g)$$

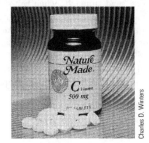

Charles D. Winters

What is an antioxidant? Assign oxidation numbers. Is vitamin C oxidized or reduced in this reaction?

BUILDING YOUR KNOWLEDGE

87. For the formation of 1.00 mol of water, which reaction uses the most nitric acid?
    (a) $3Cu(s) + 8HNO_3(aq) \longrightarrow$
    $$3Cu(NO_3)_2(aq) + 2NO(g) + 4H_2O(\ell)$$
    (b) $Al_2O_3(s) + 6HNO_3(aq) \longrightarrow$
    $$2Al(NO_3)_3(aq) + 3H_2O(\ell)$$
    (c) $4Zn(s) + 10HNO_3(aq) \longrightarrow$
    $$4Zn(NO_3)_2(aq) + NH_4NO_3(aq) + 3H_2O(\ell)$$

88. Limonite is an ore of iron that contains $2Fe_2O_3 \cdot 3H_2O$. A 0.5166-g sample of limonite is dissolved in acid and treated so that all the iron is converted to ferrous ions, Fe^{2+}. This sample requires 42.96 mL of 0.02130 M sodium dichromate solution, $Na_2Cr_2O_7$, for titration. Fe^{2+} is oxidized to Fe^{3+}, and $Cr_2O_7^{2-}$ is reduced to Cr^{3+}. What is the percent iron in the limonite? If your answer had been over 100% limonite, what conclusion could you make, presuming that the analytical data are correct?

89. One of the troublesome products of a water treatment plant in some areas of the country is $Mg(OH)_2$, a gelatinous precipitate formed during water softening. A suggestion was made that instead of shoveling the precipitate out of the pool during cleaning, the $Mg(OH)_2$ could be neutralized with hydrochloric acid to produce a soluble compound, $MgCl_2$. Then the pool could be flushed out with fresh water. Calculate the volume of 12.0 M HCl necessary to neutralize 4750 L of solution containing 1.50 g of $Mg(OH)_2$ per liter.

90. Silver nitrate and calcium chloride solutions produce a heavy, white precipitate when mixed. Chemical analysis indicates that the precipitate is silver chloride. What mass of silver chloride would be produced if 45 mL of 6.0 M silver nitrate is mixed with 45 mL of 6.0 M calcium chloride?

91. A 0.500-g sample of a crystalline monoprotic acid was dissolved in sufficient water to produce 100. mL of solution. Neutralization of the resulting solution required 75.0 mL of 0.150 M NaOH. How many moles of the acid were present in the initial acid solution?

92. The typical concentration of HCl in stomach acid (digestive juice) is a concentration of about 8.0×10^{-2} M. One experiences "acid stomach" when the stomach contents reach about 1.0×10^{-1} M HCl. One antacid tablet contains 334 mg of active ingredient, $NaAl(OH)_2CO_3$. Assume that you have acid stomach and that your stomach contains 800. mL of 1.0×10^{-1} M HCl. Calculate the number of mmol of HCl in the stomach and the number of mmol of HCl that the tablet *can* neutralize. Which is

greater? (The neutralization reaction produces NaCl, $AlCl_3$, CO_2, and H_2O.)

93. Refer to Exercises 18 and 19. Notice that the percent by mass of solute is nearly the same for both solutions. How many moles of solute are present per liter of each solution? Are the moles of solute per liter also nearly equal? Why or why not?

94. The etching of glass by hydrofluoric acid may be represented by the simplified reaction of silica with HF.

$$SiO_2(s) + HF(aq) \longrightarrow H_2SiF_6(aq) + H_2O(\ell)$$

This is an acid–base reaction in which a weak acid is used to produce an even weaker acid. Is it also an oxidation–reduction reaction? Balance the equation.

95. Write a Lewis formula for the anion SiF_6^{2-} that would be produced from the weak acid H_2SiF_6. Use the VSEPR theory to predict the shape of SiF_6^{2-}.

96. Baking soda, $NaHCO_3$, used to be a common remedy for "acid stomach." What weight of baking soda would be required to neutralize 85 mL of digestive juice, corresponding in acidity to 0.17 M HCl?

97. Oxalic acid, a poisonous compound, is found in certain vegetables such as spinach and rhubarb, but in concentrations well below toxic limits. The manufacturers of a spinach juice concentrate routinely test their product using an oxalic acid analysis to avoid any problems from an unexpectedly high concentration of this chemical. A titration with potassium permanganate is used for the oxalic acid assay, according to the following net equation.

$$5H_2C_2O_4 + 2MnO_4^- + 6H^+ \longrightarrow$$
$$10CO_2 + 2Mn^{2+} + 8H_2O(\ell)$$

Calculate the molarity of an oxalic acid solution requiring 23.2 mL of 0.127 M permanganate for a 25.0 mL portion of the solution.

BEYOND THE TEXTBOOK

Go to the textbook website at

http://www.brookscole.com/chemistry/whitten

for additional activities and exercises based on the General Chemistry Interactive CD-ROM, the World Wide Web, and library resources.

InfoTrac College Edition

For additional readings, go to InfoTrac College Edition, your online research library at:

http://infotrac.thomsonlearning.com

1 The Foundations of Chemistry

(a) Organic chemistry is the study of the chemical compounds of carbon and hydrogen and a few other elements.

(b) Forensic chemistry deals with the chemistry involved in solving crimes, including chemical analyses of crime scene artifacts, such as paint chips, dirt, fluids, blood, and hair.

(c) Physical chemistry is the study of the part of chemistry that applies the mathematical theories and methods of physics to the properties of matter and to the study of chemical processes and the accompanying energy changes.

(d) Medicinal chemistry is the study of the chemistry and biochemistry dealing with all aspects of the medical field.

1-4. *Refer to the Sections 1-1, 1-4, 1-8, 1-13 and the Key Terms for Chapter 1.*

(a) Weight is a measure of the gravitational attraction of the earth for a body. Although the mass of an object remains constant, its weight will vary depending on its distance from the center of the earth. One kilogram of mass at sea level weighs about 2.2 pounds (9.8 newtons), but that same one kilogram of mass weighs less at the top of Mt. Everest. In more general terms, it is a measure of the gravitational attraction of one body for another. The weight of an object on the moon is about 1/7th that of the same object on the earth.

(b) Potential energy is the energy that matter possesses by virtue of its position, condition, or composition. Your chemistry book lying on a table has potential energy due to its position. Energy is released if it falls from the table.

(c) Temperature is a measurement of the intensity of heat, *i.e.* the "hotness" or "coldness" of an object. The temperature at which water freezes is 0°C or 32°F.

(d) An endothermic process is a process that absorbs heat energy. The boiling of water is a physical process that requires heat and therefore is endothermic.

(e) An extensive property is a property that depends upon the amount of material in a sample. Extensive properties include mass and volume.

1-6. *Refer to the Section 1-1 and the Key Terms for Chapter 1.*

A reaction or process is exothermic, in general, if heat energy is released, but other energies may be released.

(a) The discharge of a flashlight battery in which chemical energy is converted to electrical energy is referred to as being exothermic the chemical reaction occurring in the battery releases heat.

(b) An activated light stick produces essentially no heat, but is considered to be exothermic because light is emitted.

1-8. *Refer to Sections 1-1 and 1-5, and the Key Terms for Chapter 1.*

(a) Combustion is an exothermic process in which a chemical reaction releases heat.

(b) The freezing of water is an exothermic process. Heat must be removed from the molecules in the liquid state to cause solidification.

(c) The melting of ice is an endothermic process. The system requires heat to break the attractive forces that hold solid water together.

(d) The boiling of water is an endothermic process. Molecules of liquid water must absorb energy to break away from the attractive forces that hold liquid water together in order to form gaseous molecules.

(e) The condensing of steam is an exothermic process. The heat stored in water vapor must be removed for the vapor to liquefy. The condensation process is the opposite of boiling which requires heat.

(f) The burning of paper is an exothermic process. The heat generated can be used to light the wood in a fireplace.

1-10.   *Refer to Section 1-1.*

Einstein's equation, written as $E = mc^2$, tells us that the amount of energy released when matter is transformed into energy is the product of the mass of matter transformed and the speed of light squared. From this equation, we see that energy and matter are equivalent. Known as the Law of Conservation of Matter and Energy, we can use this equation to calculate the amount of energy released in a nuclear reaction because it is proportional to the difference in mass between the products and the reactants. The energy released (in joules) equals the mass difference (in kilograms) times the square of the speed of light (in m/s).

1-12.   *Refer to Section 1-1.*

Electrical motors are less than 100% efficient in the conversion of electrical energy into useful work, since a part of that energy is converted into frictional heat which radiates away.

However, the Law of Conservation of Energy still applies:

$$\text{electrical energy } = \text{ useful work} + \text{heat}$$

1-14.   *Refer to Section 1-3 and Figures 1-7 and 1-8.*

Solids: are rigid and have definite shapes;
          they occupy a fixed volume and are thus very difficult to compress;
          the hardness of a solid is related to the strength of the forces holding the particles of a solid together; the stronger the forces, the harder is the solid object.

Liquids: occupy essentially constant volume but have variable shape;
          they are difficult to compress;
          particles can pass freely over each other;
          their boiling points increase with increasing forces of attraction among the particles.

Gases: expand to fill the entire volume of their containers;
          they are very compressible with relatively large separations between particles.

The three states are alike in that they all exhibit definite mass and volume under a given set of conditions. All consist of some combination of atoms, molecules or ions. The differences are stated above. Additional differences occur in their relative densities:

$$\text{gases} <<< \text{liquids} < \text{solids.}$$

Molecular representations of these three phases can be seen in Figure 1-8. Note that water is an exceptional compound. The density of the liquid is greater than the solid phase. That is why solid ice floats in liquid water

---

1-16.   *Refer to Section 1-6 and the Key Terms for Chapter 1.*

(a) A substance is a kind of matter in which all samples have identical chemical composition and physical properties, e.g., iron (Fe) and water (H_2O).

(b) A mixture is a sample of matter composed of two or more substances in variable composition, each substance retaining its identity and properties, e.g., soil (minerals, water, organic matter, living organisms, etc.) and seawater (water, different salts, dissolved gases, organic compounds, living organisms, etc.).

(c) An element is a substance that cannot be decomposed into simpler substances by chemical means, e.g., nickel (Ni) and nitrogen (N).

(d) A compound is a substance composed of two or more elements in fixed proportions. Compounds can be decomposed into their constituent elements by chemical means. Examples include water (H_2O) and sodium chloride (NaCl).

1-18. *Refer to Section 1-6.*

(a) Gasoline is a homogeneous liquid mixture of organic compounds distilled from oil.

(b) Tap water is a homogeneous liquid mixture, called an aqueous solution, containing water, dissolved salts, and gases such as chlorine and oxygen.

(c) Calcium carbonate is a compound, $CaCO_3$, consisting of the elements Ca, C and O in the fixed atomic ratio, 1:1:3.

(d) Ink from a ball-point pen is a homogeneous mixture of solvent, water and dyes.

(e) Vegetable soup is a heterogeneous mixture of water, vegetables and the compound, NaCl (table salt), depending on the recipe.

(f) Aluminum foil is composed of the metallic element, Al.

1-20. *Refer to Section 1-6.*

The coin is a heterogeneous mixture of gold and copper because it consists of two distinguishable elements that can be recognized on sight.

1-22. *Refer to Section 1-4.*

(a) Striking a match, causing it to burst into flames, is a chemical property, since a change in composition is occurring of the substances in the match head and new substances including carbon dioxide gas and water vapor, are being formed.

(b) The hardness of steel is a physical property. It can be determined without a composition change.

(c) The density of gold is a physical property, since it can be observed without any change in the composition of the gold.

(d) The ability of baking soda to dissolve in water with the evolution of carbon dioxide gas is a chemical property of baking soda, since during the reaction, its composition is changing and a new substance is being formed.

(e) The ability of fine steel wool to burn in air is a chemical property of steel wool since a compositional change in the steel wool occurs and heat is released.

(f) The ripening of fruit is a chemical property. When the temperature of the fruit decreases when put into a refrigerator, the rate of the chemical reaction slows. So, the lowering of the fruit's temperature is a physical change, but temperature has a definite effect on the chemical properties of the fruit.

| 1-24. | *Refer to Section 1-5.* |

The observations that identify chemical properties are: (c) ultraviolet light converts ozone into oxygen, (e) sodium metal reacts violently with water, and (f) CO_2 does not support combustion.

Some chemists think that dissolution is a chemical process, since it is actually very complex, so some chemists would include (a).

| 1-26. | *Refer to Section 1-1 and the Key Terms for Chapter 1.* |

(b), (d) and (e) are examples of potential energy. An inflated balloon (b) possesses energy which will be released if it is popped. The stored chemical energy in a flashlight battery (d) will convert to electrical energy, then into kinetic energy once it is put to use. A frozen lake (e) is stored energy. Once spring comes, the water molecules will be free to move, the lake will be circulating and the energy will convert to kinetic energy. However, a lake can also be a source of potential energy that can be converted into kinetic energy if the water is released via a dam.

(a), (c) and (f) are all examples of kinetic energy due to their motion.

| 1-28. | *Refer to Section 1-5.* |

When the sulfur is heated, some of it obviously became a gas. However, there is not enough information to tell whether or not this was the result of a physical or a chemical change.

Hypothesis 1:   Solid sulfur could be changing directly into gaseous sulfur. This is a physical change called sublimation.

Hypothesis 2:   Solid sulfur could be reacting with oxygen in the air to form a gaseous compound consisting of sulfur and oxygen. This would be a chemical change. The sharp odor may indicate the presence of SO_2, but the smell test is not conclusive.

To verify which hypothesis is correct, we need to identify the gas that is produced.

| 1-30. | *Refer to Appendix A.* |

(a) 423.<u>006</u> mL = 4.23006×10^2 mL   (6 significant figures)

(b) 0.001<u>073040</u> g = 1.073040×10^{-3} g   (7 significant figures)

(c) 1<u>081.02</u> pounds = 1.08102×10^3 pounds   (6 significant figures)

| 1-32. | *Refer to Appendix A.* |

(a) 50600   (c) 0.1610   (e) 90000.

(b) 0.0004060   (d) 0.000206   (f) 0.0009000

| 1-34. | *Refer to Appendix A.* |

? volume (cm^3) = 252.56 cm x 18.23 cm x 6.5 cm = 29927 = **3.0×10^4 cm^3**   (2 significant figures based on 6.5 cm)

Refer to Section 1-9, the conversion factors from Tables 1-6 and 1-8, and Examples 1-3 and 1-4.

(a) $? \text{ km} = 453.4 \text{ m} \times \dfrac{1 \text{ km}}{1000 \text{ m}} = \textbf{0.4534 km}$

(b) $? \text{ m} = 36.3 \text{ km} \times \dfrac{1000 \text{ m}}{1 \text{ km}} = \textbf{3.63 x 10}^{\textbf{4}} \textbf{ m}$

(c) $? \text{ g} = 487 \text{ kg} \times \dfrac{1000 \text{ g}}{1 \text{ kg}} = \textbf{4.87 x 10}^{\textbf{5}} \textbf{ g}$

(d) $? \text{ mL} = 1.32 \text{ L} \times \dfrac{1000 \text{ mL}}{1 \text{L}} = \textbf{1.32 x 10}^{\textbf{3}} \textbf{ mL}$

(e) $? \text{ L} = 55.9 \text{ dL} \times \dfrac{1 \text{ L}}{10 \text{ dL}} = \textbf{5.59 L}$

(f) $? \text{ cm}^3 = 6251 \text{ L} \times \dfrac{1000 \text{ cm}^3}{1 \text{ L}} = \textbf{6.251 x 10}^{\textbf{6}} \textbf{ cm}^{\textbf{3}}$ (Note: $1 \text{ cm}^3 = 1 \text{ mL}$)

1-38. **Refer to Section 1-9, the conversion factors listed in Table 1-8, and Example 1-9.**

$? \text{ cents/L} = \dfrac{\$3.119}{1 \text{ gal}} \times \dfrac{1 \text{ gal}}{4 \text{ qt}} \times \dfrac{1.057 \text{ qt}}{1 \text{ L}} \times \dfrac{100 \text{ cents}}{\$1} = \textbf{82.42 cents/L}$

1-40. **Refer to Section 1-10, the conversion factors from Table 1-8, and Examples 1-7 and 1-9.**

(a) $? \text{ L} = 0.750 \text{ ft}^3 \times \dfrac{(12 \text{ in})^3}{(1 \text{ ft})^3} \times \dfrac{(2.54 \text{ cm})^3}{(1 \text{ in})^3} \times \dfrac{1 \text{ L}}{1000 \text{ cm}^3} = \textbf{21.2 L}$

(b) $? \text{ pints} = 1.00 \text{ L} \dfrac{1.057 \text{ qt}}{1 \text{ L}} \times \dfrac{2 \text{ pt}}{1 \text{ qt}} = \textbf{2.11 pt}$

(c) $? \dfrac{\text{km}}{\text{L}} = \dfrac{1 \text{ mile}}{1 \text{ gal}} \times \dfrac{1.609 \text{ km}}{1 \text{ mile}} \times \dfrac{1 \text{ gal}}{4 \text{ qt}} \times \dfrac{1.057 \text{ qt}}{1 \text{ L}} = \textbf{0.4252} \dfrac{\textbf{km}}{\textbf{L}}$

Therefore, to convert miles per gallon to kilometers per liter, one multiplies the miles per gallon by the factor, 0.4252.

1-42. **Refer to Appendix A.**

$\text{Average} = \dfrac{58.2 + 56.474}{2} = 57.337 = \textbf{57.3 \%}$ since the answer must be rounded to the tenths place

---

1-44. **Refer to Section 1-9, Appendix A, the conversion factors from Table 1-8 and Example 1-9.**

(a) $18 \text{ pints} \times \dfrac{1 \text{ qt}}{2 \text{ pints}} = \textbf{9.0 qt}$

(b) $\dfrac{55.0 \text{ miles}}{\text{hr}} \times \dfrac{1.609 \text{ km}}{1 \text{ mile}} = \textbf{88.5 km/hr}$

(c) $15.45 \text{ s} + 2.2 \text{ s} + 55 \text{ s} = 72.65 \text{ s} = \textbf{73 s}$ since the answer must be rounded to the one's place.

1-46. *Refer to Section 1-11, and Examples 1-11 and 1-12.*

$$\text{Density (mg/mm}^3) = \frac{m}{V} = \frac{6.080 \text{ mg}}{(2.20 \text{ mm} \times 1.36 \text{ mm} \times 1.23 \text{ mm})} = 1.65 \text{ mg/mm}^3$$

$$\text{Density (g/cm}^3) = \frac{1.65 \text{ mg}}{1 \text{ mm}^3} \times \frac{1 \text{ g}}{1000 \text{ mg}} \times \frac{(10 \text{ mm})^3}{(1 \text{ cm})^3} = \mathbf{1.65 \text{ g/cm}^3}$$

1-48. *Refer to Section 1-11 and Example 1-12.*

(a) Method 1: $D = \frac{m}{V}$; $V (\text{cm}^3) = \frac{m \text{ (g)}}{D \text{ (g/cm}^3)} = \frac{443 \text{ g}}{10.5 \text{ g/cm}^3} = \mathbf{42.2 \text{ cm}^3}$ since $0.443 \text{ kg} \equiv 443 \text{ g}$

   Method 2:   Dimensional Analysis

$$? \text{ cm}^3 \text{ silver} = 0.443 \text{ kg} \times \frac{1000 \text{ g}}{1 \text{ kg}} \times \frac{1 \text{ cm}^3}{10.5 \text{ g}} = \mathbf{42.2 \text{ cm}^3}$$

(b) length of each edge (cm) = $\sqrt[3]{V} = \sqrt[3]{42.2 \text{ cm}^3} = \mathbf{3.48 \text{ cm}}$

(c) length of each edge (in.) = $3.48 \text{ cm} \times \frac{1 \text{ in.}}{2.54 \text{ cm}} = \mathbf{1.37 \text{ in.}}$

1-50. *Refer to Section 1-11.*

Plan: (1) Find the volume of the aluminum wire, assuming that 10-lb spool contains 10.0 lb of aluminum
        (2) Calculate the radius of the wire in meters.
        (3) Solve for the length of wire in meters, using $V = \pi r^2 \ell$

(1) $? V = 10.0 \text{ lb Al} \times \frac{453.6 \text{ g Al}}{1 \text{ lb Al}} \times \frac{1 \text{ cm}^3 \text{ Al}}{2.70 \text{ g Al}} \times \frac{1 \text{ m}^3 \text{ Al}}{(100 \text{ cm})^3 \text{ Al}} = 1.68 \times 10^{-3} \text{ m}^3 \text{ Al}$

(2) $? \text{ radius}, r = \text{diameter}/2 = \frac{0.0808 \text{ in.}}{2} \times \frac{2.54 \text{ cm}}{1 \text{ in.}} \times \frac{1 \text{ m}}{100 \text{ cm}} = 1.03 \times 10^{-3} \text{ m}$

(3) $? \text{ length}, \ell = \frac{V}{\pi r^2} = \frac{1.68 \times 10^{-3} \text{ m}^3}{3.1416(1.03 \times 10^{-3} \text{ m})^2} = \mathbf{504 \text{ m}}$

1-52. *Refer to Sections 1-10 and 1-11.*

Plan: L solution $\overset{(1)}{\Rightarrow}$ mL solution $\overset{(2)}{\Rightarrow}$ g solution $\overset{(3)}{\Rightarrow}$ g iron(III) chloride

Using 3 unit factors,

(1) Convert liters to milliliters using 1000 mL = 1 liter,
(2) Convert mL of solution to mass of solution using density, then
(3) Convert mass of solution to mass of iron(III) chloride using the definition of % by mass.

$? \text{ g iron(III) chloride} = 2.50 \text{ L soln} \times \frac{1000 \text{ mL soln}}{1 \text{ L soln}} \times \frac{1.149 \text{ g soln}}{1 \text{ mL soln}} \times \frac{11 \text{ g iron(III) chloride}}{100 \text{ g soln}} = \mathbf{3.2 \times 10^2 \text{ g}}$

1-54. *Refer to Appendix A, Section 1-12, and Examples 1-16 and 1-17.*

In determining the correct number of significant figures, note that the following values are exact: 32°F, 1°C/1.8°F, and 1°C/1 K and have an infinite number of significant figures.

(a) $? \text{ °C} = \frac{1 \text{°C}}{1.8 \text{°F}} \times (15 \text{°F} - 32 \text{°F}) = \mathbf{-9.4 \text{°C}}$

(b) $? °C = \dfrac{1°C}{1.8°F} \times (32.6°F - 32.0°F) = 0.6°C$ (1 sig. fig. due to subtraction rules)

$? K = \dfrac{1\,K}{1°C} \times (0.6°C + 273.2°C) = \mathbf{273.8\ K}$ since 0°C = 273.15°C

(c) $? °C = \dfrac{1°C}{1\,K} \times (328\,K - 273\,K) = 55°C$

$? °F = \left(55°C \times \dfrac{1.8°F}{1°C} \right) + 32°F = \mathbf{130°F}$ (2 sig. figs.)

(d) $? °F = \left(11.3°C \times \dfrac{1.8°F}{1°C} \right) + 32°F = \mathbf{52.3°F}$

1-56. *Refer to Section 1-12.*

	Freezing Point of Water (FP)	Boiling Point of Water (BP)
Celsius Scale	0°C	100°C
Fahrenheit Scale	32°F	212°F
Réamur Scale	0°R	80°R

(a) $\dfrac{BP_{water} - FP_{water} \text{ on Celsius Scale}}{BP_{water} - FP_{water} \text{ on Réamur Scale}} = \dfrac{100°C - 0°C}{80°R - 0°R} = \dfrac{100°C}{80°R} = \dfrac{1.0°C}{0.8°R} = \dfrac{5°C}{4°R}$

Therefore, since both scales set the freezing point of water = 0°, then $? °C = \left(x°R \times \dfrac{5°C}{4°R} \right)$

(b) $\dfrac{BP_{water} - FP_{water} \text{ on Fahrenheit Scale}}{BP_{water} - FP_{water} \text{ on Réamur Scale}} = \dfrac{212°F - 32°F}{80°R - 0°R} = \dfrac{180°F}{80°R} = \dfrac{9°F}{4°R}$

Therefore, $? °F = \left(x°R \times \dfrac{9°F}{4°R} \right) + 32°F$

Note that we must add 32°F to account for the fact that 0°R is equivalent to 32°F.

(c) From (a), $? °C = \left(x°R \times \dfrac{5°C}{4°R} \right)$ Rearranging, we have $? °R = \left(x°C \times \dfrac{4°R}{5°C} \right)$

$BP_{mercury}\ (°R) = 356.6°C \times \dfrac{4°R}{5°C} = \mathbf{285.3°R}$

1-58. *Refer to Section 1-12 and Examples 1-16 and 1-17.*

For Al: $? °C = \dfrac{1°C}{1\,K} \times (933.6\,K - 273.2\,K) = \mathbf{660.4°C}$

$? °F = \left(660.4°C \times \dfrac{1.8°F}{1°C} \right) + 32°F = \mathbf{1221°F}$

For Ag: $? °C = \dfrac{1°C}{1\,K} \times (1235.1\,K - 273.2\,K) = \mathbf{961.9°C}$

$? °F = \left(961.9°C \times \dfrac{1.8°F}{1°C} \right) + 32°F = \mathbf{1763°F}$

$$? \, °C = \frac{1°C}{1.8°F} \times (102.0°F - 32.0°F) = \mathbf{38.9°C}$$

$$? \, K = 38.9 \, °C + 273.2 \, ° = \mathbf{312.1 \, K}$$

amount of heat *gained* (J) = (mass of substance)(specific heat)(temp. change)

$\qquad\qquad\qquad\qquad = 45.3 \text{ g} \times 0.895 \text{ J/g·°C} \times (62.5°C - 27.0°C)$

$\qquad\qquad\qquad\qquad = \mathbf{1440 \, J}$ (3 sig. figs.)

(a) amount of heat *gained* (J) = (mass of substance)(specific heat)(temp. change)

$\qquad\qquad\qquad\qquad\quad = (69{,}700 \text{ g})(0.818 \text{ J/g·°C})(41.0°C - 25.0°C)$

$\qquad\qquad\qquad\qquad\quad = \mathbf{9.12 \times 10^5 \, J}$

(b) Note that we will follow the convention of representing temperature (°C) as t and temperature (K) as T.

In any insulated system, the Law of Conservation of Energy states:

$\qquad\qquad$ the amount of heat lost by Substance 1 = amount of heat gained by Substance 2

As will be discussed in later chapters, "heat lost" is a negative quantity and "heat gained" is a positive quantity. However, the "*amount* of heat lost" and the "*amount* of heat gained" quoted here call for *absolute* quantities without a sign associated with them. In other words, because we are using the words "lost" and "gained" the heat involved is positive and the differences in temperature are positive values as well in this exercise.

$\qquad\qquad |$ the amount of heat lost by Substance 1 $| = |$ amount of heat gained by Substance 2 $|$

$\qquad\qquad |$ (mass)(Sp. Ht.)(temp. change) $|_1 = |$ (mass)(Sp. Ht.)(temp. change) $|_2$

In this exercise,

$\qquad\qquad |$ (mass)(Sp. Ht.)(temp. change) $|_{\text{limestone}} = |$ (mass)(Sp. Ht.)(temp. change) $|_{\text{air}}$

Since any "change" is always defined as the final value minus the initial value, we have

$\qquad$ (temp. change)$_{\text{limestone}} = (30.0°C - 41.0°C)$ and (temp. change)$_{\text{air}} = (t_{\text{final}} - 10.0°C)$

$\qquad$ for the limestone, $\qquad |30.0°C - 41.0°C| = |$ negative value $| = (41.0°C - 30.0°C) = 11.0°C$

$\qquad$ for the interior air, $\qquad |t_{\text{final}} - 10.0°C| = |$ positive value $| = (t_{\text{final}} - 10.0°C)$

Before we start, we must first calculate the mass of air inside the house:

$$? \text{ g air} = 2.83 \times 10^5 \text{ liters} \times \frac{1000 \text{ mL}}{1 \text{ L}} \times \frac{1.20 \times 10^{-5} \text{ g}}{1 \text{ mL}} = 3.40 \times 10^5 \text{ g}$$

$69{,}700 \text{ g limestone} \times 0.818 \text{ J/g·°C} \times (41.0°C - 30.0°C) = 3.40 \times 10^5 \text{ g air} \times 1.004 \text{ J/g·°C} \times (t_{\text{final}} - 10.0°C)$

$\qquad\qquad\qquad\qquad 6.27 \times 10^5 \text{ J} = (3.41 \times 10^5 \times t_{\text{final}}) \text{ J} - 3.41 \times 10^6 \text{ J}$

$\qquad\qquad\qquad\qquad 4.04 \times 10^6 \text{ J} = (3.41 \times 10^5 \text{ J/°C}) \times t_{\text{final}}$

$\qquad\qquad\qquad\qquad\qquad t_{\text{final}} = \mathbf{11.8°C}$

$$\left| \text{the amount of heat lost by Substance 1} \right| = \left| \text{amount of heat gained by Substance 2} \right|$$

$$\left| \text{(mass)(Sp. Ht.)(temp. change)} \right|_{\text{metal}} = \left| \text{(mass)(Sp. Ht.)(temp. change)} \right|_{\text{water}}$$

$$50.0 \text{ g} \times \text{(Sp. Ht.)} \times (75.0°C - 18.3°C) = 100. \text{ g} \times 4.18 \text{ J/g°C} \times (18.3°C - 15.0°C)$$

(Sp. Ht.) $\times$ 2835 (remember: it has only 3 sig. figs.*) = 1379 (only 2 sig. figs.)

Solving, Sp. Ht. of the metal = **0.49 J/g°C** (2 significant figures set by the temperature change of the water)

* Note: it is better to carry all the numbers in your calculator and do your rounding to the correct number of significant figures at the end.

1-68.   *Refer to Sections 1-9 and 1-10.*

(a) ? tons ore = 5.79 tons hematite $\times \dfrac{100 \text{ tons ore}}{9.24 \text{ tons hematite}}$ = **62.7 tons ore**

(b) ? kg ore = 6.40 kg hematite $\times \dfrac{100 \text{ kg ore}}{9.24 \text{ kg hematite}}$ = **69.3 kg ore**

1-70.   *Refer to Appendix A, Section 1-9 and the conversion factors from Table 1-8.*

? m = 23.5 ft $\times \dfrac{12 \text{ in.}}{1 \text{ ft}} \times \dfrac{2.54 \text{ cm}}{1 \text{ in}} \times \dfrac{1 \text{ m}}{100 \text{ cm}}$ = **7.16 m**

1-72.   *Refer to Section 1-9 and Table 1-8.*

? lethal dose = 165 lb body wt $\times \dfrac{453.6 \text{ g body wt}}{1 \text{ lb body wt}} \times \dfrac{1 \text{ kg body wt}}{1000 \text{ g body wt}} \times \dfrac{1.5 \text{ mg drug}}{1 \text{ kg body wt}}$ = **110 mg drug** (2 sig. figs.)

1-74.   *Refer to Sections 1-10 and 1-11.*

$\qquad\qquad\qquad\quad$ (1) $\qquad\qquad$ (2)

Plan: g ammonia $\Rightarrow$ g solution $\Rightarrow$ mL solution

Using 2 unit factors,   (1) Convert mass of ammonia to mass of solution using the definition of % by mass, then

$\qquad\qquad\qquad\qquad$ (2) Convert mass of solution to volume (in mL) of solution using density

? L solution = 25.8 g ammonia $\times \dfrac{100 \text{ g soln}}{5 \text{ g ammonia}} \times \dfrac{1 \text{ mL soln}}{1.006 \text{ g soln}}$ = **500 mL** (1 significant figure due to 5% ammonia)

1-76.   *Refer to Sections 1-3 and 1-11, Example 1-2, and Figure 1-7.*

(a) Box (i) represents the very ordered, dense solid state.

(b) Box (iii) represents the less ordered, slightly less dense liquid state.

(c) Box (ii) represents the disordered, much less dense gaseous state.

(d) The physical states rank from least dense to most dense: gaseous state $\ll$ liquid state $<$ solid state

Physical properties: zinc metal is a gray and shiny solid
zinc metal piece can be cut with scissors
copper chloride solution is blue in color
the new product is brown and granular

Physical changes: the zinc pieces reduced in size when cut with scissors
the zinc pieces reduced in size during the reaction
the solution became colorless and became warmer

Chemical changes: some of the zinc disappeared. It must have reacted, because zinc metal is not soluble in water
a new brown granular product formed
the reaction is exothermic and heat was released, making the flask warm to the touch

1-80. *Refer to Sections 1-4 and 1-5, and Exercise 1-79.*

Water is more dense than ice at 0°C because a cube of ice (less dense) will float in a glass of water (more dense). The first drawing shows liquid water molecules that are disorganized and slightly closer together, whereas the second drawing depicts the water molecules in a very rigid, ordered structure. When a sample has more mass per unit volume, it is more dense, so liquid water is more dense than solid water because its molecules are closer together.

1-82. *Refer to your life story.*

Chemical vocabulary and understanding can come from many experiences, besides the classroom. Perhaps you visited a science museum, or had a chemistry "magic show" come to your school. You may have been given a chemistry set as a present. There are many science-related shows on television and the internet has many, many links to science pages. Use your own life experiences to answer this question.

1-84. *Refer to Appendix A, Table 1-8 for conversion factors, and Example 1-4.*

Each cesium atom has a diameter = 2 x 2.65 Å = 5.30 Å

? Cs atoms = 1.00 inch x $\dfrac{2.54 \text{ cm}}{1 \text{ in}}$ x $\dfrac{1 \text{ m}}{100 \text{ cm}}$ x $\dfrac{1 \text{ Å}}{10^{-10} \text{ m}}$ x $\dfrac{1 \text{ atom}}{5.30 \text{ Å}}$ = **4.79 x 10^7 atoms**

1-86. *Refer to Section 1-5 and your common sense.*

As a student writes out an End-of-Chapter Exercise, the direct chemical changes that occur include

(1) reactions (including irreversible adsorption) of the ink in the pen with the paper,
(2) the body's biochemical reactions,
(3) the creation of new neural pathways in the student's brain due to the new information she/he is learning.

More indirect chemical changes include the burning of coal or natural gas to provide the power for electricity, heat and light. If the student is doing a problem outside on a beautiful day, chemical changes might involve photosynthesis occurring in the plants around her/him providing oxygen for the student to breathe and the fusion reactions in the sun which provide heat and light, etc.

The complete answer is limited only by the student's imagination and understanding of the meaning of chemical changes. So, definitely yes, the answer involves knowledge not covered in Chapter 1.

1-88.	**_Refer to Section 1-12 and Example 1-16._**

$$? \text{ °C of iron} = \frac{1°C}{1.8°F} \times (65°F - 32°F) = \mathbf{18°C}$$

Therefore, the **water sample** at 65°C has a higher temperature than the iron sample at only 18°C.

1-90.	**_Refer to Section 1-2._**

From left to right: NO, NO_2, N_2O, N_2O_3, N_2O_4 and N_2O_5.

1-92.	**_Refer to Section 1-2, Figures 1-3 and 1-4, and Example 1-1._**

At room temperature, sulfur (rhombic) is a solid with formula, S_8, oxygen is a diatomic gas, O_2 and sulfur dioxide is a gas, SO_2.

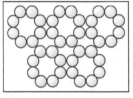 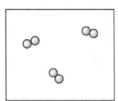 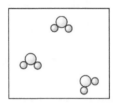 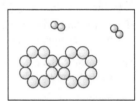

| Sulfur, $S_8(s)$ | Oxygen, $O_2(g)$ | Sulfur dioxide, $SO_2(g)$ | Mixture of S_8 and O_2 |

One similarity between S_8 and O_2 is that they are both elements composed of molecules. However, S_8 is a solid, with the molecular units arranged close together in a systematic way and O_2 is a gas, with its diatomic molecules relatively far apart.

The compound, SO_2, and the sample of S_8 mixed with O_2 both contain the elements, sulfur and oxygen, but SO_2 sample contains S and O in the definite ratio of 1:2 in each molecule and the individual gaseous SO_2 molecules are far apart. The mixture of S_8 and O_2 contains solid sulfur and molecular oxygen and the ratio of S to O can be variable. The mixture is heterogeneous, because $S_8(s)$ and $O_2(g)$ are present in different phases.

1-94.	**_Refer to Section 1-11 and Appendix A._**

The calculation only involves multiplying and dividing. The number of significant figures in the answer is then set by the value with the least number of significant figures. Since density (=8.92 g/mL) has only 3 significant figures, the answer can only have 3 significant figures, which includes the first doubtful digit. The answer is V = 475 cm^3 and "5" is the first doubtful digit.

1-96.	**_Refer to Section 1-9 and Appendix A._**

Many calculations in chemistry can be done in different ways. Consider the conversion of 3475 cm to miles.

$$(1) \, ? \text{ miles} = 3475 \text{ cm} \times \frac{1 \text{ in.}}{2.54 \text{ cm}} \times \frac{1 \text{ ft}}{12 \text{ in.}} \times \frac{1 \text{ mile}}{5280 \text{ ft}} = 0.021592649 \text{ miles or } 0.02159 \text{ miles}$$

Note: The following conversions are exact: 1 in. = 2.54 cm, 1 ft = 12 in., 1 mile = 5280 ft, so 2.54, 12, and 5280 have infinite numbers of significant figures. The number of significant figures in the answer is then set by the data: 4.

(2) ? miles = 3475 cm $\times$ $\dfrac{1\ m}{100\ cm}$ $\times$ $\dfrac{1\ km}{1000\ m}$ $\times$ $\dfrac{1\ mile}{1.609\ km}$ = 0.021597265 miles or 0.02160 miles

Note: Exact conversions: 1 m = 100 cm, 1 km = 1000 m. Inexact conversion: 1 mile = 1.609 km to 4 significant figures. The number of significant figures in the answer is set by the data (4 sig. figs.) but the answer has extra source of error since the conversion from kilometers to miles is only good to 4 sig. figs.

Method (1) uses all exact conversions and will give a more accurate answer than Method (2). If you really wanted to use Method (2), be sure that the inexact conversion contains more significant figures than your data. For example, if you used 1 mile = 1.6093 km, your answer would have been 0.021593239, and to 4 significant figures, both methods would have given essentially the same answer, differing only in the doubtful digit.

1-98. *Refer to Sections 1-12 and 1-13, and the Key Terms for Chapter 1.*

Students often get the terms, heat, specific heat and temperature confused. Here are the formal definitions:

Heat: A form of energy that flows between two samples of matter because of their difference in temperature, measured in joules (J).

Specific heat: The amount of heat required to raise the temperature of one gram of a substance one degree Celsius. Its units are J/g·°C.

Temperature: A measure of the intensity of heat, that is, the hotness or coldness of a sample or object. Temperature also refers to molecular motion. The warmer a substance is, the more its molecules are moving. Scientists usually work in °C or K.

If two samples of the same element are at different temperatures, their atoms have different kinetic energies and are moving at different average speeds. If the two samples touch, energy (heat) will transfer from the hotter to the colder element until their temperatures are the same and the average speed of their respective molecules are the same.

Different substances require different amounts of heat to change their temperatures. Specific heat is the constant that gives that information. It has units of J/g·°C and is the amount of heat required (in joules) to heat up 1 gram of a substance by 1°C.

As a final note, consider a 5.0 gram block of iron and a 15 gram block of iron, both at 25°C. They are both at the same temperature, so if they came into contact, neither would change temperature. However, the 15 g iron block contains three times more heat than the 5.0 gram block. In other words, three times more heat is required to change the temperature of the 15 gram block of iron to 26°C, as the 5.0 gram block of iron.

2 Chemical Formulas and Composition Stoichiometry

2-2. *Refer to Section 2-1 and the Key Terms for Chapter 2.*

Allotropes are defined as different forms of the same element in the same physical state. Two examples of allotropes are:

  (1) oxygen, O_2 (a diatomic molecule) and ozone, O_3 (a triatomic molecule), and

  (2) carbon as graphite, $C_{graphite}$, and carbon as diamond, $C_{diamond}$.

2-4. *Refer to Section 2-1 and Figure 2-1.*

The structural formulas and ball-and-stick models of water and ethanol are given in Figure 2-1. You can see that the general shape and bond angles are similar around the oxygen atom.

2-6. *Refer to Section 2-1 and Figure 2-1.*

Organic compounds can be distinguished from inorganic compounds because organic compounds contain C–C or C–H bonds or both. Refer to Figure 2-1. According to this definition, water, H_2O, hydrogen peroxide, H_2O_2, and carbon tetrachloride, CCl_4, are considered inorganic molecules, whereas ethanol, C_2H_5OH, is an organic molecule.

2-8. *Refer to Section 2-1, Table 2-1, and Figure 1-5.*

Ball-and-stick model of ethane, CH_3CH_3:

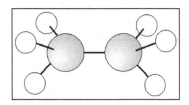

2-10. *Refer to Section 2-1 and Table 2-1.*

(a) O_3, HNO_3, SO_3

(b) H_2, H_2O, H_2O_2, H_2SO_4

(c) H_2O_2, NH_3, SO_3

(d) CH_3COOH, C_2H_6

(e) $CH_3CH_2CH_3$, $CH_3CH_2CH_2OH$

2-12. *Refer to Sections 2-1 and 2-2, and Tables 2-1 and 2-2.*

(a) HNO_3 nitric acid

(b) C_5H_{12} pentane

(c) NH_3 ammonia

(d) CH_3OH methanol

2-14. *Refer to Section 2-2 and Table 2-2.*

(a) Mg^{2+} monatomic cation

(b) SO_3^{2-} polyatomic anion

(c) Cu^+ monatomic cation

(d) NH_4^+ polyatomic cation

(e) O^{2-} monatomic anion

barium sulfate $BaSO_4$ Ba^{2+} barium ion SO_4^{2-} sulfate ion
magnesium nitrate $Mg(NO_3)_2$ Mg^{2+} magnesium ion NO_3^- nitrate ion
sodium acetate $NaCH_3COO$ Na^+ sodium ion CH_3COO^- acetate ion

(a) $CuCO_3$ copper(II) carbonate   (b) $SrBr_2$ strontium bromide

(c) $(NH_4)_2CO_3$ ammonium carbonate   (d) ZnO zinc oxide

(e) $Fe_2(SO_4)_3$ iron(III) sulfate

(a) Na_2CO_3 (b) $MgCl_2$ (c) $Zn(OH)_2$ (d) $(NH_4)_2S$ (e) NaI

(a) $NaBr$ sodium bromide   (b) $MgBr_2$ magnesium bromide

(c) SO_2 sulfur dioxide or SO_3 sulfur trioxide   (d) CaO calcium oxide

(e) K_2S potassium sulfide   (f) $AlBr_3$ aluminum bromide

The mass ratio of a rubidium atom (85.4678 amu) to a bromine atom (79.904 amu) is 85.4678/79.904 = 1.0696 (to 5 significant figures) or **1.070** (to 4 significant figures).

(a) The atomic weight of an element is the weighted average of the masses of all the element's constituent isotopes.

(b) Atomic weights can be referred to as relative numbers, because all atomic weights are determined relative to the mass of a particular carbon isotope, called carbon-12. The atomic mass unit (amu) is defined as exactly 1/12 of the mass of the carbon-12 isotope.

(a) bromine, Br_2 2 x Br = 2 x 79.904 amu = **159.808 amu**

(b) hydrogen peroxide, H_2O_2 2 x H = 2 x 1.008   amu =   2.016 amu
                                        2 x O = 2 x 15.999   amu = 31.998 amu
                                                    formula weight = **34.014 amu**

(c) saccharin, $C_7H_5NSO_3$ 7 x C = 7 x 12.011   amu = 84.077 amu
                                        5 x H = 5 x 1.008   amu =   5.040 amu
                                        1 x N = 1 x 14.007   amu = 14.007 amu
                                        1 x S = 1 x 32.06   amu = 32.06   amu
                                        3 x O = 3 x 15.999   amu = 47.997 amu
                                                  formula weight = **183.18   amu**

(d) potassium chromate, K_2CrO_4

$$2 \times K = 2 \times 39.0983 \text{ amu} = 78.1966 \text{ amu}$$
$$1 \times Cr = 1 \times 51.9961 \text{ amu} = 51.9961 \text{ amu}$$
$$4 \times O = 4 \times 15.999 \text{ amu} = 63.996 \text{ amu}$$
$$\text{formula weight} = \mathbf{194.189} \text{ amu}$$

2-30.   Refer to Section 2-6 and Example 2-8.

All atomic weights are rounded to 2 decimal places.

(a) hydrogen sulfide, H_2S

$$2 \times H = 2 \times 1.01 \text{ amu} = 2.02 \text{ amu}$$
$$1 \times S = 1 \times 32.06 \text{ amu} = 32.06 \text{ amu}$$
$$\text{formula weight} = \mathbf{34.08} \text{ amu}$$

(b) phosphorus trichloride, PCl_3

$$1 \times P = 1 \times 30.97 \text{ amu} = 30.97 \text{ amu}$$
$$3 \times Cl = 3 \times 35.45 \text{ amu} = 106.3_5 \text{ amu*}$$
$$\text{formula weight} = \mathbf{137.3} \text{ amu}$$

(c) hypochlorous acid, $HClO$

$$1 \times H = 1 \times 1.01 \text{ amu} = 1.01 \text{ amu}$$
$$1 \times Cl = 1 \times 35.45 \text{ amu} = 35.45 \text{ amu}$$
$$1 \times O = 1 \times 16.00 \text{ amu} = 16.00 \text{ amu}$$
$$\text{formula weight} = \mathbf{52.46} \text{ amu}$$

(d) hydrogen iodide, HI

$$1 \times H = 1 \times 1.01 \text{ amu} = 1.01 \text{ amu}$$
$$1 \times I = 1 \times 126.90 \text{ amu} = 126.90 \text{ amu}$$
$$\text{formula weight} = \mathbf{127.91} \text{ amu}$$

* The number was not rounded to the correct number of significant figures until after addition.

2-32.   Refer to Section 2-6.

Method 1:   Use the units of formula weight to derive a formula relating grams, moles and formula weight:

$$\text{formula weight, FW} \left(\frac{g}{mol}\right) = \frac{\text{grams of compound}}{\text{moles of compound}}$$

Therefore, grams of compound = moles of compound $\times$ FW

(1) ? g CCl_4 = 2.371 mol $CCl_4 \times 153.8$ g/mol = **364.7 g CCl_4**

(2) ? kg CCl_4 = 374.7 g $CCl_4 \times \dfrac{1 \text{ kg}}{1000 \text{ g}}$ = **0.3647 kg CCl_4**

Method 2: Dimensional Analysis

(2) ? kg CCl_4 = 2.371 mol $CCl_4 \times \dfrac{153.8 \text{ g } CCl_4}{1 \text{ mol } CCl_4} \times \dfrac{1 \text{ kg}}{1000 \text{ g}}$ = **0.3647 kg CCl_4**

2-34.   Refer to Section 2-6, and Examples 2-10 and 2-11.

The molecular mass of C_3H_8 is 44.1 g/mol. Each C_3H_8 molecule contains 8 hydrogen atoms.

Plan: g $C_3H_8 \Rightarrow$ mol $C_3H_8 \Rightarrow$ molecules $C_3H_8 \Rightarrow$ atoms H

? H atoms = 167 g $C_3H_8 \times \dfrac{1 \text{ mol } C_3H_8}{44.1 \text{ g } C_3H_8} \times \dfrac{6.02 \times 10^{23} \text{ } C_3H_8 \text{ molecules}}{1 \text{ mol } C_3H_8} \times \dfrac{8 \text{ H atoms}}{1 \text{ } C_3H_8 \text{ molecule}}$ = **1.82 $\times$ 10^{25} H atoms**

Method 1:   Use the units of formula weight to derive a formula relating grams, moles and formula weight:

$$\text{formula weight, FW} \left(\frac{\text{g}}{\text{mol}}\right) = \frac{\text{grams of substance}}{\text{moles of substance}}$$

Therefore, $\text{moles of substance} = \dfrac{\text{grams of substance}}{\text{formula weight (g/mol)}}$

$? \text{ mol NH}_3 = \dfrac{12.50 \text{ g}}{17.03 \text{ g/mol}} = \textbf{0.7340 mol NH}_3$

> (Note: be sure you use <u>at least</u> as many significant figures in the formula weight as you have significant figures in your data.)

Method 2: Dimensional Analysis

$? \text{ mol NH}_3 = 12.50 \text{ g NH}_3 \times \dfrac{1 \text{ mol NH}_3}{17.03 \text{ g NH}_3} = \textbf{0.7340 mol NH}_3$

Plan: g substance $\overset{(1)}{\Rightarrow}$ moles substance $\overset{(2)}{\Rightarrow}$ molecules substance

Method 1:   Recall: $\text{mol substance} = \dfrac{\text{g substance}}{\text{formula weight}}$ and   Avogadro's Number, $N = 6.02 \times 10^{23}$ molecules/mol

As an example:

(a) (1) $? \text{ mol CO}_2 = \dfrac{\text{g CO}_2}{\text{FW CO}_2} = \dfrac{31.6 \text{ g}}{44.0 \text{ g/mol}} = 0.718 \text{ mol CO}_2$

   (2) $? \text{ molecules CO}_2 = 0.718 \text{ mol CO}_2 \times (6.02 \times 10^{23} \text{ molecules/mol}) = \textbf{4.32} \times \textbf{10}^{23} \textbf{ molecules CO}_2$

Method 2:   Dimensional Analysis. Each unit factor corresponds to a step in the Plan.

$$\qquad\qquad\qquad\qquad\qquad\qquad \textbf{Step 1} \qquad\qquad \textbf{Step 2}$$

(a) $? \text{ molecules CO}_2 = 31.6 \text{ g CO}_2 \times \dfrac{1 \text{ mol CO}_2}{44.0 \text{ g CO}_2} \times \dfrac{6.02 \times 10^{23} \text{ molecules CO}_2}{1 \text{ mol CO}_2} = \textbf{4.32} \times \textbf{10}^{23} \textbf{ molecules CO}_2$

(b) $? \text{ molecules N}_2 = 31.6 \text{ g N}_2 \times \dfrac{1 \text{ mol N}_2}{28.0 \text{ g N}_2} \times \dfrac{6.02 \times 10^{23} \text{ molecules N}_2}{1 \text{ mol N}_2} = \textbf{6.79} \times \textbf{10}^{23} \textbf{ molecules N}_2$

(c) $? \text{ molecules P}_4 = 31.6 \text{ g P}_4 \times \dfrac{1 \text{ mol P}_4}{124 \text{ g P}_4} \times \dfrac{6.02 \times 10^{23} \text{ molecules P}_4}{1 \text{ mol P}_4} = \textbf{1.53} \times \textbf{10}^{23} \textbf{ molecules P}_4$

(d) $? \text{ molecules P}_2 = 31.6 \text{ g P}_2 \times \dfrac{1 \text{ mol P}_2}{62.0 \text{ g P}_2} \times \dfrac{6.02 \times 10^{23} \text{ molecules P}_2}{1 \text{ mol P}_2} = \textbf{3.07} \times \textbf{10}^{23} \textbf{ molecules P}_2$

(e) $? \text{ atoms P in (c)} = 1.53 \times 10^{23} \text{ molecules P}_4 \times \dfrac{4 \text{ atoms P}}{1 \text{ P}_4 \text{ molecule}} = 6.12 \times 10^{23} \text{ atoms P in (c)}$

   $? \text{ atoms P in (d)} = 3.07 \times 10^{23} \text{ molecules P}_2 \times \dfrac{2 \text{ atoms P}}{1 \text{ P}_2 \text{ molecule}} = 6.14 \times 10^{23} \text{ atoms P in (d)}$

Yes, there is the same number of P atoms in 31.6 g of pure phosphorus, regardless of whether the phosphorus is in the form of P_4 or P_2. The difference is due to rounding error only.

2-40. *Refer to Section 2-5 and the inside front page of this textbook.*

	Element	Atomic Weight (amu)	Mass of 1 Mole of Atoms (g)
(a)	Sn	**118.710**	**118.710**
(b)	**Br**	79.904	**79.904**
(c)	Mg	**24.3050**	**24.3050**
(d)	**Cr**	**51.9961**	51.9961

2-42. *Refer to Section 2-6 and Table 2-5.*

Moles of compound	Moles of cations	Moles of anions
1 mol $NaClO_4$	**1** mol Na^+	**1** mol ClO_4^-
2 mol K_2SO_4	**4** mol K^+	**2** mol SO_4^{2-}
0.2 mol calcium sulfate, $CaSO_4$	**0.2** mol Ca^{2+}	**0.2** mol SO_4^{2-}
0.25 mol $(NH_4)_2SO_4$	0.50 mol NH_4^+	0.25 mol SO_4^{2-}

2-44. *Refer to Section 2-6 and Example 2-9.*

$$\text{Plan: molecules } CH_4 \overset{(1)}{\Rightarrow} \text{ moles } CH_4 \overset{(2)}{\Rightarrow} \text{ g } CH_4$$

The molecular mass of CH_4 is 16.0 g/mol.

$$? \text{ g } CH_4 = 6.00 \times 10^6 \text{ molecules } CH_4 \times \frac{1 \text{ mol } CH_4}{6.02 \times 10^{23} \text{ molecules } CH_4} \times \frac{16.0 \text{ g } CH_4}{1 \text{ mol } CH_4} = \mathbf{1.59 \times 10^{-16} \text{ g } CH_4}$$

2-46. *Refer to Section 2-1, Exercise 30 and Figure 2-1.*

$$? \text{ mol atoms in } H_2S = 100.0 \text{ g } H_2S \times \frac{1 \text{ mol } H_2S}{34.08 \text{ g } H_2S} \times \frac{3 \text{ mol atoms in } H_2S}{1 \text{ mol } H_2S} = \mathbf{8.803 \text{ mol atoms}}$$

$$? \text{ mol atoms in } PCl_3 = 100.0 \text{ g } PCl_3 \times \frac{1 \text{ mol } PCl_3}{137.3 \text{ g } PCl_3} \times \frac{4 \text{ mol atoms in } PCl_3}{1 \text{ mol } PCl_3} = \mathbf{2.913 \text{ mol atoms}}$$

$$? \text{ mol atoms in } HClO = 100.0 \text{ g } HClO \times \frac{1 \text{ mol } HClO}{52.46 \text{ g } HClO} \times \frac{3 \text{ mol atoms in } HClO}{1 \text{ mol } HClO} = \mathbf{5.719 \text{ mol atoms}}$$

$$? \text{ mol atoms in } HI = 100.0 \text{ g } HI \times \frac{1 \text{ mol } HI}{127.91 \text{ g } HI} \times \frac{2 \text{ mol atoms in } HI}{1 \text{ mol } HI} = \mathbf{1.564 \text{ mol atoms}}$$

Therefore, 100.0 g **H_2S** contains more moles of atoms that 100.0 g of the other compounds.

2-48. *Refer to Section 2-7 and Example 2-12.*

mass of 1 mol Ag_2CO_3

$$
\begin{array}{llll}
2 \times Ag = 2 \times 107.9 \text{ g} = & 215.8 & \text{g} \\
1 \times C = 1 \times 12.01 \text{ g} = & 12.01 & \text{g} \\
3 \times O = 3 \times 16.00 \text{ g} = & \underline{48.00} & \text{g} \\
\text{mass of 1 mol} & = 275.8 & \text{g}
\end{array}
$$

percent Ag by mass

%Ag = (215.8/275.8) x 100% = **78.25%**

2-50. *Refer to Sections 2-8 and 2-9, and Example 2-17.*

(a) First, we must calculate the % by mass of N in skatole.

? % N = 100.00% - (% C + % H) = 100.00% - (82.40% + 6.92%) = 10.68% N

To find the simplest formula, assume 100 g of skatole.

$? \text{ mol C} = \dfrac{g \text{ C}}{AW \text{ C}} = \dfrac{82.40 \text{ g}}{12.01 \text{ g/mol}} = 6.861 \text{ mol C}$ $\qquad \text{Ratio} = \dfrac{6.861}{0.7623} = 9$

$? \text{ mol H} = \dfrac{g \text{ H}}{AW \text{ H}} = \dfrac{6.92 \text{ g}}{1.008 \text{ g/mol}} = 6.87 \text{ mol H}$ $\qquad \text{Ratio} = \dfrac{6.87}{0.7623} = 9$

$? \text{ mol N} = \dfrac{g \text{ N}}{AW \text{ N}} = \dfrac{10.68 \text{ g}}{14.01 \text{ g/mol}} = 0.7623 \text{ mol N}$ $\qquad \text{Ratio} = \dfrac{0.7623}{0.7623} = 1$

The simplest formula is the true formula, C_9H_9N.

(b) The molecular weight of skatole:

$$\begin{aligned} 9 \times C &= 9 \times & 12.01 \text{ g} &= 108.1 \text{ g} \\ 9 \times H &= 9 \times & 1.008 \text{ g} &= 9.07 \text{ g} \\ 1 \times N &= 1 \times & 14.01 \text{ g} &= 14.01 \text{ g} \\ \hline & & \text{mass of 1 mol } C_9H_9N &= \mathbf{131.2 \text{ g}} \end{aligned}$$

2-52. *Refer to Sections 2-8 and 2-9, and Examples 2-13 and 2-17.*

(a) Assume 100 g of timolol.

$? \text{ mol C} = \dfrac{49.4 \text{ g C}}{12.0 \text{ g/mol}} = 4.12 \text{ mol C}$ $\qquad \text{Ratio} = \dfrac{4.12}{0.316} = 13$

$? \text{ mol H} = \dfrac{7.64 \text{ g H}}{1.008 \text{ g/mol}} = 7.58 \text{ mol H}$ $\qquad \text{Ratio} = \dfrac{7.58}{0.316} = 24$

$? \text{ mol N} = \dfrac{17.7 \text{ g N}}{14.0 \text{ g/mol}} = 1.26 \text{ mol N}$ $\qquad \text{Ratio} = \dfrac{1.26}{0.316} = 4$

$? \text{ mol O} = \dfrac{15.2 \text{ g O}}{16.0 \text{ g/mol}} = 0.950 \text{ mol O}$ $\qquad \text{Ratio} = \dfrac{0.950}{0.316} = 3$

$? \text{ mol S} = \dfrac{10.1 \text{ g S}}{32.1 \text{ g/mol}} = 0.315 \text{ mol S}$ $\qquad \text{Ratio} = \dfrac{0.315}{0.315} = 1$

The simplest formula for timolol is $C_{13}H_{24}N_4O_3S$ (FW = 316 g/mol)

(b) $\text{MW (g/mol)} = \dfrac{g \text{ timolol}}{\text{mol timolol}} = \dfrac{3.16 \text{ g}}{0.0100 \text{ mol}} = 316 \text{ g/mol}$

$n = \dfrac{\text{molecular weight}}{\text{simplest formula weight}} = \dfrac{316}{316} = 1$

The simplest formula is therefore the true molecular formula, $C_{13}H_{24}N_4O_3S$.

2-54. *Refer to Section 2-8 and Example 2-13.*

Plan: (1) If percentage composition instead of sample mass is given, assume a 100 g sample.
(2) Calculate the moles of each element in the 100 g sample.
(3) Divide each of the mole values by the smallest number obtained as a mole value for the 100 g sample.
(4) Determine a whole number ratio.

General Rule: do not round to a whole number unless very close (within about 0.1) to a whole number. For example, if you obtain 2.75 as one value, do not round to 3, but multiply by 4 to convert to 11).

Let us assume we have a 100.0 g sample of norepinephrine with 56.8 g C, 6.56 g H, 28.4 g O and 8.28 g N.

$? \text{ mol C} = \dfrac{\text{g C}}{\text{AW C}} = \dfrac{56.8 \text{ g}}{12.01 \text{ g/mol}} = 4.73 \text{ mol}$ $\text{Ratio} = \dfrac{4.73}{0.591} = 8$

$? \text{ mol H} = \dfrac{\text{g}}{\text{AW H}} = \dfrac{6.56 \text{ g}}{1.008 \text{ g/mol}} = 6.51 \text{ mol}$ $\text{Ratio} = \dfrac{6.51}{0.591} = 11$

$? \text{ mol O} = \dfrac{\text{g O}}{\text{AW O}} = \dfrac{28.4 \text{ g}}{16.00 \text{ g/mol}} = 1.78 \text{ mol}$ $\text{Ratio} = \dfrac{1.78}{0.591} = 3.01 = 3$

$? \text{ mol N} = \dfrac{\text{g N}}{\text{AW N}} = \dfrac{8.28 \text{ g}}{14.01 \text{ g/mol}} = 0.591 \text{ mol}$ $\text{Ratio} = \dfrac{0.591}{0.591} = 1$

Therefore, the simplest formula is $C_8H_{11}O_3N$.

2-56. *Refer to Section 2-8 and Example 2-13.*

Let us assume we have a 100.00 g sample of the kitchen product.

It contains 27.37 g Na, 1.20 g H, 14.30 g C and 57.14 g O.

$? \text{ mol Na} = \dfrac{\text{g Na}}{\text{AW Na}} = \dfrac{27.37 \text{ g}}{22.99 \text{ g/mol}} = 1.191 \text{ mol}$ $\text{Ratio} = \dfrac{1.191}{1.19} = 1$

$? \text{ mol H} = \dfrac{\text{g}}{\text{AW H}} = \dfrac{1.20 \text{ g}}{1.008 \text{ g/mol}} = 1.19 \text{ mol}$ $\text{Ratio} = \dfrac{1.19}{1.19} = 1$

$? \text{ mol C} = \dfrac{\text{g C}}{\text{AW C}} = \dfrac{14.30 \text{ g}}{12.01 \text{ g/mol}} = 1.191 \text{ mol}$ $\text{Ratio} = \dfrac{1.191}{1.19} = 1$

$? \text{ mol O} = \dfrac{\text{g O}}{\text{AW O}} = \dfrac{57.14 \text{ g}}{16.00 \text{ g/mol}} = 3.571 \text{ mol}$ $\text{Ratio} = \dfrac{3.571}{1.19} = 3$

Therefore, the simplest formula is $NaHCO_3$ or **sodium bicarbonate** (also called sodium hydrogen carbonate.) Its common name is **baking soda**.

2-58. *Refer to Sections 2-8 and 2-9, and Examples 2-13 and 2-17.*

Let us assume we have a 100.0 g sample of lysine, So, we have 19.2 g N, 9.64 g H, 49.3 g C and 21.9 g O.

$? \text{ mol N} = \dfrac{\text{g N}}{\text{AW N}} = \dfrac{19.2 \text{ g}}{14.01 \text{ g/mol}} = 1.37 \text{ mol}$ $\text{Ratio} = \dfrac{1.37}{1.37} = 1$

$? \text{ mol H} = \dfrac{\text{g}}{\text{AW H}} = \dfrac{9.64 \text{ g}}{1.008 \text{ g/mol}} = 9.56 \text{ mol}$ $\text{Ratio} = \dfrac{9.56}{1.37} = 7$

$? \text{ mol C} = \dfrac{\text{g C}}{\text{AW C}} = \dfrac{49.3 \text{ g}}{12.01 \text{ g/mol}} = 4.10 \text{ mol}$ $\text{Ratio} = \dfrac{4.10}{1.37} = 3$

$? \text{ mol O} = \dfrac{\text{g O}}{\text{AW O}} = \dfrac{21.9 \text{ g}}{16.00 \text{ g/mol}} = 1.37 \text{ mol}$ $\text{Ratio} = \dfrac{1.37}{1.37} = 1$

Therefore, the simplest formula of lysine is C_3H_7NO (arranging the atoms in alphabetical order). Since each molecule of lysine has 2 nitrogen atoms, the molecular formula of lysine must be $C_6H_{14}N_2O_2$.

Assume 100 g of the compound found in photochemical smog.

$? \text{ mol C} = \dfrac{42.9 \text{ g C}}{12.0 \text{ g/mol}} = 3.58 \text{ mol C}$ $\text{Ratio} = \dfrac{3.58}{3.57} = 1$

$? \text{ mol O} = \dfrac{57.1 \text{ g O}}{16.0 \text{ g/mol}} = 3.57 \text{ mol O}$ $\text{Ratio} = \dfrac{3.57}{3.57} = 1$

The simplest formula for this compound is **CO** (FW = 28 g/mol)

$n = \dfrac{\text{molecular weight}}{\text{simplest formula weight}} = \dfrac{56}{28} = 2$

The true molecular formula is $\mathbf{C_2O_2}$.

(a)   mass of 1 mole of L-DOPA, $C_9H_{11}NO_4$

$9 \times C = 9 \times 12.01 \text{ g}$ $= 108.1 \text{ g}$ $? \% C = (108.1 \text{ g}/197.2 \text{ g}) \times 100\% = \mathbf{54.82 \% C}$
$11 \times H = 11 \times 1.008 \text{ g}$ $= 11.09 \text{ g}$ $? \% H = (11.09 \text{ g}/197.2 \text{ g}) \times 100\% = \mathbf{5.624 \% H}$
$1 \times N = 1 \times 14.01 \text{ g}$ $= 14.01 \text{ g}$ $? \% N = (14.01 \text{ g}/197.2 \text{ g}) \times 100\% = \mathbf{7.104 \% N}$
$\underline{4 \times O = 4 \times 16.00 \text{ g}}$ $= \underline{64.00 \text{ g}}$ $? \% O = (64.00 \text{ g}/197.2 \text{ g}) \times 100\% = \mathbf{32.45 \% O}$
mass of 1 mol $= 197.2 \text{ g}$

(b)   mass of 1 mole of Vitamin E, $C_{29}H_{50}O_2$

$29 \times C = 29 \times 12.01 \text{ g}$ $= 348.3 \text{ g}$ $? \% C = (348.3 \text{ g}/430.7 \text{ g}) \times 100\% = \mathbf{80.87 \% C}$
$50 \times H = 50 \times 1.008 \text{ g}$ $= 50.40 \text{ g}$ $? \% H = (50.40 \text{ g}/430.7 \text{ g}) \times 100\% = \mathbf{11.70 \% H}$
$\underline{2 \times O = 2 \times 16.00 \text{ g}}$ $= \underline{32.00 \text{ g}}$ $? \% O = (32.00 \text{ g}/430.7 \text{ g}) \times 100\% = \mathbf{7.430 \% O}$
mass of 1 mol $= 430.7 \text{ g}$

(c)   mass of 1 mole of vanillin, $C_8H_8O_3$

$8 \times C = 8 \times 12.01 \text{ g}$ $= 96.08 \text{ g}$ $? \% C = (96.08 \text{ g}/152.14 \text{ g}) \times 100\% = \mathbf{63.15 \% C}$
$8 \times H = 8 \times 1.008 \text{ g}$ $= 8.064 \text{ g}$ $? \% H = (8.064 \text{ g}/152.14 \text{ g}) \times 100\% = \mathbf{5.300 \% H}$
$\underline{3 \times O = 3 \times 16.00 \text{ g}}$ $= \underline{48.00 \text{ g}}$ $? \% O = (48.00 \text{ g}/152.14 \text{ g}) \times 100\% = \mathbf{31.55 \% O}$
mass of 1 mol $= 152.14 \text{ g}$

---

mass of 1 mol $Cu_3(CO_3)_2(OH)_2$ **percent Cu by mass**

$3 \times Cu = 3 \times 63.55 \text{ g}$ $= 190.6 \text{ g}$ $\% Cu = (190.6/344.6) \times 100\% = 55.31\%$
$2 \times C = 2 \times 12.01 \text{ g}$ $= 24.02 \text{ g}$
$8 \times O = 8 \times 16.00 \text{ g}$ $= 128.0 \text{ g}$
$\underline{2 \times H = 2 \times 1.01 \text{ g}}$ $= \underline{2.02 \text{ g}}$
mass of 1 mol $= 344.6 \text{ g}$

mass of 1 mol Cu_2S   **percent Cu by mass**

$2 \times Cu = 2 \times 63.55 \text{ g}$ $= 127.1 \text{ g}$ $\% Cu = (127.1/159.2) \times 100\% = 79.84\%$
$\underline{1 \times S = 1 \times 32.07 \text{ g}}$ $= \underline{32.07 \text{ g}}$
mass of 1 mol $= 159.2 \text{ g}$

mass of 1 mol CuFeS$_2$

1 x Cu = 1 x 63.55 g	=	63.55 g	
1 x Fe = 1 x 55.85 g	=	55.85 g	
2 x S = 2 x 32.06 g	=	64.12 g	
mass of 1 mol	=	183.52 g	

percent Cu by mass

% Cu = (63.55/183.52) x 100% = 34.63%

mass of 1 mol CuS

1x Cu = 1 x 63.55 g	=	63.55 g
1 x S = 1 x 32.06g	=	32.06 g
mass of 1 mol	=	95.61 g

percent Cu by mass

% Cu = (63.55/95.61) x 100% = 66.47%

mass of 1 mol Cu$_2$O

2 x Cu = 2 x 63.55 g	=	127.1 g
1 x 0 = 1 x 16.00 g	=	16.00 g
mass of 1 mol	=	143.1 g

percent Cu by mass

% Cu = (127.1/143.1) x 100% = 88.82%

mass of 1 mol Cu$_2$CO$_3$(OH)$_2$

2 x Cu = 2 x 63.55 g	=	127.1 g
1 x C = 1 x 12.01 g	=	12.01 g
5 x O = 5 x 16.00 g	=	80.00 g
2 x H = 2 x 1.01 g	=	2.02 g
mass of 1 mol	=	221.1 g

percent Cu by mass

% Cu = (127.1/221.1) x 100% = 57.49%

Therefore, **chalcopyrite, CuFeS$_2$,** has the lowest copper content on a percent by mass basis.

2-66. *Refer to Section 2-8, and Examples 2-15 and 2-16.*

Plan: (1) Use the masses of CO_2 and H_2O to calculate the masses of C and H respectively.
(2) Calculate the percentages of C and H in the sample.

(1) $? \text{ g C} = 0.3986 \text{ g CO}_2 \times \dfrac{12.01 \text{ g C}}{44.01 \text{ g CO}_2} = \textbf{0.1088 g C}$

$? \text{ g H} = 0.0578 \text{ g H}_2\text{O} \times \dfrac{2.016 \text{ g H}}{18.02 \text{ g H}_2\text{O}} = \textbf{0.00647 g H}$

(2) ? g sample = mass of C + mass of H = 0.1088 g C + 0.00647 g H = 0.1153 g sample

$? \text{ \% C} = \dfrac{0.1088 \text{ g C}}{0.1153 \text{ g sample}} \times 100\% = \textbf{94.36 \% C}$

$? \text{ \% H} = \dfrac{0.00647 \text{ g H}}{0.1153 \text{ g sample}} \times 100\% = \textbf{5.61 \% H}$

2-68. *Refer to Section 2-9 and Example 2-16.*

Plan: g C_2H_5OH $\overset{(1)}{\Rightarrow}$ mol C_2H_5OH $\overset{(2)}{\Rightarrow}$ mol CO_2 $\overset{(3)}{\Rightarrow}$ g CO_2

$? \text{ g CO}_2 = 0.377 \text{ g C}_2\text{H}_5\text{OH} \times \underset{\textbf{Step 1}}{\dfrac{1 \text{ mol C}_2\text{H}_5\text{OH}}{46.1 \text{ g C}_2\text{H}_5\text{OH}}} \times \underset{\textbf{Step 2}}{\dfrac{2 \text{ mol CO}_2}{1 \text{ mol C}_2\text{H}_5\text{OH}}} \times \underset{\textbf{Step 3}}{\dfrac{44.0 \text{ g CO}_2}{1 \text{ mol CO}_2}} = \textbf{0.720 g CO}_2$

2-70. *Refer to Sections 2-8 and 2-9, and Examples 2-13 and 2-15.*

Plan: (1) Use the masses of CO_2 and H_2O to calculate the masses of C and H respectively.
      (2) Calculate the mass of O in the sample by difference: g O = g sample - g C - g H
          since the compound contains only C, H and O.
      (3) Determine the simplest formula.

(1) $? \text{ g C} = 1.913 \text{ g } CO_2 \times \dfrac{12.01 \text{ g C}}{44.01 \text{ g } CO_2} = 0.5220 \text{ g C}$ $? \text{ g H} = 1.174 \text{ g } H_2O \times \dfrac{2.016 \text{ g H}}{18.02 \text{ g } H_2O} = 0.1313 \text{ g H}$

(2) $? \text{ g O} = 1.000 \text{ g compound} - 0.5220 \text{ g C} - 0.1313 \text{ g H} = 0.347 \text{ g O}$

(3) $? \text{ mol C} = \dfrac{0.5220 \text{ g C}}{12.01 \text{ g/mol}} = 0.04346 \text{ mol C}$ $\text{Ratio} = \dfrac{0.04346}{0.0217} = 2$

       $? \text{ mol H} = \dfrac{0.1313 \text{ g H}}{1.008 \text{ g/mol}} = 0.1303 \text{ mol H}$ $\text{Ratio} = \dfrac{0.1303}{0.0217} = 6$

       $? \text{ mol O} = \dfrac{0.347 \text{ g O}}{16.00 \text{ g/mol}} = 0.0217 \text{ mol O}$ $\text{Ratio} = \dfrac{0.0217}{0.0217} = 1$

The simplest formula for this alcohol is $\mathbf{C_2H_6O}$.

2-72. *Refer to Section 2-9 and Example 2-18.*

(a) in NO: $? \text{ g O} = 3.00 \text{ g N} \times \dfrac{16.0 \text{ g O}}{14.0 \text{ g N}} = \mathbf{3.43 \text{ g O}}$

(b) in NO_2: $? \text{ g O} = 3.00 \text{ g N} \times \dfrac{32.0 \text{ g O}}{14.0 \text{ g N}} = \mathbf{6.86 \text{ g O}}$

One can easily see that the ratio: $\dfrac{\text{g O in NO}}{\text{g O in } NO_2} = \dfrac{3.43}{6.86} = \dfrac{1}{2}$

This result illustrates the **Law of Multiple Proportions** which states that when elements form more than one compound, the ratio of the masses of one element that combine with a given mass of another element in each of the compounds can be expressed by small whole numbers.

2-74. *Refer to Section 2-9.*

(a) in SO_2: $? \text{ g O} = 9.04 \text{ g S} \times \dfrac{32.0 \text{ g O}}{32.06 \text{ g S}} = \mathbf{9.02 \text{ g O}}$

(b) in SO_3: $? \text{ g O} = 9.04 \text{ g S} \times \dfrac{48.0 \text{ g O}}{32.06 \text{ g S}} = \mathbf{13.5 \text{ g O}}$

2-76. *Refer to Section 2-10 and Example 2-19.*

$$\text{Plan: g HgS} \overset{(1)}{\Rightarrow} \text{mol HgS} \overset{(2)}{\Rightarrow} \text{mol Hg} \overset{(3)}{\Rightarrow} \text{g Hg}$$

$$? \text{ g Hg} = 578 \text{ g HgS} \times \underset{\textbf{Step 1}}{\dfrac{1 \text{ mol HgS}}{232.65 \text{ g HgS}}} \times \underset{\textbf{Step 2}}{\dfrac{1 \text{ mol Hg}}{1 \text{ mol HgS}}} \times \underset{\textbf{Step 3}}{\dfrac{200.6 \text{ g Hg}}{1 \text{ mol Hg}}} = \mathbf{498 \text{ g Hg}}$$

Plan: g Mn $\underset{(1)}{\Rightarrow}$ mol Mn $\underset{(2)}{\Rightarrow}$ mol $KMnO_4$ $\underset{(3)}{\Rightarrow}$ g $KMnO_4$

$$? \text{ g } KMnO_4 = 72.6 \text{ g Mn} \times \underset{\textbf{Step 1}}{\frac{1 \text{ mol Mn}}{54.9 \text{ g Mn}}} \times \underset{\textbf{Step 2}}{\frac{1 \text{ mol } KMnO_4}{1 \text{ mol Mn}}} \times \underset{\textbf{Step 3}}{\frac{158 \text{ g } KMnO_4}{1 \text{ mol } KMnO_4}} = \textbf{209 g } KMnO_4$$

Plan: lb $CuFeS_2$ $\underset{(1)}{\Rightarrow}$ lb Cu in $CuFeS_2$ $\underset{(2)}{=}$ lb Cu in Cu_2S $\underset{(3)}{\Rightarrow}$ lb Cu_2S

Note: Because there is a constant conversion factor between grams and pounds, we can work totally in pounds. Since the formula weights are: $CuFeS_2$ (183.5 g/mol), Cu_2S (159.2 g/mol) and Cu (63.55 g/mol), we have

$$? \text{ lb } Cu_2S = 418 \text{ lb } CuFeS_2 \times \underset{\textbf{Step 1}}{\frac{63.55 \text{ lb Cu in } CuFeS_2}{183.5 \text{ lb } CuFeS_2}} \times \underset{\textbf{Step 2}}{\frac{1 \text{ lb Cu in } Cu_2S}{1 \text{ lb Cu in } CuFeS_2}} \times \underset{\textbf{Step 3}}{\frac{159.2 \text{ lb } Cu_2S}{2 \times 63.55 \text{ lb Cu in } Cu_2S}}$$

$$= \textbf{181 lb } Cu_2S$$

(a) Plan: g $CuSO_4 \cdot 5H_2O$ $\Rightarrow$ mol $CuSO_4 \cdot 5H_2O$ $\Rightarrow$ mol $CuSO_4 \cdot H_2O$ $\Rightarrow$ g $CuSO_4 \cdot H_2O$

$$? \text{ g } CuSO_4 \cdot H_2O = 495 \text{ g } CuSO_4 \cdot 5H_2O \times \frac{1 \text{ mol } CuSO_4 \cdot 5H_2O}{249.7 \text{ g } CuSO_4 \cdot 5H_2O} \times \frac{1 \text{ mol } CuSO_4 \cdot H_2O}{1 \text{ mol } CuSO_4 \cdot 5H_2O} \times \frac{177.6 \text{ g } CuSO_4 \cdot H_2O}{1 \text{ mol } CuSO_4 \cdot H_2O}$$

$$= \textbf{352 g } CuSO_4 \cdot H_2O$$

(b) Plan: g $CuSO_4 \cdot 5H_2O$ $\Rightarrow$ mol $CuSO_4 \cdot 5H_2O$ $\Rightarrow$ mol $CuSO_4$ $\Rightarrow$ g $CuSO_4$

$$? \text{ g } CuSO_4 = 463 \text{ g } CuSO_4 \cdot 5H_2O \times \frac{1 \text{ mol } CuSO_4 \cdot 5H_2O}{249.7 \text{ g } CuSO_4 \cdot 5H_2O} \times \frac{1 \text{ mol } CuSO_4}{1 \text{ mol } CuSO_4 \cdot 5H_2O} \times \frac{159.6 \text{ g } CuSO_4}{1 \text{ mol } CuSO_4}$$

$$= \textbf{296 g } CuSO_4$$

Plan: g ore $\Rightarrow$ g $FeCr_2O_7$ $\Rightarrow$ g Cr present $\Rightarrow$ g Cr recovered   (FW of $FeCr_2O_7$ is 271.85 g/mol)

(1) $? \text{ g Cr present} = 234 \text{ g ore} \times \dfrac{55.0 \text{ g } FeCr_2O_7}{100 \text{ g ore}} \times \dfrac{2 \times 52.0 \text{ g Cr}}{271.85 \text{ g } FeCr_2O_7} = \textbf{49.2 g Cr}$

(2) $? \text{ g Cr recovered} = 400.0 \text{ g ore} \times \dfrac{49.2 \text{ g Cr present}}{234 \text{ g ore}} \times \dfrac{90.0 \text{ g Cr recovered}}{100.0 \text{ g Cr present}} = \textbf{75.7 g Cr recovered}$

(a) $? \text{ lb } MgCO_3 = 275 \text{ lb ore} \times \dfrac{26.7 \text{ lb } MgCO_3}{100 \text{ lb ore}} = \textbf{73.4 lb } MgCO_3$

(b) $? \text{ lb impurities} = 275 \text{ lb ore} - 73.4 \text{ lb } MgCO_3 = \textbf{202 lb impurity}$

(c) $? \text{ lb Mg} = 275 \text{ lb ore} \times \dfrac{26.7 \text{ lb } MgCO_3}{100 \text{ lb ore}} \times \dfrac{24.3 \text{ lb Mg}}{84.3 \text{ lb } MgCO_3} = \textbf{21.2 lb Mg}$

(24.3 is AW of Mg; 84.3 is FW of $MgCO_3$)

(a) Let us assume that we have 1 mole of $CuSO_4 \cdot 5H_2O$

$$\% \text{ } CuSO_4 \text{ by mass} = \frac{\text{FW } CuSO_4}{\text{FW } CuSO_4 \cdot 5H_2O} \times 100\% = \frac{159.6 \text{ g } CuSO_4}{249.7 \text{ g } CuSO_4 \cdot 5H_2O} \times 100\% = \textbf{63.92\%}$$

(b) $\% \text{ } CuSO_4 \text{ by mass} = \dfrac{74.4 \text{ g } CuSO_4 \cdot 5H_2O}{100.0 \text{ g sample}} \times \dfrac{63.92 \text{ g } CuSO_4}{100.0 \text{ g } CuSO_4 \cdot 5H_2O} \times 100\% = \textbf{47.6\%}$

(a) Formula Weight, $\text{FW} \left(\dfrac{g}{mol} \right) = \dfrac{\text{g substance}}{\text{mol substance}}$

$? \text{ mol } O_3 = \dfrac{\text{g } O_3}{\text{FW}} = \dfrac{96.0 \text{ g } O_3}{48.0 \text{ g/mol}} = \textbf{2.00 mol } O_3$

(b) Plan: $\text{g } O_3 \Rightarrow \text{mol } O_3 \Rightarrow \text{mol O}$

$? \text{ mol O} = 96.0 \text{ g } O_3 \times \dfrac{1 \text{ mol } O_3}{48.0 \text{ g } O_3} \times \dfrac{3 \text{ mol O}}{1 \text{ mol } O_3} = \textbf{6.00 mol O}$

(c) Plan: $\text{g } O_3 \Rightarrow \text{mol } O_3 \Rightarrow \text{mol O} \Rightarrow \text{mol } O_2 \Rightarrow \text{g } O_2$

$? \text{ g } O_2 = 96.0 \text{ g } O_3 \times \dfrac{1 \text{ mol } O_3}{48.0 \text{ g } O_3} \times \dfrac{3 \text{ mol O}}{1 \text{ mol } O_3} \times \dfrac{1 \text{ mol } O_2}{2 \text{ mol O}} \times \dfrac{32.0 \text{ g } O_2}{1 \text{ mol } O_2} = \textbf{96.0 g } O_2$

Note: Samples with the same number of atoms or moles of an element have the same mass.

(d) Plan: $\text{g } O_3 \Rightarrow \text{mol } O_3 \Rightarrow \text{molecules } O_3 = \text{molecules } O_2 \Rightarrow \text{mol } O_2 \Rightarrow \text{g } O_2$

$? \text{ g } O_2 = 96.0 \text{ g } O_3 \times \dfrac{1 \text{ mol } O_3}{48.0 \text{ g } O_3} \times \dfrac{6.02 \times 10^{23} \text{ molecules } O_3}{1 \text{ mol } O_3} \times \dfrac{1 \text{ molecule } O_2}{1 \text{ molecule } O_3} \times \dfrac{1 \text{ mole } O_2}{6.02 \times 10^{23} \text{ molecules } O_2}$

$\times \dfrac{32.0 \text{ g } O_2}{1 \text{ mol } O_2}$

$= \textbf{64.0 g } O_2$

Plan: (1) Use the masses of CO_2 and H_2O to calculate the masses of C and H respectively.

(2) The masses of C and H do not add up to the mass of the sample, therefore there must be O in the sample as well. Determine the mass of O by subtracting the masses of C and H from the mass of the sample.

(3) Determine the empirical (simplest) formula of Vitamin E.

(1) $? \text{ g C} = 1.47 \text{ g } CO_2 \times \dfrac{12.01 \text{ g C}}{44.01 \text{ g } CO_2} = 0.401 \text{ g C}$

$? \text{ g H} = 0.518 \text{ g } H_2O \times \dfrac{2.016 \text{ g H}}{18.02 \text{ g } H_2O} = 0.0580 \text{ g H}$

(2) $? \text{ g O} = \text{mass of sample} - (\text{mass of C} + \text{mass of H}) = 0.497 \text{ g } - (0.401 \text{ g C} + 0.0580 \text{ g H}) = 0.038 \text{ g O}$

(3) $? \text{ mol C} = \dfrac{0.401 \text{ g C}}{12.01 \text{ g/mol}} = 0.0334 \text{ mol C}$ $\qquad$ $\text{Ratio} = \dfrac{0.0334}{0.0024} = 14$

$? \text{ mol H} = \dfrac{0.0580 \text{ g H}}{1.008 \text{ g/mol}} = 0.0575 \text{ mol H}$ $\qquad$ $\text{Ratio} = \dfrac{0.0575}{0.0024} = 24$

$? \text{ mol O} = \dfrac{0.038 \text{ g O}}{16.00 \text{ g/mol}} = 0.0024 \text{ mol O}$ $\qquad$ $\text{Ratio} = \dfrac{0.0024}{0.0024} = 1$

The calculated simplest formula for Vitamin E is $\textbf{C}_{14}\textbf{H}_{24}\textbf{O}$. The actual simplest formula for Vitamin E is actually $\textbf{C}_{29}\textbf{H}_{50}\textbf{O}_2$. If the original data had been measured to 4 significant figures, we could have determined the formula correctly.

Sample 1: $\dfrac{1.60 \text{ g O}}{2.43 \text{ g Mg}} = 0.658$ Sample 2: $\dfrac{0.658 \text{ g O}}{1.00 \text{ g Mg}} = 0.658$ Sample 3: $\dfrac{2.29 \text{ g O}}{3.48 \text{ g Mg}} = 0.658$

All three samples of magnesium oxide had the same O/Mg mass ratio. This is an example of the **Law of Constant Composition.**

2-96.   *Refer to Section 2-9 and Examples 2-13, 2-16 and 2-17.*

(a) Plan: (1) Use the masses of CO_2 and H_2O to calculate the masses of C and H respectively.
  (2) The masses of C and H do not add up to the mass of the sample, therefore there must be O in the sample as well. Determine the mass of O by subtracting the masses of C and H from the mass of the sample.
  (3) Determine the empirical (simplest) formula of adipic acid.

(1) $? \text{ g C} = 2.960 \text{ g CO}_2 \times \dfrac{12.01 \text{ g C}}{44.01 \text{ g CO}_2} = 0.8078 \text{ g C}$ $? \text{ g H} = 1.010 \text{ g H}_2\text{O} \times$

$\dfrac{2.016 \text{ g H}}{18.02 \text{ g H}_2\text{O}} = 0.1130 \text{ g H}$

(2) $? \text{ g O} = 1.6380 \text{ g adipic acid} - 0.8078 \text{ g C} - 0.1130 \text{ g H} = 0.7172 \text{ g O}$

(3) $? \text{ mol C} = \dfrac{0.8078 \text{ g C}}{12.01 \text{ g/mol}} = 0.06726 \text{ mol C}$ $\text{Ratio} = \dfrac{0.06726}{0.04483} = 1.5$

  $? \text{ mol H} = \dfrac{0.1130 \text{ g H}}{1.008 \text{ g/mol}} = 0.1121 \text{ mol H}$ $\text{Ratio} = \dfrac{0.1121}{0.04483} = 2.5$

  $? \text{ mol O} = \dfrac{0.7172 \text{ g O}}{16.00 \text{ g/mol}} = 0.04483 \text{ mol O}$ $\text{Ratio} = \dfrac{0.04483}{0.04483} = 1$

A 1.5:2.5:1 ratio converts to 3:5:2 by multiplying by 2. Therefore, the simplest formula for adipic acid is **$C_3H_5O_2$** (FW = 73.07 g/mol).

(b) $n = \dfrac{\text{molecular weight}}{\text{simplest formula weight}} = \dfrac{146.1 \text{ g/mol}}{73.07 \text{ g/mol}} = 2$

The true molecular formula for adipic acid is $(C_3H_5O_2)_2 = $ **$C_6H_{10}O_4$**.

2-98.   *Refer to Section 2-1 and Example 2-1.*

β-hydroxybutyric acid (3-hydroxybutanoic acid):

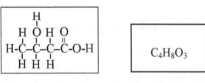

Structural formula   Chemical formula

Since each line connecting two chemical symbols represents 2 electrons being shared in a bond, we can see that each carbon atom seems to share 4 pairs of electrons with its neighbors. An oxygen atom seems to share 2 pairs of electrons and a hydrogen atom only shares 1 pair of electrons with its neighbor.

2-100. *Refer to Section 2-3 and Example 2-2.*

Correct formula: LiF Fe_2S_3 $Al(OH)_3$ $Zn(NO_3)_2$ $CaCl_2$

2-102. *Refer to Section 2-7.*

(1) % Re by mass in each compound:

ReO_2:

$$\% \text{ Re} = \frac{\text{AW Re}}{\text{FW ReO}_2} \times 100\% = \frac{186.207 \text{ g}}{218.205 \text{ g}} \times 100\% = \textbf{85.3358\% Re}$$

ReO_3:

$$\% \text{ Re} = \frac{\text{AW Re}}{\text{FW ReO}_3} \times 100\% = \frac{186.207 \text{ g}}{234.204 \text{ g}} \times 100\% = \textbf{79.5063\% Re}$$

Re_2O_3:

$$\% \text{ Re} = \frac{2 \times \text{AW Re}}{\text{FW Re}_2\text{O}_3} \times 100\% = \frac{372.414 \text{ g}}{420.411 \text{ g}} \times 100\% = \textbf{88.5833\% Re}$$

Re_2O_7:

$$\% \text{ Re} = \frac{2 \times \text{AW Re}}{\text{FW Re}_2\text{O}_7} \times 100\% = \frac{372.414 \text{ g}}{484.407 \text{ g}} \times 100\% = \textbf{76.8804\% Re}$$

(2) Since the charge of any compound equals 0, the charge of Re is determined algebraically knowing that in most ionic compounds, oxygen has a -2 charge.

ReO_2 0 = 1(charge on Re) + 2(charge on O) = 1(x) + 2(−2) = x − 4, so x = +4

ReO_3 0 = 1(charge on Re) + 3(charge on O) = 1(x) + 3(−2) = x − 6, so x = +6

Re_2O_3 0 = 2(charge on Re) + 3(charge on O) = 2(x) + 3(−2) = 2x − 6, so x= +3

Re_2O_7 0 = 2(charge on Re) + 7(charge on O) = 2(x) + 7(−2) = 2x − 14, so x= +7

(3) In order of increasing charge on Re: Re_2O_3 (Re=+3) < ReO_2 (Re=+4) < ReO_3 (Re=+6) < Re_2O_7 (Re=+7)

(4) As the charge on Re increased, the percentage of Re in the rhenium oxide decreased.

2-104. *Refer to Section 2-6.*

When organic compounds are combusted, all the hydrogen present is converted to water. So, the moles of water produced are equal to 1/2 the moles of hydrogen in the compound. In other words,

for 1 mole of compound: $? \text{ mol H}_2\text{O} = \text{moles H in compound} \times \dfrac{1 \text{ mol H}_2\text{O}}{2 \text{ mol H}}$

(a) for CH_3CH_2OH: $? \text{ mol H}_2\text{O} = 3.2 \text{ mol compound} \times \dfrac{6 \text{ moles H in compound}}{1 \text{ mol compound}} \times \dfrac{1 \text{ mol H}_2\text{O}}{2 \text{ mol H}} = 9.6 \text{ moles H}_2\text{O}$

(b) for CH_3OH: $? \text{ mol H}_2\text{O} = 3.2 \text{ mol compound} \times \dfrac{4 \text{ moles H in compound}}{1 \text{ mol compound}} \times \dfrac{1 \text{ mol H}_2\text{O}}{2 \text{ mol H}} = 6.4 \text{ moles H}_2\text{O}$

(c) for CH_3OCH_3: $? \text{ mol H}_2\text{O} = 3.2 \text{ mol compound} \times \dfrac{6 \text{ moles H in compound}}{1 \text{ mol compound}} \times \dfrac{1 \text{ mol H}_2\text{O}}{2 \text{ mol H}} = 9.6 \text{ moles H}_2\text{O}$

CH_3CH_2OH and CH_3OCH_3 will produce the most water (9.6 moles) and CH_3OH will make the least (6.4 moles).

2-106. *Refer to Section 2-10.*

Plan: $\text{g MgCl}_2 \Rightarrow \text{mol MgCl}_2 \Rightarrow \text{mol ions} \Rightarrow \text{mol NaCl} \Rightarrow \text{g NaCl}$ (FW of $MgCl_2$ is 95.2 g/mol)

$? \text{ g NaCl} = 284 \text{ g MgCl}_2 \times \dfrac{1 \text{ mol MgCl}_2}{95.2 \text{ g MgCl}_2} \times \dfrac{3 \text{ mol ions}}{1 \text{ mol MgCl}_2} \times \dfrac{1 \text{ mol NaCl}}{2 \text{ mol ions}} \times \dfrac{58.4 \text{ g NaCl}}{1 \text{ mol NaCl}} = \textbf{261 g NaCl}$

Plan: Determine the % Zn by mass in each compound. The compound with the greater % Zn for the same price will be the cheaper source of Zn.

$ZnSO_4$: $\qquad$ % Zn $= \dfrac{AW\ Zn}{FW\ ZnSO_4} \times 100\% = \dfrac{65.39\ g}{161.44\ g} \times 100\% = 40.50\%\ Zn$

$Zn(CH_3COO)_2 \cdot 2H_2O$: $\qquad$ % Zn $= \dfrac{AW\ Zn}{FW\ Zn(CH_3CO_2)_2 \cdot 2H_2O} \times 100\% = \dfrac{65.39\ g}{219.51\ g} \times 100\% = 29.79\%\ Zn$

Therefore, **$ZnSO_4$** is the cheaper source of Zn.

You would get $\dfrac{(40.50 - 29.79)}{29.79} \times 100\% = \textbf{35.95\%}$ more Zn for your money buying $ZnSO_4$, rather than $Zn(CH_3CO_2)_2 \cdot 2H_2O$.

2-110. *Refer to Sections 2-6 and 2-10.*

(a) ? g C_2H_3Cl = 13.5 mol $C_2H_3Cl \times \dfrac{62.49\ g\ C_2H_3Cl}{1\ mol\ C_2H_3Cl} = \textbf{844 g } \mathbf{C_2H_3Cl}$

(b) ? g $C_{18}H_{27}NO_3$ = 13.5 mol $C_{18}H_{27}NO_3 \times \dfrac{305.4\ g\ C_{18}H_{27}NO_3}{1\ mol\ C_{18}H_{27}NO_3} = \textbf{4.12 x 10}^3\ \mathbf{C_{18}H_{27}NO_3}$

(b) ? g $C_{18}H_{36}O_2$ = 13.5 mol $C_{18}H_{36}O_2 \times \dfrac{284.5\ g\ C_{18}H_{36}O_2}{1\ mol\ C_{18}H_{36}O_2} = \textbf{3.84 x 10}^3\ \mathbf{C_{18}H_{36}O_2}$

2-112. *Refer to Sections 2-8 and 2-9, and Examples 2-13, 2-15 and 2-17.*

Plan: (1) Use the masses of CO_2 and H_2O to calculate the masses of C and H respectively.
$\quad$ (2) The masses of C and H do not add up to the mass of the sample, therefore there must be O in the sample as well. Determine the mass of O by subtracting the masses of C and H from the mass of the sample.
$\quad$ (3) Determine the empirical (simplest) formula

(1) ? g C = 1.114 g $CO_2 \times \dfrac{12.01\ g\ C}{44.01\ g\ CO_2} = 0.3040\ g\ C$

$\quad$? g H = 0.455 g $H_2O \times \dfrac{2.016\ g\ H}{18.02\ g\ H_2O} = 0.0509\ g\ H$

(2) ? g O = 0.625 g unknown compound - 0.3040 g C - 0.0509 g H = 0.270 g O

(3) ? mol C $= \dfrac{0.3040\ g\ C}{12.01\ g/mol} = 0.0253\ mol\ C$ $\qquad\qquad$ Ratio $= \dfrac{0.0253}{0.0169} = 1.50$

$\quad$? mol H $= \dfrac{0.0509\ g\ H}{1.008\ g/mol} = 0.0505\ mol\ H$ $\qquad\qquad$ Ratio $= \dfrac{0.0505}{0.0169} = 2.99$

$\quad$? mol O $= \dfrac{0.270\ g\ O}{16.00\ g/mol} = 0.0169\ mol\ O$ $\qquad\qquad$ Ratio $= \dfrac{0.0169}{0.0169} = 1.00$

A 1.50:2.99:1.00 ratio converts to 3:6:2 by multiplying by 2. Therefore, the simplest formula for this compound is **$C_3H_6O_2$** (FW = 74.1 g/mol). The true molecular formula for the compound is the same, **$C_3H_6O_2$**, because the true molecular formula is the same as the empirical formula.

Plan: (1) Determine the number of molecules in 380 mL of H_2O.
(2) Determine the volume of ethanol that contains the same number of molecules.

(1) $? H_2O$ molecules $= 380.$ mL $H_2O \times \dfrac{1.00 \text{ g } H_2O}{1.00 \text{ mL } H_2O} \times \dfrac{1 \text{ mol } H_2O}{18.0 \text{ g } H_2O} \times \dfrac{6.02 \times 10^{23} \text{ } H_2O \text{ molecules}}{1 \text{ mol } H_2O}$

$\qquad = 1.27 \times 10^{25}$ molecules

(2) $?$ mL ethanol $= 1.27 \times 10^{25}$ molecules $\times \dfrac{1 \text{ mol}}{6.02 \times 10^{23} \text{ molecules}} \times \dfrac{46.1 \text{ g}}{1 \text{ mol}} \times \dfrac{1.00 \text{ mL}}{0.789 \text{ g}}$

$\qquad = \textbf{1230 mL ethanol}$ (to 3 significant figures)

(a) $?$ density $NaHCO_3$ (g/mL) $= \dfrac{1 \text{ mol } NaHCO_3}{0.0389 \text{ L}} \times \dfrac{84.0 \text{ g } NaHCO_3}{1 \text{ mol } NaHCO_3} \times \dfrac{1 \text{ L}}{1000 \text{ mL}} = \textbf{2.16 g/mL}$

(b) $?$ density I_2 (g/mL) $= \dfrac{1 \text{ mol } I_2}{0.05148 \text{ L}} \times \dfrac{253.8 \text{ g } I_2}{1 \text{ mol } I_2} \times \dfrac{1 \text{ L}}{1000 \text{ mL}} = \textbf{4.930 g/mL}$

(c) $?$ density Hg (g/mL) $= \dfrac{1 \text{ mol } Hg}{0.01476 \text{ L}} \times \dfrac{200.59 \text{ g } Hg}{1 \text{ mol } Hg} \times \dfrac{1 \text{ L}}{1000 \text{ mL}} = \textbf{13.59 g/mL}$

(d) $?$ density $NaCl$ (g/mL) $= \dfrac{1 \text{ mol } NaCl}{0.02699 \text{ L}} \times \dfrac{58.44 \text{ g } NaCl}{1 \text{ mol } NaCl} \times \dfrac{1 \text{ L}}{1000 \text{ mL}} = \textbf{2.165 g/mL}$

3 Chemical Equations and Reaction Stoichiometry

3-2.   *Refer to Section 3-1.*

The Law of Conservation of Matter provides the basis for balancing a chemical equation. It states that matter is neither created nor destroyed during an ordinary chemical reaction. Therefore, a balanced chemical equation must always contain the same number of each kind of atom on both sides of the equation.

3-4.   *Refer to Section 3-1.*

(a) balanced equation: $2H_2(g) + O_2(g) \rightarrow 2H_2O(g)$

(b)

3-6.   *Refer to Section 3-1.*

When 1 atom of solid sulfur reacts with 1 molecule of oxygen gas, 1 molecule of sulfur dioxide gas is produced.

3-8.   *Refer to Section 3-1 and Example 3-1.*

Hints for balancing equations:

(1) Use smallest whole number coefficients. However, it may be useful to temporarily use a fractional coefficient, then for the last step, multiply all the terms by a factor to change the fractions to whole numbers.

(2) Look for special groups of elements that appear unchanged on both sides of the equation, e.g., NO_3, PO_4, SO_4. Treat them as units when balancing.

(3) Begin by balancing both the special groups and the elements that appear only once on both sides of the equation.

(4) Any element that appears more than once on one side of the equation is normally the last element to be balanced.

(5) If free, uncombined elements appear on either side, balance them last. They are always the easiest to balance.

(6) When an element has an "odd" number of atoms on one side of the equation and an "even" number on the other side, it is often advisable to multiply the "odd" side by 2, then finish balancing. For example, if you have 3 carbon atoms on one side and 2 carbon atoms on the other, multiply the coefficients of the first side by 2 and the other side by 3. This way you'll have 6 carbons on both sides of the equation.

(a) unbalanced: $Na + O_2 \rightarrow Na_2O$

Step 1: $Na + O_2 \rightarrow \boxed{2}Na_2O$ balance O

Step 2: $\boxed{4}Na + O_2 \rightarrow 2Na_2O$ balance Na

(b) unbalanced: $Mg_3N_2 + H_2O \rightarrow NH_3 + Mg(OH)_2$

Step 1: $Mg_3N_2 + H_2O \rightarrow NH_3 + \boxed{3}Mg(OH)_2$ balance Mg

Step 2: $Mg_3N_2 + H_2O \rightarrow \boxed{2}NH_3 + 3Mg(OH)_2$ balance N

Step 3: $Mg_3N_2 + \boxed{6}H_2O \rightarrow 2NH_3 + 3Mg(OH)_2$ balance H, O

(c) unbalanced: $LiCl + Pb(NO_3)_2 \rightarrow PbCl_2 + LiNO_3$

Step 1: $LiCl + Pb(NO_3)_2 \rightarrow PbCl_2 + \boxed{2}LiNO_3$ balance NO_3

Step 2: $\boxed{2}LiCl + Pb(NO_3)_2 \rightarrow PbCl_2 + 2LiNO_3$ balance Li, Cl

(d) unbalanced: $H_2O + KO_2 \rightarrow KOH + O_2$

Step 1: $H_2O + KO_2 \rightarrow \boxed{2}KOH + O_2$ balance H

Step 2: $H_2O + \boxed{2}KO_2 \rightarrow 2KOH + O_2$ balance K

Step 3: $H_2O + 2KO_2 \rightarrow 2KOH + \boxed{3/2}O_2$ balance O

Step 4: $\boxed{2}H_2O + \boxed{4}KO_2 \rightarrow \boxed{4}KOH + \boxed{3}O_2$ multiply by 2 whole number coefficients

(e) unbalanced: $H_2SO_4 + NH_3 \rightarrow (NH_4)_2SO_4$

Step 1: $H_2SO_4 + \boxed{2}NH_3 \rightarrow (NH_4)_2SO_4$ balance N, H

3-10. *Refer to Section 3-1, Example 3-1 and Exercise 3-8 Solution.*

(a) unbalanced: $Fe_2O_3 + CO \rightarrow Fe + CO_2$

Step 1: $Fe_2O_3 + \boxed{3}CO \rightarrow Fe + \boxed{3}CO_2$ balance C, O

Step 2: $Fe_2O_3 + 3CO \rightarrow \boxed{2}Fe + 3CO_2$ balance Fe

(b) unbalanced: $Rb + H_2O \rightarrow RbOH + H_2$

Step 1: $Rb + H_2O \rightarrow RbOH + \boxed{1/2}H_2$ balance H

Step 2: $\boxed{2}Rb + \boxed{2}H_2O \rightarrow \boxed{2}RbOH + \boxed{1}H_2$ multiply by 2 whole number coefficients

(c) unbalanced: $K + KNO_3 \rightarrow K_2O + N_2$

Step 1: $K + \boxed{2}KNO_3 \rightarrow K_2O + N_2$ balance N

Step 2: $K + 2KNO_3 \rightarrow \boxed{6}K_2O + N_2$ balance O

Step 3: $\boxed{10}K + 2KNO_3 \rightarrow 6K_2O + N_2$ balance K

(d) unbalanced: $(NH_4)_2Cr_2O_7 \rightarrow N_2 + H_2O + Cr_2O_3$

Step 1: $(NH_4)_2Cr_2O_7 \rightarrow N_2 + \boxed{4}\,H_2O + Cr_2O_3$ balance H, O

(e) unbalanced: $Al + Cr_2O_3 \rightarrow Al_2O_3 + Cr$

Step 1: $\boxed{2}\,Al + Cr_2O_3 \rightarrow Al_2O_3 + Cr$ balance Al

Step 2: $2Al + Cr_2O_3 \rightarrow Al_2O_3 + \boxed{2}\,Cr$ balance Cr

---

3-12. *Refer to Section 3-2 and Example 3-2.*

(a) $N_2 + 3H_2 \rightarrow 2NH_3$

(b) ? molecules H_2 = 150. molecules $N_2 \times \dfrac{3 \text{ molecules } H_2}{1 \text{ molecule } N_2}$ = **450. molecules H_2**

(c) ? molecules NH_3 = 150. molecules $N_2 \times \dfrac{2 \text{ molecules } NH_3}{1 \text{ molecule } N_2}$ = **300. molecules NH_3**

3-14. *Refer to Section 3-2 and Example 3-3.*

(a) $CaCO_3 + 2HCl \rightarrow CaCl_2 + CO_2 + H_2O$

(b) ? mol HCl = 2.6 mol $CaCO_3 \times \dfrac{2 \text{ mol HCl}}{1 \text{ mol } CaCO_3}$ = **5.2 mol HCl**

(c) ? mol H_2O = 2.6 mol $CaCO_3 \times \dfrac{1 \text{ mol } H_2O}{1 \text{ mol } CaCO_3}$ = **2.6 mol H_2O**

3-16. *Refer to Section 2-10 and Examples 2-19 and 2-20.*

Plan: mol C $\overset{(1)}{\Rightarrow}$ mol $NaHCO_3 \overset{(2)}{\Rightarrow}$ g $NaHCO_3$

            Step 1   **Step 2**

? g $NaHCO_3$ = 10.5 mol C $\times \dfrac{1 \text{ mol } NaHCO_3}{1 \text{ mol C}} \times \dfrac{84.0 \text{ g } NaHCO_3}{1 \text{ mol } NaHCO_3}$ = **882 g $NaHCO_3$**

3-18. *Refer to Section 3-2 and Example 3-3.*

(a) balanced equation: $2KClO_3 \rightarrow 2KCl + 3O_2$

    ? mol O_2 = 6.4 mol $KClO_3 \times \dfrac{3 \text{ mol } O_2}{2 \text{ mol } KClO_3}$ = **9.6 mol O_2**

(b) balanced equation: $2H_2O_2 \rightarrow 2H_2O + O_2$

    ? mol O_2 = 6.4 mol $H_2O_2 \times \dfrac{1 \text{ mol } O_2}{2 \text{ mol } H_2O_2}$ = **3.2 mol O_2**

(c) balanced equation: $2HgO \rightarrow 2Hg + O_2$

    ? mol O_2 = 6.4 mol $HgO \times \dfrac{1 \text{ mol } O_2}{2 \text{ mol } HgO}$ = **3.2 mol O_2**

(d) balanced equation: $2NaNO_3 \rightarrow 2NaNO_2 + O_2$

    ? mol O_2 = 6.4 mol $NaNO_3 \times \dfrac{1 \text{ mol } O_2}{2 \text{ mol } NaNO_3}$ = **3.2 mol O_2**

(e) balanced equation: $KClO_4 \rightarrow KCl + 2O_2$

    ? mol O_2 = 6.40 mol $KClO_4 \times \dfrac{2 \text{ mol } O_2}{1 \text{ mol } KClO_4}$ = **13 mol O_2**

unbalanced:	$NH_3 + O_2 \rightarrow NO + H_2O$	
Step 1:	$\boxed{2}NH_3 + O_2 \rightarrow NO + \boxed{3}H_2O$	balance H
Step 2:	$2NH_3 + O_2 \rightarrow \boxed{2}NO + 3H_2O$	balance N
Step 3:	$2NH_3 + \boxed{5/2}O_2 \rightarrow 2NO + 3H_2O$	balance O
Step 4:	$\boxed{4}NH_3 + \boxed{5}O_2 \rightarrow \boxed{4}NO + \boxed{6}H_2O$	whole number coefficients

(a) $? \text{ mol } O_2 = 6.40 \text{ mol } NH_3 \times \dfrac{5 \text{ mol } O_2}{4 \text{ mol } NH_3} = \textbf{8.00 mol O}_2$

(b) $? \text{ mol } NO = 6.40 \text{ mol } NH_3 \times \dfrac{4 \text{ mol } NO}{4 \text{ mol } NH_3} = \textbf{6.40 mol NO}$

(c) $? \text{ mol } H_2O = 6.40 \text{ mol } NH_3 \times \dfrac{6 \text{ mol } H_2O}{4 \text{ mol } NH_3} = \textbf{9.60 mol H}_2\textbf{O}$

Balanced equation: $CH_4 + 2O_2 \rightarrow CO_2 + 2H_2O$

Method 1:   Use units as formulas: Plan: $g \ CH_4 \overset{(1)}{\Rightarrow} mol \ CH_4 \overset{(2)}{\Rightarrow} mol \ O_2 \overset{(3)}{\Rightarrow} g \ O_2$

(1) $? \text{ mol } CH_4 = \dfrac{g \ CH_4}{FW \ CH_4} = \dfrac{44.5 \text{ g}}{16.0 \text{ g/mol}} = 2.78 \text{ mol } CH_4$ (Note: since FW=g/mol, then mol=g/FW)

(2) $? \text{ mol } O_2 = \text{mol } CH_4 \times 2 \text{ mol } O_2/1 \text{ mol } CH_4 = 2.78 \text{ mol} \times 2 = 5.56 \text{ mol } O_2$

(3) $? \text{ g } O_2 = \text{mol } O_2 \times FW \ O_2 = 5.56 \text{ mol} \times 32.0 \text{ g/mol} = \textbf{178 g O}_2$

Note: To minimize rounding errors, keep all your numbers in your calculator until the end, then round to the appropriate number of significant figures.

Method 2:   Dimensional Analysis (Each unit factor corresponds to a step in Method 1.)

$$\qquad\qquad\qquad\quad \text{Step 1}\qquad \text{Step 2}\qquad \text{Step 3}$$
$$? \text{ g } O_2 = 44.5 \text{ g } CH_4 \times \dfrac{1 \text{ mol } CH_4}{16.0 \text{ g } CH_4} \times \dfrac{2 \text{ mol } O_2}{1 \text{ mol } CH_4} \times \dfrac{32.0 \text{ g } O_2}{1 \text{ mol } O_2} = \textbf{178 g } O_2$$

Method 3:   Proportion or Ratio Method

$$\dfrac{? \text{ g } O_2}{\text{g } CH_4} = \dfrac{2 \times FW \ O_2}{1 \times FW \ CH_4}$$

Solving, $? \text{ g } O_2 = \text{g } CH_4 \times \dfrac{2 \times FW \ O_2}{1 \times FW \ CH_4} = 44.5 \text{ g} \times \dfrac{2 \times 32.0 \text{ g}}{1 \times 16.0 \text{ g}}$

$$= \textbf{178 g } O_2$$

3-24. *Refer to Section 3-2 and Example 3-8.*

Balanced equation: $Fe_3O_4 + 4H_2 \rightarrow 3Fe + 4H_2O$

Method 1: Plan: $\underset{(1)}{g\ H_2O} \Rightarrow \underset{(2)}{mol\ H_2O} \Rightarrow \underset{(3)}{mol\ Fe_3O_4} \Rightarrow g\ Fe_3O_4$

(1) $?\ mol\ H_2O = \dfrac{g\ H_2O}{FW\ H_2O} = \dfrac{27.15\ g}{18.02\ g/mol} = 1.507\ mol\ H_2O$

(2) $?\ mol\ Fe_3O_4 = mol\ H_2O \times 1\ mol\ Fe_3O_4/4\ mol\ H_2O = 1.507\ mol \times 1/4 = 0.3767\ mol\ Fe_3O_4$

(3) $?\ g\ Fe_3O_4 = mol\ Fe_3O_4 \times FW\ Fe_3O_4 = 0.3767\ mol \times 231.55\ g/mol = \mathbf{87.22\ g\ Fe_3O_4}$

Note: Remember to use at least as many significant figures in your formula weights as your data. To minimize rounding errors, keep all your numbers in your calculator until the end, then round to the appropriate number of significant figures.

Method 2: Dimensional Analysis (Each unit factor corresponds to a step in Method 1.)

$$?\ g\ Fe_3O_4 = 27.15\ g\ H_2O \times \overset{\textbf{Step 1}}{\dfrac{1\ mol\ H_2O}{18.02\ g\ H_2O}} \times \overset{\textbf{Step 2}}{\dfrac{1\ mol\ Fe_3O_4}{4\ mol\ H_2O}} \times \overset{\textbf{Step 3}}{\dfrac{231.55\ g\ Fe_3O_4}{1\ mol\ Fe_3O_4}} = \mathbf{87.22\ g\ Fe_3O_4}$$

Method 3: Proportion or Ratio Method

$$\dfrac{?\ g\ Fe_3O_4}{g\ H_2O} = \dfrac{1 \times FW\ Fe_3O_4}{4 \times FW\ H_2O}$$

Solving, $?\ g\ Fe_3O_4 = g\ H_2O \times \dfrac{FW\ Fe_3O_4}{4 \times FW\ H_2O} = 27.15\ g \times \dfrac{1 \times 231.55\ g}{4 \times 18.02\ g} = \mathbf{87.22\ g\ Fe_3O_4}$

3-26. *Refer to Sections 3-2 and 2-10, and Examples 3-7, 2-19 and 2-20.*

(a) Balanced equation: $2Na + I_2 \rightarrow 2NaI$

(b) *Method 1*: Plan: $\underset{(1)}{g\ I_2} \Rightarrow \underset{(2)}{mol\ I_2} \Rightarrow \underset{(3)}{mol\ NaI} \Rightarrow g\ NaI$

(1) $?\ mol\ I_2 = \dfrac{g\ I_2}{FW\ I_2} = \dfrac{47.24\ g}{253.8\ g/mol} = 0.1861\ mol\ I_2$

(2) $?\ mol\ NaI = mol\ I_2 \times 2\ mol\ NaI/1\ mol\ I_2 = 0.1861\ mol \times 2 = 0.3723\ mol\ NaI$

(3) $?\ g\ NaI = mol\ NaI \times FW\ NaI = 0.3723\ mol \times 149.9\ g/mol = \mathbf{55.80\ g\ NaI}$

Note 1: To minimize rounding errors, keep all your numbers in your calculator until the end, then round to the appropriate number of significant figures.

Note 2: The number of significant figures of your calculated formula weight should have at least as many significant figures as the number of significant figures in your data.

Method 2: Dimensional Analysis (Each unit factor corresponds to a step in Method 1.)

$$?\ g\ NaI = 47.24\ g\ I_2 \times \overset{\textbf{Step 1}}{\dfrac{1\ mol\ I_2}{253.8\ g\ I_2}} \times \overset{\textbf{Step 2}}{\dfrac{2\ mol\ NaI}{1\ mol\ I_2}} \times \overset{\textbf{Step 3}}{\dfrac{149.9\ g\ NaI}{1\ mol\ NaI}} = \mathbf{55.80\ g\ NaI}$$

3-28. *Refer to Sections 3-2 and 2-6, and Example 3-8.*

Balanced equation: $C_3H_8 + 5O_2 \rightarrow 3CO_2 + 4H_2O$

Method 1: Plan: $\overset{(1)}{\text{mol } H_2O} \Rightarrow \overset{(2)}{\text{mol } C_3H_8} \Rightarrow g\ C_3H_8$

(1) ? mol C_3H_8 = mol H_2O × 1 mol C_3H_8/4 mol H_2O = 7.25 mol × 1/4 = 1.81 mol C_3H_8

(2) ? g C_3H_8 = mol C_3H_8 × FW C_3H_8 = 1.81 mol × 44.09 g/mol = **79.9 g C_3H_8**

Note: To minimize rounding errors, keep all your numbers in your calculator until the end, then round to the appropriate number of significant figures.

Method 2: Dimensional Analysis (Each unit factor corresponds to a step in Method 1.)

Step 1　　**Step 2**

? g C_3H_8= 7.25 mol H_2O × $\dfrac{1\ \text{mol } C_3H_8}{4\ \text{mol } H_2O}$ × $\dfrac{44.09\ \text{g } C_3H_8}{1\ \text{mol } C_3H_8}$ = **79.9 g C_3H_8**

3-30. *Refer to Section 3-3, and Examples 3-9 and 3-10.*

Balanced equation: $2CO + O_2 \rightarrow 2CO_2$

This is a limiting reactant problem.

(a) Reactants: 8 CO and 6 O_2 molecules　　　　(b) Products: 8 CO_2 and 2 O_2 molecules

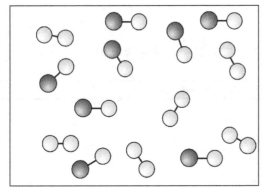　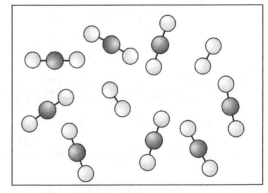

(c) Plan: (1) Find the limiting reactant.
　　　　　(2) Do the stoichiometric problem based on amount of limiting reactant.

(1) Convert the mass of reactants to moles and compare the required ratio to the available ratio.

? mol CO = $\dfrac{\text{g CO}}{\text{FW CO}}$ = $\dfrac{134.67\ g}{28.010\ \text{g/mol}}$ = 4.8079 mol CO　　? mol O_2 = $\dfrac{\text{g } O_2}{\text{FW } O_2}$ = $\dfrac{77.25\ g}{32.00\ \text{g/mol}}$ = 2.414 mol O_2

Required ratio = $\dfrac{2\ \text{mol CO}}{1\ \text{mol } O_2}$ = 2　　　　　Available ratio = $\dfrac{4.8079\ \text{mol CO}}{2.414\ \text{mol } O_2}$ = 1.992

The available ratio < required ratio. Therefore, we do not have enough CO to react with all the O_2, and so CO is the limiting reactant.

(2) The amount of CO_2 is determined by the amount of limiting reactant, 134.67 g of CO.

$$? \text{ g } CO_2 = 134.67 \text{ g CO} \times \frac{1 \text{ mol CO}}{28.010 \text{ g CO}} \times \frac{2 \text{ mol } CO_2}{2 \text{ mol CO}} \times \frac{44.009 \text{ g } CO_2}{1 \text{ mol } CO_2} = \mathbf{211.59 \text{ g } CO_2}$$

3-32.   *Refer to Section 3-3, Examples 3-9 and 3-10, and Exercise 3-30 Solution.*

Balanced equation: $Ca_3(PO_4)_2 + 2H_2SO_4 \rightarrow Ca(H_2PO_4)_2 + 2CaSO_4$

This is a limiting reactant problem.

(1) Convert to moles and compare required ratio to available ratio to find the limiting reactant.

$$? \text{ mol } Ca_3(PO_4)_2 = \frac{\text{g } Ca_3(PO_4)_2}{\text{FW } Ca_3(PO_4)_2} = \frac{200.0 \text{ g}}{310.2 \text{ g/mol}} = 0.6447 \text{ mol } Ca_3(PO_4)_2$$

$$? \text{ mol } H_2SO_4 = \frac{\text{g } H_2SO_4}{\text{FW } H_2SO_4} = \frac{133.5 \text{ g}}{98.08 \text{ g/mol}} = 1.361 \text{ mol } H_2SO_4$$

$$\text{Required ratio} = \frac{2 \text{ mol } H_2SO_4}{1 \text{ mol } Ca_3(PO_4)_2} = 2 \qquad\qquad \text{Available ratio} = \frac{1.361 \text{ mol } H_2SO_4}{0.6447 \text{ mol } Ca_3(PO_4)_2} = 2.11$$

Available ratio > required ratio; $Ca_3(PO_4)_2$ is the limiting reactant.

(2) First, find the mass of H_2SO_4 that reacted, then determine the mass of superphosphate (triple phosphate).

The Law of Conservation of Mass states that the mass of reactants that react equal the mass of products formed. Therefore, we can calculate the mass of superphosphate.

$$? \text{ g } H_2SO_4 = 200.0 \text{ g } Ca_3(PO_4)_2 \times \frac{1 \text{ mol } Ca_3(PO_4)_2}{310.2 \text{ g } Ca_3(PO_4)_2} \times \frac{2 \text{ mol } H_2SO_4}{1 \text{ mol } Ca_3(PO_4)_2} \times \frac{98.08 \text{ g } H_2SO_4}{1 \text{ mol } H_2SO_4} = 126.5 \text{ g } H_2SO_4$$

$$? \text{ g } [Ca(H_2PO_4)_2 + 2CaSO_4]_{\text{formed}} = \text{g } [H_2SO_4 + Ca_3(PO_4)_2]_{\text{reacted}}$$
$$= 126.5 \text{ g } H_2SO_4 + 200.0 \text{ g } Ca_3(PO_4)_2$$
$$= \mathbf{326.5 \text{ g superphosphate } [Ca(H_2PO_4)_2 + 2CaSO_4]}$$

3-34.   *Refer to Section 3-3, Examples 3-9 and 3-10, and Exercise 3-30 Solution.*

Balanced equation: $S_8(\ell) + 4Cl_2(g) \rightarrow 4S_2Cl_2(\ell)$

This is a limiting reactant problem.

(1) Convert to moles and compare the required ratio to the available ratio to find the limiting reactant.

$$? \text{ mol } S_8 = \frac{\text{g } S_8}{\text{FW } S_8} = \frac{32.0 \text{ g}}{256.6 \text{ g/mol}} = 0.125 \text{ mol } S_8$$

$$? \text{ mol } Cl_2 = \frac{\text{g } Cl_2}{\text{FW } Cl_2} = \frac{71.0 \text{ g}}{70.90 \text{ g/mol}} = 1.00 \text{ mol } Cl_2$$

$$\text{Required ratio} = \frac{1 \text{ mol } S_8}{4 \text{ mol } Cl_2} = 0.25 \qquad\qquad \text{Available ratio} = \frac{0.125 \text{ mol } S_8}{1.00 \text{ mol } Cl_2} = 0.125$$

Available ratio < required ratio; $\mathbf{S_8}$ is the limiting reactant.

(2) The theoretical yield of S_2Cl_2 produced is determined by the mass of S_8.

$$? \text{ g } S_2Cl_2 = 32.0 \text{ g } S_8 \times \frac{1 \text{ mol } S_8}{256.5 \text{ g } S_8} \times \frac{4 \text{ mol } S_2Cl_2}{1 \text{ mol } S_8} \times \frac{135.02 \text{ g } S_2Cl_2}{1 \text{ mol } S_2Cl_2} = \mathbf{67.4 \text{ g } S_2Cl_2}$$

(3) The mass of the excess reactant, Cl_2, can be determined by first calculating the amount of Cl_2 that reacted, then subtracting that amount from the initial amount of Cl_2.

$$? \text{ g } Cl_2 \text{ reacted} = 32.0 \text{ g } S_8 \times \frac{1 \text{ mol } S_8}{256.5 \text{ g } S_8} \times \frac{4 \text{ mol } Cl_2}{1 \text{ mol } S_8} \times \frac{70.9 \text{ g } Cl_2}{1 \text{ mol } Cl_2} = 35.4 \text{ g } Cl_2$$

$? \text{ g } Cl_2 \text{ in excess} = 71.0 - 35.4 = \mathbf{35.6 \text{ g } Cl_2 \text{ unreacted}}$

3-36. *Refer to Section 3-3, Examples 3-9 and 3-10, and Exercise 3-30 Solution.*

Balanced equation: $3Ca(OH)_2 + 2H_3PO_4 \rightarrow Ca_3(PO_4)_2 + 6H_2O$

This is a limiting reactant problem.

(1) Convert to moles and compare the required ratio to the available ratio to find the limiting reactant.

$$? \text{ mol } Ca(OH)_2 = \frac{\text{g } Ca(OH)_2}{\text{FW } Ca(OH)_2} = \frac{12.9 \text{ g}}{74.10 \text{ g/mol}} = 0.174 \text{ mol } Ca(OH)_2$$

$$? \text{ mol } H_3PO_4 = \frac{\text{g } H_3PO_4}{\text{FW } H_3PO_4} = \frac{18.37 \text{ g}}{97.99 \text{ g/mol}} = 0.1875 \text{ mol } H_3PO_4$$

$$\text{Required ratio} = \frac{3 \text{ mol } Ca(OH)_2}{2 \text{ mol } H_3PO_4} = 1.5 \qquad \text{Available ratio} = \frac{0.174 \text{ mol } Ca(OH)_2}{0.1875 \text{ mol } H_3PO_4} = 0.928$$

Available ratio < required ratio; $Ca(OH)_2$ is the limiting reactant.

(2) The mass of $Ca_3(PO_4)_2$ produced is determined by the mass of $Ca(OH)_2$.

$$? \text{ g } Ca_3(PO_4)_2 = 12.9 \text{ g } Ca(OH)_2 \times \frac{1 \text{ mol } Ca(OH)_2}{74.10 \text{ g } Ca(OH)_2} \times \frac{1 \text{ mol } Ca_3(PO_4)_2}{3 \text{ mol } Ca(OH)_2} \times \frac{310.2 \text{ g } Ca_3(PO_4)_2}{1 \text{ mol } Ca_3(PO_4)_2}$$

$$= \mathbf{18.0 \text{ g } Ca_3(PO_4)_2}$$

3-38. *Refer to Section 3-3, Examples 3-9 and 3-10, and Exercise 3-30 Solution.*

Balanced equation: $2AgNO_3 + BaCl_2 \rightarrow 2AgCl + Ba(NO_3)_2$

(a) Convert to moles and compare the required ratio to the available ratio to find the limiting reactant.

$$? \text{ mol } AgNO_3 = \frac{\text{g } AgNO_3}{\text{FW } AgNO_3} = \frac{62.4 \text{ g}}{169.9 \text{ g/mol}} = 0.367 \text{ mol } AgNO_3$$

$$? \text{ mol } BaCl_2 = \frac{\text{g } BaCl_2}{\text{FW } BaCl_2} = \frac{53.1 \text{ g}}{208.2 \text{ g/mol}} = 0.255 \text{ mol } BaCl_2$$

$$\text{Required ratio} = \frac{2 \text{ mol } AgNO_3}{1 \text{ mol } BaCl_2} = 2 \qquad \text{Available ratio} = \frac{0.367 \text{ mol } AgNO_3}{0.255 \text{ mol } BaCl_2} = 1.44$$

Available ratio < required ratio; $\mathbf{AgNO_3}$ is the limiting reactant.

(b) The reactant in excess will be $BaCl_2$ and its mass depends on the limiting reactant, $AgNO_3$.

$$? \text{ g } BaCl_2 \text{ that reacted} = 62.4 \text{ g } AgNO_3 \times \frac{1 \text{ mol } AgNO_3}{169.9 \text{ g } AgNO_3} \times \frac{1 \text{ mol } BaCl_2}{2 \text{ mol } AgNO_3} \times \frac{208.2 \text{ g } BaCl_2}{1 \text{ mol } BaCl_2} = 38.2 \text{ g } BaCl_2$$

$? \text{ g } BaCl_2 \text{ that remain} = $ initial mass - mass that reacted

$= 53.1 \text{ g} - 38.2 \text{ g}$

$= \mathbf{14.9 \text{ g } BaCl_2}$

(c) The mass of $AgCl$ produced is determined by the mass of $AgNO_3$.

$$? \text{ g } AgCl = 62.4 \text{ g } AgNO_3 \times \frac{1 \text{ mol } AgNO_3}{169.9 \text{ g } AgNO_3} \times \frac{2 \text{ mol } AgCl}{2 \text{ mol } AgNO_3} \times \frac{143.4 \text{ g } AgCl}{1 \text{ mol } AgCl} = \mathbf{52.7 \text{ g } AgCl}$$

Balanced equation: $PCl_3 + Cl_2 \rightarrow PCl_5$

Step 1. Calculate the theoretical yield of PCl_5.

Plan: $g\ PCl_3 \overset{(1)}{\Rightarrow} mol\ PCl_3 \overset{(2)}{\Rightarrow} mol\ PCl_5 \overset{(3)}{\Rightarrow} g\ PCl_5$ (theoretical)

(1) $?\ mol\ PCl_3 = \dfrac{g\ PCl_3}{FW\ PCl_3} = \dfrac{92.5\ g}{137\ g/mol} = 0.675\ mol\ PCl_3$

(2) $?\ mol\ PCl_5 = mol\ PCl_3 = 0.675\ mol\ PCl_5$

(3) $?\ g\ PCl_5 = mol\ PCl_5 \times FW\ PCl_5 = 0.675\ mol \times 208\ g/mol = 140.\ g\ PCl_5$

Alternatively by dimensional analysis:

$?\ g\ PCl_5 = 92.5\ g\ PCl_3 \times \dfrac{1\ mol\ PCl_3}{137\ g\ PCl_3} \times \dfrac{1\ mol\ PCl_5}{1\ mol\ PCl_3} \times \dfrac{208\ g\ PCl_5}{1\ mol\ PCl_5} = \mathbf{140.\ g\ PCl_5}$

Step 2. Solve for the actual yield of PCl_5.

$?\ \%\ yield = \dfrac{actual\ yield}{theoretical\ yield} \times 100\%$ Substituting, $76.5\% = \dfrac{?\ actual\ yield}{140.\ g} \times 100\%$

Therefore, $?\ actual\ yield = \dfrac{76.5\% \times 140.\ g}{100\%} = \mathbf{107\ g\ PCl_5}$

Balanced equation: $2KClO_3 \rightarrow 2KCl + 3O_2$

(a) Calculate the theoretical yield of O_2.

Plan: $g\ KClO_3 \overset{(1)}{\Rightarrow} mol\ KClO_3 \overset{(2)}{\Rightarrow} mol\ O_2 \overset{(3)}{\Rightarrow} g\ O_2$ (theoretical)

(1) $?\ mol\ KClO_3 = \dfrac{g\ KClO_3}{FW\ KClO_3} = \dfrac{5.79\ g}{122.55\ g/mol} = 0.0472\ mol\ KClO_3$

(2) $?\ mol\ O_2 = 0.0472\ mol\ KClO_3 \times \dfrac{3\ mol\ O_2}{2\ mol\ KClO_3} = 0.0709\ mol\ O_2$

(3) $?\ g\ O_2 = mol\ O_2 \times AW\ O_2 = 0.0709\ mol \times 32.0\ g/mol = \mathbf{2.27\ g\ O_2}$ (theoretical yield)

Alternatively by dimensional analysis:

$?\ g\ O_2 = 5.79\ g\ KClO_3 \times \dfrac{1\ mol\ KClO_3}{122.55\ g\ KClO_3} \times \dfrac{3\ mol\ O_2}{2\ mol\ KClO_3} \times \dfrac{32.0\ g\ O_2}{1\ mol\ O_2} = \mathbf{2.27\ g\ O_2}$

(b) Calculate the percent yield of O_2.

$\%\ yield = \dfrac{actual\ yield}{theoretical\ yield} \times 100\% = \dfrac{1.05\ g}{2.27\ g} \times 100\% = \mathbf{46.3\%}$

Balanced equation: $2AgNO_3 \rightarrow 2Ag + 2NO_2 + O_2$

Step 1. Calculate the theoretical yield of Ag.

Plan: $g\ AgNO_3 \overset{(1)}{\Rightarrow} mol\ AgNO_3 \overset{(2)}{\Rightarrow} mol\ Ag \overset{(3)}{\Rightarrow} g\ Ag$ (theoretical)

(1) $?\ mol\ AgNO_3 = \dfrac{g\ AgNO_3}{FW\ AgNO_3} = \dfrac{1.099\ g}{169.9\ g/mol} = 6.469 \times 10^{-3}\ mol\ AgNO_3$

(2) ? mol Ag = mol $AgNO_3$ = 6.469 x 10^{-3} mol Ag

(3) ? g Ag = mol Ag x AW Ag = (6.469 x 10^{-3} mol) x 107.9 g/mol = 0.6980 g Ag (theoretical yield)

Alternatively by dimensional analysis:

$$? \text{ g Ag} = 1.099 \text{ g AgNO}_3 \times \frac{1 \text{ mol AgNO}_3}{169.9 \text{ g AgNO}_3} \times \frac{2 \text{ mol Ag}}{2 \text{ mol AgNO}_3} \times \frac{107.9 \text{ g Ag}}{1 \text{ mol Ag}} = 0.6980 \text{ g Ag}$$

Step 2. Calculate the percent yield of Ag.

$$\% \text{ yield} = \frac{\text{actual yield}}{\text{theoretical yield}} \times 100\% = \frac{0.665 \text{ g}}{0.6980 \text{ g}} \times 100\% = \textbf{95.3\%}$$

3-46.   *Refer to Section 3-4 and Example 3-11.*

Balanced equation: $CS_2 + 3O_2 \rightarrow CO_2 + 2SO_2$

Step 1. Calculate the theoretical yield of SO_2. To minimize the number of steps, you could work in mg and mmol.

$$\text{Plan: mg CS}_2 \overset{(1)}{\Rightarrow} \text{g CS}_2 \overset{(2)}{\Rightarrow} \text{mol CS}_2 \overset{(3)}{\Rightarrow} \text{mol SO}_2 \overset{(4)}{\Rightarrow} \text{g SO}_2 \text{ (theoretical)} \overset{(5)}{\Rightarrow} \text{mg SO}_2 \text{ (theoretical)}$$

$$\underset{}{? \text{ mg SO}_2} = 85.9 \text{ mg CS}_2 \times \underset{\text{Step 1}}{\frac{1 \text{ g CS}_2}{1000 \text{ mg CS}_2}} \times \underset{\text{Step 2}}{\frac{1 \text{ mol CS}_2}{76.13 \text{ g CS}_2}} \times \underset{\text{Step 3}}{\frac{2 \text{ mol SO}_2}{1 \text{ mol CS}_2}} \times \underset{\text{Step 4}}{\frac{64.1 \text{ g SO}_2}{1 \text{ mol SO}_2}} \times \underset{\text{Step 5}}{\frac{1000 \text{ mg SO}_2}{1 \text{ g SO}_2}}$$

$$= \textbf{145 mg SO}_2$$

Step 2. Calculate the percent yield of SO_2.

$$\% \text{ yield} = \frac{\text{actual yield}}{\text{theoretical yield}} \times 100\% = \frac{108 \text{ mg}}{145 \text{ mg}} \times 100\% = \textbf{74.5\%}$$

3-48.   *Refer to Sections 3-3 and 3-4.*

Balanced equation: $Fe_2O_3 + 2Al \rightarrow 2Fe + Al_2O_3$

(a) Plan: (1) Find the limiting reactant.
         (2) Calculate the theoretical yield of Fe, based on the limiting reactant.

(1) $? \text{ mol Al} = \dfrac{\text{g Al}}{\text{AW Al}} = \dfrac{500.0 \text{ g}}{26.98 \text{ g/mol}} = 18.53 \text{ mol Al}$

$? \text{ mol Fe}_2O_3 = \dfrac{\text{g Fe}_2O_3}{\text{FW Fe}_2O_3} = \dfrac{500.0 \text{ g}}{159.7 \text{ g/mol}} = 3.131 \text{ mol Fe}_2O_3$

Required ratio $= \dfrac{2 \text{ mol Al}}{1 \text{ mol Fe}_2O_3} = 2$ Available ratio $= \dfrac{18.53 \text{ mol Al}}{3.131 \text{ mol Fe}_2O_3} = 5.918$

Available ratio > required ratio; Fe_2O_3 is the limiting reactant.

(2) The mass of Fe that should be produced from the limiting reactant, Fe_2O_3, is the theoretical yield.

$$? \text{ g Fe (theoretical yield)} = 500.0 \text{ g Fe}_2O_3 \times \frac{1 \text{ mol Fe}_2O_3}{159.7 \text{ g Fe}_2O_3} \times \frac{2 \text{ mol Fe}}{1 \text{ mol Fe}_2O_3} \times \frac{55.85 \text{ g Fe}}{1 \text{ mol Fe}} = \textbf{349.7 g Fe}$$

(b) Calculate the percent yield of Fe.

$$\% \text{ yield} = \frac{\text{actual yield}}{\text{theoretical yield}} \times 100\% = \frac{166.5 \text{ g}}{349.7 \text{ g}} \times 100\% = \textbf{47.61\%}$$

Balanced equations: $$TeO_2 + 2OH^- \rightarrow TeO_3^{2-} + H_2O$$
$$TeO_3^{2-} + 2H^+ \rightarrow H_2TeO_3$$

Plan: $g\ TeO_2 \overset{(1)}{\Rightarrow} mol\ TeO_2 \overset{(2)}{\Rightarrow} mol\ TeO_3^{2-} \overset{(3)}{\Rightarrow} mol\ H_2TeO_3 \overset{(4)}{\Rightarrow} g\ H_2TeO_3$

$$? g\ H_2TeO_3 = 74.2\ g\ TeO_2 \times \underset{\text{Step 1}}{\frac{1\ mol\ TeO_2}{159.6\ g\ TeO_2}} \times \underset{\text{Step 2}}{\frac{1\ mol\ TeO_3^{2-}}{1\ mol\ TeO_2}} \times \underset{\text{Step 3}}{\frac{1\ mol\ H_2TeO_3}{1\ mol\ TeO_3^{2-}}} \times \underset{\text{Step 4}}{\frac{177.6\ g\ H_2TeO_3}{1\ mol\ H_2TeO_3}} = \mathbf{82.6\ g\ H_2TeO_3}$$

Balanced equations: $$2KClO_3 \rightarrow 2KCl + 3O_2$$
$$CH_4 + 2O_2 \rightarrow CO_2 + 2H_2O$$

Plan: $g\ CH_4 \overset{(1)}{\Rightarrow} mol\ CH_4 \overset{(2)}{\Rightarrow} mol\ O_2 \overset{(3)}{\Rightarrow} mol\ KClO_3 \overset{(4)}{\Rightarrow} g\ KClO_3$

$$? g\ KClO_3 = 78.88\ g\ CH_4 \times \underset{\text{Step 1}}{\frac{1\ mol\ CH_4}{16.04\ g\ CH_4}} \times \underset{\text{Step 2}}{\frac{2\ mol\ O_2}{1\ mol\ CH_4}} \times \underset{\text{Step 3}}{\frac{2\ mol\ KClO_3}{3\ mol\ O_2}} \times \underset{\text{Step 4}}{\frac{122.6\ g\ KClO_3}{1\ mol\ KClO_3}} = \mathbf{803.9\ g\ KClO_3}$$

(a) Balanced equations:
$$4NH_3 + 5O_2 \rightarrow 4NO + 6H_2O$$
$$2NO + O_2 \rightarrow 2NO_2$$
$$3NO_2 + H_2O \rightarrow 2HNO_3 + NO$$
$$HNO_3 + NH_3 \rightarrow NH_4NO_3$$

(b) $? mol\ N\ atoms = 1\ mol\ NH_4NO_3 \times \dfrac{2\ mol\ N\ atoms}{1 mol\ NH_4NO_3} = \mathbf{2\ mol\ N\ atoms}$

(c) Step 1: Determine how many <u>total</u> moles of NH_3 are necessary to produce 1 mole of NH_4NO_3.
In the last reaction, we know we need 1 mole NH_3 and 1 mole HNO_3 to make 1 mole of NH_4NO_3.
To determine the number of moles of NH_3 required to make 1 mole of HNO_3:

$$? mol\ NH_3\ (in\ first\ reaction) = 1\ mol\ NH_4NO_3 \times \frac{1\ mol\ HNO_3}{1\ mol\ NH_4NO_3} \times \frac{3\ mol\ NO_2}{2\ mol\ HNO_3} \times \frac{2\ mol\ NO}{2\ mol\ NO_2} \times \frac{4\ mol\ NH_3}{4\ mol\ NO}$$
$$= 1.5\ moles\ NH_3$$

Therefore, the total moles of NH_3 required to make 1 mole of NH_4NO_3 is $(1 + 1.5)$ mol $= 2.5$ mol NH_3
This assumes that the NO formed in the third reaction is lost and is not recycled.

Step 2: Do the normal stoichiometric problem.

$$? g\ NH_3 = 200.0\ g\ NH_4NO_3 \times \underset{\text{Step 1}}{\frac{1\ mol\ NH_4NO_3}{80.05\ g\ NH_4NO_3}} \times \underset{\text{Step 2}}{\frac{2.5\ mol\ NH_3}{1\ mol\ NH_4NO_3}} \times \underset{\text{Step 3}}{\frac{17.03\ g\ NH_3}{1\ mol\ NH_3}} = \mathbf{106.4\ g\ NH_3}$$

3-56. *Refer to Section 3-5 and Example 3-13.*

Balanced equations:

ZnS in ore $\rightarrow$ ZnS	flotation	89.6% efficient
$2ZnS + 3O_2 \rightarrow 2ZnO + 2SO_2$	heat in air	100% efficient
$ZnO + H_2SO_4 \rightarrow ZnSO_4 + H_2O$	acid treatment	100% efficient
$2ZnSO_4 + 2H_2O \rightarrow 2Zn + 2H_2SO_4 + O_2$	electrolysis	92.2% efficient

Plan: kg ZnS in ore $\Rightarrow$ kg ZnS $\Rightarrow$ g ZnS $\Rightarrow$ mol ZnS $\Rightarrow$ mol ZnO $\Rightarrow$ mol $ZnSO_4$
$\Rightarrow$ mol Zn (theoretical) $\Rightarrow$ mol Zn (actual) $\Rightarrow$ g Zn $\Rightarrow$ kg Zn

$$? \text{ kg Zn} = 454 \text{ kg ZnS in ore} \times \frac{89.6 \text{ kg ZnS}}{100 \text{ kg ZnS in ore}} \times \frac{1000 \text{ g ZnS}}{1 \text{ kg ZnS}} \times \frac{1 \text{ mol ZnS}}{97.5 \text{ g ZnS}} \times \frac{2 \text{ mol ZnO}}{2 \text{ mol ZnS}}$$

$$\times \frac{1 \text{ mol ZnSO}_4}{1 \text{ mol ZnO}} \times \frac{2 \text{ mol Zn}}{2 \text{ mol ZnSO}_4} \times \frac{0.922 \text{ mol Zn (actual)}}{1 \text{ mol Zn (theoretical)}} \times \frac{65.39 \text{ g Zn}}{1 \text{ mol Zn}} \times \frac{1 \text{ kg Zn}}{1000 \text{ g Zn}} = \textbf{252 kg Zn}$$

3-58. *Refer to Section 3-6 and Example 3-16.*

We know $\qquad D\left(\dfrac{\text{g}}{\text{mL}}\right) = \dfrac{\text{g soln}}{\text{mL soln}}$ $\qquad$ and $\qquad$ % by mass $= \dfrac{\text{g (NH}_4)_2\text{SO}_4}{\text{g soln}} \times 100\%$

$$? \text{ g (NH}_4)_2\text{SO}_4 = 750.0 \text{ mL soln} \times \frac{1.10 \text{ g soln}}{1.00 \text{ mL soln}} \times \frac{18.0 \text{ g (NH}_4)_2\text{SO}_4}{100 \text{ g soln}} = \textbf{149 g (NH}_4)_2\textbf{SO}_4$$

3-60. *Refer to Section 3-6, Exercise 3-58, and Example 3-17.*

$$? \text{ mL soln} = 125 \text{ g (NH}_4)_2\text{SO}_4 \times \frac{100 \text{ g soln}}{18.0 \text{ g (NH}_4)_2\text{SO}_4} \times \frac{1.00 \text{ mL soln}}{1.10 \text{ g soln}} = \textbf{631 mL soln}$$

3-62. *Refer to Section 3-6 and Example 3-18.*

Method 1: Use the units of molarity as an equation: $M\left(\dfrac{\text{mol}}{\text{L}}\right) = \dfrac{\text{mol substance}}{\text{L soln}}$

Plan: g Na_3PO_4 $\overset{(1)}{\Rightarrow}$ mol Na_3PO_4 $\overset{(2)}{\Rightarrow}$ M Na_3PO_4

(1) $? \text{ mol Na}_3\text{PO}_4 = \dfrac{\text{g Na}_3\text{PO}_4}{\text{FW Na}_3\text{PO}_4} = \dfrac{355 \text{ g}}{163.94 \text{ g/mol}} = 2.17 \text{ mol Na}_3\text{PO}_4$

(2) $? \ M \text{ Na}_3\text{PO}_4 = \dfrac{\text{mol Na}_3\text{PO}_4}{\text{L soln}} = \dfrac{2.17 \text{ mol}}{2.50 \text{ L}} = \textbf{0.866} \ \boldsymbol{M} \textbf{ Na}_3\textbf{PO}_4$

Method 2: Dimensional Analysis

$$? \ M \text{ Na}_3\text{PO}_4 = \frac{355 \text{ g Na}_3\text{PO}_4}{2.50 \text{ L soln}} \times \frac{1 \text{ mol Na}_3\text{PO}_4}{163.94 \text{ g Na}_3\text{PO}_4} = \textbf{0.866} \ \boldsymbol{M} \textbf{ Na}_3\textbf{PO}_4$$

3-64. *Refer to Section 3-6 and Example 3-19.*

$$? \text{ L NaOH} = 25.0 \text{ g NaOH} \times \frac{1 \text{ mol NaOH}}{40.00 \text{ g NaOH}} \times \frac{1 \text{ L soln}}{0.123 \text{ mol NaOH}} = \textbf{5.08 L or 5080 mL NaOH soln}$$

3-66. *Refer to Section 3-6 and Example 3-20.*

(a) % by mass = $\dfrac{g\ CaCl_2}{g\ soln} \times 100\% = \dfrac{16.0\ g\ CaCl_2}{64.0\ g\ H_2O + 16.0\ g\ CaCl_2} \times 100\% = \mathbf{20.0\%\ CaCl_2}$

(b) Assume we have 1 liter of solution

Plan: $1\ L\ soln \overset{(1)}{\Rightarrow} g\ soln\ in\ 1\ L \overset{(2)}{\Rightarrow} g\ CaCl_2\ in\ 1\ L \overset{(3)}{\Rightarrow} mol\ CaCl_2\ in\ 1\ L = M\ CaCl_2$

(1) ? g soln in 1 L = $1000\ mL \times \dfrac{1.180\ g}{mL} = 1180\ g\ soln$

(2) ? g $CaCl_2$ in 1 L = $1180\ g\ soln \times 20.0\%\ CaCl_2 = 236\ g\ CaCl_2$

(3) ? mol $CaCl_2$ in 1 L = $\dfrac{236\ g\ CaCl_2\ in\ 1\ L\ soln}{111\ g/mol} = 2.13\ mol\ CaCl_2\ in\ 1\ L = \mathbf{2.13\ \textit{M}\ CaCl_2}$

3-68. *Refer to Section 3-6 and Example 3-18.*

Method 1: Plan: $g\ BaCl_2 \cdot 2H_2O \overset{(1)}{\Rightarrow} mol\ BaCl_2 \cdot 2H_2O \overset{(2)}{=} mol\ BaCl_2 \overset{(3)}{\Rightarrow} M\ BaCl_2$

(1) ? mol $BaCl_2 \cdot 2H_2O = \dfrac{g\ BaCl_2 \cdot 2H_2O}{FW\ BaCl_2 \cdot 2H_2O} = \dfrac{1.72\ g}{244\ g/mol} = 0.00705\ mol\ BaCl_2 \cdot 2H_2O$

(2) ? mol $BaCl_2 = mol\ BaCl_2 \cdot 2H_2O = 0.00705\ mol\ BaCl_2$

(3) ? $M\ BaCl_2 = \dfrac{mol\ BaCl_2}{L\ soln} = \dfrac{0.00705\ mol}{0.750\ L} = \mathbf{0.00940\ \textit{M}\ BaCl_2}$

Method 2:   Dimensional Analysis

? $M\ BaCl_2 = \dfrac{1.72\ g\ BaCl_2 \cdot 2H_2O}{750.\ mL\ soln} \times \dfrac{1000\ mL}{1\ L} \times \dfrac{1\ mol\ BaCl_2 \cdot 2H_2O}{244\ g\ BaCl_2 \cdot 2H_2O} \times \dfrac{1\ mol\ BaCl_2}{1\ mol\ BaCl_2 \cdot 2H_2O} = \mathbf{0.00940\ \textit{M}\ BaCl_2}$

3-70. *Refer to Section 3-6, Example 3-20, and Exercise 3-66 Solution.*

? $M\ HF = \dfrac{1000\ mL\ soln}{1\ L} \times \dfrac{1.17\ g\ soln}{1\ mL\ soln} \times \dfrac{49.0\ g\ HF}{100\ g\ soln} \times \dfrac{1\ mol\ HF}{20.0\ g\ HF} = \mathbf{28.7\ \textit{M}\ HF}$

3-72. *Refer to Section 3-7 and Example 3-21.*

For a dilution problem, $M_1 \times V_1 = M_2 \times V_2$

Therefore, $V_1 = \dfrac{M_2 \times V_2}{M_1} = \dfrac{1.50\ M \times 2.00\ L}{12.0\ M} = \mathbf{0.250\ L\ conc.\ HCl\ soln}$

3-74. *Refer to Section 3-7 and Example 3-21.*

For a dilution problem, $M_1 \times V_1 = M_2 \times V_2$, therefore, $M_2 = M_1 \times \dfrac{V_1}{V_2}$

(a) $M_2 = M_1 \times \dfrac{V_1}{V_2} = 0.500\ M \times \dfrac{1.00\ mL}{1.00 \times 10^3\ mL} = 0.000500\ M$ solution remaining in flask

(b) $M_2 = 0.500\ M \times \dfrac{1.00\ mL}{10.00\ mL} \times \dfrac{1.00\ mL}{10.00\ mL} \times \dfrac{1.00\ mL}{10.00\ mL} = 0.000500\ M$ solution remaining in flask

Remember that V_2 is the total volume = 1.00 mL in flask + 9.00 mL of solvent added = 10.00 mL

(c) Both methods resulted in the same solute concentration for the 1.00 mL remaining in the volumetric flask. However, the single rinse used 1.00 L of solvent, whereas the three rinses used only 27.00 mL of solvent.

(d) The triple rinse technique is much more economical than the single rinse and still gives the same result.

3-76. *Refer to Section 3-7 and Example 3-21.*

For a dilution problem, $M_1 \times V_1 = M_2 \times V_2$

Therefore, $V_2 = \dfrac{M_1 \times V_1}{M_2} = \dfrac{12.0\ M \times 100.\ \text{mL}}{5.20\ M} = $ **231 mL NaOH soln**

3-78. *Refer to Section 3-8, and Example 3-23.*

Balanced equation: $KOH + CH_3COOH \rightarrow KCH_3COO + H_2O$

Plan: $\underset{(1)}{g\ CH_3COOH} \Rightarrow \underset{(2)}{mol\ CH_3COOH} \Rightarrow \underset{(3)}{mol\ KOH} \Rightarrow L\ KOH\ soln$

Method 1:

(1) $?\ mol\ CH_3COOH = \dfrac{g\ CH_3COOH}{FW\ CH_3COOH} = \dfrac{0.385\ g}{60.05\ g/mol} = 6.41 \times 10^{-3}\ mol\ CH_3COOH$

(2) $?\ mol\ KOH = 6.41 \times 10^{-3}\ mol\ CH_3COOH \times (1\ mol\ KOH/1\ mol\ CH_3COOH) = 6.41 \times 10^{-3}\ mol\ KOH$

(3) $?\ L\ KOH\ soln = \dfrac{mol\ KOH}{M\ KOH} = \dfrac{6.41 \times 10^{-3}\ mol\ KOH}{0.157\ M} = $ **0.0408 L KOH soln**

Method 2: Dimensional Analysis

$?\ L\ KOH = 0.385\ g\ CH_3COOH \times \dfrac{1\ mol\ CH_3COOH}{60.05\ g\ CH_3COOH} \times \dfrac{1\ mol\ KOH}{1\ mol\ CH_3COOH} \times \dfrac{1\ L\ soln}{0.157\ mol\ KOH}$

$= $ **0.0408 L KOH soln**

3-80. *Refer to Section 3-8 and Example 3-24.*

Balanced equation: $Ba(OH)_2 + 2HNO_3 \rightarrow Ba(NO_3)_2 + 2H_2O$

Plan: $\underset{(1)}{M, L\ Ba(OH)_2\ soln} \Rightarrow \underset{(2)}{mol\ Ba(OH)_2} \Rightarrow \underset{(3)}{mol\ HNO_3} \Rightarrow L\ HNO_3\ soln$

Method 1:

(1) $?\ mol\ Ba(OH)_2 = 0.0515\ M \times 0.04555\ L = 2.35 \times 10^{-3}\ mol\ Ba(OH)_2$

(2) $?\ mol\ HNO_3 = 2.35 \times 10^{-3}\ mol\ Ba(OH)_2 \times (2\ mol\ HNO_3/1\ mol\ Ba(OH)_2) = 4.69 \times 10^{-3}\ mol\ HNO_3$

(3) $?\ L\ HNO_3 = \dfrac{mol\ HNO_3}{M\ HNO_3} = \dfrac{4.69 \times 10^{-3}\ mol}{0.558\ M} = $ **0.00841 L or 8.41 mL HNO₃ soln**

Method 2: Dimensional Analysis

$?\ L\ HNO_3 = 0.04555\ L\ Ba(OH)_2 \times \dfrac{0.0515\ mol\ Ba(OH)_2}{1\ L\ soln} \times \dfrac{2\ mol\ HNO_3}{1\ mol\ Ba(OH)_2} \times \dfrac{1\ L\ soln}{0.558\ mol\ HNO_3}$

$= $ **0.00841 L or 8.41 mL HNO₃ soln**

Balanced equation: $AlCl_3 + 3AgNO_3 \rightarrow 3AgCl + Al(NO_3)_3$

Plan: $\overset{(1)}{g\ AgCl} \Rightarrow \overset{(2)}{mol\ AgCl} \Rightarrow \overset{(3)}{mol\ AlCl_3} \Rightarrow M\ AlCl_3$

Recall: $M = \dfrac{\text{mol substance}}{\text{L soln}}$

Method 1:

(1) $?\ mol\ AgCl = \dfrac{g\ AgCl}{FW\ AgCl} = \dfrac{0.215\ g}{143.3\ g/mol} = 1.50 \times 10^{-3}\ mol\ AgCl$

(2) $?\ mol\ AlCl_3 = mol\ AgCl \times 1\ mol\ AlCl_3/3\ mol\ AgCl = 5.00 \times 10^{-4}\ mol\ AlCl_3$

(3) $?\ M\ AlCl_3 = \dfrac{mol\ AlCl_3}{L\ soln} = \dfrac{5.00 \times 10^{-4}\ mol\ AlCl_3}{0.1105\ L\ soln} = \textbf{0.00453}\ \textbf{\textit{M}}\ \textbf{AlCl}_3\ \textbf{soln}$

Method 2:   Dimensional Analysis

$?\ mol\ AlCl_3 = 0.215\ g\ AgCl \times \dfrac{1\ mol\ AgCl}{143.3\ g\ AgCl} \times \dfrac{1\ mol\ AlCl_3}{3\ mol\ AgCl} = 5.00 \times 10^{-4}\ mol\ AlCl_3$

$?\ M\ AlCl_3 = \dfrac{mol\ AlCl_3}{L\ soln} = \dfrac{5.00 \times 10^{-4}\ mol\ AlCl_3}{0.1105\ L\ soln} = \textbf{0.00453}\ \textbf{\textit{M}}\ \textbf{AlCl}_3\ \textbf{soln}$

Balanced equation: $Fe_3O_4 + 2C \rightarrow 3Fe + 2CO_2$

Plan: $g\ Fe \Rightarrow mol\ Fe \Rightarrow mol\ Fe_3O_4 \Rightarrow g\ Fe_3O_4 \Rightarrow \%Fe_3O_4\ in\ ore$

$?\ g\ Fe_3O_4 = 2.11\ g\ Fe\ in\ ore \times \dfrac{1\ mol\ Fe}{55.85\ g\ Fe} \times \dfrac{1\ mol\ Fe_3O_4}{3\ mol\ Fe} \times \dfrac{231.55\ g\ Fe_3O_4}{1\ mol\ Fe_3O_4} = 2.92\ g\ Fe_3O_4$

$?\ \%Fe_3O_4\ in\ ore = \dfrac{2.92\ g\ Fe_3O_4}{75.0\ g\ ore} \times 100\% = \textbf{3.89\% Fe}_3\textbf{O}_4\ \textbf{in ore}$

Balanced equation: $2KBr + Cl_2 \rightarrow 2KCl + Br_2$

Method 1:   Plan: $\overset{(1)}{g\ Cl_2} \Rightarrow \overset{(2)}{mol\ Cl_2} \Rightarrow \overset{(3)}{mol\ Br_2} \Rightarrow g\ Br_2$

(1) $?\ mol\ Cl_2 = \dfrac{g\ Cl_2}{FW\ Cl_2} = \dfrac{0.631\ g}{70.9\ g/mol} = 8.90 \times 10^{-3}\ mol\ Cl_2$

(2) $?\ mol\ Br_2 = mol\ Cl_2 = 8.90 \times 10^{-3}\ mol\ Br_2$

(3) $?\ g\ Br_2 = mol\ Br_2 \times FW\ Br_2 = (8.90 \times 10^{-3}\ mol) \times 159.8\ g/mol = \textbf{1.42 g Br}_2$

Method 2:   Dimensional Analysis (The unit factors correspond to the steps in Method 1.)

$$\overset{\textbf{Step 1}}{} \quad \overset{\textbf{Step 2}}{} \quad \overset{\textbf{Step 3}}{}$$

$?\ g\ Br_2 = 0.631\ g\ Cl_2 \times \dfrac{1\ mol\ Cl_2}{70.9\ g\ Cl_2} \times \dfrac{1\ mol\ Br_2}{1\ mol\ Cl_2} \times \dfrac{159.8\ g\ Br_2}{1\ mol\ Br_2} = \textbf{1.42 g Br}_2$

Method 3:   Proportion or Ratio Method

$\dfrac{?\ g\ Br_2}{g\ Cl_2} = \dfrac{1 \times FW\ Br_2}{1 \times FW\ Cl_2}$ Solving, $?\ g\ Br_2 = g\ Cl_2 \times \dfrac{1 \times FW\ Br_2}{1 \times FW\ Cl_2} = 0.631\ g \times \dfrac{159.8\ g}{70.9\ g} = \textbf{1.42 g Br}_2$

A chemical reaction involves a chemical change in which

(1) one or more substances are used up (at least partially),
(2) one or more new substances are formed and
(3) energy is absorbed or released.

Here is an example of the chemical reaction, presented in Exercise 3-4:

$$2H_2(g) + O_2(g) \rightarrow 2H_2O(g)$$

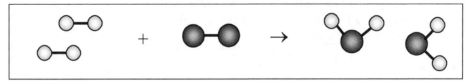

Balanced equation: $3\ CoCl_2(aq) + 2\ K_3PO_4(aq) \rightarrow Co_3(PO_4)_2(s) + 6\ KCl(aq)$

Balanced equation: $3\ Be(s) + N_2(g) \rightarrow Be_3N_2(s)$

(1) ? mol Be = 1 mol N_2 × (3 mol Be/1 mol N_2) = **3.0 mol Be**

(2) ? g Be = 1.00 g N_2 × $\dfrac{1\ mol\ N_2}{28.0\ g\ N_2}$ × $\dfrac{3\ mol\ Be}{1\ mol\ N_2}$ × $\dfrac{9.0122\ g\ Be}{1.00\ mol\ Be}$ = **0.966 g Be**

(3) If the mass of Be is less than the mass of N_2, then Be may or may not be the limiting reactant. Be will only be limiting if (mass of Be/mass of N_2) < 0.966/1. See part (2). If the moles of Be is less than the moles of N_2, then Be will always be the limiting reactant.

(4) In comparing the amounts to make your decision, working in moles is easier than mass, but as long as you do the correct calculations, the result will be the same.

A 1.0% solution means there is 1.0 g of solute in 100 g of solution. Since the densities of the solutions are assumed to be nearly identical, as the solute decreases in formula weight, the moles (g/FW) of the solute will increase and the molarity of the solution will increase. In order of increasing molarity:

1.0% $SnCl_2$ (FW=189.6 g/mol) < 1.0% $AlCl_3$ (FW=133.3 g/mol) < 1.0% NaCl (FW=58.4 g/mol)

Balanced equation: $Bi + 4HNO_3 + 3H_2O \rightarrow Bi(NO_3)_3 \cdot 5H_2O + NO$

Plan: (1) Calculate the grams of HNO_3 required to react with the Bi,
 (2) Determine the volume of HNO_3 that will contain the desired mass of HNO_3 using the unit factors for % by mass and density.

(1) $? \text{ g HNO}_3 = 20.0 \text{ g Bi } \times \dfrac{1 \text{ mol Bi}}{209.0 \text{ g Bi}} \times \dfrac{4 \text{ mol HNO}_3}{1 \text{ mol Bi}} \times \dfrac{63.02 \text{ g HNO}_3}{1 \text{ mol HNO}_3} = 24.1 \text{ g HNO}_3$

(2) $? \text{ mL HNO}_3 = 24.1 \text{ g HNO}_3 \dfrac{100 \text{ g soln}}{30.0 \text{ g HNO}_3} \times \dfrac{1 \text{ mL soln}}{1.182 \text{ g soln}} = \textbf{68.0 mL HNO}_3$

3-98. *Refer to Section 3-6.*

The concentration of particles in each container is determined by counting the number of dissolved particles and dividing by the volume of solution.

Solution	Concentration
A	12 particles/0.5 L = 24 particles/L
B	6 particles/0.5 L = 12 particles/L
C	3 particles/0.5 L = 6 particles/L
D	8 particles/0.5 L = 16 particles/L
E	3 particles/0.25 L = 12 particles/L
F	5 particles/0.25 L = 20 particles/L

(a) **Solution A** is the most concentrated.

(b) **Solution C** is the least concentrated.

(c) **Solutions B and E** have the same concentration.

(d) When solutions E and F are combined, the resulting solution has the concentration:

8 particles/0.5 L = 32 particles/2 L = 16 particles/L, which is the same as **Solution D**.

3-100. *Refer to Sections 3-3 and 3-4, and Exercise 3-48 Solution.*

Balanced equation: $\text{Zn}(s) + 2\text{AgNO}_3(aq) \rightarrow \text{Zn(NO}_3)_2(aq) + 2\text{Ag}(s)$

(a) This problem involves both the limiting reactant and the percent yield concepts.

(1) Find the limiting reactant.
(2) Calculate the theoretical yield of Ag, based on the limiting reactant.
(3) Determine the percent yield of Ag.

(1) $? \text{ mol Zn} = \dfrac{\text{g Zn}}{\text{AW Zn}} = \dfrac{100.0 \text{ g}}{65.41 \text{ g/mol}} = 1.529 \text{ mol Zn}$

$? \text{ mol AgNO}_3 = \text{mol Ag}^+ = 1.330 \ M \text{ AgNO}_3 \times 1\text{L} = 1.330 \text{ mol AgNO}_3$

Required ratio $= \dfrac{1 \text{ mol Zn}}{2 \text{ mol AgNO}_3} = 0.5$ 　　　　 Available ratio $= \dfrac{1.529 \text{ mol Zn}}{1.330 \text{ mol AgNO}_3} = 1.150$

Available ratio > required ratio; AgNO_3 is the limiting reactant.

(2) The mass of Ag produced from the limiting reactant, AgNO_3, is the theoretical yield.

$? \text{ g Ag (theoretical yield)} = 1.330 \text{ mol AgNO}_3 \times \dfrac{2 \text{ mol Ag}}{2 \text{ mol AgNO}_3} \times \dfrac{107.9 \text{ g Ag}}{1 \text{ mol Ag}} = 143.5 \text{ g Ag}$

(3) % yield of Ag $= \dfrac{\text{actual yield}}{\text{theoretical yield}} \times 100\% = \dfrac{90.0 \text{ g}}{143.5 \text{ g}} \times 100\% = \mathbf{62.7\%}$

(b) The yield might be less than 100% because (1) the zinc might not be pure or (2) the technician or student who collected the silver may have been careless. She or he may have not recovered all of it or even may have spilled some. (3) Some of the zinc may not have reacted because it became coated with silver, or (4) some of the zinc may not have been added to the reaction vessel in the first place.

3-102.   *Refer to Sections 3-3 and 3-4.*

Step 1:   Balance the equation for the reaction.

Step 2:   Find the limiting reactant by first converting the reactant masses to moles, then calculate the required molar ratio of one reactant to another and comparing the required ratio to the available ratio. If the available molar ratio is greater than the required molar ratio for a reactant, then it will be in excess and the other reactant is the limiting reactant.

Step 3:   Calculate the theoretical yield of product in grams or moles, based on the limiting reactant using simple stoichiometry.

Step 4:   Calculate the percent yield by dividing the amount of product the experimenter actually made by the theoretical yield, then multiplying by 100.

The percent yield calculated by using moles or grams would be the same.

3-104.   *Refer to Sections 3-3, 3-4 and 1-12, and Tables 1-2 and 1-9.*

Balanced equation:

$$CH_3COOH \quad + \quad CH_3CH_2OH \quad \rightarrow \quad CH_3COOCH_2CH_3 \quad + \quad H_2O$$

acetic acid   ethanol   ethyl acetate
              (ethyl alcohol)

FW (g/mol)   60.05   46.07   88.10
Density (g/mL)   1.05   0.789   0.902
          (from Table 1-2)   (from Table 1-9)

(a) Plan: (1) Convert the volume of reactants to the mass of reactants.
          (2) Evaluate the limiting reactant.

(1) ? g CH_3COOH = 20.2 mL CH_3COOH x 1.05 g/mL = 21.2 g CH_3COOH

   ? g CH_3CH_2OH = 20.1 mL CH_3CH_2OH x 0.789 g/mL = 15.9 g CH_3CH_2OH

(2) Convert the mass of reactants to moles and compare the required ratio to the available ratio.

$$? \text{ mol } CH_3COOH = \dfrac{\text{g } CH_3COOH}{\text{FW } CH_3COOH} = \dfrac{21.2 \text{ g}}{60.05 \text{ g/mol}} = 0.353 \text{ mol } CH_3COOH$$

$$? \text{ mol } CH_3CH_2OH = \dfrac{\text{g } CH_3CH_2OH}{\text{FW } CH_3CH_2OH} = \dfrac{15.9 \text{ g}}{46.07 \text{ g/mol}} = 0.345 \text{ mol } CH_3CH_2OH$$

Required ratio $= \dfrac{1 \text{ mol } CH_3CH_2OH}{1 \text{ mol } CH_3COOH} = 1$ Available ratio $= \dfrac{0.345 \text{ mol } CH_3CH_2OH}{0.353 \text{ mol } CH_3COOH} = 0.977$

Available ratio < required ratio; **CH_3CH_2OH is the limiting reactant**.

(b) Plan: (1) Calculate the actual yield of ethyl acetate, $CH_3COOCH_2CH_3$, in grams.
          (2) Calculate the theoretical yield of ethyl acetate from 0.345 mol CH_3CH_2OH.
          (3) Calculate the percent yield of ethyl acetate.

(1) ? g ethyl acetate = 27.5 mL ethyl acetate $\times$ 0.902 g/mL = 24.8 g ethyl acetate (actual yield)

(2) ? mol ethyl acetate = mol CH_3CH_2OH $\times$ 1 = 0.345 mol ethyl acetate

    ? g ethyl acetate = mol ethyl acetate $\times$ FW ethyl acetate = 0.345 mol $\times$ 88.1 g/mol

                  = 30.4 g ethyl acetate (theoretical yield)

(3) ? % yield ethyl acetate $= \dfrac{\text{actual yield}}{\text{theoretical yield}} \times 100\% = \dfrac{24.8\ g}{30.4\ g} \times 100\% =$ **81.6%**

3-106. *Refer to Section 3-6.*

Plan: This is a complex dilution problem.

    (1) Find the moles of NaCl in each solution

    (2) Add the moles of NaCl together and divide by the total volume to get the new molarity.

(1)   mol NaCl in Solution 1 = 0.375 M $\times$ 0.0350 L = 0.0131 mol NaCl
      mol NaCl in Solution 2 = 0.632 M $\times$ 0.0475 L = 0.0300 mol NaCl

(2)   ? M NaCl $= \dfrac{\text{total moles of NaCl}}{\text{total volume}} = \dfrac{(0.0131\ \text{mol} + 0.0300\ \text{mol})}{(0.0350\ \text{L} + 0.0475\ \text{L})} =$ **0.522 M NaCl**

3-108. *Refer to Section 3-5 and Example 3-13.*

(a) Balanced equations: $P_4 + 5O_2 \rightarrow P_4O_{10}$ 89.5% efficient
                                $P_4O_{10} + 6H_2O \rightarrow 4H_3PO_4$ 97.8% efficient

(b) Plan: g P_4 $\Rightarrow$ mol P_4 $\Rightarrow$ mol P_4O_{10} (theoretical) $\Rightarrow$ mol P_4O_{10} (actual) $\Rightarrow$ mol H_3PO_4 (theoretical)
            $\Rightarrow$ mol H_3PO_4 (actual) $\Rightarrow$ g H_3PO_4

? g H_3PO_4 = 225 g P_4 $\times \dfrac{1\ \text{mol}\ P_4}{124\ \text{g}\ P_4} \times \dfrac{1\ \text{mol}\ P_4O_{10}\ \text{(theoretical)}}{1\ \text{mol}\ P_4} \times \dfrac{89.5\ \text{mol}\ P_4O_{10}\ \text{(actual)}}{100.\ \text{mol}\ P_4O_{10}\ \text{(theoretical)}}$

         $\times \dfrac{4\ \text{mol}\ H_3PO_4\ \text{(theoretical)}}{1\ \text{mol}\ P_4O_{10}} \times \dfrac{97.8\ \text{mol}\ H_3PO_4\ \text{(actual)}}{100.\ \text{mol}\ H_3PO_4\ \text{(theoretical)}} \times \dfrac{98.0\ \text{g}\ H_3PO_4\ \text{(actual)}}{1\ \text{mol}\ H_3PO_4}$

    = **623 g H_3PO_4**

3-110. *Refer to Sections 3-3 and 3-8.*

Balanced equation: $NaCl(aq) + AgNO_3(aq) \rightarrow AgCl(s) + NaNO_3(aq)$

Plan: (1) Calculate the mass (in grams) of NaCl in the 1.20% solution using density.
        (2) Determine the limiting reactant.
        (3) Determine the mass of AgCl produced.

(1) ? g NaCl = 10.0 mL NaCl $\times \dfrac{1.02\ \text{g soln}}{1\ \text{mL soln}} \times \dfrac{1.20\ \text{g NaCl}}{100\ \text{g soln}} = 0.122$ g NaCl

(2) Convert each reactant to moles and compare required ratio to available ratio to find the limiting reactant.

$$? \text{ mol NaCl} = \frac{\text{g NaCl}}{\text{FW NaCl}} = \frac{0.122 \text{ g}}{58.4 \text{ g/mol}} = 0.00209 \text{ mol NaCl}$$

$$? \text{ mol AgNO}_3 = M \text{ AgNO}_3 \text{ x L soln} = (1.21 \text{ x } 10^{-2} M) \text{ x } 0.0500 \text{ L} = 6.05 \text{ x } 10^{-4} \text{ mol AgNO}_3$$

$$\text{Required ratio} = \frac{1 \text{ mol NaCl}}{1 \text{ mol AgNO}_3} = 1 \qquad \text{Available ratio} = \frac{0.00209 \text{ mol NaCl}}{6.05 \text{ x } 10^{-4} \text{ mol AgNO}_3} = 3.45$$

Available ratio > required ratio; $AgNO_3$ is the limiting reactant.

(3) $$? \text{ g AgCl} = 0.0500 \text{ L x } \frac{1.21 \text{ x } 10^{-2} \text{ mol AgNO}_3}{1 \text{ L soln}} \text{ x } \frac{1 \text{ mol AgCl}}{1 \text{ mol AgNO}_3} \text{ x } \frac{143.3 \text{ g AgCl}}{1 \text{ mol AgCl}} = \textbf{0.0867 g AgCl}$$

3-112. *Refer to Section 3-2.*

Balanced equations: $\text{Zn} + 2\text{HCl} \rightarrow \text{ZnCl}_2 + \text{H}_2$

$2\text{Al} + 6\text{HCl} \rightarrow 2\text{AlCl}_3 + 3\text{H}_2$

Assume: (1) 1 mol of H_2 is produced.

(2) Zn costs \$1.00/g Zn; Al costs \$2.00/g Al

Plan: mol H_2 $\Rightarrow$ mol metal $\Rightarrow$ g metal $\Rightarrow$ \$ required/mol H_2

(1) For Zn: $$1 \text{ mol H}_2 \text{ x } \frac{1 \text{ mol Zn}}{1 \text{ mol H}_2} \text{ x } \frac{65.4 \text{ g Zn}}{1 \text{ mol Zn}} \text{ x } \frac{\$1.00}{1 \text{ g Zn}} = \$65.4/\text{mol H}_2$$

(2) For Al: $$1 \text{ mol H}_2 \text{ x } \frac{2 \text{ mol Al}}{3 \text{ mol H}_2} \text{ x } \frac{27.0 \text{ g Al}}{1 \text{ mol Al}} \text{ x } \frac{\$2.00}{1 \text{ g Al}} = \$36.0/\text{mol H}_2$$

Therefore, Al is less expensive for the production of equal amounts of hydrogen gas.

4 The Structure of Atoms

If any oil droplets in Millikan's oil drop experiment had possessed a deficiency of electrons, the droplets would have been positively charged and would have been attracted to, not repelled by, the negatively charged plate. There would have been no voltage setting possible where the electrical and gravitational forces on the drop would have balanced.

4-4. *Refer to Sections 4-2 and 4-3, and Figures 4-1 and 4-3.*

(a) Canal rays, also produced in the cathode ray tube, move toward the cathode (the negative electrode). Therefore, they must be positively charged. Canal rays are positively charged ions created when cathode rays knock electrons from the gaseous atoms in the tube.

(b) Cathode rays are electrons and are independent of source. Canal rays are the positive ions from the specific gas used after a loss of electrons; they are therefore dependent upon the gas used.

4-6. *Refer to Sections 4-2 and 4-3, and Figure 4-2.*

(a) We must modify the Millikan oil drop experiment in order to determine the charge-to-mass ratio of the positively charged whizatron by

    (1) in some way producing an excess of whizatrons on the oil droplets, and
    (2) switching the leads to the plates to make the bottom plate positively charged.

The positively charged whizatrons on the oil droplets will be repulsed by the plate.

(b) Since all of the charges on the droplets will be integral multiples of the charge on the whizatron, we will identify the droplet with the smallest charge and test to see if the other droplets have charges that are multiples of its charge.

From the results shown in the table below, we can deduce that the charge on the whizatron is 1/2 of the smallest observed charge:

$$1/2 \times (2.44 \times 10^{-19}) = 1.22 \times 10^{-19} \text{ coulombs.}$$

All the droplets have charges that are integral multiples of **1.22×10^{-19} coulombs**.

Charge on Droplets (coulombs)	Ratio
4.88×10^{-19}	$\dfrac{4.88 \times 10^{-19}}{1.22 \times 10^{-19}} = 4.0$
6.10×10^{-19}	$\dfrac{6.10 \times 10^{-19}}{1.22 \times 10^{-19}} = 5.0$
2.44×10^{-19}	$\dfrac{2.44 \times 10^{-19}}{1.22 \times 10^{-19}} = 2.0$
8.53×10^{-19}	$\dfrac{8.53 \times 10^{-19}}{1.22 \times 10^{-19}} = 7.0$
7.32×10^{-19}	$\dfrac{7.32 \times 10^{-19}}{1.22 \times 10^{-19}} = 6.0$

Alpha particles, which are the positively-charged nuclei of helium atoms, were thought to be much more dense than gold. Hence, according to Thomson's "plum pudding" model of the atom, it was expected that these particles would pass easily through the gold foil with little deflection. The fact that some particles were greatly deflected astounded Rutherford. This led him to conclude that all the positive charges were found in one central place, instead of scattered throughout the atom.

4-10. *Refer to Section 4-4.*

Volume of a hydrogen atom = $(4/3)\pi r^3 = (4/3)\pi(5.29 \times 10^{-11} \text{ m})^3 = 6.20 \times 10^{-31} \text{ m}^3$ 　　　($1 \text{ nm} = 1 \times 10^{-9}$ m)

Volume of a hydrogen nucleus = volume of a proton = $(4/3)\pi r^3 = (4/3)\pi(1.5 \times 10^{-15} \text{ m})^3 = 1.4 \times 10^{-44} \text{ m}^3$

Therefore, the fraction of space in a hydrogen atom occupied by the nucleus is:

$$\frac{V_{\text{hydrogen nucleus}}}{V_{\text{hydrogen atom}}} = \frac{1.4 \times 10^{-44} \text{ m}^3}{6.20 \times 10^{-31} \text{ m}^3} = \textbf{2.3} \times \textbf{10}^{-14}$$

As can be seen, an atom is mostly empty space.

4-12. *Refer to Sections 4-2 and 4-7.*

Calculation of the charge-to-mass ratio:

Species	Charge	Mass Number	Charge-to-Mass Ratio
$^{12}C^+$	+1	12	$1/12 = 0.0833$
$^{12}C^{2+}$	+2	12	$2/12 = 0.167$
$^{14}N^+$	+1	14	$1/14 = 0.0714$
$^{14}N^{2+}$	+2	14	$2/14 = 0.143$

The order of increasing charge-to-mass ratios is $^{14}N^+ < {}^{12}C^+ < {}^{14}N^{2+} < {}^{12}C^{2+}$.

4-14. *Refer to Sections 4-5, 4-6 and 4-7, Table 4-1, and Example 4-1.*

A neutral atom of $^{58}_{28}\text{Ni}$ contains 28 electrons, 28 protons and (58-28) = 30 neutrons.

If we assume that the mass of the atom is simply the sum of the masses of its subatomic particles, then

$$\begin{aligned}
\text{mass of } ^{58}\text{Ni} &= (28 \; e^- \times \text{mass } e^-) + (28 \; p \times \text{mass } p) + (30 \; n \times \text{mass } n) \\
&= (28 \times 0.00054858 \text{ amu}) + (28 \times 1.0073 \text{ amu}) + (30 \times 1.0087 \text{ amu}) \\
&= 58.481 \text{ amu/atom}
\end{aligned}$$

(a) % by mass $e^- = \dfrac{\text{mass } e^-}{\text{mass } ^{58}\text{Ni}} \times 100\% = \dfrac{28 \; e^- \times 0.00054858 \text{ amu}/e^-}{58.481 \text{ amu}} \times 100\% = \textbf{0.026265\%}$

(b) % by mass $p = \dfrac{\text{mass } p}{\text{mass } ^{58}\text{Ni}} \times 100\% = \dfrac{28 \; p \times 1.0073 \text{ amu}/p}{58.481 \text{ amu}} \times 100\% = \textbf{48.228\%}$

(c) % by mass $n = \dfrac{\text{mass } n}{\text{mass } ^{58}\text{Ni}} \times 100\% = \dfrac{30 \; n \times 1.0087 \text{ amu}/n}{58.481 \text{ amu}} \times 100\% = \textbf{51.745\%}$

4-16. *Refer to the Key Terms for Chapter 4.*

(a) The atomic number of an element is the integral number of protons in the nucleus. It defines the identity of that element. For example, oxygen has an atomic number of 8 and therefore has 8 protons. All oxygen atoms have exactly 8 protons and there is no other element that has 8 protons in its nucleus (**Section 4-5**).

(b) Isotopes are two or more forms of atoms of the same element with different masses. In other words, they are atoms containing the same number of protons but they have different numbers of neutrons. ^{16}O and ^{17}O are isotopes since both have 8 protons but ^{16}O has (16 - 8) = 8 neutrons while ^{17}O has (17 - 8) = 9 neutrons (**Section 4-7**).

(c) The mass number of an element is the integral sum of the numbers of protons and neutrons in that atom. The mass number of ^{17}O is 17, the sum of protons and neutrons in the nucleus (**Section 4-7**).

(d) Nuclear charge refers to the number of protons or positive charges in the nucleus. The nuclear charge of all oxygen atoms is +8.

4-18. *Refer to Section 4-7, Table 4-2 and the Periodic Table in the textbook.*

From the Periodic Table, we see that the atomic number of strontium is 38.

Therefore, each strontium atom has 38 protons.

If it is a neutral atom then it also has 38 electrons.

If we assume that these isotopes are neutral, then

Isotope	Number of Protons	Number of Electrons	Number of Neutrons (Mass Number - Atomic Number)	
$^{84}_{38}Sr$	38	38	46	(= 84 - 38)
$^{86}_{38}Sr$	38	38	48	(= 86 - 38)
$^{87}_{38}Sr$	38	38	49	(= 87 - 38)
$^{88}_{38}Sr$	38	38	50	(= 88 - 38)

4-20. *Refer to Section 4-7.*

Remember: atomic number = number of protons = number of electrons in a neutral atom
                       mass number = number of protons + number of neutrons

Kind of Atom	Atomic Number	Mass Number	Isotope	Number of Protons	Number of Electrons	Number of Neutrons
cobalt	**27**	**59**	$^{59}_{27}\text{Co}$	**27**	**27**	32
boron	**5**	**11**	$^{11}_{5}\text{B}$	**5**	**5**	**6**
manganese	**25**	**55**	$^{55}_{25}\text{Mn}$	**25**	25	30
platinum	**78**	182	$^{182}_{78}\underline{\text{Pt}}$	**78**	78	**104**

4-22.   *Refer to Section 4-7 and Example 4-1.*

	Symbol of Species	Number of Protons	Number of Neutrons	Number of Electrons
(a)	$^{24}_{12}\text{Mg}$	12	12	12
(b)	$^{51}_{23}\text{V}$	23	28	23
(c)	$^{91}_{40}\text{Zr}$	40	51	40
(d)	$^{27}_{13}\text{Al}$	13	14	13
(e)	$^{65}_{30}\text{Zn}^{2+}$	30	35	28
(f)	$^{108}_{47}\text{Ag}^{+}$	47	61	46

4-24.   *Refer to Section 4-7.*

	Number of Protons	Number of Neutrons	Number of Electrons	Z	A	Charge	Symbol
(a)	24	28	24	24	52	0	$^{52}_{24}\text{Cr}$
(b)	20	20	20	20	40	0	$^{40}_{20}\text{Ca}$
(c)	33	42	33	33	75	0	$^{75}_{33}\text{As}$
(d)	53	74	53	53	127	0	$^{127}_{53}\text{I}$

4-26.   *Refer to Section 4-9 and Example 4-3.*

We know: AW Ga = (mass ^{69}Ga x fraction of ^{69}Ga) + (mass ^{71}Ga x fraction of ^{71}Ga)

   let   x = fraction of ^{69}Ga
   then   (1-x) = fraction of ^{71}Ga

Substituting,

$$69.723 \text{ amu} = (68.925580 \text{ amu})x + (70.9247005 \text{ amu})(1 - x)$$
$$= 68.925580x + 70.9247005 - 70.9247005x$$
$$1.202 = 1.999120x$$

fraction of ^{69}Ga = x = 0.6013   % abundance of ^{69}Ga = **60.13%**
fraction of ^{71}Ga = 1-x = 0.3987   % abundance of ^{71}Ga = **39.87%**

4-28. *Refer to Section 4-9 and Example 4-2.*

Plan: (1) For each isotope, convert the % abundance to a fraction.

   (2) Multiply the fraction of each isotope by its mass and add the terms to find the atomic weight of Sr.

$$AW \ (amu) \ = \sum \frac{(relative \ abundance)}{(total \ relative \ abundance)} \times isotope \ mass \ (amu)$$

? AW Sr = (mass #1 x fraction of #1) + (mass #2 x fraction of #2) + (mass #3 x fraction of #3)
     + (mass #4 x fraction of #4)

$= (83.9134 \ amu \times \frac{0.56}{100}) + (85.9094 \ amu \times \frac{9.86}{100}) + (86.9089 \ amu \times \frac{7.00}{100}) + (87.9056 \ amu \times \frac{82.58}{100})$

= 0.47 amu + 8.47 amu + 6.08 amu + 72.59 amu

= **87.61 amu** (to 4 significant figures)

4-30. *Refer to Section 4-9 and Example 4-2.*

Plan: (1) For each isotope, convert the % abundance to a fraction.

   (2) Multiply the fraction of each isotope by its mass and add the terms to find the atomic weight of Fe.

? AW Fe = (mass ^{54}Fe x fraction of ^{54}Fe) + (mass ^{56}Fe x fraction of ^{56}Fe) + (mass ^{57}Fe x fraction of ^{57}Fe)
     + (mass ^{58}Fe x fraction of ^{58}Fe)

$= (53.9396 \ amu \times \frac{5.82}{100}) + (55.9349 \ amu \times \frac{91.66}{100}) + (56.9354 \ amu \times \frac{2.19}{100})$

$+ (57.9333 \ amu \times \frac{0.33}{100})$

= 3.14 amu + 51.27 amu + 1.25 amu + 0.19 amu

= **55.85 amu** (to 4 significant figures)

4-32. *Refer to Section 4-9 and Example 4-3.*

We know: AW Cu = (mass ^{63}Cu x fraction of ^{63}Cu) + (mass ^{65}Cu x fraction of ^{65}Cu)

   let   x = fraction of ^{63}Cu
   then (1-x) = fraction of ^{65}Cu

Substituting,

   63.546 amu = (62.9298 amu)x + (64.9278 amu)(1 - x)

        = 62.9298x + 64.9278 - 64.9278x

      1.998x = 1.382

   fraction of ^{63}Cu = x = 0.6917

   % abundance of ^{63}Cu = **69.17%**

4-34. *Refer to Section 4-9 and Table 4-3.*

Plan: (1) For each isotope, convert the % abundance to a fraction.

   (2) Multiply the fraction of each isotope by its mass.

   (3) Add terms to obtain the atomic weight of the element.

? AW O = (mass ^{16}O x fraction of ^{16}O) + (mass ^{17}O x fraction of ^{17}O) + (mass ^{18}O x fraction of ^{18}O)

   $= (15.99492 \ amu \times \frac{99.762}{100}) + (16.99913 \ amu \times \frac{0.038}{100}) + (17.99916 \ amu \times \frac{0.200}{100})$

   = **15.999 amu** (to 5 significant figures)

? AW Cl = (mass ^{35}Cl x fraction of ^{35}Cl) + (mass ^{37}Cl x fraction of ^{37}Cl)

$$= (34.96885 \text{ amu} \times \frac{75.770}{100}) + (36.96590 \text{ amu} \times \frac{24.230}{100})$$

$$= \textbf{35.453 amu} \text{ (to 5 significant figures)}$$

Yes, the answers agree with the atomic weights given in Table 4-3.

4-36. *Refer to Section 4-9 and Example 4-2.*

If the mass spectrum were complete for germanium, the calculated atomic weight would be the weighted average of the isotopes:

$$\text{AW (amu)} = \sum \frac{\text{(relative abundance)}}{\text{(total relative abundance)}} \times \text{isotope mass (amu)}$$

$$= (5.49/15.90)71.9217 + (1.55/15.90)72.9234 + (7.31/15.90)73.9219 + (1.55/15.90)75.9219$$
$$= \textbf{73.3 amu}$$

However, the true atomic weight of germanium is 72.61 amu. The observed data gives a value that is too high. Therefore, the spectrum is incomplete and data must have been lost at the plot's low end when the recorder malfunctioned.

4-38. *Refer to Section 4-9 and Example 4-2.*

Plan: (1) For each isotope, convert the % abundance to a fraction.
(2) Multiply the fraction of each isotope by its mass and add the terms to find the atomic weight of Cr.

? AW Cr = (mass ^{50}Cr x fraction of ^{50}Cr) + (mass ^{52}Cr x fraction of ^{52}Cr) + (mass ^{53}Cr x fraction of ^{53}Cr)
$\qquad$ + (mass ^{54}Cr x fraction of ^{54}Cr)

? AW Cr = (49.9461 amu $\times \frac{4.35}{100}$) + (51.9405 amu $\times \frac{83.79}{100}$) + (52.9406 amu $\times \frac{9.50}{100}$) + (53.9389 amu $\times \frac{2.36}{100}$)

$$= \textbf{52.0 amu} \text{ (to 3 significant figures)}$$

4-40. *Refer to Section 4-10 and Figure 4-11.*

Mendeleev arranged the known elements in order of increasing atomic weight in sequence so that elements with similar chemical and physical properties fell in the same column or group. To achieve this chemical periodicity, it was necessary for Mendeleev to leave blank spaces for elements undiscovered at that time and to make assumptions concerning atomic weights not known with certainty.

The modern periodic table has elements arranged in order of increasing atomic number so that elements with similar chemical properties fall in the same column.

4-42. *Refer to Section 4-10.*

The atomic weight of an element is a weighted average of the mass of the naturally occurring isotopes of that element. Therefore, the atoms in a naturally occurring sample of argon must be heavier than the atoms in a naturally occurring sample of potassium.

Atoms of argon have 18 protons, whereas atoms of potassium have 19 protons. In order for the atomic weight of argon to be greater than that of potassium, argon atoms must have more neutrons.

Consider the isotopes for these elements:

Isotope	Percent Composition	Number of Protons	Number of Neutrons
$^{40}_{18}Ar$	99.60%	18	22
$^{39}_{19}K$	93.1%	19	20
$^{41}_{19}K$	6.88%	19	22

argon (AW: 39.948 amu)

potassium (AW: 39.0983 amu)

From these data, we can see that argon would have a higher atomic weight than potassium.

4-44.   Refer to Section 4-10, the Periodic Table and the Handbook of Chemistry and Physics.

If we look at the densities of the elements in reference to where they are on the periodic table with reference to selenium, we see that the density of Se should be between 2.07 (S) and 6.24 (Te) and between 3.12 (Br) and 5.72 (As). We can estimate it to be the average of the densities of the surrounding elements

	S 2.07 g/cm³	
As 5.72 g/cm³	Se	Br 3.12 g/cm³
	Te 6.24 g/cm³	

$$D \text{ of Se} = \frac{2.07 + 6.24 + 5.72 + 3.12}{4} = 4.29 \text{ g/cm}^3$$

The Handbook of Chemistry and Physics gives the density of Se as 4.81 g/cm³. This averaging method gave us a reasonable estimation of the density with the following relative error:

$$\% \text{ error in the density of Se} = \frac{4.81 - 4.29}{4.81} \times 100 = 11\%$$

4-46.   Refer to Section 4-10, the Periodic Table, and the Handbook of Chemistry and Physics.

The periodic trends of the element properties also apply to compound containing the elements. Therefore, the melting points of CF_4, CCl_4, CBr_4 and CI_4 should follow a trend. If we graph the melting points of these compounds versus molecular weight, we can estimate the melting point of CBr_4.

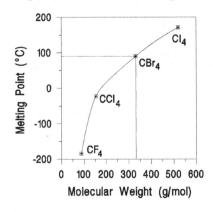

Compound	MW (g/mol)	MP (°C)
CF_4	88.0	−184
CCl_4	153.8	−23
CBr_4	331.6	?
CI_4	519.6	171

The estimated melting point of CBr_4 is about **90°C**. The actual value is 90.1°C according to the *Handbook of Chemistry and Physics*.

4-48.   Refer to Section 4-10.

Hydride formulas are related to the group number of the central element, e.g.,

2A	3A	4A	5A	6A	7A
BeH_2	BH_3	CH_4	NH_3	H_2O	HF

Arsine, the hydride of arsenic, has the formula AsH_x. Arsenic, the central element, is a 5A element. Therefore, its structure should be similar to NH_3 and is predicted to be AsH_3.

4-50. *Refer to Section 4-10 and the Periodic Table.*

(a) alkaline earth metals: beryllium (Be), magnesium (Mg), calcium (Ca), strontium (Sr), barium (Ba) and radium (Ra)

(b) Group 4A elements: carbon (C), silicon (Si), germanium (Ge), tin (Sn), lead (Pb) and ununquadium (Uuq)

(c) Group 2B elements: zinc (Zn), cadmium (Cd), mercury (Hg) and ununbium (Uub).

4-52. *Refer to Section 4-10, the Key Terms for Chapter 4 and Tables 4-5, 4-6 and 4-7.*

(a) Metals are the elements below and to the left of the stepwise division (metalloids) in the upper right corner of the periodic table. They possess metallic bonding. Approximately 80% of the known elements are metals, including potassium (K), calcium (Ca), scandium (Sc) and vanadium (V).

(b) Nonmetals are the elements above and to the right of the metalloids in the periodic table, including carbon (C), nitrogen (N), sulfur (S) and chlorine (Cl).

(c) The halogens, meaning "salt-formers," are the elements of Group 7A. They include fluorine (F), chlorine (Cl), bromine (Br), iodine (I) and astatine (At).

4-54. *Refer to Section 4-11 and Example 4-4.*

For electromagnetic radiation: frequency x wavelength = speed of light

$$\nu \ (s^{-1}) \ x \ \lambda \ (m) = c \ (m/s)$$

$$\nu \ (s^{-1}) = \frac{c \ (m/s)}{\lambda \ (m)}$$

(a) $\lambda \ (m) = 8973 \ \text{Å} \ x \ \dfrac{10^{-10} \ m}{1 \ \text{Å}} = 8.973 \ x \ 10^{-7} \ m$ $\qquad \nu \ (s^{-1}) = \dfrac{3.00 \ x \ 10^8 \ m/s}{8.973 \ x \ 10^{-7} \ m} = \mathbf{3.34 \ x \ 10^{14} \ s^{-1}}$

(b) $\lambda \ (m) = 442 \ nm \ x \ \dfrac{10^{-9} \ m}{1 \ nm} = 4.42 \ x \ 10^{-7} \ m$ $\qquad \nu \ (s^{-1}) = \dfrac{3.00 \ x \ 10^8 \ m/s}{4.42 \ x \ 10^{-7} \ m} = \mathbf{6.79 \ x \ 10^{14} \ s^{-1}}$

(c) $\lambda \ (m) = 4.92 \ cm \ x \ \dfrac{1 \ m}{100 \ cm} = 0.0492 \ m$ $\qquad \nu \ (s^{-1}) = \dfrac{3.00 \ x \ 10^8 \ m/s}{0.0492 \ m} = \mathbf{6.10 \ x \ 10^9 \ s^{-1}}$

(d) $\lambda \ (m) = 4.55 \ x \ 10^{-9} \ cm \ x \ \dfrac{1 \ m}{100 \ cm} = 4.55 \ x \ 10^{-11} \ m$ $\qquad \nu \ (s^{-1}) = \dfrac{3.00 \ x \ 10^8 \ m/s}{4.55 \ x \ 10^{-11} \ m} = \mathbf{6.59 \ x \ 10^{18} \ s^{-1}}$

4-56. *Refer to Section 4-11, Example 4-5, and Figure 4-14b.*

(a) $\nu \ (s^{-1}) = \dfrac{c \ (m/s)}{\lambda \ (m)} = \dfrac{3.00 \ x \ 10^8 \ m/s}{670.8 \ nm \ x \ 10^{-9} \ m/1 \ nm} = \mathbf{4.47 \ x \ 10^{14} \ s^{-1}}$

(b) $E = h\nu = (6.63 \ x \ 10^{-34} \ J{\cdot}s)(4.47 \ x \ 10^{14} \ s^{-1}) = \mathbf{2.96 \ x \ 10^{-19} \ J/photon}$

(c) From Figure 4-14b, the color corresponding to $\lambda = 670.8$ nm or 6708Å is **red**.

4-58. *Refer to Section 4-11 and Example 4-6.*

$E \ (J/photon) = \dfrac{hc}{\lambda} = \dfrac{(6.63 \ x \ 10^{-34} \ J{\cdot}s)(3.00 \ x \ 10^8 \ m/s)}{3400\text{Å} \ x \ (10^{-10} \ m/1 \ \text{Å})} = \mathbf{5.85 \ x \ 10^{-19} \ J/photon}$

$E \ (J/mol) = 5.85 \ x \ 10^{-19} \ J/photon \ x \ 6.02 \ x \ 10^{23} \ photons/mol = \mathbf{3.52 \ x \ 10^5 \ J/mol \ or \ 352 \ kJ/mol}$

4-60. *Refer to Tables 1-6 and 1-8.*

Plan: (1) Use dimensional analysis to determine how far (in miles) light travels in one year, which is a light year.

(2) Use this as a unit factor to determine the distance in miles between Alpha Centauri and our solar system.

(1) $? \text{ miles/light yr} = \dfrac{3.00 \times 10^8 \text{ m}}{1 \text{ s}} \times \dfrac{100 \text{ cm}}{1 \text{m}} \times \dfrac{1 \text{ in}}{2.54 \text{ cm}} \times \dfrac{1 \text{ ft}}{12 \text{ in}} \times \dfrac{1 \text{ mile}}{5280 \text{ ft}} \times \dfrac{60 \text{ s}}{1 \text{ min}} \times \dfrac{60 \text{ min}}{1 \text{ hr}} \times \dfrac{24 \text{ hr}}{1 \text{ day}} \times \dfrac{365 \text{ d}}{1 \text{ yr}}$

$= 5.88 \times 10^{12} \text{ miles/light yr}$

Therefore in 1 year, light will travel 5.88×10^{12} miles

(2) $? \text{ miles} = 4.3 \text{ light years} \times \dfrac{5.88 \times 10^{12} \text{ miles}}{1 \text{ light year}} = \mathbf{2.5 \times 10^{13} \text{ miles}}$

4-62. *Refer to Section 4-12.*

The photoelectric effect is the emission of an electron from a metal surface caused by impinging electromagnetic radiation. This radiation must have a certain minimum energy, i.e., its frequency must be greater than the threshold frequency, which is characteristic of a particular metal, for current to flow. If the frequency is below the threshold frequency, no current flows. As long as this criterion is met, the current increases with increasing intensity (brightness) of the light.

4-64. *Refer to Sections 4-10, 4-11 and 4-12, Figure 4-13 and Exercise 4-63.*

We know: $E = h\nu = \dfrac{hc}{\lambda}$

Therefore, $\lambda \text{ (m)} = \dfrac{hc}{E} = \dfrac{(6.63 \times 10^{-34} \text{ J·s})(3.00 \times 10^8 \text{ m/s})}{(3.89 \text{ eV})(1.60 \times 10^{-19} \text{ J/eV})} = 3.20 \times 10^{-7} \text{ m}$

$\lambda \text{ (nm)} = 3.20 \times 10^{-7} \text{ m} \times \dfrac{1 \text{ nm}}{10^{-9} \text{ m}} = \mathbf{320 \text{ nm}}$ $\mathbf{(3200 \text{ Å} = \text{ultraviolet})}$

4-66. *Refer to Section 4-13 and Figure 4-18b.*

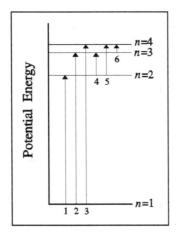

Transitions for Absorption Spectrum

1 $n = 1 \rightarrow n = 2$
2 $n = 1 \rightarrow n = 3$
3 $n = 1 \rightarrow n = 4$
4 $n = 2 \rightarrow n = 3$
5 $n = 2 \rightarrow n = 4$
6 $n = 3 \rightarrow n = 4$

The energy loss due to 1 atom emitting a photon is $E = hc/\lambda$.

The energy loss due to 1 mole of atoms each emitting a photon is $E = (hc/\lambda)N$, where N is Avogadro's Number.

Substituting, $E = \dfrac{(6.63 \times 10^{-34} \text{ J·s})(3.00 \times 10^{8} \text{ m/s})}{(5.50 \times 10^{3} \text{ Å})(1 \times 10^{-10} \text{ m/Å})} \times 6.02 \times 10^{23} \text{ mol}^{-1} = 2.18 \times 10^{5} \text{ J/mol} = \textbf{218 kJ/mol}$

4-70.   *Refer to Section 4-13.*

Using the equations, $E = h\nu$ and $c = \lambda\nu$, we can qualitatively deduce the relationships between the energies of photons, E, their wavelengths, λ, and frequency, ν. Consider the diagram at the right, drawn not entirely to scale.

(a) The photon with the smallest energy is produced by an electron in the $n = 7$ major energy level falling to the $n = 2$ major energy level. This photon therefore also has the smallest frequency since $E \propto \nu$ and the longest wavelength since $\nu \propto 1/\lambda$.

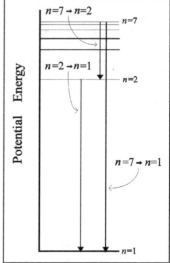

(b) The photon with the highest frequency is produced by the transition, $n = 7 \rightarrow n = 1$, since this transition involves the release of the most energy ($\nu \propto E$)

(c) The photon with the shortest wavelength also has the highest frequency ($\lambda \propto 1/\nu$) and releases the most energy. It is produced by an electron in the $n = 7$ major energy level falling to the $n = 1$ major energy level.

(d) Plan: (1) Use the Rydberg equation, $\dfrac{1}{\lambda} = R\left(\dfrac{1}{n_1^2} - \dfrac{1}{n_2^2}\right)$ where $R = 1.097 \times 10^7$ m^{-1} to evaluate $\dfrac{1}{\lambda}$.

   (2) Solve for λ and ν.

(1) $\dfrac{1}{\lambda} = 1.097 \times 10^7 \text{ m}^{-1}\left(\dfrac{1}{1^2} - \dfrac{1}{6^2}\right) = (1.097 \times 10^7 \text{ m}^{-1})(0.9722) = 1.067 \times 10^7 \text{ m}^{-1}$

(2) $\lambda = 9.376 \times 10^{-8}$ m   and $\nu = \dfrac{c}{\lambda} = \dfrac{3.00 \times 10^8 \text{ m/s}}{9.376 \times 10^{-8} \text{ m}} = \textbf{3.20} \times \textbf{10}^{\textbf{15}} \textbf{ s}^{-1}$

4-72.   *Refer to Section 4-13 and Figure 4-17.*

(a) lithium $\lambda = 4603$ Å   **blue**

(b) neon $\lambda = 540.0$ nm or 5400 Å   **greenish-yellow**

(c) calcium $\lambda = 6573$ Å   **red**

(d) potassium $\nu = 3.90 \times 10^{14}$ s^{-1} **red/infrared**

4-74.   *Refer to Section 4-13.*

The energy emitted by 1 photon is $E = hc/\lambda$. The energy emitted by n photons is $E = (hc/\lambda)n$.

The energy emitted by this laser in 2 seconds is

$$E = \text{power} \times \text{time} = 515 \text{ milliwatts} \times \frac{1 \text{ watt}}{1000 \text{ milliwatts}} \times \frac{1 \text{ J/s}}{1 \text{ watt}} \times 2.00 \text{ s} = 1.03 \text{ J}$$

Substituting,

$$1.03 \text{ J} = \frac{(6.63 \times 10^{-34} \text{ J}\cdot\text{s})(3.00 \times 10^8 \text{ m/s})}{(488.0 \text{ nm})(10^{-9} \text{ m/nm})} \times n$$

$n = 2.53 \times 10^{18}$ **photons**

4-76. *Refer to Section 4-14, Example 4-7 and Figure 5-1.*

(a) The de Broglie wavelength is given by $\lambda \text{ (m)} = \frac{h(\text{J}\cdot\text{s})}{m(\text{kg})v(\text{m/s})}$ where h is Planck's constant, v is velocity

The units are as stated because $1 \text{ J} = 1 \text{ kg}\cdot\text{m}^2/\text{s}^2$.
The mass of a proton is $1.67 \times 10^{-24} \text{ g} \times 1 \text{ kg}/1000 \text{ g} = 1.67 \times 10^{-27} \text{ kg}$.
The velocity of the proton, $v = 2.50 \times 10^7 \text{ m/s}$ (1/12 of the speed of light)

Substituting,

$$\lambda = \frac{h}{mv} = \frac{6.63 \times 10^{-34} \text{ J}\cdot\text{s}}{(1.67 \times 10^{-27} \text{ kg})(2.50 \times 10^7 \text{ m/s})} = 1.59 \times 10^{-14} \text{ m}$$

(b) For the stone, mass (kg) = 30.0 g $\times$ 1 kg/1000 g = 0.0300 kg

$$v \text{ (m/s)} = \frac{2.00 \times 10^5 \text{ m}}{1 \text{ h}} \times \frac{1 \text{ h}}{60 \text{ min}} \times \frac{1 \text{ min}}{60 \text{ s}} = 55.6 \text{ m/s}$$

$$\lambda = \frac{h}{mv} = \frac{6.63 \times 10^{-34} \text{ J}\cdot\text{s}}{(0.0300 \text{ kg})(55.6 \text{ m/s})} = 3.97 \times 10^{-34} \text{ m}$$

(c) Radii of atoms range from 0.4 Å (4×10^{-11} m) to 3 Å (3×10^{-10} m).

The wavelength of a proton, calculated in (a), is 4 orders of magnitude smaller than the radius of a typical atom.

The wavelength of a 30 g stone is much smaller by 24 orders of magnitude than a typical atom's radius.

4-78. *Refer to Section 4-14.*

Plan: (1) Calculate the mass (M) of an alpha particle (He nucleus, He^{2+}) in kilograms.

(2) Calculate the velocity (v) from $\lambda = \frac{h}{mv}$ (Note: $1 \text{ J} = 1 \text{ kg}\cdot\text{m}^2/\text{s}^2$)

(1) M = 4.003 g/mol He^{2+} $\times \dfrac{1 \text{ mol He}^{2+}}{6.02 \times 10^{23} \text{ He}^{2+} \text{ ions}} \times \dfrac{1 \text{ kg}}{10^3 \text{ g}}$

$= 6.65 \times 10^{-27}$ kg/He^{2+} ion

(2) $v = \dfrac{h}{m\lambda} = \dfrac{6.63 \times 10^{-34} \text{ J}\cdot\text{s}}{(6.65 \times 10^{-27} \text{ kg})(0.529 \text{ Å})(1 \times 10^{-10} \text{ m/Å})}$

$= \dfrac{6.63 \times 10^{-34} \text{ kg}\cdot\text{m}^2/\text{s}^2\cdot\text{s}}{(6.65 \times 10^{-27} \text{ kg})(5.29 \times 10^{-11} \text{ m})}$

$= 1.88 \times 10^3$ **m/s**

The angular momentum quantum number, ℓ, for a particular energy level as defined by the principle quantum number, n, depends on the value of n. ℓ can take integral values from 0 up to and including $(n - 1)$.

For example, when $n = 3$, $\ell = 0$, 1, or 2.

An orbital described by $n = 3$, $\ell = 1$, $m_\ell = -1$, and $m_s = -1/2$ is a **3p orbital**. See Figures 4-24 and 4-25 for illustrations.

The maximum number of electrons as designated by sets of quantum numbers:

(a) 6 electrons since quantum numbers $n = 3$ and $\ell = 1$ represent the 3p subshell with 3 orbitals.

(b) 10 electrons since $n = 3$ and $\ell = 2$ represent the 3d subshell with 5 orbitals.

(c) 0 electrons since it is impossible that $\ell = 0$ and $m_\ell = -1$. For an s orbital ($\ell = 0$), m_ℓ can only have a value of 0.

(d) 2 electrons since $n = 3$, $\ell = 1$ and $m_\ell = -1$ represent one of the 3p orbitals.

(e) 1 electron since $n = 3$, $\ell = 1$, $m_\ell = 0$ and $m_s = -1/2$ represent one of the electrons in a 3p orbital.

(a) There are **3** energy sublevels in the third major energy level, $n = 3$, corresponding to $\ell = 0$, 1, and 2.

(b) Both $\ell = 1$ and $\ell = 2$ have sets of equivalent orbitals. The $\ell = 1$ (3p) energy sublevel has 3 equivalent orbitals and the $\ell = 2$ (3d) energy sublevel has 5 equivalent orbitals.

(c) Illustrations of these orbitals can be found in Figures 4-23, 4-25, 4-26 and 4-28.

There are 9 individual orbitals in the third shell, $n = 3$

n	ℓ	m_ℓ	orbital
3	0	0	3s
3	1	−1	3p
3	1	0	3p
3	1	1	3p
3	2	−2	3d
3	2	−1	3d
3	2	0	3d
3	2	+1	3d
3	2	+2	3d

(a) $m_\ell = -1, 0, +1$ for the p energy sublevel

(b) $m_\ell = -3, -2, -1, 0, +1, +2, +3$ for the f energy sublevel

(c) $n = 3$ $\ell = 0$, so $m_\ell = 0$

   $\ell = 1$, so $m_\ell = -1, 0, +1$

   $\ell = 2$, so $m_\ell = -2, -1, 0, +1, +2$

	Designation	Number of Orbitals		Designation	Number of Orbitals
(a)	$3p$	3	(e)	$5d$	5
(b)	$4p$	3	(f)	$5f$	7
(c)	$4p_x$	1	(g)	$n = 5$	25
(d)	$6d$	5	(h)	$7s$	1

(a) A $1s$ and a $2s$ orbital, like all s orbitals, can be described as *spherically symmetrical*, i.e., round like a ball. A $2s$ orbital is larger than a $1s$ orbital and has a node.

(b) A $3p_x$ orbital resembles an equal-arm dumbbell centered on the nucleus and lying along the x-axis, whereas a $2p_y$ orbital resembles an equal-arm dumbbell as well centered on the nucleus but lying along the y-axis. They are both shaped the same. The $3p$ orbital is larger than the $2p$ orbital and they lie along different axes.

	1s	2s	2p	3s	3p	3d	4s	4p
(a) $_{15}$P	↑↓	↑↓	↑↓ ↑↓ ↑↓	↑↓	↑ ↑ ↑			
(b) $_{28}$Ni	↑↓	↑↓	↑↓ ↑↓ ↑↓	↑↓	↑↓ ↑↓ ↑↓	↑↓ ↑↓ ↑↓ ↑ ↑	↑↓	
(c) $_{31}$Ga	↑↓	↑↓	↑↓ ↑↓ ↑↓	↑↓	↑↓ ↑↓ ↑↓	↑↓ ↑↓ ↑↓ ↑↓ ↑↓	↑↓	↑ _ _
(d) $_{48}$Cd	↑↓	↑↓	↑↓ ↑↓ ↑↓	↑↓	↑↓ ↑↓ ↑↓	↑↓ ↑↓ ↑↓ ↑↓ ↑↓	↑↓	↑↓ ↑↓ ↑↓

4d	4f	5s
↑↓ ↑↓ ↑↓ ↑↓ ↑↓	_ _ _ _ _ _ _	↑↓

(a) The ground state for Si was incorrect because the $3s$ electrons should have been paired up. The corrected electronic configuration is below.

61

(b) Ni is not an exception to the filling rule, so the 4s electrons should be paired, with two unpaired electrons in the $3d$ energy level. See below for the corrected electronic configuration.

(c) For S, Hund's Rule must be obeyed. The electrons should fill up the $3p$ energy level singly before pairing begins. See below.

	1s	2s	2p	3s	3p	3d	4s	4p
(a) $_{14}$Si	↑↓	↑↓	↑↓ ↑↓ ↑↓	↑↓	↑ ↑ _			
(b) $_{28}$Ni	↑↓	↑↓	↑↓ ↑↓ ↑↓	↑↓	↑↓ ↑↓ ↑↓	↑↓ ↑↓ ↑↓ ↑ ↑	↑↓	
(c) $_{16}$S	↑↓	↑↓	↑↓ ↑↓ ↑↓	↑↓	↑↓ ↑ ↑			

4-100.   Refer to Section 4-18 and Appendix B.

From the information given, we can deduce the following ground state configuration:

$$1s^2\,2s^2\,2p^6\,3s^2\,3p^6\,4s^2.$$

(a) The element has 20 electrons. Because it is neutral, there must be 20 protons. So, the element has atomic number 20 and is calcium, Ca.

(b) The element appears in Period 4.

(c) The element appears in Group 2A.

(d) Calcium has a total of 8 s electrons.

(e) Calcium has a total of 12 p electrons.

(f) Calcium has no d electrons.

4-102.   Refer to Sections 4-18 and 4-19, and Appendix B.

The first five elements that have an unpaired electron in an s orbital are: $_1$H, $_3$Li, $_{11}$Na, $_{19}$K and $_{24}$Cr.
All but $_{24}$Cr can be found in Group 1A.

4-104.   Refer to Section 4-18, Figure 4-32 and Appendix B.

(a) 1 outer electron in the first shell: H

(b) 3 outer electrons in the second shell: B

(c) 3 outer electrons in the third shell: Al

(d) 2 outer electrons in the seventh shell: Ra, Ac, Th, Pa, U, Np, Pu, Am, Cm, Bk, Cf, Es, Fm, Md, No, Lr, Rf, Db, Sg, Bh, Hs, Mt

(e) 4 outer electrons in the third shell: Si

(f) 8 outer electrons in the fifth shell: Xe

4-106.   Refer to Sections 4-18 and 4-19, and Exercise 4-96.

(a) $_{15}$P $1s^22s^22p^63s^23p^3$ or $[Ne]3s^23p^3$

(b) $_{28}$Ni $1s^22s^22p^63s^23p^63d^84s^2$ or $[Ar]3d^84s^2$

(c) $_{31}$Ga $1s^22s^22p^63s^23p^63d^{10}4s^24p^1$ or $[Ar]3d^{10}4s^24p^1$

(d) $_{48}$Cd $1s^22s^22p^63s^23p^63d^{10}4s^24p^64d^{10}4f^05s^2$ or $[Kr]4d^{10}5s^2$

4-108.   Refer to Sections 4-18 and 4-19.

Hund's Rule states that electrons in the ground state must occupy all the orbitals of a given subshell singly before pairing begins. These unpaired electrons have parallel spins.

The electron configurations that violate Hund's Rule are

(b) $1s^22s^22p_x^2$. The second electron in $2p_x$ should have occupied other $2p$ orbitals before pairing.

(d) $1s^22s^12p_x^12p_z^1$. There should be 2 electrons in the $2s$ orbital before moving on to the $2p$ orbitals.

(e) $1s^22s^12p_x^22p_y^12p_z^1$. There should be 2 electrons in the $2s$ orbital before moving on to the $2p$ orbitals. The $2p$ orbitals were filled properly, according to Hund's Rule.

4-110.   Refer to Sections 4-19 and 4-20.

The paramagnetic elements with atomic numbers of 11 or less include: H, Li, B, C, N, O, F and Na.

4-112.   Refer to Sections 4-18 and 4-19, and Apprendix B.

$_{29}$Cu	$1s^22s^22p^63s^23p^63d^{10}4s^1$	or	$[Ar]3d^{10}4s^1$
$_8$O	$1s^22s^22p^4$	or	$[He]2s^22p^4$
$_{57}$La	$1s^22s^22p^63s^23p^63d^{10}4s^24p^64d^{10}5s^25p^65d^16s^2$	or	$[Xe]5d^16s^2$
$_{39}$Y	$1s^22s^22p^63s^23p^63d^{10}4s^24p^64d^15s^2$	or	$[Kr]4d^15s^2$
$_{56}$Ba	$1s^22s^22p^63s^23p^63d^{10}4s^24p^64d^{10}5s^25p^66s^2$	or	$[Xe]6s^2$
$_{81}$Tl	$1s^22s^22p^63s^23p^63d^{10}4s^24p^64d^{10}4f^{14}5s^25p^65d^{10}6s^26p^1$	or	$[Xe]4f^{14}5d^{10}6s^26p^1$
$_{83}$Bi	$1s^22s^22p^63s^23p^63d^{10}4s^24p^64d^{10}4f^{14}5s^25p^65d^{10}6s^26p^3$	or	$[Xe]4f^{14}5d^{10}6s^26p^3$

4-114.   Refer to Sections 4-18 and 4-19, and Appendix B.

(a) $_{33}$As

(b) $_{83}$Bi

(c) $_{102}$No

(d) $_{43}$Tc

(e) $_{22}$Ti

			Number of Electrons		
			s	p	d
(a)	$_{15}$P	$1s^22s^22p^63s^23p^3$	6	9	0
(b)	$_{36}$Kr	$1s^22s^22p^63s^23p^63d^{10}4s^24p^6$	8	18	10
(c)	$_{28}$Ni	$1s^22s^22p^63s^23p^63d^84s^2$	8	12	8
(d)	$_{30}$Zn	$1s^22s^22p^63s^23p^63d^{10}4s^2$	8	12	10
(e)	$_{22}$Ti	$1s^22s^22p^63s^23p^63d^24s^2$	8	12	2

4-118. *Refer to Sections 4-16, 4-17 and 4-18, and Example 4-8.*

(a) $_{11}$Na $1s^22s^22p^63s^1$

Electron	n	ℓ	m_ℓ	m_s
1	1	0	0	+1/2
2	1	0	0	−1/2
3	2	0	0	+1/2
4	2	0	0	−1/2
5	2	1	−1	+1/2
6	2	1	0	+1/2
7	2	1	+1	+1/2
8	2	1	−1	−1/2
9	2	1	0	−1/2
10	2	1	+1	−1/2
11	3	0	0	+1/2

(b) $_8$O $1s^22s^22p^4$

Electron	n	ℓ	m_ℓ	m_s
1	1	0	0	+1/2
2	1	0	0	−1/2
3	2	0	0	+1/2
4	2	0	0	−1/2
5	2	1	−1	+1/2
6	2	1	0	+1/2
7	2	1	+1	+1/2
8	2	1	−1	−1/2

(c) $_{20}$Ca $1s^22s^22p^63s^23p^64s^2$

Electron	n	ℓ	m_ℓ	m_s
1	1	0	0	+1/2
2	1	0	0	−1/2
3	2	0	0	+1/2
4	2	0	0	−1/2
5	2	1	−1	+1/2
6	2	1	0	+1/2
7	2	1	+1	+1/2
8	2	1	−1	−1/2
9	2	1	0	−1/2
10	2	1	+1	−1/2
11	3	0	0	+1/2
12	3	0	0	−1/2
13	3	1	−1	+1/2
14	3	1	0	+1/2
15	3	1	+1	+1/2
16	3	1	−1	−1/2
17	3	1	0	−1/2
18	3	1	+1	−1/2
19	4	0	0	+1/2
20	4	0	0	−1/2

4-120. *Refer to Sections 4-18 and 4-19.*

	ns	*np*		*ns*	*np*
1A	↑	_ _ _	5A	↑↓	↑ ↑ ↑
2A	↑↓	_ _ _	6A	↑↓	↑↓ ↑ ↑
3A	↑↓	↑ _ _	7A	↑↓	↑↓ ↑↓ ↑
4A	↑↓	↑ ↑ _	8A	↑↓	↑↓ ↑↓ ↑↓

4-122. *Refer to Sections 4-16 and 4-18, Example 4-8, Table 4-8 and Appendix B.*

(a) $_{14}Si$ $[Ne]3s^23p^2$

The highest energy or "last" electron entered a $3p$ orbital.
Therefore, $n = 3$, $\ell = 1$, and $m_\ell = -1, 0$ or $+1$.

(b) $_{89}Ac$ $[Rn]7s^26d^1$

The highest energy or "last" electron went into a $6d$ orbital.
Therefore, $n = 6$, $\ell = 2$, and $m_\ell = -2, -1, 0, +1,$ or $+2$.

(c) $_{17}Cl$ $[Ne]3s^23p^5$

The highest energy or "last" electron entered a $3p$ orbital.
Therefore, $n = 3$, $\ell = 1$, and $m_\ell = -1, 0$ or $+1$.

(d) $_{59}Pr$ $[Kr]4d^{10}4f^35s^25p^66s^2$

The highest energy or "last" electron entered a $4f$ orbital.
Therefore, $n = 4$, $\ell = 3$, and $m_\ell = -3, -2, -1, 0, +1, +2$ or $+3$.

4-124. *Refer to Sections 4-18 and 4-19, and Appendix B.*

$A \equiv {_{29}}Cu$ $1s^22s^22p^63s^23p^63d^{10}4s^1$

$B \equiv {_{40}}Zr$ $1s^22s^22p^63s^23p^63d^{10}4s^24p^64d^25s^2$

$C \equiv {_{54}}Xe$ $1s^22s^22p^63s^23p^63d^{10}4s^24p^64d^{10}5s^25p^6$

$D \equiv {_{83}}Bi$ $1s^22s^22p^63s^23p^63d^{10}4s^24p^64d^{10}4f^{14}5s^25p^65d^{10}6s^26p^3$

$E \equiv {_{4}}Be$ $1s^22s^2$

4-126. *Refer to Sections 4-18 and 4-19, Example 4-11 and Appendix B.*

Given below are the shorthand notations and number of unpaired electrons for the elements in their ground states.

	Shorthand	**Unpaired Electrons**
$_{11}Na$	$[Ne]3s^1$	1
$_{10}Ne$	$1s^22s^22p^6$	0
$_{13}Al$	$1s^22s^22p^63s^23p^1$	1
$_{4}Be$	$1s^22s^2$	0
$_{35}Br$	$[Ar]3d^{10}4s^24p^5$	1
$_{33}As$	$[Ar]\,3d^{10}4s^24p^3$	3
$_{22}Ti$	$[Ar]3d^24s^2$	2

4-128. *Refer to Sections 4-18, 4-19 and 4-20, and Appendix B.*

An element is paramagnetic if it has any unpaired electrons. Given below are the shorthand notations and number of unpaired electrons present for the elements and ions in their ground states.

		Shorthand	**Unpaired Electrons**	**Paramagnetic**
(a)	$_{35}Br$	$[Ar]3d^{10}4s^24p^5$	1	yes
(b)	$_{36}Kr$	$1s^22s^22p^63s^23p^63d^{10}4s^24p^6$	0	no
(c)	$_{10}Ne^+$	$1s^22s^22p^5$	1	yes
(d)	$_{26}Fe$	$[Ar]3d^64s^2$	4	yes
(e)	$_{35}Br^-$	$[Ar]3d^{10}4s^24p^6$ or $[Kr]$	0	no

4-130. *Refer to Section 4-9.*

The atomic mass of chlorine is reported as 35.5 to three significant figures. No single atom of chlorine has that mass because the atomic mass of any element is the weighted average of all the isotopes, not the mass of any one atom. Chlorine is ~76% ^{35}Cl and ~24% ^{37}Cl.

4-132. *Refer to Section 4-4.*

$$? \text{ diameter of atom} = 9.39 \text{ in.} \times 100{,}000 \times \frac{1 \text{ ft}}{12 \text{ in.}} \times \frac{1 \text{ mile}}{5280 \text{ ft}} = \textbf{14.8 miles}$$

4-134. *Refer to Section 4-16, and Figures 4-22, 4-23, 4-25 and 4-26.*

(a) $3p_x$ (Figure 4-25)

(b) $2s$ (Figures 4-22 and 4-23)

(c) $3d_{xy}$ (Figure 4-26)

(d) $3d_{z^2}$ (Figure 4-26)

4-136. *Refer to Section 4-16 and 4-18.*

An atom in its ground state containing 18 electrons (argon) has three s ($\ell = 0$) orbitals: $1s$, $2s$ and $3s$. These 3 orbitals hold 2 electrons each for a total of **6 electrons**.

4-138. *Refer to Section 4-18.*

For $_3Li$

(a) ground state: $1s^22s^1$

(b) excited state: $1s^22p^1$ or $1s^12s^2$

(c) forbidden or impossible state: $1s^3$

4-140. *Refer to Section 4-18.*

(a) A ground state hydrogen atom has its one electron in the lowest energy level. Every atom has an infinite number of orbitals, but only some are occupied by electrons.

(b) A lithium atom in its ground state has three electrons, two is the $1s$ sublevel and one in the $2s$ sublevel.

(c) The angular momentum quantum number, ℓ, of an electron in a p sublevel has a value of 1.

(d) Three electrons in a p sublevel will occupy separate orbitals, so one has an m_ℓ value of -1, one has an m_ℓ value of 0 and one has an m_ℓ value of $+1$.

(e) Two electrons in the same orbital must have opposite spins.

4-142. *Refer to Section 4-8.*

(a),(b) There are four different HCl molecules which can be formed from the naturally-occurring hydrogen and chlorine isotopes:

Molecules	$^1H^{35}Cl$	$^1H^{37}Cl$	$^2H^{35}Cl$	$^2H^{37}Cl$
Approximate Masses	36 amu	38 amu	37 amu	39 amu

(c) From the relative abundance of the isotopes, the expected abundances of the molecules are in the following decreasing order:

$$^1H^{35}Cl > {}^1H^{37}Cl > {}^2H^{35}Cl > {}^2H^{37}Cl$$

4-144. *Refer to Section 4-13 and Example 4-6.*

Plan: (1) Use $E = hc/\lambda$ to calculate the energy of the photon emitted by an excited sodium atom in joules.
(2) Convert energy (J) to mass (kg) using Einstein's equation, $E = mc^2$, where $1\ J = 1\ kg\cdot m^2/s^2$.

(1) $\lambda = 589\ nm = 589 \times 10^{-9}\ m = 5.89 \times 10^{-7}\ m$

$$E\ \text{per photon} = \frac{(6.63 \times 10^{-34}\ J\cdot s)(3.00 \times 10^8\ m/s)}{(5.89 \times 10^{-7}\ m)} = 3.38 \times 10^{-19}\ \text{J/photon}$$

(2) ? mass of one photon (kg) $= \dfrac{E}{c^2} = \dfrac{3.38 \times 10^{-19}\ J}{(3.00 \times 10^8\ m/s)^2} = \mathbf{3.76 \times 10^{-36}\ kg}$

4-146. *Refer to Section 4-13 and Example 4-6.*

Plan: (1) Use $E = hc/\lambda$ to calculate the energy loss in J/atom of barium
(2) Convert J/atom into kJ/mol

(1) $\lambda = 554\ nm = 554 \times 10^{-9}\ m = 5.54 \times 10^{-7}\ m$

$$E\ \text{lost per atom} = \frac{(6.63 \times 10^{-34}\ J\cdot s)(3.00 \times 10^8\ m/s)}{(5.54 \times 10^{-7}\ m)} = 3.59 \times 10^{-19}\ \text{J/atom}$$

(2) ? kJ/mol Ba atoms $= 3.59 \times 10^{-19}\ \text{J/atom} \times \dfrac{6.02 \times 10^{23}\ \text{atoms}}{1\ \text{mol}} \times \dfrac{1\ kJ}{1000\ J} = \mathbf{216\ kJ/mol}$

4-148. *Refer to Section 4-13.*

We know: $c\ (m/s) = \lambda\ (m) \times \nu\ (s^{-1})$. Since $\nu = 89.5\ MHz = 8.95 \times 10^7\ s^{-1}$ and $c = 3.00 \times 10^8\ m/s$

$$\lambda\ (m) = \frac{c\ (m/s)}{\nu\ (s^{-1})} = \frac{3.00 \times 10^8\ m/s}{8.95 \times 10^7\ s^{-1}} = \mathbf{3.35\ m}$$

(a) ? electrons per 1 mol N_2 molecules $= \dfrac{7 \text{ electrons}}{1 \text{ atom N}} \times \dfrac{2 \text{ atoms N}}{1 \text{molecule } N_2} \times \dfrac{6.02 \times 10^{23} \text{ molecules } N_2}{1 \text{ mol } N_2 \text{ molecules}}$

$$= \mathbf{8.43 \times 10^{24} \text{ electrons/mol } N_2}$$

(b) ? electrons $= 30.0 \text{ g } H_2O \times \dfrac{1 \text{ mol } H_2O}{18.0 \text{ g } H_2O} \times \dfrac{6.02 \times 10^{23} \text{ molecules } H_2O}{1 \text{ mol } H_2O} \times \dfrac{10 \text{ electrons}}{1 \text{ molecule } H_2O}$

$$= \mathbf{1.00 \times 10^{25} \text{ electrons}}$$

Note: there are 10 electrons in an H_2O molecule because there is 1 electron per hydrogen atom and 8 electrons in an oxygen atom, for a total of 10 electrons.

5 Chemical Periodicity

5-2. *Refer to Section 5-1*

The general order in which the shells are filled starting with the $n = 3$ shell is:

$$3s \quad 3p \quad 4s \quad 3d \quad 4p \text{ etc.}$$

Period 3 includes the elements whose outer electrons are in $3s$ or $3p$ subshells. The maximum number of electrons in these subshells is a total of 8. Hence Period 3 contains only 8 elements. Since the $3d$ subshell is higher in energy than the $4s$ subshell, it is not going to be filled until Period 4.

5-4. *Refer to Section 5-1 and Table 4-5.*

The atomic number of the yet-to-be discovered alkali metal in period 8 is 119. The last portion of its electron configuration after [Rn] (atomic number = 86) should be:

$7s^2 \, 5f^{14} \, 6d^{10} \, 7p^6 \, 8s^1$ (in order of increasing energy) or $5f^{14} \, 6d^{10} \, 7s^2 \, 7p^6 \, 8s^1$ (in order of distance from the nucleus)

5-6. *Refer to Section 5-1.*

(a) ns^2np^5 Group 7A (halogens)

(b) ns^1 Group 1A (alkali metals)

(c) $ns^2(n-1)d^{1-10}$ d-transition elements

(d) ns^2np^1 Group 3A

5-8. *Refer to Section 5-1 and Appendix B.*

(a) alkali metals	B	(h) actinides	D
(b) outer configuration of d^7s^2	H	(i) d-transition elements	E, H, K
(c) lanthanides	A	(j) noble gases	G
(d) p-block representative elements	C, F, G, I	(k) alkaline earth elements	J
(e) partially filled f-subshells	A		
(f) halogens	I		
(g) s-block representative elements	B, J		

5-10. *Refer to Section 5-5 and the Key Terms for Chapter 5.*

(a) The ions most likely to be formed are Cs^+ and Se^{2-}, because

(b) Cs^+ and Se^{2-} have noble gas configurations and the others do not. When ions have the same total number of electrons as a noble gas, i.e. they are isoelectronic with a noble gas and are more likely to be stable.

Electrons that are in filled sets of orbitals between the nucleus and outer shell electrons shield the outer shell electrons partially from the effect of the protons in the nucleus; this effect is called nuclear shielding.

As we move from left to right along a period, the outer shell electrons do experience a progressively stronger force of attraction to the nucleus due to the combination of an increase in the number of protons and a constant nuclear shielding by inner electrons. As a result the atomic radii decrease.

As we move down a group, the outer electrons are partially shielded from the attractive force of the nucleus by an increasing number of inner electrons. This effect is *partially* responsible for the observed increase in atomic radii going down a group.

Consider the element with atomic number 116 in Group 6A. Even though it has not been isolated, its atomic radius is expected to be somewhat larger than that of Po (1.68 Å), probably about 1.9 - 2.0 Å, since it lies just below Po on the periodic table. Its outer electrons would lie in the $n=7$ shell, which would be further away from the nucleus than Po's outermost electrons in the $n=6$ shell.

Atomic radii increase from top to bottom within a group and from right to left within a period. Therefore, in order of increasing size, we have:

(a) Be < Mg < Ca < Sr < Ba < Ra

(b) He < Ne < Ar < Kr < Xe < Rn

(c) Ar < Cl < S < P < Si < Al < Mg < Na

(d) C < Si < Sn < Pb

(a) The first ionization energy, IE_1, also called the first ionization potential, is the minimum amount of energy required to remove the most loosely bound electron from an isolated gaseous atom to form an ion with a 1+ charge.

$$X(g) + IE_1 \rightarrow X^+(g) + e^-$$

(b) The second ionization energy, IE_2, is the amount of energy required to remove a second electron from an isolated gaseous singly charged cation; i.e. to remove an electron from an ion with a 1+ charge to give an ion with a 2+ charge.

$$X^+(g) + IE_2 \rightarrow X^{2+}(g) + e^-$$

As we move down a given group, the valence electrons are further and further away from the nucleus. The first ionization energies of the elements, which is the energy required to remove an electron from an isolated gaseous atom, decrease while the atomic radii increase.

Likewise, from left to right across a period, the forces of attraction between the outermost electron and the nucleus increase. Therefore the ionization energies increase while the atomic radii decrease. Refer to Figure 5-2 for the exceptions to the general trends for ionization energy.

Electrons that are in filled sets of orbitals between the nucleus and outer shell electrons shield the outer shell electrons partially from the effect of the protons in the nucleus; this effect is called nuclear shielding. This shielding causes the effective nuclear charge, Z_{eff}, felt by the outer electrons for the positively charged nucleus to be less than the actual nuclear charge. Z_{eff} increases going from left to right across a period, because the nuclear charge is increasing. The increase in effective nuclear charge causes the outermost electrons to be held more tightly making them harder to remove. Therefore, the first ionization energies generally increase from left to right across the periodic table.

5-24. *Refer to Section 5-3, Table 5-1, Figure 5-2 and Example 5-2.*

First ionization energies increase from left to right and bottom to top in the periodic table. However, there are exceptions: elements of Group 3A generally have lower first ionization energies than elements of Group 2A, and elements of Group 6A generally have lower first ionization energies than elements of Group 5A because it is easier to remove a unpaired electron than a paired electron from an orbital. Therefore, we obtain the following orders of increasing first ionization energies:

(a) $Fr < Cs < Rb < K < Na < Li$

(b) $At < I < Br < Cl < F$

(c) $Li < B < Be < C < O < N < F < Ne$

(d) $Cs < Ga < B < Br < H < F$

5-26. *Refer to Section 5-3 and Exercise 5-24 Solution.*

As we move from left to right across Period 2 of the periodic table, there is an increase in effective nuclear charge and a decrease in atomic radii. Outer valence electrons are held more tightly and first ionization energies *generally* increase. Therefore, as the atomic radii decrease, the first ionization energies increase. Refer to Figure 5-2 for the exceptions to the general trend for ionization energy.

5-28. *Refer to Section 5-3.*

It is difficult to prepare compounds containing Li^{2+} due to the immense amount of energy that is required to remove a second electron from an ion of lithium, i.e., there is a very large amount of energy (the second ionization energy) required for this reaction:

$$Li^+(g) + 7298 \text{ kJ/mol} \rightarrow Li^{2+}(g) + e^-$$

This energy is not likely to be repaid during compound formation. The reason for such a high second ionization energy for lithium is because the electron configuration of Li^+ is $1s^2$ which has a filled s orbital. It is the special stability of the filled s orbital which prevents the formation of Li^{2+} ions. Also, the formation of Li^{2+} requires 14 times more energy than the formation of Li^+ and so is much less likely.

On the other hand, Be^{2+} has the very stable electron configuration of $1s^2$, isoelectronic with the noble gas, He. Compounds with Be^{2+} ions are to be expected.

5-30. *Refer to Section 5-4, Figure 5-3, Table 5-2, and Example 5-3.*

The electron affinity of an element is defined as the amount of energy absorbed when an electron is added to an isolated gaseous atom to form an ion with a 1– charge.

In general, electron affinities become more negative from bottom to top and from left to right in the periodic table, but there are many exceptions. According to Table 5-2, the order of increasing negative values of electron affinity is:

(least negative EA)   P < S < Br < Cl   (most negative EA)

5-32. **_Refer to Section 5-4._**

Elements that gain electrons easily to form negative ions have very negative electron affinities. The halogens, with electronic configurations of $ns^2\,np^5$, easily gain one electron to form stable ions with a filled set of p orbitals. These ions are isoelectronic with the noble gases and have noble gas electronic configurations, $ns^2\,np^6$. Therefore, the halogens have the most negative electron affinities. This does not occur when a Group 6A element gains an electron.

5-34. **_Refer to Section 5-4 and Table 5-2._**

		Electronic Configuration			
(a)	$O(g) + e^- \rightarrow O^-(g) + 141$ kJ/mol	O	$1s^2\,2s^2\,2p^4$	O^-	$1s^2\,2s^2\,2p^5$
(b)	$Cl(g) + e^- \rightarrow Cl^-(g) + 349$ kJ/mol	Cl	$[\text{Ne}]\,3s^2\,3p^5$	Cl^-	$[\text{Ar}]$
(c)	$Mg(g) + e^- + {\sim}0$ kJ/mol $\rightarrow Mg^-(g)$	Mg	$[\text{Ne}]\,3s^2$	Mg^-	$[\text{Ne}]\,3s^2\,3p^1$

5-36. **_Refer to Section 5-5, Figure 5-4 and Example 5-4._**

(a) Within an isoelectronic series, ionic radii increase with decreasing atomic number. Therefore, in order of increasing ionic radii, we have

$$Ga^{3+} < Ca^{2+} < K^+$$

(b) Ionic radii increase down a group. So, $Be^{2+} < Mg^{2+} < Ca^{2+} < Ba^{2+}$

(c) $Al^{3+} < Sr^{2+} < K^+ < Rb^+$ (See Figure 5-4)

(d) $Ca^{2+} < K^+ < Rb^+$ (See Figure 5-4)

5-38. **_Refer to Section 5-5, Figure 5-4, and Example 5-4._**

(a) In an isoelectronic series, ionic radii increase with decreasing atomic number because of decreasing nuclear charge. Therefore, in order of increasing ionic radii, we have

$$Cl^- < S^{2-} < P^{3-}$$

(b) Ionic radii increase down a group. So, $O^{2-} < S^{2-} < Se^{2-}$

(c) $S^{2-} < N^{3-} < Br^-$ and $S^{2-} < N^{3-} < P^{3-}$ but we don't know the size relationship between P^{3-} and Br^-. (See Figure 5-4)

(d) Ionic radii increase down a group. So, $Cl^- < Br^- < I^-$

The Fe^{2+} ion has 26 protons pulling on 24 electrons, whereas the Fe^{3+} ion has 26 protons pulling on 23 electrons. The electrons in the Fe^{3+} ion are more tightly held and therefore, Fe^{3+} is the smaller ion.

Likewise, the Sn^{2+} ion has 50 protons pulling on 48 electrons, whereas the Sn^{4+} ion has 50 protons attracting 46 electrons. The electrons in the Sn^{4+} ion are more tightly held and therefore, Sn^{4+} is the smaller ion.

5-42.   *Refer to Section 5-6, Table 5-3 and Example 5-5.*

Electronegativities usually increase from left to right across periods and from bottom to top within groups. Exceptions are explained in Section 5-6.

(a) Pb < Sn < Ge < C   (b) Na < Mg < S < Cl   (c) Bi < Sb < P < N   (d) Ba < Sc < Si < Se < F

5-44.   *Refer to the Sections as stated.*

(a) increasing atomic radius: S < Si < Na   (Section 5-2)

(b) increasing first ionization energy: Na < Si < S (Section 5-3)

(c) decreasing electronegativity: S < Si < Na   (Section 5-6)

5-46.   *Refer to Section 5-7, Table 5-4 and Example 5-6.*

For a compound, the sum of the oxidation numbers of the component elements must be equal to zero.

(a) Let x = oxidation number of P

PCl_3
$0 = x + 3(\text{ox. no. Cl}) = x + 3(-1) = x - 3$
$x = +3$

P_2O_5
$0 = 2x + 5(\text{ox. no. O}) = 2x + 5(-2) = 2x - 10$
$x = +5$

P_4O_{10}
$0 = 4x + 10(\text{ox. no. O}) = 4x + 10(-2) = 4x - 20$
$x = +5$

HPO_3
$0 = 1(\text{ox. no. H}) + x + 3(\text{ox. no. O}) = 1(+1) + x + 3(-2) = x - 5$
$x = +5$

H_3PO_3
$0 = 3(\text{ox. no. H}) + x + 3(\text{ox. no. O}) = 3(+1) + x + 3(-2) = x - 3$
$x = +3$

$POCl_3$
$0 = x + 1(\text{ox. no. O}) + 3(\text{ox. no. Cl}) = x + 1(-2) + 3(-1) = x - 5$
$x = +5$

$H_4P_2O_7$
$0 = 4(\text{ox. no. H}) + 2x + 7(\text{ox. no. O}) = 4(+1) + 2x + 7(-2) = 2x - 10$
$x = +5$

$Mg_3(PO_4)_2$
$0 = 3(\text{ox. no. Mg}) + 2x + 8(\text{ox. no. O}) = 3(+2) + 2x + 8(-2) = 2x - 10$
$x = +5$

(b) Let x = oxidation number of Br

Br^-
$x = -1$

BrO^-
$-1 = x + 1(\text{ox. no. O}) = x + 1(-2) = x - 2$
$x = +1$

BrO_2^- $-1 = x + 2(\text{ox. no. O}) = x + 2(-2) = x - 4$
              $x = +3$

BrO_3^- $-1 = x + 3(\text{ox. no. O}) = x + 3(-2) = x - 6$
              $x = +5$

BrO_4^- $-1 = x + 4(\text{ox. no. O}) = x + 4(-2) = x - 8$
              $x = +7$

(c) Let x = oxidation number of Mn

MnO $0 = x + 1(\text{ox. no. O}) = x + 1(-2) = x - 2$
              $x = +2$

MnO_2 $0 = x + 2(\text{ox. no. O}) = x + 2(-2) = x - 4$
              $x = +4$

$Mn(OH)_2$ $0 = x + 2(\text{ox. no. O}) + 2(\text{ox. no. H}) = x + 2(-2) + 2(+1) = x - 2$
              $x = +2$

K_2MnO_4 $0 = 2(\text{ox. no. K}) + x + 4(\text{ox. no. O}) = 2(+1) + x + 4(-2) = x - 6$
              $x = +6$

$KMnO_4$ $0 = 1(\text{ox. no. K}) + x + 4(\text{ox. no. O}) = 1(+1) + x + 4(-2) = x - 7$
              $x = +7$

Mn_2O_7 $0 = 2x + 7(\text{ox. no. O}) = 2x + 7(-2) = 2x - 14$
              $x = +7$

(d) Let x = oxidation of O

OF_2 $0 = x + 2(\text{ox. no. F}) = x + 2(-1) = x - 2$
              $x = +2$

Na_2O $0 = 2(\text{ox. no. Na}) + x = 2(+1) + x = x + 2$
              $x = -2$

Na_2O_2 $0 = 2(\text{ox. no. Na}) + 2x = 2(+1) + 2x = 2x + 2$
              $x = -1$

KO_2 $0 = 1(\text{ox. no. K}) + 2x = 1(+1) + 2x = 2x + 1$
              $x = -1/2$

5-48.   ***Refer to Section 5-7, Table 5-4 and Example 5-6.***

For an ion, the sum of the oxidation numbers of the component elements must equal the charge on the ion.

(a) Let x = oxidation number of N

N^{3-} $x = -3$

NO_2^- $-1 = x + 2(\text{ox. no. O}) = x + 2(-2) = x - 4$
              $x = +3$

NO_3^- $-1 = x + 3(\text{ox. no. O}) = x + 3(-2) = x - 6$
              $x = +5$

N_3^- $-1 = 3x$
              $x = -1/3$

NH_4^+ $+1 = x + 4(\text{ox. no. H}) = x + 4(+1) = x + 4$
              $x = -3$

(b) Let x = oxidation number of Cl

Cl_2 $0 = 2x$
                 $x = 0$

HCl $0 = 1(\text{ox. no. H}) + x = 1(+1) + x = x + 1$
                 $x = -1$

$HClO$ $0 = 1(\text{ox. no. H}) + x + 1(\text{ox. no. O}) = 1(+1) + x + 1(-2) = x - 1$
                 $x = +1$

$HClO_2$ $0 = 1(\text{ox. no. H}) + x + 2(\text{ox. no. O}) = 1(+1) + x + 2(-2) = x - 3$
                 $x = +3$

$KClO_3$ $0 = 1(\text{ox. no. K}) + x + 3(\text{ox. no. O}) = 1(+1) + x + 3(-2) = x - 5$
                 $x = +5$

Cl_2O_7 $0 = 2x + 7(\text{ox. no. O}) = 2x + 7(-2) = 2x - 14$
                 $x = +7$

$Ca(ClO_4)_2$ $0 = 1(\text{ox. no. Ca}) + 2x + 8(\text{ox. no. O}) = 1(+2) + 2x + 8(-2) = 2x - 14$
                 $x = +7$

PCl_5 $0 = +5 + 5(\text{ox. no. Cl}) = +5 + 5(x)$
                 $x = -1$

5-50.   *Refer to Sections 5-3 and 5-4, and Tables 5-1 and 5-2.*

If we compare the values of the first ionization energy and electron affinity for the Period 3 elements, we have

	Na	Mg	Al	Si	P	S	Cl	Ar
First Ionization Energy (kJ/mol)	496	738	578	786	1012	1000	1251	1521
Electron Affinity (kJ/mol)	−53	(~0)	−43	−134	−72	−200	−349	0

The magnitude of the electron affinity values is less than that of the first ionization energies. It is much more difficult and hence more energy is required to remove an electron from a neutral gaseous atom, quantified by the first ionization energy, than to add an electron to a neutral gaseous atom, quantified by the electron affinity. In fact, many atoms actually release energy when an extra electron is added as denoted by the negative sign attached to the electron affinity value.

5-52.   *Refer to Section 5-8.*

Elemental hydrogen exists as a colorless, odorless, tasteless, diatomic gas with the lowest atomic weight and density of any known substance. This flammable gas melts at −259.14°C and boils at −252.8°C.

5-54.   *Refer to Section 5-8 and Example 5-7.*

(a) Hydrogen gas reacts with the alkali metals and heavier alkaline earth metals to form ionic hydrides:

$$2Li(\text{molten}) + H_2(g) \rightarrow 2LiH(s)$$

(b) Hydrogen gas reacts with other nonmetals to form binary molecular compounds:

$$H_2(g) + Cl_2(g) \rightarrow 2HCl(g)$$

NaH, sodium hydride, is the product of hydrogen gas reacting with an active metal, sodium. A compound consisting of a metal and a nonmetal has a high degree of ionic character.

H_2S, hydrogen sulfide, is the product of hydrogen gas reacting with a nonmetal, sulfur. A compound consisting of two nonmetals is primarily covalent, and has a much smaller degree of ionic character.

5-58. *Refer to Section 5-8.*

(a) H_2S hydrogen sulfide
(b) HCl   hydrogen chloride
(c) KH   potassium hydride
(d) NH_3 ammonia
(e) H_2Se hydrogen selenide
(f) MgH_2 magnesium hydride
(g) AlH_3 aluminum hydride

5-60. *Refer to Sections 5-8 and 5-9.*

H_2, hydrogen, is a colorless, odorless, tasteless, nonpolar, diamagnetic, diatomic gas with the lowest atomic weight and density of any known substance. It has low solubility in water and is very flammable. Hydrogen is prepared by reactions of metals with water, steam or various acids, electrolysis of water, the water gas reaction and thermal cracking of hydrocarbons. It combines with metals and nonmetals to form hydrides.

O_2, oxygen, is nearly colorless, odorless, tasteless, nonpolar, paramagnetic, diatomic gas. It is nonflammable but participates in all combustion reactions. It is prepared by cooling air until it changes to a liquid, then separating the gas components, electrolysis of water and thermal decomposition of certain oxygen-containing salts. Oxygen combines with almost all other elements to form oxides and can be converted to an allotropic form, ozone, O_3.

5-62. *Refer to Section 5-9 and Table 5-5.*

The elements that react with oxygen to form primarily normal oxides include (a) Li, (d) Mg, (e) Zn and (f) Al.

5-64. *Refer to Section 5-9 and Example 5-11.*

(a) $2C(s) + O_2(g) \rightarrow 2CO(g)$ (O_2 is limited)
(b) $As_4(s) + 3O_2(g) \rightarrow 2As_2O_3(s)$ (O_2 is limited)
(c) $2Ge(s) + O_2(g) \rightarrow 2GeO(s)$ (O_2 is limited)

5-66. *Refer to Section 5-9 and Table 5-5.*

A normal oxide is a binary (two element) compound containing oxygen in the -2 oxidation state. BaO is an example of an ionic oxide and SO_2 is an example of a molecular (covalent) oxide.

A peroxide can be a binary ionic compound containing the O_2^{2-} ion, such as Na_2O_2, or a covalent compound, such as H_2O_2, with oxygen in the -1 oxidation state.

A superoxide is a binary ionic compound containing the O_2^- ion with oxygen in the $-1/2$ oxidation state, such as KO_2.

5-68. *Refer to Section 5-9 and Example 5-11.*

(a) $CO_2(g) + H_2O(\ell) \rightarrow H_2CO_3(aq)$ carbonic acid

(b) $SO_3(\ell) + H_2O(\ell) \rightarrow H_2SO_4(aq)$ sulfuric acid

(c) $SeO_3(s) + H_2O(\ell) \rightarrow H_2SeO_4(aq)$ selenic acid

(d) $N_2O_5(s) + H_2O(\ell) \rightarrow 2HNO_3(aq)$ nitric acid

(e) $Cl_2O_7(\ell) + H_2O(\ell) \rightarrow 2HClO_4(aq)$ perchloric acid

5-70. *Refer to Section 5-9.*

The acid anhydrides are:

(a) SO_3

(b) CO_2

(c) SO_2

(d) P_2O_5

(e) N_2O_3

5-72. *Refer to Section 5-9.*

Combustion is an oxidation-reduction reaction in which oxygen gas combines rapidly with oxidizable materials in highly exothermic reactions usually with a visible flame. The oxygen atoms are being reduced since the oxidation number of oxygen is changed from 0 in O_2 to –2 in the products, usually CO_2 and H_2O when oxidizing hydrocarbons, while the other reactants have elements being oxidized. When $H_2(g)$ is the fuel, the balanced equation is: $2H_2(g) + O_2(g) \rightarrow 2H_2O(g)$

5-74. *Refer to Section 5-9.*

(a) $2CH_4(g) + 3O_2(g) \rightarrow 2CO(g) + 4H_2O(g)$ (O_2 is limited)

(b) $2C_3H_8(g) + 7O_2(g) \rightarrow 6CO(g) + 8H_2O(g)$ (O_2 is limited)

5-76. *Refer to Section 5-9.*

Balanced reaction: $C_3H_8(g) + 5O_2(g) \rightarrow 3CO_2(g) + 4H_2O(g)$

However, this is a limiting reactant problem with propane, C_3H_8, being the limiting reactant since we are given 7 molecules of O_2 and not 5. When the reaction is complete, there will be 2 molecules of O_2 remaining unreacted.

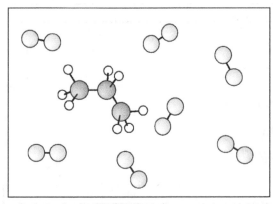 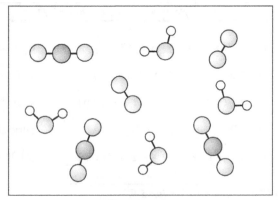

| Before Reaction | After Reaction |

5-78.   *Refer to Section 5-9.*

(a) $4C_6H_5NH_2(\ell) + 33O_2(g) \rightarrow 24CO_2(g) + 14H_2O(\ell) + 4NO(g)$

(b) $2C_2H_5SH(\ell) + 9O_2(g) \rightarrow 4CO_2(g) + 6H_2O(g) + 2SO_2(g)$

(c) $C_7H_{10}NO_2S(\ell) + 10O_2(g) \rightarrow 7CO_2(g) + 5H_2O(g) + NO(g) + SO_2(g)$

5-80.   *Refer to Section 5-2 and Figure 5-1.*

Within a family or group, atomic radii increase from top to bottom as electrons are added to shells further and further from the nucleus. As we move from left to right across a period, atomic radii decrease. Therefore, the atomic radii are most likely associated with the following atoms and Ge must be **122 pm**, where 1 pm = 1 picometer = 1×10^{-12} m.

	Si - 118 pm	P -110 pm
Ga - 135 pm	Ge - 122 pm	As - 120 pm

5-82.   *Refer to Section 5-2, and Figures 5-1 and 5-4.*

The electronic configurations for beryllium and magnesium: $_4$Be $1s^22s^2$ and $_{12}$Mg $1s^22s^22p^63s^2$ show that both elements are in Group 2A. Both are metals, exhibiting +2 oxidation number in all their compounds. They would be expected to form stable 2+ ions, with Mg having more metallic character than Be. When we compare the sizes of their most stable ions, Be^{2+} and Mg^{2+}, we see that $Mg^{2+} > Be^{2+}$.

5-84.   *Refer to Section 5-1.*

In the periodic table on the next page, each energy sublevel, e.g. 2s, is placed in the elemental box which corresponds to the element, e.g. Be, in which that energy sublevel is filled.

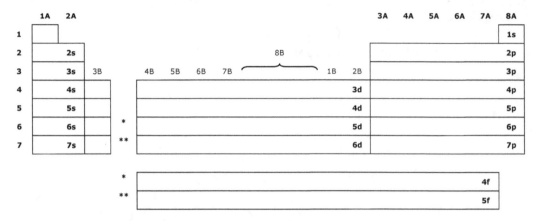

	1A	2A						8B					3A	4A	5A	6A	7A	8A
1																		1s
2	2s																	2p
3	3s	3B	4B	5B	6B	7B			1B	2B							3p
4	4s									3d							4p
5	5s									4d							5p
6	6s	*								5d							6p
7	7s	**								6d							7p

*							4f
**							5f

5-86.   Refer to Section 5-6 and Table 5-3.

The following elements have an electronegativity of 3.0 or greater: N, O, F, S and Cl. These nonmetals are located in the upper right hand corner of the periodic table, but do not include H or He.

The following elements have an electronegativity of 1.0 or less: Li, Na, K, Rb, Cs, Fr, Sr, Ca, Ra, and Yb (a lanthanide, atomic number 70). All but Yb are either alkali metals (Group1A) or alkaline earths (Group 2A).

5-88.   Refer to Section 5-7 and Figure 5-1.

Hydrogen gas obtained cheaply from the electrolysis of water: $2H_2O(\ell) \rightarrow 2H_2(g) + O_2(g)$

may be used to fuel automobiles in the future. The pollution would be greatly decreased, however, there may be problems with:

(1) safe storage and combustion of the gas which is very flammable,

(2) transferring the gas safely into the vehicle at neighborhood "hydrogen stations,"

(3) managing the high volume electrolysis plants so that the hydrologic cycle would not be overly disturbed, and

(4) pollution generated by the electricity required to electrolyze the water in the first place.

5-90.   Refer to Sections 5-3 and 5-10.

Recall: For 1 atom, E (J/atom) $= h$ (J·s) x ν (s^{-1})

          For 1 mole of atoms, E (J/mol) $= h\nu N$ where N is Avogadro's Number

Solving for ν, we have

$$\nu\ (s^{-1}) = \frac{E}{hN} = \frac{419 \text{ kJ/mol x 1000 J/kJ}}{(6.63 \times 10^{-34}\text{ J·s})(6.02 \times 10^{23}\text{ atoms/mol})} = \mathbf{1.05 \times 10^{15}\ s^{-1}} \text{ when one atom of K is involved}$$

5-92.   Refer to Section 5-3 and Table 5-1.

First Ionization Energy for Mg (kJ/mol) = 738 kJ/mol   So, $Mg(g) + 738 \text{ kJ/mol} \rightarrow Mg^+(g) + e^-$

Second Ionization Energy for Mg (kJ/mol) = 1451 kJ/mol   So, $\underline{Mg^+(g) + 1451 \text{ kJ/mol} \rightarrow Mg^{2+}(g) + e^-}$

$Mg(g) + 2189 \text{ kJ/mol} \rightarrow Mg^{2+}(g) + 2e^-$

And so, 2189 kJ/mol of energy is required to produce 1 mole of gaseous Mg^{2+} ions from gaseous Mg atoms. So, using dimensional analysis:

$$? \text{ energy (kJ)} = 1.75 \text{ g Mg} \times \frac{1 \text{ mol Mg}}{24.305 \text{ g Mg}} \times \frac{2189 \text{ kJ}}{1 \text{mol Mg}} = \textbf{158 kJ}$$

6 Some Types of Chemical Reactions

6-2. *Refer to Section 6-1.*

Three major classes of compounds are electrolytes:

	Strong Electrolytes	**Weak Electrolytes**
(1) acids	HCl, HClO$_4$	CH$_3$COOH, HF
(2) soluble bases	NaOH, Ba(OH)$_2$	NH$_3$, (CH$_3$)$_3$N
(3) soluble salts	NaCl, KNO$_3$	Pb(CH$_3$COO)$_2$*

* This is one of the very few soluble salts that is a weak electrolyte.

Therefore, the three classes of compounds which are *strong* electrolytes are strong acids, strong soluble bases and soluble salts.

6-4. *Refer to Sections 6-1 and 6-9.*

A salt is a compound that contains a cation other than H$^+$ and an anion other than the hydroxide ion, OH$^-$, or the oxide ion, O^{2-}. A salt is a product of the reaction between a particular acid and base and consists of the cation of the base and the anion of the acid. For example,

$$NaOH \ + \ HCl \ \rightarrow \ NaCl \ + \ H_2O$$
$$\textbf{base} \qquad \textbf{acid} \qquad \textbf{salt}$$

6-6. *Refer to Section 6-1.*

(a) $HCl(aq) \ \rightarrow \ H^+(aq) + Cl^-(aq)$

(b) $HNO_3(aq) \ \rightarrow \ H^+(aq) + NO_3^-(aq)$

(c) $HClO_2(aq) \ \rightleftarrows \ H^+(aq) + ClO_2^-(aq)$

(d) $H_2CO_3(aq) \ \rightleftarrows \ H^+(aq) + HCO_3^-(aq)$

    $HCO_3^-(aq) \ \rightleftarrows \ H^+(aq) + CO_3^{2-}(aq)$

Note: Because carbonic acid is diprotic, its ionization occurs in two steps.

6-8. *Refer to Section 6-1 and Table 6-3.*

Common strong soluble bases include:

lithium hydroxide	LiOH	calcium hydroxide	Ca(OH)$_2$*
sodium hydroxide	NaOH	strontium hydroxide	Sr(OH)$_2$*
potassium hydroxide	KOH	barium hydroxide	Ba(OH)$_2$
rubidium hydroxide	RbOH		
cesium hydroxide	CsOH		

* Ca(OH)$_2$ and Sr(OH)$_2$ are less soluble than Ba(OH)$_2$ and so are sometimes considered only moderately soluble or even "insoluble". As you are discovering, the concept of solubility is not a yes or no proposition.

6-10.   *Refer to Section 6-1.*

Household ammonia is the most common weak base.
It ionizes as follows:

$$NH_3(aq) + H_2O(\ell) \rightleftarrows NH_4^+(aq) + OH^-(aq)$$

6-12.   *Refer to Section 6-1 and the Key Terms at the end of Chapter 6.*

Ionization refers to the process in which a molecular compound, such as HCl, separates or reacts with water to form ions in solution. Dissociation refers to the process in which a solid ionic compound, such as NaCl, separates into its ions in aqueous solution.

6-14.   *Refer to Section 6-1.*

(a) Na_2S is a soluble salt and is a strong electrolyte: $Na_2S(aq) \rightarrow 2Na^+(aq) + S^{2-}(aq)$.

(b) $Ba(OH)_2$ is a strong base and is a strong electrolyte: $Ba(OH)_2(aq) \rightarrow Ba^{2+}(aq) + 2OH^-(aq)$.

(c) CH_3OH, methanol, is a nonelectrolyte.

(d) HCN is a weak acid and is a weak electrolyte.

(e) $Al(NO_3)_3$ is a soluble salt and is a strong electrolyte: $Al(NO_3)_3(aq) \rightarrow Al^{3+}(aq) + 3NO_3^-(aq)$.

6-16.   *Refer to Section 6-1, Table 6-4, and the Solubility Guidelines in Section 6-1.*

Ionic Substance	Soluble	Insoluble
Chloride	NaCl, KCl	$AgCl$, Hg_2Cl_2
Sulfate	Na_2SO_4, K_2SO_4	$BaSO_4$, $PbSO_4$
Hydroxide	NaOH, KOH	$Cu(OH)_2$, $Mg(OH)_2$

6-18.   *Refer to Section 6-1 and Tables 6-1, 6-2 and 6-3.*

(a) perchloric acid ($HClO_4$) – strong acid

(b) cesium hydroxide (CsOH) – strong base

(c) carbonic acid (H_2CO_3) – weak acid

(d) ethylamine ($C_2H_5NH_2$) – weak base

6-20.   *Refer to Section 6-1, Figure 6-1 and the Key Terms to Chapter 6.*

Electrolytes are defined as substances whose aqueous solutions conduct electricity due to the presence of ions in solution. Acids, soluble bases and soluble salts are electrolytes. Measuring the extent to which a substance's aqueous solution conducts electricity is how chemists determine whether it is a strong or weak electrolyte. If the solution conducts electricity well, the solute is a strong electrolyte, like the strong acid, HCl; if it conducts electricity poorly, the solute is a weak electrolyte, like the weak acid, HF.

6-22.   *Refer to Section 6-1, Table 6-4 and Example 6-3.*

soluble: $Ca(CH_3COO)_2$, NH_4Cl, $AgNO_3$, $(NH_4)_3PO_4$ insoluble: $PbCl_2$ (except in hot water)

6-24.   *Refer to Section 6-1.*

Acidic household "chemicals":	vinegar (dilute acetic acid)
	vitamin C (ascorbic acid)
	lemon juice (citric acid)

Basic household "chemicals":	ammonia
	drain cleaner (sodium hydroxide)
	Milk of Magnesia (magnesium hydroxide)

6-26.   *Refer to Section 6-1.*

Many organic acids, like acetic acid, occur in living systems and are generally weak acids so as not to disrupt living cells. Note that stomach acid, HCl, is a strong acid, but the stomach tissue protects itself with a heavy mucous layer.

6-28.   *Refer to Section 6-3 and Table 6-6.*

(a) Li^+ lithium ion   (c) Ca^{2+} calcium ion   (e) Ag^+ silver ion

(b) Au^{3+} gold(III) ion   (d) Zn^{2+} zinc ion

6-30.   *Refer to Sections 6-3 and 6-4, and Table 6-6.*

(a) chloride ion Cl^- (c) telluride ion Te^{2-} (e) nitrite ion NO_2^-

(b) hydrogen sulfide ion HS^- (d) hydroxide ion OH^-

6-32.   *Refer to Sections 6-3 and 6-4, and Table 6-6.*

(a) CuI_2 copper(II) iodide   (d) $MnCl_2$ manganese(II) chloride

(b) Hg_2Cl_2 mercury(I) chloride   (e) $CuCO_3$ copper(II) carbonate

(c) Li_3N lithium nitride   (f) FeO iron(II) oxide

6-34.   *Refer to Section 6-4 and Table 6-6.*

(a) copper(II) chlorite $Cu(ClO_2)_2$ (c) barium phosphate $Ba_3(PO_4)_2$ (e) sodium sulfite Na_2SO_3

(b) potassium nitrate KNO_3 (d) copper(I) sulfate Cu_2SO_4

6-36.   *Refer to Section 6-4.*

| H_3PO_4 | phosphoric acid | $H_2PO_4^-$ | dihydrogen phosphate ion |
| HPO_4^{2-} | hydrogen phosphate ion | PO_4^{3-} | phosphate ion |

6-38.   *Refer to Section 6-3.*

(a) AsF_3 arsenic trifluoride   (d) CSe_2 carbon diselenide

(b) Br_2O dibromine oxide   (e) N_2O_4 dinitrogen tetroxide

(c) BrF_5 bromine pentafluoride

6-40. *Refer to Section 6-3.*

(a) diboron trioxide B_2O_3

(b) dinitrogen pentasulfide N_2S_5

(c) phosphorus triiodide PI_3

(d) sulfur tetrafluoride SF_4

(e) silicon sulfide SiS_2

(f) hydrogen sulfide H_2S

(g) tetraphosphorus hexoxide P_4O_6

6-42. *Refer to 2-1 and Table 2-1.*

(a) CH_4 methane

(b) NH_3 ammonia

6-44. *Refer to Sections 6-3 and 6-4.*

(a) CN^- cyanide ion

(b) NO_3^- nitrate ion

6-46. *Refer to Sections 4-5 and 4-6.*

(a) NH_4Br ammonium bromide $CuBr_2$ copper(II) bromide

$NaBr$ sodium bromide $FeBr_3$ iron(III) bromide or ferric bromide

$MgBr_2$ magnesium bromide $AgBr$ silver bromide

(b) - $Cu(OH)_2$ copper(II) hydroxide

$NaOH$ sodium hydroxide $Fe(OH)_3$ iron(III) hydroxide or ferric hydroxide

$Mg(OH)_2$ magnesium hydroxide $AgOH$ silver hydroxide

(c) $(NH_4)_2SO_4$ ammonium sulfate $CuSO_4$ copper(II) sulfate

Na_2SO_4 sodium sulfate $Fe_2(SO_4)_3$ iron(III) sulfate or ferric sulfate

$MgSO_4$ magnesium sulfate Ag_2SO_4 silver sulfate

(d) $(NH_4)_3PO_4$ ammonium phosphate $Cu_3(PO_4)_2$ copper(II) phosphate

Na_3PO_4 sodium phosphate $FePO_4$ iron(III) phosphate or ferric phosphate

$Mg_3(PO_4)_2$ magnesium phosphate Ag_3PO_4 silver phosphate

(e) NH_4NO_3 ammonium nitrate $Cu(NO_3)_2$ copper(II) nitrate

$NaNO_3$ sodium nitrate $Fe(NO_3)_3$ iron(III) nitrate or ferric nitrate

$Mg(NO_3)_2$ magnesium nitrate $AgNO_3$ silver nitrate

6-48. *Refer to Section 6-3.*

(a) $N_2(g) + O_2(g) \overset{heat}{\rightarrow} 2NO(g)$

(b) $PbS(s) + PbSO_4(s) \overset{heat}{\rightarrow} 2Pb(s) + 2SO_2(g)$

6-50. *Refer to Section 6-5.*

Due to the Law of Conservation of Matter, electrons cannot be created or destroyed in chemical reactions. The electrons that cause the reduction of one substance must be produced from the oxidation of another substance. Therefore, oxidation and reduction always occur simultaneously in ordinary chemical reactions.

Reaction (b) is the only oxidation-reduction reaction.

In reactions (a), (c) and (d), there are no elements that are changing oxidation number.

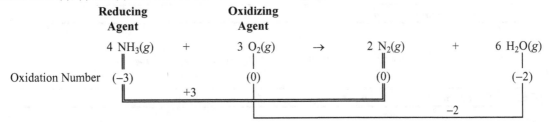

	Oxidizing Agent		Reducing Agent		
(a)	$3H_2SO_4$	+	$2Al$	$\rightarrow$	$Al_2(SO_4)_3 + 3H_2$
(b)	N_2	+	$3H_2$	$\rightarrow$	$2NH_3$
(c)	$3O_2$	+	$2ZnS$	$\rightarrow$	$2ZnO + 2SO_2$
(d)	$4HNO_3$	+	C	$\rightarrow$	$4NO_2 + CO_2 + 2H_2O$
(e)	H_2SO_4	+	$2HI$	$\rightarrow$	$SO_2 + I_2 + 2H_2O$

(a) formula unit: $\qquad$ $Zn(s) + 2HCl(aq) \rightarrow H_2(g) + ZnCl_2(aq)$

   total ionic: $\qquad$ $Zn(s) + 2H^+(aq) + 2Cl^-(aq) \rightarrow H_2(g) + Zn^{2+}(aq) + 2Cl^-(aq)$

   net ionic: $\qquad$ $Zn(s) + 2H^+(aq) \rightarrow H_2(g) + Zn^{2+}(aq)$

(b) formula unit: $\qquad$ $Mg(OH)_2(s) + 2HCl(aq) \rightarrow MgCl_2(aq) + 2H_2O(\ell)$

   total ionic: $\qquad$ $Mg(OH)_2(s) + 2H^+(aq) + 2Cl^-(aq) \rightarrow Mg^{2+}(aq) + 2Cl^-(aq) + 2H_2O(\ell)$

   net ionic: $\qquad$ $Mg(OH)_2(s) + 2H^+(aq) \rightarrow Mg^{2+}(aq) + 2H_2O(\ell)$

(c) formula unit: $\qquad$ $2HNO_3(aq) + CaCO_3(s) \rightarrow Ca(NO_3)_2(aq) + H_2O(\ell) + CO_2(g)$

   total ionic: $\qquad$ $2H^+(aq) + 2NO_3^-(aq) + CaCO_3(s) \rightarrow Ca^{2+}(aq) + 2NO_3^-(aq) + H_2O(\ell) + CO_2(g)$

   net ionic: $\qquad$ $2H^+(aq) + CaCO_3(s) \rightarrow Ca^{2+}(aq) + H_2O(\ell) + CO_2(g)$

(d) formula unit: $\qquad$ $4HCl(aq) + MnO_2(s) \rightarrow MnCl_2(aq) + Cl_2(g) + 2H_2O(\ell)$

   total ionic: $\qquad$ $4H^+(aq) + 4Cl^-(aq) + MnO_2(s) \rightarrow Mn^{2+}(aq) + 2Cl^-(aq) + Cl_2(g) + 2H_2O(\ell)$

   net ionic: $\qquad$ $4H^+(aq) + 2Cl^-(aq) + MnO_2(s) \rightarrow Mn^{2+}(aq) + Cl_2(g) + 2H_2O(\ell)$

6-58. *Refer to Sections 6-5 and 6-6.*

(a) $Be + F_2 \rightarrow BeF_2$ (b) $Ca + Br_2 \rightarrow CaBr_2$ (c) $Ba + Cl_2 \rightarrow BaCl_2$

6-60. *Refer to Sections 6-5 and 6-6.*

(a) $\overset{+6}{3SO_3} + \overset{+3}{Al_2O_3} \rightarrow \overset{+3\ +6}{Al_2(SO_4)_3}$ (b) $\overset{+7}{Cl_2O_7} + H_2O \rightarrow \overset{+7}{2HClO_4}$ (c) $\overset{+2}{CaO} + \overset{+4}{SiO_2} \rightarrow \overset{+2\ +4}{CaSiO_3}$

6-62. *Refer to Sections 6-5 and 6-7.*

(a) $\overset{-3\ +1}{(NH_4)_2}\overset{+6\ -2}{Cr_2O_7}(s) \rightarrow \overset{0}{N_2}(g) + \overset{+3\ -2}{Cr_2O_3}(s) + \overset{+1\ -2}{4H_2O}(g)$

(b) $\overset{+1\ +5\ -2}{2NaNO_3}(s) \rightarrow \overset{+1\ +3\ -2}{2NaNO_2}(s) + \overset{0}{O_2}(g)$

6-64. *Refer to Section 6-8, Table 6-9 and Example 6-6.*

Zn, Fe and Ni are more active metals than Cu and will displace Cu from an aqueous solution of $CuSO_4$.

$Hg(\ell) + CuSO_4(aq) \rightarrow$ no reaction

total ionic equation: $Zn(s) + Cu^{2+}(aq) + SO_4^{2-}(aq) \rightarrow Zn^{2+}(aq) + SO_4^{2-}(aq) + Cu(s)$
net ionic equation: $Zn(s) + Cu^{2+}(aq) \rightarrow Zn^{2+}(aq) + Cu(s)$

total ionic equation: $Fe(s) + Cu^{2+}(aq) + SO_4^{2-}(aq) \rightarrow Fe^{2+}(aq) + SO_4^{2-}(aq) + Cu(s)$
net ionic equation: $Fe(s) + Cu^{2+}(aq) \rightarrow Fe^{2+}(aq) + Cu(s)$

total ionic equation: $Ni(s) + Cu^{2+}(aq) + SO_4^{2-}(aq) \rightarrow Ni^{2+}(aq) + SO_4^{2-}(aq) + Cu(s)$
net ionic equation: $Ni(s) + Cu^{2+}(aq) \rightarrow Ni^{2+}(aq) + Cu(s)$

6-66. *Refer to Section 6-8, Table 6-9, Exercise 6-64 and Example 6-7.*

In order of increasing activity: Hg < Cu < Ni < Fe < Zn

6-68. *Refer to Section 6-8, Table 6-9, Exercise 6-67 and Example 6-7.*

In order of increasing activity: Ag < Cr < Na < Ca

6-70. *Refer to Section 6-8, Table 6-9, and Example 6-7.*

Five elements that will react with steam, but not cold water are magnesium (Mg), aluminum (Al), manganese (Mn), zinc (Zn) and chromium (Cr).

4-72. *Refer to Section 6-8 and Example 6-8.*

Each halogen will displace less electronegative (heavier) halogens from their binary salts.
Hence, reactions (b) and (c) will occur and reactions (a) and (d) will not occur.

6-74. *Refer to Section 6-8 and Table 6-9.*

(a) no   (b) no   (c) yes   (d) yes

6-76. *Refer to Section 6-8, Solubility Guidelines in Section 6-1, Table 6-4, and Examples 6-12 and 6-13.*

(a) formula unit:

$$3CaCl_2(aq) + 2K_3PO_4(aq) \rightarrow Ca_3(PO_4)_2(s) + 6KCl(aq)$$

total ionic:

$$3Ca^{2+}(aq) + 6Cl^-(aq) + 6K^+(aq) + 2PO_4^{3-}(aq) \rightarrow Ca_3(PO_4)_2(s) + 6K^+(aq) + 6Cl^-(aq)$$

net ionic:

$$3Ca^{2+}(aq) + 2PO_4^{3-}(aq) \rightarrow Ca_3(PO_4)_2(s)$$

(b) formula unit:

$$Hg(NO_3)_2(aq) + Na_2S(aq) \rightarrow HgS(s) + 2NaNO_3(aq)$$

total ionic:

$$Hg^{2+}(aq) + 2NO_3^-(aq) + 2Na^+(aq) + S^{2-}(aq) \rightarrow HgS(s) + 2Na^+(aq) + 2NO_3^-(aq)$$

net ionic:

$$Hg^{2+}(aq) + S^{2-}(aq) \rightarrow HgS(s)$$

(c) formula unit:

$$2CrCl_3(aq) + 3Ca(OH)_2(aq) \rightarrow 2Cr(OH)_3(s) + 3CaCl_2(aq)$$

total ionic:

$$2Cr^{3+}(aq) + 6Cl^-(aq) + 3Ca^{2+}(aq) + 6OH^-(aq) \rightarrow 2Cr(OH)_3(s) + 3Ca^{2+}(aq) + 6Cl^-(aq)$$

net ionic:

$$2Cr^{3+}(aq) + 6OH^-(aq) \rightarrow 2Cr(OH)_3(s)$$

therefore,

$$Cr^{3+}(aq) + 3OH^-(aq) \rightarrow Cr(OH)_3(s)$$

6-78. *Refer to Section 6-9, and Examples 6-9, 6-10 and 6-11.*

(a) formula unit:

$$CH_3COOH(aq) + KOH(aq) \rightarrow KCH_3COO(aq) + H_2O(\ell)$$

total ionic:

$$CH_3COOH(aq) + K^+(aq) + OH^-(aq) \rightarrow K^+(aq) + CH_3COO^-(aq) + H_2O(\ell)$$

net ionic:

$$CH_3COOH(aq) + OH^-(aq) \rightarrow CH_3COO^-(aq) + H_2O(\ell)$$

(b) formula unit:

$$H_2SO_3(aq) + 2NaOH(aq) \rightarrow Na_2SO_3(aq) + 2H_2O(\ell)$$

total ionic:

$$H_2SO_3(aq) + 2Na^+(aq) + 2OH^-(aq) \rightarrow 2Na^+(aq) + SO_3^{2-}(aq) + 2H_2O(\ell)$$

net ionic:

$$H_2SO_3(aq) + 2OH^-(aq) \rightarrow SO_3^{2-}(aq) + 2H_2O(\ell)$$

(c) formula unit:

$$HF(aq) + NaOH(aq) \rightarrow NaF(aq) + H_2O(\ell)$$

total ionic:

$$HF(aq) + Na^+(aq) + OH^-(aq) \rightarrow Na^+(aq) + F^-(aq) + H_2O(\ell)$$

net ionic:

$$HF(aq) + OH^-(aq) \rightarrow F^-(aq) + H_2O(\ell)$$

6-80. *Refer to Section 6-9, and Examples 6-9, 6-10 and 6-11.*

(a) formula unit:

$$2LiOH(aq) + H_2SO_4(aq) \rightarrow Li_2SO_4(aq) + 2H_2O(\ell)$$

total ionic:

$$2Li^+(aq) + 2OH^-(aq) + 2H^+(aq) + SO_4^{2-}(aq) \rightarrow 2Li^+(aq) + SO_4^{2-}(aq) + 2H_2O(\ell)$$

net ionic:

$$2OH^-(aq) + 2H^+(aq) \rightarrow 2H_2O(\ell)$$

therefore,

$$OH^-(aq) + H^+(aq) \rightarrow H_2O(\ell)$$

(b) formula unit:

$$3Ca(OH)_2(aq) + 2H_3PO_4(aq) \rightarrow Ca_3(PO_4)_2(s) + 6H_2O(\ell)$$

total ionic: $3Ca^{2+}(aq) + 6OH^-(aq) + 2H_3PO_4(aq) \rightarrow Ca_3(PO_4)_2(s) + 6H_2O(\ell)$

net ionic: $3Ca^{2+}(aq) + 6OH^-(aq) + 2H_3PO_4(aq) \rightarrow Ca_3(PO_4)_2(s) + 6H_2O(\ell)$

(c) formula unit: $Cu(OH)_2(s) + 2HNO_3(aq) \rightarrow Cu(NO_3)_2(aq) + 2H_2O(\ell)$

total ionic: $Cu(OH)_2(s) + 2H^+(aq) + 2NO_3^-(aq) \rightarrow Cu^{2+}(aq) + 2NO_3^-(aq) + 2H_2O(\ell)$

net ionic: $Cu(OH)_2(s) + 2H^+(aq) \rightarrow Cu^{2+}(aq) + 2H_2O(\ell)$

6-82. *Refer to Section 6-9 and Example 6-11.*

(a) formula unit: $2HClO_4(aq) + Ca(OH)_2(aq) \rightarrow Ca(ClO_4)_2(aq) + 2H_2O(\ell)$

total ionic: $2H^+(aq) + 2ClO_4^-(aq) + Ca^{2+}(aq) + 2OH^-(aq) \rightarrow Ca^{2+}(aq) + 2ClO_4^-(aq) + 2H_2O(\ell)$

net ionic: $2H^+(aq) + 2OH^-(aq) \rightarrow 2H_2O(\ell)$

therefore, $H^+(aq) + OH^-(aq) \rightarrow H_2O(\ell)$

(b) formula unit: $H_2SO_4(aq) + 2NH_3(aq) \rightarrow (NH_4)_2SO_4(aq)$

total ionic: $2H^+(aq) + SO_4^{2-}(aq) + 2NH_3(aq) \rightarrow 2NH_4^+(aq) + SO_4^{2-}(aq)$

net ionic: $2H^+(aq) + 2NH_3(aq) \rightarrow 2NH_4^+(aq)$

therefore, $H^+(aq) + NH_3(aq) \rightarrow NH_4^+(aq)$

(c) formula unit: $2CH_3COOH(aq) + Cu(OH)_2(s) \rightarrow Cu(CH_3COO)_2(aq) + 2H_2O(\ell)$

total ionic: $2CH_3COOH(aq) + Cu(OH)_2(s) \rightarrow Cu^{2+}(aq) + 2CH_3COO^-(aq) + 2H_2O(\ell)$

net ionic: $2CH_3COOH(aq) + Cu(OH)_2(s) \rightarrow Cu^{2+}(aq) + 2CH_3COO^-(aq) + 2H_2O(\ell)$

6-84. *Refer to Section 6-9 and Example 6-11.*

(a) formula unit: $H_2S(aq) + 2NaOH(aq) \rightarrow Na_2S(aq) + 2H_2O(\ell)$

total ionic: $H_2S(aq) + 2Na^+(aq) + 2OH^-(aq) \rightarrow 2Na^+(aq) + S^{2-}(aq) + 2H_2O(\ell)$

net ionic: $H_2S(aq) + 2OH^-(aq) \rightarrow S^{2-}(aq) + 2H_2O(\ell)$

(b) formula unit: $H_3PO_4(aq) + Al(OH)_3(s) \rightarrow AlPO_4(s) + 3H_2O(\ell)$

total ionic: $H_3PO_4(aq) + Al(OH)_3(s) \rightarrow AlPO_4(s) + 3H_2O(\ell)$

net ionic: $H_3PO_4(aq) + Al(OH)_3(s) \rightarrow AlPO_4(s) + 3H_2O(\ell)$

(c) formula unit: $H_2CO_3(aq) + Pb(OH)_2(s) \rightarrow PbCO_3(s) + 2H_2O(\ell)$

total ionic: $H_2CO_3(aq) + Pb(OH)_2(s) \rightarrow PbCO_3(s) + 2H_2O(\ell)$

net ionic: $H_2CO_3(aq) + Pb(OH)_2(s) \rightarrow PbCO_3(s) + 2H_2O(\ell)$

6-86. *Refer to Section 6-9 and Example 6-11.*

(a) $Mg(OH)_2(s) + 2HNO_3(aq) \rightarrow Mg(NO_3)_2(aq) + 2H_2O(\ell)$

(b) $2Al(OH)_3(s) + 3H_2SO_3(aq) \rightarrow Al_2(SO_3)_3(aq) + 6H_2O(\ell)$

(c) $2KOH(aq) + H_2CO_3(aq) \rightarrow K_2CO_3(aq) + 2H_2O(\ell)$

(d) $Zn(OH)_2(s) + 2HClO_3(aq) \rightarrow Zn(ClO_3)_2(aq) + 2H_2O(\ell)$

(e) $LiOH(aq) + CH_3COOH(aq) \rightarrow LiCH_3COO(aq) + H_2O(\ell)$

6-88. *Refer to Sections 6-1 and 6-9, the Solubility Guidelines, Table 6-4, and Examples 6-12 and 6-13.*

(a) $2AgNO_3(aq) + CaCl_2(aq) \rightarrow 2AgCl(s) + Ca(NO_3)_2(aq)$

(b) The reaction goes to completion because the ions, Ag^+ and Cl^-, are being removed from solution due to the precipitation of AgCl.

6-90. *Refer to Sections 6-1 and 6-9, Exercise 6-89 and the Solubility Guidelines summarized in Table 6-4.*

	In Formula Unit Equation	In Total Ionic Equation
(a)	$(NH_4)_2SO_4(aq)$	$2NH_4^+(aq) + SO_4^{2-}(aq)$
(b)	$NaBr(aq)$	$Na^+(aq) + Br^-(aq)$
(c)	$SrCl_2(aq)$	$Sr^{2+}(aq) + 2Cl^-(aq)$
(d)	$MgF_2(s)$	$MgF_2(s)$
(e)	$Na_2CO_3(aq)$	$2Na^+(aq) + CO_3^{2-}(aq)$

6-92. *Refer to Section 6-1 and 6-9, Exercise 6-91 and the Solubility Guidelines summarized in Table 6-4.*

(a) $BaSO_4$ insoluble

(b) $Al(NO_3)_3$ soluble

(c) CuS insoluble

(d) Na_3AsO_4 soluble

(e) $Ca(CH_3COO)_2$ soluble

6-94. *Refer to Section 6-1 and the Solubility Guidelines summarized in Tables 6-4 and 6-5.*

(a) $KClO_3$ soluble

(b) NH_4Cl soluble

(c) NH_3 soluble

(d) HNO_2 soluble

(e) PbS insoluble

6-96. *Refer to Section 6-1 and Examples 6-12 and 6-13.*

(a) formula unit: $Cu(NO_3)_2(aq) + Na_2S(aq) \rightarrow CuS(s) + 2NaNO_3(aq)$

total ionic: $Cu^{2+}(aq) + 2NO_3^-(aq) + 2Na^+(aq) + S^{2-}(aq) \rightarrow CuS(s) + 2Na^+(aq) + 2NO_3^-(aq)$

net ionic: $Cu^{2+}(aq) + S^{2-}(aq) \rightarrow CuS(s)$

(b) formula unit: $CdSO_4(aq) + H_2S(aq) \rightarrow CdS(s) + H_2SO_4(aq)$

total ionic: $Cd^{2+}(aq) + SO_4^{2-}(aq) + H_2S(aq) \rightarrow CdS(s) + 2H^+(aq) + SO_4^{2-}(aq)$

net ionic: $Cd^{2+}(aq) + H_2S(aq) \rightarrow CdS(s) + 2H^+(aq)$

(c) formula unit: $Bi_2(SO_4)_3(aq) + 3(NH_4)_2S(aq) \rightarrow Bi_2S_3(s) + 3(NH_4)_2SO_4(aq)$

total ionic: $2Bi^{3+}(aq) + 3SO_4^{2-}(aq) + 6NH_4^+(aq) + 3S^{2-}(aq) \rightarrow Bi_2S_3(s) + 6NH_4^+(aq) + 3SO_4^{2-}(aq)$

net ionic: $2Bi^{3+}(aq) + 3S^{2-}(aq) \rightarrow Bi_2S_3(s)$

6-98.   *Refer to Sections 6-9 and 6-10, the Solubility Guidelines in Section 6-1, and Example 6-11.*

(a) precipitation reaction $MnCl_2(aq) + Na_2S(aq) \rightarrow MnS(s) + 2NaCl(aq)$

(b) precipitation reaction $Na_2CO_3(aq) + ZnCl_2(aq) \rightarrow ZnCO_3(s) + 2NaCl(aq)$

(c) gas-forming reaction $K_2CO_3(aq) + 2HClO_4(aq) \rightarrow 2KClO_4(s) + CO_2(g) + H_2O(\ell)$

6-100.   *Refer to Section 6-11 and Example 6-14.*

The acid-base reactions are (a) and (k) only, in which an acid reacts with a base to give a salt and water. In all acid-base reactions, no oxidation or reduction is involved.

(a) $H_2SO_4(aq) + 2KOH(aq) \rightarrow K_2SO_4(aq) + 2H_2O(\ell)$

(k) $RbOH(aq) + HNO_3(aq) \rightarrow RbNO_3(aq) + H_2O(\ell)$

6-102.   *Refer to Section 6-5 and Example 6-4.*

The oxidation-reduction reactions are the following. Underlined elements are the ones actually being oxidized or reduced.

Net Ionic Equation	Oxidizing Agent	Reducing Agent
(b) $2Rb(s) + Br_2(\ell) \overset{heat}{\rightarrow} 2RbBr(s)$	$Br_2(\ell)$	$Rb(s)$
(c) $2I^-(aq) + F_2(g) \rightarrow 2F^-(aq) + I_2(s)$	$F_2(g)$	$I^-(aq)$
(e) $S(s) + O_2(g) \overset{heat}{\rightarrow} SO_2(g)$	$O_2(g)$	$S(s)$
(g) $HgS(s) + O_2(g) \overset{heat}{\rightarrow} Hg(\ell) + SO_2(g)$	$H\underline{g}S(s), O_2(g)$	$Hg\underline{S}(s)$
(i) $Pb(s) + 2H^+(aq) + 2Br^-(aq) \rightarrow PbBr_2(s) + H_2(g)$	$H^+(aq)$	$Pb(s)$
(j) $2H^+(aq) + 2I^-(aq) + H_2O_2(aq) \rightarrow I_2(s) + 2H_2O(\ell)$	$H_2\underline{O}_2(aq)$	$I^-(aq)$
(m) $H_2O(g) + CO(g) \overset{heat}{\rightarrow} H_2(g) + CO_2(g)$	$\underline{H}_2O(g)$	$\underline{C}O(g)$
(o) $PbSO_4(s) + PbS(s) \overset{heat}{\rightarrow} 2Pb(s) + 2SO_2(g)$	$Pb\underline{S}O_4(s), Pb\underline{S}(s)$	$Pb\underline{S}(s)$

6-104.   *Refer to Section 6-9.*

The metathesis (also called double displacement) reactions are those in which the positive and negative ions in two compounds "change partners," with no change in oxidation numbers, to form two new compounds. There are three:

(a) $H_2SO_4(aq) + 2KOH(aq) \rightarrow K_2SO_4(aq) + 2H_2O(\ell)$

(h) $AgNO_3(aq) + HCl(aq) \rightarrow AgCl(s) + HNO_3(aq)$

(k) $RbOH(aq) + HNO_3(aq) \rightarrow RbNO_3(aq) + H_2O(\ell)$

The decomposition reactions can be identified easily as one compound breaking down, i.e., decomposing, to other compounds, elements or a combination of element(s) and compound(s). There is only one: (f).

(f) $BaCO_3(s) \overset{heat}{\rightarrow} BaO(s) + CO_2 (s)$

6-108. *Refer to Sections 6-5 and 6-10.*

(a) The oxidation-reduction reactions that form gaseous products are (e), (g), (i), (m) and (o).

(b) The redox reactions that also fit the definition of gas-formation reactions because they do not have any gaseous reactants are only (i) and (o).

6-110. *Refer to Sections as stated.*

(a) Copper metal is formed by a displacement reaction. (Refer to Section 6-8 and Table 6-9.)

$$Cu(NO_3)_2(aq) + Mg(s) \rightarrow Mg(NO_3)_2(aq) + Cu(s)$$

(b) Solid barium phosphate is formed in a precipitation reaction.
(Refer to Sections 6-1, 6-9, and the Solubility Guidelines given in Table 6-4.)

$$3Ba(NO_3)_2(aq) + 2Na_3PO_4(aq) \rightarrow Ba_3(PO_4)_2(s) + 6NaNO_3(aq)$$

(c) There is no reaction because Al is a less active metal than Ca.
(Refer to Section 6-8 and Table 6-9.)

(d) Solid silver iodide is formed in a precipitation reaction.
(Refer to Sections 6-1, 6-9, and the Solubility Guidelines given in Table 6-4.)

$$AgNO_3(aq) + NaI(aq) \rightarrow AgI(s) + NaNO_3(aq)$$

6-112. *Refer to Sections as stated.*

(a) Both 1.2 M CH_3COOH and 0.12 M CH_3COOH are equally weak acids, only their concentrations are different (Section 6-1). In fact, the more dilute CH_3COOH solution actually ionizes a little more into its ions (Chapter 18).

(b) The salt produced when nitric acid, HNO_3, reacts with potassium hydroxide, KOH, is KNO_3, not KNO_4 (Section 6-9).

(c) The first two statements are correct - nickel reacts with HCl and not steam, but magnesium is active enough to react with steam. Therefore magnesium is more reactive than nickel (Section 6-8).

6-114. *Refer to Section 6-11 and Table 6-10.*

Displacement reactions are always oxidation-reduction reactions, while metathesis reactions are never redox reactions.

6-116. *Refer to Section 6-5.*

(a)
$$\overset{-2.5\,+1}{2\;C_4H_{10}(g)} + \overset{0}{13\;O_2(g)} \rightarrow \overset{+4\,-2}{8\;CO_2(g)} + \overset{+1\,-2}{10\;H_2O(g)}$$ (O_2 is in excess)

(b)
$$\overset{-2.5\,+1}{2\;C_4H_{10}(g)} + \overset{0}{9\;O_2(g)} \rightarrow \overset{+2\,-2}{8\;CO(g)} + \overset{+1\,-2}{10\;H_2O(g)}$$ (O_2 is limited)

(c) $C_4H_{10}(g) + O_2(g) \rightarrow C_2H_2(g) + 2\ CO(g) + 4\ H_2(g)$ (O_2 is very limited)

6-118. *Refer to Sections 6-1 and 6-10.*

(a) Calcite is primarily $CaCO_3$, while dolomite is a mixture of $CaCO_3$ and $MgCO_3$. This is not surprising because both Ca^{2+} and Mg^{2+} behave similarly. They are neighboring 2A elements than have lost 2 electrons to form their stable ions. In excess CO_3^{2-} ions, both $CaCO_3$ and $MgCO_3$ would precipitate out of solution as insoluble carbonates.

(b) The bubbles resulting when cold $HCl(aq)$ is applied to limestone are composed of carbon dioxide gas formed in the metathesis gas-forming reaction: $CaCO_3(s) + 2HCl(aq) \rightarrow CaCl_2(aq) + H_2O(\ell) + CO_2(g)$

6-120. *Refer to Chapter 3.*

Balanced equation: $P_4(s) + 6Cl_2(g) \rightarrow 4PCl_3(\ell)$

Explanation (particle level): When 1 molecule of solid phosphorus (P_4) reacts with 6 molecules of gaseous chlorine (Cl_2), 4 molecules of liquid phosphorus trichloride (PCl_3) are formed.

Explanation (mole level): When 1 mole of solid phosphorus molecules reacts with 6 moles of gaseous chlorine molecules, 4 moles of liquid phosphorus trichloride molecules are formed.

6-122. *Refer to Section 6-11.*

(1) formula unit: $2HNO_3(aq) + Sr(OH)_2(aq) \rightarrow Sr(NO_3)_2(aq) + 2H_2O(\ell)$

total ionic: $2H^+(aq) + 2NO_3^-(aq) + Sr^{2+}(aq) + 2OH^-(aq) \rightarrow Sr^{2+}(aq) + 2NO_3^-(aq) + 2H_2O(\ell)$

net ionic: $2H^+(aq) + 2OH^-(aq) \rightarrow 2H_2O(\ell)$

$H^+(aq) + OH^-(aq) \rightarrow H_2O(\ell)$

(2) formula unit: $H_2SO_4(aq) + 2RbOH(aq) \rightarrow Rb_2SO_4(aq) + 2H_2O(\ell)$

total ionic: $2H^+(aq) + 2SO_4^{2-}(aq) + 2Rb^+(aq) + 2OH^-(aq) \rightarrow 2Rb^+(aq) + 2SO_4^{2-}(aq) + 2H_2O(\ell)$

net ionic: $2H^+(aq) + 2OH^-(aq) \rightarrow 2H_2O(\ell)$

$H^+(aq) + OH^-(aq) \rightarrow H_2O(\ell)$

The net ionic equations for these two reactions are the same because both acid-base reactions involve a strong acid and a strong soluble base forming a soluble salt.

6-124. *Refer to Section 6-11.*

(a) acid-base reaction: $Ba(OH)_2(aq) + H_2SO_4(aq) \rightarrow BaSO_4(s) + 2H_2O(\ell)$

(b) precipitation reaction: $Ba(OH)_2(aq) + Na_2SO_4(aq) \rightarrow BaSO_4(s) + 2NaOH(aq)$

(c) gas-forming reaction: $BaCO_3(s) + H_2SO_4(aq) \rightarrow BaSO_4(s) + CO_2(g) + H_2O(\ell)$

(a) $AB + CD \rightarrow AD + CB$ metathesis reaction   (c) $A + BC \rightarrow AC + B$ displacement reaction
("switching partners")

(b) $AB \rightarrow A + B$ decomposition reaction   (d) $A + B \rightarrow AB$ combination reaction

6-128. *Refer to Chapter 3.*

(a) Balanced equation: $2KClO_3(s) \rightarrow 2KCl(s) + 3O_2(g)$

? mol O_2 = 24.0 g $KClO_3 \times \dfrac{1 \text{ mol } KClO_3}{122.6 \text{ g } KClO_3} \times \dfrac{3 \text{ mol } O_2}{2 \text{ mol } KClO_3}$ = **0.294 mol O_2**

(b) Balanced equation: $2H_2O_2(aq) \rightarrow 2H_2O(\ell) + O_2(g)$

? mol O_2 = 24.0 g $H_2O_2 \times \dfrac{1 \text{ mol } H_2O_2}{34.02 \text{ g } H_2O_2} \times \dfrac{1 \text{ mol } O_2}{2 \text{ mol } H_2O_2}$ = **0.353 mol O_2**

(c) Balanced equation: $2HgO(s) \rightarrow 2 \, Hg(\ell) + O_2(g)$

? mol O_2 = 24.0 g $HgO \times \dfrac{1 \text{ mol } HgO}{216.6 \text{ g } HgO} \times \dfrac{1 \text{ mol } O_2}{2 \text{ mol } HgO}$ = **0.0554 mol O_2**

7 Chemical Bonding

7-2. *Refer to Sections 7-2 and 7-3.*

Ionic bonding results from electrostatic interactions between ions, which can be formed by the *transfer* of one or more electrons from a *metal* to a *nonmetal* or group of nonmetals (forming a polyatomic ion, like NO_3^-). Covalent bonding, on the other hand, results from *sharing* one or more electron pairs between two *nonmetal* atoms.

(a) $K + Cl_2$ ionic bonding, since K is a metal and Cl is a nonmetal

(b) $C + O_2$ covalent bonding, since both C and O are nonmetals

(c) $N_2 + O_2$ covalent bonding, since both N and O are nonmetals

(d) $S + O_2$ covalent bonding, since both S and O are nonmetals

7-4. *Refer to Section 7-1 and Table 7-1.*

(a) Lewis dot representations for the representative elements show only the valence electrons in the outermost occupied *s* and *p* orbitals. Paired and unpaired electrons are also indicated.

(b) He: Ṡi·   ·P̈·   :N̈e: Mg: ·Ï:

7-6. *Refer to Sections 7-2 and 7-3.*

In $NaClO_3$, there is ionic bonding occurring between the Na^+ ion and the ClO_3^- ion, and covalent bonding between the O and Cl atoms in the ClO_3^- ion.

7-8. *Refer to Sections 7-2 and 7-3.*

In general, the bond between a metal and a nonmetal is ionic, whereas the bond between two nonmetals is covalent. In other words, the further apart across the periodic table the two elements are, the more likely they are to form an ionic bond.

(a) Ca (metal) and Cl (nonmetal)   ionic bond

(b) P (nonmetal) and O (nonmetal)   covalent bond

(c) Br (nonmetal) and I (nonmetal)   covalent bond

(d) Na (metal) and I (nonmetal)   ionic bond

(e) Si (metalloid) and Br (nonmetal)   covalent bond

(f) Ba (metal) and F (nonmetal)   ionic bond

7-10. *Refer to Sections 7-2 and 7-3.*

In general, whenever a metal and a nonmetal are together in a compound, it is ionic. If the compound consists only of nonmetals, it is covalent. In other words, the further apart two elements are on the periodic table, the more likely they are to form an ionic compound.

(a) $Ca(NO_3)_2$ metal + nonmetals   ionic (within the NO_3^- ion, there are covalent bonds)

(b) H_2Se nonmetals   covalent

(c) KNO_3 metal + nonmetals   ionic (within the NO_3^- ion, there are covalent bonds)

(d) $CaCl_2$ metal + nonmetal   ionic

(e)	H_2CO_3	nonmetals	covalent (H is not a metal)
(f)	NCl_3	nonmetals	covalent
(g)	Li_2O	metal + nonmetal	ionic
(h)	N_2H_4	nonmetals	covalent
(i)	$SOCl_2$	nonmetals	covalent

7-12.   *Refer to Section 7-2 and Chapter 13.*

An ionic crystal is a solid characterized by a regular, ordered arrangement of ions in three-dimensional space. The specific geometrical arrangement of the ions is controlled by

(1) the compound formula, i.e., the ratio of cations to anions,
(2) the size of the ions and
(3) the conditions (temperature and pressure) under which the solid exists.

7-14.   *Refer to Section 7-2 and Table 7-2.*

(a) $Ca + Cl_2 \rightarrow$ **$CaCl_2$**

(b) $Ba + Cl_2 \rightarrow$ **$BaCl_2$**

(c) $Na + 1/2Cl_2 \rightarrow$ **NaCl**

7-16.   *Refer to Section 7-2 and Appendix B.*

(a) Cr^{3+} [Ar] $3d^3$ (e) Cu^{2+} [Ar] $3d^9$

(b) Mn^{2+} [Ar] $3d^5$ (f) Sc^{2+} [Ar] $3d^1$ (Note: Sc^{3+} is more stable ion)

(c) Ag^+ [Kr] $4d^{10}$ (g) Fe^{2+} [Ar] $3d^6$

(d) Fe^{3+} [Ar] $3d^5$

7-18.   *Refer to Section 7-2.*

Stable binary ionic compounds are formed from ions that have noble gas configurations. None of the compounds meet this requirement. First of all, CO_4 is not an ionic compound at all because it is a covalent compound, made from 2 nonmetals. Even so, CO_4 is not stable because with O^{2-}, C would have an oxidation number of +8, which is very unlikely. Consider the following ionic compounds composed of a metal and nonmetals:

MgI ($Mg^+ + I^-$) $Al(OH)_2$ ($Al^{2+} + 2OH^-$) InF_2 ($In^{2+} + 2F^-$)

$RbCl_2$ ($Rb^{2+} + 2Cl^-$)   CsS ($Cs^{2+} + S^{2-}$) Be_3O ($3Be^+ + O^{3-}$).

Neither Mg^+, Al^{2+}, In^{2+}, Rb^{2+}, Cs^{2+}, Be^+ nor O^{3-} have noble gas configurations.

7-20.   *Refer to Section 7-2.*

(a) Cations with ....$3s^2\,3p^6$ electronic configurations are isoelectronic with argon. Examples: K^+, Ca^{2+}

(b) Cations with ....$6s^2\,6p^6$ electronic configurations are isoelectronic with radon. Examples: Fr^+, Ra^{2+}

7-22. *Refer to Section 7-3 and Figure 7-4.*

Figure 7-4 is a plot of potential energy versus the distance between 2 hydrogen atoms. The resulting function is the sum of two opposing forces: (1) the attractive force between the negatively charged electron of one H atom and the positively charged nucleus of the other H atom, and (2) the repulsive force between the two positively charged nuclei.

When the two atoms are relatively far apart, there is essentially no interaction at all between them; both the attractive and repulsive forces are about zero. As the two atoms get closer, the attractive forces dominate, and the potential energy decreases to a minimum at a distance of 0.74 Å, which is the H–H bond length. At distances less than 0.74 Å, the repulsive forces become more important and the energy increases sharply.

7-24. *Refer to Section 7-3.*

(a) A single covalent bond contains 2 shared electrons.

(b) A double covalent bond contains 4 shared electrons.

(c) A triple covalent bond contains 6 shared electrons.

7-26. *Refer to Section 7-4, and Tables 7-3 and 7-4.*

Here is the listing of the bond energies and bond lengths of C–O, C=O, and C≡O:

	Single bond C–O	Double bond C=O	Triple bond C≡O
Bond energy (kJ/mol)	358	732 (799 in CO_2)	1072
Bond length (Å)	1.43	1.22	1.13

We can easily see that as we go from single bond to double bond to triple bond between carbon and oxygen, the bond energies increase while the bond lengths decrease.

	Single bond C–C	Double bond C=C	Triple bond C≡C
Bond energy (kJ/mol)	346	602	835
Bond length (Å)	1.54	1.34	1.21

The same relationships are seen as we go from single bond to double bond to triple bond between carbon and carbon; the bond energies increase while the bond lengths decrease.

Overall, the bond energies are less for C–C bonds and the bond lengths are greater than for the corresponding C–O bonds

7-28. *Refer to Section 7-5.*

Lewis formulas are representations of molecules or ions which show

- the element symbols,
- the order in which the atoms are connected,
- the number of valence electrons linking the atoms together,
- the number of lone pairs of valence electrons not used for bonding,
- and the number and kind of bonds.

They do not show the shape of a chemical species.

96

H_2O H:Ö:H   H-Ö-H

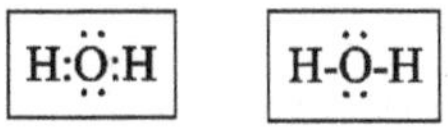

$S = N - A$
$= [2 \times 2(\text{for H}) + 1 \times 8(\text{for O})] - [2 \times 1(\text{for H}) + 1 \times 6(\text{for O})]$
$= 12 - 8$
$= 4$ (there are 4 electrons shared in the molecule)

NH_3 H:N:H / H   H-N-H / H

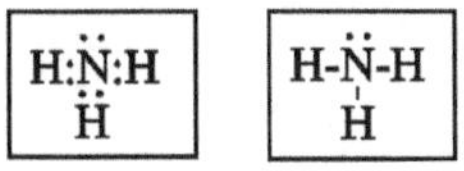

$S = N - A$
$= [3 \times 2(\text{for H}) + 1 \times 8(\text{for N})] - [3 \times 1(\text{for H}) + 1 \times 5(\text{for N})]$
$= 14 - 8$
$= 6$ (there are 6 electrons shared in the molecule)

OH^- [:Ö:H]⁻   [:Ö-H]⁻

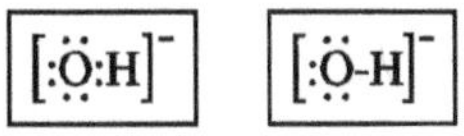

$S = N - A$
$= [1 \times 2(\text{for H}) + 1 \times 8(\text{for O})] - [1 \times 1(\text{for H}) + 1 \times 6(\text{for O}) + 1e^-]$
$= 10 - 8$
$= 2$ (there are 2 electrons shared in the diatomic ion)

Br^- :Br:⁻

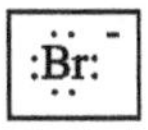

(a) SCl_2 :Cl:S:Cl:

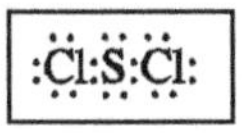

$S = N - A$
$= [1 \times 8(\text{for S}) + 2 \times 8(\text{for Cl})] - [1 \times 6(\text{for S}) + 2 \times 7(\text{for Cl})]$
$= 4$ (there are 4 electrons shared)

(b) AsF_3 :F:As:F: / :F:

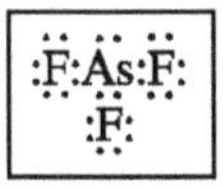

$S = N - A$
$= [1 \times 8(\text{for As}) + 3 \times 8(\text{for F})] - [1 \times 5(\text{for As}) + 3 \times 7(\text{for F})]$
$= 6$ (there are 6 electrons shared)

(c) ICl :I:Cl:

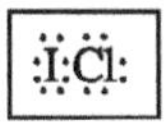

$S = N - A$
$= [1 \times 8(\text{for I}) + 1 \times 8(\text{for Cl})] - [1 \times 7(\text{for I}) + 1 \times 7(\text{for Cl})]$
$= 2$ (there are 2 electrons shared)

(d) $SeCl_2$:Cl:Se:Cl:

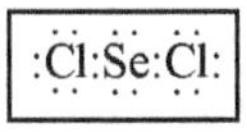

$S = N - A$
$= [1 \times 8(\text{for Se}) + 2 \times 8(\text{for Cl})] - [1 \times 6(\text{for Se}) + 2 \times 7(\text{for Cl})]$
$= 4$ (there are 4 electrons shared)

The number of valence electrons in a compound is the sum of the valence electrons of each atom in the compound. If the species is a positively-charged ion, one must subtract the charge on the ion to determine the total number of valence electrons. If the species is negatively-charged, one must add the charge on the ion to determine the number of valence electrons.

(a) H_2Se $2 \times 1(\text{for H}) + 1 \times 6(\text{for Se}) = 8$ valence electrons

(b) PCl_3 $1 \times 5(\text{for P}) + 3 \times 7(\text{for Cl}) = 26$ valence electrons

(c) ClO_4^- $1 \times 7(\text{for Cl}) + 4 \times 6(\text{for O}) + 1\ e^- = 32$ valence electrons

(d) OH^- $1 \times 6(\text{for O}) + 1 \times 1(\text{for H}) + 1\ e^- = 8$ valence electrons

(a) H_2Se H:S̈e:H

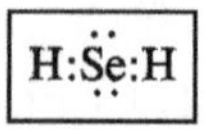

$S = N - A$
$= [2 \times 2(\text{for H}) + 1 \times 8(\text{for Se})] - [2 \times 1(\text{for H}) + 1 \times 6(\text{for Se})]$
$= 4$ shared electrons

(b) PCl_3 :C̈l : P̈ : C̈l:
                  :C̈l:

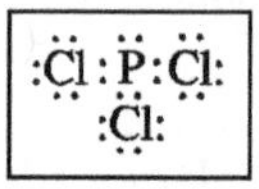

$S = N - A$
$= [1 \times 8(\text{for P}) + 3 \times 8(\text{for Cl})] - [1 \times 5(\text{for P}) + 3 \times 7(\text{for Cl})]$
$= 6$ shared electrons

(c) ClO_4^-
$\begin{bmatrix} & :\ddot{O}: & \\ :\ddot{O}:Cl:\ddot{O}: & \\ & :\ddot{O}: & \end{bmatrix}^-$

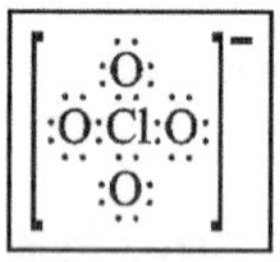

$S = N - A$
$= [1 \times 8(\text{for Cl}) + 4 \times 8(\text{for O})] - [1 \times 7(\text{for Cl}) + 4 \times 6(\text{for O}) + 1 \, e^-]$
$= 8$ shared electrons

(d) OH^- $\left[:\ddot{O}:H \right]^-$

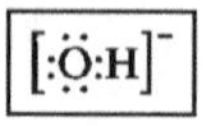

$S = N - A$
$= [1 \times 2(\text{for H}) + 1 \times 8(\text{for O})] - [1 \times 1(\text{for H}) + 1 \times 6(\text{for O}) + 1e^-]$
$= 10 - 8$
$= 2$ shared electrons

(a) H_2CO H
                C::Ö
                H

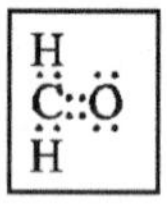

$S = N - A$
$= [2 \times 2(\text{for H}) + 1 \times 8(\text{for C}) + 1 \times 8(\text{for O})]$
$\qquad - [2 \times 1(\text{for H}) + 1 \times 4(\text{for C}) + 1 \times 6(\text{for O})]$
$= 8$ shared electrons

(b) ClF :C̈l:B̈r:

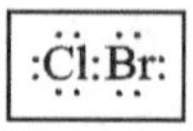

$S = N - A$
$= [1 \times 8(\text{for Cl}) + 1 \times 8(\text{for Br})] - [1 \times 7(\text{for Cl}) + 1 \times 7(\text{for Br})]$
$= 2$ shared electrons

(c) BF_4^-
$\begin{bmatrix} & :\ddot{F}: & \\ :\ddot{F}:B:\ddot{F}: & \\ & :\ddot{F}: & \end{bmatrix}^-$

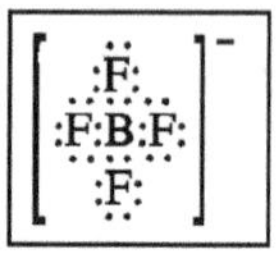

$S = N - A$
$= [1 \times 8(\text{for B}) + 4 \times 8(\text{for F})] - [1 \times 3(\text{for B}) + 4 \times 7(\text{for F}) + 1e^-]$
$= 8$ shared electrons

(d) PO_4^{3-}
$\begin{bmatrix} & :\ddot{O}: & \\ :\ddot{O}:P:\ddot{O}: & \\ & :\ddot{O}: & \end{bmatrix}^{3-}$

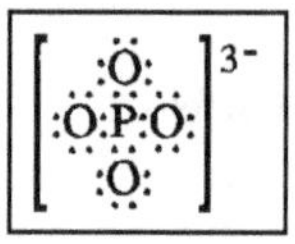

$S = N - A$
$= [1 \times 8(\text{for P}) + 4 \times 8(\text{for O})] - [1 \times 5(\text{for P}) + 4 \times 6(\text{for O}) + 3e^-]$
$= 8$ shared electrons

(e) $HClO_3$ H:Ö:Cl:Ö:
                    :Ö:

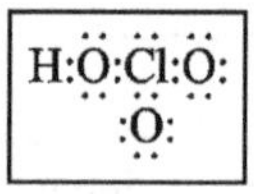

$S = N - A$
$= [1 \times 8(\text{for Cl}) + 3 \times 8(\text{for O}) + 1 \times 2(\text{for H})]$
$\qquad - [1 \times 7(\text{for Cl}) + 3 \times 6(\text{for O}) + 1 \times 1(\text{for H})]$
$= 8$ shared electrons

Nonmetal atoms must gain noble gas configuration by sharing electrons with each other when forming covalent compounds, rather than transferring electrons from one atom to another as is done when forming ionic compounds, because nonmetals have similar electronegativity values. The electronegativity difference between two nonmetal atoms is not great enough for electron transfer to happen.

CCl₄

:Cl:
:Cl:C:Cl:
:Cl:

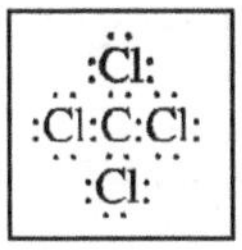

$S = N - A$
$= [1 \times 8(\text{for C}) + 4 \times 8(\text{for Cl})] - [1 \times 4(\text{for C}) + 4 \times 7(\text{for Cl})]$
$= 8$ shared electrons

SiF₄

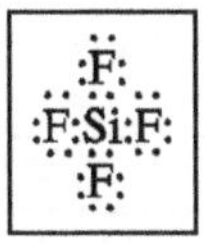

:F:
:F:Si:F:
:F:

$S = N - A$
$= [1 \times 8(\text{for Si}) + 4 \times 8(\text{for F})] - [1 \times 4(\text{for Si}) + 4 \times 7(\text{for F})]$
$= 8$ shared electrons

PbI₄

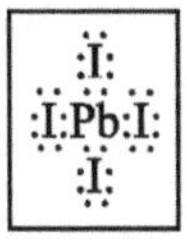

:I:
:I:Pb:I:
:I:

$S = N - A$
$= [1 \times 8(\text{for Pb}) + 4 \times 8(\text{for I})] - [1 \times 4(\text{for Pb}) + 4 \times 7(\text{for I})]$
$= 8$ shared electrons

All three compounds obey the octet rule and are formed from a 4A element bonded to four atoms of a 7A element and, therefore, look very similar.

The formal charge, FC = (Group No.) - [(No. of bonds) + (No. of unshared e^-)]

(a)

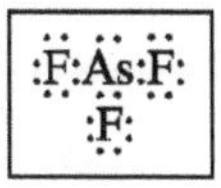

:F:As:F:
:F:

for As, FC = 5 - (3 + 2) = 0
for F,   FC = 7 - (1 + 6) = 0

(b)

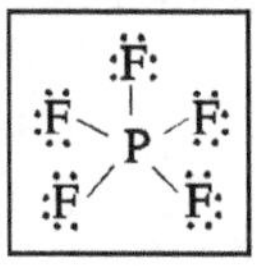

:F:
:F:-P-:F:
:F: :F:

for P,   FC = 5 - (5 + 0) = 0
for F,   FC = 7 - (1 + 6) = 0

(c)

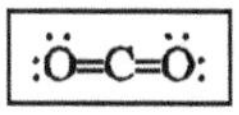

:Ö=C=Ö:

for C,   FC = 4 - (4 + 0) = 0
for O,   FC = 6 - (2 + 4) = 0

(d)

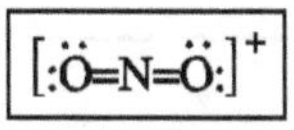

[:Ö=N=Ö:]⁺

for N,   FC = 5 - (4 + 0) = +1
for O,   FC = 6 - (2 + 4) = 0

(e)

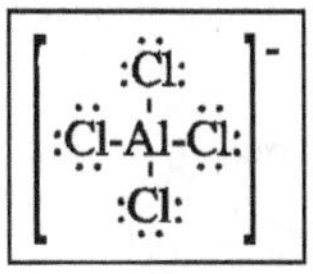

[:Cl:]⁻
:Cl-Al-Cl:
:Cl:

for Al, FC = 3 - (4 + 0) = -1
for Cl, FC = 7 - (1 + 6) = 0

Although one can draw a dot structure for the sulfate ion that obeys the octet rule, a better structure with more accurate bond lengths can be produced using the concept of formal charge and the $3d$ orbitals available to sulfur. Here are six resonance forms of the sulfate ion. The singly bonded oxygen atoms have a formal charge of -1; all the other atoms have a formal charge of 0. The true structure is the average of all the resonance structures.

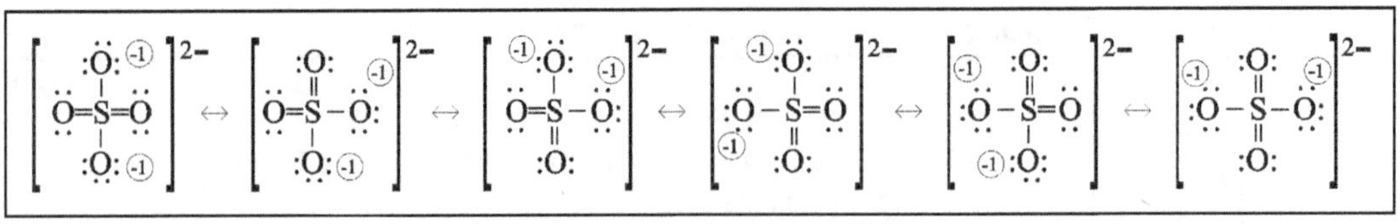

$$\left[\begin{array}{c} :\!\ddot{O}\!:\!\overset{\text{-}\textcircled{1}}{} \\ \overset{..}{O}=\overset{}{S}=\overset{..}{O} \\ :\!\ddot{O}\!:\!\overset{\text{-}\textcircled{1}}{} \end{array}\right]^{2-} \leftrightarrow \left[\begin{array}{c} :\!\ddot{O}\!: \\ \overset{..}{O}=\overset{\parallel}{S}-\overset{..}{O}\!:\!\overset{\text{-}\textcircled{1}}{} \\ :\!\ddot{O}\!:\!\overset{\text{-}\textcircled{1}}{} \end{array}\right]^{2-} \leftrightarrow \left[\begin{array}{c} \overset{\text{-}\textcircled{1}}{}:\!\ddot{O}\!:\!\overset{\text{-}\textcircled{1}}{} \\ \overset{..}{O}=\overset{\parallel}{S}-\overset{..}{O}\!: \\ :\!\ddot{O}\!: \end{array}\right]^{2-} \leftrightarrow \left[\begin{array}{c} \overset{\text{-}\textcircled{1}}{}:\!\ddot{O}\!: \\ :\!\overset{|}{O}-\overset{|}{S}=\overset{..}{O} \\ \overset{\text{-}\textcircled{1}}{}\;:\!\ddot{O}\!: \end{array}\right]^{2-} \leftrightarrow \left[\begin{array}{c} \overset{\text{-}\textcircled{1}}{}\quad:\!\ddot{O}\!: \\ :\!\overset{|}{O}-\overset{\parallel}{S}=\overset{..}{O} \\ \overset{\text{-}\textcircled{1}}{}:\!\ddot{O}\!: \end{array}\right]^{2-} \leftrightarrow \left[\begin{array}{c} \overset{\text{-}\textcircled{1}}{}\quad:\!\ddot{O}\!:\!\overset{\text{-}\textcircled{1}}{} \\ :\!\overset{|}{O}-\overset{|}{S}-\overset{..}{O}\!: \\ :\!\ddot{O}\!: \end{array}\right]^{2-}$$

All the arrangements have the same stability. Since the ion is actually tetrahedral in shape and not square planar, all the bonds are equidistant from each other, even though it doesn't look that way on paper.

7-48. *Refer to Sections 7-5 and 7-6, and Example 7-1.*

butane:

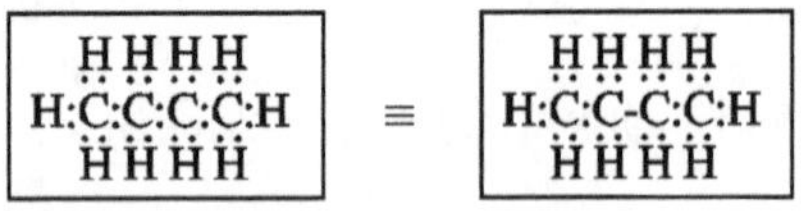

$S = N - A$
$= [4 \times 8(\text{for C}) + 10 \times 2(\text{for H})]$
$\qquad - [4 \times 4(\text{for C}) + 10 \times 1(\text{for H})]$
$= 26$ shared electrons

The indicated bond in butane is a nonpolar covalent single bond between two carbon atoms.

propane:

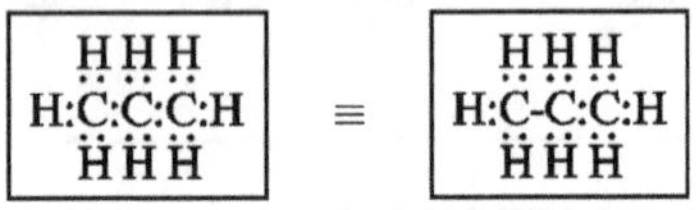

$S = N - A$
$= [3 \times 8(\text{for C}) + 8 \times 2(\text{for H})]$
$\qquad - [3 \times 4(\text{for C}) + 8 \times 1(\text{for H})]$
$= 20$ shared electrons

The indicated bond in propane is also a nonpolar covalent single bond between two carbon atoms.

7-50. *Refer to Sections 7-5 and 7-6, and Examples 7-1 and 7-2.*

(a) C_2F_4

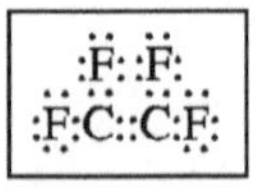

$S = N - A$
$= [2 \times 8(\text{for C}) + 4 \times 8(\text{for F})] - [2 \times 4(\text{for C}) + 4 \times 7(\text{for F})]$
$= 12$ shared electrons

(b) CH_2CHCN

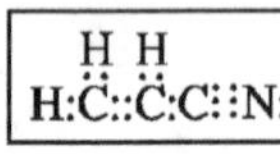

$S = N - A$
$= [3 \times 8(\text{for C}) + 3 \times 2(\text{for H}) + 1 \times 8(\text{for N})]$
$\qquad - [3 \times 4(\text{for C}) + 3 \times 1(\text{for H}) + 1 \times 5(\text{for N})]$
$= 18$ shared electrons

7-52. *Refer to Sections 7-5, 7-6 and 7-8, and Examples 7-1, 7-4 and 7-5.*

(a) $BeBr_2$

The octet rule is not valid without modification (Section 7-8, Limitation A).

$A = 1 \times 2(\text{for Be}) + 2 \times 7(\text{for Br}) = 16$
$\qquad$ (total number of valence electrons)

(b) BBr_3

:Br:
:Br: B :Br: :Br:
                :Br-B-Br:

The octet rule is not valid without modification (Section 7-8, Limitation B).

$A = 1 \times 3(\text{for B}) + 3 \times 7(\text{for Br}) = 24$
$\qquad$ (total number of valence electrons)

(c) NCl_3

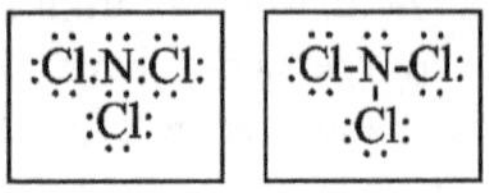

:Cl:N:Cl: :Cl-N-Cl:
   :Cl: :Cl:

$S = N - A$
$= [1 \times 8(\text{for N}) + 3 \times 8(\text{for Cl})] - [1 \times 5(\text{for N}) + 3 \times 7(\text{for Cl})]$
$= 6$ shared electrons

(d) $AlCl_3$ The octet rule is not valid without modification
        (Section 7-8, Limitation B).
        A = 1 × 3(for Al) + 3 × 7(for Cl) = 24 (total no. of valence electrons)

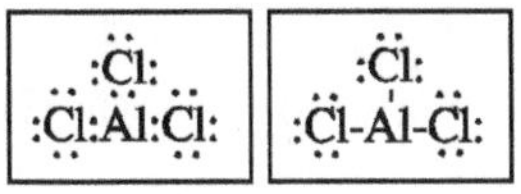

Compounds (a), (b) and (d) have a central atom that disobeys the octet rule with a share in less than an octet of valence electrons.

7-54.   Refer to Sections 7-5, 7-6 and 7-8, and Examples 7-1 and 7-5.

(a) CH_2Cl_2 $S = N - A$
        = [1 × 8(for C) + 2 × 2(for H) + 2 × 8(for Cl)]
                - [1 × 4(for C) + 2 × 1(for H) + 2 × 7(for Cl)]
        = 8 shared electrons

(b) BF_3 The octet rule is not valid without modification
        (Section 7-8, Limitation B).
        A = 1 × 3(for B) + 3 × 7(for Br) = 24
                (total no. of valence electrons)

(c) BCl_4^- $S = N - A$
        = [1 × 8(for B) + 4 × 8(for Cl)]
                - [1 × 3(for B) + 4 × 7(for Cl) + 1e$^-$]
        = 8 shared electrons

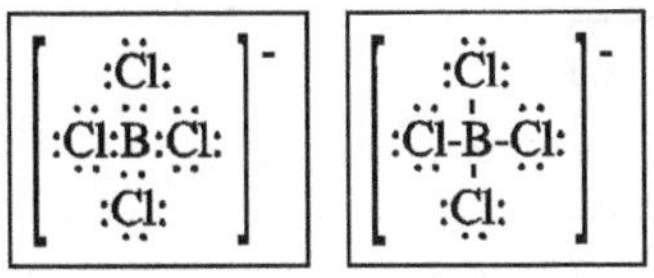

(d) AlF_4^- $S = N - A$
        = [1 × 8(for Al) + 4 × 8(for F)]
                - [1 × 3(for Al) + 4 × 7(for F) + 1e$^-$]
        = 8 shared electrons

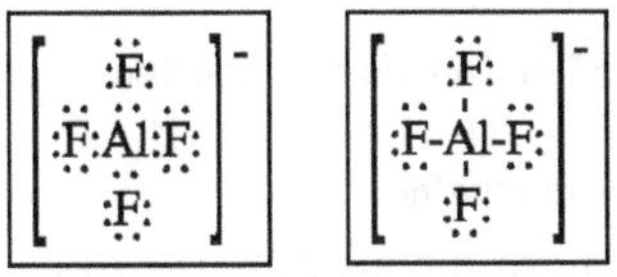

Only **Compound (b)** has a central atom that disobeys the octet rule with a share in less than an octet of valence electrons.

7-56.   Refer to Sections 7-5, 7-6 and 7-8, and Examples 7-1 and 7-5.

(1) NO_2 The octet rule is not valid without modification (Section 7-8, Limitation
        (1 of 4 resonance   C).
        structures) A = 1 × 5(for N) + 2 × 6(for O) = 17 (total number of valence electrons)

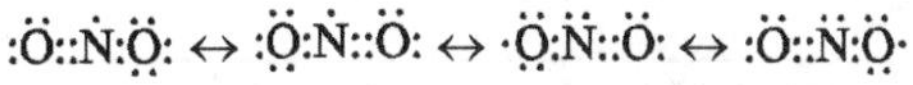

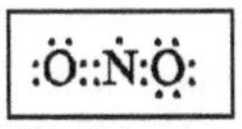

        :Ö::N:Ö: ↔ :Ö:N::Ö: ↔ ·Ö:N::Ö: ↔ :Ö::N:Ö·

(2) SF_4 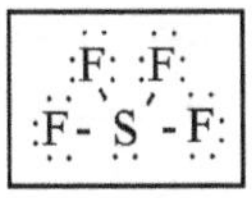   The octet rule is not valid without modification (Section 7-8, Limitation
        D).
        A = 1 × 6(for S) + 4 × 7(for F) = 34 (total no. of valence electrons)

(3) NH_3 $S = N - A$
        = [3 × 2(for H) + 1 × 8(for N)] - [3 × 1(for H) + 1 × 5(for N)]
        = 14 - 8 = 6 (there are 6 electrons shared in the molecule)

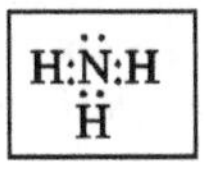

(4) SO_3

$$\boxed{\begin{array}{c} \ddot{O}::S:\ddot{O} \\ :\ddot{O}: \end{array}}$$

(1 of 3 resonance structures)

$S = N - A$
$= [1 \times 8(\text{for S}) + 3 \times 8(\text{for O})] - [1 \times 6(\text{for S}) + 3 \times 6(\text{for S})]$
$= 32 - 24 = 8$ shared electrons

(5) ClO_2

$$\boxed{:\ddot{O}:\ddot{Cl}:\ddot{O}:}$$

The octet rule is not valid without modification (Section 7-8, Limitation C).
$A = 1 \times 7(\text{for Cl}) + 2 \times 6(\text{for O}) = 19$ (total number of valence electrons)

(6) ClO_2^-

$$\boxed{[:\ddot{O}:\ddot{Cl}:\ddot{O}:]^-}$$

$S = N - A$
$= [1 \times 8(\text{for Cl}) + 2 \times 8(\text{for O})] - [1 \times 7(\text{for Cl}) + 2 \times 6(\text{for O}) + 1\ e^-]$
$= 24 - 20 = 4$ shared electrons

Only **NH_3 , SO_3 and ClO_2^-** have central atoms that obey the octet rule. **NO_2 and ClO_2** are odd-electron molecules.

7-58. *Refer to Section 7-9 and Example 7-9.*

Ozone, O_3 exhibits resonance, obeying the octet rule: $S = N - A = [3 \times 8(\text{for O})] - [3 \times 6(\text{for O})] = 6$ shared e^-

$$\boxed{:\ddot{O}::\ddot{O}:\ddot{O}: \quad \leftrightarrow \quad :\ddot{O}:\ddot{O}::\ddot{O}:}$$

7-60. *Refer to Sections 7-4 and 7-9, and Table 7-4.*

As the number of electrons in a bond increases, the energy of the bond increases, and the length of the bond decreases. Therefore,

$$C–C > C=C > C\equiv C \qquad \text{in bond length}$$

From the discussion of resonance, the carbon-carbon bond length in the six-membered ring of toluene is intermediate in length between a single bond and a double bond. Therefore, this bond would be shorter than a regular single bond found between the CH_3 group and the carbon atom on the ring.

7-62. *Refer to Section 7-8 and 7-9, and Example 7-9.*

(a) NO_2^-

$$\boxed{[:\ddot{O}:\ddot{N}:\ddot{O}:]^- \leftrightarrow [:\ddot{O}::\ddot{N}:\ddot{O}:]^-}$$

$S = N - A$
$= [1 \times 8(\text{for N}) + 2 \times 8(\text{for O})]$
$\quad - [1 \times 5(\text{for N}) + 2 \times 6(\text{for O}) + 1e^-]$
$= 6$ shared electrons

(b) BrO_3^-

$$\boxed{\begin{array}{c}\ddot{O}::Br::\ddot{O} \\ :\ddot{O}:\end{array}}^- \leftrightarrow \boxed{\begin{array}{c}\ddot{O}::Br:\ddot{O} \\ :\ddot{O}:\end{array}}^- \leftrightarrow \boxed{\begin{array}{c}:\ddot{O}:Br::\ddot{O} \\ :\ddot{O}:\end{array}}^-$$

The octet rule is not valid.
$A = 1 \times 7(\text{for Br}) + 3 \times 6(\text{for O}) + 1e^-$
$= 26$ available electrons

(c) PO_4^{3-}

$$\boxed{\begin{array}{c}:\ddot{O}: \\ \ddot{O}:P:\ddot{O} \\ :\ddot{O}:\end{array}}^{3-} \leftrightarrow \boxed{\begin{array}{c}:\ddot{O}: \\ :\ddot{O}:P::\ddot{O} \\ :\ddot{O}:\end{array}}^{3-} \leftrightarrow \boxed{\begin{array}{c}:\ddot{O}: \\ :\ddot{O}:P:\ddot{O}: \\ :\ddot{O}:\end{array}}^{3-} \leftrightarrow \boxed{\begin{array}{c}:\ddot{O}: \\ :\ddot{O}:P:\ddot{O}: \\ :\ddot{O}:\end{array}}^{3-}$$

The octet rule is not valid.
$A = 1 \times 5(\text{for P}) + 4 \times 6(\text{for O}) + 3e^-$
$= 32$ available electrons

(a) $ElBr_3$

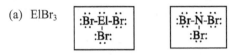

El is located in Group 5A because it brings 5 valence electrons to the compound. The example shown is NBr_3.

(b) ElO_2

:Ö::El::Ö: :Ö::C::Ö:

El is located in Group 4A because it brings 4 valence electrons to the compound. The example shown is CO_2.

(c) ElH_4^+

$\begin{bmatrix} H \\ H:El:H \\ H \end{bmatrix}^+$ $\begin{bmatrix} H \\ H:N:H \\ H \end{bmatrix}^+$

El is located in Group 5A because it brings 5 valence electrons to the ion. One electron was lost giving the ion a 1+ charge. The example shown is NH_4^+.

(d) ElH_3^+

$\begin{bmatrix} H:El:H \\ H \end{bmatrix}^+$ $\begin{bmatrix} H:Ö:H \\ H \end{bmatrix}^+$

El is located in Group 6A because it brings 6 valence electrons to the ion. One electron was lost giving the ion a 1+ charge. The example shown is the hydronium ion, H_3O^+.

(a) SO_2 exhibits resonance and obeys the octet rule:

Ö::S:Ö: ↔   :Ö:S::Ö

$S = N - A$ = [1 x 8(for S) + 2 x 8(for O)] - [1 x 6(for S) + 2 x 6(for O)] = 6 shared electrons

(b) NO_2 exhibits resonance, but it violates the octet rule because the compound contains an odd number of valence electrons, 17 (Section 7-8, Limitation C).

:Ö::N:Ö: ↔   :Ö:N::Ö: ↔   ·Ö:N::Ö: ↔   :Ö::N:Ö·

A = 1 x 5(for N) + 2 x 6(for O) = 17 (total number of valence electrons)

(c) CO exhibits resonance. It is known from experiments that the C-O bond in CO is intermediate between a typical double and triple bond length. Only one resonance structure obeys the octet rule.

:C:::O: ↔   :C::Ö

$S = N - A$
= [1 x 8(for C) + 1 x 8(for O)] - [1 x 4(for C) + 1 x 6(for O)]
= 16 - 10
= 6 shared electrons

(d) O_3 exhibits resonance and obeys the octet rule.

:Ö::O:Ö: ↔   :Ö:O::Ö:

$S = N - A$ = [3 x 8(for O)] - [3 x 6(for O)] = 24 - 18 = 6 shared electrons

(e) SO_3 exhibits resonance and obeys the octet rule.

Ö::S:Ö: ↔   :Ö:S:Ö: ↔   :Ö:S::Ö
:Ö: :Ö: :Ö:

$S = N - A$ = [1 x 8(for S) + 3 x 8(for O)] - [1 x 6(for S) + 3 x 6(for O)] = 8 shared electrons

(f) $(NH_4)_2SO_4$ is an ionic solid composed of covalently bonded polyatomic ions; both obey the octet rule:

NH_4^+

$$\begin{bmatrix} \text{H} \\ \text{H:N:H} \\ \text{H} \end{bmatrix}^+$$

$S = N - A$
$= [4 \times 2(\text{for H}) + 1 \times 8(\text{for N})] - [4 \times 1(\text{for H}) + 1 \times 5(\text{for N}) - 1\ e^-]$
$= 16 - 8$
$= 8$ shared electrons

SO_4^{2-}

$$\begin{bmatrix} \text{:Ö:} \\ \text{:Ö:S:Ö:} \\ \text{:Ö:} \end{bmatrix}^{2-}$$

$S = N - A$
$= [4 \times 8(\text{for O}) + 1 \times 8(\text{for S})] - [4 \times 6(\text{for O}) + 1 \times 6(\text{for S}) + 2\ e^-]$
$= 40 - 32 = 8$ shared electrons

(See Exercise 7-46 Solution for more appropriate Lewis formulas due to formal charge examination.)

7-68.   *Refer to Section 7-10 and Example 7-10.*

An HCl molecule is a heteronuclear diatomic molecule composed of H (EN = 2.1) and Cl (EN = 3.0). Because the electronegativities of the elements are different, the pull on the electrons in the covalent bond between them is unequal. Hence HCl is a polar molecule.

A homonuclear diatomic molecule contains a nonpolar bond, since the electron pair between the two atoms is shared equally. Cl_2 is an example of a homonuclear diatomic molecule.

7-70.   *Refer to Section 7-10.*

In the periodic table, values of electronegativities increase from left to right across a period and from bottom to top within a group.

So if we examine the bonds, (a) C–F, (b) S–F, (c) Si–F and (d) O–F, and want to know which one is the most polar, we see that what we really want to know is which atom (C, S, Si, or O) has an electronegativity value that is most different from that of F (Period 2 and Group 7A). That would be Si, since it in the 4A group and in Period 3.

7-72.   *Refer to Section 7-10, Table 6-3 and Example 7-10.*

Electronegativity is defined as the tendency of an atom to attract electrons to itself in a chemical bond.

Electrons are more attracted to the fluorine atom in the C–F bond than to the bromine atom in the C–Br bond because the F atom has a higher electronegativity value (EN = 4.0) than the bromine atom (EN = 2.8).

7-74.   *Refer to Sections 7-10, 7-11 and 7-12, Table 6-3 and Example 7-10.*

(a) $\overset{\delta+}{C} - \overset{\delta-}{O}$ (ΔEN = 1.0) is more polar than $\overset{\delta+}{C} - \overset{\delta-}{N}$ (ΔEN = 0.5)

(b) Both the C – S (ΔEN = 0) bond and the N – Cl (ΔEN = 0) bond are non-polar bonds and as such, have no dipole moment.

(c) $\overset{\delta+}{P} - \overset{\delta-}{N}$ (ΔEN = 0.9) is more polar than P – H (ΔEN = 0.0)

(d) $\overset{\delta+}{B} - \overset{\delta-}{I}$ (ΔEN = 0.5) is more polar than $\overset{\delta+}{B} - \overset{\delta-}{H}$ (ΔEN = 0.1)

(a) The two pairs of elements most likely to form ionic bonds are (1) Ba (metal) and F (nonmetal) and (2) K (metal) and O (nonmetal).

(b) We know that bond polarity increases with increasing Δ(EN), the difference in electronegativity between 2 atoms that are bonded together.

Bond	I – H	C – F	N – F
EN	2.5 2.1	2.5 4.0	3.0 4.0
Δ(EN)	0.4	1.5	1.0

Therefore, the least polar bond is I–H and the most polar bond is C–F.

The use of ΔEN alone to distinguish between ionic and polar covalent bonds will lead to the mis-labeling of some bonds, especially when the elements, H and F are involved.

Position on the periodic table can also be used as an indicator:

metal + nonmetal $\rightarrow$ ionic bond, and the compound is generally a solid and melts at high temperatures, and nonmetal + nonmetal $\rightarrow$ covalent bond, and the compound is generally a liquid or gas at room temperature.

However, there are also many exceptions, especially when Be is involved.

	ΔEN	Bonding Type
(a) K (metal, EN = 0.9) and O (nonmetal, EN = 3.5)	2.6	ionic (K_2O, decomposes at 350°C)
(b) Br (nonmetal, EN = 2.8) and I (nonmetal, EN = 2.5)	0.3	polar covalent (IBr, m.p. 42°C)
(c) Na (metal, EN = 1.0) and H (nonmetal, EN = 2.1)	1.1	ionic (NaH, m.p. 800°C)
(d) O (nonmetal, EN = 3.5) and O (nonmetal, EN = 3.5)	0.0	nonpolar covalent (O_2, gas)
(e) H (nonmetal, EN = 2.1) and O (nonmetal, EN = 3.5)	1.4	polar covalent (H_2O is a liquid)

The bond with the greater "ionic character" is the bond between atoms with the greater difference in electronegativity.

(a) Na–Cl (ΔEN = 2.0) has more ionic character than Mg–Cl (ΔEN = 1.8)

(b) Ca–S (ΔEN = 1.5) has more ionic character than Fe–S (ΔEN = 0.8)

(c) Al–Br (ΔEN = 1.3) has more ionic character than O–Br (ΔEN = 0.7)

(d) Ra–H (ΔEN = 1.1) has more ionic character than C–H (ΔEN = 0.4)

A molecule or polyatomic ion for which two or more Lewis formulas with the same arrangements of atoms can be drawn to describe the bonding is said to exhibit resonance. The two structures given here do not have the same arrangement of atoms, and hence are not resonance structures.

A chemical bond exhibiting 100% "covalent character" and 0% "ionic character" occurs between identical nonmetals atoms in which the difference in electronegativity (ΔEN) is zero. An example is the H–H bond. There are atoms with essentially the same electronegativity, e.g. N and Cl both have an electronegativity equal to 3.0 to 2 significant figures, so the N–Cl bond would exhibit close to 100% "covalent character" and 0% "ionic character".

7-86. *Refer to Sections 7-10 and 7-11.*

Electrostatic charge potential (ECP) plots integrate dipole moment, electronegativity, and partial charges. It is a visual representation of the **relative polarity** of a molecule.

Both Cl_2 and F_2 are nonpolar molecules with nonpolar bonds. However, Cl_2 is larger than F_2, so it is easy to see which is which.

7-88. *Refer to Sections 7-10 and 7-11, and Table 7-4.*

From Table 7-4, there are indications that there is a trend of longer bond lengths as we move down a group.

VIA Group: H–O (0.94 Å) < H–S (1.32 Å) looking at X–O vs. X–S bond lengths

C–O (1.43 Å) < C–S (1.81 Å)

N–O (1.36 Å) < N–S (1.74 Å)

F–O (1.30 Å) < F–S (1.68 Å)

S–O (1.70 Å) < S–S (2.08 Å)

O–O (1.32 Å) < O–S (1.70 Å)

VIIA Group: H–H (0.74 Å) < H–F (0.92 Å) looking at X–H vs. X–F bond lengths

C–H (1.10 Å) < C–F (1.41 Å)

N–H (0.98 Å) < N–F (1.34 Å)

O–H (0.94 Å) < O–F (1.30 Å)

F–H (0.92 Å) < F–F (1.28 Å)

S–H (1.32 Å) < S–F (1.68 Å)

Looking at these examples, in every case X–O < X–S in bond length and X–H < X–F in bond length.

7-90. *Refer to the Introduction to Chapter 7 and Section 7-12.*

Ionic compounds, as compared to covalent compounds, tend to have greater densities, higher melting and boiling points, and can be soluble in the very polar solvent, water, if the ionic bond is not too strong.

Compounds with more ionic character: $SnCl_2$, $SnBr_2$, SnI_2, and $PbCl_2$
Compounds with more covalent character: $SnCl_4$, SnI_4, $SnBr_4$ and $PbCl_4$

Metals with +4 charge appear to have more covalent character than those with +2 charge.

7-92. *Refer to Sections 7-10 and 7-11.*

(a) Ca_3N_2 calcium nitride (ionic)

(b) Al_2O_3 aluminum oxide (ionic)

(c) K₂Se   potassium selenide (ionic)

(d) SrBr₂   strontium bromide (ionic)

7-94.   *Refer to Sections 6-2, 7-5, 7-6 and 7-9.*

(a) formula unit: $HCN(aq) + NaOH(aq) \rightarrow NaCN(aq) + H_2O(\ell)$

     total ionic: $HCN(aq) + Na^+(aq) + OH^-(aq) \rightarrow Na^+(aq) + CN^-(aq) + H_2O(\ell)$

     net ionic: $HCN(aq) + OH^-(aq) \rightarrow CN^-(aq) + H_2O(\ell)$

(b) formula unit: $HCl(aq) + NaOH(aq) \rightarrow NaCl(aq) + H_2O(\ell)$

     total ionic: $H^+(aq) + Cl^-(aq) + Na^+(aq) + OH^-(aq) \rightarrow Na^+(aq) + Cl^-(aq) + H_2O(\ell)$

     net ionic: $H^+(aq) + OH^-(aq) \rightarrow H_2O(\ell)$

(c) formula unit: $CaCl_2(aq) + Na_2CO_3(aq) \rightarrow 2NaCl(aq) + CaCO_3(s)$

     total ionic: $Ca^{2+}(aq) + 2Cl^-(aq) + 2Na^+(aq) + CO_3^{2-}(aq) \rightarrow 2Na^+(aq) + 2Cl^-(aq) + CaCO_3(s)$

     net ionic: $Ca^{2+}(aq) + CO_3^{2-}(aq) \rightarrow CaCO_3(s)$

Note: Only one of the three resonance structures of the carbonate ion is shown.

7-96.   *Refer to Sections 7-5 and 7-6.*

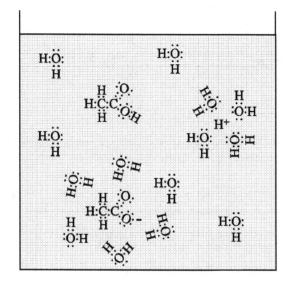

There are three solute species present due to the partial ionization of acetic acid, CH_3COOH:

$$CH_3COOH(aq) \rightleftarrows CH_3COO^-(aq) + H^+(aq)$$

The solvent species, H_2O, is a very polar molecule. The water molecules arrange themselves around the ions so that the slightly positive ends of the water molecules point toward the negative ions, and the slightly negative ends of the water molecules point toward the positive ions.

In the actual solution, because acetic acid is a weak acid, there are very many more acetic acid molecules, CH_3COOH, than there are acetate ions, CH_3COO^-, or hydrogen ions, H^+.

8 Molecular Structure and Covalent Bonding Theories

8-2.   *Refer to Sections 7-10 and 8-8.*

(a) "Bonding pair" is a term that refers to a pair of electrons that is shared between two nuclei in a covalent bond, while the term "lone pair" refers to an unshared pair of electrons that is associated with a single nucleus.

(b) Lone pairs of electrons occupy more space than bonding pairs. This fact was determined experimentally from measurements of bond angles of many molecules and polyatomic ions. An explanation for this is the fact that a lone pair has only one atom exerting strong attractive forces on it, and it exists closer to the nucleus than bonding pairs.

(c) The relative magnitudes of the repulsive forces between pairs of electrons on an atom are as follows:

$$bp/bp < lp/bp << lp/lp$$

where *lp* refers to lone pairs and *bp* refers to bonding pairs of valence shell electrons.

8-4.   *Refer to Section 8-2.*

When VSEPR theory is used to predict molecular geometries, double and triple bonds are treated identically to single bonds: as a single electron group, i.e. as a single place where you can find electrons.

A single unshared nonbonding electron is also counted as one electron group.

8-6.   *Refer to Sections 8-2, 8-11 and 8-15, and Tables 8-3 and 8-4.*

Three possible arrangements of AB_2U_3 with 2 atoms of B and 3 lone pairs around the central A atom are:

(1) 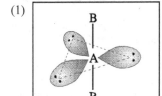   (2) 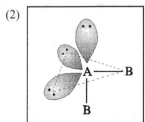   (3)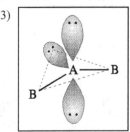

According to VSEPR theory, the most stable arrangement of the three lone pairs of electrons would be in the equatorial position, as shown in (1), where they would be less crowded. Therefore, a linear structure is the correct molecular geometry of the molecule.

8-8.   *Refer to Sections 8-4 and 8-5, and Table 8-2.*

(a) The number of electron groups (also called the regions of high electron density) on an atom is equal to the number of its pure atomic orbitals that hybridize.

(b) The number of atomic orbitals that hybridize equals the number of hybrid orbitals formed.

(a) *sp*

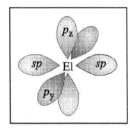

(b) *sp²*

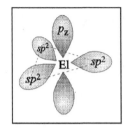

(c) *sp³*

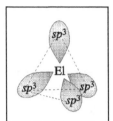

(d) *sp³d*

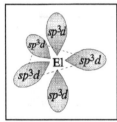

(e) *sp³d²*

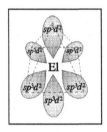

(a) ABU_5 *sp³d²*

(b) AB_2U_4 *sp³d²*

(c) AB_3 *sp²*

(d) AB_3U_2 *sp³d*

(e) AB_5 *sp³d*

From the sketch, we can see that two *p* orbitals and one *s* orbital are being hybridized, forming three new *sp²* hybrid orbitals. See the following figure in Section 8-6. The three *sp²* hybrid orbitals are arranged as so:

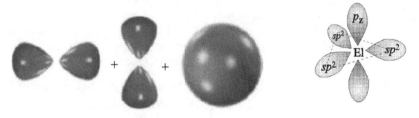

(a) *sp*   180°

(b) *sp²*   120°

(c) *sp³*   109.5°

(d) *sp³d*   90°, 120°, 180°

(e) *sp³d²*   90°, 180°

8-18. *Refer to Section 8-5.*

The hybridization at the central atoms in linear nonpolar Group 2A (also called IIA) compounds, like $BeCl_2$, is *sp*.

8-20. *Refer to Sections 8-5, 8-6 and 8-7.*

The molecular or ionic geometry is identical to its electronic geometry when there are no lone pairs on the central atom.

8-22. *Refer to Section 8-2.*

The central atom is an atom that is bonded to more than one other atom.

Central Atom

(a) HCO_3^- C

O (can also be considered a central atom when bonded to both the carbon and hydrogen)

(b) SiO_2 Si

(c) SO_3 S

(d) $Al(OH)_4^-$ Al

(e) $BeBr_2$ Be

(f) $(CH_3)_4Pb$ Pb

8-24. *Refer to Table 8-4 and the Sections as stated.*

(a) $CdCl_2$

:Cl:Cd:Cl:

This molecule (type AB_2) does not obey the octet rule without modification.

Available electrons, $A = 2 \times 7$(for Cl) $+ 1 \times 2$(for Cd) $= 16$ (total number of valence e^-)

The Lewis formula predicts 2 electron groups around the central Be atom and a linear electronic geometry. There are no lone pairs on the Cd atom, so the molecular geometry is the same as the electronic geometry: linear (Section 8-5).

(b) $SnCl_4$

:Cl:
:Cl:Sn:Cl:
:Cl:

Sn is a 4A element and has 4 valence electrons.

$S = N - A = [4 \times 8$(for Cl) $+ 1 \times 8$(for Sn)$] - [4 \times 7$(for Cl) $+ 1 \times 4$(for Sn)$]$
            $= 8$ shared electrons

The Lewis formula for the molecule (type AB_4) predicts 4 electron groups around the central Sn atom and a tetrahedral electronic geometry. Since there are no lone pairs on Sn, the molecular geometry is also tetrahedral (Section 8-7).

(c) BrF_3

:F:Br:F:
:F:

This molecule (type AB_3U_2) does not obey the octet rule without modification.

Available electrons, $A = 3 \times 7$(for F) $+ 1 \times 7$(for Br) $= 28$ (total number of valence e^-)

The Lewis formula predicts 5 electron groups around the central Br atom and a trigonal bipyramidal electronic geometry. There are two lone pairs on the Br atom, so the molecular geometry is T-shaped (Section 8-11).

(d) SbF_6^-

$$\begin{bmatrix} \text{:F:} \\ \text{:F} \ \ \text{:F:} \\ \text{:F} \ \text{Sb} \ \text{:F:} \\ \text{:F} \ \ \text{:F:} \\ \text{:F:} \end{bmatrix}^-$$

This polyatomic ion (type AB_6), like (c), does not obey the octet rule without modification since 12 electrons must be shared to form 6 Sb-F bonds. Sb is a 5A element, but the charge on the ion gives an extra electron which participates in bonding. The Lewis formula predicts 6 electron groups around the central Sb atom and an octahedral electronic geometry. There are no lone pairs on the Sb atom, so the ionic geometry is the same as the electronic geometry (Section 8-12).

8-26. *Refer to Exercise 8-24 Solution and Table 8-1.*

(a) $CdCl_2$ The ideal bond angles would be 180° since the molecule is linear.

     $SnCl_4$ The ideal bond angles would be 109.5° since the structure is tetrahedral.

     BrF_3 The ideal bond angles would be those for a trigonal bipyramidal electronic geometry (type AB_3U_2): 90° and 180°. One F atom and the 2 lone pairs on the Br atom are separated by 120°.

     SbF_6^- The ideal bond angles would be those for an octahedron, 90° and 180°.

(b) These bond angles differ from the actual bond angles only for BrF_3, since this species has lone pairs of electrons on the central atom. Lone pairs of electrons require more space than bonding pairs of electrons: the F–Br–F bond angles in BrF_3 are slightly reduced from the ideal case.

8-28. *Refer to Sections 8-7, 8-8 and 8-9.*

(a) $H^+ + H_2O \rightarrow H_3O^+$

	Lewis Formula	Electronic Geometry	Molecular (Ionic) Geometry
H_2O	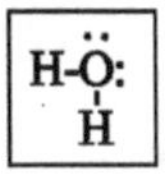 H-Ö: ⏋ H	tetrahedral	angular (bent)
H_3O^+	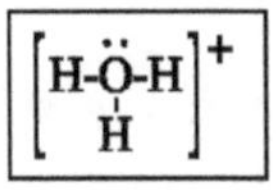 [H-Ö-H]⁺ H	tetrahedral	trigonal pyramidal

(b) $NH_3 + H^+ \rightarrow NH_4^+$

	Lewis Formula	Electronic Geometry	Molecular (Ionic) Geometry
NH_3	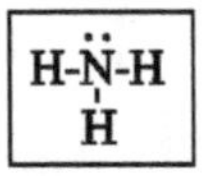 H-N̈-H H	tetrahedral	trigonal pyramidal
NH_4^+	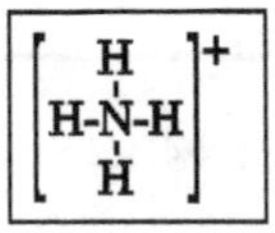 [H-N-H]⁺ H H	tetrahedral	tetrahedral

8-30. *Refer to Tables 8-3 and 8-4, and the Sections as stated.*

(a) H_3O^+

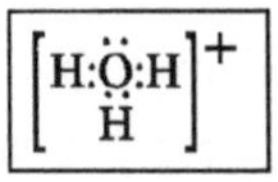

[H:Ö:H]⁺
  H

$S = N - A$ = [3 x 2(for H) + 1 x 8(for O)] - [3 x 1(for H) + 1 x 6(for O) - 1e^-]
             = 6 shared electrons

The Lewis formula for the ion (type AB_3U) predicts 4 electron groups around O including 1 lone pair of electrons. The electronic geometry is tetrahedral and the ionic geometry is trigonal pyramidal (Section 8-8).

(b) PCl_6^-

The ion (type AB_6) does not obey the octet rule.

$A = 6 \times 7(\text{for Cl}) + 1 \times 5(\text{for P}) + 1\ e^- = 48$ (total number of valence electrons)

The Lewis formula shows 6 electron groups around the central P atom. The electronic geometry and the ionic geometry are both octahedral because there are no lone pairs of electrons on P (Section 8-12).

(c) PCl_4^-

The ion (type AB_4U) does not obey the octet rule.

$A = 4 \times 7(\text{for Cl}) + 1 \times 5(\text{for P}) + 1\ e^- = 34$ (total number of valence electrons)

The Lewis formula shows 5 electron groups around the central P atom and its electronic geometry is trigonal bipyramidal. The ionic geometry is a seesaw due to the presence of 1 lone pair of electrons on the central P atom (Section 8-11).

(d) $SbCl_4^+$

$S = N - A\ = [4 \times 8(\text{for Cl}) + 1 \times 8(\text{for Sb})] - [4 \times 7(\text{for Cl}) + 1 \times 5(\text{for Sb})$
$\qquad - 1e^-]$
$= 8$ shared electrons

The Lewis formula for the ion (type AB_4) predicts 4 electron groups around the central Sb atom and a tetrahedral electronic geometry. Since there are no lone pairs on Sb, the ionic geometry is also tetrahedral (Section 8-7).

(a)

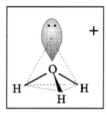

(b)

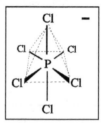

(c)

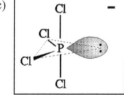

(d)

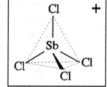

8-32. *Refer to Sections 8-7, 8-11 and 8-12.*

(a) SiF_4

$S = N - A\ = [4 \times 8(\text{for F}) + 1 \times 8(\text{for Si})] - [4 \times 7(\text{for F}) + 1 \times 4(\text{for Si})]$
$\qquad = 8$ shared electrons

The Lewis formula for the molecule (type AB_4) predicts 4 electron groups around the central Si atom with no lone pairs of electrons. The molecular geometry is the same as the electronic geometry: tetrahedral.

SF_4

The molecule (type AB_4U) does not obey the octet rule.

$A = 4 \times 7(\text{for F}) + 1 \times 6(\text{for S}) = 34$ (total number of valence electrons)

The Lewis formula shows 5 electron groups around the central S atom and its electronic geometry is trigonal bipyramidal. The molecular geometry is a seesaw due to the presence of 1 lone pair of electrons on the central S atom.

XeF$_4$

This molecule (type AB$_4$U$_2$) does not obey the octet rule.

$A = 4 \times 7$(for F) $+ 1 \times 8$(for Xe) $= 36$ (total number of valence electrons)

The Lewis formula predicts 6 electron groups around the central Xe atom and its electronic geometry is octahedral. The molecular geometry is square planar due to the presence of 2 lone pairs of electrons on the central Xe atom.

(b) It is obvious that the molecular geometries of SiF$_4$, SF$_4$ and XeF$_4$ are not the same even though their molecular formulas are similar. The differences are due to the different number of valence electrons that must be accommodated by the central atom as lone pairs of electrons.

8-34.   *Refer to Table 8-3 and the Sections as stated.*

(a) I$_3^-$

The ion (type AB$_2$U$_3$) does not obey the octet rule.

$A = 3 \times 7$(for I) $+ 1\ e^- = 22$ (total number of valence electrons)

The Lewis formula predicts 5 electron groups around the central I atom and a trigonal bipyramidal electronic geometry. This ionic geometry is linear.

(b) TeCl$_4$

The molecule (type AB$_4$U) does not obey the octet rule.

$A = 4 \times 7$(for Cl) $+ 1 \times 6$(for Te) $= 34$ (total number of valence electrons)

The Lewis formula predicts 5 electron groups around Te with 1 lone pair of electrons. The electronic geometry is trigonal bipyramidal and the molecular geometry is a seesaw (Section 8-11).

(c) XeO$_3$

$S = N - A = [3 \times 8$(for O) $+ 1 \times 8$(for Xe)$] - [3 \times 6$(for O) $+ 1 \times 8$(for Xe)$]$
$= 6$ shared electrons

The Lewis formula for the molecule (type AB$_3$U) predicts 4 electron groups around Xe including 1 lone pair of electrons. The electronic geometry is tetrahedral and the molecular geometry is trigonal pyramidal (Section 8-8).

(d) BrNO

:B̈r:N̈::Ö:

$S = N - A = [1 \times 8$(for Br) $+ 1 \times 8$(for N) $+ 1 \times 8$(for O)$]$
$\qquad - [1 \times 7$(for Br) $+ 1 \times 5$(for N) $+ 1 \times 6$(for O)$]$
$= 6$ shared electrons

The Lewis formula for the molecule (type AB$_2$U) predicts 3 electron groups around the central N atom including 1 lone pair of electrons. The electronic geometry is trigonal planar and the molecular geometry is angular or bent (Table 8-3).

(e) ClNO$_2$

$S = N - A = [1 \times 8$(for Cl) $+ 1 \times 8$(for N) $+ 2 \times 8$(for O)$]$
$\qquad - [1 \times 7$(for Cl) $+ 1 \times 5$(for N) $+ 2 \times 6$(for O)$]$
$= 8$ shared electrons

The Lewis formula for the molecule (type AB$_3$) predicts 3 electron groups around the central N atom. Only 1 of the two resonance structures is shown. The electronic and molecular geometries are the same, trigonal planar, because there are no lone pairs of electrons on the N atom (Section 8-6).

(f) Cl$_2$SO

$S = N - A = [2 \times 8$(for Cl) $+ 1 \times 8$(for S) $+ 1 \times 8$(for O)$]$
$\qquad - [2 \times 7$(for Cl) $+ 1 \times 6$(for S) $+ 1 \times 6$(for O)$]$
$= 6$ shared electrons

The Lewis formula for the molecule (type AB$_3$U) predicts 4 electron groups around the central S atom including 1 lone pair of electrons. The electronic geometry is tetrahedral and the molecular geometry is trigonal pyramidal (Section 8-8).

The magnitude of bond polarity depends on the difference in electronegativity (ΔEN) between the two atoms involved.

For the N–O bond, ΔEN = 3.5 - 3.0 = 0.5. For the H–O bond, ΔEN = 3.5 - 2.1 = 1.4. Since the H–O bond has the greater ΔEN, the H–O bond is predicted to be more polar than the N–O bond.

8-38. *Refer to Section 8-3 and the Sections as stated.*

(a) CdI_2

This molecule (type AB_2) has a linear electronic and molecular geometry. The Cd–I bonds are polar. Since the molecule is symmetric, the bond dipoles cancel to give a nonpolar molecule (Section 8-5).

(b) BCl_3

This molecule (type AB_3) has a trigonal planar electronic geometry and trigonal planar molecular geometry. The B–Cl bonds are polar, but since the molecule is symmetrical, the bond dipoles cancel to give a nonpolar molecule (Section 8-6).

(c) $AsCl_3$

This molecule (type AB_3U) has a tetrahedral electronic geometry and a pyramidal molecular geometry. Cl (EN = 3.0) is more electronegative than As (EN = 2.1). The polar As–Cl bond dipoles oppose the effect of the lone pair. The molecule is only slightly polar (Section 8-8).

(d) H_2O

This molecule (type AB_2U_2) has a tetrahedral electronic geometry and an angular molecular geometry. Oxygen (EN = 3.5) is more electronegative than H (EN = 2.1). The O–H bond dipole reinforces the effect of the two lone pairs of electrons and so, H_2O is very polar (Section 8-9).

(e) SF_6

This molecule (type AB_6) has an octahedral electronic and molecular geometry. The S-F bonds are polar, but the molecule is symmetrical. The S–F bond dipoles cancel to give a nonpolar molecule (Section 8-12).

8-40. *Refer to Section 8-3 and the Sections as stated.*

(a) BF_3

This molecule (type AB_3) has a trigonal planar electronic and molecular geometry. The B–F bonds are polar. Since the molecule is symmetric, the bond dipoles cancel to give a nonpolar molecule (Section 8-6).

(b) CF_4

This molecule (type AB_4) has a tetrahedral electronic geometry and tetrahedral molecular geometry. The C–F bonds are polar, but since the molecule is symmetrical, the bond dipoles cancel to give a nonpolar molecule (Section 8-7).

(c) NF_3

This molecule (type AB_3U) has a tetrahedral electronic geometry and a pyramidal molecular geometry. F (EN = 4.0) is more electronegative than N (EN = 3.0). The polar N–F bond dipoles oppose the effect of the lone pair. The molecule is only slightly polar (Section 8-8).

(d) OF_2

This molecule (type AB_2U_2) has a tetrahedral electronic geometry and an angular molecular geometry. Oxygen (EN = 3.5) is less electronegative than F (EN = 4.0). The O–F bond dipole opposes the effect of the two lone pairs of electrons and so, OF_2 is polar (Section 8-9).

(e) HF

This molecule (type ABU_3) has a linear electronic and molecular geometry. The H-F bond is polar and the molecule is polar (Section 8-10).

BF_3 and CF_4 are nonpolar molecules. CF_4, NF_3, OF_2 and HF have tetrahedral electronic geometries, but have different molecular geometries since they have 0, 1, 2, and 3 lone pairs of electrons around the center atom, respectively.

8-42. *Refer to Section 8-8.*

PCl_3

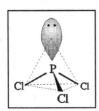

The P–Cl bond in phosphorus trichloride is a polar bond because the difference in electronegativity, ΔEN, between the two atoms is not zero.

$$\Delta EN = 3.0 \text{ (for Cl)} - 2.1 \text{ (for P)} = 0.9$$

This molecule (type AB_3U) has a tetrahedral electronic geometry and a trigonal pyramidal molecular geometry. The polar P–Cl bond dipoles oppose the effect of the lone pair. The molecule is polar.

8-44. *Refer to Section 8-3, Table 5-3 and the Sections as stated.*

(a) CS_2

This molecule (type AB_2) has a linear electronic and molecular geometry. The C–S bonds are nonpolar, since ΔEN = 2.5 (for S) - 2.5 (for C) = 0. Moreover, the molecule is symmetric giving a nonpolar molecule (Section 8-5).

(b) AlF_3

This molecule (type AB_3) has a trigonal planar electronic geometry and trigonal planar molecular geometry. The Al–F bonds are polar, but since the molecule is symmetrical, the bond dipoles cancel to give a nonpolar molecule (Section 8-6).

(c) H_2S

This molecule (type AB_2U_2) has a tetrahedral electronic geometry and an angular molecular geometry. Sulfur (EN = 2.5) is more electronegative than H (EN = 2.1). The S–H bond dipole reinforces the effect of the two lone pairs of electrons and so, H_2S is very polar (Section 8-9).

(d) SnF_2

This molecule (type AB_2U) has a trigonal planar electronic geometry and an angular molecular geometry. F (EN = 4.0) is more electronegative than Sn (EN = 1.8). The Sn–F bond dipoles lessens the effect of the lone pair of electrons and so, SnF_2 is polar, but not extremely so (Table 8-3).

8-46. *Refer to Sections 8-1 and 8-4.*

The orbital overlap model of covalent bonding, described in *valence bond* (VB) *theory*, starts by describing covalent bonding as electron pair sharing that results from the overlap of orbitals from two atoms. VB theory describes the atomic orbitals that overlap to produce the bonding that generates molecules or ions that have a certain geometry. It is also assumed that each unshared pair of electrons occupies a separate orbital. Many times, pure atomic orbitals do not have the correct energies or orientations to describe where the electrons are when atoms are bonded to other atoms. So a process called hybridization is used, in which atomic orbitals are "mixed" together to form new hybrid orbitals which do have a lower total energy and are in the appropriate spatial arrangement to explain the molecular and ionic geometries that are observed.

8-48. *Refer to Table 8-2, Section 8-4 and Exercise 8-10 Solution.*

(a) NCl_3 sp^3

(b) $AlCl_3$ sp^2

(c) CF_4 sp^3

(d) SF_6 sp^3d^2

(e) IO_4^- sp^3

8-50. *Refer to Table 8-2.*

	Lewis Formula	Hybridization	Electronic Geometry	Molecular Geometry
(i) $CHCl_3$	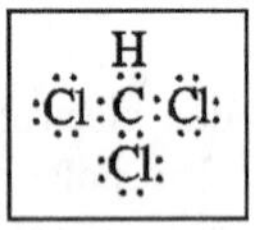	sp^3	tetrahedral	tetrahedral (distorted)
(ii) CH_2Cl_2	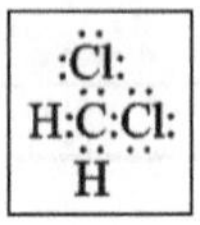	sp^3	tetrahedral	tetrahedral (distorted)
(iii) NF_3	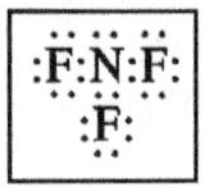	sp^3	tetrahedral	trigonal pyramidal (1 lone pair of e^-)
(iv) PO_4^{3-}	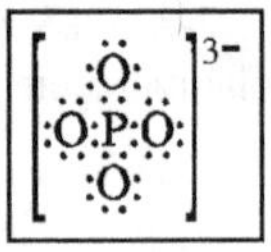	sp^3	tetrahedral	tetrahedral
(v) IF_6^+	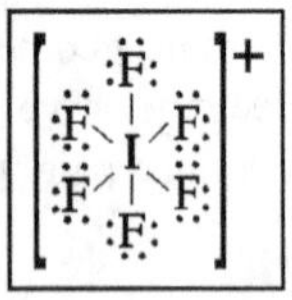	sp^3d^2	octahedral	octahedral
(vi) SiF_6^{2-}	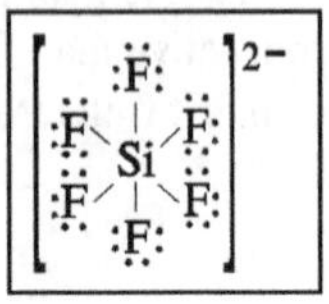	sp^3d^2	octahedral	octahedral

$CH_3CCl=CH_2$

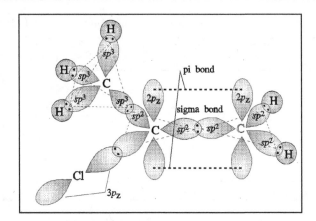

(a)

H O H
H-C-C-C-H
  1 2 3
  H   H

C_1 sp^3 hybridization (4 electron groups)

C_2 sp^2 hybridization (3 electron groups)

C_3 sp^3 hybridization (4 electron groups)

(b)

H
:N-H :O.
H-C-C
  1   2
  H   .O.-H

C_1 sp^3 hybridization (4 electron groups)

C_2 sp^2 hybridization (3 electron groups)

(c)

    H   H
    C-C
H-C   C-N   O
    C=C   O
    H   H

C (all C atoms) sp^2 hybridization (3 electron groups)

(d)

H H Cl H
H-C=C-C=C-H
  1 2 3 4

C_1 sp^2 hybridization (3 electron groups)

C_2 sp^2 hybridization (3 electron groups)

C_3 sp^2 hybridization (3 electron groups)

C_4 sp^2 hybridization (3 electron groups)

(e)

    H H
H-C=C-C-C≡C-H
  1 2 3 4 5
      H

C_1 sp^2 hybridization (3 electron groups)

C_2 sp^2 hybridization (3 electron groups)

C_3 sp^3 hybridization (4 electron groups)

C_4 sp hybridization (2 electron groups)

C_5 sp hybridization (2 electron groups)

117

(a) *s-s* overlap (b) *s-p* overlap (c) *p-p* overlap along bond axis (d) *p-p* overlap perpendicular to bond axis

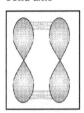

8-58. *Refer to Sections 8-14 and 8-15, and Figures 8-6 and 8-8.*

(a) The molecule contains 10 single bonds (10 sigma bonds) and 1 double bond (1 sigma bond, 1 pi bond) for a total of 11 sigma bonds and 1 pi bond.

(b) The molecule contains 4 single bonds (4 sigma bonds) and 2 double bonds (2 sigma bonds, 2 pi bonds) for a total of 6 sigma bonds and 2 pi bonds.

(c) The molecule contains 9 single bonds (9 sigma bonds) and 1 double bond (1 sigma bond, 1 pi bond) for a total of 10 sigma bonds and 1 pi bond.

(d) The molecule contains 5 single bonds (5 sigma bonds), 1 double bond (1 sigma bond and 1 pi bond) and 1 triple bond (1 sigma bonds, 2 pi bonds) for a total of 7 sigma bonds and 3 pi bonds.

8-60. *Refer to Table 8-2.*

Note: This discussion ignores formal charge considerations.

(a) BO_3^{3-}

$$\left[:\ddot{O}:B:\ddot{O}: \atop :\ddot{O}: \right]^{3-}$$

This ion (type AB_3) has a trigonal planar electronic and ionic geometry. We don't use the word, molecular, since these species are not molecules, but ions (Section 8-6).

(b) CO_3^{2-}

$$\left[:\ddot{O}:C::\ddot{O} \atop :\ddot{O}: \right]^{2-}$$

This ion (type AB_3) has a trigonal planar electronic and ionic geometry. Only one of its three resonance structures is shown (Section 8-6).

(c) SO_3^{2-}

$$\left[:\ddot{O}:\ddot{S}:\ddot{O}: \atop :\ddot{O}: \right]^{2-}$$

This ion (type AB_3U) has a tetrahedral electronic geometry and a pyramidal ionic geometry (Section 8-8). These geometries would still be the same if formal charges were considered.

(d) ClO_3^-

$$\left[:\ddot{O}:\ddot{Cl}:\ddot{O}: \atop :\ddot{O}: \right]^{-}$$

This ion (type AB_3U) has a tetrahedral electronic geometry and a pyramidal ionic geometry (Section 8-8). These geometries would still be the same if formal charges were considered.

All four ions have three oxygen atoms surrounding a nonmetal, but the nonmetals (B, C, S and Cl) are from different groups. The borate ion (Group 3A) does not obey the octet rule, but the carbonate, sulfite and chlorate ions can be drawn so that the ions obey the octet rule. The carbonate ion clearly exhibits resonance.

(a) butane

C_4H_{10}

H H H H
H-C-C-C-C-H
H H H H

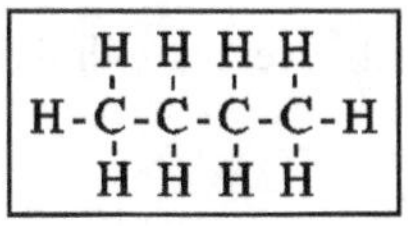

C_1, C_2, C_3, C_4 sp^3 hybridized with bond angles of 109.5°

(b) propene

$H_2C=CHCH_3$

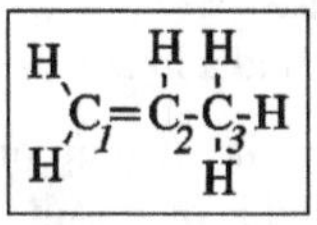

H   H H
 C$_1$=C$_2$-C$_3$-H
H   H

C_1, C_2 sp^2 hybridized with bond angles of 120°
C_3 sp^3 hybridized with bond angles of 109.5°

(c) 1-butyne

$HC≡CCH_2CH_3$

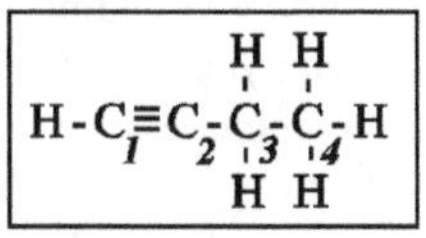

            H H
H-C$_1$≡C$_2$-C$_3$-C$_4$-H
            H H

C_1, C_2 sp hybridized with bond angles of 180°.
C_3, C_4 sp^3 hybridized with bond angles of 109.5°.

(d) acetaldehyde

CH_3CHO

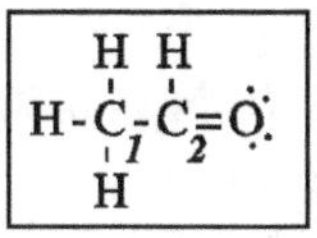

H H
H-C$_1$-C$_2$=Ö
H

C_1 sp^3 hybridized with bond angles of 109.5°.
C_2 sp^2 hybridized with bond angles of 120°.

(a) butane, $CH_3CH_2CH_2CH_3$

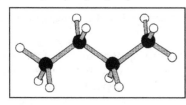

(b) propene, CH_2CHCH_3

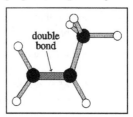

double
bond

(c) 1-butyne, $CHCCH_2CH_3$

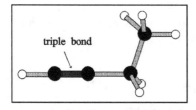

triple bond

(d) acetaldehyde, CH_3CHO

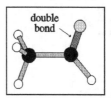

double
bond

(i) NH_3

H-N̈-H
H

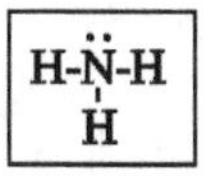

(a) The N atom is sp^3 hybridized because the molecule (type AB_3U) has 4 electron groups around the central N atom.

(b) Three of the sp^3 hybrid orbitals overlap with the $1s$ orbitals of the H atoms to form sigma bonds, leaving the fourth hybrid orbital to contain 1 lone pair of electrons on the N.

119

(ii) NH_4^+

(a) The N atom is sp^3 hybridized because the ion (type AB_4) has 4 electron groups around the central N atom.

(b) Each of the four sp^3 hybrid orbitals overlap with the $1s$ orbital of an H atom to form a sigma bond.

(iii) N_2H_2

(a) Each N atom is sp^2 hybridized because there are 3 electron groups around each N atom (a single bond, a double bond and a lone pair of electrons).

(b) Each N-H single bond is formed from the overlap of an sp^2 hybrid orbital of N with a $1s$ orbital of H. The double bond is the result of the side-on overlap of the unhybridized $2p$ orbitals on the N atoms, yielding a pi bond, and the head-on overlap of two sp^2 hybrid orbitals, yielding a sigma bond. The third sp^2 hybrid orbital on each N atom is used to accommodate the lone pair of electrons.

(iv) HCN

(a) The N atom is sp hybridized because there are 2 electron groups around the N atom.

(b) A lone pair of electrons occupies one sp hybrid orbital on N. The other sp hybrid orbital on N overlaps head-on with an sp hybrid orbital on C forming a sigma bond. The unhybridized $2p$ orbitals on C and N overlap side-on to form 2 pi bonds. The one sigma bond with the two pi bonds creates a C–N triple bond. The H–C bond is formed from the overlap of a $1s$ H orbital with an sp hybrid orbital on C.

(v) H_2NNH_2

(a) Both N atoms are sp^3 hybridized because there are 4 electron groups around each N atom.

(b) Each N–H single bond is formed from the overlap of an sp^3 hybrid orbital of N with a $1s$ orbital of H. The single N–N bond is the result of the head-on overlap of an sp^3 hybrid orbital on each N atom, yielding a sigma bond. The fourth sp^3 hybrid orbital on each N atom is used to accommodate the lone pair of electrons.

8-66.   *Refer to Sections 8-7, 8-14 and 8-15.*

(i) H_2CO

(a) The carbon atom is sp^2 hybridized.

(b) Since there are no lone pairs of electrons on C, the electronic and molecular geometries are trigonal planar. The molecule is planar (flat) with H–C–H and H–C–O bond angles of 120°.

(ii) HCN

(a) The carbon atom is sp hybridized.

(b) The molecular geometry is linear and the H–C–N bond angle is 180°.

(iii) $CH_3CH_2CH_3$

(a) All three carbon atoms are sp^3 hybridized.

(b) The molecular geometry about each carbon atom is tetrahedral with H–C–H, C–C–C and H–C–C bond angles of 109.5°.

(iv) H_2C_2O

(a) Carbon-1 is sp^2 hybridized and carbon-2 is sp hybridized.

(b) The molecular geometry at carbon-1 is trigonal planar with H–C–H and H–C–C bond angles of 120°. The molecular geometry at carbon-2 is linear with C–C–O bond angle of 180°.

See Table below for answers to (a), (b) and (c).

	(a) Lewis Formula	(b) Hybridization	(c) Molecular (or Ionic) Geometry
(i) IF		sp^3	linear
(ii) IF$_3$		sp^3d	T-shaped
(iii) IF$_4^-$		sp^3d^2	square planar
(iv) IF$_5$		sp^3d^2	square pyramidal
(v) IF$_6^-$			
(vi) IF$_7$			

hydroxylamine

Since there are 4 electron groups around both the N and O atoms, the ideal bond angles about these atoms should be 109.5°. The lone pair of electrons on the N atom would make the H–N–H and the H–N–O bond angles less than 109.5°. The two lone pairs of electrons on the O atom should make the N–O–H bond angle even smaller. In fact, the observed bond angles are 107° for H–N–H and H–N–O, and 102° for N–O–H.

Experimental evidence demonstrates that ·CH$_3$, the methyl free radical, has bond angles of about 120°, indicating a trigonal planar arrangement. This fact indicates that a single unpaired electron does not have much, if any, repulsive force. The species can be treated as if the central carbon atom had only 3 electron groups, sp^2 hybridization and a resulting trigonal planar geometry.

The methyl carbanion, :CH$_3^-$, has bond angles close to that in a tetrahedral arrangement of atoms, 109°, indicating 4 electron groups around the central C atom and sp^3 hybridization. The lone pair of electrons exerts significant repulsive force on the electrons in bonding orbitals and must be counted as an electron group.

(a) NO_2^+

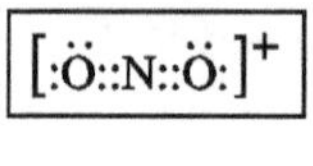

$[:\ddot{O}::N::\ddot{O}:]^+$

$S = N - A = [1 \times 8(\text{for N}) + 2 \times 8(\text{for O})] - [1 \times 5(\text{for N}) + 2 \times 6(\text{for O})$
$- 1e^-]$
$= 8$ shared electrons

The Lewis formula of NO_2^+ (type AB_2) shows 2 electron groups around the central N atom.

The hybridization of N is *sp*.

NO_2^-

$[:\ddot{O}:N::\ddot{O}:]^- \leftrightarrow [:\ddot{O}::N:\ddot{O}:]^-$

$S = N - A = [1 \times 8(\text{for N}) + 2 \times 8(\text{for O})]$
$- [1 \times 5(\text{for N}) + 2 \times 6(\text{for O}) + 1e^-]$
$= 6$ shared electrons

The Lewis resonance structures of NO_2^- (type AB_2U) show 3 electron groups around the central N atom.

The hybridization of N is sp^2.

(b) The bond angle for the linear ion, NO_2^+, is 180°. The ideal bond angle for the angular ion, NO_2^-, is 120°.

The actual O–N–O bond angle is slightly less than 120°, because a lone pair of electrons requires more room than a bonding pair.

(a) PF_5

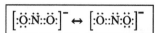

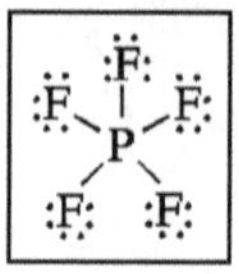

The Lewis formulas predict sp^3d hybridization of P in PF_5 (5 electron groups), changing to sp^3d^2 hybridization of P in PF_6^- (6 electron groups).

PF_6^-

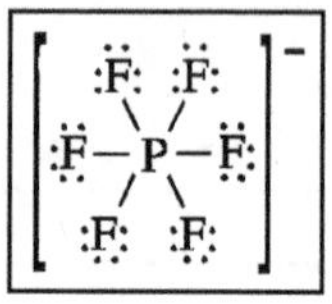

(b) CO

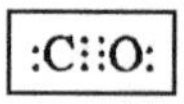

$:C::O:$

The Lewis formulas predict *sp* hybridization of C in both molecules since both C atoms have 2 electron groups around them.

CO_2

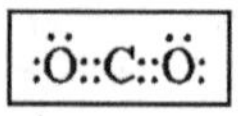

$:\ddot{O}::C::\ddot{O}:$

(c) AlI_3

The Lewis formulas predict sp^2 hybridization of Al in AlI_3 (3 electron groups) changing to sp^3 hybridization of Al in AlI_4^- (4 electron groups).

AlI_4^-

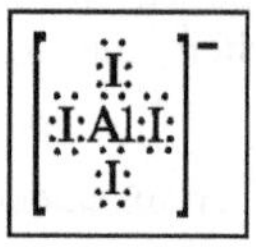

(d) NH_3

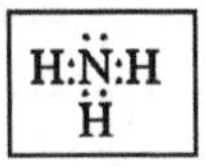

BF_3

$H_3N:BF_3$

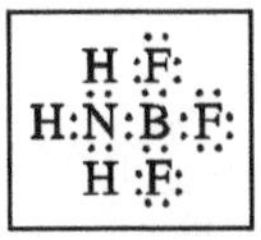

The Lewis formulas predict sp^3 hybridization of N in NH_3 (4 electron groups) and sp^2 hybridization of B in BF_3 (3 electron groups). The product of the reaction, $H_3N:BF_3$, contains both N and B atoms with sp^3 hybridization.

8-78. *Refer to Sections 8-8 and 8-9.*

Using Valence Bond (VB) theory, the central atoms of the molecules with formulas AB_2U_2 and AB_3U should undergo sp^3 hybridized with predicted bond angles of 109.5°. If no hybridization occurs, bonds would be formed by the use of p orbitals. Since the p orbitals are oriented at 90° from each other, the bond angles would be 90°. Note that hybridization is only invoked if the actual molecular geometry data indicate that it is necessary.

The actual B–A–B bond angles for molecules of some representative elements are:

H_2O	104.5°	NH_3	106.7°
H_2S	92.2°	PH_3	93.7°
H_2Se	91.0°	AsH_3	91.8°
H_2Te	89.5°	SbH_3	91.3°

It is not necessary to invoke hybridization for the larger elements (Period 3 and greater). The above data show it is only the molecules containing the smaller Period 2 elements (O and N) that have bond angles approaching those for sp^3 hybridization, 109.5°. The other molecules formed from the larger elements have bond angles closer to 90°, so the application of the hybridization concept is not necessary to explain their molecular geometries.

8-80. *Refer to Table 8-4.*

Molecule or Ion	Electronic Geometry	Molecular Geometry	Hybridization of S Atom
SO_2	trigonal planar	bent or angular	sp^2
SCl_2	tetrahedral	bent or angular	sp^3
SO_3	trigonal planar	trigonal planar	sp^2
SO_3^{2-}	tetrahedral	trigonal pyramidal	sp^3
SF_4	trigonal bipyramidal	see-saw	sp^3d
SO_4^{2-}	tetrahedral	tetrahedral	sp^3
SF_5^+	trigonal bipyramidal	trigonal bipyramidal	sp^3d
SF_6	octahedral	octahedral	sp^3d^2

(a) The molecule, tetrafluoromethane (CF_4), is nonpolar because its four polar C−F bonds are arranged symmetrically around the C in a tetrahedral arrangement. The dipole moments associated with these bonds cancel each other out.

The molecule, trifluoromethane (HCF_3) is tetrahedral, like CF_4, but is polar because the dipole moments associated with the three C−F bonds are not cancelled by the one C−H bond.

(b) An example of a linear triatomic polar molecule is hydrogen cyanide, H−C≡N.

(c) The valence electrons in a polar molecule may or may not be distributed evenly. If they are not, the molecule is definitely polar. In CF_4 and $CBrF_3$, the valence electrons are distributed evenly about the center carbon atom, but now one must examine whether or not the dipole moments associated with the bonds cancel each other out. CF_4 is nonpolar, but $CBrF_3$ is polar.

8-84. *Refer to Section 8-16 and Table 8-4.*

(a) The five different electronic geometries are linear, trigonal planar, tetrahedral, trigonal bipyramidal and octahedral.

(b) Here is the listing of the molecular geometries that are associated with each of the electronic geometries:

Electronic Geometry	Molecular Geometry
linear	linear
trigonal planar	trigonal planar (no lone pairs) bent (1 lone pair)
tetrahedral	tetrahedral (no lone pairs) trigonal pyramidal (1 lone pair) bent (2 lone pairs)
trigonal bipyramidal	trigonal bipyramidal (no lone pairs) see-saw (1 lone pair) T-shaped (2 lone pairs) linear (3 lone pairs)
octahedral	octahedral (no lone pairs) square pyramidal (1 lone pair) square planar (2 lone pairs)

(c)

Description	Molecular Geometry
2 bonded atoms, 1 lone pair (AB_2U)	angular or bent
3 bonded atoms, 1 lone pair (AB_3U)	trigonal pyramidal
2 bonded atoms, 2 lone pairs (AB_2U_2)	bent
4 bonded atoms, 1 lone pair (AB_4U)	see-saw
3 bonded atoms, 2 lone pairs (AB_3U_2)	T-shaped
2 bonded atoms, 3 lone pairs (AB_2U_3)	linear
5 bonded atoms, 1 lone pair (AB_5U_1)	square pyramidal
4 bonded atoms, 2 lone pairs (AB_4U_2)	square planar

Evidence can be presented to show that rotation around a C–C single bond happens readily, but rotation around a C=C double bond does not. Consider the compound, CH_2ClCH_2Cl. No matter how this compound is synthesized, there is only one compound that is made with that formula. However, when CHClCHCl is prepared, there are two different compounds made with that formula. We call these two compounds geometric isomers. One is labeled "cis" and the other is "trans." They have different physical and chemical properties. If there were free rotation around a double bond, this could not happen.

| CH_2ClCH_2Cl | cis-CHClCHCl (bp = 333.2 K) | trans-CHClCHCl (bp = 320.7 K) |

C_3O_2 $S = N - A = [2 \times 8(\text{for O}) + 3 \times 8(\text{for C})] - [2 \times 6(\text{for O}) + 3 \times 4(\text{for C})] = 16$ shared electrons

The Lewis formula can be represented as:

or

The Lewis formula predicts 2 electron groups around each C atom, resulting in the linear structure of C_3O_2.

The correct Lewis formula is:

9 Molecular Orbitals in Chemical Bonding

9-2. **_Refer to the Introduction to Chapter 9 and Section 9-1._**

A molecular orbital (MO) is an orbital resulting from the overlap and combination of atomic orbitals on different atoms. An MO and the electrons in it belong to the molecule as a whole. Molecular orbitals calculations are used to develop (1) mathematical representations of the orbital shapes, and (2) energy level diagrams for the molecules.

The mathematical pictures called "electron density maps" are used to determine molecular structures and the energy level diagrams are used to determine the energies of bond formation and to interpret spectroscopy data.

9-4. **_Refer to Section 8-4._**

A set of hybridized atomic orbitals holds the same maximum number of electrons as the set of atomic orbitals from which the hybridized atomic orbitals were formed. A hybridized atomic orbital can hold a maximum of 2 electrons having opposite spin.

9-6. **_Refer to Section 9-1, and Figures 9-2 and 9-3._**

A σ (sigma) and a σ* (sigma star) molecular orbital result from the head-on overlap and the subsequent combination of atomic orbitals on adjacent atoms. Both molecular orbitals are cylindrically symmetrical about the axis linking the two atoms. There is a high electron density in the region between the atoms for the bonding σ orbital, promoting bonding and stabilizing the system.

However, the electron density between the atoms approaches zero at the nodal plane for the anti-bonding σ* orbital, which destabilizes the system. As an example, see below for the overlap of 2 $1s$ orbitals (from Figure 9-2). Figure 9-3 shows the bonding and antibonding sigma orbitals formed by the combining head-on of two p orbitals.

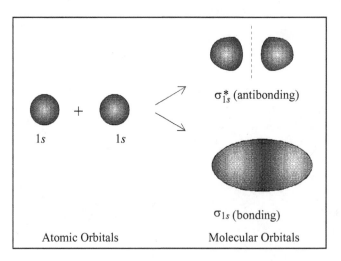

$1s$ $1s$

σ_{1s}^* (antibonding)

σ_{1s} (bonding)

Atomic Orbitals   Molecular Orbitals

Rules for placing electrons in molecular orbitals:

(1) Choose the correct molecular orbital energy level diagram.

(2) Determine the *total* number of electrons in the molecule or ion.

(3) Put the electrons into the energy level diagram as follows:

- Each electron is placed in the lowest possible energy level.

- A maximum of 2 electrons can be placed in an orbital, but they must have opposite spins (Pauli Exclusion Principle).

- Electrons must occupy all the orbitals of a given energy level singly with the same spin before pairing begins (Hund's Rule).

| 9-10. | *Refer to Sections 9-1 and 9-6, and Figures 9-2, 9-3, 9-4, 9-10 and 9-11.* |

(a) Atomic orbitals are *pure* orbitals that have not mixed with other orbitals in the same atom, molecule or ion. Molecular orbitals are orbitals resulting from the overlapping and mixing of atomic orbitals from *all* the atoms in a molecule. A molecular orbital belongs to the molecule as a whole and not simply to a particular atom in the molecule.

For example, each H atom has a $1s$ atomic orbital, but in the H_2 molecule, the σ_{1s} molecular orbital belongs to the entire H_2 molecule.

(b) A bonding molecular orbital (MO) results when two atomic orbitals overlap in phase. The energy of the bonding MO is always lower than the original atomic orbitals and is therefore more stable. An antibonding MO results when two atomic orbitals overlap out of phase; its energy is higher than the original atomic orbitals. Refer to Figure 9-2.

(c) A sigma (σ) molecular orbital results from the head-on overlap of two atomic orbitals. A pi (π) molecular orbital results from the side-on overlap of atomic orbitals. See Figures 9-2, 9-3 and 9-4.

(d) A localized molecular orbital is an MO which is associated with one or two particular atoms in a molecule. The bonding orbitals are localized between the atoms that are bonded together, the nonbonding orbitals are localized on one particular atom. Delocalized molecular orbitals, on the other hand, cover the entire molecule. These orbitals cannot easily be labeled as specific bonds. See Figures 9-10 and 9-11.

| 9-12. | *Refer to Section 9-1.* |

Bonding molecular orbitals (MOs) have energies that are lower than those of the original atomic orbitals. Antibonding molecular orbitals have energies that are higher than those of the original atomic orbitals. Therefore, bonding MOs are more stable than the original atomic orbitals, whereas, antibonding MOs are less stable than the original atomic orbitals.

| 9-14. | *Refer to the Key Terms for Chapter 9.* |

(a) A homonuclear molecule or ion is a species containing only one type of element. For example, O_2, O_3 and O_2^+ are homonuclear.

(b) A heteronuclear molecule or ion is a species containing different elements. For example, HF, CN^- and H_2O are heteronuclear.

(c) A diatomic molecule or ion is a species containing two atoms. It can either be homonuclear (O_2, O_2^-) or heteronuclear (HF, CN^-).

Recall: Bond Order $= \dfrac{\text{No. bonding electrons - No. antibonding electrons}}{2}$

		No. Bonding Electrons	No. Antibonding Electrons	Bond Order
(a) Be_2	$\sigma_{1s}^2 \; \sigma_{1s}^{*\,2} \; \sigma_{2s}^2 \; \sigma_{2s}^{*\,2}$	4	4	0
Be_2^+	$\sigma_{1s}^2 \; \sigma_{1s}^{*\,2} \; \sigma_{2s}^2 \; \sigma_{2s}^{*\,1}$	4	3	0.5
Be_2^-	$\sigma_{1s}^2 \; \sigma_{1s}^{*\,2} \; \sigma_{2s}^2 \; \sigma_{2s}^{*\,2} \; \pi_{2p_v}^1$	5	4	0.5
(b) B_2	$\sigma_{1s}^2 \; \sigma_{1s}^{*\,2} \; \sigma_{2s}^2 \; \sigma_{2s}^{*\,2} \; \pi_{2p_v}^1 \; \pi_{2p_z}^1$	6	4	1
B_2^+	$\sigma_{1s}^2 \; \sigma_{1s}^{*\,2} \; \sigma_{2s}^2 \; \sigma_{2s}^{*\,2} \; \pi_{2p_v}^1$	5	4	0.5
B_2^-	$\sigma_{1s}^2 \; \sigma_{1s}^{*\,2} \; \sigma_{2s}^2 \; \sigma_{2s}^{*\,2} \; \pi_{2p_v}^2 \; \pi_{2p_z}^1$	7	4	1.5

In Molecular Orbital Theory, the greater the bond order, the more stable is the molecule or ion. Therefore, we predict:

> Unstable: Be_2
> Somewhat stable: Be_2^+, Be_2^-, B_2^+
> Stable: B_2, B_2^-

This means that although Be_2 is unstable, both its 1+ cation and 1− anion are somewhat stable. It also shows that the stability of the boron species is in the order: $B_2^+ < B_2 < B_2^-$.

All these predictions are generally correct. The fact that many of these supposed stable species are not observed in nature is because they are chemically very reactive and are observed only at high temperatures and reduced pressures. Therefore, the chemical reactivity of a species is also instrumental when considering the survival probability of the species with stable chemical bonding.

Note: Bond Order $= \dfrac{\text{No. bonding electrons - No. antibonding electrons}}{2}$

		No. Bonding Electrons	No. Antibonding Electrons	Bond Order
(a) Ne_2^+	$\sigma_{1s}^2 \; \sigma_{1s}^{*\,2} \; \sigma_{2s}^2 \; \sigma_{2s}^{*\,2} \; \sigma_{2p}^2 \; \pi_{2p_v}^2 \; \pi_{2p_z}^2 \; \pi_{2p_v}^{*\,2} \; \pi_{2p_z}^{*\,2} \; \sigma_{2p}^{*\,1}$	10	9	0.5
(b) Ne_2	$\sigma_{1s}^2 \; \sigma_{1s}^{*\,2} \; \sigma_{2s}^2 \; \sigma_{2s}^{*\,2} \; \sigma_{2p}^2 \; \pi_{2p_v}^2 \; \pi_{2p_z}^2 \; \pi_{2p_v}^{*\,2} \; \pi_{2p_z}^{*\,2} \; \sigma_{2p}^{*\,2}$	10	10	0
(c) Ne_2^{2+}	$\sigma_{1s}^2 \; \sigma_{1s}^{*\,2} \; \sigma_{2s}^2 \; \sigma_{2s}^{*\,2} \; \sigma_{2p}^2 \; \pi_{2p_v}^2 \; \pi_{2p_z}^2 \; \pi_{2p_v}^{*\,2} \; \pi_{2p_z}^{*\,2}$	10	8	1

The ions Ne_2^+ and Ne_2^{2+} have non-zero bond orders and would exist, but Ne_2 has a bond order of zero and would not exist.

9-22. ***Refer to Sections 9-2, 9-3, 9-4, Exercise 9-19, Table 9-1, and Example 9-1.***

Recall: Bond Order = $\frac{\text{No. bonding electrons - No. antibonding electrons}}{2}$

		No. Bonding Electrons	No. Antibonding Electrons	Bond Order
(a) Li_2	$\sigma_{1s}^2\ \sigma_{1s}^{*2}\ \sigma_{2s}^2$	4	2	1
(b) Li_2^+	$\sigma_{1s}^2\ \sigma_{1s}^{*2}\ \sigma_{2s}^1$	3	2	0.5
(c) O_2^{2-}	$\sigma_{1s}^2\ \sigma_{1s}^{*2}\ \sigma_{2s}^2\ \sigma_{2s}^{*2}\ \sigma_{2p}^2\ \pi_{2p_y}^2\ \pi_{2p_z}^2\ \pi_{2p_y}^{*2}\ \pi_{2p_z}^{*2}$	10	8	1

All these species would exist since their bond order is greater than zero.

9-24. ***Refer to Section 9-3 and Exercise 9-23.***

Recall: Bond Order = $\frac{\text{No. bonding electrons - No. antibonding electrons}}{2}$

(a) X_2 bond order = $\frac{10 - 4}{2} = 3$

(b) X_2 bond order = $\frac{10 - 6}{2} = 2$

(c) X_2^- bond order = $\frac{10 - 5}{2} = 2.5$

9-26. ***Refer to Sections 9-3 and 9-4, Example 9-1, and Exercise 9-25.***

In Exercise 9-25, the following electron configurations were obtained:

F_2 $\sigma_{1s}^2\ \sigma_{1s}^{*2}\ \sigma_{2s}^2\ \sigma_{2s}^{*2}\ \sigma_{2p}^2\ \pi_{2p_y}^2\ \pi_{2p_z}^2\ \pi_{2p_y}^{*2}\ \pi_{2p_z}^{*2}$

F_2^- $\sigma_{1s}^2\ \sigma_{1s}^{*2}\ \sigma_{2s}^2\ \sigma_{2s}^{*2}\ \sigma_{2p}^2\ \pi_{2p_y}^2\ \pi_{2p_z}^2\ \pi_{2p_y}^{*2}\ \pi_{2p_z}^{*2}\ \sigma_{2p}^{*1}$

F_2^+ $\sigma_{1s}^2\ \sigma_{1s}^{*2}\ \sigma_{2s}^2\ \sigma_{2s}^{*2}\ \sigma_{2p}^2\ \pi_{2p_y}^2\ \pi_{2p_z}^2\ \pi_{2p_y}^{*2}\ \pi_{2p_z}^{*1}$

C_2 $\sigma_{1s}^2\ \sigma_{1s}^{*2}\ \sigma_{2s}^2\ \sigma_{2s}^{*2}\ \pi_{2p_y}^2\ \pi_{2p_z}^2$

C_2^+ $\sigma_{1s}^2\ \sigma_{1s}^{*2}\ \sigma_{2s}^2\ \sigma_{2s}^{*2}\ \pi_{2p_y}^2\ \pi_{2p_z}^1$

C_2^- $\sigma_{1s}^2\ \sigma_{1s}^{*2}\ \sigma_{2s}^2\ \sigma_{2s}^{*2}\ \pi_{2p_y}^2\ \pi_{2p_z}^2\ \sigma_{2p}^1$

(a) Recall: Bond Order $= \dfrac{\text{No. bonding electrons - No. antibonding electrons}}{2}$

	F_2	F_2^-	F_2^+	C_2	C_2^+	C_2^-
Bonding e^-	10	10	10	8	7	9
Antibonding e^-	8	9	7	4	4	4
Bond order	1	0.5	1.5	2	1.5	2.5
(b) Unpaired e^-	0	1	1	0	1	1
Paramagnetic or Diamagnetic	D	P	P	D	P	P

(c) Based on bond orders, we have the following order of stability:

Somewhat stable: F_2^-

Stable: F_2, F_2^+, C_2, C_2^+, and C_2^-

Order of stability: $F_2^- < F_2 < F_2^+$ and $C_2^+ < C_2 < C_2^-$

9-28. *Refer to Sections 9-3 and 9-4.*

(a) N_2 $\qquad$ $\sigma_{1s}^2 \; \sigma_{1s}^{*2} \; \sigma_{2s}^2 \; \sigma_{2s}^{*2} \; \pi_{2p_y}^2 \; \pi_{2p_z}^2 \; \sigma_{2p}^2$

N_2^- $\qquad$ $\sigma_{1s}^2 \; \sigma_{1s}^{*2} \; \sigma_{2s}^2 \; \sigma_{2s}^{*2} \; \pi_{2p_y}^2 \; \pi_{2p_z}^2 \; \sigma_{2p}^2 \; \pi_{2p_y}^{*1}$

N_2^+ $\qquad$ $\sigma_{1s}^2 \; \sigma_{1s}^{*2} \; \sigma_{2s}^2 \; \sigma_{2s}^{*2} \; \pi_{2p_y}^2 \; \pi_{2p_z}^2 \; \sigma_{2p}^1$

(b) Recall: Bond Order $= \dfrac{\text{No. bonding electrons - No. antibonding electrons}}{2}$

N_2 $\qquad$ bond order $= \dfrac{10 - 4}{2} = 3$

N_2^- $\qquad$ bond order $= \dfrac{10 - 5}{2} = 2.5$

N_2^+ $\qquad$ bond order $= \dfrac{9 - 4}{2} = 2.5$

(c) The species with the greatest bond order has the greatest bond energy and the shortest bond length.

Therefore, the N_2 molecule with a bond order of 3 has the shortest bond.

Both N_2^- and N_2^+ ions with bond orders of 2.5, should have slightly longer bond lengths.

in bond length: $\quad N_2 < N_2^-$ and N_2^+

NO^+

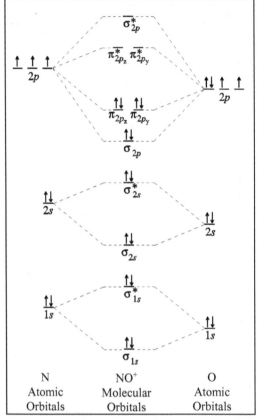

The bond order of NO^+ is

$$\text{bond order} = \frac{\text{bonding } e^- \text{ - antibonding } e^-}{2}$$

$$= \frac{10 - 4}{2}$$

$$= 3$$

There are no lone pairs of electrons, so the molecular ion is **diamagnetic**.

The NO^+ ion is **very stable**, since its bond order is high.

N	NO^+	O
Atomic	Molecular	Atomic
Orbitals	Orbitals	Orbitals

Recall: Bond Order $= \dfrac{\text{No. bonding electrons - No. antibonding electrons}}{2}$

CN $\sigma_{1s}^{2}\ \sigma_{1s}^{*\,2}\ \sigma_{2s}^{2}\ \sigma_{2s}^{*\,2}\ \pi_{2p_z}^{2}\ \pi_{2p_y}^{2}\ \sigma_{2p}^{1}$

CN^+ $\sigma_{1s}^{2}\ \sigma_{1s}^{*\,2}\ \sigma_{2s}^{2}\ \sigma_{2s}^{*\,2}\ \pi_{2p_z}^{2}\ \pi_{2p_y}^{2}$

CN^{2+} $\sigma_{1s}^{2}\ \sigma_{1s}^{*\,2}\ \sigma_{2s}^{2}\ \sigma_{2s}^{*\,2}\ \pi_{2p_z}^{2}\ \pi_{2p_y}^{1}$

CN^- $\sigma_{1s}^{2}\ \sigma_{1s}^{*\,2}\ \sigma_{2s}^{2}\ \sigma_{2s}^{*\,2}\ \pi_{2p_z}^{2}\ \pi_{2p_y}^{2}\ \sigma_{2p}^{2}$

CN^{2-} $\sigma_{1s}^{2}\ \sigma_{1s}^{*\,2}\ \sigma_{2s}^{2}\ \sigma_{2s}^{*\,2}\ \pi_{2p_z}^{2}\ \pi_{2p_y}^{2}\ \sigma_{2p}^{2}\ \pi_{2p_y}^{*\,1}$

Bond order calculations:

bond order of CN $= \dfrac{9 - 4}{2} = 2.5$ bond order of $CN^+ = \dfrac{8 - 4}{2} = 2.0$ bond order of $CN^{2+} = \dfrac{7 - 4}{2} = 1.5$

bond order of $CN^- = \dfrac{10 - 4}{2} = 3$ bond order of $CN^{2-} = \dfrac{10 - 5}{2} = 2.5$

The most stable species is **CN⁻** since it has the largest bond order. The species, CN, CN²⁺ and CN²⁻, are predicted to be paramagnetic because they have one unpaired electron.

9-34. *Refer to Section 9-5 and the Molecular Orbital Diagram before Exercise 9-29.*

(a) NF

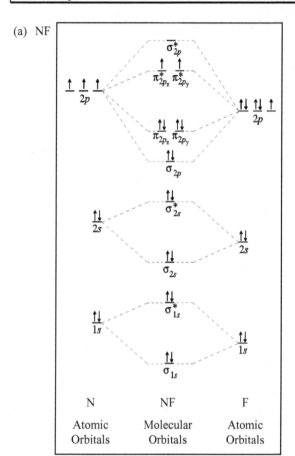

NF⁺

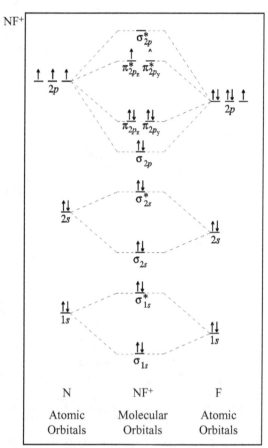

(b) NF $\quad \sigma_{1s}^2 \; \sigma_{1s}^{*\,2} \; \sigma_{2s}^2 \; \sigma_{2s}^{*\,2} \; \sigma_{2p}^2 \; \pi_{2p_z}^2 \; \pi_{2p_y}^2 \; \pi_{2p_z}^{*\,1} \; \pi_{2p_y}^{*\,1}$

NF⁺ $\quad \sigma_{1s}^2 \; \sigma_{1s}^{*\,2} \; \sigma_{2s}^2 \; \sigma_{2s}^{*\,2} \; \sigma_{2p}^2 \; \pi_{2p_z}^2 \; \pi_{2p_y}^2 \; \pi_{2p_z}^{*\,1}$

(c) Recall: Bond Order $= \dfrac{\text{No. bonding electrons - No. antibonding electrons}}{2}$

	NF	NF⁺
Bonding e^-	10	10
Antibonding e^-	6	5
Bond order	2	2.5
Unpaired e^-	2	1

(d) Paramagnetic or   P   P
    Diamagnetic
_____

Both NF and NF$^+$ are stable, but NF$^+$ is slightly more stable than NF due to its higher bond order.

| 9-36. | *Refer to Sections 9-3 and 9-5, and the Molecular Orbital Diagram before Exercise 9-29.* |

BC

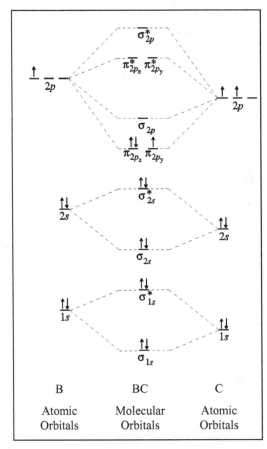

To decrease the strength of the B–C bond, an electron is removed from the BC molecule, forming the BC$^+$ ion. One of the electrons from the bonding orbital, π_{2p_z} is removed.

The bond order decreases from 1.5 for BC to 1.0 for BC$^+$. Likewise, the bond strength also decreases.

| 9-38. | *Refer to Section 9-6 and Figure 9-10.* |

(a) SO$_2$

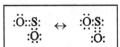

(b) O$_3$

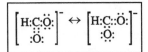

(c) HCO$_2^-$

$$\left[H\!:\!\ddot{C}\!:\!\ddot{\ddot{O}}\!: \atop :\!\ddot{O}\!: \right]^- \leftrightarrow \left[H\!:\!\ddot{C}\!:\!:\!\ddot{O}\!: \atop :\!\ddot{O}\!: \right]^-$$

Molecular Orbital Descriptions:

(a)

(b)

(c)

9-40. *Refer to Sections 9-3, 9-4 and 9-5, and Figure 9-9.*

(a) O_2^{2+} σ_{1s}^2 σ_{1s}^{*2} σ_{2s}^2 σ_{2s}^{*2} σ_{2p}^2 $\pi_{2p_y}^2$ $\pi_{2p_z}^2$ bond order $= \dfrac{10-4}{2} = 3$

The ion is diamagnetic and very stable.

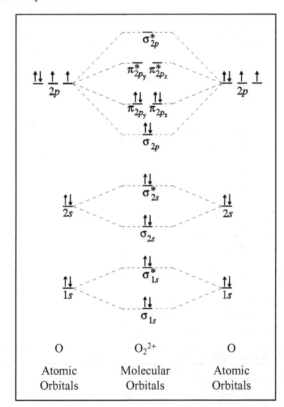

(b) HO^- $1s^2$ $2s^2$ σ_{sp}^2 $2p_x^2$ $2p_y^2$ bond order $= \dfrac{2-0}{2} = 1$

The ion is diamagnetic and stable.

134

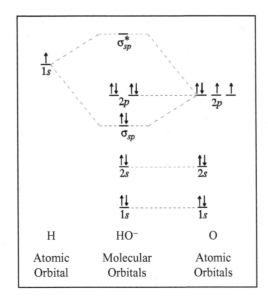

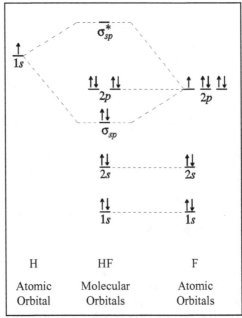

(c) HF $1s^2\ 2s^2\ \sigma_{sp}^2\ 2p_x^2\ 2p_y^2$

bond order $= \dfrac{2 - 0}{2} = 1$

The HF molecule is diamagnetic and stable.

9-42. *Refer to Section 9-4, Figure 9-5, and Table 9-1.*

(a) If a diatomic species has 20 or fewer electrons, its bond order cannot be greater than three. The difference between the number of bonding electrons and the number of antibonding electrons is never more than 6 according to Figure 9-5. Since bond order equals (no. bonding electrons - antibonding electrons)/2, the maximum bond order can never be more than three.

(b) Bond order must be a value that is divisible by 0.5 because the difference between the number of bonding electrons and antibonding electrons is always a whole number. When the difference is divided by 2 to determine bond order, the answer must be a multiple of 0.5.

135

9-44. *Refer to Section 9-4, Figure 9-5, and Table 9-1.*

The homonuclear diatomic molecules of the second row of the periodic table are predicted by MO theory to (1) be paramagnetic: B_2 and O_2, (2) have a bond order of 1: Li_2, B_2 and F_2, (3) have a bond order of 2: C_2, O_2, and (4) have the highest bond order: N_2 with bond order of 3.

9-46. *Refer to Section 9-4, Figure 9-7 and Exercise 9-30 Solution.*

To explain how the bonds in N–O, N–O$^+$ and N–O$^-$ compare, let's first find their electron configurations and bond order:

NO (15 e$^-$) $\qquad \sigma_{1s}^2 \; \sigma_{1s}^{*\,2} \; \sigma_{2s}^2 \; \sigma_{2s}^{*\,2} \; \sigma_{2p}^2 \; \pi_{2p_z}^2 \; \pi_{2p_y}^2 \; \pi_{2p_z}^{*\,1}$ $\qquad\qquad$ bond order = (10 - 5)/2 = 2.5

NO$^+$ (14 e$^-$) $\qquad \sigma_{1s}^2 \; \sigma_{1s}^{*\,2} \; \sigma_{2s}^2 \; \sigma_{2s}^{*\,2} \; \sigma_{2p}^2 \; \pi_{2p_z}^2 \; \pi_{2p_y}^2$ $\qquad\qquad\qquad$ bond order = (10 - 4)/2 = 3

NO$^-$ (16 e$^-$) $\qquad \sigma_{1s}^2 \; \sigma_{1s}^{*\,2} \; \sigma_{2s}^2 \; \sigma_{2s}^{*\,2} \; \sigma_{2p}^2 \; \pi_{2p_z}^2 \; \pi_{2p_y}^2 \; \pi_{2p_z}^{*\,1} \; \pi_{2p_y}^{*\,1}$ $\qquad$ bond order = (10 - 6)/2 = 2

The atoms in each of these three species are connected by a strong bond, since their bond orders are large, so they should definitely exist. As bond order increases, bond strength increases and bond length decreases. Therefore, in order of increasing bond length (decreasing bond strength), we have:

$$\text{in bond length:} \qquad NO^+ < NO < NO^-$$

9-48. *Refer to Sections 9-3 and 9-4, and Table 9-1.*

Valence bond theory does agree fairly well with molecular orbital (MO) theory for homonuclear diatomic molecules that can obey the octet rule: H_2 (single bond, bond order = 1), Li_2 (single bond, bond order = 1), N_2 (triple bond, bond order = 3), O_2 (double bond, bond order = 2), F_2 (single bond, bond order = 1). However, for those molecules that don't, it is more difficult to know if they exist or not and what bond orders they have. MO theory allows us to predict that He_2, Be_2 and Ne_2 do not exist since they have bond orders = 0, and that B_2 has bond order = 1 and C_2 has bond order = 2.

Bond order is somewhat useful in predicting bond lengths and bond energies. Molecules with a bond order of 1 have bond lengths ranging from 0.74 Å for H_2 (short due the small atomic size of H) to 2.67 Å for Li_2 (much less stable). Molecules with a bond order of 2 have shorter bond lengths: 1.31 Å for C_2 and 1.21 Å for O_2. N_2 with bond order of 3 has the shortest bond length (except for H_2): 1.09 Å. Bond energies are inversely related to the bond lengths. The exception, H_2, has a bond energy closer to O_2, because of its small size. As a note, although Be_2 is predicted not to exist (bond order = 0), there is a small but observable bond energy of 9 kJ/mol.

9-50. *Refer to Sections 9-3 and 9-4, and Table 9-1.*

The addition of electrons to bonding orbitals increases the bond strength, while the addition of electrons to antibonding orbitals does the reverse and decreases the bond strength. Adding electrons to nonbonding orbitals will not affect the bond strength.

(a) N and P are both VA elements but N_2 is much more stable than P_2 because N is a smaller atom than P and therefore can effectively participate in pi bonding, whereas P cannot. The $3p$ orbitals of a P atom do not overlap side-on in a pi bond with the corresponding $3p$ orbitals of another P atom nearly as well as the corresponding $2p$ orbitals of the much smaller nitrogen atoms. Therefore, as explained by valence bond theory, P forms 3 sigma bonds instead and acquires an octet of electrons using sp^3 hybridization to form P_4 molecules.

(b) O and S are both VIA elements. However, O_2 and O_3 are much more stable than S_2 because O is a smaller atom than S and therefore can effectively participate in pi bonding, whereas S cannot. The $3p$ orbitals of a S atom do not overlap side-on with the corresponding $3p$ orbitals of another S atom nearly as well as the corresponding $2p$ orbitals of the smaller O atoms. As a result, S forms 2 sigma bonds and obtains its octet of electrons using sp^3 hybridization to form S_8 molecules.

10 Reactions in Aqueous Solutions I: Acids, Bases, and Salts

10-2.   *Refer to Section 10-2.*

(a) According to Arrhenius, an acid is a substance that contains hydrogen and produces hydrogen ions in aqueous solution. A base is a substance that contains the OH group and produces hydroxide ions in aqueous solution. Neutralization is the reaction between hydrogen ions and hydroxide ions yielding water molecules.

(b) acid: $HBr(aq) \rightarrow H^+(aq) + Br^-(aq)$
   base: $Ba(OH)_2(aq) \rightarrow Ba^{2+}(aq) + 2OH^-(aq)$
   neutralization: $2HBr(aq) + Ba(OH)_2(aq) \rightarrow BaBr_2(aq) + 2H_2O(\ell)$

10-4.   *Refer to Section 6-1 and Figure 6-1.*

To distinguish between strong electrolytes, weak electrolytes and nonelectrolytes, prepare equimolar aqueous solutions of the compounds and test their electrical conductivity. If a compound's solution conducts electricity well, it is a strong electrolyte; if its solution conducts electricity poorly, it is a weak electrolyte. A solution of a nonelectrolyte does not conduct electricity at all.

strong electrolyte: Na_2SO_4, $HClO_4$
weak electrolyte: HCN, CH_3COOH, HF, $HCOOH$, NH_3
nonelectrolyte: CH_3OH

10-6.   *Refer to Section 10-3.*

A hydrated hydrogen ion, called the hydronium ion, contains only one water of hydration: $H^+(H_2O)$ or H_3O^+

10-8.   *Refer to Section 10-3 and Exercise 10-6 Solution.*

The statement, "The hydrated hydrogen ion should always be represented as H_3O^+," has two main flaws. First, the true extent of hydration of the H^+ in many solutions is unknown. Secondly, when balancing equations, it is generally much easier to use H^+ rather than H_3O^+.

10-10.   *Refer to Section 10-4 and Example 10-1.*

In accordance with Brønsted-Lowry terminology,

(a) acid: a proton donor, e.g. HCl, NH_4^+, H_2O, H_3O^+

(b) conjugate base: a species that is produced when an acid donates a proton,
   e.g. Cl^- is the conjugate base of HCl OH^- is the conjugate base of H_2O
        NH_3 is the conjugate base of NH_4^+ H_2O is the conjugate base of H_3O^+

(c) base: a proton acceptor, e.g., NH_3, H_2O, OH^-

(d) conjugate acid: a species that is produced when a base accepts a proton,
   e.g. HCl is the conjugate acid of Cl^- H_2O is the conjugate acid of OH^-
        NH_4^+ is the conjugate acid of NH_3 H_3O^+ is the conjugate acid of H_2O

(e) conjugate acid-base pair: two species with formulas that differ only by a proton, e.g., HCl and Cl^-, NH_4^+ and NH_3, $H_2PO_4^-$ and HPO_4^{2-}. The species with the extra proton is the conjugate acid, whereas the other is the conjugate base.

(a) In dilute aqueous solution, ammonia is a Brønsted-Lowry base and water is a Brønsted-Lowry acid. The reaction produces an ammonium ion (the conjugate acid of ammonia) and a hydroxide ion (the conjugate base of water).

$$NH_3(aq) + H_2O(\ell) \rightleftarrows NH_4^+(aq) + OH^-(aq)$$

(b) In the gaseous state, ammonia also behaves as a Brønsted-Lowry base when reacting with gaseous hydrogen chloride. It takes a proton from the gaseous acid and produces the ionic salt, ammonium chloride.

$$NH_3(g) + HCl(g) \rightleftarrows NH_4Cl(s)$$

These species are Brønsted-Lowry bases in water (none are Arrhenius bases) since they are proton acceptors and OH^- ions are produced: NH_3, HS^-, CH_3COO^- and O^{2-}.

$$NH_3 + H_2O \rightleftarrows NH_4^+ + OH^- \qquad\qquad HS^- + H_2O \rightleftarrows H_2S + OH^-$$
$$CH_3COO^- + H_2O \rightleftarrows CH_3COOH + OH^- \qquad O^{2-} + H_2O \rightleftarrows 2OH^-$$

(a) $NH_4^+ + CH_3COO^- \rightarrow NH_3 + CH_3COOH$
    acid$_1$ base$_2$ base$_1$ acid$_2$

(c) $HClO_4 + [H_2NNH_3]^+ \rightarrow ClO_4^- + [H_3NNH_3]^{2+}$
    acid$_1$ base$_2$ base$_1$ acid$_2$

(b) $S^{2-} + H_2SO_4 \rightarrow HS^- + HSO_4^-$
    base$_1$ acid$_2$ acid$_1$ base$_2$

(d) $NH_2^- + H_2O \rightarrow NH_3 + OH^-$
    base$_1$ acid$_2$ acid$_1$ base$_2$

Acid	H_2O	HS^-	HBr	PH_4^+	$HOCH_3$
Conjugate Base	OH^-	S^{2-}	Br^-	PH_3	CH_3O^-

	Brønsted-Lowry Acids	**Brønsted-Lowry Bases**
(a)	H_2O, HCN	CN^-, OH^-
(b)	H_2CO_3, H_2SO_4	HSO_4^-, HCO_3^-
(c)	CH_3COOH, HNO_2	NO_2^-, CH_3COO^-
(d)	H_2O, NH_3	NH_2^-, OH^-

(a) $C_5H_5N + CH_3CO_2H \rightleftarrows C_5H_5NH^+ + CH_3CO_2^-$
    base$_1$ acid$_2$ acid$_1$ base$_2$

(b) $N_2H_4 + HSO_4^- \rightleftarrows N_2H_5^+ + SO_4^{2-}$
    base$_1$ acid$_2$ acid$_1$ base$_2$

(c) $[Al(H_2O)_6]^{3+} + OH^- \rightleftarrows [Al(H_2O)_5(OH^-)]^{2+} + H_2O$
    acid$_1$ base$_2$ base$_1$ acid$_2$

10-24. *Refer to Section 10-4 and Example 10-1.*

(a) H_2SO_4 + H_2O ⇄ HSO_4^- + H_3O^+
acid$_1$ base$_2$ base$_1$ acid$_2$

HSO_4^- + H_2O ⇄ SO_4^{2-} + H_3O^+
acid$_1$ base$_2$ base$_1$ acid$_2$

(b) H_2SO_3 + H_2O ⇄ HSO_3^- + H_3O^+
acid$_1$ base$_2$ base$_1$ acid$_2$

HSO_3^- + H_2O ⇄ SO_3^{2-} + H_3O^+
acid$_1$ base$_2$ base$_1$ acid$_2$

10-26. *Refer to Section 10-1.*

Aqueous solutions of strong soluble bases (1) have a bitter taste, (2) have a slippery feeling, (3) change the colors of many acid-base indicators, (4) react with protic acids (acids that have an H) to form salts and water, and (5) conduct an electrical current since they contain ions.

Aqueous ammonia reacts with protic acids to form salts (and no water), but exhibits all the other traits to a lesser degree since it is a weak base exhibiting limited ionization and providing a lower OH^- concentration.

10-28. *Refer to Section 10-6 and Table 10-1.*

Amphoteric metal or metalloid hydroxides can act either as an acid or as a base. Such compounds include $Be(OH)_2$, $Zn(OH)_2$, $As(OH)_3$ and $Sb(OH)_3$.

(a) As acids:
$Be(OH)_2 + 2OH^- \rightarrow [Be(OH)_4]^{2-}$
$Zn(OH)_2 + 2OH^- \rightarrow [Zn(OH)_4]^{2-}$
$As(OH)_3 + OH^- \rightarrow [As(OH)_4]^-$
$Sb(OH)_3 + OH^- \rightarrow [Sb(OH)_4]^-$

(b) As bases:
$Be(OH)_2 + 2H^+ \rightarrow Be^{2+} + 2H_2O$
$Zn(OH)_2 + 2H^+ \rightarrow Zn^{2+} + 2H_2O$
$As(OH)_3 + 3H^+ \rightarrow As^{3+} + 3H_2O$
$Sb(OH)_3 + 3H^+ \rightarrow Sb^{3+} + 3H_2O$

10-30. *Refer to Section 10-7 and the Key Terms at the end of Chapter 10.*

Consider the following reaction: $K_2O(s) + H_2O(\ell) \rightarrow 2K^+(aq) + 2OH^-(aq)$

The leveling effect is the effect by which all acids stronger than the acid that is characteristic of the solvent react with the solvent to produce that acid. For example, in water, the strongest acid and base that can exist in water is H^+ and OH^-, respectively. In our example, the oxide ion (O^{2-}) is a stronger base than OH^-. When K_2O dissolves in water, the O^{2-} cannot exist in the solution. O^{2-} immediately removes a proton from H_2O, forming OH^-:

$$O^{2-}(aq) + H_2O(\ell) \rightarrow 2OH^-(aq).$$

Because any base stronger than OH^- will undergo a similar reaction, we say that water does not allow us to discriminate between these bases with regard to strength. Therefore, water is called a leveling solvent.

10-32. *Refer to Sections 10-4 and 10-7.*

Base strength refers to the relative tendency to produce OH^- ions in aqueous solution by (1) the dissociation of soluble metal hydroxides or (2) by ionization reactions with water using Arrhenius theory. A more general definition, applying Brønsted-Lowry theory, is that base strength is a measure of the relative tendency to accept a proton from any acid.

Acid strength refers to the relative tendency of a substance to produce H_3O^+ ions in aqueous solutions, according to Arrhenius. Using Brønsted-Lowry theory, acid strength is a measure of the relative tendency of a species to donate a proton.

10-34. *Refer to Section 10-4.*

(a) A binary protic acid is a covalent compound consisting of hydrogen atom(s) and one other element. The compound can act as a proton donor.

(b) hydrofluoric acid $HF(aq)$
     hydrosulfuric acid $H_2S(aq)$
     hydrobromic acid $HBr(aq)$
     hydroselenic acid $H_2Se(aq)$

10-36. *Refer to Section 10-7.*

In order of decreasing acidity:
(a) $H_2Se > H_2S > H_2O$ (b) $HI > HBr > HCl > HF$ (c) $H_2S > HS^- > S^{2-}$ (S^{2-} is not an acid)

10-38. *Refer to Section 10-4.*

Brønsted-Lowry bases: NH_3, H_2O and $:H^-$ in ionic NaH Brønsted-Lowry acids: H_2O, HF

The compounds, BeH_2, BH_3 and CH_4 are *generally* considered as neither Brønsted-Lowry acids nor Brønsted-Lowry bases.

10-40. *Refer to Section 10-7.*

Ternary acids, including nitric and perchloric acids, can be described as hydroxyl compounds of nonmetals since they contain 1 or more -O-H groups attached to the central nonmetal atom. For example,

$$HNO_3 \equiv NO_2(OH) \qquad\qquad HClO_4 \equiv ClO_3(OH)$$

10-42. *Refer to Section 10-7.*

Consider phosphoric acid, H_3PO_4 (a triprotic acid), and phosphorous acid, H_3PO_3 (a diprotic acid). Two structures that show this acidic behavior are:

phosphoric acid   phosphorous acid

Each H atoms attached to an O atom is an acidic hydrogen and can be released by the acid to a base. Phosphoric acid has 3 such H atoms and thus is triprotic. Although phosphorous acid has 3 H atoms, only 2 H atoms are bonded to an O atom, the other one is attached directly to the P atom. Thus phosphorous acid is only diprotic. A way to write this is H_2PHO_3.

10-44. *Refer to Section 10-7.*

(a) Acid strengths of most ternary acids containing different elements in the same oxidation state from the same group in the periodic table increase with increasing electronegativity of the central element.

(b) In order of increasing acid strength:

   (1) $H_3PO_4 < HNO_3$ (2) $H_3AsO_4 < H_3PO_4$*   (3) $H_2TeO_4 < H_2SeO_4$ (4) $HIO_3 < HBrO_3 < HClO_3$

   *Although to 2 significant figures, As and P have the same electronegativity value of 2.1, because P is directly above As in Group 5A, I'm predicting that P is very slightly more electronegative than As.

Acid-base reactions are called neutralization reactions because the reaction of an acid with a base generally produces a salt with little or no acid-base character and, in many cases, water.

10-48. *Refer to Section 4-2.*

The electrolytes are NH_4Cl, HI, RaF_2, $Zn(CH_3COO)_2$, $Cu(NO_3)_2$, CH_3COOH, KOH, $KHCO_3$, $NaClO_4$ and $La_2(SO_4)_3$. The nonelectrolytes are C_6H_6, $C_{12}H_{22}O_{11}$ (table sugar) and I_2.

10-50. *Refer to Section 10-8 and Examples 10-2 and 10-3.*

(a) formula unit:
$$HNO_2(aq) + LiOH(aq) \rightarrow LiNO_2(aq) + H_2O(\ell)$$

nitrous   lithium   lithium
acid   hydroxide   nitrite

total ionic:
$$HNO_2(aq) + Li^+(aq) + OH^-(aq) \rightarrow Li^+(aq) + NO_2^-(aq) + H_2O(\ell)$$

net ionic:
$$HNO_2(aq) + OH^-(aq) \rightarrow NO_2^-(aq) + H_2O(\ell)$$

(b) formula unit:
$$H_2SO_4(aq) + 2KOH(aq) \rightarrow K_2SO_4(aq) + 2H_2O(\ell)$$

sulfuric   potassium   potassium
acid   hydroxide   sulfate

total ionic:
$$2H^+(aq) + SO_4^{2-}(aq) + 2K^+(aq) + 2OH^-(aq) \rightarrow 2K^+(aq) + SO_4^{2-}(aq) + 2H_2O(\ell)$$

net ionic:
$$2H^+(aq) + 2OH^-(aq) \rightarrow 2H_2O(\ell)$$

therefore,
$$H^+(aq) + OH^-(aq) \rightarrow H_2O(\ell)$$

(c) formula unit:
$$HCl(aq) + NH_3(aq) \rightarrow NH_4Cl(aq)$$
hydrochloric   ammonia   ammonium
acid   chloride

total ionic:
$$H^+(aq) + Cl^-(aq) + NH_3(aq) \rightarrow NH_4^+(aq) + Cl^-(aq)$$
net ionic:
$$H^+(aq) + NH_3(aq) \rightarrow NH_4^+(aq)$$
$$\rightarrow$$

(d) formula unit:
$$CH_3COOH(aq) + NaOH(aq) \rightarrow NaCH_3COO(aq) + H_2O(\ell)$$

acetic   sodium   sodium
acid   hydroxide   acetate

total ionic:
$$CH_3COOH(aq) + Na^+(aq) + OH^-(aq) \rightarrow Na^+(aq) + CH_3COO^-(aq) + H_2O(\ell)$$

net ionic:
$$CH_3COOH(aq) + OH^-(aq) \rightarrow CH_3COO^-(aq) + H_2O(\ell)$$

(e) formula unit:
$$HI(aq) + NaOH(aq) \rightarrow NaI(aq) + H_2O(\ell)$$

hydriodic   sodium   sodium
acid   hydroxide   iodide

total ionic:
$$H^+(aq) + I^-(aq) + Na^+(aq) + OH^-(aq) \rightarrow Na^+(aq) + I^-(aq) + H_2O(\ell)$$

net ionic:
$$H^+(aq) + OH^-(aq) \rightarrow H_2O(\ell)$$

(a) formula unit:

$$2HClO_4(aq) + Ba(OH)_2(aq) \rightarrow Ba(ClO_4)_2(aq) + 2H_2O(\ell)$$

perchloric   barium   barium
acid   hydroxide   perchlorate

total ionic: $2H^+(aq) + 2ClO_4^-(aq) + Ba^{2+}(aq) + 2OH^-(aq) \rightarrow Ba^{2+}(aq) + 2ClO_4^-(aq) + 2H_2O(\ell)$

net ionic: $2H^+(aq) + 2OH^-(aq) \rightarrow 2H_2O(\ell)$

therefore, $H^+(aq) + OH^-(aq) \rightarrow H_2O(\ell)$

(b) formula unit:

$$2HI(aq) + Ca(OH)_2(aq) \rightarrow CaI_2(aq) + 2H_2O(\ell)$$

hydroiodic   calcium   calcium
acid   hydroxide   iodide

total ionic: $2H^+(aq) + 2I^-(aq) + Ca^{2+}(aq) + 2OH^-(aq) \rightarrow Ca^{2+}(aq) + 2I^-(aq) + 2H_2O(\ell)$

net ionic: $2H^+(aq) + 2OH^-(aq) \rightarrow 2H_2O(\ell)$

therefore, $H^+(aq) + OH^-(aq) \rightarrow H_2O(\ell)$

(c) formula unit:

$$H_2SO_4(aq) + 2NH_3(aq) \rightarrow (NH_4)_2SO_4(aq)$$

sulfuric   ammonia   ammonium
acid   sulfate

total ionic: $2H^+(aq) + SO_4^{2-}(aq) + 2NH_3(aq) \rightarrow 2NH_4^+(aq) + SO_4^{2-}(aq)$

net ionic: $2H^+(aq) + 2NH_3(aq) \rightarrow 2NH_4^+(aq)$

therefore, $H^+(aq) + NH_3(aq) \rightarrow NH_4^+(aq)$

(d) formula unit:

$$3H_2SO_4(aq) + 2Fe(OH)_3(s) \rightarrow Fe_2(SO_4)_3(aq) + 6H_2O(\ell)$$

sulfuric   iron(III)   iron(III)
acid   hydroxide   sulfate

total ionic: $6H^+(aq) + 3SO_4^{2-}(aq) + 2Fe(OH)_3(s) \rightarrow 2Fe^{3+}(aq) + 3SO_4^{2-}(aq) + 6H_2O(\ell)$

net ionic: $6H^+(aq) + 2Fe(OH)_3(s) \rightarrow 2Fe^{3+}(aq) + 6H_2O(\ell)$

therefore, $3H^+(aq) + Fe(OH)_3(s) \rightarrow Fe^{3+}(aq) + 3H_2O(\ell)$

(e) formula unit:

$$H_2SO_4(aq) + Ba(OH)_2(aq) \rightarrow BaSO_4(s) + 2H_2O(\ell)$$

sulfuric   barium   barium
acid   hydroxide   sulfate

total ionic: $2H^+(aq) + SO_4^{2-}(aq) + Ca^{2+}(aq) + 2OH^-(aq) \rightarrow BaSO_4(s) + 2H_2O(\ell)$

net ionic: same as the total ionic equation

(a) formula unit:

$$2HNO_3(aq) + Pb(OH)_2(s) \rightarrow Pb(NO_3)_2(aq) + 2H_2O(\ell)$$

total ionic: $2H^+(aq) + 2NO_3^-(aq) + Pb(OH)_2(s) \rightarrow Pb^{2+}(aq) + 2NO_3^-(aq) + 2H_2O(\ell)$

net ionic: $2H^+(aq) + Pb(OH)_2(s) \rightarrow Pb^{2+}(aq) + 2H_2O(\ell)$

(b) formula unit:

$$2HCl(aq) + Sr(OH)_2(aq) \rightarrow SrCl_2(aq) + 2H_2O(\ell)$$

total ionic: $2H^+(aq) + 2Cl^-(aq) + Sr^{2+}(aq) + 2OH^-(aq) \rightarrow Sr^{2+}(aq) + 2Cl^-(aq) + 2H_2O(\ell)$

net ionic: $2H^+(aq) + 2OH^-(aq) \rightarrow 2H_2O(\ell)$

therefore, $H^+(aq) + OH^-(aq) \rightarrow H_2O(\ell)$

143

(c) formula unit:

$$H_2SO_4(aq) + 2NH_3(aq) \rightarrow (NH_4)_2SO_4(aq)$$

total ionic:

$$2H^+(aq) + SO_4{}^{2-}(aq) + 2NH_3(aq) \rightarrow 2NH_4{}^+(aq) + SO_4{}^{2-}(aq)$$

net ionic:

$$2H^+(aq) + 2NH_3(aq) \rightarrow 2NH_4{}^+(aq)$$

therefore,

$$H^+(aq) + NH_3(aq) \rightarrow NH_4{}^+(aq)$$

(d) formula unit:

$$2HClO_4(aq) + Ca(OH)_2(aq) \rightarrow Ca(ClO_4)_2(aq) + 2H_2O(\ell)$$

total ionic:

$$2H^+(aq) + 2ClO_4{}^-(aq) + Ca^{2+}(aq) + 2OH^-(aq) \rightarrow Ca^{2+}(aq) + 2ClO_4{}^-(aq) + 2H_2O(\ell)$$

net ionic:

$$2H^+(aq) + 2OH^-(aq) \rightarrow 2H_2O(\ell)$$

therefore,

$$H^+(aq) + OH^-(aq) \rightarrow H_2O(\ell)$$

(e) formula unit:

$$3H_2SO_4(aq) + 2Al(OH)_3(s) \rightarrow Al_2(SO_4)_3(aq) + 6H_2O(\ell)$$

total ionic:

$$6H^+(aq) + 3SO_4{}^{2-}(aq) + 2Al(OH)_3(s) \rightarrow 2Al^{3+}(aq) + 3SO_4{}^{2-}(aq) + 6H_2O(\ell)$$

net ionic:

$$6H^+(aq) + 2Al(OH)_3(s) \rightarrow 2Al^{3+}(aq) + 6H_2O(\ell)$$

therefore,

$$3H^+(aq) + Al(OH)_3(s) \rightarrow Al^{3+}(aq) + 3H_2O(\ell)$$

10-56.   *Refer to Section 10-8 and Example 10-4.*

(a) The salts are (1) $KMnO_4$, (2) $CaSO_4$, (4) SnF_2 and (5) K_3PO_4. Compound (3) P_4O_{10} is an oxide, not a salt.

(b) Acid-base equations that account for salt formation are:

(1) $KOH(aq) + HMnO_4(aq) \rightarrow KMnO_4(aq) + H_2O(\ell)$

(2) $Ca(OH)_2(aq) + H_2SO_4(aq) \rightarrow CaSO_4(aq) + 2H_2O(\ell)$

(4) $Sn(OH)_2(s) + 2HF(aq) \rightarrow SnF_2(s) + 2H_2O(\ell)$

(5) $3KOH(aq) + H_3PO_4(aq) \rightarrow K_3PO_4(aq) + 3H_2O(\ell)$

10-58.   *Refer to Section 10-9.*

An acidic salt is a salt that contains an ionizable hydrogen atom. It is the product formed when less than the amount of base required for complete neutralization (reaction) reacts with a polyprotic acid:

$$H_2SO_3(aq) + NaOH(aq) \rightarrow NaHSO_3(aq) + H_2O(\ell)$$

$$H_2CO_3(aq) + NaOH(aq) \rightarrow NaHCO_3(aq) + H_2O(\ell)$$

$$H_3PO_4(aq) + KOH(aq) \rightarrow KH_2PO_4(aq) + H_2O(\ell)$$

$$H_3PO_4(aq) + 2NaOH(aq) \rightarrow Na_2HPO_4(aq) + 2H_2O(\ell)$$

$$H_2S(aq) + NaOH(aq) \rightarrow NaHS(aq) + H_2O(\ell)$$

10-60.   *Refer to Sections 10-8 and 10-9.*

(a) $HNO_3 + NH_3 \rightarrow NH_4NO_3$

(b) $H_3PO_4 + NH_3 \rightarrow NH_4H_2PO_4$

(c) $H_3PO_4 + 2NH_3 \rightarrow (NH_4)_2HPO_4$

(d) $H_3PO_4 + 3NH_3 \rightarrow (NH_4)_3PO_4$

(e) $H_2SO_4 + 2NH_3 \rightarrow (NH_4)_2SO_4$

10-62. *Refer to Section 10-9.*

A basic salt is a salt containing an ionizable OH group and can therefore neutralize acids.

(a),(b)　　$HCl(aq)$　　$+$　　$Ca(OH)_2(aq)$　　$\rightarrow$　　$Ca(OH)Cl(aq)$　　$+$　　$H_2O(\ell)$
　　　　　　1 mol　　　　　　**1 mol**

　　　　$HCl(aq)$　　$+$　　$Al(OH)_3(s)$　　$\rightarrow$　　$Al(OH)_2Cl(aq)$　　$+$　　$H_2O(\ell)$
　　　　1 mol　　　　　　**1 mol**

　　　　$2HCl(aq)$　　$+$　　$Al(OH)_3(s)$　　$\rightarrow$　　$Al(OH)Cl_2(aq)$　　$+$　　$2H_2O(\ell)$
　　　　2 mol　　　　　　**1 mol**

10-64. *Refer to Section 10-7 and Appendix F.*

(a) Protonation of the carbonate ion, CO_3^{2-}:　$CO_3^{2-}(aq) + H^+(aq) \rightleftarrows HCO_3^-(aq)$
　　　　　　　　　　　　　　　　　　　　　$HCO_3^-(aq) + H^+(aq) \rightleftarrows H_2CO_3(aq)$

(b) Deprotonation of arsenic acid, H_3AsO_3:　$H_3AsO_3(aq) \rightleftarrows H^+(aq) + H_2AsO_3^-(aq)$
　　　　　　　　　　　　　　　　　　　　　　$H_2AsO_3^-(aq) \rightleftarrows H^+(aq) + HAsO_3^{2-}(aq)$
　　　　　　　　　　　　　　　　　　　　　　$HAsO_3^{2-}(aq) \rightleftarrows H^+(aq) + AsO_3^{3-}(aq)$

(c) Protonation of the glycinate ion,
　　$NH_2CH_2COO^-$: $NH_2CH_2COO^-(aq) + H^+(aq) \rightleftarrows NH_2CH_2COOH(aq)$
　　(glycinate ion is a diprotic base) $NH_2CH_2COOH(aq) + H^+(aq) \rightleftarrows NH_3CH_2COOH^+(aq)$

10-66. *Refer to Section 10-7 and Appendix F.*

Ionization of citric acid, $C_6H_8O_7$ or $C_3H_5O(COOH)_3$:
　　　　$C_3H_5O(COOH)_3(aq) \rightleftarrows H^+(aq) + C_3H_5O(COO)(COOH)_2^-(aq)$
　　　　$C_3H_5O(COO)(COOH)_2^-(aq) \rightleftarrows H^+(aq) + C_3H_5O(COO)_2(COOH)^{2-}(aq)$
　　　　$C_3H_5O(COO)_2(COOH)^{2-}(aq) \rightleftarrows H^+(aq) + C_3H_5O(COO)_3^{3-}(aq)$

10-68. *Refer to Section 10-10.*

(a)　H:Ö:　+　H:Ö:　→　H:Ö:H$^+$　+　H:Ö:$^-$
　　　 H　　　　 H　　　　 H
　　 base　　 **acid**　　 **acid**　　　**base**

(b)　H:Cl̈:　+　H:Ö:　→　:Cl̈:$^-$　+　H:Ö:H$^+$
　　　　　　　　　 H　　　　　　　　　　 H
　　 acid　　 **base**　　 **base**　　　 **acid**

(c)　H:N̈:H　+　H:Ö:　→　　H$^+$　　+　H:Ö:$^-$
　　　 H　　　　 H　　　　 H:N:H
　　　　　　　　　　　　　　 H
　　 base　　 **acid**　　 **acid**　　　**base**

(d)　H:N̈:H　+　H:Br̈:　→　$\left[\begin{array}{c} H \\ H:N:H \\ H \end{array}\right]^+$:Br̈:$^-$
　　　 H
　　 base　　 **acid**　　　　**acid**　 **base**

(a) I_2 + I^- → I_3^-
Lewis acid   Lewis base

(b) SO_2 + BF_3 → $O_2S:BF_3$
Lewis base   Lewis acid

(c) Au^+ + $2CN^-$ → $[Au(CN)_2]^-$
Lewis acid   Lewis base

(d) CO_2 + H_2O → H_2CO_3
Lewis acid   Lewis base

(a)
Lewis base   Lewis acid

(b)
Lewis base   Lewis acid

(a) HF + SbF_5 → $H(SbF_6)$ (b) HF + BF_3 → $H(BF_4)$
Lewis   Lewis   **Lewis   Lewis**
base   acid   **base   acid**

(b)   In $H(SbF_6)$, H is bonded to the SbF_6^- ion through an ionic bond. In $H(BF_4)$, the H is bonded to the BF_4^- ion through an ionic bond.

(a) Hydrogen sulfide, $H_2S(g)$, can be prepared by combining elemental sulfur with hydrogen gas.
$$S_8(s) + 8H_2(g) \rightarrow 8H_2S(g)$$

(b) Hydrogen chloride, $HCl(g)$, can be prepared in small quantities by dropping concentrated nonvolatile acids such as phosphoric acid, onto an appropriate salt such as $NaCl(s)$.
$$H_3PO_4(\ell) + NaCl(s) \rightarrow HCl(g) + NaH_2PO_4(s)$$

(c) An aqueous solution of the weak acid acetic acid, $CH_3COOH(aq)$, can be produced by using sulfuric acid and an acetate salt:
$$H_2SO_4(aq) + Ca(CH_3COO)_2(aq) \rightarrow 2CH_3COOH(aq) + CaSO_4(aq)$$

(a) acidic oxides: CO_2, SO_2, SO_3
(b) amphoteric oxides: Al_2O_3, Ga_2O_3, SnO_2
(c) basic oxides: Na_2O, K_2O, CaO, BaO

(a) H_2S Arrhenius acid, Brønsted-Lowry acid
(b) $PO(OH)_3 \equiv H_3PO_4$ Arrhenius acid, Brønsted-Lowry acid
(c) $H_2CaO_2 \equiv Ca(OH)_2$ Arrhenius base, Brønsted-Lowry base
(d) $ClO_3(OH) \equiv HClO_4$ Arrhenius acid, Brønsted-Lowry acid
(e) $Sb(OH)_3$ amphoteric hydroxide (can act as either an acid or base)

10-82.   *Refer to Section 10-4 and Example 10-1.*

(a)

Acid	Conjugate base	Name of conjugate base	Base	Conjugate Acid	Name of conjugate acid
H_3PO_4	$H_2PO_4^-$	dihydrogen phosphate ion	HSO_4^-	H_2SO_4	sulfuric acid
NH_4^+	NH_3	ammonia	PH_3	PH_4^+	phosphonium ion
OH^-	O^{2-}	oxide ion	PO_4^{3-}	HPO_4^{2-}	hydrogen phosphate ion

(b) We know that the weaker a base, the stronger is its conjugate acid. Therefore, given that NO_2^- is a stronger base than NO_3^-, then HNO_3 (the conjugate acid of NO_3^-) is a stronger acid than HNO_2 (the conjugate acid of NO_2^-).

10-84.   *Refer to Section 10-8 and Figure 6-1.*

In a conductivity experiment, the indicator light bulb glows brightly when the electrodes are placed in an aqueous solution containing a high concentration of ions, such as can be found in aqueous solutions of strong electrolytes (strong acids, strong soluble bases and soluble salts). The bulb will only glow dimly in the presence of weak electrolytes because there are few ions present to conduct electricity through the solution.

(a) $NaOH(aq)$ and $HCl(aq)$ are both strong electrolytes. The light bulb glows brightly for these solutions. The neutralization reaction between NaOH and HCl that results when the two solutions are mixed can be represented as follows:

formula unit: $NaOH(aq) + HCl(aq) \rightarrow NaCl(aq) + H_2O(\ell)$

dissociation of the product, $NaCl(aq)$: $NaCl(aq) \rightarrow Na^+(aq) + Cl^-(aq)$

Even though ions are lost as the reaction proceeds, due to H^+ and OH^- ions combining to form water, there are still plenty of Na^+ and Cl^- ions remaining in the solution to cause the indicator bulb to glow brightly, but not quite as brightly as the initial solution.

(b) $NH_3(aq)$ and $CH_3COOH(aq)$ are both weak electrolytes and the light bulb will only glow dimly for these solutions. The neutralization reaction between the weak base, NH_3, and the weak acid, CH_3COOH, is as follows:

formula unit: $NH_3(aq) + CH_3COOH(aq) \rightarrow NH_4CH_3COO(aq)$

dissociation   of   the   product, $NH_4CH_3COO(aq) \rightarrow NH_4^+(aq) + CH_3COO^-(aq)$
$NH_4CH_3COO(aq)$:

As can readily be seen, the product formed is a soluble salt, the strong electrolyte, NH_4CH_3COO, which dissociates completely into NH_4^+ and CH_3COO^- ions. The indicator bulb glows brightly in this solution.

10-86.   *Refer to Sections 10-4 and 10-8, and the Key Terms for Chapter 10.*

Solubility refers to the extent to which a substance will dissolve in a solvent. Molecular substances that do dissolve in water may or may not ionize into ions. If they do ionize, they may or may not ionize completely.

HCl(aq), a soluble gas, ionizes almost totally into its ions in aqueous solution, whereas glucose, a soluble molecular solid, does not ionize at all. Weak acids, such as HF, are soluble in water but ionize only slightly into ions.

10-88. Refer to Section 10-7.

(a) Hydrochloric acid is a strong acid and ionizes completely in aqueous solution:
$$HCl(aq) \rightarrow H^+(aq) + Cl^-(aq)$$
It is best represented by Diagram (d).

(b) Hydrofluoric acid is a weak acid and only ionizes slightly in aqueous solution:
$$HF(aq) \rightleftarrows F^-(aq) + H^+(aq)$$
It is best represented by Diagram (b).

10-90. Refer to Section 10-5.

On planet Baseacidopolous, ammonia is the primary solvent: $NH_3 + NH_3 \rightleftarrows NH_2^- + NH_4^+$

(a) The cation that would indicate that a compound is an acid is NH_4^+.

(b) The anion that would indicate that a compound is a base is NH_2^-.

(c) NaCl could be a salt on this planet. It would be formed as follows: $NaNH_2 + NH_4Cl \rightarrow NaCl + 2NH_3$

10-92. Refer to Section 10-7.

In a solution of $1M$ HCl, a strong acid, in order of decreasing concentration, we have:

$$H_2O > H_3O^+ > Cl^- > OH^- > HCl$$

Note: H_3O^+ is only very slightly more concentrated than Cl^- because of the ionization of water.

10-94. Refer to Sections 10-2, 10-4 and 10-7.

(a) Arrhenius acid: HCl   Arrhenius base: NaOH

(b) Brønsted-Lowry acid that is not an Arrhenius acid: H_2O or NH_3

(c) Brønsted-Lowry base that is not an Arrhenius base: H_2O or NH_3

(d) There are no Arrhenius acids or bases that are not acids or bases under Brønsted-Lowry theory.

10-96. Refer to Section 10-10.

The Lewis bases are the following. They all have at least one lone pair of electrons.

$$:\overset{..}{\underset{..}{I}}:^- \qquad :H:\overset{..}{N}:H: \qquad :\overset{..}{\underset{..}{F}}:^- \qquad :C::\overset{..}{\underset{..}{O}}:$$
$$\qquad \qquad :\overset{..}{H}:$$

$$I^- \qquad \qquad NH_3 \qquad \qquad F^- \qquad \qquad CO$$

10-98. Refer to Sections 10-8 and 10-9.

(1) H_2S (weak acid) + NaOH (strong base) $\rightarrow$ NaHS (acidic salt) + H_2O

(2) NaHS (acidic salt) + NaOH (strong base) $\rightarrow$ Na_2S (normal salt) + H_2O

Autoionization of PCl_5:

| PCl_5 | + | PCl_5 | $\rightarrow$ | PCl_4^+ | + | PCl_6^- |

trigonal bipyramidal   trigonal bipyramidal   tetrahedral   octahedral

(a) $CH_3COOH(aq) + NaHCO_3(aq) \rightarrow NaCH_3COO(aq) + CO_2(g) + H_2O(\ell)$

The "fizz" is caused by the gaseous product, carbon dioxide, escaping from the solution.

(b) $CH_3CH(OH)COOH(aq) + NaHCO_3(aq) \rightarrow NaCH_3CH(OH)COO(aq) + CO_2(g) + H_2O(\ell)$

"Quick" bread "rises" during baking due to the reaction between baking soda and lactic acid found in the added milk. The resulting carbon dioxide gas bubbles are caught in the bread dough, giving the bread more volume. Yeast breads "rise" due to carbon dioxide bubbles released in the fermentation of sugar by yeast.

11 Reactions in Aqueous Solutions II: Calculations

Molarity is defined as the number of moles of solute per 1 liter of solution and has units of mol/L. If we multiply molarity by unity = $10^{-3}/10^{-3}$,

$$\text{Molarity, } M\left(\frac{\text{mol}}{\text{L}}\right) = \frac{\text{mol solute}}{\text{L soln}} \times \frac{10^{-3}}{10^{-3}} = \frac{\text{mmol solute}}{\text{mL soln}}$$

Plan: (1) Calculate the moles of $MgSO_4$ present in the solution.
       (2) Calculate the molarity.

(1) ? mol $MgSO_4 = \dfrac{41.4 \text{ g } MgSO_4}{120.4 \text{ g/mol}} = 0.344$ mol $MgSO_4$

(2) ? M $MgSO_4 = \dfrac{0.344 \text{ mol } MgSO_4}{3.00 \text{ L}} = \textbf{0.115 } \textbf{\textit{M}} \textbf{ MgSO}_4 \textbf{ soln}$

Dimensional Analysis: ? M $MgSO_4 = \dfrac{41.4 \text{ g } MgSO_4}{3.00 \text{ L}} \times \dfrac{1 \text{ mol } MgSO_4}{120.4 \text{ g } MgSO_4} = \textbf{0.115 } \textbf{\textit{M}} \textbf{ MgSO}_4$

Assume a 1 liter solution of 39.77% H_2SO_4 with density of 1.305 g/mL (density = specific gravity $\times$ 1.00 g/mL)

? g H_2SO_4 soln in 1 L soln $= \dfrac{1.305 \text{ g soln}}{1 \text{ mL soln}} \times 1000$ mL soln = 1305 g soln

? g H_2SO_4 in 1 L soln = 1305 g soln $\times \dfrac{39.77 \text{ g } H_2SO_4}{100 \text{ g soln}} = 519.0$ g H_2SO_4

? mol H_2SO_4 in 1 L soln $= \dfrac{519.0 \text{ g } H_2SO_4}{98.08 \text{ g/mol}} = 5.292$ mol H_2SO_4

Therefore, ? M $H_2SO_4 = \textbf{5.292 } \textbf{\textit{M}}$

This is a possible limiting reactant problem.

Plan: (1) Calculate the number of moles of HCl and NaOH.
       (2) Determine the limiting reactant, if there is one.
       (3) Calculate the moles of NaCl formed.
       (4) Determine the molarity of NaCl in the solution.

Balanced equation: $HCl(aq) + NaOH(aq) \rightarrow NaCl(aq) + H_2O(\ell)$

(1) ? mol HCl = 3.35 M HCl $\times$ 0.225 L = 0.754 mol HCl
     ? mol NaOH = 1.77 M NaOH $\times$ 0.426 L = 0.754 mol NaOH

(2) This is not a problem with a single limiting reactant since we have stoichiometric amounts of HCl and NaOH. Our final solution is a salt solution with no excess acid or base.

(3) ? mol NaCl = mol HCl = mol NaOH = 0.754 mol NaCl

(4) $? \, M \, \text{NaCl} = \dfrac{\text{mol NaCl}}{\text{total volume}} = \dfrac{0.754 \text{ mol}}{(0.225 \text{ L} + 0.426 \text{ L})} = \mathbf{1.16 \, \textit{M} \, NaCl}$

11-10. *Refer to Section 11-1 and Example 11-1.*

This is a possible limiting reactant problem.

Plan: (1) Calculate the number of moles of HI and KOH.
　　　　(2) Determine the limiting reactant, if there is one.
　　　　(3) Calculate the moles of KI formed.
　　　　(4) Determine the molarity of KI in the solution.

Balanced equation: $\text{HI}(aq) + \text{KOH}(aq) \rightarrow \text{KI}(aq) + \text{H}_2\text{O}(\ell)$

(1) ? mol HI = 8.99 M HI x 0.0555 L = 0.499 mol HI
　　 ? mol KOH = 14.1 M KOH x 0.0354 L = 0.499 mol KOH

(2) This is not a problem with a single limiting reactant since we have stoichiometric amounts of HI and KOH. Our final solution is a salt solution with no excess acid or base.

(3) ? mol KI = mol HI = mol KOH = 0.499 mol KI

(4) $? \, M \, \text{KI} = \dfrac{\text{mol KI}}{\text{total volume}} = \dfrac{0.499 \text{ mol}}{(0.0555 \text{ L} + 0.0354 \text{ L})} = \mathbf{5.49 \, \textit{M} \, KI}$

Note: The answers to each step were rounded to the correct number of significant figures. However, the entire number has been kept in the calculator and used throughout the entire calculation to minimize rounding errors.

11-12. *Refer to Section 11-1 and Examples 11-2 and 11-4.*

This is a possible limiting reactant problem.

Plan: (1) Calculate the number of millimoles of HI and Ba(OH)$_2$.
　　　　(2) Determine the limiting reactant, if there is one.
　　　　(3) Calculate the millimoles of BaI$_2$ formed.
　　　　(4) Determine the molarity of BaI$_2$ in the solution.

Balanced equation: $2\text{HI}(aq) + \text{Ba(OH)}_2(aq) \rightarrow \text{BaI}_2(aq) + 2\text{H}_2\text{O}(\ell)$

(1) ? mmol HI = 0.104 M HI x 19.4 mL = 2.02 mmol HI
　　 ? mmol Ba(OH)$_2$ = 0.135 M Ba(OH)$_2$ x 7.50 mL = 1.01 mmol Ba(OH)$_2$

(2)　　Required ratio $= \dfrac{2 \text{ mmol HI}}{1 \text{ mmol Ba(OH)}_2} = 2$　　　　Available ratio $= \dfrac{2.02 \text{ mmol HI}}{1.01 \text{ mmol Ba(OH)}_2} = 2$

　　Available ratio = required ratio; we have stoichiometric amounts of both reactants.
　　We can use either reactant to calculate the amount of product.

(3) ? mmol BaI$_2$ = 2.02 mmol HI x $\dfrac{1 \text{ mmol BaI}_2}{2 \text{ mmol HI}}$ = 1.01 mmol BaI$_2$

(4) $? \, M \, \text{BaI}_2 = \dfrac{\text{mmol BaI}_2}{\text{total volume in mL}} = \dfrac{1.01 \text{ mmol}}{(19.4 \text{ mL} + 7.50 \text{ mL})} = \mathbf{0.0375 \, \textit{M} \, BaI_2}$

Note: When doing these calculations, do not round off your answers until the end. The answers here are rounded after each step to illustrate the concept of significant figures.

Balanced equation: $H_3PO_4(aq) + 3NaOH(aq) \rightarrow Na_3PO_4(aq) + 3H_2O(\ell)$

Plan: (1) Calculate the moles of H_3PO_4 and NaOH.
(2) Determine the limiting reactant, if there is one.
(3) Calculate the moles of Na_3PO_4 formed.
(4) Determine the molarity of the salt in the solution.
(5) Determine the moles and concentration of excess reactant in the solution.

(1) ? mol H_3PO_4 = 5.52 M H_3PO_4 x 0.250 L = 1.38 mol H_3PO_4
? mol NaOH = 5.52 M NaOH x 0.775 L = 4.28 mol NaOH

(2) In the balanced equation, H_3PO_4 reacts with NaOH in a 1:3 mole ratio.
mol H_3PO_4:mol NaOH = 1.38 mol:4.28 mol = 1:3.10

We do not have stoichiometric amounts of both reactants; this is a limiting reactant problem. We have less H_3PO_4 than is necessary to react with all of the NaOH, so H_3PO_4 is the limiting reactant and NaOH is in excess. The amount of salt formed is set then by the amount of H_3PO_4.

(3) ? mol Na_3PO_4 = mol H_3PO_4 = 1.38 mol Na_3PO_4

(4) ? M $Na_3PO_4 = \dfrac{1.38 \text{ mol } Na_3PO_4}{(0.250 \text{ L} + 0.775 \text{ L})}$ = **1.35 M Na_3PO_4**

(5) The moles of NaOH consumed are determined from the amount of limiting reactant, H_3PO_4. The moles and molarity of NaOH remaining is determined by subtraction.
? mol NaOH consumed = 3 x 1.38 mol H_3PO_4 = 4.14 mol NaOH
? excess mol NaOH = total mol NaOH - mol NaOH consumed by H_3PO_4 = 4.28 mol – 4.14 mol = 0.14 mol
? M NaOH $= \dfrac{0.14 \text{ mol NaOH}}{(0.250 \text{ L} + 0.775 \text{ L})}$ = **0.137 M NaOH in excess**

Note: When doing these calculations, do not round off your answers until the end. The answers here are rounded after each step to illustrate the concept of significant figures.

Assume a 1 liter solution of 5.11% CH_3COOH.
? g CH_3COOH soln in 1 L soln $= \dfrac{1.007 \text{ g soln}}{1 \text{ mL soln}}$ x 1000 mL soln = 1007 g soln

? g CH_3COOH in 1 L soln = 1007 g soln x $\dfrac{5.11 \text{ g } CH_3COOH}{100 \text{ g soln}}$ = 51.5 g CH_3COOH

? mol CH_3COOH in 1 L soln $= \dfrac{51.5 \text{ g } CH_3COOH}{60.1 \text{ g/mol}}$ = 0.857 mol CH_3COOH

Therefore, ? M CH_3COOH = **0.857 M**

(a) Balanced equation: $3NaOH(aq) + H_3PO_4(aq) \rightarrow Na_3PO_4(aq) + 3H_2O(\ell)$

Plan: (1) Calculate the moles of NaOH and H_3PO_4 required to form 1 mole of Na_3PO_4.
(2) Find the volumes of each solution.

(1) ? mol NaOH = mol Na_3PO_4 x $\dfrac{3 \text{ mol NaOH}}{1 \text{ mol } Na_3PO_4}$ = 1.00 mol x 3 = 3.00 mol NaOH
? mol H_3PO_4 = mol Na_3PO_4 = 1.00 mol H_3PO_4

(2) $? \text{ L NaOH soln} = \dfrac{3.00 \text{ mol NaOH}}{3.25 \, M \text{ NaOH}} = \textbf{0.923 L NaOH soln}$

$\quad\quad ? \text{ L H}_3\text{PO}_4 \text{ soln} = \dfrac{1.00 \text{ mol H}_3\text{PO}_4}{4.50 \, M \text{ H}_3\text{PO}_4} = \textbf{0.222 L H}_3\textbf{PO}_4 \textbf{ soln}$

(b) Balanced equation: $2\text{NaOH}(aq) + \text{H}_3\text{PO}_4(aq) \rightarrow \text{Na}_2\text{HPO}_4(aq) + 2\text{H}_2\text{O}(\ell)$

   Plan: (1) Calculate the moles of NaOH and H_3PO_4 required to form 1 mole of Na_2HPO_4.
   (2) Find the volumes of each solution.

(1) $? \text{ mol NaOH} = \text{mol Na}_2\text{HPO}_4 \times \dfrac{2 \text{ mol NaOH}}{1 \text{ mol Na}_2\text{HPO}_4} = 1.00 \text{ mol} \times 2 = 2.00 \text{ mol NaOH}$

$\quad\quad ? \text{ mol H}_3\text{PO}_4 = \text{mol Na}_2\text{HPO}_4 = 1.00 \text{ mol H}_3\text{PO}_4$

(2) $? \text{ L NaOH soln} = \dfrac{2.00 \text{ mol NaOH}}{3.25 \, M \text{ NaOH}} = \textbf{0.615 L NaOH soln}$

$\quad\quad ? \text{ L H}_3\text{PO}_4 \text{ soln} = \dfrac{1.00 \text{ mol H}_3\text{PO}_4}{4.50 \, M \text{ H}_3\text{PO}_4} = \textbf{0.222 L H}_3\textbf{PO}_4 \textbf{ soln}$

11-20. *Refer to Sections 11-2 and 11-3.*

A standard solution of NaOH cannot be prepared directly because the solid is hydroscopic and absorbs moisture and CO_2 from the air.

Step 1: Weigh out an amount of solid NaOH and dissolve it in water to obtain a solution with the approximate concentration.

Step 2: Weigh out an appropriate amount of an acidic material, suitable for use as a primary standard, such as potassium hydrogen phthalate (KHP).

Step 3: Titrate the KHP sample with the NaOH solution and calculate the molarity of the NaOH solution using the fact that KHP and NaOH react in a 1:1 stoichiometric ratio.

The prepared NaOH solution is a secondary standard because its concentration is determined by titration against a primary standard.

11-22. *Refer to Section 11-3 and Example 11-6.*

(a) Potassium hydrogen phthalate (KHP) is the acidic salt, $\text{KC}_6\text{H}_4(\text{COO})(\text{COOH})$.

(b) KHP is used as a primary standard for the standardization of strong bases.

11-24. *Refer to Sections 11-1 and 11-3, and Example 11-3.*

Balanced equation: $2\text{CH}_3\text{COOH} + \text{Ba(OH)}_2 \rightarrow \text{Ba(CH}_3\text{COO)}_2 + 2\text{H}_2\text{O}$

$\qquad\qquad\qquad\qquad\quad$ (1) $\qquad\qquad$ (2) $\qquad\qquad\qquad$ (3)

Plan: M, L Ba(OH)_2 soln $\Rightarrow$ mol Ba(OH)_2 $\Rightarrow$ mol CH_3COOH $\Rightarrow$ $V \text{ CH}_3\text{COOH}$ soln

(1) $? \text{ mol Ba(OH)}_2 = 0.105 \, M \times 0.02158 \text{ L} = 0.00227 \text{ mol Ba(OH)}_2$

(2) $? \text{ mol CH}_3\text{COOH} = 0.00227 \text{ mol Ba(OH)}_2 \times \dfrac{2 \text{ mol CH}_3\text{COOH}}{1 \text{ mol Ba(OH)}_2} = 0.00453 \text{ mol CH}_3\text{COOH}$

(3) $? \text{ L CH}_3\text{COOH soln} = \dfrac{0.00453 \text{ mol CH}_3\text{COOH}}{0.145 \, M \text{ CH}_3\text{COOH}} = \textbf{0.0313 L} \textbf{ or } \textbf{31.3 mL of CH}_3\textbf{COOH soln}$

Dimensional Analysis:

$? \text{ L CH}_3\text{COOH soln} = 0.02158 \text{ L Ba(OH)}_2 \text{ soln} \times \dfrac{0.105 \text{ mol Ba(OH)}_2}{1 \text{ L Ba(OH)}_2 \text{ soln}} \times \dfrac{2 \text{ mol CH}_3\text{COOH}}{1 \text{ mol Ba(OH)}_2})$

$\qquad\qquad\qquad\qquad\quad \times \dfrac{1 \text{ L CH}_3\text{COOH soln}}{0.145 \text{ mol CH}_3\text{COOH}}$

$\qquad\qquad\qquad = \textbf{0.0313 L or 31.3 mL of CH}_3\textbf{COOH soln}$

11-26. *Refer to Section 11-3 and Example 11-5.*

Balanced equation: $2HNO_3(aq) + Na_2CO_3(s) \rightarrow 2NaNO_3(aq) + CO_2(g) + H_2O(\ell)$

$$\text{Plan: } \underset{(1)}{g\,Na_2CO_3} \Rightarrow \underset{(2)}{mol\,Na_2CO_3} \Rightarrow \underset{(3)}{mol\,HNO_3} \Rightarrow M\,HNO_3\,soln$$

(1) $? \text{ mol } Na_2CO_3 = 0.2040 \text{ g } Na_2CO_3 \times \dfrac{1 \text{ mol } Na_2CO_3}{106.0 \text{ g } Na_2CO_3} = 1.925 \times 10^{-3} \text{ mol } Na_2CO_3$

(2) $? \text{ mol } HNO_3 = 1.925 \times 10^{-3} \text{ mol } Na_2CO_3 \times \dfrac{2 \text{ mol } HNO_3}{1 \text{ mol } Na_2CO_3} = 3.849 \times 10^{-3} \text{ mol } HNO_3$

(3) $? M\,HNO_3 \text{ soln} = \dfrac{3.849 \times 10^{-3} \text{ mol } HNO_3}{0.01955 \text{ L } HNO_3} = \mathbf{0.1969\ \textit{M}\ HNO_3}$

Dimensional Analysis (start by setting up the ratio of mass to volume, then convert to moles and do stochiometry):

$? M\,HNO_3 \text{ soln} = \dfrac{0.2040 \text{ g } Na_2CO_3}{0.01955 \text{ L } HNO_3 \text{ soln}} \times \dfrac{1 \text{ mol } Na_2CO_3}{106.0 \text{ g } Na_2CO_3} \times \dfrac{2 \text{ mol } HNO_3}{1 \text{ mol } Na_2CO_3} = \mathbf{0.1969\ \textit{M}\ HNO_3}$

11-28. *Refer to Section 11-3 and Example 11-6.*

Balanced equation: $NaOH + KHP \rightarrow NaKP + H_2O$

$$\text{Plan: } \underset{(1)}{g\,KHP} \Rightarrow \underset{(2)}{mmol\,KHP} \Rightarrow \underset{(3)}{mmol\,NaOH} \Rightarrow M\,NaOH$$

(1) $? \text{ mmol } KHP = \dfrac{0.5536 \text{ g } KHP}{204.2 \text{ g/mol}} \times \dfrac{1000 \text{ mmol}}{1 \text{ mol}} = 2.711 \text{ mmol } KHP$

(2) $? \text{ mmol } NaOH = \text{mmol } KHP = 2.711 \text{ mmol } NaOH$

(3) $? M\,NaOH = \dfrac{2.711 \text{ mmol } NaOH}{(37.26 \text{ mL - } 0.23 \text{ mL})} = \mathbf{0.07321\ \textit{M}\ NaOH}$

11-30. *Refer to Section 11-3 and Example 11-7.*

Balanced equation: $2HCl(aq) + CaCO_3(s) \rightarrow CaCl_2(aq) + CO_2(g) + H_2O(\ell)$

$$\text{Plan: } \underset{(1)}{g\,CaCO_3} \Rightarrow \underset{(2)}{mol\,CaCO_3} \Rightarrow \underset{(3)}{mol\,HCl} \Rightarrow L\,HCl\,soln$$

(1) $? \text{ mol } CaCO_3 = 0.900 \text{ g } CaCO_3 \times \dfrac{1 \text{ mol } CaCO_3}{100.1 \text{ g } CaCO_3} = 0.00899 \text{ mol } CaCO_3$

(2) $? \text{ mol } HCl = 0.00899 \text{ mol } CaCO_3 \times \dfrac{2 \text{ mol } HCl}{1 \text{ mol } CaCO_3} = 0.0180 \text{ mol } HCl$

(3) $? \text{ L } HCl \text{ soln} = \dfrac{0.0180 \text{ mol } HCl}{1.0\ M\,HCl} = \mathbf{0.018 \text{ L or 18 mL } HCl}$

Dimensional Analysis:

$? \text{ L } HCl \text{ soln} = 0.900 \text{ g } CaCO_3 \times \dfrac{1 \text{ mol } CaCO_3}{100.1 \text{ g } CaCO_3} \times \dfrac{2 \text{ mol } HCl}{1 \text{ mol } CaCO_3} \times \dfrac{1.0 \text{ L soln}}{1.0 \text{ mol } HCl} = \mathbf{0.018 \text{ L or 18 mL } HCl}$

11-32. *Refer to Section 11-2.*

(a) An ideal primary standard:
  (1) does not react with or absorb water vapor, oxygen or carbon dioxide,
  (2) reacts according to a single known reaction,
  (3) is available in high purity,
  (4) has a high formula weight,
  (5) is soluble in the solvent of interest,
  (6) is nontoxic,

(7) is inexpensive, and

(8) is environmentally friendly.

(b) The significance of each factor is given below.

(1) The compound must be weighed accurately and must not undergo composition change due to reaction with atmospheric components.

(2) The reaction must be one of known stoichiometry with no side reactions.

(3) Solutions of precisely known concentration must be prepared by directly weighing the primary standard.

(4) The high formula weight is necessary to minimize the effect of weighing errors.

(5),(6),(7),(8) The significance is self-explanatory.

11-34. *Refer to Section 11-3 and Example 11-9.*

Balanced equation: $(COOH)_2 + 2NaOH \rightarrow Na_2(COO)_2 + 2H_2O$

Plan: M, L NaOH $\overset{(1)}{\Rightarrow}$ mol NaOH $\overset{(2)}{\Rightarrow}$ mol $(COOH)_2$ $\overset{(3)}{\Rightarrow}$ mol $(COOH)_2 \cdot 2H_2O$ $\overset{(4)}{\Rightarrow}$ g $(COOH)_2 \cdot 2H_2O$ $\overset{(5)}{\Rightarrow}$ % purity

(1) ? mol NaOH = 0.298 M NaOH x 0.01916 L = 0.00571 mol NaOH

(2) ? mol $(COOH)_2$ = mol NaOH x $\dfrac{1 \text{ mol } (COOH)_2}{2 \text{ mol NaOH}}$ = 0.00571 mol NaOH x 1/2 = 0.00285 mol $(COOH)_2$

(3) ? mol $(COOH)_2 \cdot 2H_2O$ = mol $(COOH)_2$ = 0.00285 mol $(COOH)_2 \cdot 2H_2O$

(4) ? g $(COOH)_2 \cdot 2H_2O$ = 0.00285 mol $(COOH)_2 \cdot 2H_2O$ x 126 g/mol = 0.360 g $(COOH)_2 \cdot 2H_2O$

(5) ? % $(COOH)_2 \cdot 2H_2O$ = $\dfrac{\text{g } (COOH)_2 \cdot 2H_2O}{\text{g sample}}$ x 100 = $\dfrac{0.360 \text{ g}}{1.00 \text{ g}}$ x 100 = **36.0% $(COOH)_2 \cdot 2H_2O$**

11-36. *Refer to Section 11-3.*

Balanced equation: $2HCl + CaCO_3 \rightarrow CaCl_2 + CO_2 + H_2O$

Plan: M, L HCl $\overset{(1)}{\Rightarrow}$ mol HCl $\overset{(2)}{\Rightarrow}$ mol $CaCO_3$ $\overset{(3)}{\Rightarrow}$ g $CaCO_3$

(1) ? mol HCl = 0.112 M HCl x 0.0268 L = 0.00300 mol HCl

(2) ? mol $CaCO_3$ = 0.00300 mol HCl x (1 mol $CaCO_3$/2 mol HCl) = 0.00150 mol $CaCO_3$

(3) ? g $CaCO_3$ = 0.00150 mol $CaCO_3$ x 100.1 g/mol = **0.150 g $CaCO_3$**

Dimensional Analysis:

? g $CaCO_3$ = 0.0268 L HCl soln x $\dfrac{0.112 \text{ mol HCl}}{1 \text{ L HCl soln}}$ x $\dfrac{1 \text{ mol } CaCO_3}{2 \text{ mol HCl}}$ x $\dfrac{100.1 \text{ g } CaCO_3}{1 \text{ mol } CaCO_3}$ = **0.150 g $CaCO_3$**

11-38. *Refer to Section 11-3 and Examples 11-7 and 11-8.*

Balanced equation: $HNO_3 + NaOH \rightarrow NaNO_3 + H_2O$

Plan: M, L HNO_3 soln $\overset{(1)}{\Rightarrow}$ mol HNO_3 $\overset{(2)}{\Rightarrow}$ mol NaOH $\overset{(3)}{\Rightarrow}$ M NaOH soln

(1) ? mol HNO_3 = 0.0342 M x 0.0375 L = 1.28 x 10^{-3} mol HNO_3

(2) ? mol NaOH = 1.28 x 10^{-3} mol HNO_3 x (1 mol NaOH/1 mol HNO_3) = 1.28 x 10^{-3} mol NaOH

(3) ? M NaOH = $\dfrac{\text{mol NaOH}}{\text{L NaOH}}$ = $\dfrac{1.28 \times 10^{-3} \text{ mol}}{0.0414 \text{ L}}$ = **0.0310 M NaOH soln**

(1) Plan: $\underset{(1)}{g\ H_3PO_4} \Rightarrow \underset{(2)}{mol\ H_3PO_4} \Rightarrow M\ H_3PO_4\ soln$

   (1) $?\ mol\ H_3PO_4 = \dfrac{g\ H_3PO_4}{FW\ H_3PO_4} = \dfrac{0.978\ g}{97.99\ g/mol} = 0.00998\ mol\ H_3PO_4$

   (2) $?\ M\ H_3PO_4 = \dfrac{mol\ H_3PO_4}{L\ soln} = \dfrac{0.00998\ mol}{0.185\ L} =$ **0.0539 *M* H$_3$PO$_4$**

Dimensional Analysis (start by setting up the ratio of mass to volume, then convert to moles):

$?\ M\ H_3PO_4\ soln = \dfrac{0.978\ g\ H_3PO_4}{0.185\ L\ H_3PO_4\ soln} \times \dfrac{1\ mol\ H_3PO_4}{97.99\ g\ H_3PO_4} =$ **0.0539 *M* H$_3$PO$_4$**

(2) Balanced equation: $H_3PO_4 + 3NaOH \rightarrow Na_3PO_4 + 3H_2O$

$?\ mL\ H_3PO_4\ soln = 11.58\ mL\ NaOH\ soln \times \dfrac{0.454\ mol\ NaOH}{1000\ mL\ NaOH\ soln} \times \dfrac{1\ mol\ H_3PO_4}{3\ mol\ NaOH} \times \dfrac{1000\ mL\ H_3PO_4\ soln}{0.0539\ mol\ H_3PO_4}$

   $=$ **32.5 mL of H$_3$PO$_4$ soln**

(1) $?\ M\ H_3AsO_4 = \dfrac{mol\ H_3AsO_4}{L\ soln} = \dfrac{(8.6\ g\ H_3AsO_4)/(142\ g/mol)}{0.475\ L} =$ **0.13 *M* H$_3$AsO$_4$**

(2) Balanced equation: $H_3AsO_4 + 3NaOH \rightarrow Na_3AsO_4 + 3H_2O$

$?\ mL\ H_3AsO_4\ soln = 11.58mL\ NaOH\ soln \times \dfrac{0.454\ mol\ NaOH}{1000\ mL\ NaOH\ soln} \times \dfrac{1\ mol\ H_3AsO_4}{3\ mol\ NaOH} \times \dfrac{1000\ mL\ H_3AsO_4\ soln}{0.13\ mol\ H_3AsO_4}$

   $=$ **14 mL H$_3$AsO$_4$ soln**

Balanced equation: $2HCl + Na_2CO_3 \rightarrow 2NaCl + CO_2 + H_2O$

Plan: $\underset{(1)}{g\ Na_2CO_3} \Rightarrow \underset{(2)}{mol\ Na_2CO_3} \Rightarrow \underset{(3)}{mol\ HCl} \Rightarrow M\ HCl$

$?\ mol\ HCl = 0.483\ g\ Na_2CO_3 \times \dfrac{1\ mol\ Na_2CO_3}{106.0\ g\ Na_2CO_3} \times \dfrac{2\ mol\ HCl}{1\ mol\ Na_2CO_3} = 0.00911\ mol\ HCl$

$?\ M\ HCl = \dfrac{0.00911\ mol\ HCl}{0.0391\ L\ soln} =$ **0.233 *M* HCl**

Balanced equations: $Mg(OH)_2(s) + 2HCl(aq) \rightarrow MgCl_2(aq) + 2H_2O(\ell)$

   $HCl(aq) + NaOH(aq) \rightarrow NaCl(aq) + H_2O(\ell)$

This is an example of the method of back titration, in which more acid (HCl) is added than is necessary to stoichiometrically react with the base ($Mg(OH)_2$), in order to be certain that all the base has reacted. One then titrates the excess acid with a standardized base solution (NaOH) and in a series of calculations, determines the amount of unknown base ($Mg(OH)_2$).

Plan: (1) Calculate the total moles of HCl that were added to the tablet.
   (2) Calculate the moles of HCl in excess, which are equal to the moles of NaOH added.
   (3) Calculate the moles of HCl that reacted with $Mg(OH)_2$ in the tablet = (1) - (2).
   (4) Determine the mass of $Mg(OH)_2$ that reacted with the HCl.
   (5) Determine the mass % of $Mg(OH)_2$ in the tablet.

(1) ? mol HCl added = 0.953 M HCl x 0.02500 L = 0.0238 mol HCl

(2) ? mol HCl in excess = mol NaOH titrated = 0.602 M NaOH x 0.01229 L = 0.00740 mol HCl

(3) ? mol HCl reacted = 0.0238 mol HCl - 0.00740 mol HCl = 0.0164 mol HCl

(4) ? g $Mg(OH)_2$ = 0.0164 mol HCl x $\dfrac{1 \text{ mol } Mg(OH)_2}{2 \text{ mol HCl}}$ x $\dfrac{58.32 \text{ g } Mg(OH)_2}{1 \text{ mol } Mg(OH)_2}$ = 0.478 g $Mg(OH)_2$

(5) ? % $Mg(OH)_2$ = $\dfrac{0.478 \text{ g } Mg(OH)_2}{1.462 \text{ g tablet}}$ x 100 = **32.7%**

11-48.   *Refer to Sections 3-1 and 11-4.*

(a) $Fe(s) + 2HCl(aq) \rightarrow FeCl_2(aq) + H_2(g)$

(b) $2Cr(s) + 3H_2SO_4(aq) \rightarrow Cr_2(SO_4)_3(aq) + 3H_2(g)$

(c) $Sn(s) + 4HNO_3(aq) \rightarrow SnO_2(s) + 4NO_2(g) + 2H_2O(\ell)$

11-50.   *Refer to Section 11-4 and Examples 11-1 and, 11-11.*

Determining the net ionic equation by balancing the oxidation-reduction reaction:

skeletal equation:	$Cu(s) + HNO_3(aq) \rightarrow Cu^{2+}(aq) + NO(g)$
ox. half-rxn:	$Cu(s) \rightarrow Cu^{2+}(aq)$
balanced ox. half-rxn:	$Cu(s) \rightarrow Cu^{2+}(aq) + 2e^-$
red. half-rxn:	$NO_3^-(aq) \rightarrow NO(g)$ since HNO_3 is a strong acid
balanced red. half-rxn:	$3e^- + 4H^+(aq) + NO_3^-(aq) \rightarrow NO(g) + 2H_2O(\ell)$

Now, we balance the electron transfer and add the half-reactions term-by-term and cancel electrons:

oxidation:	$3[Cu(s) \rightarrow Cu^{2+}(aq) + 2e^-]$
reduction:	$2[3e^- + 4H^+(aq) + NO_3^-(aq) \rightarrow NO(g) + 2H_2O(\ell)]$

balanced net ionic eq.: $3Cu(s) + 8H^+(aq) + 2NO_3^-(aq) \rightarrow 3Cu^{2+}(aq) + 2NO(g) + 4H_2O(\ell)$

The formula unit equation is obtained by recognizing that there is no net charge in a solution, so all the cations are paired with anions to neutralize the charge. In this case the Cu^{2+} and H^+ are paired with NO_3^-. This does mean that some NO_3^- did not react but remained as spectator ions.

balanced formula unit eq.: $3Cu(s) + 8HNO_3(aq) \rightarrow 3Cu(NO_3)_2(aq) + 2NO(g) + 4H_2O(\ell)$

11-52.   *Refer to Sections 11-4 and 11-5, and Examples 11-10 and 11-11.*

(a) skeletal equation:	$MnO_4^-(aq) + Br^-(aq) \rightarrow Mn^{2+}(aq) + Br_2(\ell)$
ox. half-rxn:	$Br^-(aq) \rightarrow Br_2(\ell)$
balanced ox. half-rxn:	$2Br^-(aq) \rightarrow Br_2(\ell) + 2e^-$
red. half-rxn:	$MnO_4^-(aq) \rightarrow Mn^{2+}(aq)$
balanced red. half-rxn:	$5e^- + 8H^+(aq) + MnO_4^-(aq) \rightarrow Mn^{2+}(aq) + 4H_2O(\ell)$

Now, we balance the electron transfer and add the half-reactions term-by-term and cancel electrons:

oxidation:	$5[2Br^-(aq) \rightarrow Br_2(\ell) + 2e^-]$
reduction:	$2[5e^- + 8H^+(aq) + MnO_4^-(aq) \rightarrow Mn^{2+}(aq) + 4H_2O(\ell)]$

balanced.: $16H^+(aq) + 2MnO_4^-(aq) + 10Br^-(aq) \rightarrow 2Mn^{2+}(aq) + 5Br_2(\ell) + 8H_2O(\ell)$

Br is oxidized from -1 (in Br⁻) to 0 (in Br₂), therefore, Br⁻ is the reducing agent.

Mn is reduced from +7 (in MnO_4^-) to +2 (in Mn^{2+}), therefore, MnO_4^- is the oxidizing agent.

(b) skeletal equation: $\qquad$ $Cr_2O_7^{2-}(aq) + I^-(aq) \rightarrow Cr^{3+}(aq) + I_2(s)$

ox. half-rxn: $\qquad$ $I^-(aq) \rightarrow I_2(s)$

balanced ox. half-rxn: $\qquad$ $2I^-(aq) \rightarrow I_2(s) + 2e^-$

red. half-rxn: $\qquad$ $Cr_2O_7^{2-}(aq) \rightarrow Cr^{3+}(aq)$

balanced red. half-rxn: $\qquad$ $6e^- + 14H^+(aq) + Cr_2O_7^{2-}(aq) \rightarrow 2Cr^{3+}(aq) + 7H_2O(\ell)$

Now, we balance the electron transfer and add the half-reactions term-by-term and cancel electrons:

oxidation: $\qquad$ $3[2I^-(aq) \rightarrow I_2(s) + 2e^-]$

reduction: $\qquad$ $[6e^- + 14H^+(aq) + Cr_2O_7^{2-}(aq) \rightarrow 2Cr^{3+}(aq) + 7H_2O(\ell)]$

---

balanced.: $\qquad$ $14H^+(aq) + Cr_2O_7^{2-}(aq) + 6I^-(aq) \rightarrow 2Cr^{3+}(aq) + 3I_2(s) + 7H_2O(\ell)$

I is oxidized from -1 (in I⁻) to 0 (in I₂), therefore, I⁻ is the reducing agent.

Cr is reduced from +6 (in $Cr_2O_7^{2-}$) to +3 (in Cr^{3+}), therefore, $Cr_2O_7^{2-}$ is the oxidizing agent.

(c) oxidation: $\qquad$ $5[H_2O(\ell) + SO_3^{2-}(aq) \rightarrow SO_4^{2-}(aq) + 2H^+(aq) + 2e^-]$

reduction: $\qquad$ $2[5e^- + 8H^+(aq) + MnO_4^-(aq) \rightarrow Mn^{2+}(aq) + 4H_2O(\ell)]$

---

balanced.: $\qquad$ $2MnO_4^-(aq) + 5SO_3^{2-}(aq) + 6H^+(aq) \rightarrow 2Mn^{2+}(aq) + 5SO_4^{2-}(aq) + 3H_2O(\ell)$

S is oxidized from +4 (in SO_3^{2-}) to +6 (in SO_4^{2-}), therefore, SO_3^{2--} is the reducing agent.

Mn is reduced from +7 (in MnO_4^-) to +2 (in Mn^{2+}), therefore, MnO_4^- is the oxidizing agent.

(d) oxidation: $\qquad$ $6[Fe^{2+}(aq) \rightarrow Fe^{3+}(aq) + e^-]$

reduction: $\qquad$ $[6e^- + 14H^+(aq) + Cr_2O_7^{2-}(aq) \rightarrow 2Cr^{3+}(aq) + 7H_2O(\ell)]$

---

balanced.: $\qquad$ $Cr_2O_7^{2-}(aq) + 6Fe^{2+}(aq) + 14H^+(aq) \rightarrow 2Cr^{3+}(aq) + 6Fe^{3+}(aq) + 7H_2O(\ell)$

Fe is oxidized from +2 (in Fe^{2+}) to +3 (in Fe^{3+}), therefore, Fe^{2+} is the reducing agent.

Cr is reduced from +6 (in $Cr_2O_7^{2-}$) to +3 (in Cr^{3+}), therefore, $Cr_2O_7^{2-}$ is the oxidizing agent.

11-54. *Refer to Sections 11-4 and 11-5, and Example 11-13.*

The net ionic equation is obtained by balancing the oxidation-reduction reaction. First we determine the half-reactions:

skeletal equation: $\qquad$ $Al(s) + OH^-(aq) + H_2O(\ell) \rightarrow [Al(OH)_4]^-(aq) + H_2(g)$

ox. half-rxn: $\qquad$ $Al(s) \rightarrow [Al(OH)_4]^-(aq)$

balanced ox. half-rxn: $\qquad$ $Al(s) + 4OH^-(aq) \rightarrow [Al(OH)_4]^-(aq) + 3e^-$

red. half-rxn: $\qquad$ $H_2O(\ell) \rightarrow H_2(g)$

balanced red. half-rxn: $\qquad$ $2e^- + 2H_2O(\ell) \rightarrow H_2(g) + 2OH^-(aq)$

Now, we balance the electron transfer and add the half-reactions term-by-term and cancel electrons:

oxidation: $\qquad$ $2[Al(s) + 4OH^-(aq) \rightarrow [Al(OH)_4]^-(aq) + 3e^-]$

reduction: $\qquad$ $3[2e^- + 2H_2O(\ell) \rightarrow H_2(g) + 2OH^-(aq)]$

---

balanced: $\qquad$ $6e^- + 2Al(s) + 8OH^-(aq) + 6H_2O(\ell) \rightarrow 2[Al(OH)_4]^-(aq) + 3H_2(g) + 6OH^-(aq) + 6e^-$

simplifying: $\qquad$ $2Al(s) + 2OH^-(aq) + 6H_2O(\ell) \rightarrow 2[Al(OH)_4]^-(aq) + 3H_2(g)$

The formula unit equation is obtained by recognizing that there is no net charge in a solution, so all the cations are paired with anions to neutralize the charge. In this case the anions are paired with Na^+ ions from the NaOH, giving:

formula unit equation: $2Al(s) + 2NaOH(aq) + 6H_2O(\ell) \rightarrow 2NaAl(OH)_4(aq) + 3H_2(g)$

11-56. *Refer to Sections 11-4 and 11-5, and Example 11-11.*

(a) Balanced reaction: $Cr_2O_7^{2-}(aq) + 3\,Sn^{2+}(aq) + 14\,H_3O^+(aq) \rightarrow 2\,Cr^{3+}(aq) + 3\,Sn^{2+}(aq) + 21\,H_2O(\ell)$

Sn^{2+} is the reactant being oxidized since the oxidation state of Sn is increasing from +2 to +4. Therefore, Sn^{2+} is the reducing agent.

$Cr_2O_7^{2-}$ is the reactant being reduced since the oxidation state of Cr is decreasing from +6 to +3. Therefore, $Cr_2O_7^{2-}$ is the oxidizing agent.

(b) Balanced reaction: $FeS(s) + 3\,NO_3^-(aq) + 4\,H_3O^+(aq) \rightarrow 3\,NO(g) + SO_4^{2-}(aq) + Fe^{3+}(aq) + 6\,H_2O(\ell)$

FeS is the reactant being oxidized since the oxidation state of Fe is increasing from +2 to +3 and that of S is increasing from –2 to +6.

Therefore, FeS is the reducing agent.

NO_3^- is the reactant being reduced since the oxidation state of N is decreasing from +5 to +2.

Therefore, NO_3^- is the oxidizing agent.

11-58. *Refer to Sections 11-4 and 11-5, and Examples 11-11 and 11-12.*

(a) The net ionic equation is obtained by balancing the oxidation-reduction reaction. First we determine the half-reactions. Then we balance the electron transfer and add the half-reactions term-by-term and cancel electrons:

skeletal equation:	$MnO_4^-(aq) + C_2O_4^{2-}(aq) \rightarrow Mn^{2+}(aq) + CO_2(g)$
ox. half-rxn:	$C_2O_4^{2-}(aq) \rightarrow CO_2(g)$
balanced ox. half-rxn:	$C_2O_4^{2-}(aq) \rightarrow 2\,CO_2(g) + 2e^-$
red. half-rxn:	$MnO_4^-(aq) \rightarrow Mn^{2+}(aq)$
balanced red. half-rxn:	$5e^- + 8H^+(aq) + MnO_4^-(aq) \rightarrow Mn^{2+}(aq) + 4H_2O(\ell)$
oxidation:	$5[C_2O_4^{2-}(aq) \rightarrow 2\,CO_2(g) + 2e^-]$
reduction:	$2[5e^- + MnO_4^-(aq) + 8H^+(aq) \rightarrow Mn^{2+}(aq) + 4H_2O(\ell)]$
balanced:	$2MnO_4^-(aq) + 5C_2O_4^{2-}(aq) + 16H^+(aq) \rightarrow 2Mn^{2+}(aq) + 10\,CO_2(g) + 8H_2O(\ell)$

Balanced formula unit equation (cations = K^+, anions Cl^-):
$2KMnO_4(aq) + 5K_2C_2O_4(aq) + 16HCl(aq) \rightarrow 2MnCl_2(aq) + 12KCl(aq) + 10\,CO_2(g) + 8H_2O(\ell)$

(b)

skeletal equation:	$Zn(s) + NO_3^-(aq) \rightarrow Zn^{2+}(aq) + NH_4^+(aq)$
ox. half-rxn:	$Zn(s) \rightarrow Zn^{2+}(aq)$
balanced ox. half-rxn:	$Zn(s) \rightarrow Zn^{2+}(aq) + 2e^-$
red. half-rxn:	$NO_3^-(aq) \rightarrow NH_4^+(aq)$
balanced red. half-rxn:	$8e^- + 10H^+(aq) + NO_3^-(aq) \rightarrow NH_4^+(aq) + 3H_2O(\ell)$

oxidation: $4[Zn(s) \rightarrow Zn^{2+}(aq) + 2e^-]$

reduction: $1[8e^- + 10H^+(aq) + NO_3^-(aq) \rightarrow NH_4^+(aq) + 3H_2O(\ell)]$

balanced: $4Zn(s) + NO_3^-(aq) + 10H^+(aq) \rightarrow 4Zn^{2+}(aq) + NH_4^+(aq) + 3H_2O(\ell)$

Balanced formula unit equation (cations = H^+, anions = unreacted NO_3^-):

$4Zn(s) + 10\ HNO_3(aq) \rightarrow 4Zn(NO_3)_2(aq) + NH_4NO_3(aq) + 3H_2O(\ell)$

11-60. *Refer to Sections 11-4 and 11-5, and Examples 11-11 and 11-12.*

(a) The net ionic equation is obtained by balancing the oxidation-reduction reaction. First we determine the half-reactions. Then we balance the electron transfer and add the half-reactions term-by-term and cancel electrons:

Balanced net ionic equation:

oxidation: $Zn(s) \rightarrow Zn^{2+}(aq) + 2e^-$

reduction: $2e^- + Cu^{2+}(aq) \rightarrow Cu(s)$

balanced: $Zn(s) + Cu^{2+}(aq) \rightarrow Zn^{2+}(aq) + Cu(s)$

Balanced formula unit equation (anion = SO_4^{2-}): $Zn(s) + CuSO_4(aq) \rightarrow ZnSO_4(aq) + Cu(s)$

(b) Balanced net ionic equation:

oxidation: $2[Cr(s) \rightarrow Cr^{3+}(aq) + 3e^-]$

reduction: $3[2e^- + 2H^+(aq) \rightarrow H_2(g)]$

balanced: $2Cr(s) + 6H^+(aq) \rightarrow 2Cr^{3+}(aq) + 3H_2(g)$

Balanced formula unit equation (anion = SO_4^{2-}): $2Cr(s) + 3H_2SO_4(aq) \rightarrow Cr_2(SO_4)_3(aq) + 3H_2(g)$

11-62. *Refer to Section 11-6 and Example 11-14.*

Balanced <u>net ionic</u> equation is:

$5Fe^{2+}(aq) + MnO_4^-(aq) + 8H^+(aq) \rightarrow 5Fe^{3+}(aq) + Mn^{2+}(aq) + 4H_2O(\ell)$

Note: This exercise uses $KMnO_4$ and $FeSO_4$. These are both soluble salts which dissociate into their ions. The K^+ and SO_4^{2-} ions are spectator ions and are omitted from the balanced net ionic equation.

Plan: M, mL $FeSO_4$ soln $\overset{(1)}{\Rightarrow}$ mmol $FeSO_4$ $\overset{(2)}{\Rightarrow}$ mmol $KMnO_4$ $\overset{(3)}{\Rightarrow}$ mL $KMnO_4$

(1) ? mmol $FeSO_4$ = 0.150 M x 25.0 mL = 3.75 mmol $FeSO_4$

(2) ? mmol $KMnO_4$ = 3.75 mmol $FeSO_4$ x $\dfrac{1\ \text{mmol } KMnO_4}{5\ \text{mmol } FeSO_4}$ = 0.750 mmol $KMnO_4$

(3) ? mL $KMnO_4$ = $\dfrac{0.750\ \text{mmol } KMnO_4}{0.233\ M\ KMnO_4}$ = **3.22 mL $KMnO_4$ soln**   (since molarity can have units: mmol/mL)

Alternative: Dimensional Analysis (Each step above is a separate unit factor):

? mL $KMnO_4$ = 25.0 mL $FeSO_4$ x $\dfrac{0.150\ \text{mmol } FeSO_4}{1\ \text{mL } FeSO_4}$ x $\dfrac{1\ \text{mmol } KMnO_4}{5\ \text{mmol } FeSO_4}$ x $\dfrac{1\ \text{mL } KMnO_4}{0.233\ \text{mmol } KMnO_4}$

            = **3.22 mL $KMnO_4$ soln**

Balanced <u>net</u> <u>ionic</u> equation - you need to balance this before you can begin:

$$2MnO_4^-(aq) + 16H^+(aq) + 10\ I^-(aq) \rightarrow 2Mn^{2+}(aq) + 5I_2(s) + 8H_2O(\ell)$$

Note: This exercise uses $KMnO_4$ and KI, which are both soluble salts that dissociate into their ions. The K^+ ions are spectator ions and are omitted from the balanced net ionic equation.

Plan: M, L KI soln $\overset{(1)}{\Rightarrow}$ mol KI $\overset{(2)}{\Rightarrow}$ mol $KMnO_4$ $\overset{(3)}{\Rightarrow}$ V $KMnO_4$ soln

(1) ? mol KI = 0.150 M x 0.0270 L = 0.00405 mol KI

(2) ? mol $KMnO_4$ = 0.00405 mol KI x $\dfrac{1\ mol\ KMnO_4}{5\ mol\ KI}$ = 0.000810 mol $KMnO_4$

Note: The ratio of mol $KMnO_4$ to mol KI was simplified from 2/10 to 1/5.

(3) ? L $KMnO_4$ soln = $\dfrac{0.000810\ mol\ KMnO_4}{0.190\ M\ KMnO_4}$ = **0.00426 L or 4.26 mL $KMnO_4$ soln**

Alternative: Dimensional Analysis (Each step above is a separate unit factor):

? mL $KMnO_4$ = 0.0270 L KI x $\dfrac{0.150\ mol\ KI}{1\ L\ KI}$ x $\dfrac{1\ mol\ KMnO_4}{5\ mol\ KI}$ x $\dfrac{1\ L\ KMnO_4}{0.190\ mol\ KMnO_4}$

$\qquad$ = **0.00426 L or 4.26 mL $KMnO_4$ soln**

11-66. *Refer to Section 11-6 and Example 11-15.*

(a) Balanced equation: $2Na_2S_2O_3 + I_2 \rightarrow Na_2S_4O_6 + 2NaI$

$\quad$ Plan: M, L $Na_2S_2O_3$ soln $\overset{(1)}{\Rightarrow}$ mol $Na_2S_2O_3$ $\overset{(2)}{\Rightarrow}$ mol I_2 $\overset{(3)}{\Rightarrow}$ M I_2 soln

$\quad$ (1) ? mol $Na_2S_2O_3$ = 0.1442 M x 0.03700 L = 0.005335 mol $Na_2S_2O_3$

$\quad$ (2) ? mol I_2 = 0.005335 mol $Na_2S_2O_3$ x $\dfrac{1\ mol\ I_2}{2\ mol\ Na_2S_2O_3}$ = 0.002668 mol I_2

$\quad$ (3) ? $M\ I_2$ = $\dfrac{mol\ I_2}{L\ I_2}$ = $\dfrac{0.002668\ mol\ I_2}{0.02885\ L\ I_2}$ = **0.09247 $M\ I_2$**

(b) Balanced equation: $As_2O_3 + 5H_2O + 2I_2 \rightarrow 2H_3AsO_4 + 4HI$

$\quad$ Plan: M, L I_2 soln $\overset{(1)}{\Rightarrow}$ mol I_2 $\overset{(2)}{\Rightarrow}$ mol As_2O_3 $\overset{(3)}{\Rightarrow}$ g As_2O_3

$\quad$ (1) ? mol I_2 = 0.09247 M x 0.03532 L = 0.003266 mol I_2

$\quad$ (2) ? mol As_2O_3 = 0.003266 mol I_2 x $\dfrac{1\ mol\ As_2O_3}{2\ mol\ I_2}$ = 0.001633 mol As_2O_3

$\quad$ (3) ? g As_2O_3 = 0.001633 mol As_2O_3 x 197.8 g/mol = **0.3230 g As_2O_3**

$\quad$ Alternative: Dimensional Analysis (Each step above is a separate unit factor):

? g As_2O_3 = 0.03532 L I_2 x $\dfrac{0.09247\ mol\ I_2}{1\ L\ I_2}$ x $\dfrac{1\ mol\ As_2O_3}{2\ mol\ I_2}$ x $\dfrac{197.8\ g\ As_2O_3}{1\ mol\ As_2O_3}$ = **0.3230 g As_2O_3**

11-68. *Refer to Sections 11-6 and Example 11-14.*

Balanced <u>net</u> <u>ionic</u> equation - you need to balance this before you can begin:

$$2NO_3^-(aq) + 3S^{2-}(aq) + 8H^+(aq) \rightarrow 2NO(g) + 3S(s) + 4H_2O(\ell)$$

Plan: M, L S^{2-} soln $\overset{(1)}{\Rightarrow}$ mol S^{2-} $\overset{(2)}{\Rightarrow}$ mol NO_3^- $\overset{(3)}{\Rightarrow}$ V NO_3^- soln

(1) $? \text{ mol } S^{2-} = 0.75 \ M \times 0.035 \ L = 0.026 \text{ mol } S^{2-}$

(2) $? \text{ mol } NO_3^- = 0.026 \text{ mol } S^{2-} \times \dfrac{2 \text{ mol } NO_3^-}{3 \text{ mol } S^{2-}} = 0.018 \text{ mol } NO_3^-$

(3) $? \text{ L } NO_3^- \text{ soln} = \dfrac{0.018 \text{ mol } NO_3^-}{5.0 \ M \ NO_3^-} =$ **0.0035 L or 3.5 mL NO_3^- soln**

Note: when doing calculations step-wise, it is critical that you keep the entire number in your calculator and don't round between steps. Otherwise, major rounding errors can develop. Rounding was done in this manual at every step only to illustrate the concept of significant figures.

Dimensional Analysis:

$? \text{ L } NO_3^- = 0.035 \text{ L } S^{2-} \text{ soln} \times \dfrac{0.75 \text{ mol } H_2S}{1 \text{ L } H_2S \text{ soln}} \times \dfrac{2 \text{ mol } NO_3^-}{3 \text{ mol } S^{2-}} \times \dfrac{1 \text{ L } NO_3^- \text{ soln}}{5.0 \text{ mol } NO_3^-} =$ **0.0035 L or 3.5 mL NO_3^- soln**

11-70.   *Refer to Sections 3-6 and 11-6 and Examples 3-18 and 11-15.*

Plan: $\overset{(1)}{\text{g KMnO}_4 \Rightarrow} \overset{(2)}{\text{mol KMnO}_4 \Rightarrow} M \text{ KMnO}_4$

(1) $? \text{ mol KMnO}_4 = \dfrac{14.6 \text{ g KMnO}_4}{158 \text{ g/mol}} = 0.0924 \text{ mol KMnO}_4$

(2) $? \ M \text{ KMnO}_4 = \dfrac{0.0924 \text{ mol KMnO}_4}{0.750 \text{ L}} =$ **0.123 M KMnO$_4$**

The balanced half-reaction involving the reduction of MnO_4^- to MnO_4^{2-} requires 1 electron:

$$e^- + MnO_4^-(aq) \rightarrow MnO_4^{2-}(aq)$$

This fact is irrelevant since the molarity of a solution is *independent* of the number of electrons involved in the reaction. The molarity depends only on the moles of solute and the liters of solution.

11-72.   *Refer to Sections 3-6 and 11-3, and Example 11-7.*

(a) $? \ M \text{ MgNH}_4\text{PO}_4 = \dfrac{0.0618 \text{ g MgNH}_4\text{PO}_4}{0.250 \text{ L soln}} \times \dfrac{1 \text{ mol MgNH}_4\text{PO}_4}{137.3 \text{ g MgNH}_4\text{PO}_4} =$ **1.80 x 10^{-3} M MgNH$_4$PO$_4$**

(b) $? \ M \text{ NaCH}_3\text{COO} = \dfrac{16.8 \text{ g NaCH}_3\text{COO}}{0.300 \text{ L soln}} \times \dfrac{1 \text{ mol NaCH}_3\text{COO}}{82.03 \text{ g NaCH}_3\text{COO}} =$ **0.683 M NaCH$_3$COO**

(c) $? \ M \text{ CaC}_2\text{O}_4 = \dfrac{0.0250 \text{ g CaC}_2\text{O}_4}{0.750 \text{ L soln}} \times \dfrac{1 \text{ mol CaC}_2\text{O}_4}{128.1 \text{ g CaC}_2\text{O}_4} =$ **2.60 x 10^{-4} M CaC$_2$O$_4$**

(d) $? \ M \text{ (NH}_4)_2\text{SO}_4 = \dfrac{2.20 \text{ g (NH}_4)_2\text{SO}_4}{0.400 \text{ L soln}} \times \dfrac{1 \text{ mol (NH}_4)_2\text{SO}_4}{132.2 \text{ g (NH}_4)_2\text{SO}_4} =$ **0.0416 M (NH$_4$)$_2$SO$_4$**

11-74.   *Refer to Section 11-3 and Examples 11-5 and 11-6.*

Balanced equation: $HCl + NaOH \rightarrow NaCl + H_2O$

(1) Plan: $\overset{(1)}{M, \text{ mL NaOH} \Rightarrow} \overset{(2)}{\text{mmol NaOH} \Rightarrow} \text{mmol HCl}$

$? \text{ mmol HCl} = 25.5 \text{ mL NaOH} \times \dfrac{0.298 \text{ mmol NaOH}}{1 \text{ mL NaOH}} \times \dfrac{1 \text{ mmol HCl}}{1 \text{ mmol NaOH}} =$ **7.60 mmol HCl**

(2) $? \text{ mL HCl} = 7.60 \text{ mmol HCl} \times \dfrac{1 \text{ mL HCl}}{0.606 \text{ mmol HCl}} =$ **12.5 mL HCl**

11-76. *Refer to Section 11-1 and Example 11-3.*

Balanced equation: $2HCl + Ca(OH)_2 \rightarrow CaCl_2 + 2H_2O$

Plan: $g\ Ca(OH)_2 \overset{(1)}{\Rightarrow} mol\ Ca(OH)_2 \overset{(2)}{\Rightarrow} mol\ HCl \overset{(3)}{\Rightarrow} V\ HCl$

(1) $?\ mol\ Ca(OH)_2 = \frac{1.98\ g\ Ca(OH)_2}{74.1\ g/mol} = 0.0267\ mol\ Ca(OH)_2$

(2) $?\ mol\ HCl = 0.0267\ mol\ Ca(OH)_2 \times (2\ mol\ HCl/1\ mol\ Ca(OH)_2) = 0.0534\ mol\ HCl$

(3) $?\ L\ HCl = \frac{0.0534\ mol\ HCl}{0.1153\ M\ HCl}$ = **0.463 L or 463 mL HCl soln**

Dimensional Analysis:

$?\ L\ HCl = 1.98\ g\ Ca(OH)_2 \times \frac{1\ mol\ Ca(OH)_2}{74.1\ g\ Ca(OH)_2} \times \frac{2\ mol\ HCl}{1\ mol\ Ca(OH)_2} \times \frac{1\ L\ HCl\ soln}{0.1153\ mol\ HCl}$

= **0.463 L or 463 mL HCl soln**

11-78. *Refer to Section 11-1 and Example 11-3.*

Balanced equation: $H_2SO_4 + 2KOH \rightarrow K_2SO_4 + 2H_2O$

Plan: $M, L\ KOH \overset{(1)}{\Rightarrow} mol\ KOH \overset{(2)}{\Rightarrow} mol\ H_2SO_4 \overset{(3)}{\Rightarrow} V\ H_2SO_4$

(1) $?\ mol\ KOH = 0.296\ M \times 0.0344\ L = 0.0102\ mol\ KOH$

(2) $?\ mol\ H_2SO_4 = 0.0102\ mol\ KOH \times (1\ mol\ H_2SO_4/2\ mol\ KOH) = 0.00509\ mol\ H_2SO_4$

(3) $?\ L\ H_2SO_4 = \frac{0.00509\ mol\ H_2SO_4}{0.296\ M\ H_2SO_4}$ = **0.0172 L or 17.2 mL H_2SO_4 soln**

Dimensional Analysis:

$?\ L\ H_2SO_4 = 0.0344\ L\ KOH\ soln \times \frac{0.296\ mol\ KOH}{1\ L\ KOH\ soln} \times \frac{1\ mol\ H_2SO_4}{2\ mol\ KOH} \times \frac{1\ L\ H_2SO_4\ soln}{0.296\ mol\ H_2SO_4}$

= **0.0172 L or 17.2 mL H_2SO_4 soln**

11-80. *Refer to Sections 11-1 and Example 11-3.*

Balanced equation: $H_2SO_4 + 2NaOH \rightarrow Na_2SO_4 + 2H_2O$

Plan: $M, L\ H_2SO_4 \overset{(1)}{\Rightarrow} mol\ H_2SO_4 \overset{(2)}{\Rightarrow} mol\ NaOH \overset{(3)}{\Rightarrow} V\ NaOH$

(1) $?\ mol\ H_2SO_4 = 0.1023\ M \times 0.02941\ L = 0.003009\ mol\ H_2SO_4$

(2) $?\ mol\ NaOH = 0.003009\ mol\ H_2SO_4 \times (2\ mol\ NaOH/1\ mol\ H_2SO_4) = 0.006017\ mol\ NaOH$

(3) $?\ L\ NaOH = \frac{0.006017\ mol\ NaOH}{0.1945\ M\ NaOH}$ = **0.03094 L or 30.94 mL NaOH soln**

Dimensional Analysis:

$?\ L\ NaOH = 0.02941\ L\ H_2SO_4\ soln \times \frac{0.1023\ mol\ H_2SO_4}{1\ L\ H_2SO_4\ soln} \times \frac{2\ mol\ NaOH}{1\ mol\ H_2SO_4} \times \frac{1\ L\ NaOH\ soln}{0.1945\ mol\ NaOH}$

= **0.03094 L or 30.94 mL NaOH soln**

11-82. *Refer to Sections 11-3 and 11-6.*

(a) Balanced equation: $HI + NaOH \rightarrow NaI + H_2O$

Plan: $M, L\ NaOH\ soln \overset{(1)}{\Rightarrow} mol\ NaOH \overset{(2)}{\Rightarrow} mol\ HI \overset{(3)}{\Rightarrow} V\ HI\ soln$

(1) $?\ mol\ NaOH = 0.100\ M \times 0.0250\ L = 0.00250\ mol\ NaOH$

(2) ? mol HI = mol NaOH = 0.00250 mol HI

(3) ? L HI soln $= \dfrac{0.00250 \text{ mol HI}}{0.245 \, M \text{ HI}} = \textbf{0.0102 L or 10.2 mL of HI soln}$

Dimensional Analysis:

? L HI soln $= 0.0250$ L NaOH soln $\times \dfrac{0.100 \text{ mol NaOH}}{1 \text{ L NaOH soln}} \times \dfrac{1 \text{ mol HI}}{1 \text{ mol NaOH}} \times \dfrac{1 \text{ L HI soln}}{0.245 \text{ mol HI}} = \textbf{0.0102 L of HI}$

(b) Balanced net ionic equation: $Ag^+ + I^- \rightarrow AgI$

Plan: $\underset{(1)}{\text{g AgNO}_3} \Rightarrow \underset{(2)}{\text{mol AgNO}_3} \Rightarrow \underset{(3)}{\text{mol HI}} \Rightarrow V \text{ HI soln}$

(1) ? mol $AgNO_3 = \dfrac{0.503 \text{ g AgNO}_3}{169.9 \text{ g/mol}} = 0.00296$ mol $AgNO_3$

(2) ? mol HI = mol $AgNO_3$ = 0.00296 mol HI

(3) ? L HI soln $= \dfrac{0.00296 \text{ mol HI}}{0.245 \, M \text{ HI}} = \textbf{0.0121 L or 12.1 mL of HI soln}$

(c) Balanced equation: $2Cu^{2+} + 4I^- \rightarrow 2CuI + I_2$

Plan: $\underset{(1)}{\text{g CuSO}_4} \Rightarrow \underset{(2)}{\text{mol CuSO}_4} \Rightarrow \underset{(3)}{\text{mol HI}} \Rightarrow \text{L HI soln}$

(1) ? mol $CuSO_4 = \dfrac{0.621 \text{ g CuSO}_4}{159.6 \text{ g/mol}} = 0.00389$ mol $CuSO_4$

(2) ? mol HI = 0.00389 mol $CuSO_4 \times (4 \text{ mol HI}/2 \text{ mol CuSO}_4) = 0.00778$ mol HI

(3) ? L HI $= \dfrac{0.00778 \text{ mol HI}}{0.245 \, M \text{ HI}} = \textbf{0.0318 L or 31.8 mL of HI soln}$

11-84. *Refer to Section 5-7 and Example 5-6.*

An antioxidant is a compound that opposes oxidation or inhibits reactions promoted by oxygen or peroxides. Such a compound is ascorbic acid, $H_2C_6H_6O_6$, also called Vitamin C, which can undergo a decomposition reaction as follows:

Oxidation Numbers: $\underset{}{+1 \; +\frac{2}{3} \; +1 \; -2} \qquad \underset{}{+1 \; +1 \; -2} \qquad 0$

$$H_2C_6H_6O_6 \rightarrow C_6H_6O_6 + H_2$$

Vitamin C is both oxidized ($C = +2/3 \rightarrow C = +1$) and reduced ($H = +1 \rightarrow H = 0$) in this reaction.

11-86. *Refer to Section 11-3.*

Balanced equation: $HCl + NaOH \rightarrow NaCl + H_2O$

(1) ? g H_2O produced when 0.0100 mol NaCl is produced

$= 0.0100$ mol NaCl $\times \dfrac{1 \text{ mol H}_2\text{O}}{1 \text{ mol NaCl}} \times \dfrac{18.0 \text{ g H}_2\text{O}}{1 \text{ mol H}_2\text{O}} = 0.180$ g H_2O = 0.180 mL H_2O since density is 1.00 g/mL

(2) The amount of water is negligible when working with 3 significant figures, i.e. volume of 200. mL is the same as a volume of 200.180 mL when working with 3 significant figures. However, the volume is significant when working with 4 significant figures. The volume of water would then become 200.2 mL.

11-88. *Refer to Section 11-6 and Examples 11-14 and 11-15.*

Balanced equation: $Cr_2O_7^{2-} + 6Fe^{2+} + 14H^+ \rightarrow 2Cr^{3+} + 6Fe^{3+} + 7H_2O$

Plan: $M, L \text{ Na}_2\text{Cr}_2\text{O}_7 \underset{(1)}{\Rightarrow} \text{mol Na}_2\text{Cr}_2\text{O}_7 (= \text{mol Cr}_2\text{O}_7^{2-}) \underset{(2)}{\Rightarrow} \text{mol Fe}^{2+} \underset{(3)}{\Rightarrow} \text{g Fe}^{2+} (= \text{g Fe}) \underset{(4)}{\Rightarrow} \%\text{Fe}$

(1) $? \text{ mol } Cr_2O_7^{2-} = 42.96 \text{ mL } Na_2Cr_2O_7 \times \dfrac{1.000 \text{ L } Na_2Cr_2O_7}{1000 \text{ mL } Na_2Cr_2O_7} \times \dfrac{0.02130 \text{ mol } Na_2Cr_2O_7}{1.000 \text{ L } Na_2Cr_2O_7} \times \dfrac{1 \text{ mol } Cr_2O_7^{2-}}{1 \text{ mol } Na_2Cr_2O_7}$

$\qquad = 9.150 \times 10^{-4} \text{ mol } Cr_2O_7^{2-}$

(2) $? \text{ mol } Fe^{2+} = 9.150 \times 10^{-4} \text{ mol } Cr_2O_7^{2-} \times \dfrac{6 \text{ mol } Fe^{2+}}{1 \text{ mol } Cr_2O_7^{2-}} = 5.490 \times 10^{-3} \text{ mol } Fe^{2+}$

(3) $? \text{ g Fe} = 5.490 \times 10^{-3} \text{ mol } Fe^{2+} \times \dfrac{1 \text{ mol Fe}}{1 \text{ mol } Fe^{2+}} \times \dfrac{55.85 \text{ g Fe}}{1 \text{ mol Fe}} = 0.3066 \text{ g Fe}$

(4) $? \text{ \%Fe} = \dfrac{0.3066 \text{ g Fe}}{0.5166 \text{ g sample}} \times 100 = \textbf{59.36\% Fe}$

Pure limonite, $2Fe_2O_3 \cdot 3H_2O$ (FW = 373.4 g/mol), is 59.83% Fe by mass.

$\qquad \text{\% Fe by mass} = \dfrac{\text{AW Fe} \times 4}{\text{FW}} \times 100\% = \dfrac{223.4 \text{ g}}{373.4 \text{ g}} \times 100\% = 59.83\% \text{ Fe}$

If the percentage of Fe in the ore had been calculated to be greater than 59.83%, one might conclude that there were other components in the dissolved ore solution in addition to Fe^{2+} that could reduce $Cr_2O_7^{2-}$ to Cr^{3+}, (assuming of course that the analytical data were correct). Therefore, the $Na_2Cr_2O_7$ volume necessary to reach the equivalence point would increase, and the amount of Fe present would appear to be larger than it really was.

11-90. *Refer to Section 11-1 and Example 11-2.*

This is a possible limiting reactant problem.
Plan: (1) Calculate the number of moles of $AgNO_3$ and $CaCl_2$.
  (2) Determine the limiting reactant, if there is one.
  (3) Calculate the moles of AgCl formed.
  (4) Determine the mass of AgCl produced.

Balanced equation: $2AgNO_3(aq) + CaCl_2(aq) \rightarrow 2AgCl(s) + Ca(NO_3)_2(aq)$

(1) $? \text{ mol } AgNO_3 = 6.0 \ M \ AgNO_3 \times 0.095 \text{ L} = 0.57 \text{ mol } AgNO_3$
    $? \text{ mol } CaCl_2 = 6.0 \ M \ CaCl_2 \times 0.040 \text{ L} = 0.24 \text{ mol } CaCl_2$

(2) In the balanced equation, $AgNO_3$ reacts with $CaCl_2$ in a 2:1 mole ratio.
    mol $AgNO_3$:mol $CaCl_2$ = 0.57 mol:0.24 mol = 2.4:1
    We do not have stoichiometric amounts of both reactants; this is a limiting reactant problem. We have more $AgNO_3$ than is necessary to react with all of the $CaCl_2$, so $CaCl_2$ is the limiting reactant and $AgNO_3$ is in excess. The amount of salt formed is set then by the amount of $CaCl_2$.

(3) $? \text{ mol AgCl} = 0.24 \text{ mol } CaCl_2 \times (2 \text{ mol AgCl}/1 \text{ mol } CaCl_2) = 0.48 \text{ mol AgCl}$

(4) $? \text{ g AgCl} = 0.48 \text{ mol AgCl} \times \dfrac{143 \text{ g AgCl}}{1 \text{ mol AgCl}} = \textbf{69 g AgCl}$

11-92. *Refer to Section 11-2.*

Balanced equation: $NaAl(OH)_2CO_3 + 4HCl \rightarrow NaCl + AlCl_3 + CO_2 + 3H_2O$

Plan: (1) Calculate the mmoles of HCl in your stomach acid.
  (2) Calculate the mmoles of $NaAl(OH)_2CO_3$ in one antacid tablet.
  (3) Calculate the mmoles of HCl that can be neutralized by the antacid tablet.

(1) $? \text{ mmol HCl in stomach} = 0.10 \text{ M HCl} \times 800. \text{ mL} = \textbf{80. mmol HCl in stomach}$

(2) $? \text{ mmol } NaAl(OH)_2CO_3 = \dfrac{334 \text{ mg } NaAl(OH)_2CO_3}{144 \text{ mg/mmol}} = 2.32 \text{ mmol } NaAl(OH)_2CO_3$

(3) $? \text{ mmol neutralized HCl} = 2.32 \text{ mmol } NaAl(OH)_2CO_3 \times \dfrac{4 \text{ mmol HCl}}{1 \text{ mmol } NaAl(OH)_2CO_3} = \textbf{9.28 mmol HCl}$

The number of **mmoles of HCl in your stomach** is roughly nine times greater than the number of mmoles of HCl that can be neutralized by a single antacid tablet. However, about 2 tablets are sufficient to neutralize the excess HCl in the stomach by reducing its concentration down to the normal 8.0×10^{-2} M level.

11-94. *Refer to Section 11-5.*

The net ionic equation is obtained by balancing the redox reaction. First we determine the half-reactions:

skeletal equation: $\qquad\qquad\qquad$ $CrI_3(aq) + H_2O_2(aq) \rightarrow CrO_4^{2-}(aq) + IO_4^-(aq)$

ox. half-rxn: $\qquad\qquad\qquad\qquad$ $CrI_3(aq) \rightarrow CrO_4^{2-}(aq) + IO_4^-(aq)$

balanced ox. half-rxn: $\quad$ $32OH^-(aq) + CrI_3(aq) \rightarrow CrO_4^{2-}(aq) + 3IO_4^-(aq) + 16H_2O(\ell) + 27e^-$

red. half-rxn: $\qquad\qquad\qquad\qquad$ $H_2O_2(aq) \rightarrow 2OH^-(aq)$

balanced red. half-rxn: $\qquad$ $2e^- + H_2O_2(aq) \rightarrow 2OH^-(aq)$

Now, we balance the electron transfer and add the half-reactions term-by-term and cancel electrons:

oxidation: $\qquad\quad$ $2[32OH^-(aq) + CrI_3(aq) \rightarrow CrO_4^{2-}(aq) + 3IO_4^-(aq) + 16H_2O(\ell) + 27e^-]$

reduction: $\qquad\qquad$ $27[2e^- + H_2O_2(aq) \rightarrow 2OH^-(aq)]$

---

balanced: $\quad$ $54e^- + 27H_2O_2(aq) + 64OH^-(aq) + 2CrI_3(aq) \rightarrow 2CrO_4^{2-}(aq) + 6IO_4^-(aq) + 32H_2O(\ell) + 54OH^-(aq) +$

$54e^-$

simplifying: $\qquad$ $27H_2O_2(aq) + 10OH^-(aq) + 2CrI_3(aq) \rightarrow 2CrO_4^{2-}(aq) + 6IO_4^-(aq) + 32H_2O(\ell)$

The elements being oxidized: Cr ($+3 \rightarrow +6$) and I ($-1 \rightarrow +7$) and the element being reduced: O ($-1 \rightarrow -2$)
The oxidizing agent is H_2O_2 and the reducing agent is CrI_3.

11-96. *Refer to Section 5-7.*

Balanced equation: $SiO_2(s) + 6HF(aq) \rightarrow H_2SiF_6(aq) + 2H_2O(\ell)$

The etching of glass, SiO_2, by hydrofluoric acid, HF, is **not** an oxidation-reduction reaction, since no element in the reaction is undergoing a change in oxidation number.

11-98. *Refer to Section 11-3 and Example 11-6.*

If we consider the two electrostatic charge potential plots for potassium hydrogen phthalate (KHP), the only difference between them is the location of the hydrogen in the −COOH group. The figure on the left is more stable because the hydrogen is oriented in such a way as to promote intramolecular H-bonding within the compound. The figure on the right has two oxygen atoms with partial negative charges adjacent to each other; this is not as stable a configuration.

12 Gases and the Kinetic-Molecular Theory

12-2.   *Refer to Sections 12-1 and 12-2.*

All gases are (a) transparent to light. Some gases are (b) colorless and (e) odorless. However, no gas (c) is unable to pass through filter paper, (d) is more difficult to compress than water and (f) settles on standing.

12-4.   *Refer to Section 12-3 and Figure 12-1.*

A manometer is a device employing the change in liquid levels to measure gas pressure differences between a standard and an unknown system. For example, a typical mercury manometer consists of a glass tube partially filled with mercury. One arm is open to the atmosphere and the other is connected to a container of gas. When the pressure of the gas in the container is greater than atmospheric pressure, the level of the mercury in the open side will be higher and

$$P_{gas} = P_{atm} + \Delta h$$

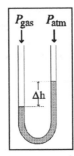

where Δh is the difference in mercury levels

However, when the pressure of the gas is less than atmospheric pressure, the level of the mercury in the side connected to the gas will be higher, and

$$P_{gas} = P_{atm} - \Delta h$$

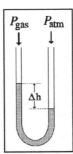

where Δh is the difference in mercury levels

12-6.   *Refer to Section 12-3 and Appendix C.*

(a) ? psi = 742 torr $\times \dfrac{1 \text{ atm}}{760 \text{ torr}} \times \dfrac{14.70 \text{ psi}}{1 \text{ atm}} =$ **14.4 psi**

(b) ? cm Hg = 742 torr $\times \dfrac{1 \text{ mm Hg}}{1 \text{ torr}} \times \dfrac{1 \text{ cm Hg}}{10 \text{ mm Hg}} =$ **74.2 cm Hg**

(c) ? inches Hg = 742 torr $\times \dfrac{1 \text{ mm Hg}}{1 \text{ torr}} \times \dfrac{1 \text{ cm Hg}}{10 \text{ mm Hg}} \times \dfrac{1 \text{ in Hg}}{2.54 \text{ cm Hg}} =$ **29.2 in Hg**

(d) ? kPa = 742 torr $\times \dfrac{1 \text{ atm}}{760 \text{ torr}} \times \dfrac{1.013 \times 10^5 \text{ Pa}}{1 \text{ atm}} \times \dfrac{1 \text{ kPa}}{1000 \text{ Pa}} =$ **98.9 kPa**

(e) $\quad ? \text{ atm} = 742 \text{ torr} \times \dfrac{1 \text{ atm}}{760 \text{ torr}} = \textbf{0.976 atm}$

(f) $\quad ? \text{ ft } H_2O = 742 \text{ torr} \times \dfrac{1 \text{ mm Hg}}{1 \text{ torr}} \times \dfrac{1 \text{ cm Hg}}{10 \text{ mm Hg}} \times \dfrac{1 \text{ in. Hg}}{2.54 \text{ cm Hg}} \times \dfrac{1 \text{ ft Hg}}{12 \text{ in. Hg}} \times \dfrac{13.59 \text{ ft } H_2O}{1.00 \text{ ft Hg}} = \textbf{33.1 ft } H_2O$

Note: The final unit factor uses the relative densities of water and mercury at 25°C. Since the density of water is only 1/13.59 that of mercury, a 13.59 ft column of H_2O has the same mass as a 1.00 ft column of mercury.

12-8. *Refer to Sections 12-1 and 12-2.*

(a) The material is not a gas. If the container did hold a gas and was opened to the atmosphere, the material would expand without limit.

(b) The material discharging from the smokestack is not a gas, but a colloidal mixture that light cannot penetrate.

(c) The material is not a gas because its density, 8.2 g/mL, is far too great.

(d) The material is a gas for two reasons. (1) It is much less dense than fresh water since it rises rapidly to the surface. (2) At 30 ft below the water's surface the material is exposed to 2 atm pressure: 1 atm (760 mm Hg) atmospheric pressure and 1 atm (76 cm Hg) of water pressure. As the pressure on the material decreased as the material rises to the surface, its volume increased. This is an illustration of Boyle's Law (Section 12-4).

(e) The material may be a gas, but insufficient information is given.

(f) The material is definitely a gas.

12-10. *Refer to Section 12-3.*

Since 1 atm = 14.7 psi,

$? \text{ psi} = 150. \text{ atm} \times \dfrac{14.7 \text{ psi}}{1 \text{ atm}} = \textbf{2.20} \times \textbf{10}^3 \textbf{ psi}$

12-12. *Refer to Section 12-4 and Figures 12-3 and 12-4.*

(a) Boyle studied the effect of changing pressure on a volume of a known mass of gas at constant temperature. Boyle's Law states: at a given temperature, the product of pressure and volume of a definite mass of gas is constant.

(b) When the mathematical relationship, XY = constant, is plotted on the X-Y axes, a hyperbola results. Boyle's Law can be stated as

$$\text{pressure} \times \text{volume} = \text{constant} \qquad (\text{at constant } n, T)$$

resulting in the graph shown in Figure 12-4. Since pressure and volume can never have negative values, the other branch of the hyperbola is omitted.

12-14. *Refer to Section 12-4 and Examples 12-1 and 12-2.*

Boyle's Law states: $\quad P_1V_1 = P_2V_2 \qquad$ at constant n and T

Substituting, $\qquad P_2 = \dfrac{P_1V_1}{V_2} = \dfrac{2.00 \text{ atm} \times 300. \text{ mL}}{567 \text{ mL}} = \textbf{1.06 atm}$

Refer to Section 12-4 and Examples 12-1 and 12-2.

Recall Boyle's Law: $P_1V_1 = P_2V_2$ at constant n and T

(a) Given: $P_1 = 59.4 \text{ torr} \times \dfrac{1 \text{ atm}}{760 \text{ torr}} = 7.82 \times 10^{-2} \text{ atm}$ $V_1 = 35.0 \text{ L}$

$P_2 = ?$ $V_2 = 150. \text{ mL} \times \dfrac{1 \text{ L}}{1000 \text{ mL}} = 0.150 \text{ L}$

$P_2 = \dfrac{P_1V_1}{V_2} = \dfrac{7.82 \times 10^{-2} \text{ atm} \times 35.0 \text{ L}}{0.150 \text{ L}} = \mathbf{18.2 \ atm}$

(b) Given: $P_1 = 7.82 \times 10^{-2} \text{ atm}$ $V_1 = 35.0 \text{ L}$
$P_2 = 10.0 \text{ atm}$ $V_2 = ?$

$V_2 = \dfrac{P_1V_1}{P_2} = \dfrac{7.82 \times 10^{-2} \text{ atm} \times 35.0 \text{ L}}{10.0 \text{ atm}} = \mathbf{0.274 \ L}$

12-18. **Refer to Section 12-4.**

Plan: (1) Use Boyle's Law to find the maximum volume occupied by the gas at 1.1 atm.
(2) After subtracting out the volume of the cylinder, divide the remaining volume by the volume of each balloon to get the number of balloons.

(1) Recall Boyle's Law: $P_1V_1 = P_2V_2$ at constant n and T

Given: $P_1 = 165 \text{ atm}$ $V_1 = 10.0 \text{ L}$
$P_2 = 1.1 \text{ atm}$ $V_2 = ?$

Solving, $V_2 = \dfrac{P_1V_1}{P_2} = \dfrac{165 \text{ atm} \times 10.0 \text{ L}}{1.1 \text{ atm}} = 1500 \text{ L}$ (2 significant figures)

(2) This volume of gas is distributed between the balloons and the "empty" cylinder.

$N \times V_{balloon} = V_2 - V_{cylinder}$ where N = number of balloons (a whole number)
$N \times 2.5 \text{ L} = 1500 \text{ L} - 10.0 \text{ L}$

$N = \dfrac{1500 \text{ L} - 10.0 \text{ L}}{2.5 \text{ L}} = \mathbf{6.0 \times 10^2 \ balloons}$ (2 significant figures)

12-20. **Refer to Section 12-5 and Figure 12-5.**

(a) An "absolute temperature scale" is a scale in which properties such as gas volume change linearly with temperature while the origin of the scale is set at absolute zero. The Kelvin scale is a typical example of it.

(b) Boyle, in his experiments, noticed that temperature affected gas volume. About 1800, Charles and Gay-Lussac found that the rate of gas expansion with increased temperature was constant at constant pressure. Later, Lord Kelvin noticed that for a series of constant pressure systems, volume decreased as temperature decreased and the extrapolation of these different T-V lines back to zero volume yielded a common intercept, -273.15°C on the temperature axis. He defined this temperature as absolute zero. The relationship between the Celsius and Kelvin temperature scales is

$$K = °C + 273.15°.$$

(c) Absolute zero may be thought of as the limit of thermal contraction for an ideal gas. In other words, an ideal gas would have zero volume at absolute zero temperature. Theoretically, it is also the temperature at which molecular motion ceases.

(a) Experiments have shown that at constant pressure, the volume of a definite mass of gas is directly proportional to its absolute temperature (in K).

(b) This is known as Charles's Law and is expressed as V/T = constant at constant n and P. Therefore, for a sample of gas when volume is plotted against temperature, a straight line results. See line A in the graph above.

12-24. *Refer to Section 12-5 and Figure 12-5.*

In the graph above, we see that for the real gas B, the volume drops to nearly zero at about 50°C. This is because the gas must have liquefied at that temperature, i.e., its boiling point must be about 50°C. Since liquids are much more dense than gases, the volume would have decreased greatly at that temperature.

From the graph, we can read that at 100°C (373 K), the volume of the gas is 13 mL and at 400°C (673 K), the volume is about 22 mL. Charles's Law states that for an ideal gas, V/T = constant at constant n and P.

At 373 K $V/T = 0.035$ mL/K
At 673 K $V/T = 0.033$ mL/K

Since V/T is approximately the same within the reading error of the graph, the gas does behave ideally above 50°C.

It is expected that most real gases would exhibit similar ideal behavior above their liquefaction points, i.e., their boiling points.

12-26. *Refer to Section 12-5.*

This is a Charles's Law calculation: $\dfrac{V_1}{T_1} = \dfrac{V_2}{T_2}$ at constant n and P

Given: $V_1 = 0.82$ L $T_1 = 26°C + 273° = 299$ K
         $V_2 = ?$ L $T_2 = 21°C + 273° = 294$ K

$V_2 = \dfrac{V_1 T_2}{T_1} = \dfrac{0.82 \text{ L x } 294 \text{ K}}{299 \text{ K}} = \mathbf{0.81 \text{ L}}$

12-28. *Refer to Section 12-5.*

(a) Recall Charles's Law: $\dfrac{V_1}{T_1} = \dfrac{V_2}{T_2}$ at constant n and P

Given: $V_1 = 1.400$ L $T_1 = 0.0°C + 273.15° = 273.2$ K
         $V_2 = ?$ $T_2 = 8.0°C + 273.15° = 281.2$ K

$V_2 = \dfrac{V_1 T_2}{T_1} = \dfrac{1.400 \text{ L x } 281.2 \text{ K}}{273.2 \text{ K}} = \mathbf{1.441 \text{ L}}$

(b) The volume change corresponding to the temperature change from 0.0°C to 8.0°C is (1.441 - 1.400) L = 0.041 L or 41 mL or 41 cm^3. When the cross-sectional area of the graduated arm is 1.0 cm^2, the difference in height (cm) is equivalent to the difference in volume (cm^3). Hence, the height will increase by **41 cm**.

(c) To improve the thermometer's sensitivity (measured in Δheight/°C) for the same volume change, the cross-sectional area of the graduated arm should be decreased. This will cause the height difference to increase. Also, a larger volume of gas could be used.

Recall Charles's Law: $\dfrac{V_1}{T_1} = \dfrac{V_2}{T_2}$ at constant n and P

Dry ice: volume at $-78.5°C$: $V_2 = \dfrac{V_1 T_2}{T_1} = \dfrac{5.00 \text{ L} \times (-78.5°C + 273.15°)}{25.0°C + 273.15°} = \mathbf{3.26\ L}$

Liquid N_2: volume at $-195.8°C$: $V_2 = \dfrac{V_1 T_2}{T_1} = \dfrac{5.00 \text{ L} \times (-195.8°C + 273.15°)}{25.0°C + 273.15°} = \mathbf{1.30\ L}$

Liquid He: volume at $-268.9°C$: $V_2 = \dfrac{V_1 T_2}{T_1} = \dfrac{5.00 \text{ L} \times (-268.9°C + 273.15°)}{25.0°C + 273.15°} = \mathbf{0.0713\ L}$

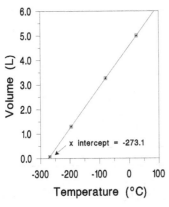

If the line is extrapolated to the x axis, the x intercept is the temperature at which zero volume is theoretically reached. That temperature is $-273.1°C$, also known as absolute zero, 0.0 K.

(a) $P \times V = $ constant

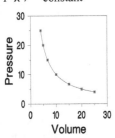

(b) $P = $ constant $\times 1/V$

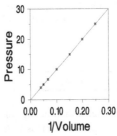

(c) $V = $ constant $\times T$ or $V/T = $ constant

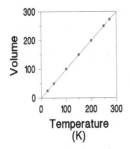

(d) $P = $ constant $\times T$ or $P/T = $ constant

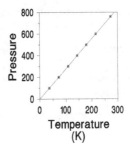

The graphs were obtained by plotting the hypothetical data given below. It is assumed that for (a) and (b), n and T are constant; for (c), n and P are constant; and for (d), n and V are constant.

(a),(b)					(c)				(d)		
P	**V**	**PxV**	**1/V**		**V**	**T(K)**	**V/T**		**P**	**T(K)**	**P/T**
4.00	25	100	0.0400		273	273	1.00		760	273	2.78
5.00	20.0	100	0.0500		250	250	1.00		600	216	2.78
6.67	15.0	100	0.0667		200	200	1.00		500	180	2.78
10.0	10.0	100	0.100		150	150	1.00		400	144	2.78
15.0	6.67	100	0.150		100	100	1.00		300	108	2.78
20.0	5.00	100	0.200		50	50	1.00		200	71.8	2.78
25.0	4.00	100	0.250		25	25	1.00		100	35.9	2.78

12-34. *Refer to Section 12-7, and Examples 12-4 and 12-5.*

Given: $T_1 = 26°C + 273.15° = 299$ K $\qquad V_1 = 385$ mL $\qquad P_1 = 670.$ torr
$\qquad\quad T_2 = ?$ $\qquad\qquad\qquad\qquad\qquad V_2 = 560.$ mL $\qquad P_2 = 940.$ torr

Combined Gas Law: $\qquad \dfrac{P_1 V_1}{T_1} = \dfrac{P_2 V_2}{T_2} \quad$ at constant n

$$\frac{670. \text{ torr} \times 385 \text{ mL}}{299 \text{ K}} = \frac{940. \text{ torr} \times 560. \text{ mL}}{T_2}$$

$$T_2 = \textbf{610. K or 337°C}$$

12-36. *Refer to Sections 12-4, 12-5 and 12-7.*

Boyle's Law and Charles's Law can both be derived from the Combined Gas Law: $\dfrac{P_1 V_1}{T_1} = \dfrac{P_2 V_2}{T_2}$ at constant n

(1) When applying Boyle's Law, we are working at constant temperature and with a constant number of moles of gas. In this case, $T_1 = T_2$, and the Combined Gas Law simplifies to

$\qquad\qquad\qquad$ Boyle's Law: $\qquad P_1 V_1 = P_2 V_2 \qquad$ at constant n and T

(2) When applying Charles's Law, we are working at constant pressure and with a constant number of moles of gas. In this case, $P_1 = P_2$, and the Combined Gas Law simplifies to

$\qquad\qquad\qquad$ Charles's Law: $\qquad \dfrac{V_1}{T_1} = \dfrac{V_2}{T_2} \qquad$ at constant n and P

12-38. *Refer to Section 12-8.*

(a) Avogadro's Law states that, at the same temperature and pressure, equal volumes of all gases contain the same number of molecules. This means that equal number of moles of any gas take up equal volumes as long as the temperature and pressure are the same.

(b) The standard molar volume is the volume occupied by 1 mole of an ideal gas under standard conditions. It is 22.4 L/mol at STP, where STP is defined as 1 atmosphere pressure (760 torr) and 0.00°C (273.15 K).

(c) The term "standard molar volume" does not apply to liquids and solids. "Molar volume" is defined as the volume that one mole of liquid or solid occupies at standard conditions, usually 1 atmosphere pressure (760 torr) and 0.00°C (273.15 K). However, the molar volume for different liquids and solids is different, not a standard value.

(d) Yes, there are other temperature and pressure conditions at which 1 mole of any ideal gas would occupy 22.4 L.

The law we need here that is applied to situations where the number of moles of gas and the volume stay constant can be derived from the Combined Gas Law:

$$\frac{P_1 V_1}{T_1} = \frac{P_2 V_2}{T_2} \quad \text{at constant } n$$

We want the volume to remain constant, so the equation simplifies to $\dfrac{P_1}{T_1} = \dfrac{P_2}{T_2}$ at constant n and V

We know that 1 mole of any ideal gas occupies 22.4 L at 1 atmosphere and 273.15 K, so plugging in, we can determine that any time the pressure to temperature ratio is 1 atm/273.15 K = 0.00366 atm/K, the volume will be 22.4 L.

12-40. *Refer to Section 12-9, and Examples 12-6 and 12-11.*

Plan: (1) Find the volume of 1.00 mole of EDB vapor using the ideal gas equation.
(2) Calculate the density, D (g/L), of the EDB vapor.

(1) $? \, V \, \text{EDB (in L)} = \dfrac{nRT}{P} = \dfrac{(1.00 \text{ mol})(0.0821 \text{ L·atm/mol·K})(165°C + 273°)}{1.00 \text{ atm}} = 36.0 \text{ L EDB}$

(2) $\text{Density (g/L)} = \dfrac{\text{mass of vapor (g)}}{\text{volume of vapor (L)}} = \dfrac{188 \text{ g}}{36.0 \text{ L}} = \textbf{5.23 g/L}$

12-42. *Refer to Section 12-8, and Examples 12-6 and 12-12.*

Recall: at STP, 1 mol of gas having a mass equal to its molecular weight occupies 22.4 L. Therefore at STP for a gas that behaves ideally,

$$\text{Density (g/L)} = \dfrac{\text{molecular weight (g/mol)}}{22.4 \text{ L/mol}}$$

(a) Plan: Using the above formula, calculate the molecular weights of the 2 unknown gases and identify them.

Cylinder #1: $D = 3.74$ g/L
MW (g/mol) = D (g/L) x 22.4 L/mol = 3.74 g/L x 22.4 L/mol = 83.8 g/mol
Therefore, the gas must be **krypton, Kr**.

Cylinder #2: $D = 0.900$ g/L
MW (g/mol) = D (g/L) x 22.4 L/mol = 0.900 g/L x 22.4 L/mol = 20.2 g/mol
Therefore, the gas must be **neon, Ne**.

(b) It is possible using the tools we now have to identify the gases if the density had been made at a different temperature and pressure than STP.

Plan: (1) Use the Combined Gas Law to calculate the volume that 1 L of the gas would have occupied at STP.
(2) Calculate the new density at STP, which is equal to the same number of grams of gas divided by the newly calculated volume at STP.
(3) Calculate the MW of the gas as above.

Note: However, it is standard procedure to solve this problem using the variation of the ideal gas law. See Example 12-12.

12-44. *Refer to Section 12-9.*

(a) An "ideal gas" is a hypothetical gas that follows all of the postulates of the kinetic molecular theory. It also obeys exactly all of the gas laws.

(b) The ideal gas equation, also called the ideal gas law, is the relationship, $PV = nRT$.

(c) The ideal gas law is derived by combining Boyle's Law, Charles's Law and Avogadro's Law, obtaining

$$V \propto \dfrac{nT}{P} \quad \text{with no restrictions}$$

(d) The symbol for the proportionality constant for the conversion of the above proportion to an equality is R. The formula obtained is

$$V = R\left(\frac{nT}{P}\right)$$

which can be rearranged to give

$$PV = nRT.$$

The value of R is obtained by experimentally measuring a complete set of P, V, n and T values, then solving for R by substituting into the ideal gas law.

12-46.   *Refer to Section 12-9 and Example 12-8.*

Recall the ideal gas law: $PV = nRT$

$$P = \frac{nRT}{V} = \frac{(2.54 \text{ mol})(0.0821 \text{ L·atm/mol·K})(45°C + 273°)}{12.75 \text{ L}} = \textbf{5.20 atm}$$

12-48.   *Refer to Section 12-9, Table 1-8, and Example 12-9.*

Plan: (a) (1) Calculate the moles of Cl_2 involved.
   (2) Determine the volume (in L and ft³) of Cl_2 at 750. torr and 18°C using $PV = nRT$.
   (b) Determine the length (ft) of the Cl_2 cloud knowing that V (ft³) = length (ft) x width (ft) x depth(ft).

(a) (1) ? mol Cl_2 = 565 tons $\times \dfrac{2000 \text{ lb}}{1 \text{ ton}} \times \dfrac{453.6 \text{ g}}{1 \text{ lb}} \times \dfrac{1 \text{ mol}}{70.9 \text{ g}} = 7.23 \times 10^6$ mol Cl_2

   (2) ? V Cl_2 (in L) $= \dfrac{nRT}{P} = \dfrac{(7.23 \times 10^6 \text{ mol})(0.0821 \text{ L·atm/mol·K})(18.0°C + 273°)}{(750./760.) \text{ atm}} = \textbf{1.75} \times \textbf{10}^{\textbf{8}}$ **L Cl_2**

   ? V Cl_2 (in ft³) = 1.75 x 10⁸ L $\times \dfrac{1 \text{ ft}^3}{28.32 \text{ L}} = \textbf{6.18} \times \textbf{10}^{\textbf{6}}$ **ft³ Cl_2**

(b) ? length of Cl_2 cloud (ft) $= \dfrac{V \text{ (ft}^3)}{\text{width (ft) x depth (ft)}} = \dfrac{6.18 \times 10^6 \text{ ft}^3}{(0.500 \text{ mi} \times 5280 \text{ ft/mi}) \times 60.0 \text{ ft}} = \textbf{39.0 ft}$ (3 sig. fig.)

12-50.   *Refer to Section 12-10 and Example 12-10.*

Plan: (1) Calculate the moles of He involved using $PV = nRT$.
   (2) Determine the mass of He.

(1) ? $n = \dfrac{PV}{RT} = \dfrac{(1.1 \text{ atm})(5.0 \text{ L})}{(0.0821 \text{ L·atm/mol·K})(25°C + 273°)} = 0.22$ mol He

(2) ? g He = 0.22 mol x 4.003 g/mol = **0.88 g He**

12-52.   *Refer to Section 12-8 and Table 12-3.*

Plan: Standard molar volume, referring to the volume that one mole of gas occupies at STP, can be calculated by dividing the formula weight of the gas (g/mol) by the gas' density at STP (g/L), giving units of L/mol.

Standard molar volume of $SF_6 = \dfrac{146.07 \text{ g/mol}}{6.65 \text{ g/L}} = \textbf{22.0 L/mol}$

Standard molar volume of HF $= \dfrac{20.01 \text{ g/mol}}{0.922 \text{ g/L}} = \textbf{21.7 L/mol}$

12-54. *Refer to Section 12-10 and Example 12-12.*

Plan: (1) Use the ideal gas law, $PV = nRT$, to calculate the moles of ethane in the container at STP.
(2) Determine the experimental molecular weight of ethane and compare it to the theoretical value.

(1) $n = \dfrac{PV}{RT} = \dfrac{(1\ atm)(0.185\ L)}{(0.0821\ L \cdot atm/mol \cdot K)(273\ K)} = 8.25 \times 10^{-3}\ mol\ C_2H_6$

(2) $MW\ C_2H_6 = \dfrac{0.244\ g\ C_2H_6}{8.25 \times 10^{-3}\ mol} = \textbf{29.6 g/mol}$

The actual molecular weight of ethane, C_2H_6, is 30.1 g/mol.

$Percent\ error = \dfrac{actual\ MW - experimental\ MW}{actual\ MW} \times 100\% = \dfrac{30.1 - 29.6}{30.1} \times 100\% = \textbf{2\%}$

Possible sources of error which would result in a slightly low experimental molecular weight include:
   (a) the container volume is slightly less than 185 mL,
   (b) the mass of ethane is slightly more than 0.244 g, and
   (c) ethane deviates slightly from ideality under STP conditions   (Refer to methane, CH_4, in Table 12-5.)

12-56. *Refer to Section 12-10 and Example 12-12.*

Plan: (1) Use the ideal gas law, $PV = nRT$, to find the number of moles of gas.
(2) Calculate the molecular weight of the gas.

(1) $n = \dfrac{PV}{RT} = \dfrac{[(745/760)\ atm](0.00413\ L)}{(0.0821\ L \cdot atm/mol \cdot K)(23°C + 273°)} = 1.67 \times 10^{-4}\ mol$

(2) $MW\ (g/mol) = \dfrac{0.00500\ g\ gas}{1.67 \times 10^{-4}\ mol} = \textbf{30.0 g/mol}$

Within experimental error, the gaseous hydrocarbon could be **ethane (C_2H_6)** with MW of 30.1 g/mol.

12-58. *Refer to Section 12-10 and Example 12-13.*

Plan: (1) Find the volume, V, of the container. In this case, you cannot assume that the flask is 250. mL.
(2) Determine the number of moles of gas, using $PV = nRT$.
(3) Determine the mass of the gas in the flask.
(4) Calculate the molecular weight of the gas.

(1) ? V, volume of container = volume of water in container (we are calibrating the 250. mL flask)

$\quad\quad\quad\quad = \dfrac{mass\ of\ water\ (g)}{density\ of\ water\ (g/mL)}$ $\left(since\ D = \dfrac{mass}{volume} \right)$

$\quad\quad\quad\quad = \dfrac{mass\ of\ flask\ filled\ with\ water - empty\ flask}{density\ of\ water}$

$\quad\quad\quad\quad = \dfrac{327.4\ g - 65.347\ g}{0.997\ g/mL}$

$\quad\quad\quad\quad = 263\ mL$

(2) $n = \dfrac{PV}{RT} = \dfrac{[(743.3/760)\ atm](0.263\ L)}{(0.0821\ L \cdot atm/mol \cdot K)(99.8°C + 273°)} = 0.00840\ mol$

(3) mass of gas = mass of condensed liquid = mass of flask and condensed liquid - mass of empty flask
$\quad\quad\quad\quad\quad\quad\quad\quad\quad\quad = 65.739\ g - 65.347\ g$
$\quad\quad\quad\quad\quad\quad\quad\quad\quad\quad = 0.392\ g$

(4) $MW\ (g/mol) = \dfrac{0.392\ g\ gas}{0.00840\ mol} = 46.7\ g/mol\ or\ \textbf{46.7 amu/molecule}$

(a) The partial pressure of a gas is the pressure it exerts in a mixture of gases. It is equal to the pressure the gas would exert if it were alone in the container at the same temperature.

(b) Dalton's Law states that the total pressure exerted by a mixture of ideal gases is the sum of the partial pressures of those gases: $P_{total} = P_A + P_B + P_C \ldots$ at constant V, T

From Dalton's Law of Partial Pressures,

$$P_{total} = \frac{n_{total}RT}{V} \qquad \text{where } n_{total} = n_{CHCl_3} + n_{CH_4} = \frac{3.23 \text{ g CHCl}_3}{119.4 \text{ g/mol}} + \frac{1.22 \text{ g CH}_4}{16.04 \text{ g/mol}}$$

$$= 0.0271 \text{ mol} + 0.0761 \text{ mol}$$

$$= 0.1031 \text{ mol (4 sig. figs. due to rules of addition)}$$

$$P_{total} = \frac{(0.1031 \text{ mol gas})(0.0821 \text{ L·atm/mol·K})(275°C + 273°)}{0.0500 \text{ L}} = \textbf{92.8 atm}$$

$$P_{CHCl_3} = \left(\frac{n_{CHCl_3}}{n_{CHCl_3} + n_{CH_4}}\right)P_{total} = \left(\frac{0.0271 \text{ mol}}{0.0271 \text{ mol} + 0.0761 \text{ mol}}\right) 92.8 \text{ atm} = \textbf{24.4 atm}$$

Alternative method: use $P_{CHCl_3} = \dfrac{n_{CHCl_3}RT}{V}$

mole fraction of He $X_{He} = \dfrac{P_{He}}{P_{total}} = \dfrac{0.467 \text{ atm He}}{0.467 \text{ atm He} + 0.317 \text{ atm Ar} + 0.277 \text{ atm Xe}} = \dfrac{0.467 \text{ atm}}{1.061 \text{ atm}} = \textbf{0.440}$

mole fraction of Ar $X_{Ar} = \dfrac{P_{Ar}}{P_{total}} = \dfrac{0.317 \text{ atm}}{1.061 \text{ atm}} = \textbf{0.299}$

mole fraction of Xe $X_{Xe} = \dfrac{P_{Xe}}{P_{total}} = \dfrac{0.277 \text{ atm}}{1.061 \text{ atm}} = \textbf{0.261}$ Note: $X_{He} + X_{Ar} + X_{Xe} = 1$

(a) Boyle's Law states that $P_1V_1 = P_2V_2$.

     For each gas, $P_2 = \dfrac{P_1V_1}{V_2} = \dfrac{1.50 \text{ atm} \times 2.50 \text{ L}}{1.00 \text{ L}} = 3.75 \text{ atm}$

     Dalton's Law of Partial Pressures states that $P_{total} = P_1 + P_2 + P_3 + \ldots$ at constant V, T

     Therefore, $P_{total} = P_{O_2} + P_{N_2} + P_{He} = 3.75 \text{ atm} + 3.75 \text{ atm} + 3.75 \text{ atm} = \textbf{11.25 atm}$

(b) partial pressure of O_2, $P_{O_2} = \textbf{3.75 atm}$

(c) partial pressure of N_2, P_{N_2} = partial pressure of He, $P_{He} = \textbf{3.75 atm}$

Plan: (1) Calculate the partial pressure of nitrogen in the container at 25°C and 750. torr.
            (2) Use the Combined Gas Law to calculate the volume of gas (N_2 + H_2O) at the new conditions.

(1) $P_{N_2} = P_{atm} - P_{H_2O} = 750. \text{ torr} - 24 \text{ torr} = 726 \text{ torr}$

(2) Combined Gas Law: $\dfrac{P_1V_1}{T_1} = \dfrac{P_2V_2}{T_2}$

$$\frac{760 \text{ torr} \times 249 \text{ mL}}{273 \text{ K}} = \frac{726 \text{ torr} \times V_2}{25°C + 273°} \qquad \text{Solving, } V_2 = \textbf{285 mL}$$

(a) Recall Boyle's Law: $P_1V_1 = P_2V_2$ at constant n, T
The total volume of the flasks = 2.00 L + 4.00 L = 6.00 L
for He: 6.00 atm x 4.00 L = P_2 x 6.00 L   for N_2: 3.00 atm x 2.00 L = P_2 x 6.00 L
P_2 = **4.00 atm** P_2 = **1.00 atm**

(b) According to Dalton's Law of Partial Pressures, $P_{total} = P_1 + P_2 + \ldots$.
Therefore, $P_{total} = P_{He} + P_{N_2}$ = 4.00 atm + 1.00 atm = **5.00 atm**

(c) mole fraction of He, $X_{He} = \dfrac{P_{He}}{P_{total}} = \dfrac{4.00 \text{ atm}}{5.00 \text{ atm}} = \textbf{0.800}$

Balanced equation: $2NaN_3(s) \rightarrow 2Na(s) + 3N_2(g)$

Plan: $\underset{(1)}{V\,N_2} \Rightarrow \underset{(2)}{mol\,N_2} \Rightarrow \underset{(3)}{mol\,NaN_3} \Rightarrow g\,NaN_3$

(1) ? mol $N_2 = n = \dfrac{PV}{RT} = \dfrac{(1.40 \text{ atm})(25.0 \text{ L})}{(0.0821 \text{ L·atm/mol·K})(25°C + 273°)} = 1.43$ mol N_2

(2) ? mol $NaN_3 = \dfrac{2 \text{ mol } NaN_3}{3 \text{ mol } N_2}$ x 1.43 mol N_2 = 0.954 mol NaN_3

(3) ? g NaN_3 = 0.954 mol NaN_3 x 65.0 g/mol = **62.0 g NaN₃**

Note: When doing an extensive calculation, keep all the numbers in your calculator. The answers here are rounded off to the appropriate number of significant figures after each step only to illustrate the concept of significant figures.

Balanced equation: $S_8(g) + 8O_2(g) \rightarrow 8SO_2(g)$

In reality, above 444°C, sulfur boils to give a vapor containing a mixture of S_8, S_6, S_4 and S_2 molecules. However, we are assuming at this temperature that the sulfur exists primarily as S_8.

Plan: $\underset{(1)}{V\,S_8} \Rightarrow \underset{(2)}{mol\,S_8} \Rightarrow \underset{(3)}{mol\,SO_2} \Rightarrow g\,SO_2$

(1) ? mol $S_8 = n = \dfrac{PV}{RT} = \dfrac{(1.00 \text{ atm})(1.00 \text{ L})}{(0.0821 \text{ L·atm/mol·K})(600.°C + 273°)} = 0.0140$ mol S_8

(2) ? mol $SO_2 = \dfrac{8 \text{ mol } SO_2}{1 \text{ mol } S_8}$ x 0.0140 mol S_8 = 0.112 mol SO_2

(3) ? g SO_2 = 0.112 mol SO_2 x 64.07 g/mol = **7.15 g SO₂**

Balanced equation: $2KClO_3(s) \rightarrow 2KCl(s) + 3O_2(g)$

Plan: $\underset{(1)}{V_{actual}\,O_2} \Rightarrow \underset{(2)}{V_{theoretical}\,O_2} \Rightarrow \underset{(3)}{mol\,O_2} \Rightarrow \underset{(4)}{mol\,KClO_3} \Rightarrow g\,KClO_3$

(1) In order to fill four 250. mL bottles, 1.00 L O_2 is actually required. However, more than 1.00 L O_2 must be produced since some O_2 will be lost in the process. If 25% of O_2 will be wasted, the percentage yield of the process is 75%. The theoretical amount of O_2 that must be produced can be calculated:

Recall: percentage yield $= \dfrac{\text{actual yield}}{\text{theoretical yield}}$ x 100%.   Therefore, theoretical volume of O_2 needed $= \dfrac{\text{actual volume of } O_2 \text{ needed}}{75\%} \times 100\% = \dfrac{1.00 \text{ L}}{75\%} \times 100\% = 1.33 \text{ L } O_2$

(2) ? mol $O_2 = n = \dfrac{PV}{RT} = \dfrac{[(762/760) \text{ atm}](1.33 \text{ L})}{(0.0821 \text{ L·atm/mol·K})(25°C + 273°)} = 0.0545 \text{ mol } O_2$

(3) ? mol $KClO_3 = 0.0545$ mol O_2 x (2 mol $KClO_3$/3 mol O_2) = 0.0363 mol $KClO_3$

(4) ? g $KClO_3 = 0.0363$ mol $KClO_3$ x 122.6 g/mol = **4.45 g $KClO_3$**

12-78. *Refer to Section 12-12.*

Balanced equation: $N_2(g) + 3H_2(g) \rightarrow 2NH_3(g)$

This is a limiting reactant problem. Due to Gay-Lussac's Law, we can work directly in volumes instead of moles.

(1) Compare the required ratio to the available ratio of reactants to find the limiting reactant.

Required ratio $= \dfrac{1 \text{ volume } N_2}{3 \text{ volumes } H_2} = 0.333$ Available ratio $= \dfrac{3.00 \text{ L } N_2}{7.00 \text{ L } H_2} = 0.429$

Available ratio > required ratio; H_2 is the limiting reactant.

(2) ? L $NH_3 = 7.00$ L H_2 x $\dfrac{2 \text{ L } NH_3}{3 \text{ L } H_2} = $ **4.67 L NH_3**

12-80. *Refer to Section 12-12, and Examples 12-20 and 12-21.*

Balanced equation: $2KNO_3(s) \rightarrow 2KNO_2(s) + O_2(g)$

Recall that 1 mole of ideal gas at STP occupies 22.4 L.

Plan: $V_{STP} O_2 \overset{(1)}{\Rightarrow} \text{mol } O_2 \overset{(2)}{\Rightarrow} \text{mol } KNO_3 \overset{(3)}{\Rightarrow} \text{g } KNO_3$

Method 1:

(1) ? mol $O_2 = \dfrac{21.1 \text{ L}_{STP} O_2}{22.4 \text{ L}_{STP}/\text{mol}} = 0.942 \text{ mol } O_2$

(2) ? mol $KNO_3 = 0.942$ mol O_2 x (2 mol KNO_3/1 mol O_2)= 1.88 mol KNO_3

(3) ? g $KNO_3 = 1.88$ mol KNO_3 x 101 g/mol = **190. g KNO_3**

Method 2: Dimensional Analysis

? g $KNO_3 = 21.1$ L$_{STP}$ O_2 x $\dfrac{1 \text{ mol } O_2}{22.4 \text{ L}_{STP} O_2}$ x $\dfrac{2 \text{ mol } KNO_3}{1 \text{ mol } O_2}$ x $\dfrac{101 \text{ g } KNO_3}{1 \text{ mol } KNO_3}$ = **190. g KNO_3**

12-82. *Refer to Section 12-12.*

Plan: $V \, SO_2 \overset{(1)}{\Rightarrow} \text{mol } SO_2 \overset{(2)}{\Rightarrow} \text{mol } S \overset{(3)}{\Rightarrow} \text{g } S \overset{(4)}{\Rightarrow} \%S \text{ by mass}$

(1) ? mol $SO_2 = n = \dfrac{PV}{RT} = \dfrac{[(755/760) \text{ atm}](1.177 \text{ L})}{(0.0821 \text{ L·atm/mol·K})(35.0°C + 273°)} = 0.0462 \text{ mol } SO_2$

(2) ? mol S = mol SO_2 = 0.0462 mol S

(3) ? g S = 0.0462 mol S x 32.066 g/mol = 1.48 g S

(4) ? %S by mass $= \dfrac{\text{g } S}{\text{g sample}} \times 100 = \dfrac{1.48 \text{ g}}{5.913 \text{ g}} \times 100 = $ **25.1% S by mass**

Balanced equations: A: $2C_8H_{18} + 25O_2 \rightarrow 16CO_2 + 18H_2O$

B: $2C_8H_{18} + 17O_2 \rightarrow 16CO + 18H_2O$

(a) Plan: CO concentration $\overset{(1)}{\Rightarrow}$ g CO $\overset{(2)}{\Rightarrow}$ mol CO $\overset{(3)}{\Rightarrow}$ mol C_8H_{18} (from Reaction B) $\overset{(4)}{\Rightarrow}$ mol C_8H_{18} (total)

$\overset{(5)}{\Rightarrow}$ g C_8H_{18} (total) $\overset{(6)}{\Rightarrow}$ $V\,C_8H_{18}$

Method 1:

(1) ? g CO = concentration (g/m^3) x volume (m^3) = 2.00 g/m^3 x 97.5 m^3 = 195 g CO produced

(2) ? mol CO = $\dfrac{195 \text{ g CO}}{28.0 \text{ g/mol}}$ = 6.96 mol CO

(3) ? mol C_8H_{18} (Reaction B) = (2/16) x 6.96 mol CO = 0.871 mol C_8H_{18} (Reaction B)

(4) ? mol C_8H_{18} (total) = $\dfrac{0.871 \text{ mol } C_8H_{18} \text{ (Reaction B)}}{0.050}$ = 17.4 mol C_8H_{18} (total)

since only 5.0% of the total amount of C_8H_{18} burned in the engine produced CO.

(5) ? g C_8H_{18} (total) = 17.4 mol C_8H_{18} x 114 g/mol = 1980 g C_8H_{18} (total)

(6) ? $V\,C_8H_{18}$ = $\dfrac{\text{mass (g)}}{\text{Density (g/mL)}}$ = $\dfrac{1980 \text{ g } C_8H_{18}}{0.702 \text{ g/mL}}$ = 2830 mL or **2.83 L C_8H_{18}**   (g/mL) = $\dfrac{\text{mass (g)}}{\text{volume (mL)}}$

Method 2: Dimensional Analysis

? L C_8H_{18} = 97.5 m^3 x $\dfrac{2.00 \text{ g CO}}{1 \text{ m}^3}$ x $\dfrac{1 \text{ mol CO}}{28.0 \text{ g CO}}$ x $\dfrac{2 \text{ mol } C_8H_{18} \text{ (Reaction B)}}{16 \text{ mol CO}}$ x $\dfrac{1.00 \text{ mol } C_8H_{18} \text{ (total)}}{0.050 \text{ mol } C_8H_{18} \text{ (Reaction B)}}$

x $\dfrac{114 \text{ g } C_8H_{18} \text{ (total)}}{1 \text{ mol } C_8H_{18} \text{ (total)}}$ x $\dfrac{1 \text{ mL } C_8H_{18}}{0.702 \text{ g } C_8H_{18}}$ x $\dfrac{1 \text{ L } C_8H_{18}}{1000 \text{ mL } C_8H_{18}}$ = **2.83 L C_8H_{18}**

(b) fuel rate $\left(\dfrac{\text{L}}{\text{min}}\right) = \dfrac{\text{volume of fuel burned (L)}}{\text{time (min)}}$

therefore, time (min) = $\dfrac{\text{volume of fuel burned (L)}}{\text{fuel rate (L/min)}}$ = $\dfrac{2.83 \text{ L}}{0.0631 \text{ L/min}}$ = **44.8 min**

12-86. *Refer to Section 12-13.*

According to the Kinetic-Molecular Theory, all gas molecules have the same average kinetic energy (= $1/2\,m\bar{u}^2$) at the same temperature. Therefore, lighter molecules will have higher average molecular speeds ($\bar{u}$). So, in order of increasing speeds at 25°C (or any temperature where all are gases):

CH_2Cl_2 (84.9 g/mol) < Kr (83.8 g/mol) < N_2 (28.0 g/mol) < CH_4 (16.0 g/mol)

12-88. *Refer to Section 12-13 and Exercise 12-86 Solution.*

According to the Kinetic-Molecular Theory, all gas molecules have the same average kinetic energy (= $1/2\,m\bar{u}^2$) at the same temperature, where $\bar{u}$ is the average velocity. Hence, at the same T:

$$1/2(m_{SiH_4})(\bar{u}_{SiH_4})^2 = 1/2\,(m_{CH_4})(\bar{u}_{CH_4})^2$$

$$\dfrac{\bar{u}_{CH_4}}{\bar{u}_{SiH_4}} = \sqrt{\dfrac{m_{SiH_4}}{m_{CH_4}}} = \sqrt{\dfrac{MW_{SiH_4}}{MW_{CH_4}}} = \sqrt{\dfrac{32}{16}} = 1.4$$

SiH_4 is heavier than CH_4; however, both molecules have the same average kinetic energy. This is due to the fact that methane molecules have an average speed which is 1.4 times faster than that of silane molecules.

(a) The third assumption of the Kinetic-Molecular Theory states that the average kinetic energy of gaseous molecules is directly proportional to the absolute temperature of the sample.

Average kinetic energy $= 1/2m\bar{u}^2 \propto T$ where m = mass (g)

$\bar{u}$ = average molecular speed (m/s)

T = absolute temperature (K)

We see that the average molecular speed is directly proportional to the square root of the absolute temperature.

(b) $\dfrac{\text{rms speed of N}_2 \text{ molecules at } 100°C}{\text{rms speed of N}_2 \text{ molecules at } 0°C} = \sqrt{\dfrac{100°C + 273°}{0°C + 273°}} = \textbf{1.17}$

According to Kinetic-Molecular Theory, the pressure exerted by a gas upon the walls of its container is caused by gas molecules hitting the walls. Pressure depends on

(1) the number of molecules hitting the walls per unit time and
(2) how vigorously the molecules hit the walls.

(a) When a gaseous sample in a fixed volume is heated, the pressure increases. Recall that the average kinetic energy is directly proportional to the absolute temperature. As temperature increases, so does the energy and also the velocity of the molecules. At higher temperatures, there is an increase in the force and number of collisions and the pressure increases.

(b) When the volume of a gaseous sample is reduced at constant temperature, the pressure increases. When the volume is reduced, more molecules hit a given area on the walls per unit time, increasing the pressure. This is Boyle's Law.

For H_2, F_2 and HF under the same conditions, H_2 would behave the most ideally, because for such small nonpolar molecules, the dispersion forces would be small and therefore the intermolecular attractions would be negligible. The behavior of HF, on the other hand, would deviate the most from ideality, because even though HF is smaller than F_2, it is very polar and its molecules exhibit great attraction for one another.

(a) The effect of molecular volume on the properties of a gas becomes more important when a gas is compressed at constant temperature.

(b) Molecular volume also becomes more important when more gas molecules are added to a system.

(c) When the temperature of the gas is raised at constant pressure, the volume expands. At a larger occupied volume, the effect of molecular volume on the properties of a gas becomes less significant.

(a) Assuming CCl_4 obeys the ideal gas law: $PV = nRT$

$$P = \frac{nRT}{V} = \frac{(1.00 \text{ mol})(0.0821 \text{ L·atm/mol·K})(77.0°C + 273°)}{35.0 \text{ L}} = \textbf{0.821 atm}$$

(b) Assuming CCl_4 obeys the van der Waals equation: $\left(P + \dfrac{n^2 a}{V^2}\right)(V-nb) = nRT$

$$\text{for } CCl_4, \quad a = 20.39 \text{ L}^2\cdot\text{atm/mol}^2, \ b = 0.1383 \text{ L/mol}$$

$$\left[P + \dfrac{(1.00 \text{ mol})^2(20.39 \text{ L}^2\cdot\text{atm/mol}^2)}{(35.0 \text{ L})^2}\right]\left[35.0 \text{ L} - (1.00 \text{ mol})\left(0.1383 \dfrac{\text{L}}{\text{mol}}\right)\right]$$

$$= (1.00 \text{ mol})(0.0821 \text{ L}\cdot\text{atm/mol}\cdot\text{K})(77°\text{C} + 273°)$$

$$[P + 0.0166 \text{ atm}][34.9 \text{ L}] = 28.7 \text{ L}\cdot\text{atm}$$

$$P + 0.0166 \text{ atm} = 0.822 \text{ atm}$$

$$\boldsymbol{P = 0.805 \text{ atm}}$$

(c) (1) Assuming CCl_4 obeys the ideal gas law: $PV = nRT$

$$P = \dfrac{nRT}{V} = \dfrac{(3.10 \text{ mol})(0.0821 \text{ L}\cdot\text{atm/mol}\cdot\text{K})(135°\text{C} + 273°)}{5.75 \text{ L}} = \boldsymbol{18.1 \text{ atm}}$$

(2) Assuming CCl_4 obeys the van der Waals equation: $\left(P + \dfrac{n^2 a}{V^2}\right)(V-nb) = nRT$

$$\text{for } CCl_4, \ a = 20.39 \text{ L}^2\cdot\text{atm/mol}^2, \ b = 0.1383 \text{ L/mol}$$

$$\left[P + \dfrac{(3.10 \text{ mol})^2(20.39 \text{ L}^2\cdot\text{atm/mol}^2)}{(5.75 \text{ L})^2}\right]\left[5.75 \text{ L} - (3.10 \text{ mol})\left(0.1383 \dfrac{\text{L}}{\text{mol}}\right)\right]$$

$$= (3.10 \text{ mol})(0.0821 \text{ L}\cdot\text{atm/mol}\cdot\text{K})(135°\text{C} + 273°)$$

$$[P + 5.93 \text{ atm}][5.32 \text{ L}] = 104 \text{ L}\cdot\text{atm}$$

$$P + 5.93 \text{ atm} = 19.5 \text{ atm}$$

$$\boldsymbol{P = 13.6 \text{ atm}}$$

12-100. *Refer to Section 12-15, Table 12-5 and Example 12-23.*

First, calculate the moles of CO_2: ? mol CO_2 = 165 g/44.01 g/mol = 3.75 mol

(a) Assuming CO_2 obeys the ideal gas law: $PV = nRT$

$$P = \dfrac{nRT}{V} = \dfrac{(3.75 \text{ mol})(0.0821 \text{ L}\cdot\text{atm/mol}\cdot\text{K})(25°\text{C} + 273°)}{12.5 \text{ L}} = \boldsymbol{7.34 \text{ atm}}$$

(b) Assuming CCl_4 obeys the van der Waals equation: $\left(P + \dfrac{n^2 a}{V^2}\right)(V-nb) = nRT$

$$\text{for } CO_2, \ a = 3.59 \text{ L}^2\cdot\text{atm/mol}^2, \ b = 0.0427 \text{ L/mol}$$

$$\left[P + \dfrac{(3.75 \text{ mol})^2(3.59 \text{ L}^2\cdot\text{atm/mol}^2)}{(12.5 \text{ L})^2}\right]\left[12.5 \text{ L} - (3.75 \text{ mol})\left(0.0427 \dfrac{\text{L}}{\text{mol}}\right)\right]$$

$$= (3.75 \text{ mol})(0.0821 \text{ L}\cdot\text{atm/mol}\cdot\text{K})(25°\text{C} + 273°)$$

$$[P + 0.323 \text{ atm}][12.3 \text{ L}] = 91.7 \text{ L}\cdot\text{atm}$$

$$P + 0.323 \text{ atm} = 7.46 \text{ atm}$$

$$\boldsymbol{P = 7.14 \text{ atm}}$$

12-102. *Refer to Section 12-1 and Table 12-1.*

The molar volume of compounds is the volume that one mole of compound will occupy at a particular temperature. It can be calculated by dividing the atomic weight, AW, of an element by its density.

Molar volume of liquid iron at 1600.°C:

$$\text{Molar volume (cm}^3\text{/mol)} = \dfrac{\text{AW}}{D} = \dfrac{55.85 \text{ g/mol}}{6.88 \text{ g/cm}^3} = \boldsymbol{8.12 \text{ cm}^3\text{/mol}}$$

Alternatively, by dimensional analysis: molar volume (cm^3/mol) $= \dfrac{55.85 \text{ g}}{1 \text{ mol Fe}} \times \dfrac{1 \text{ cm}^3}{6.88 \text{ g}} = \boldsymbol{8.12 \text{ cm}^3\text{/mol}}$

Molar volume of solid iron at 20°C:

$$\text{Molar volume (cm}^3\text{/mol)} = \frac{AW}{D} = \frac{55.85 \text{ g/mol}}{7.86 \text{ g/cm}^3} = \textbf{7.11 cm}^3\textbf{/mol}$$

Alternatively, by dimensional analysis: $\text{molar volume (cm}^3\text{/mol)} = \dfrac{55.85 \text{ g}}{1 \text{ mol Fe}} \times \dfrac{1 \text{ cm}^3}{7.86 \text{ g}} = \textbf{7.11 cm}^3\textbf{/mol}$

Most substances have a slightly smaller molar volume as a solid than as a liquid; substances generally decrease in volume when they freeze. Water is the notable exception; it expands (increases in molar volume) upon freezing. That is why closed containers holding water and other aqueous solutions will break in freezing weather. Although iron is much more dense overall than the compounds in Table 12-1, and its molar volumes are much less than those of benzene and carbon tetrachloride, iron still behaves normally. The molar volume of liquid iron is still greater than that of solid iron.

12-104. _Refer to Section 12-12 and Example 12-20._

Balanced equation: $2H_2O(\ell) \;\rightarrow\; 2H_2(g) + O_2(g)$

Plan: $V\,O_2 \overset{(1)}{\Rightarrow} \text{mol } O_2 \overset{(2)}{\Rightarrow} \text{mol } H_2O \overset{(3)}{\Rightarrow} \text{g } H_2O$

(1) $\;?\text{ mol } O_2 = n = \dfrac{PV}{RT} = \dfrac{(1.00 \text{ atm})(0.085 \text{ L})}{(0.0821 \text{ L·atm/mol·K})(25°C + 273°)} = 0.0035 \text{ mol } O_2$

(2) $\;?\text{ mol } H_2O = \dfrac{2 \text{ mol } H_2O}{1 \text{ mol } O_2} \times 0.0035 \text{ mol } N_2 = 0.0069 \text{ mol } H_2O$

(3) $\;?\text{ g } H_2O = 0.0069 \text{ mol } H_2O \times 18.0 \text{ g/mol} = \textbf{0.13 g } \textbf{H}_2\textbf{O}$ (2 significant figures)

Note: When doing an extensive calculation, keep all the numbers in your calculator. The answers here are rounded off to the appropriate number of significant figures after each step only to illustrate the concept of significant figures.

12-106. _Refer to Section 12-5._

Recall Charles' Law: $\quad \dfrac{V_1}{T_1} = \dfrac{V_2}{T_2} \qquad$ at constant n and P

Given: $\;\; V_1 = 175 \text{ m}^3 \qquad T_1 = 10.°C + 273° = 283 \text{ K}$
$\qquad\;\; V_2 = ? \qquad\qquad\;\; T_2 = 18°C + 273° = 291 \text{ K}$

$$V_2 = \frac{V_1 T_2}{T_1} = \frac{175 \text{ m}^3 \times 291 \text{ K}}{283 \text{ K}} = 180. \text{ m}^3$$

Therefore, **5 m³** (= 180. m³ - 175 m³) of air had been forced out of the cabin.

$?\text{ L air forced from cabin} = 5 \text{ m}^3 \times \dfrac{(100 \text{ cm})^3}{(1 \text{ m})^3} \times \dfrac{1 \text{ mL}}{1 \text{ cm}^3} \times \dfrac{1 \text{ L}}{1000 \text{ mL}} = \textbf{5000 L air}$

12-108. _Refer to Section 12-10 and Example 12-12._

Plan: (1) Use the ideal gas law, $PV = nRT$, to find the moles of Freon-12.
$\qquad$ (2) Calculate the molecular weight of Freon-12.

(1) $\;n = \dfrac{PV}{RT} = \dfrac{[(790./760) \text{ atm}](8.29 \text{ L})}{(0.0821 \text{ L·atm/mol·K})(200.°C + 273°)} = 0.222 \text{ mol Freon-12}$

(2) $\;\text{MW (g/mol)} = \dfrac{26.8 \text{ g Freon-12}}{0.222 \text{ mol}} = \textbf{121 g/mol}$

(1) Thought Process #1: Consider the ideal gas law, $PV = nRT$. We know that

Boyle's Law: P is inversely proportional to V at constant n and T.

Charles's Law: V is directly proportional to T at constant P and n.

Avogadro's Law: V is directly proportional to n at constant P and T.

So, what we see is that variables on the same side of the ideal gas law equality are inversely proportional to each other and variables on opposite sides of the equality are directly proportional to each other.

Therefore, we can deduce that P is directly proportional T at constant n and V.

(2) Thought Process #2: Another way to figure out the relationship is to say that at constant n and V,

$$P = \frac{nRT}{V} = \text{constant} \times T \quad \text{and } P \text{ is directly proportional } T \text{ since } n, R \text{ and } V \text{ are all constants}$$

We have a formula that is similar to Charles's Law: $\frac{P_1}{T_1} = \frac{P_2}{T_2}$ at constant n and V

A non-laboratory application of this law is that in a closed constant volume container holding a gas, the pressure increases with increasing temperature. In a fire, supposedly empty sealed containers containing air or vapor can become lethal weapons if the container is incapable of handling the increased stress provided by increased pressure. This fact would be invaluable to fire fighters.

(a) Plan: (1) Determine the actual partial pressure of H_2O vapor before and after air conditioning.

(2) Calculate the moles and mass of water present before and after air conditioning using the ideal gas law, $PV = nRT$.

(3) Determine the mass of water removed by the air conditioning process.

(1) From Appendix E,   vapor pressure of water at 33°C = 37.7 torr

vapor pressure of water at 25°C = 23.8 torr

Given: $\text{relative humidity} = \dfrac{\text{actual partial pressure of } H_2O \text{ vapor}}{\text{partial pressure of } H_2O \text{ vapor if saturated}}$

before air conditioning at 33.0°C: $P_{H_2O,\text{actual}} = \text{relative humidity} \times P_{H_2O,\text{sat}}$
$= 0.800 \times 37.7 \text{ torr}$
$= 30.2 \text{ torr}$

after air conditioning at 25.0°C: $P_{H_2O,\text{actual}} = \text{relative humidity} \times P_{H_2O,\text{sat}}$
$= 0.150 \times 23.8 \text{ torr}$
$= 3.57 \text{ torr}$

(2) $? V_{\text{house}} (L) = 245 \text{ m}^3 \times \dfrac{(100 \text{ cm})^3}{(1 \text{ m})^3} \times \dfrac{1 \text{ mL}}{1 \text{ cm}^3} \times \dfrac{1 \text{ L}}{1000 \text{ mL}} = 2.45 \times 10^5 \text{ L}$

before air conditioning: $n = \dfrac{PV}{RT} = \dfrac{[(30.2/760) \text{ atm}](2.45 \times 10^5 \text{ L})}{(0.0821 \text{ L·atm/mol·K})(33.0°\text{C} + 273°)} = 388 \text{ mol } H_2O$

$? \text{ g } H_2O = 388 \text{ mol} \times 18.0 \text{ g/mol} = 6980 \text{ g } H_2O$

after air conditioning: $n = \dfrac{PV}{RT} = \dfrac{[(3.57/760) \text{ atm}](2.45 \times 10^5 \text{ L})}{(0.0821 \text{ L·atm/mol·K})(25.0°\text{C} + 273°)} = 47.0 \text{ mol } H_2O$

$? \text{ g } H_2O = 47.0 \text{ mol} \times 18.0 \text{ g/mol} = 846 \text{ g } H_2O$

(3) The mass of water removed = 6980 g - 846 g = **6130 g H_2O**

(b) $? \text{ mL } H_2O \text{ at } 25°\text{C} = \dfrac{6130 \text{ g } H_2O}{0.997 \text{ g/cm}^3} = \textbf{6150 cm}^3 \textbf{ } \textbf{H}_2\textbf{O}$ since $\text{Density (g/mL)} = \dfrac{\text{mass (g)}}{\text{volume (mL)}}$

12-114. *Refer to Section 12-15, Example 12-23 and Table 12-5.*

(1) Assuming NH_3 obeys the ideal gas law: $PV = nRT$

$$P = \frac{nRT}{V} = \frac{(4.00 \text{ mol})(0.0821 \text{ L·atm/mol·K})(100°C + 273°)}{25.0 \text{ L}} = \textbf{4.90 atm}$$

(2) Assuming NH_3 obeys the van der Waals equation: $\left(P + \frac{n^2a}{V^2}\right)(V-nb) = nRT$

for NH_3, $\quad a = 4.17 \text{ L}^2\text{·atm/mol}^2$, $b = 0.0371$ L/mol

$$\left[P + \frac{(4.00 \text{ mol})^2(4.17 \text{ L}^2\text{·atm/mol}^2)}{(25.0 \text{ L})^2}\right]\left[25.0 \text{ L} - (4.00 \text{ mol})\left(0.0371 \frac{\text{L}}{\text{mol}}\right)\right]$$
$$= (4.00 \text{ mol})(0.0821 \text{ L·atm/mol·K})(100°C + 273°)$$

Simplifying, $\quad [P + 0.107 \text{ atm}][24.9 \text{ L}] = 122 \text{ L·atm}$

$$P + 0.116 \text{ atm} = 4.90 \text{ atm}$$
$$P = \textbf{4.78 atm}$$

(3) % difference $= \dfrac{P_{\text{ideal}} - P_{\text{real}}}{P_{\text{ideal}}} \times 100 = \dfrac{4.90 - 4.78}{4.90} \times 100 = \textbf{2.4\%}$ (2 significant figures)

12-116. *Refer to Section 12-10 and Examples 12-13 and 12-14.*

Plan: (1) Find the empirical formula for cyanogen.
(2) Calculate the molecular weight of cyanogen, using the ideal gas law, $PV = nRT$.
(3) Determine the molecular formula.

(1) Assume 100 g of cyanogen.

$? \text{ mol C} = \dfrac{46.2 \text{ g C}}{12.0 \text{ g/mol}} = 3.85 \text{ mol C}$ $\qquad$ Ratio $= \dfrac{3.85}{3.84} = 1.00$

$? \text{ mol N} = \dfrac{53.8 \text{ g N}}{14.0 \text{ g/mol}} = 3.84 \text{ mol N}$ $\qquad$ Ratio $= \dfrac{3.84}{3.84} = 1.00$

The empirical formula for cyanogen is C_1N_1 or CN (formula weight = 26.0 g/mol)

(2) $? \text{ mol cyanogen} = n = \dfrac{PV}{RT} = \dfrac{[(750./760) \text{ atm}](0.476 \text{ L})}{(0.0821 \text{ L·atm/mol·K})(25°C + 273°)} = 0.0192 \text{ mol}$

MW (g/mol) $= \dfrac{1.00 \text{ g}}{0.0192 \text{ mol}} = 52.1 \text{ g/mol}$

(3) let $n = \dfrac{\text{molecular weight}}{\text{simplest formula weight}} = \dfrac{52.1 \text{ g/mol}}{26.0 \text{ g/mol}} = 2$

Therefore, the true molecular formula for cyanogen is $\textbf{C}_2\textbf{N}_2$.

Note that italicized n represents moles, whereas n is the ratio between the masses of the molecular formula and the empirical formula.

12-118. *Refer to Section 1-13.*

(1) Winter in London: **38°F**

(2) Summer in London: **22°C** since 22°C is $\left(22°C \times \dfrac{1.8°F}{1°C}\right) + 32°F = 72°F$

(3) Shaded part of moon: **40 K** since we know that should be very, very cold.

12-120. *Refer to Section 12-11.*

Plan: (1) Determine the partial pressure of acetic acid, CH_3COOH, and carbon dioxide, CO_2, in the mixture.
(2) Determine the moles of each gas in the mixture using the ideal gas law.
(3) Calculate the mass of each gas and the total mass of the sample.

(1) $P_{\text{acetic acid}} = 400.$ torr
$P_{\text{carbon dioxide}} = P_{\text{total}} - P_{\text{acetic acid}} = 760.$ torr $- 400.$ torr $= 360.$ torr

(2) n of acetic acid $= \dfrac{P_{\text{acetic acid}}V}{RT} = \dfrac{[(400./760.) \text{ atm}](0.500 \text{ L})}{(0.0821 \text{ L·atm/mol·K})(16.0°C + 273°)} = 0.0111$ mol CH_3COOH

n of carbon dioxide $= \dfrac{P_{\text{carbon dioxide}}V}{RT} = \dfrac{[(360./760.) \text{ atm}](0.500 \text{ L})}{(0.0821 \text{ L·atm/mol·K})(16.0°C + 273°)} = 0.00998$ mol CO_2

(3) ? g $CH_3COOH = 0.0111$ mol $CH_3COOH \times \dfrac{60.05 \text{ g } CH_3COOH}{1 \text{ mol } CH_3COOH} = 0.667$ g CH_3COOH

? g $CO_2 = 0.00998$ mol $CO_2 \times \dfrac{44.01 \text{ g } CO_2}{1 \text{ mol } CO_2} = 0.439$ g CO_2

The total mass of the sample $= 0.667$ g $CH_3COOH + 0.439$ g $CO_2 = \mathbf{1.106\ g}$

12-122. *Refer to Section 12-13 and Figure 12-12.*

Use your imagination in this drawing and have fun. You might make the gas cylinders narrower to accentuate the decrease in volume between the molecules. To show changes in kinetic energy, recall that as the kinetic energy of the gas molecules decrease with temperature, so does the molecules' average velocity. You could put comic strip-like lines off each molecule indicating the speed and direction the molecules are traveling - longer lines for molecules moving faster and shorter lines for the slower molecules, such as:

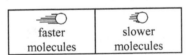

faster molecules	slower molecules

12-124. *Refer to Section 12-12.*

According to Gay-Lussac's Law, we can think directly in volumes instead of moles or molecules if the temperature and pressure are constant during a reaction.

(a) In the figure denoting the initial conditions, there are 6 reactant molecules in 2.5 L. After the reaction, the volume is only 1.25 L. Therefore, since the volume halved, the number of product molecules must have also halved. The only two answers involving 3 molecules are (i) and (ii). Answer (i) is wrong, because mass, i.e., the number of atoms before and after the reaction, was not conserved. Therefore, the answer must be **(ii)**.

(b) Balanced equation: $2AB_2(g) \rightarrow A_2B_4(g)$ where A are the pink atoms and B are the yellow atoms

12-126. *Refer to Sections 3-6 and 12-11.*

In Chapter 3, we discussed percent by mass as a concentration unit:

$$\% \text{ by mass} = \dfrac{\text{g solute}}{\text{g solution}} \times 100\%$$

We can similarly equate mole percent and mole fraction: mole percent = mole fraction $\times$ 100%

Plan: (1) Calculate the moles of Xe in one liter of air, assuming 25°C.
  (2) Calculate the atoms of Xe.

(1) $? \text{ mol Xe} = n = \dfrac{PV}{RT} = \dfrac{(8.7 \times 10^{-8} \text{ atm})(1.00 \text{ L})}{(0.0821 \text{ L·atm/mol·K})(25°C + 273°)} = 3.6 \times 10^{-9} \text{ mol Xe}$

(2) $? \text{ atoms Xe} = 3.6 \times 10^{-9} \text{ mol Xe} \times \dfrac{6.02 \times 10^{23} \text{ atoms Xe}}{1 \text{ mol Xe}} = \mathbf{2.1 \times 10^{15} \text{ atoms Xe}}$

12-130. *Refer to Section 12-13 and Figures 12-8 and 12-9.*

According to the Kinetic-Molecular Theory, all gas molecules have the same average kinetic energy ($= 1/2\, m\bar{u}^2$) at the same temperature. Therefore, lighter molecules will have higher average molecular speeds ($\bar{u}$), so the average speed of H_2 molecules will be faster than that of O_2 molecules at 25°C.

However, because of the Maxwellian distribution function for molecular speeds, not all H_2 molecules will be faster than all O_2 molecules and some H_2 molecules will have velocities near 0 m/s. Some O_2 molecules will be moving faster than the average speed of H_2 molecules.

12-132. *Refer to Sections 12-9 and 12-12.*

Since $PV = nRT$; $P = \dfrac{nRT}{V}$. Therefore, at constant T and V, $P \propto n$.

As a result, at constant T and V, pressure can be used to measure the relative amount of compounds.

Balanced equation: $2H_2(g) + O_2(g) \rightarrow 2H_2O(g)$

Compare the required ratio of reactants (using moles) to the available ratio of reactants using partial pressures to find the limiting reactant.

Required ratio $= \dfrac{2 \text{ moles H}_2}{1 \text{ mole O}_2} = 2.00$ Available ratio $= \dfrac{0.588 \text{ atm H}_2}{0.302 \text{ atm O}_2} = 1.95$

Available ratio < required ratio; $\mathbf{H_2}$ **is the limiting reactant.**

12-134. *Refer to Section 12-12.*

Balanced equations: $C(s) + O_2(g) \rightarrow CO_2(g)$
$CO_2(g) + 2NaOH(aq) \rightarrow Na_2CO_3(aq) + H_2O(\ell)$
$HCl(aq) + NaOH(aq) \rightarrow NaCl(aq) + H_2O(\ell)$

This is an example of the method of back titration, in which there is stoichiometrically more base, NaOH, present than is necessary to react with CO_2 dissolved in the water. One then titrates the excess NaOH with a standardized HCl solution and in a series of calculations, calculates the initial moles of CO_2. In this problem, the calculations are taken even further to determine the volume of O_2.

Plan: (1) Calculate the total moles of NaOH present.
  (2) Calculate the moles of NaOH in excess after the CO_2 was bubbled in, which are equal to the moles of HCl reacted.
  (3) Calculate the total moles of NaOH that reacted with CO_2 = (1) - (2).
  (4) Determine the moles of CO_2.
  (5) Determine the moles and volume of O_2 involved in the first equation.

(1) ? mol $NaOH_{total}$ = 0.437 M NaOH x 3.50 L = 1.53 mol NaOH

(2) ? mol $NaOH_{excess}$ = 1.71 L HCl soln x $\dfrac{0.350 \text{ mol HCl}}{1 \text{ L HCl}}$ x $\dfrac{1 \text{ mol NaOH}}{1 \text{ mol HCl}}$ = 0.598 mol NaOH

(3) ? mol $NaOH_{reacted}$ = 1.53 mol NaOH - 0.60 mol NaOH = 0.93 mol NaOH

(4) ? mol CO_2 = 0.93 mol NaOH x $\dfrac{1 \text{ mol } CO_2}{2 \text{ mol NaOH}}$ = 0.46 mol CO_2

(5) ? mol O_2 = 0.46 mol CO_2 x $\dfrac{1 \text{ mol } O_2}{1 \text{ mol } CO_2}$ = 0.46 mol O_2

   ? $V\,O_2 = \dfrac{nRT}{P} = \dfrac{[(0.46 \text{ mol } O_2)(0.0821 \text{ L·atm/mol·K})(20.°C + 273°)]}{8.6 \text{ atm}}$ = **1.3 L O_2**

12-136. *Refer to Section 12-12.*

Balanced equation: $Mg^{2+}(aq) + SiO_2(s,dispersed) + 2HCO_3^-(aq) \rightarrow MgSiO_3(s) + 2CO_2(g) + H_2O(\ell)$

Plan: $\overset{(1)}{\text{L } CO_2} \Rightarrow \overset{(2)}{\text{mol } CO_2} \Rightarrow \overset{(3)}{\text{mol } MgSiO_3} \Rightarrow \text{g } MgSiO_3$

(1) ? mol $CO_2 = n = \dfrac{PV}{RT} = \dfrac{[(775/760.) \text{ atm}](100. \text{ L})}{(0.0821 \text{ L·atm/mol·K})(30.°C + 273°)}$ = 4.10 mol CO_2

(2) ? mol $MgSiO_3$ = 4.10 mol CO_2 x (1 mol $MgSiO_3$/2 mol CO_2) = 2.05 mol $MgSiO_3$

(3) ? g $MgSiO_3$ = 2.05 mol $MgSiO_3$ x 100.4 g/mol = **206 g $MgSiO_3$**

12-138. *Refer to Section 12-12.*

(a) ? molarity SO_2 (mol/L) = $\dfrac{0.135 \text{ mg } SO_2}{1 \text{ L}}$ x $\dfrac{1 \text{ g}}{1000 \text{ mg}}$ x $\dfrac{1 \text{ mol } SO_2}{64.1 \text{ g } SO_2}$ = **2.11 x 10^{-6} M SO_2**

(b) (1) We must first determine the average FW of an air molecule. From Table 12-2, using the average composition of air, we can calculate:

FW_{air} = weighted average of the major gases' formula weights

   = (fractional composition of N_2)(FW N_2) + (fractional composition of O_2)(FW O_2)
      + (fractional composition of Ar)(FW Ar) + (fractional composition of CO_2)(FW CO_2)

   = (0.7809)(28.01 g/mol) + (0.2094)(32.00 g/mol) + (0.0093)(39.95 g/mol) + (0.0003)(44.0 g/mol)

   = 29.0 g/mol   (this is close to 29.2 g/mol given in Exercise 12-41)

(2) Using the density of the air, we can determine how many moles of air are present in 1 liter of air

   ? mol/L of air = $\dfrac{1 \text{ mol air}}{29.0 \text{ g air}}$ x $\dfrac{1.29 \text{ g air}}{1 \text{ L air}}$ = 0.0445 mol of air molecules per liter

(3) We can now calculate the mole fraction of SO_2 in one liter of air:

   ? mole fraction $SO_2 = \dfrac{\text{mol } SO_2}{\text{mol air} + \text{mol } SO_2} = \dfrac{2.11 \text{ x } 10^{-6} \text{ mol } SO_2}{0.0445 \text{ mol air} + 2.11 \text{ x } 10^{-6} \text{ mol } SO_2}$ = **4.74 x 10^{-5}**

15 Chemical Thermodynamics

15-2. *Refer to the Key Terms for Chapters 1 and 15.*

(a) Heat is a form of energy that flows between two samples of matter due to their differences in temperature.
(b) Temperature is a measure of the intensity of heat, i.e., the hotness or coldness of an object.
(c) The system refers to the substances of interest in a process, i.e., it is the part of the universe that is under investigation.
(d) The surroundings refer to everything in the environment of the system of interest.
(e) The thermodynamic state of a system refers to a set of conditions that completely specifies all of the thermodynamic properties of the system.
(f) Work is the application of a force through a distance. For physical or chemical changes that occur at constant pressure, the work done on the system is $-P\Delta V$.

15-4. *Refer to Sections 1-1, 15-1 and 15-10, and Figure 15-1.*

(a) When heat is given off by a system, that system is labeled an exothermic process. Figure 15-1 describes such a process: the combustion of 1 mole of methane at 25°C:

$$CH_4(g) + 2O_2(g) \rightarrow CO_2(g) + 2H_2O(\ell) + 890 \text{ kJ}$$

(b) In this example, the system's volume at constant pressure decreases since the system initially has 3 moles of gas, but produces only 1 mole of gas, since volume is directly proportional to moles of gas at constant temperature and pressure. When gas is consumed in a process (e.g. in this process: 3 moles gaseous reactants → 1 mole gaseous product), the surroundings are doing work on the system.

Note: When we look at the volume of a system, we generally consider only the gases, since the volume of 1 mole of gas is so much greater than the volume of 1 mole of a liquid or solid, which are much more dense.

15-6. *Refer to Sections 1-1 and 15-1.*

An endothermic process absorbs heat energy from its surroundings; an exothermic process releases heat energy to its surroundings. If a reaction is endothermic in one direction, it is exothermic in the opposite direction. For example, the melting of 1 mole of ice water is an endothermic process requiring 6.02 kJ of heat:

$$H_2O(s) + 6.02 \text{ kJ} \rightarrow H_2O(\ell)$$

The reverse process, the freezing of 1 mole of liquid water, releasing 6.02 kJ of heat, is an exothermic process:

$$H_2O(\ell) \rightarrow H_2O(s) + 6.02 \text{ kJ}$$

15-8. *Refer to Section 15-1.*

According to the First Law of Thermodynamics, the total amount of energy in the universe is constant. When an incandescent light is turned on, electrical energy is converted mainly into light and heat energy. A small fraction of the energy is converted to chemical energy, which is why the filament eventually burns out.

15-10. *Refer to Sections 1-7 and 15-2.*

A state function is a variable that defines the state of a system; it is a function that is independent of the pathway by which a process occurs. Therefore, the change in a state function depends only on the initial and the final value, not on how that change occurred.

(a) Your bank balance is a state function, because it depends only on the difference between your deposits and withdrawals.

(b) The mass of a candy bar is a state function, since it is a constant wherever you are.

(c) However, your weight is not a state function. Weight depends on the gravitational attraction of your body to the center of the earth, which changes depending on where you are on the earth.

(d) The heat lost by perspiration during a climb up a mountain along a fixed path is not a state function, because it depends on the person - her/his size, build, metabolism and degree of fitness.

15-12.   *Refer to Sections 15-5, 15-6 and 15-17.*

(a) ΔH, the enthalpy change or heat of reaction, is the heat change of a reaction occurring at some constant pressure and temperature.

ΔH° is the standard enthalpy change of a reaction that occurs at 1 atm pressure. Unless otherwise stated, the reaction temperature is 25°C.

(b) As stated in (a), ΔH°_{rxn} is the standard enthalpy change of a reaction occurring at 1 atm pressure.

ΔH°_f, the standard molar enthalpy of formation of a substance, is the enthalpy change for a reaction in which 1 mole of the substance in a specific state is formed from its elements in their standard states.

15-14.   *Refer to Sections 15-4 and 15-5.*

(i) Since the reaction is endothermic, (a) enthalpy increases, (b) $H_{product} > H_{reactant}$ and (c) ΔH is positive.

(ii) Since the reaction is exothermic, (a) enthalpy decreases, (b) $H_{reactant} > H_{product}$ and (c) ΔH is negative.

15-16.   *Refer to Section 15-5 and Example 15-5.*

Balanced equation: $CH_3OH(g) + \frac{3}{2}O_2(g) \rightarrow CO_2(g) + 2H_2O(\ell)$ $\qquad\qquad$ $\Delta H_{rxn} = -764$ kJ/mol

(a) Plan: heat evolved/mol rxn $\overset{(1)}{\Rightarrow}$ heat evolved/mol CH_3OH $\overset{(2)}{\Rightarrow}$ heat evolved/g CH_3OH $\overset{(3)}{\Rightarrow}$ heat evolved

? heat evolved (kJ) $= \dfrac{764 \text{ kJ}}{\text{mol rxn}} \times \dfrac{1 \text{ mol rxn}}{1 \text{ mol } CH_3OH} \times \dfrac{1 \text{ mol } CH_3OH}{32.0 \text{ g } CH_3OH} \times 115.0 \text{ g } CH_3OH = \textbf{2750 kJ evolved}$

(b) Plan: heat evolved $\overset{(1)}{\Rightarrow}$ mol reaction $\overset{(2)}{\Rightarrow}$ mol O_2 $\overset{(3)}{\Rightarrow}$ g O_2

? g O_2 = 925 kJ $\times \dfrac{1 \text{ mol rxn}}{764 \text{ kJ}} \times \dfrac{1.5 \text{ mol } O_2}{1 \text{ mol rxn}} \times \dfrac{32.0 \text{ g } O_2}{1 \text{ mol } O_2} = \textbf{58.1 g } O_2$

15-18.   *Refer to Section 15-5 and Example 15-5.*

Balanced equation: $PbO(s) + C(s) \rightarrow Pb(s) + CO(g)$

Since the equation involves one mole of PbO, ΔH can be expressed in the units of kJ/mol PbO.

? heat supplied to the reaction $= \dfrac{5.95 \text{ kJ}}{13.43 \text{ g PbO}} \times \dfrac{223.2 \text{ g PbO}}{1 \text{ mol PbO}} = 98.9$ kJ/mol PbO

Therefore, since the heat is being added to the reaction, $\Delta H = \textbf{+98.9 kJ/mol rxn}$

15-20.   *Refer to Section 15-3 and Appendix K.*

The standard molar enthalpy of formation, ΔH°_f, is the amount of heat absorbed when 1 mole of the substance is produced from its elements in their standard states. At 25°C, ΔH°_f of liquid water is −285.8 kJ/mol and ΔH°_f of water vapor is −241.8 kJ/mol. This means that more heat is released when liquid water is formed from its elements, then when gaseous water is formed from its elements. So, the formation reaction of liquid water is more exothermic, which means that $H_2O(\ell)$ has a lower enthalpy than $H_2O(g)$. See the solution to Exercise 15-22.

15-22. *Refer to Sections 15-1 and 15-5.*

Consider the balanced reactions: (1) $CH_4(g) + 2O_2(g) \rightarrow CO_2(g) + 2H_2O(\ell)$ $\Delta H_1 = (-)$

(2) $CH_4(g) + 2O_2(g) \rightarrow CO_2(g) + 2H_2O(g)$ $\Delta H_2 = (-)$

The only difference between them is that Reaction (1) involves water in the liquid phase and Reaction (2) involves water as water vapor. Since more heat is released when $H_2O(g) \rightarrow H_2O(\ell)$, as shown in the adjacent diagram, Reaction (1) is more exothermic than Reaction (2).

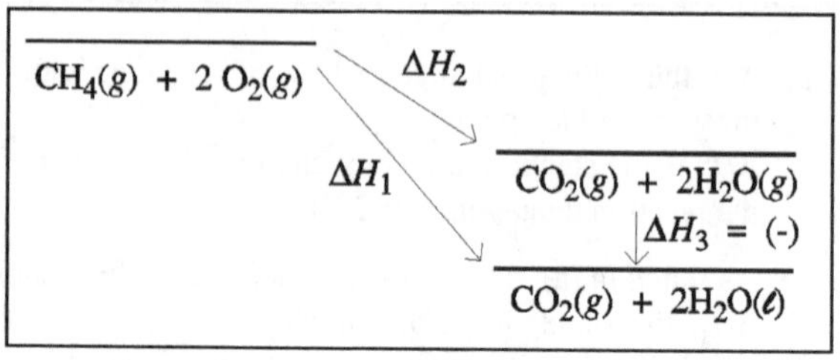

15-24. *Refer to Section 15-6 and the Key Terms for Chapter 15.*

The thermodynamic standard state of a substance is its most stable state under standard pressure (1 atm) and at some specific temperature (usually 25°C). "Thermodynamic" refers to the observation, measurement and prediction of energy changes that accompany physical changes or chemical reaction. "Standard" refers to the set conditions of 1 atm pressure and 25°C. The "state" of a substance is its phase: gas, liquid or solid. "Substance" is any kind of matter all specimens of which have the same chemical composition and physical properties.

15-26. *Refer to Section 15-7 and Appendix K.*

The standard molar enthalpy of formation, ΔH_f°, of elements in their standard states is zero. From the tabulated values of standard molar enthalpies in Appendix K, we can identify the standard states of elements.

(a) chlorine $Cl_2(g)$

(b) chromium $Cr(s)$

(c) bromine $Br_2(\ell)$

(d) iodine $I_2(s)$

(e) sulfur $S(s, \text{rhombic})$

(f) nitrogen $N_2(g)$

15-28. *Refer to Section 15-7, Example 15-6 and Appendix K.*

Hint: Use Appendix K to identify an element's standard state since its ΔH_f° value is equal to zero.

(a) $Ca(s) + O_2(g) + H_2(g) \rightarrow Ca(OH)_2(s)$

(b) $6C(s, \text{graphite}) + 3H_2(g) \rightarrow C_6H_6(\ell)$

(c) $Na(s) + \frac{1}{2}H_2(g) + C(s,\text{graphite}) + \frac{3}{2}O_2(g) \rightarrow NaHCO_3(s)$

(d) $Ca(s) + F_2(g) \rightarrow CaF_2(s)$

(e) $\frac{1}{4}P_4(s,\text{white}) + \frac{3}{2}H_2(g) \rightarrow PH_3(g)$

(f) $3C(s,\text{graphite}) + 4H_2(g) \rightarrow C_3H_8(g)$

(g) $S(s,\text{rhombic}) \rightarrow S(g)$

(h) $H_2(g) + \frac{1}{2}O_2(g) \rightarrow H_2O(\ell)$

15-30. *Refer to Section 15-5.*

The balanced equation for the standard molar enthalpy of formation of $Li_2O(s)$ is: $2Li(s) + \frac{1}{2}O_2(g) \rightarrow Li_2O(s)$

$? \text{ kJ/mol } Li_2O(s) = \dfrac{146 \text{ kJ}}{3.47 \text{ g Li}} \times \dfrac{6.94 \text{ g Li}}{1 \text{ mol Li}} \times \dfrac{2 \text{ mol Li}}{1 \text{ mol } Li_2O} = 584 \text{ kJ/mol}$

And so, $\Delta H^\circ_{f\ Li_2O(s)} = \textbf{–584 kJ/mol}$ since the reaction is exothermic.

15-32. *Refer to Section 15-8 and Examples 15-7 and 15-8.*

To obtain the desired equation,
(1) divide the first equation by 2 to give 2 moles of HCl on the reactant side,
(2) multiply the second equation by 2, giving 2 moles of HF on the product side. Then,
(3) reverse the third equation, so that H_2O, H_2 and $\frac{1}{2}O_2$ are eliminated when the modified equations are added together.

$$\begin{array}{ll} & \Delta H^\circ \\ 2HCl(g) + \frac{1}{2}O_2(g) \rightarrow H_2O(\ell) + Cl_2(g) & -101.2 \text{ kJ/mol rxn} \\ H_2(g) + F_2(g) \rightarrow 2HF(\ell) & -1200.0 \text{ kJ/mol rxn} \\ H_2O(\ell) \rightarrow H_2(g) + \frac{1}{2}O_2(g) & +285.8 \text{ kJ/mol rxn} \\ \hline 2HCl(g) + F_2(g) \rightarrow 2HF(\ell) + Cl_2(g) & \textbf{–1015.4 kJ/mol rxn} \end{array}$$

15-34. *Refer to Section 15-8 and Examples 15-7 and 15-8.*

To obtain the desired equation,
(1) multiply the first equation by 2 to give 2 moles of SO_2 on the product side, then
(2) reverse the second equation and multiply by 2, giving 2 moles of SO_3 on the reactant side.

$$\begin{array}{ll} & \Delta H^\circ \\ 2S(s) + 2O_2(g) \rightarrow 2SO_2(g) & -593.6 \text{ kJ/mol rxn} \\ 2SO_3(g) \rightarrow 2S(s) + 3O_2(g) & +791.2 \text{ kJ/mol rxn} \\ \hline 2SO_3(g) \rightarrow 2SO_2(g) + O_2(g) & \textbf{+197.6 kJ/mol rxn} \end{array}$$

15-36. *Refer to Section 15-8 and Examples 15-7 and 15-8.*

To obtain the desired hydrogenation equation,
(1) use the first equation as it is to give 2 moles of H_2 on the reactant side,
(2) use the second equation as it is to give 1 mole of C_3H_4 on the reactant side, then
(3) reverse the third equation to give 1 mole of C_3H_8 on the product side.

$$\begin{array}{ll} & \Delta H^\circ \\ 2H_2(g) + O_2(g) \rightarrow 2H_2O(\ell) & -571.6 \text{ kJ/mol rxn} \\ C_3H_4(g) + 4O_2(g) \rightarrow 3\,CO_2(g) + 2H_2O(\ell) & -1937 \text{ kJ/mol rxn} \\ 3CO_2(g) + 4H_2O(\ell) \rightarrow C_3H_8(g) + 5O_2(g) & +2220.\text{ kJ/mol rxn} \\ \hline C_3H_4(g) + 2H_2(g) \rightarrow C_3H_8(g) & \textbf{–289 kJ/mol rxn} \end{array}$$

15-38. *Refer to Section 15-8, Example 15-9 and Appendix K.*

(a) Balanced equation: $NH_4NO_3(s) \rightarrow N_2O(g) + 2H_2O(\ell)$

$\Delta H^\circ_{rxn} = [\Delta H^\circ_{f\ N_2O(g)} + 2\Delta H^\circ_{f\ H_2O(\ell)}] - [\Delta H^\circ_{f\ NH_4NO_3(s)}]$
$= [(1\ mol)(82.05\ kJ/mol) + (2\ mol)(-285.8\ kJ/mol)] - [(1\ mol)(-365.6\ kJ/mol)]$
$= \mathbf{-124.0\ kJ/mol\ rxn}$

(b) Balanced equation: $2FeS_2(s) + \frac{11}{2}O_2(g) \rightarrow Fe_2O_3(s) + 4SO_2(g)$

$\Delta H^\circ_{rxn} = [\Delta H^\circ_{f\ Fe_2O_3(s)} + 4\Delta H^\circ_{f\ SO_2(g)}] - [2\Delta H^\circ_{f\ FeS_2(s)} + \frac{11}{2}\Delta H^\circ_{f\ O_2(g)}]$
$= [(1\ mol)(-824.2\ kJ/mol) + (4\ mol)(-296.8\ kJ/mol)] - [(2\ mol)(-177.5\ kJ/mol) + (\frac{11}{2}mol)(0\ kJ/mol)]$
$= \mathbf{-1656\ kJ/mol\ rxn}$

(c) Balanced equation: $SiO_2(s) + 3C(s,graphite) \rightarrow SiC(s) + 2CO(g)$

$\Delta H^\circ_{rxn} = [\Delta H^\circ_{f\ SiC(s)} + 2\Delta H^\circ_{f\ CO(g)}] - [\Delta H^\circ_{f\ SiO_2(s)} + 3\Delta H^\circ_{f\ C(s,graphite)}]$
$= [(1\ mol)(-65.3\ kJ/mol) + (2\ mol)(-110.5\ kJ/mol)] - [(1\ mol)(-910.9\ kJ/mol) + (3\ mol)(0\ kJ/mol)]$
$= \mathbf{+624.6\ kJ/mol\ rxn}$

15-40. *Refer to Section 15-5 and Examples 15-4 and 15-5.*

(1) Balanced equation for combustion of propane: $C_3H_8(g) + 5O_2(g) \rightarrow 3CO_2(g) + 4H_2O(g)$

$\Delta H^\circ_{combustion} = [3\Delta H^\circ_{f\ CO_2(g)} + 4\Delta H^\circ_{f\ H_2O(g)}] - [\Delta H^\circ_{f\ C_3H_8(g)} + 5\Delta H^\circ_{f\ O_2(g)}]$
$= [(3\ mol)(-393.5\ kJ/mol) + (4\ mol)(-241.8\ kJ/mol)]$
$\qquad\qquad - [(1\ mol)(-103.8\ kJ/mol) + (5\ mol)(0\ kJ/mol)]$
$= -2043.9\ kJ/mol\ C_3H_8$

heat released (kJ/g) $= \dfrac{2043.9\ kJ}{1\ mol\ C_3H_8} \times \dfrac{1\ mol\ C_3H_8}{44.09\ g\ C_3H_8} = \mathbf{46.36\ kJ/g\ C_3H_8}$

(2) Balanced equation for combustion of octane: $C_8H_{18}(\ell) + \frac{25}{2}O_2(g) \rightarrow 8CO_2(g) + 9H_2O(g)$

$\Delta H^\circ_{combustion} = [8\Delta H^\circ_{f\ CO_2(g)} + 9\Delta H^\circ_{f\ H_2O(g)}] - [\Delta H^\circ_{f\ C_8H_{18}(\ell)} + \frac{25}{2}\Delta H^\circ_{f\ O_2(g)}]$
$= [(8\ mol)(-393.5\ kJ/mol) + (9\ mol)(-241.8\ kJ/mol)]$
$\qquad\qquad - [(1\ mol)(-268.8\ kJ/mol) + (\frac{25}{2}mol)(0\ kJ/mol)]$
$= -5055.4\ kJ/mol\ C_8H_{18}$

heat released (kJ/g) $= \dfrac{5055.4\ kJ}{1\ mol\ C_8H_{18}} \times \dfrac{1\ mol\ C_8H_{18}}{114.2\ g\ C_8H_{18}} = \mathbf{44.27\ kJ/g\ C_8H_{18}}$

Note: The sign convention for ΔH° tells the reader whether heat is being released or absorbed. However, when the question asks for "heat released" or "heat absorbed," the value of heat is a positive number. When the words "released" or "absorbed" are used, the sign convention is *not* used.

15-42. *Refer to Section 15-5 and Example 15-4.*

Balanced equation: $8Al(s) + 3Fe_3O_4(s) \rightarrow 4Al_2O_3(s) + 9Fe(s)$ $\qquad\qquad \Delta H^\circ = -3350.\ kJ/mol\ rxn$

Plan: (1) Determine the limiting reactant.
(2) Calculate the heat released based on the limiting reactant.

(1) $? \text{ mol Al} = \dfrac{27.6 \text{ g Al}}{27.0 \text{ g/mol}} = 1.02 \text{ mol Al}$ $\qquad ? \text{ mol Fe}_3\text{O}_4 = \dfrac{69.12 \text{ g Fe}_3\text{O}_4}{231.6 \text{ g/mol}} = 0.2984 \text{ mol Fe}_3\text{O}_4$

$\text{Required ratio} = \dfrac{8 \text{ mol Al}}{3 \text{ mol Fe}_3\text{O}_4} = 2.67$ $\qquad \text{Available ratio} = \dfrac{1.02 \text{ mol Al}}{0.2984 \text{ mol Fe}_3\text{O}_4} = 3.42$

Available ratio > Required ratio; Fe_3O_4 is the limiting reactant.

(2) $\Delta H° = 69.12 \text{ g Fe}_3\text{O}_4 \times \dfrac{1 \text{ mol Fe}_3\text{O}_4}{231.6 \text{ g Fe}_3\text{O}_4} \times \dfrac{-3350. \text{ kJ}}{3 \text{ mol Fe}_3\text{O}_4} = -333.3 \text{ kJ}$

Therefore, there are **+333 kJ** of heat released.

Note: The sign convention for $\Delta H°$ tells the reader whether heat is being released or absorbed. However, when the question asks for "heat released" or "heat absorbed," the value of heat is a positive number. When the words "released" or "absorbed" are used, the sign convention is *not* used.

15-44. *Refer to Section 15-9, Tables 15-2 and 15-3, and Examples 15-11 and 15-12.*

Balanced equations: oxidation of sucrose: $\qquad C_{12}H_{22}O_{11}(s) + 12O_2\,(g) \;\rightarrow\; 12CO_2(g) + 11H_2O(g)$

oxidation of tristearin: $\qquad C_{57}H_{110}O_6(s) + 163/2\;O_2\,(g) \;\rightarrow\; 57CO_2(g) + 55H_2O(g)$

Sucrose, $C_{12}H_{22}O_{11}$ contains 10 C-C bonds, 14 C-O bonds, 14 C-H bonds and 8 O-H bonds
Tristearin, $C_{57}H_{110}O_6$ contains 53 C-C bonds, 6 C-O bonds, 3 C=O bonds and 110 C-H bonds

Oxidation of 1 mol sucrose:

$\Delta H°_{\text{rxn}} = \Sigma \text{ B.E.}_{\text{reactants}} - \Sigma \text{ B.E.}_{\text{products}}$
$= [10\text{B.E.}_{\text{C-C}} + 14\text{B.E.}_{\text{C-O}} + 14\text{B.E.}_{\text{C-H}} + 8\text{B.E.}_{\text{O-H}} + 12\text{B.E.}_{\text{O=O}}] - [24\text{B.E.}_{\text{C=O}} + 22\text{B.E.}_{\text{O-H}}]$
$= [(10 \text{ mol})(346 \text{ kJ/mol}) + (14 \text{ mol})(358 \text{ kJ/mol}) + (14 \text{ mol})(413 \text{ kJ/mol}) + (8 \text{ mol})(463 \text{ kJ/mol})$
$\qquad + (12 \text{ mol})(498 \text{ kJ/mol})]$
$\qquad - [(24 \text{ mol})(799 \text{ kJ/mol})^* + (22 \text{ mol})(463 \text{ kJ/mol})]$
$= 23930 \text{ kJ} - 29360 \text{ kJ}$
$= \mathbf{-5430 \text{ kJ/mol sucrose}}$
$= \dfrac{-5430 \text{ kJ}}{1 \text{ mol sucrose}} \times \dfrac{1 \text{ mol}}{342.3 \text{ g}} = \mathbf{-15.9 \text{ kJ/g sucrose}}$
$= \dfrac{-5430 \text{ kJ}}{1 \text{ mol sucrose}} \times \dfrac{1 \text{ mol}}{342.3 \text{ g}} \times \dfrac{1 \text{ kcal}}{4.184 \text{ kJ}} = \mathbf{-3.79 \text{ kcal/g sucrose}}$

Oxidation of 1 mol tristearin:

$\Delta H°_{\text{rxn}} = \Sigma \text{ B.E.}_{\text{reactants}} - \Sigma \text{ B.E.}_{\text{products}}$
$= [53\text{B.E.}_{\text{C-C}} + 6\text{B.E.}_{\text{C-O}} + 110\text{B.E.}_{\text{C-H}} + 3\text{B.E.}_{\text{C=O}} + 163/2\text{B.E.}_{\text{O=O}}] - [114\text{B.E.}_{\text{C=O}} + 110\text{B.E.}_{\text{O-H}}]$
$= [(53 \text{ mol})(346 \text{ kJ/mol}) + (6 \text{ mol})(358 \text{ kJ/mol}) + (110 \text{ mol})(413 \text{ kJ/mol}) + (3 \text{ mol})(732 \text{ kJ/mol})$
$\qquad + (163/2 \text{ mol})(498 \text{ kJ/mol})]$
$\qquad - [(114 \text{ mol})(799 \text{ kJ/mol})^* + (110 \text{ mol})(463 \text{ kJ/mol})]$
$= 68100 \text{ kJ} - 71000 \text{ kJ}$
$= \mathbf{-2900 \text{ kJ/mol tristearin}}$
$= \dfrac{-2900 \text{ kJ}}{1 \text{ mol sucrose}} \times \dfrac{1 \text{ mol}}{891.5 \text{ g}} = \mathbf{-3.3 \text{ kJ/g tristearin}}$
$= \dfrac{-2900 \text{ kJ}}{1 \text{ mol sucrose}} \times \dfrac{1 \text{ mol}}{891.5 \text{ g}} \times \dfrac{1 \text{ kcal}}{4.184 \text{ kJ}} = \mathbf{-0.78 \text{ kcal/g tristearin}}$

Sucrose has the greater energy density, meaning that for 1 g of compound, more energy is released when sucrose is oxidized than when tristearin is oxidized.

* See extra information for the C=O bond in Table 15-3. C=O has different bond energies in CO_2 than in other compounds.

(a) For a reaction occurring in the gaseous phase, the net enthalpy change, ΔH°_{rxn}, equals the sum of the bond energies in the reactants minus the sum of the bond energies in the products:

$$\Delta H^\circ_{rxn} = \Sigma \text{ B.E.}_{reactants} - \Sigma \text{ B.E.}_{products}$$

If the products have higher bond energy and are therefore more stable than the reactants, the reaction is exothermic. If the opposite is true, the reaction is endothermic.

(b) Consider $O_2(g)$: $\quad \Delta H^\circ_{f\ O_2(g)} = 0$ kJ/mol since the standard state of oxygen is $O_2(g)$

$$-\Sigma \text{ B.E.}_{O_2(g)} = -\text{B.E.}_{O=O} = -498 \text{ kJ/mol}$$

Therefore, one cannot say that $\Delta H^\circ_{f\ substance} = -\Sigma \text{ B.E.}_{substance}$. Bond energies are a measure of the energy involved in breaking of one mole of bonds in a gaseous substance to form gaseous atoms of the elements. The value of ΔH°_f is a measure of the energy involved in making one mole of the substance from its elements in their standard states. They differ in two major aspects: (1) In bond energy considerations, all the bonds are broken to give free atoms, while in ΔH°_f determinations, some bonds may still be maintained as diatomic or polyatomic free elements (e.g., $O_2(g)$ or $P_4(s)$). (2) The standard states of the elements are not necessarily the gaseous state. Moreover, the ΔH°_f equation is an exact calculation, but the bond energy equation is only an estimation of ΔH°_f because bond energies are average values from many different compounds.

(a) Balanced equation in terms of Lewis structures of the reactants and products:

ΔH°_{rxn} $= \Sigma \text{ B.E.}_{reactants} - \Sigma \text{ B.E.}_{products}$ $\quad$ in the gas phase

$\quad = [\text{B.E.}_{C=C} + 4\text{B.E.}_{C-H} + \text{B.E.}_{Br-Br}] - [\text{B.E.}_{C-C} + 4\text{B.E.}_{C-H} + 2\text{B.E.}_{C-Br}]$

$\quad = [(1 \text{ mol})(602 \text{ kJ/mol}) + (4 \text{ mol})(413 \text{ kJ/mol}) + (1 \text{ mol})(193 \text{ kJ/mol})]$

$\qquad - [(1 \text{ mol})(346 \text{ kJ/mol}) + (4 \text{ mol})(413 \text{ kJ/mol}) + (2 \text{ mol})(285 \text{ kJ/mol})]$

$\quad = \mathbf{-121 \text{ kJ/mol rxn}}$

(b) Balanced equation in terms of Lewis structures of the reactants and products:

$\Delta H^\circ_{rxn} = \Sigma \text{ B.E.}_{reactants} - \Sigma \text{ B.E.}_{products}$ $\quad$ in the gas phase

$\quad = [2\text{B.E.}_{O-H} + \text{B.E.}_{O-O}] - [2\text{B.E.}_{O-H} + 1/2 \text{ B.E.}_{O=O}]$

$\quad = [(2 \text{ mol})(463 \text{ kJ/mol}) + (1 \text{ mol})(146 \text{ kJ/mol})] - [(2 \text{ mol})(463 \text{ kJ/mol}) + (1/2 \text{ mol})(498 \text{ kJ/mol})]$

$\quad = \mathbf{-103 \text{ kJ/mol rxn}}$

Balanced equation: $CCl_2F_2(g) + F_2(g) \rightarrow CF_4(g) + Cl_2(g)$

$\Delta H^\circ_{rxn} = \Sigma \text{ B.E.}_{reactants} - \Sigma \text{ B.E.}_{products}$ $\quad$ in the gas phase

$\quad = [2\text{B.E.}_{C-Cl} + 2\text{B.E.}_{C-F} + \text{B.E.}_{F-F}] - [4\text{B.E.}_{C-F} + \text{B.E.}_{Cl-Cl}]$

$\quad = [(2 \text{ mol})(339 \text{ kJ/mol}) + (2 \text{ mol})(485 \text{ kJ/mol}) + (1 \text{ mol})(155 \text{ kJ/mol})]$

$\qquad\qquad - [(4 \text{ mol})(485 \text{ kJ/mol}) + (1 \text{ mol})(242 \text{ kJ/mol})]$

$\quad = \mathbf{-379 \text{ kJ/mol rxn}}$

(1) Balanced equation for standard heat of formation of HCl: $\frac{1}{2} H_2(g) + \frac{1}{2} Cl_2(g) \rightarrow HCl(g)$

$\Delta H^\circ_{rxn} = \Sigma$ B.E.$_{reactants} - \Sigma$ B.E.$_{products}$ in the gas phase

$\quad\quad = [\frac{1}{2}$ B.E.$_{H-H} + \frac{1}{2}$ B.E.$_{Cl-Cl}$] - [B.E.$_{H-Cl}$]

$\quad\quad = [(0.5 \text{ mol})(436 \text{ kJ/mol}) + (0.5 \text{ mol})(242 \text{ kJ/mol})] - [(1 \text{ mol})(432 \text{ kJ/mol})]$

$\quad\quad = $ **−93 kJ/mol HCl**

For HCl(g), $\Delta H^\circ_f = -92.31$ kJ/mol

(2) Balanced equation for standard heat of formation of HF: $\frac{1}{2} H_2(g) + \frac{1}{2} F_2(g) \rightarrow HF(g)$

$\Delta H^\circ_{rxn} = \Sigma$ B.E.$_{reactants} - \Sigma$ B.E.$_{products}$ in the gas phase

$\quad\quad = [\frac{1}{2}$ B.E.$_{H-H} + \frac{1}{2}$ B.E.$_{F-F}$] - [B.E.$_{H-F}$]

$\quad\quad = [(0.5 \text{ mol})(436 \text{ kJ/mol}) + (0.5 \text{ mol})(155 \text{ kJ/mol})] - [(1 \text{ mol})(565 \text{ kJ/mol})]$

$\quad\quad = $ **−270 kJ/mol HF**

For HF(g), $\Delta H^\circ_f = -271$ kJ/mol

The ΔH°_{rxn} of this reaction: $PCl_3(g) \rightarrow P(g) + 3Cl(g)$ is equal to 3 times the average P-Cl bond energy in $PCl_3(g)$ since this reaction involves the breaking of 3 P-Cl bonds.

$\Delta H^\circ_{rxn} = [\Delta H^\circ_f\ _{P(g)} + 3\Delta H^\circ_f\ _{Cl(g)}] - [\Delta H^\circ_f\ _{PCl_3(g)}]$

$\quad\quad = [(1 \text{ mol})(314.6 \text{ kJ/mol}) + (3 \text{ mol})(121.7 \text{ kJ/mol})] - [(1 \text{ mol})(-306.4 \text{ kJ/mol})]$

$\quad\quad = 986$ kJ/mol rxn

Therefore, the average bond energy of an P-Cl bond in $PCl_3(g)$ is (986/3) kJ or **329 kJ**.

The ΔH°_{rxn} of the reaction: $PCl_5(g) \rightarrow P(g) + 5Cl(g)$
is equal to 5 times the average P-Cl bond energy in PCl_5, since this reaction involves the breaking of 5 P-Cl bonds.

$\Delta H^\circ_{rxn} = [\Delta H^\circ_f\ _{P(g)} + 5\Delta H^\circ_f\ _{Cl(g)}] - [\Delta H^\circ_f\ _{PCl_5(g)}]$

$\quad\quad = [(1 \text{ mol})(314.6 \text{ kJ/mol}) + (5 \text{ mol})(121.7 \text{ kJ/mol})] - [(1 \text{ mol})(-398.9 \text{ kJ/mol})]$

$\quad\quad = 1322$ kJ/mol rxn

Therefore, the average bond energy of a P-Cl bond in $PCl_5(g)$ is (1322/5) kJ or **264 kJ**.

It takes less energy to break an average P-Cl bond in PCl_5 than one in PCl_3 because P is a relatively small atom and Cl is relatively large. It is more difficult to squeeze 5 atoms of Cl around a P than 3 atoms of Cl. Therefore, those 5 atoms of Cl in PCl_5 are not held as tightly and have weaker P-Cl bonds.

$\Delta H^\circ_{rxn} = [5$B.E.$_{C-H} + $B.E.$_{C-C} + $B.E.$_{C-N} + 2$B.E.$_{N-H}] - [4$B.E.$_{C-H} + $B.E.$_{C=C} + 3$B.E.$_{N-H}]$

Substituting,

$53.6 \text{ kJ} = [(5 \text{ mol})(413 \text{ kJ/mol}) + (1 \text{ mol})(346 \text{ kJ/mol}) + (1 \text{ mol})(B.E._{C-N}) + (2 \text{ mol})(391 \text{ kJ/mol})]$
$\quad\quad\quad\quad - [(4 \text{ mol})(413 \text{ kJ/mol}) + (1 \text{ mol})(602 \text{ kJ/mol}) + (3 \text{ mol})(391 \text{ kJ/mol})]$

$53.6 \text{ kJ} = (1 \text{ mol})(B.E._{C-N}) - 234 \text{ kJ}$

B.E.$_{C-N} = $ **288 kJ/mol**

Table 15-2 gives the bond energy for an average C-N bond as 305 kJ/mol.

Plan: (1) Determine the heat gained by the calorimeter.
(2) Find the heat capacity of the calorimeter (calorimeter constant).

(1)
$$|\text{heat lost}|_{\text{iron}} = |\text{heat gained}|_{\text{water}} + |\text{heat gained}|_{\text{calorimeter}}$$
$$|\text{specific heat} \times \text{mass} \times \Delta t|_{\text{iron}} = |\text{specific heat} \times \text{mass} \times \Delta t|_{\text{water}} + |\text{heat gained}|_{\text{calorimeter}}$$

$(0.444 \text{ J/g·°C})(93.3 \text{ g})(65.58°C - 19.68°C) = (4.184 \text{ J/g·°C})(75.0 \text{ g})(19.68°C - 16.95°C) + |\text{heat gained}|_{\text{calorimeter}}$

$$1.90 \times 10^3 \text{ J} = 8.57 \times 10^2 \text{ J} + |\text{heat gained}|_{\text{calorimeter}}$$

Therefore, $|\text{heat gained}|_{\text{calorimeter}} = 1.90 \times 10^3 \text{ J} - 857 \text{ J} = 1.04 \times 10^3 \text{ J}$

(2) heat capacity of calorimeter (J/°C) $= \dfrac{|\text{heat gained}|_{\text{calorimeter}}}{\Delta T} = \dfrac{1.04 \times 10^3 \text{ J}}{19.68°C - 16.95°C} = \textbf{381 J/°C}$

$$|\text{heat lost}|_{\text{metal}} = |\text{heat gained}|_{\text{water}} + |\text{heat gained}|_{\text{calorimeter}}$$
$$|\text{specific heat} \times \text{mass} \times \Delta t|_{\text{metal}} = |\text{specific heat} \times \text{mass} \times \Delta t|_{\text{water}} + |\text{calorimeter constant} \times \Delta t|_{\text{cal}}$$

$(\text{Sp. Ht.})(36.5 \text{ g})(100.0°C - 32.5°C) = (4.184 \text{ J/g·°C})(50.0 \text{ mL} \times 0.997 \text{ g/mL})(32.5°C - 25.0°C)$
$$+ (1.87 \text{ J/°C})(32.5°C - 25.0°C)$$
$$(\text{Sp. Ht.})(2.46 \times 10^3 \text{ J}) = 1.6 \times 10^3 \text{ J} + 14 \text{ J}$$
Specific heat of the metal $= \textbf{0.66 J/g·°C}$

Balanced equation: $Pb(NO_3)_2(aq) + 2NaI(aq) \rightarrow PbI_2(s) + 2NaNO_3(aq)$

(a) $|\text{heat released}| = |\text{heat gained}|_{\text{soln}} + |\text{heat gained}|_{\text{calorimeter}}$
$\qquad = |\text{specific heat} \times \text{mass} \times \Delta t|_{\text{soln}} + |\text{heat capacity} \times \Delta t|_{\text{calorimeter}}$
$\qquad = (4.184 \text{ J/g·°C})(200. \text{ g})(24.2°C - 22.6°C)$
$\qquad\qquad + (472 \text{ J/°C})(24.2°C - 22.6°C)$
$\qquad = 1.3 \times 10^3 \text{ J} + 7.6 \times 10^2 \text{ J}$
$\qquad = \textbf{2.1} \times \textbf{10}^3 \textbf{ J}$

(b) This is a possible limiting reactant problem because amounts of both reactants are given. In this case, we are given stoichiometric amounts of both reactants.

$\text{mol Pb(NO}_3)_2 = \dfrac{6.62 \text{ g}}{331 \text{g/mol}} = 0.0200 \text{ mol}$

$\text{mol NaI} = \dfrac{6.00 \text{ g}}{149.9 \text{g/mol}} = 0.0400 \text{ mol}$

$\Delta H_{\text{rxn}} = \dfrac{-2.1 \times 10^3 \text{ J}}{0.0200 \text{ mol Pb(NO}_3)_2} \times \dfrac{1 \text{ mol Pb(NO}_3)_2}{1 \text{ mol rxn}} = \textbf{--1.0} \times \textbf{10}^5 \textbf{ J/mol rxn or --1.0} \times \textbf{10}^2 \textbf{ kJ/mol rxn}$

(a) $2C_6H_6(\ell) + 15 O_2(g) \rightarrow 12CO_2(g) + 6H_2O(\ell)$

(b) |heat released| = |heat gained|$_{water}$ + |heat gained|$_{calorimeter}$

= |specific heat $\times$ mass $\times \Delta t$|$_{water}$ + |heat capacity $\times \Delta t$|$_{calorimeter}$

= (4.184 J/g·°C)(945 g)(32.692°C - 23.640°C) + (891 J/°C)(32.692°C - 23.640°C)

= 3.58 $\times$ 10^4 J + 8.07 $\times$ 10^3 J

= 4.39 $\times$ 10^4 J or 43.9 kJ

Since heat is released in this reaction (the temperature of the water increased), ΔE is a negative quantity.

$$\Delta E = -\frac{43.9 \text{ kJ}}{1.048 \text{ g } C_6H_6(\ell)} = \textbf{--41.9 kJ/g } \mathbf{C_6H_6}(\ell)$$

$$\Delta E = -\frac{43.9 \text{ kJ}}{1.048 \text{ g } C_6H_6(\ell)} \times \frac{78.11 \text{ g}}{1 \text{ mol}} = \textbf{--3270 kJ/mol } \mathbf{C_6H_6}(\ell) \qquad \text{(to 3 significant figures)}$$

15-68. *Refer to Sections 15-4 and 15-5, Examples 15-2, 15-3 and 15-4, and Exercise 1-60 Solution.*

Balanced equation: Mg(s) + 2HCl(aq) $\rightarrow$ MgCl$_2$(aq) + H$_2$(g)

(1) |heat released| = |heat gained|$_{soln}$ + |heat gained|$_{calorimeter}$

= |specific heat $\times$ mass $\times \Delta t$|$_{soln}$ + |heat capacity $\times \Delta t$|$_{calorimeter}$

= (4.184 J/g·°C)[(100. mL $\times$ 1.10 g/mL) + 1.22 g](45.5°C - 23.0°C)

+ (562 J/°C)(45.5°C - 23.0°C)

= 1.05 $\times$ 10^4 J + 1.26 $\times$ 10^4 J

= **2.31 $\times$ 10^4 J**

Note: The mass of the solution equals the mass of the HCl solution plus the mass of the magnesium strip.

(2) This is a possible limiting reactant problem because amounts of both reactants are given. In this case, it is clear that Mg is the limiting reactant, since

$$\text{mol Mg} = \frac{1.22 \text{ g}}{24.3 \text{ g/mol}} = 0.0502 \text{ mol} \qquad\qquad \text{mol HCl} = 6.02 \text{ } M \times 0.100 \text{ L} = 0.612 \text{ mol}$$

$$\Delta H_{rxn} = \frac{-2.31 \times 10^4 \text{ J}}{0.0502 \text{ mol Mg}} \times \frac{1 \text{ mol Mg}}{1 \text{ mol rxn}} = \textbf{--4.60} \times \textbf{10}^5 \textbf{ kJ or --460. kJ/mol rxn}$$

15-70. *Refer to Sections 15-4 and 15-10, and Examples 15-2 and 15-14.*

Balanced equation: 2C$_{10}$H$_{22}$(ℓ) + 31 O$_2$(g) $\rightarrow$ 20CO$_2$(g) + 22H$_2$O(ℓ)

|heat released| = |heat gained|$_{water}$ + |heat gained|$_{calorimeter}$

= |specific heat $\times$ mass $\times \Delta t$|$_{water}$ + |heat capacity $\times \Delta t$|$_{calorimeter}$

= (4.184 J/g·°C)(1250.0 g)(26.4°C - 24.6°C) + (2450 J/°C)(26.4°C - 24.6°C)

= 9400 J + 4400 J (each value has 2 significant figures)

= 13800 J (3 significant figures - see rules for adding numbers)

Since heat is released in this reaction (the temperature of the water increased), ΔE is a negative quantity.

$$\Delta E = -\frac{13800 \text{ J}}{6.620 \text{ g } C_{10}H_{22}(\ell)} = \textbf{--2.08} \times \textbf{10}^3 \textbf{ J/g } \mathbf{C_{10}H_{22}}(\ell)$$

$$\Delta E = -\frac{13800 \text{ J}}{6.620 \text{ g } C_{10}H_{22}(\ell)} \times \frac{142.3 \text{ g}}{1 \text{ mol}} \times \frac{1 \text{ kJ}}{1000 \text{ J}} = \textbf{--297 kJ/mol } \mathbf{C_{10}H_{22}}(\ell)$$

15-72. *Refer to Sections 15-10.*

(a) When heat is absorbed by a system or added to a system, q is "+." When heat is released or removed from a system, q is "–."

(b) When work is done on a system, w is "+." When work is done by a system, w is "–."

15-74. *Refer to Section 15-10 and Example 15-13.*

Balanced equation: $2NH_4NO_3(s) \rightarrow 2N_2(g) + 4H_2O(g) + O_2(g)$

(a) Work (w) is "–". The change in the moles of gas, Δn_{gas} (= $n_{gaseous\ products}$ - $n_{gaseous\ reactants}$) is a positive value. The sign of the work term is opposite that of Δn_{gas} since $w = -P\Delta V = -\Delta n_{gas}RT$ at constant P and T, so work is "–".

(b) This reaction is responsible for many explosions, so intuitively we know that the system is doing work on the surroundings. The created gases of the system are expanding against the atmosphere and doing work on the surroundings.

15-76. *Refer to Section 15-10.*

For the system: $q = -175$ J, $w_{electrical} = +96$ J and $w_{PV} = -257$ J
$\Delta E = q + w_{total} = q + (w_{electrical} + w_{PV}) = -175\ \text{J} + [+96\ \text{J} + (-257\ \text{J})] = \mathbf{-336\ J}$

15-78. *Refer to Section 15-10, Example 15-13 and Exercise 15-77.*

Plan: Evaluate $\Delta n_{gas} = n_{gaseous\ products}$ - $n_{gaseous\ reactants}$. The sign of the work term is opposite that of Δn_{gas} since $w = -P\Delta V = -\Delta n_{gas}RT$ at constant P and T.

(a) $2SO_2(g) + O_2(g) \rightarrow 2SO_3(g)$
$\Delta n_{gas} = 2\ \text{mol} - 3\ \text{mol} = -1\ \text{mol}$. Therefore, $w > 0$ and work is done by the surroundings on the system.

(b) $CaCO_3(s) \rightarrow CaO(s) + CO_2(g)$
$\Delta n_{gas} = 1\ \text{mol} - 0\ \text{mol} = +1\ \text{mol}$. Therefore, work < 0, and work is done by the system on the surroundings.

(c) $CO_2(g) + H_2O(\ell) + CaCO_3(s) \rightarrow Ca^{2+}(aq) + 2HCO_3^-(aq)$
$\Delta n_{gas} = 0\ \text{mol} - 1\ \text{mol} = -1\ \text{mol}$. Therefore, work > 0 and work is done on the system by the surroundings.

15-80. *Refer to Sections 15-10 and 15-11.*

(a) The balanced equation for the oxidation of 1 mole of HCl: $HCl(g) + 1/4\ O_2(g) \rightarrow 1/2\ Cl_2(g) + 1/2\ H_2O(g)$

$$\text{work} = -P\Delta V = -\Delta n_{gas}RT = -(n_{gaseous\ products} - n_{gaseous\ reactants})RT$$
$$= -(1\ \text{mol} - 5/4\ \text{mol})(8.314\ \text{J/mol·K})(200°C + 273°)$$
$$= \mathbf{+983\ J}$$

Work is a positive number, therefore, work is done on the system by the surroundings. As the system "shrinks" from 5/4 mole of gas to 1 mole of gas, work is done on the system by the surroundings to decrease the volume. (Recall that $V \propto n$ at constant T and P.)

(b) The balanced reaction for the decomposition of 1 mole of NO: $NO(g) \rightarrow 1/2\ N_2(g) + 1/2\ O_2(g)$

$$\text{work} = -P\Delta V = -\Delta n_{gas}RT = -(1\ \text{mol} - 1\ \text{mol})RT = \mathbf{0\ J}$$

There is no work done since the number of moles of gas, and hence the volume of the system, remains constant.

15-82. *Refer to the Introduction to Section 15-12, Sections 15-12 and 15-15.*

When fuel, e.g., gasoline, is burned, it first undergoes a physical change as it is converted from a liquid to the gaseous state. In the carburetor, the fuel is mixed with oxygen, and a spark ignites the mixture. The fuel then undergoes a chemical change as it reacts with oxygen gas to produce carbon dioxide and water. This reaction happens spontaneously. Let us consider gasoline as being primarily octane; the reaction in the engine is:

$$2C_8H_{18}(g) + 25\ O_2(g) \rightarrow 16CO_2(g) + 18H_2O(g) + \text{heat}$$

and it is exothermic, producing a great deal of heat. The Second Law of Thermodynamics states that in spontaneous changes, the universe tends toward a state of increasing entropy, $\Delta S_{universe} > 0$.

Does this make sense in this case? Absolutely. We are first going from a system containing 2 moles of liquid fuel to 2 moles of gaseous fuel - a big increase in entropy. Then before reaction we have 27 moles of gas, and after reaction we have a system containing 34 moles of gas. Entropy involves an increase in the relative positions of the molecules with respect to each other and the energies they can have. The entropy of this system has definitely increased after the combustion reaction has occurred.

15-84. *Refer to Section 15-14.*

The Third Law of Thermodynamics states that the entropy of a pure, perfect crystalline substance is zero at 0 K.

This means that all substances have some entropy (dispersal of energy and/or matter, i.e. disorder) except when the substance is a pure, perfect, motionless, vibrationless crystal at absolute zero Kelvin. This also implies that the entropy of a substance can be expressed on an absolute basis.

15-86. *Refer to Section 15-13.*

(a) The probability that a coin will come up heads in one flip is ½ = **0.5**.

(b) The probability that a coin comes up heads two times in a row is ½ x ½ = ¼ = **0.25**.

(c) The probability that the coin comes up heads 10 times in a row is $(½)^{10} = 1/1024 = \textbf{0.000977}$.

15-88. *Refer to Section 15-13, Exercise 15-87 and Figure 15-13.*

Consider the following arrangements of molecules:

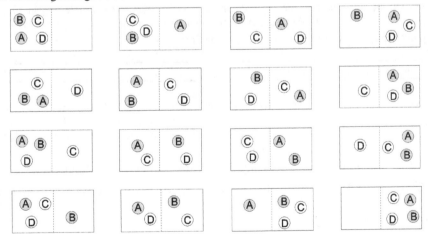

(a) A total of **16** different arrangements are possible.

(b) A mixture of unlike molecules in at least one of the flasks can be found in **14 out of 16** arrangements.

(c) The probability that at least one of the flasks contains a mixture of unlike molecules is 14/16 or **7/8**.

(d) The probability that the gases are not mixed is 2/16 or **1/8**.

15-90. *Refer to Section 15-13.*

(a) heating glass to its softening temperature   entropy is increasing for the glass, so ΔS is positive

(b) sugar dissolving in coffee   entropy is increasing for both sugar and coffee, so ΔS is positive

(c) $CaCO_3$ is precipitating   entropy is decreasing for $CaCO_3$, so ΔS is negative

---

15-92. *Refer to Section 15-14 and Table 15-4.*

There is an increase in entropy (dispersal of energy) in only the process (c) sublimation of dry ice, $CO_2(s) \rightarrow CO_2(g)$. In the other physical processes, the systems are becoming more ordered and the entropy is decreasing.

15-94. *Refer to Section 15-14.*

When the volume occupied by one mole of Ar at 0°C is halved, there is a *decrease* in entropy (dispersal of energy), as signified by the negative sign of the entropy change, -5.76 J/(mol rxn)·K. In the smaller volume there are fewer energy levels available for the argon molecules to occupy and so, there is a decrease in entropy in the smaller volume.

15-96. *Refer to Sections 15-13 and 15-14, and Table 15-4.*

(a) increase in entropy   When the NaCl dissolves, the ions disperse throughout the water. This allows the ions and the water molecules to transfer energy to each other. Dispersal of matter allows for more dispersal of energy.

(b) decrease in entropy   When some of the NaCl precipitates out as the saturated solution cools, there are fewer number of ways to distribute the same total energy.

(c) decrease in entropy   The solid phase is always more ordered than the liquid phase of a substance.

(d) increase in entropy   The gas phase is always more disordered than the liquid phase of a substance.

(e) increase in entropy   The reaction is producing 2 moles of gas from 1 mole of gas. Energy is more dispersed in a system with 2 moles of gas than in a system with 1 mole of gas.

(f) decrease in entropy   The reaction is the opposite of (e).

15-98. *Refer to Section 15-14 and Example 15-18.*

(a) $S°$ of MgO(s) $< S°$ of NaF(s)   The higher ion charges in MgO (2+ and 2−) as compared to the ion charges in NaF (1+ and 1−) hold the MgO ionic solid together more tightly so the ions vibrate less, leading to lower absolute entropy.

(b) $S°$ of Au(s) $< S°$ of Hg(ℓ)   Solids generally have lower entropy than liquids.

(c) $S°$ of $H_2O(g) < S°$ of $H_2S(g)$ For similar molecules, absolute entropy generally increases with increasing size.

(d) $S°$ of $CH_3OH(\ell) < S°$ of $C_2H_5OH(\ell)$ See (c).

(e) $S°$ of NaOH(s) $< S°$ of NaOH(aq)   When substances are mixed, in this case, dissolved in water, the absolute entropy is always higher than either substance by itself.

Entropy increases and the change in entropy is positive when a reaction occurs
    (1) when there are more gaseous products than gaseous reactants ($\Delta n_{gas} > 0$) and
    (2) when there are more aqueous products than aqueous reactants if no gases are present.

(a) entropy change is negative   2 mol gaseous products → 1 mol gaseous product
(b) entropy change is negative   4 mol gaseous products → 2 mol gaseous product
(c) entropy change is positive   0 mol gaseous products → 1 mol gaseous product
(d) entropy change is negative   1/2 mol gaseous products → 0 mol gaseous product
(e) entropy change is negative   2 mol aqueous products → 0 mol gaseous product

---

15-102. *Refer to Sections 15-13 and 15-14.*

Consider the boiling of a pure liquid at constant pressure.   (a) $\Delta S_{system} > 0$ (b) $\Delta H_{system} > 0$ (c) $\Delta T_{system} = 0$

15-104. *Refer to Section 15-13 and Example 15-15.*

(a) Balanced equation: $4HCl(g) + O_2(g) \rightarrow 2Cl_2(g) + 2H_2O(g)$

$\Delta S^\circ_{rxn} = [2S^\circ_{Cl_2(g)} + 2S^\circ_{H_2O(g)}] - [4S^\circ_{HCl(g)} + S^\circ_{O_2(g)}]$
$= [(2\text{ mol})(+223.0 \text{ J/mol·K}) + (2\text{ mol})(+188.7 \text{ J/mol·K})]$
$\quad - [(4\text{ mol})(+186.8 \text{ J/mol·K}) + (1\text{ mol})(+205.0 \text{ J/mol·K})]$
$= \mathbf{-128.8 \text{ J/(mol rxn)·K}}$

The reaction is producing 4 moles of gas from 5 moles of gas. The energy and mass in the system is becoming less dispersed as the number of moles of gas decreases; entropy is decreasing and the change in entropy is expected to be negative.

(b) Balanced equation: $PCl_3(g) + Cl_2(g) \rightarrow PCl_5(g)$

$\Delta S^\circ_{rxn} = [S^\circ_{PCl_5(g)}] - [S^\circ_{PCl_3(g)} + S^\circ_{Cl_2(g)}]$
$= [(1\text{ mol})(+353 \text{ J/mol·K})] - [(1\text{ mol})(+311.7 \text{ J/mol·K}) + (1\text{ mol})(+223.0 \text{ J/mol·K})]$
$= \mathbf{-182 \text{ J/(mol rxn)·K}}$

The reaction is producing 1 mole of gas from 2 moles of gas. For the same reasoning as shown in (a), the entropy is decreasing and the change in entropy is expected to be negative.

(c) Balanced equation: $2N_2O(g) \rightarrow 2N_2(g) + O_2(g)$

$\Delta S^\circ_{rxn} = [2S^\circ_{N_2(g)} + S^\circ_{O_2(g)}] - [2S^\circ_{N_2O(g)}]$
$= [(2\text{ mol})(+191.5 \text{ J/mol·K}) + (1\text{ mol})(+205.0 \text{ J/mol·K})] - [(2\text{ mol})(+219.7 \text{ J/mol·K})]$
$= \mathbf{+148.6 \text{ J/(mol rxn)·K}}$

The reaction is producing 3 mole of gas from 2 moles of gas. The entropy is increasing and the change in entropy is expected to be positive.

15-106. *Refer to Sections 15-15 and 15-16, and Table 15-7.*

(a) always spontaneous: (iii) $\Delta H < 0, \Delta S > 0$
(b) always nonspontaneous: (ii) $\Delta H > 0, \Delta S < 0$
(c) spontaneous or nonspontaneous, depending on T and the magnitudes of ΔH and ΔS: (i)$\Delta H > 0, \Delta S > 0$
                                                              (iv) $\Delta H < 0, \Delta S < 0$

15-108. *Refer to Section 15-14, Example 15-16 and Appendix K.*

Balanced equation: $SiH_4(g) + 2O_2(g) \rightarrow SiO_2(s) + 2H_2O(\ell)$

$\Delta S^\circ_{rxn} = [S^\circ_{SiO_2(s)} + 2S^\circ_{H_2O(\ell)}] - [S^\circ_{SiH_4(g)} + 2S^\circ_{O_2(g)}]$

$$= [(1 \text{ mol})(+41.84 \text{ J/mol·K}) + (2 \text{ mol})(+69.91 \text{ J/mol·K})] - [(1 \text{ mol})(+204.5 \text{ J/mol·K})$$
$$+ (2 \text{ mol})(+205.0 \text{ J/mol·K})]$$
$$= \mathbf{-432.8 \text{ J/(mol rxn)·K}}$$

15-110. *Refer to Sections 15-8 and 15-16.*

Since $\Delta G°$ is a state function like $\Delta H°$, we can use Hess's Law type of manipulations to determine the $\Delta G_f°$. The balanced equation representing the $\Delta G_f°$ of HBr(g) is: $\frac{1}{2}H_2(g) + \frac{1}{2}Br_2(\ell) \rightarrow HBr(g)$

	$\Delta G°$
$\frac{1}{2}Br_2(\ell) \rightarrow \frac{1}{2}Br_2(g)$	1.57 kJ
$H(g) + Br(g) \rightarrow HBr(g)$	−339.09 kJ
$\frac{1}{2}Br_2(g) \rightarrow Br(g)$	80.85 kJ
$\frac{1}{2}H_2(g) \rightarrow H(g)$	203.247 kJ
$\frac{1}{2}H_2(g) + \frac{1}{2}Br_2(\ell) \rightarrow HBr(g)$	**−53.42 kJ/mol rxn**

15-112. *Refer to Section 15-16, Example 15-20 and Appendix K.*

Plan: Calculate $\Delta H°_{rxn}$ and $\Delta S°_{rxn}$, then use the Gibbs free energy change equation, $\Delta G = \Delta H - T\Delta S$, to determine $\Delta G°_{rxn}$.

(a) Balanced equation: $3NO_2(g) + H_2O(\ell) \rightarrow 2HNO_3(\ell) + NO(g)$

$\Delta H°_{rxn} = [2\Delta H_f°{}_{HNO_3(\ell)} + \Delta H_f°{}_{NO(g)}] - [3\Delta H_f°{}_{NO_2(g)} + \Delta H_f°{}_{H_2O(\ell)}]$
$= [(2 \text{ mol})(-174.1 \text{ kJ/mol}) + (1 \text{ mol})(+90.25 \text{ kJ/mol})]$
$\qquad - [(3 \text{ mol})(+33.2 \text{ kJ/mol}) + (1 \text{ mol})(-285.8 \text{ kJ/mol})]$
$= \mathbf{-71.75 \text{ kJ/mol rxn}}$

$\Delta S°_{rxn} = [2S°_{HNO_3(\ell)} + S°_{NO(g)}] - [3S°_{NO_2(g)} + S°_{H_2O(\ell)}]$
$= [(2 \text{ mol})(+155.6 \text{ J/mol·K}) + (1 \text{ mol})(+210.7 \text{ J/mol·K})]$
$\qquad - [(3 \text{ mol})(+240.0 \text{ J/mol·K}) + (1 \text{ mol})(+69.91 \text{ J/mol·K})]$
$= \mathbf{-268.0 \text{ J/(mol rxn)·K}}$

$\Delta G°_{rxn} = \Delta H°_{rxn} - T\Delta S°_{rxn} = -71.75 \text{ kJ} - (298.15 \text{ K})(-0.268 \text{ kJ/K}) = \mathbf{+8.15 \text{ kJ/mol rxn}}$

(b) Balanced equation: $SnO_2(s) + 2CO(g) \rightarrow 2CO_2(g) + Sn(s,\text{white})$

$\Delta H°_{rxn} = [2\Delta H_f°{}_{CO_2(g)} + \Delta H_f°{}_{Sn(s)}] - [\Delta H_f°{}_{SnO_2(s)} + 2\Delta H_f°{}_{CO(g)}]$
$= [(2 \text{ mol})(-393.5 \text{ J/mol}) + (1 \text{ mol})(0 \text{ kJ/mol})] - [(1 \text{ mol})(-580.7 \text{ kJ/mol}) + (2 \text{ mol})(-110.5 \text{ kJ/mol})]$
$= \mathbf{+14.7 \text{ kJ/mol rxn}}$

$\Delta S°_{rxn} = [2S°_{CO_2(g)} + S°_{Sn(s)}] - [S°_{SnO_2(s)} + 2S°_{CO(g)}]$
$= [(2 \text{ mol})(+213.6 \text{ J/mol·K}) + (1 \text{ mol})(+51.55 \text{ J/mol·K})]$
$\qquad - [(1 \text{ mol})(+52.3 \text{ J/mol·K}) + (2 \text{ mol})(+197.6 \text{ J/mol·K})]$
$= \mathbf{+31.2 \text{ J/(mol rxn)·K}}$

$\Delta G°_{rxn} = \Delta H°_{rxn} - T\Delta S°_{rxn} = +14.7 \text{ kJ} - (298.15 \text{ K})(+0.0312 \text{ kJ/K}) = \mathbf{+5.4 \text{ kJ/mol rxn}}$

(c) Balanced equation: $2Na(s) + 2H_2O(\ell) \rightarrow 2NaOH(aq) + H_2(g)$

$\Delta H°_{rxn} = [2\Delta H_f°{}_{NaOH(aq)} + \Delta H_f°{}_{H_2(g)}] - [2\Delta H_f°{}_{Na(s)} + 2\Delta H_f°{}_{H_2O(\ell)}]$
$= [(2 \text{ mol})(-469.6 \text{ kJ/mol}) + (1 \text{ mol})(0 \text{ kJ/mol})] - [(2 \text{ mol})(0 \text{ kJ/mol}) + (2 \text{ mol})(-285.8 \text{ kJ/mol})]$
$= \mathbf{-367.6 \text{ kJ/mol rxn}}$

$$\Delta S^\circ_{rxn} = [2S^\circ_{NaOH(aq)} + S^\circ_{H_2(g)}] - [2S^\circ_{Na(s)} + 2S^\circ_{H_2O(\ell)}]$$
$$= [(2 \text{ mol})(+49.8 \text{ J/mol·K}) + (1 \text{ mol})(+130.6 \text{ J/mol·K})]$$
$$- [(2 \text{ mol})(+51.0 \text{ J/mol·K}) + (2 \text{ mol})(+69.91 \text{ J/mol·K})]$$
$$= \mathbf{-11.62 \text{ J/(mol rxn)·K}}$$

$$\Delta G^\circ_{rxn} = \Delta H^\circ_{rxn} - T\Delta S^\circ_{rxn} = -367.6 \text{ kJ} - (298.15 \text{ K})(-0.01162 \text{ kJ/K}) = \mathbf{-364.1 \text{ kJ/mol rxn}}$$

15-114. *Refer to Sections 15-16 and 15-17.*

Recall: Gibbs free energy change equation: $\Delta G = \Delta H - T\Delta S$

(a) false   An exothermic reaction ($\Delta H < 0$) will be spontaneous ($\Delta G < 0$) only if either ΔS is positive, or, in the event ΔS is negative, the absolute value of $T\Delta S$ is smaller than that of ΔH.

(b) true   From the Gibbs free energy change equation; the $T\Delta S$ term has a negative sign in front.

(c) false   A reaction with $\Delta S_{sys} > 0$ will be spontaneous ($\Delta G < 0$) only if either ΔH is negative, or, in the event ΔH is positive, its absolute value is smaller than that of $T\Delta S$.

15-116. *Refer to Sections 15-16 and 15-17, and Appendix K.*

Balanced equation: $2H_2O_2(\ell) \rightarrow 2H_2O(\ell) + O_2(g)$

(a) $\Delta H^\circ_{rxn} = [2\Delta H^\circ_{f\,H_2O(\ell)} + \Delta H^\circ_{f\,O_2(g)}] - [2\Delta H^\circ_{f\,H_2O_2(\ell)}]$
$$= [(2 \text{ mol})(-285.8 \text{ kJ/mol}) + (1 \text{ mol})(0 \text{ kJ/mol})] - [(2 \text{ mol})(-187.8 \text{ kJ/mol})]$$
$$= \mathbf{-196.0 \text{ kJ/mol rxn}}$$

$\Delta G^\circ_{rxn} = [2\Delta G^\circ_{f\,H_2O(\ell)} + \Delta G^\circ_{f\,O_2(g)}] - [2\Delta G^\circ_{f\,H_2O_2(\ell)}]$
$$= [(2 \text{ mol})(-237.2 \text{ kJ/mol}) + (1 \text{ mol})(0 \text{ kJ/mol})] - [(2 \text{ mol})(-120.4 \text{ kJ/mol})]$$
$$= \mathbf{-233.6 \text{ kJ/mol rxn}}$$

$\Delta S^\circ_{rxn} = [2S^\circ_{H_2O(\ell)} + S^\circ_{O_2(g)}] - [2S^\circ_{H_2O_2(\ell)}]$
$$= [(2 \text{ mol})(+69.91 \text{ J/mol·K}) + (1 \text{ mol})(+205.0 \text{ J/mol·K})] - [(2 \text{ mol})(+109.6 \text{ J/mol·K})]$$
$$= \mathbf{+125.6 \text{ J/(mol rxn)·K}}$$

(b) Hydrogen peroxide, $H_2O_2(\ell)$, will be stable if $\Delta G^\circ > 0$ for the above balanced reaction at some temperature, i.e., if the above reaction is non-spontaneous. However, $\Delta H^\circ_{rxn} < 0$ and $\Delta S^\circ_{rxn} > 0$ for the decomposition of $H_2O_2(\ell)$ and the reaction is spontaneous ($\Delta G^\circ < 0$) for all temperatures. Hence, there is no temperature at which $H_2O_2(\ell)$ is stable at 1 atm.

15-118. *Refer to Section 15-17.*

Dissociation reactions, such as $HCl(g) \rightarrow H(g) + Cl(g)$, require energy to break bonds and therefore are endothermic with positive ΔH values. The ΔS values for such reactions are positive since 2 or more particles are being formed from 1 molecule, causing the system to become more energetically dispersed. Under the circumstances when ΔH and ΔS are both positive, the spontaneity of the reaction is favored at higher temperatures.

15-120. *Refer to Section 15-17, Examples 15-22 and 15-23, and Appendix K.*

Plan: Evaluate ΔH_{rxn} and ΔS_{rxn}. To assess the temperature range over which the reaction is spontaneous, use the signs of ΔH and ΔS and the Gibbs free energy change equation, $\Delta G = \Delta H - T\Delta S$. Assume that ΔH and ΔS are independent of temperature.

(a) Balanced equation: $CaCO_3(s) + H_2SO_4(\ell) \rightarrow CaSO_4(s) + H_2O(\ell) + CO_2(g)$

$\Delta H^\circ_{rxn} = [\Delta H^\circ_{f\,CaSO_4(s)} + \Delta H^\circ_{f\,H_2O(\ell)} + \Delta H^\circ_{f\,CO_2(g)}] - [\Delta H^\circ_{f\,CaCO_3(s)} + \Delta H^\circ_{f\,H_2SO_4(\ell)}]$

$\quad = [(1\text{ mol})(-1433\text{ kJ/mol}) + (1\text{ mol})(-285.8\text{ kJ/mol}) + (1\text{ mol})(-393.5\text{ kJ/mol})]$
$\qquad - [(1\text{ mol})(-1207\text{ kJ/mol}) + (1\text{ mol})(-814.0\text{ kJ/mol})]$

$\quad = -91.3\text{ kJ/mol rxn}$

$\Delta S^\circ_{rxn} = [S^\circ_{CaSO_4(s)} + S^\circ_{H_2O(\ell)} + S^\circ_{CO_2(g)}] - [S^\circ_{CaCO_3(s)} + S^\circ_{H_2SO_4(\ell)}]$

$\quad = [(1\text{ mol})(+107\text{ J/mol·K}) + (1\text{ mol})(+69.91\text{ J/mol·K}) + (1\text{ mol})(+213.6\text{ J/mol·K})]$
$\qquad - [(1\text{ mol})(+92.9\text{ J/mol·K}) + (1\text{ mol})(+156.9\text{ J/mol·K})]$

$\quad = +141\text{ J/(mol rxn)·K}$

Since ΔH is negative and ΔS is positive, the reaction is **spontaneous at all temperatures**.

(b) Balanced equation: $2HgO(s) \rightarrow 2Hg(\ell) + O_2(g)$

$\Delta H^\circ_{rxn} = [2\Delta H^\circ_{f\,Hg(\ell)} + \Delta H^\circ_{f\,O_2(g)}] - [2\Delta H^\circ_{f\,HgO(s)}]$

$\quad = [(2\text{ mol})(0\text{ kJ/mol}) + (1\text{ mol})(0\text{ kJ/mol})] - [(2\text{ mol})(-90.83\text{ kJ/mol})]$

$\quad = +181.7\text{ kJ/mol rxn}$

$\Delta S^\circ_{rxn} = [2S^\circ_{Hg(\ell)} + S^\circ_{O_2(g)}] - [2S^\circ_{HgO(s)}]$

$\quad = [(2\text{ mol})(+76.02\text{ J/mol·K}) + (1\text{ mol})(+205.0\text{ J/mol·K})] - [(2\text{ mol})(+70.29\text{ J/mol·K})]$

$\quad = +216.5\text{ J/(mol rxn)·K}$

At equilibrium, $\Delta G^\circ_{rxn} = 0 = \Delta H^\circ_{rxn} - T\Delta S^\circ_{rxn}$, and solving for T_{eq}

$T_{eq} = \dfrac{\Delta H_{rxn}}{\Delta S_{rxn}} = \dfrac{181.7\text{ kJ}}{0.2165\text{ kJ/K}} = 839.3\text{ K}$

Since ΔH and ΔS are positive, the reaction is **spontaneous at $T > 839.3$ K**.

(c) Balanced equation: $CO_2(g) + C(s) \rightarrow 2CO(g)$

$\Delta H^\circ_{rxn} = [2\Delta H^\circ_{f\,CO(g)}] - [\Delta H^\circ_{f\,CO_2(g)} + \Delta H^\circ_{f\,C(s)}]$

$\quad = [(2\text{ mol})(-110.5\text{ kJ/mol})] - [(1\text{ mol})(-393.5\text{ kJ/mol}) + (1\text{ mol})(0\text{ kJ/mol})]$

$\quad = +172.5\text{ kJ/mol rxn}$

$\Delta S^\circ_{rxn} = [2S^\circ_{CO(g)}] - [S^\circ_{CO_2(g)} + S^\circ_{C(s)}]$

$\quad = [(2\text{ mol})(+197.6\text{ J/mol·K})] - [(1\text{ mol})(+213.6\text{ J/mol·K}) + (1\text{ mol})(+5.740\text{ J/mol·K})]$

$\quad = +175.9\text{ J/(mol rxn)·K}$

At equilibrium, $\Delta G^\circ_{rxn} = 0 = \Delta H^\circ_{rxn} - T\Delta S^\circ_{rxn}$, and solving for T_{eq}

$T_{eq} = \dfrac{\Delta H_{rxn}}{\Delta S_{rxn}} = \dfrac{172.5\text{ kJ}}{0.1759\text{ kJ/K}} = 980.7\text{ K}$

Since ΔH and ΔS are positive, the reaction is **spontaneous at $T > 980.7$ K**.

(d) Balanced equation: $2Fe_2O_3(s) \rightarrow 4Fe(s) + 3O_2(g)$

$\Delta H^\circ_{rxn} = [4\Delta H^\circ_{f\,Fe(s)} + 3\Delta H^\circ_{f\,O_2(g)}] - [2\Delta H^\circ_{f\,Fe_2O_3(s)}]$

$\quad = [(4\text{ mol})(0\text{ kJ/mol}) + (3\text{ mol})(0\text{ kJ/mol})] - [(2\text{ mol})(-824.2\text{ kJ/mol})]$

$\quad = +1648\text{ kJ/mol rxn}$

$\Delta S^\circ_{rxn} = [4S^\circ_{Fe(s)} + 3S^\circ_{O_2(g)}] - [2S^\circ_{Fe_2O_3(s)}]$

$\quad = [(4\text{ mol})(+27.3\text{ J/mol·K}) + (3\text{ mol})(+205.0\text{ J/mol·K})] - [(2\text{ mol})(+87.40\text{ J/mol·K})]$

$\quad = +549.4\text{ J/(mol rxn)·K}$

$T_{eq} = \dfrac{\Delta H_{rxn}}{\Delta S_{rxn}} = \dfrac{1648\text{ kJ}}{0.5494\text{ kJ/K}} = 3000.\text{ K}$

Since ΔH and ΔS are positive, the reaction is **spontaneous at $T > 3000.$ K**.

244

15-122. *Refer to Section 15-17, Appendix K and Example 15-21.*

(a) The process is: $H_2O(\ell) \rightarrow H_2O(g)$

$\Delta H^{\circ}_{rxn} = \Delta H^{\circ}_{f\ H_2O(g)} - \Delta H^{\circ}_{f\ H_2O(\ell)} = (1\ \text{mol})(-241.8\ \text{kJ/mol}) - (1\ \text{mol})(-285.8\ \text{kJ/mol}) = +44.0\ \text{kJ}$

$\Delta S^{\circ}_{rxn} = S^{\circ}_{H_2O(g)} - S^{\circ}_{H_2O(\ell)} = (1\ \text{mol})(+188.7\ \text{J/mol·K}) - (1\ \text{mol})(+69.91\ \text{J/mol·K}) = +118.8\ \text{J/K}$

$T_{eq} = \dfrac{\Delta H_{rxn}}{\Delta S_{rxn}} = \dfrac{44.0\ \text{kJ}}{0.1188\ \text{kJ/K}} = 370\ \text{K or } \mathbf{97°C}$

(b) The known boiling point of water is, of course, 100°C. The discrepancy is because we assumed that the standard values of enthalpy of formation and entropy in Appendix K are independent of temperature. However, these tabulated values were determined at 25°C; we are using them to solve a problem at 100°C. Nevertheless, this assumption allows us to estimate the boiling point of water with reasonable accuracy.

15-124. *Refer to Sections 15-16 and 15-17, and Appendix K.*

Balanced equation: $2NiO(s) \rightarrow 2Ni(s) + O_2(g)$

(1) The decomposition of NiO(s) is product-favored (spontaneous) at 25°C if $\Delta G^{\circ}_{rxn} < 0$ at that temperature.
$\Delta G^{\circ}_{rxn} = -2\Delta H^{\circ}_{f\ NiO(s)} = -(2\ \text{mol})(-216\ \text{kJ/mol}) = +432\ \text{kJ}$
Since $\Delta G^{\circ}_{rxn} > 0$, the reaction is reactant-favored, not product favored at 25°C.

(2) To determine how this reaction is affected by temperature, let's calculate ΔS°_{rxn} and ΔH°_{rxn}.
$\Delta H^{\circ}_{rxn} = -2\Delta H^{\circ}_{f\ NiO(s)} = -(2\ \text{mol})(-244\ \text{kJ/mol}) = +488\ \text{kJ/mol rxn}$
$\Delta S^{\circ}_{rxn} = [2S^{\circ}_{Ni(s)} + S^{\circ}_{O_2(g)}] - [2S^{\circ}_{NiO(s)}]$
$\qquad = [(2\ \text{mol})(+30.1\ \text{J/mol·K}) + (1\ \text{mol})(+205.0\ \text{J/mol·K})] - [(2\ \text{mol})(+38.6\ \text{J/mol·K})]$
$\qquad = +188\ \text{J/(mol rxn)·K}$
$T_{eq} = \dfrac{\Delta H_{rxn}}{\Delta S_{rxn}} = \dfrac{+488\ \text{kJ}}{0.188\ \text{kJ/K}} = \mathbf{2.60 \times 10^3\ K\ or\ 2320°C}$

15-126. *Refer to Sections 15-16 and 15-17, and Appendix K.*

Balanced equation: $C_2H_4(g) + H_2O(g) \rightarrow C_2H_5OH(\ell)$

$\Delta S^{\circ}_{rxn} = [S^{\circ}_{C_2H_5OH(\ell)}] - [S^{\circ}_{C_2H_4(g)} + S^{\circ}_{H_2O(g)}]$
$\qquad = [(1\ \text{mol})(+161\ \text{J/mol·K})] - [(1\ \text{mol})(+219.5\ \text{J/mol·K}) + (1\ \text{mol})(+188.7\ \text{J/mol·K})]$
$\qquad = \mathbf{-247\ J/(mol\ rxn)·K}$

Since $\Delta S^{\circ}_{rxn} < 0$, we know that the reaction is becoming more ordered, but we don't know if the reaction is spontaneous (product-favored) or not. We would also need to know ΔH°_{rxn}.

$\Delta H^{\circ}_{rxn} = [\Delta H^{\circ}_{f\ C_2H_5OH(\ell)}] - [\Delta H^{\circ}_{f\ C_2H_4(g)} + \Delta H^{\circ}_{f\ H_2O(g)}]$
$\qquad = [(1\ \text{mol})(-277.7\ \text{kJ/mol})] - [(1\ \text{mol})(+52.26\ \text{kJ/mol}) + (1\ \text{mol})(-241.8\ \text{kJ/mol})]$
$\qquad = \mathbf{-88.2\ kJ/mol\ rxn}$

Since ΔH is negative and ΔS is negative, the reaction will be spontaneous at lower temperatures. Let's now find the temperature at which the reaction is at equilibrium:

$\Delta G^{\circ}_{rxn} = \Delta H^{\circ}_{rxn} - T\Delta S^{\circ}_{rxn} = 0$ at equilibrium
$T_{eq} = \dfrac{\Delta H_{rxn}}{\Delta S_{rxn}} = \dfrac{-88.2\ \text{kJ}}{-0.247\ \text{kJ/K}} = 357\ \text{K,}$

Therefore, the reaction is only product-favored at **temperatures below 357 K**.

Plan: Use Hess's Law and solve for ΔH_f° of the organic compound.

(a) Balanced equation: $C_6H_{12}(\ell) + 9O_2(g) \rightarrow 6CO_2(g) + 6H_2O(\ell)$

$\Delta H^\circ_{combustion} = [6\Delta H_f^\circ\, CO_2(g) + 6\Delta H_f^\circ\, H_2O(\ell)] - [\Delta H_f^\circ\, C_6H_{12}(\ell) + 9\Delta H_f^\circ\, O_2(g)]$

$-3920 \text{ kJ} = [(6 \text{ mol})(-393.5 \text{ kJ/mol}) + (6 \text{ mol})(-285.8 \text{ kJ/mol})]$
$\qquad\qquad\qquad\quad - [(1 \text{ mol})\Delta H_f^\circ\, C_6H_{12}(\ell) + (9 \text{ mol})(0 \text{ kJ/mol})]$

$-3920 \text{ kJ} = -4075.8 \text{ kJ} - (1 \text{ mol})\Delta H_f^\circ\, C_6H_{12}(\ell)$

$\Delta H_f^\circ\, C_6H_{12}(\ell) = \mathbf{-156 \text{ kJ/mol } C_6H_{12}(\ell)}$

(b) Balanced equation: $C_6H_5OH(s) + 7O_2(g) \rightarrow 6CO_2(g) + 3H_2O(\ell)$

$\Delta H^\circ_{combustion} = [6\Delta H_f^\circ\, CO_2(g) + 3\Delta H_f^\circ\, H_2O(\ell)] - [\Delta H_f^\circ\, C_6H_5OH(s) + 7\Delta H_f^\circ\, O_2(g)]$

$-3053 \text{ kJ} = [(6 \text{ mol})(-393.5 \text{ kJ/mol}) + (3 \text{ mol})(-285.8 \text{ kJ/mol})]$
$\qquad\qquad\qquad\quad - [(1 \text{ mol})\Delta H_f^\circ\, C_6H_5OH(s) + (7 \text{ mol})(0 \text{ kJ/mol})]$

$-3053 \text{ kJ} = -3218.4 \text{ kJ} - (1 \text{ mol})\Delta H_f^\circ\, C_6H_5OH(s)$

$\Delta H_f^\circ\, C_6H_5OH(s) = \mathbf{-165 \text{ kJ/mol } C_6H_5OH(s)}$

15-130. *Refer to Sections 15-10 and 15-11.*

The vaporization process is: ethanol$(\ell) \rightarrow$ ethanol(g)

$\Delta E = q + w$ $\qquad\qquad$ where $\qquad\qquad$ ΔE = change in internal energy
$\qquad\qquad\qquad\qquad\qquad\qquad\qquad\qquad\qquad q$ = heat absorbed by the system
$\qquad\qquad\qquad\qquad\qquad\qquad\qquad\qquad\qquad w$ = work done on the system

(1) The heat absorbed by the system, $q = \Delta H_{vap} \times$ g ethanol = +855 J/g $\times$ 12.5 g = **+10700 J**

(2) The work done on the system in going from a liquid to a gas,

$w = -P\Delta V = -P(V_{gas} - V_{liquid})$

$\qquad$ where $\quad V_{gas} = \dfrac{nRT}{P} = \dfrac{(12.5 \text{ g}/46.1 \text{ g/mol})(0.0821 \text{ L·atm/mol·K})(78.0°C + 273.15°)}{1.00 \text{ atm}} = 7.82 \text{ L}$

$\qquad\qquad\qquad V_{liquid} = 12.5 \text{ g ethanol} \times \dfrac{1.00 \text{ mL ethanol}}{0.789 \text{ g ethanol}} = 15.8 \text{ mL or } 0.0158 \text{ L}$

Therefore,

$w = -P\Delta V = -(1 \text{ atm})(7.82 \text{ L} - 0.02 \text{ L}) = -7.80$ L·atm (the negative value means the system is doing work)

To find a factor to convert L·atm to J, we can equate two values of the molar gas constant, R
$\qquad\qquad\qquad$ 0.0821 L·atm/mol·K = 8.314 J/mol·K
$\qquad\qquad\qquad\qquad$ 1 L·atm = 101 J

And so, $w = -7.80$ L·atm $\times \dfrac{101 \text{ J}}{1 \text{ L·atm}} = \mathbf{-788 \text{ J}}$

(3) Finally, $\Delta E = q + w = 10700 \text{ J} + (-788 \text{ J}) = \mathbf{9900 \text{ J}}$

15-132. *Refer to Section 15-4.*

(a) heat gained by calorimeter = 0.01520 g $C_{10}H_8 \times \dfrac{1 \text{ mol } C_{10}H_8}{128.16 \text{ g } C_{10}H_8} \times \dfrac{5156.8 \text{ kJ}}{1 \text{ mol } C_{10}H_8} = 0.6116 \text{ kJ}$

We know: |heat gained by calorimeter| = |heat capacity $\times \Delta t$| $\qquad$ where t is temperature in °C

Therefore, $\quad$ heat capacity $= \dfrac{|\text{heat gained by calorimeter}|}{|\Delta t|} = \dfrac{0.6116 \text{ kJ}}{0.212°C} = \mathbf{2.88 \text{ kJ/°C}}$

(b) $|\text{heat released in the reaction}| = 0.1040 \text{ g } C_8H_{18} \times \dfrac{1 \text{ mol } C_8H_{18}}{114.22 \text{ g/mol}} \times \dfrac{5451.4 \text{ kJ}}{1 \text{ mol } C_8H_{18}} = 4.964 \text{ kJ}$

We also know:
$$|\text{heat released in the reaction}| = |\text{heat gained by calorimeter}|$$

Substituting,
$$4.964 \text{ kJ} = |\text{heat capacity} \times \Delta t|$$
$$= |2.88 \text{ kJ/°C} \times \Delta t|$$
$$\Delta t = 1.72\text{°C}$$

Therefore, $t_{\text{final}} = t_{\text{initial}} + \Delta t = 22.102\text{°C} + 1.72\text{°C} = \textbf{23.82°C}$.

15-134. *Refer to Sections 15-14, 15-15 and 15-16.*

When a rubber band is stretched: $\Delta H < 0$, since heat is released

$\Delta S < 0$, since the rubber band is becoming more ordered (more linear);

therefore, $\Delta G > 0$, since the process does not occur spontaneously

When the stretched rubber band is relaxed, the signs of the thermodynamic state functions change:

$\Delta H > 0$, since heat is absorbed (that's why your hand feels colder)

$\Delta S > 0$, since the rubber band is becoming more disordered; therefore

$\Delta G < 0$, since the process occurs spontaneously

The spontaneous process that occurs when the stretched rubber band is allowed to return to its original, random arrangement of polymer molecules, must be driven by the increase in the mass and energy dispersal of the system, since the reaction is endothermic ($\Delta H > 0$).

15-136. *Refer to Sections 1-13 and 15-4.*

(a)
$$|\text{heat lost}|_{\text{metal}} = |\text{heat gained}|_{\text{water}}$$
$$|\text{specific heat} \times \text{mass} \times \Delta t|_{\text{metal}} = |\text{specific heat} \times \text{mass} \times \Delta t|_{\text{water}}$$
$$(\text{specific heat of metal})(32.6 \text{ g})(99.83\text{°C} - 24.41\text{°C}) = (4.184 \text{ J/g·°C})(100.0 \text{ g})(24.41\text{°C} - 23.62\text{°C})$$
$$(\text{specific heat of metal})(2.46 \times 10^3) = 330$$
$$\text{specific heat of metal} = \textbf{0.13 J/g·°C}$$

Therefore, according to this calculation, the metal is **tungsten, W** (specific heat = 0.135 J/g·°C).

(b)
$$|\text{heat lost}|_{\text{metal}} = |\text{heat gained}|_{\text{water}} + |\text{heat gained}|_{\text{calorimeter}}$$
$$|\text{specific heat} \times \text{mass} \times \Delta t|_{\text{metal}} = |\text{specific heat} \times \text{mass} \times \Delta t|_{\text{water}}$$
$$+ |\text{heat capacity} \times \Delta t|_{\text{calorimeter}}$$
$$(\text{specific heat of metal})(32.6 \text{ g})(99.83\text{°C} - 24.41\text{°C}) = (4.184 \text{ J/g·°C})(100.0 \text{ g})(24.41\text{°C} - 23.62\text{°C})$$
$$+ (410 \text{ J/°C})(24.41\text{°C} - 23.62\text{°C})$$
$$(\text{specific heat of metal})(2.46 \times 10^3) = 330 + 320$$
$$\text{specific heat of metal} = 0.26 \text{ J/g·°C}$$

Yes, the identification of the metal was different. When the heat capacity of the calorimeter is taken into account, the specific heat of the metal is 0.26 J/g·°C and the metal is identified as molybdenum, Mo (specific heat = 0.250 J/g·°C).

15-138. *Refer to Sections 15-13, 15-14. 15-16 and 15-17.*

(a) crystal growth from supersaturated solution:

$\Delta S < 0$ since the system is becoming more ordered; there are fewer number of ways to distribute the same total energy.

$\Delta G < 0$ since crystals spontaneously will form from a supersaturated solution

(b) sugar cube dissolving into hot tea

$\Delta S > 0$ since the system is becoming more disordered, i.e. the sugar molecules disperse throughout the tea., allowing the sugar molecules and the aqueous tea solution to transfer energy to each other. Dispersal of matter allows for more dispersal of energy.

$\Delta G < 0$ since the sugar cube easily and spontaneously dissolves into hot tea

(c) $H_2O(s) \rightarrow H_2O(\ell)$

$\Delta S > 0$ since the system is becoming more disordered; liquids always have higher entropy than solids
The sign of ΔG depends on the temperature. When $T > 0°C$, $\Delta G < 0$, since ice will spontaneously melt. When $T < 0°C$, $\Delta G > 0$, since liquid water will spontaneously freeze and when $T = 0°C$, $\Delta G = 0$, since that is the melting point of water and the reaction is at equilibrium.

15-140. *Refer to Section 15-10.*

Calculation: Activity Time Equivalent (min) $= \dfrac{\text{Food Fuel Value (kcal)}}{\text{Energy Output (kcal/min)}}$

Food	Fuel Value (kcal)	Activity Time Equivalent (min)				
		Sitting (1.7 kcal/min)	Walking (5.5 kcal/min)	Cycling (10 kcal/min)	Swimming (8.4 kcal/min)	Running (19 kcal/min)
Apple	100	59	18	10	12	5.3
Cola	105	62	19	11	13	5.5
Malted milk	500	290	91	50	60	26
Pasta	195	110	35	20	23	10
Hamburger	350	210	64	35	42	18
Steak	1000	590	180	100	120	53

15-142. *Refer to Section 15-3 and Fundamental Algebra.*

? kJ of energy found in 100. g protein = 100. g protein $\times \dfrac{17 \text{ kJ}}{1 \text{ g protein}} = 1700$ kJ

? kJ of energy found in 100. g fat = 100. g fat $\times \dfrac{39 \text{ kJ}}{1 \text{ g fat}} = 3900$ kJ

The difference in energy content is the amount of energy that must be burned up by walking instead of resting, so that the person doesn't gain weight:

difference in energy content = 3900 - 1700 = 2200 kJ

? time required to walk instead of rest to burn off 2200 kJ $= \dfrac{\text{difference in energy content}}{\text{difference in utilization rate}}$

$= \dfrac{(3900 - 1700) \text{ kJ}}{(1250 - 335) \text{ kJ/hr}}$

$= \dfrac{2200 \text{ kJ}}{915 \text{ kJ/hr}}$

$= \mathbf{2.4 \text{ hr}}$

15-144. *Refer to Sections 1-13 and 15-4.*

$|\text{heat lost}|_{\text{lead}} = |\text{heat gained}|_{\text{water}} + |\text{heat gained}|_{\text{calorimeter}}$

$|\text{specific heat} \times \text{mass} \times \Delta t|_{\text{lead}} = |\text{specific heat} \times \text{mass} \times \Delta t|_{\text{water}} + |\text{heat capacity} \times \Delta t|_{\text{calorimeter}}$

(Sp. Ht. of Pb)(43.6 g)(100.0°C − 26.8°C) = (4.184 J/g·°C)(50.0 g)(26.8°C - 25.0°C)

$+ (18.6 \text{ J/°C})(26.8°C - 25.0°C)$

(Specific heat of Pb)(3190) = 380 + 33

$$\text{Specific heat of Pb} = \textbf{0.13 J/g·°C}$$
$$\text{Molar heat capacity of Pb} = 0.13 \text{ J/g·°C} \times 207.2 \text{ g/mol} = \textbf{27 J/mol·°C}$$

15-146. *Refer to Section 15-4.*

(a) Heat gain by calorimeter $= (4572 \text{ J/°C})(27.93°C - 24.76°C) = 1.449 \times 10^4 \text{ J or } 14.49 \text{ kJ}$

Fuel value of butter $= \dfrac{14.49 \text{ kJ}}{0.483 \text{ g}} = \textbf{30.0 kJ/g}$

(b) Nutritional Calories/g butter $= \dfrac{30.0 \text{ kJ/g}}{4.184 \text{ kJ/kilocalorie}} = \textbf{7.17 kilocalorie/g}$

(c) Nutritional Calories/5.00 g pat of butter $= (7.17 \text{ kilocalorie/g}) \times 5.00 \text{ g} = \textbf{35.9 kilocalorie}$

Element Colors for Models

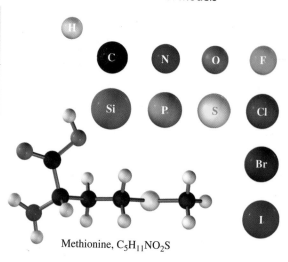

Methionine, $C_5H_{11}NO_2S$

Color Scale for Electrical Charge Potential (ECP) Surfaces

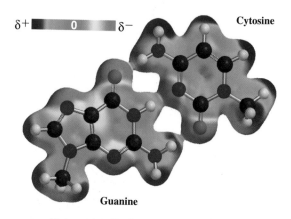

$\delta+$ 0 $\delta-$

Cytosine

Guanine

Hydrogen bonding between two DNA base pairs

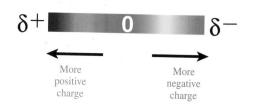

$\delta+$ 0 $\delta-$

More positive charge   More negative charge